THE ENCYCLOPEDIA OF
ANIMALS

THE ENCYCLOPEDIA OF
ANIMALS

Consultant Editor:

Dr. Per Christiansen

amber
BOOKS

First published in 2006 by
Amber Books Ltd
Bradley's Close
74–77 White Lion Street
London N1 9PF
United Kingdom
www.amberbooks.co.uk

13-ISBN: 978-1-905704-07-1
10-ISBN: 1-905704-07-0

Project Editor: Michael Spilling
Design: Hawes Design
Picture Research: Terry Forshaw

Printed in Singapore

In this book the featured animals have been arranged alphabetically using the hierarchy of order, family, species and common name. To find an animal under its common name, please refer to the index on pages 502–507.

Introduction   8

ACCIPITRIFORMES   10
ACIPENSERIFORMES   11
ACTINIARIA   12
ANGUILLIFORMES   13
ANSERIFORMES   14
ANURA   25
APODIFORMES   31
ARANEAE   33
ARTIODACTYLA   37
BATIFORMES   99
BLATTARIA   100
CAPRIMULGIFORMES   101
CARCHARHINIFORMES   102
CARCHARHINOIDIFORMES   104
CARNIVORA   105
CASUARIIFORMES   181
CETACEA   183
CHARACIFORMES   192
CHARADRIIFORMES   193
CHELONIA   205
CHIROPTERA   209
CHONDRICHTHYES   219
CICONIIFORMES   220
COLEOPTERA   227
CORACIIFORMES   230

CONTENTS

CONTENTS

CROCODYLIA 234

CUCULIFORMES 239

CYPRINIFORMES 241

DECAPODA 243

DERMOPTERA 247

DIPROTODONTA 248

EDENTATA 250

FALCONIFORMES 253

GALLIFORMES 269

GASTEROSTEIFORMES 272

GAVIIFORMES 274

GRUIFORMES 275

HYDROZOA 279

HYMENOPTERA 280

HYRACOIDEA 284

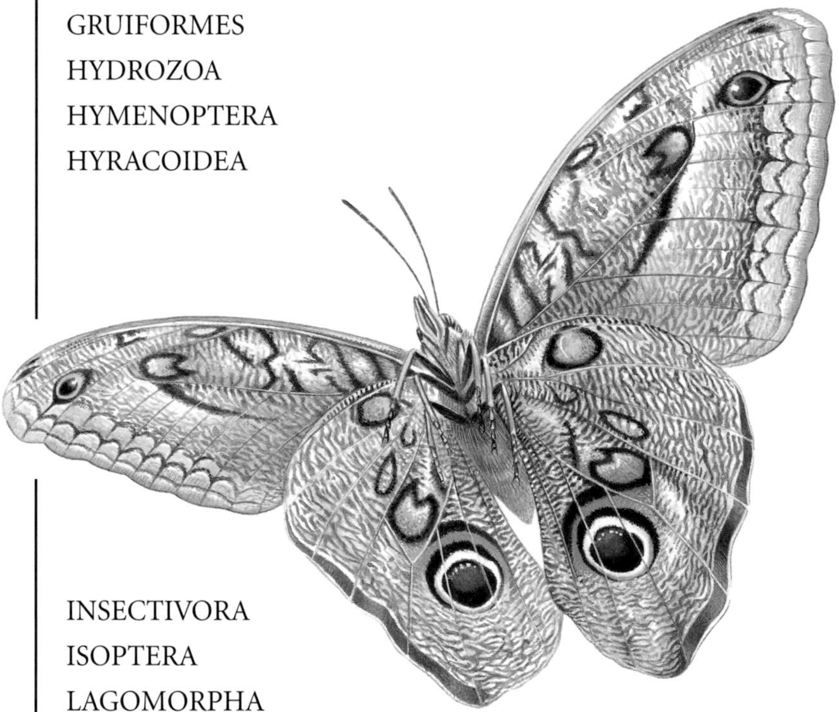

INSECTIVORA 285

ISOPTERA 292

LAGOMORPHA 293

LAMNIFORMES 297

LEPIDOPTERA 298

LITHOBIIDA 302

LOPHIIFORMES 303

MACROSCELIDEA 304

MANTODEA 305

MARSUPIALIA 306

MONOTREMATA 325

NEUROPTERA 327

OCTOPODA 328

ODONATA 330

ORTHOPTERA 331

PASSERIFORMES 332

PELICANIFORMES 344

PERCIFORMES 348

PERISSODACTYLA 357

CONTENTS

PHOENICOPTERIFORMES 364

PHOLIDOTA 365

PICIFORMES 366

PINNIPEDIA 367

PLEURONECTIFORMES 379

PODICIPEDIFORMES 380

PRIMATES 381

PROBOSCIDEA 418

PROCELLARIIFORMES 420

PSITTACIFORMES 421

RODENTIA 424

SALMONIFORMES 457

SCLERACTINIA 460

SCORPAENIFORMES 461

SCORPIONES 462

SCYLIORHINIFORMES 463

SEMAEOSTOMEAE 464

SILURIFORMES 465

SIRENIA 466

SPHENISCIFORMES 468

SPINULOSIDA 469

SQUAMATA 470

STRIGIFORMES 489

STRUTHIONIFORMES 492

TETRAODONTIFORMES 494

TINAMIFORMES 495

TUBULIDENTATA 496

URODELA 497

URODELES 498

XENARTHRA 499

XIPHOSURA 501

Animal Name Index 502

General Index 508

Picture Credits 511

Introduction

THE EARTH IS TEEMING with animal life. Life on Earth is very old, some 3700 millions years or more. This is why there are so many different kinds of plants and animals: they have had a long time to change into the numerous species found in the world today. Animals can roughly be divided into two, large groups: invertebrates and vertebrates. Invertebrates include animals such as insects, spiders and worms, and vertebrates are fish, amphibians, reptiles, mammals and birds.

The two groups are very different from each other. Invertebrates are extremely numerous — they do not have a skeleton, but, rather, a hard outer casing. This means that they cannot grow very large and explains why most invertebrates are smaller than the nail on your thumb. The only exceptions are ocean-dwelling octopuses and squid. Some of these grow to be an enormous size and can weigh several hundred kilos or pounds. Vertebrates have a backbone made of a strong material. In primitive vertebrates, such as sharks, the backbone is made of cartilage, like the human nose. But most vertebrates have a real skeleton of bone. This enabled them to grow to large sizes on dry land, where animals have to support their body weight without the help of water. This requires a strong skeleton, and is why all the large land animals that ever lived are vertebrates.

EVOLVING WORLD

Today there are many fantastic vertebrates. Lakes, rivers and oceans are teeming with fish. The forests across the world are filled with a huge variety of birds and mammals, and on the open plains and prairies are found many different kinds of mammals, often living in big, spectacular herds. In the oceans are the largest animals that have ever lived, the whales. Some of them are much larger than even the largest dinosaur. Like other mammals, whales nourish their young with milk — this is why they can grow to be so large. Whale milk is extremely fat and rich, so the whale baby grows incredibly fast. A blue whale baby can increase its weight by up to 100 kilos (267lbs) every day!

Scientists have studied life on Earth for a long time to find out how animals live, hoping to discover why there are so many different kinds of plants and animals. Life on our planet has changed through time,

A fox hunts in a snow-bound midwinter landscape. Foxes scavenge carrion and hunt small prey such as rodents, rabbits and birds. Unlike its cousin the wolf, the fox is a solitary animal, and does not hunt in a pack: this is because the fox hunts only enough food to feed one animal.

because of a process known as evolution. Evolution is a very complicated scientific area that deals with how life changes over time. Animals adapt to certain conditions in their particular environment. Forest-dwelling animals have developed the ability to find food, shelter and raise their young in a forest environment. They would have difficulty surviving outside the forest. Birds in a forest often have short, strong beaks for eating nuts and seeds, or have adapted to eating local insects by having long, sharp beaks. Birds along the coasts, however, often feed on invertebrates hidden in the sand. They need very different kinds of beaks to find their food.

This is why so many different species of animal can live together in one place. They have all become adapted for living in slightly different ways to the other species, so as to avoid competing directly for the same resources. But environments often change over time. The climate changes — it may become drier or wetter, hotter or colder. When this occurs, most animals and plants change too, adapting to the new conditions. Those that are unable to change fast enough dwindle, and may become extinct. Extinction is a normal process in the evolution of life. But when some species disappear, others will quickly change to fill the niches that are now left vacant.

A CHANGING ENVIRONMENT

In today's world, however, this has changed. Man is exploiting so much of the natural world that the environments are changing at an accelerated speed. Under normal conditions a forest may turn into an open grassy plain if it rains less: but this will take a long time, decades or even centuries. But a group of lumber workers with chainsaws can turn a forest into a grassy field in just a few weeks. Animals simply cannot adapt that fast. Thus, unfortunately a lot of animals are becoming extinct because manmade changes impact the environment so quickly.

In this book we have selected a vast array of animals that illustrate the fantastic variety of life on Earth. Our selection includes common animals, such as the duck, fox and zebra, more fantastic creatures, such as narwhal, pangolin and gharial, and many that are on the verge of extinction, such as the white rhino. With so many animals in danger of dying out, it is important that we learn about our shared environment before it changes irrevocably.

A leopard prowls in long grass in southern Africa. Leopards are shy, nocturnal animals that are difficult to observe. They can survive in a variety of environments, including jungle and desert. They are also good climbers and swimmers. Their adaptability may explain why they are one of the most numerous and widely distributed 'big cats'.

• **ORDER** • *Accipitriformes* • **FAMILY** • *Pandionidae* • **GENUS & SPECIES** • *Pandion haliaetus*

OSPREY

KEY FEATURES

- Remarkably powerful for its size, it can seize and fly off with prey almost as heavy as itself.
- Spiny-soled feet, tipped with razor-sharp talons, enable it to grip the most slippery of prey.
- Most widespread of all birds of prey, occurring on every continent except Antarctica.

VITAL STATISTICS

WEIGHT	Male 1.4kg (3.1lb); female 1.6kg (3.5lb)
LENGTH	Male 55–58cm (21.6–22.8in); female 60–64cm (23.6–25.2in)
WINGSPAN	1.45–1.6m (4ft 8 in–5ft 2in)
SEXUAL MATURITY	3 years
BREEDING SEASON	Varies according to range
NUMBER OF EGGS	2 to 5; usually 3
INCUBATION PERIOD	34–40 days
FLEDGING PERIOD	49–57 days
BREEDING INTERVAL	1 year
TYPICAL DIET	Freshwater and marine fish, juveniles may take small mammals
LIFESPAN	5–15 years

Sharp eyes, narrow wings and dexterous, powerfully taloned feet, equip the osprey to find, capture and kill the fish on which it feeds.

FEMALE
Slightly larger than the male, the female also has a more prominent band of brown feathers across the breast.

BILL
Sharply hooked for piercing and ripping open the tough and scaly skin of fish.

PLUMAGE
Denser and more oily than the plumage of most birds of prey, the osprey's feathers shrug off water with ease.

WINGS
For a bird of prey with such a wide wingspan, the wings are unusually narrow, but wider wings would trap too much water in the feathers, making it much harder for the osprey to get airborne again after a dive to catch prey.

FEET
The outer toe on each powerful foot can be rotated to face backwards to help the bird grasp prey more firmly. Spiny soles help hook the fish to the feet.

LEGS
Long legs increase the bird's reach, enabling it to catch fish without submerging its body in the water.

CREATURE COMPARISONS

Significantly larger than the osprey, with a wingspan of 1.9–2.4m (6ft 2in–7ft 9in) and weighing up to 3kg (6.6lb), the African fish eagle (Haliaeetus vocifer) is also a far more accomplished predator. Having spotted a flash of silver from its waterside perch, the eagle flies swiftly over the water and snatches its victim with a single foot, barely missing a wingbeat. Only when catching very large fish does the eagle ever partly submerge itself. Where its range overlaps with that of the osprey, the eagle will often bully its smaller relative into giving up its catch.

African fish eagle

Osprey

WHERE IN THE WORLD?

Breeds throughout much of Europe and Asia, North America, Southeast Asia and Australasia. Winters in South America, Africa and India.

RELATED SPECIES

The unique structure of the osprey's feet has led to it being classified in a separate family: the Pandionidae, of which it is the sole member. Among the 220 or so species of Accipitriformes there are several fish-eaters, including, the white-tailed sea eagle, Haliaetus albicilla.

• **ORDER** • *Acipenseriformes* • **FAMILY** • *Acipenseridae* • **GENUS & SPECIES** • *Acipenser sturio*

EUROPEAN STURGEON

The European sturgeon betrays its primitive origins by its unusual spinal structure and the strange ridges and bony plates that stud its skin.

KEY FEATURES

- A giant, solitary fish that spends most of its life at sea, each year it swims inland up large rivers to breed.
- A 'living fossil' that still closely resembles its prehistoric ancestors, which swam the seas in the age of the dinosaurs.
- Its roe (eggs) is one of the sources of caviar, and overfishing for this valuable delicacy is causing its overall decline.

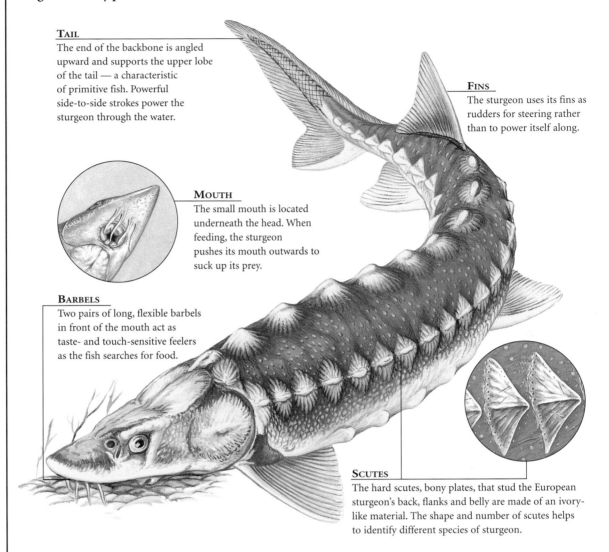

TAIL
The end of the backbone is angled upward and supports the upper lobe of the tail — a characteristic of primitive fish. Powerful side-to-side strokes power the sturgeon through the water.

FINS
The sturgeon uses its fins as rudders for steering rather than to power itself along.

MOUTH
The small mouth is located underneath the head. When feeding, the sturgeon pushes its mouth outwards to suck up its prey.

BARBELS
Two pairs of long, flexible barbels in front of the mouth act as taste- and touch-sensitive feelers as the fish searches for food.

SCUTES
The hard scutes, bony plates, that stud the European sturgeon's back, flanks and belly are made of an ivory-like material. The shape and number of scutes helps to identify different species of sturgeon.

VITAL STATISTICS

WEIGHT	Up to 300kg (661.4lb)
LENGTH	Male 1–1.5m (3ft 3in–4ft 9in); female 1.3–2m (4ft 3in–6ft 6in). Occasionally, both sexes may reach 3.5m (11ft 5in)
SEXUAL MATURITY	Male 7–9 years; female 8–14 years
BREEDING SEASON	Spring to early summer
NUMBER OF EGGS	Up to 2.5 million
HATCHING INTERVAL	3–7 days
BREEDING INTERVAL	1 year
TYPICAL DIET	Crustaceans, molluscs, insect larvae, worms and small fish
LIFESPAN	Unknown, possibly 100 years or more

CREATURE COMPARISONS

A relative of the European sturgeon, the American paddlefish, Polyodon spathula, lives in the silty, slow-flowing waters of the Mississippi River in the USA. Apart from its paddle-like nose the paddlefish is similar in shape to the European sturgeon, although it is generally smaller, growing to 1.5m (4ft 9in) and weighing up to 80kg (176.4lb). It feeds by cruising along the riverbed, stirring up mud to flush out small prey and straining water through its gills to trap tiny planktonic animals.

European sturgeon

American paddlefish

WHERE IN THE WORLD?

Found in the northern Mediterranean, Baltic Sea and Black Sea, and coastal Atlantic waters around Europe and Scandinavia. Swims up rivers to breed.

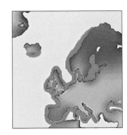

RELATED SPECIES

The European sturgeon is one of 23 species of sturgeon found in rivers, lakes and seas in Europe, Asia and North America. They range in size from the sterlet, Acipenser ruthenus, which grows up to 1m (3ft 3in) long, to the beluga, Huso huso, which can reach 5m and weigh over 1000kg (2205lb).

• **ORDER** • *Actiniaria* • **FAMILY** • *Various* • **GENUS & SPECIES** • *Various*

SEA ANEMONE

KEY FEATURES

- Colourful, soft-bodied marine creatures that anchor themselves to rocks, reefs or the seabed.
- Use concentric rows of tentacles to sting prey and inject powerful venom.
- Reproduce either sexually or by budding off parts of the body, which regenerate into clones of the parent.

VITAL STATISTICS

WEIGHT	Varies according to species; mass mainly made up of water
DIAMETER	1–100cm (0.4–39.4in)
SEXUAL MATURITY	Not known
BREEDING SEASON	Year-round
NUMBER OF YOUNG	Hundreds or even thousands in a lifetime
BIRTH INTERVAL	Continual breeding process
TYPICAL DIET	Plankton, invertebrates, fish, depending on species and size of anemone
LIFESPAN	Up to 70 years or more in some species

Swaying with the water currents, the sea anemone's stinging tentacles wait to ensnare any vulnerable creature that brushes past.

CROSS-SECTION
The mouth (A) is the only opening into the the animal's inner cavity (B). The body wall is made up of two layers (C) enclosing a digestive cavity and sexual organs (D).

HARPOONS
Each sting cell on a tentacle has a capsule called a nematocyst (A) containing a coiled tube. When triggered, the tube shoots outwards (B) and penetrates the prey's body.

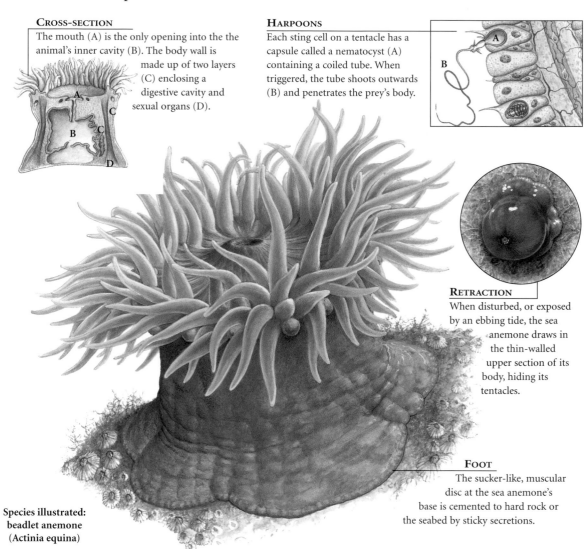

RETRACTION
When disturbed, or exposed by an ebbing tide, the sea anemone draws in the thin-walled upper section of its body, hiding its tentacles.

FOOT
The sucker-like, muscular disc at the sea anemone's base is cemented to hard rock or the seabed by sticky secretions.

Species illustrated:
**beadlet anemone
(Actinia equina)**

CREATURE COMPARISONS

Most sea anemones in the genus Actinia attach themselves to rocks and lead static lives. Those of other genera may lead a very different life: a number of Isosicyonis species have developed an intimate association with hermit crabs. A hermit crab takes over an abandoned seashell, and the sea anemone attaches itself to the occupied shell — or the crab may actually lift the anemone onto its new home. As the crab moves about, so does the sea anemone. It seems the association is beneficial to both: the sea anemone picks up scraps of food as the crab forages, while the crab obtains a crown of stinging tentacles to deter predators. Some species of crab even carry anemones on their claws to thrust at attacking fish and octopuses.

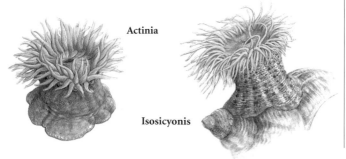

Actinia

Isosicyonis

WHERE IN THE WORLD?

Found in all the seas of the world, from coastal waters to the ocean depths. Absent from freshwater.

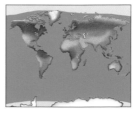

RELATED SPECIES
Belonging to the order Actinaria, Heteractis magnifica is one of the largest sea anemones. Along with 11 orders of coral, this sea anemone order makes up the class Anthozoa, which contains approximately 6500 species.

• ORDER • *Anguilliformes* • FAMILY • *Anguillidae* • GENUS & SPECIES • *Anguilla anguilla*

EUROPEAN EEL

KEY FEATURES

- Migrates thousands of kilometres or miles across the ocean as part of its breeding cycle, but its route is mystery.

- An elongated fish that is able to live in both saltwater and freshwater — it can even wriggle overland.

- In moist surroundings, is able to stay out of water for hours or even days at a time.

The eel's slippery, snake-like body changes to suit its habitat. During its freshwater phase, the eel can even travel overland when necessary.

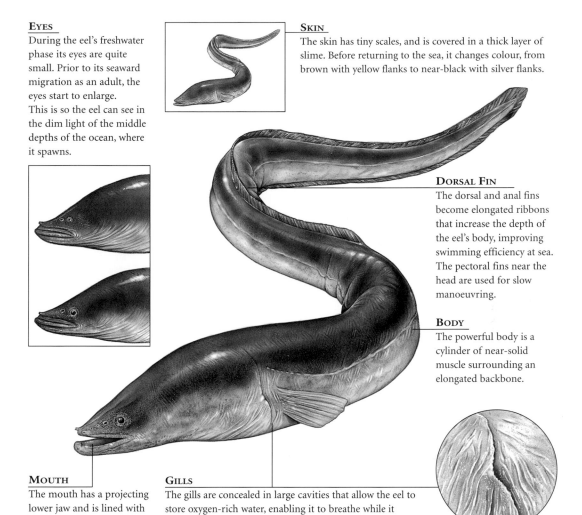

EYES
During the eel's freshwater phase its eyes are quite small. Prior to its seaward migration as an adult, the eyes start to enlarge. This is so the eel can see in the dim light of the middle depths of the ocean, where it spawns.

SKIN
The skin has tiny scales, and is covered in a thick layer of slime. Before returning to the sea, it changes colour, from brown with yellow flanks to near-black with silver flanks.

DORSAL FIN
The dorsal and anal fins become elongated ribbons that increase the depth of the eel's body, improving swimming efficiency at sea. The pectoral fins near the head are used for slow manoeuvring.

BODY
The powerful body is a cylinder of near-solid muscle surrounding an elongated backbone.

MOUTH
The mouth has a projecting lower jaw and is lined with small, blunt teeth.

GILLS
The gills are concealed in large cavities that allow the eel to store oxygen-rich water, enabling it to breathe while it wriggles overland through wet grass to isolated ponds.

VITAL STATISTICS

WEIGHT	Normally up to 3.6kg (7.9lb) but females have been recorded up to12.7kg (28lb)
LENGTH	Male up to 51cm (20.1in); female up to 1m (3ft 3in)
SPAWNING	Deep mid-Atlantic water
NUMBER OF EGGS	Clear, 1cm (0.4in) spheres; quantity unknown
BREEDING INTERVAL	Breeds only once; dies after spawning
TYPICAL DIET	Aquatic insects, small fish, molluscs; almost anything, including carrion
LIFESPAN	Up to 30 years

CREATURE COMPARISONS

Some 16 species of eel share the European eel's migratory habits, spending their adult lives in freshwater but returning to the ocean to breed. But many of the European eel's relatives spend their whole lives in a single habitat. Among those that do are the conger and the moray eel, which are strictly marine fish. Freshwater eels spend their lives in rivers and streams. They are generally smaller than their ocean relatives, but they have the same basic body shape and swim in the same, characteristic way.

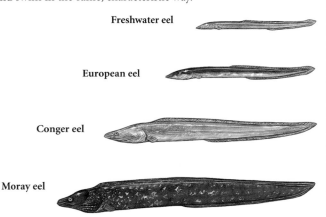

Freshwater eel

European eel

Conger eel

Moray eel

WHERE IN THE WORLD?

Hatches in the Sargasso Sea in the mid-Atlantic and drifts with the Gulf Stream. Adults live in freshwater and coastal habitats in Europe and North Africa.

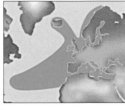

RELATED SPECIES

The European eel is one of a group of about 600 snake-like fish including the American eel, the conger eel, the moray eels and odd species like the gulper eel that live in the dark ocean depths. The American eel, Anguilla rostrata, looks like the European eel, but is often shorter. It has a similar lifecycle, although it lives in the USA and spawns in another area of the Sargasso Sea. Some scientists believe the two eels are one species.

• **ORDER** • *Anseriformes* • **FAMILY** • *Anatidae* • **GENUS & SPECIES** • *Aix galericulata*

MANDARIN DUCK

KEY FEATURES

- The extravagant plumage of the drake (male) makes it one of the most easily recognized of all ducks.
- Native to Asia, but escapees from waterfowl collections have established populations in mainland Britain.
- Prefers wooded habitats near water and usually nests in tree-holes.

VITAL STATISTICS

WEIGHT	500–650g (17.6–22.9oz)
LENGTH	41–49cm (16.1–19.3in)
WINGSPAN	68–74cm (26.8–29.1in)
SEXUAL MATURITY	1 year
BREEDING SEASON	Spring
NUMBER OF EGGS	9 to 12
INCUBATION PERIOD	4 weeks
FLEDGING PERIOD	6 weeks
BREEDING INTERVAL	1 year
TYPICAL DIET	Seeds and nuts, with some insects and snails
LIFESPAN	3–6 years

Adorned with rich colours, ornate patterns and fanciful 'whiskers' and 'sails', the male mandarin duck is one of the most beautiful of all waterfowl.

PLUMAGE
Immediately after the breeding season, the drake moults his colourful feathers and takes on 'eclipse' plumage, which is similar to that of the female.

FEMALE
Though dowdy in comparison with the drake, the female's prominent eyering and eyestripe help distinguish her from other grey-brown ducks.

WING FEATHERS
The most unusual feature of the drake's ornamental plumage is the pair of orange 'sails' formed from an enlarged and upturned set of wing feathers.

WINGS AND TAIL
Strong wings that beat rapidly and a long tail give the bird excellent manoeuvrability, compared to other ducks, when flying at speed among trees.

FEET
Sharp claws on the toes of its webbed feet help the mandarin duck get a secure grip when perching on branches.

CREATURE COMPARISONS

The Carolina wood duck of North America is a cousin of the mandarin duck. It, too, is a woodland dweller that nests in tree-holes, and it is also a popular captive bird in Europe. Though similar in size and shape to the mandarin drake, the male has strikingly different plumage embellished with glossy greens and browns and bold, white stripes. The female, like that of the mandarin duck, is predominantly grey-brown.

Male mandarin duck

Male Carolina wood duck

WHERE IN THE WORLD?

Occurs naturally in the east of China, eastern Russia and Japan. Feral populations also exist in parts of Europe, the majority being found in southeast England.

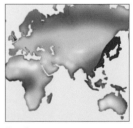

RELATED SPECIES

The mandarin duck is one of 13 species of perching ducks and perching geese that belong to the Cairinini tribe. Although the different species are scattered across the globe, all share adaptations for living in wooded habitats. The largest is the spur-winged goose of Africa; others in the group include the muscovy duck of Central and South America, the African pygmy goose and the maned wood duck of Australia.

• ORDER • *Anseriformes* • FAMILY • *Anatidae* • GENUS & SPECIES • *Anas platyrhynchos*

MALLARD

A highly versatile bodyplan allows the mallard to exploit a wide range of feeding opportunities, making it the world's most successful duck.

KEY FEATURES

- The world's most abundant species of duck.
- Feeds on submerged plants by upending and pushing its long neck underwater.
- Male abandons his mate after egg-laying.
- Ducklings stay close to their mother for protection, often swimming behind her in a long line.

VITAL STATISTICS

WEIGHT	750–1575g (26.4–55.6oz)
LENGTH	50–65cm (19.7–25.6in)
WINGSPAN	75–100cm (29.5–39.4in)
SEXUAL MATURITY	1 year
BREEDING SEASON	February to June
NUMBER OF EGGS	9 to 13
INCUBATION PERIOD	About 28 days
FLEDGING PERIOD	50–60 days
BREEDING INTERVAL	1 year
TYPICAL DIET	Shoots and seeds of aquatic plants, grass, insects, snails and worms
LIFESPAN	Up to 29 years

FEMALE
The female, or duck, is slightly smaller than the male, or drake, and has a drab, brown-streaked plumage to camouflage her when sitting on the nest.

BILL
The sharp 'nail' on the tip of the bill is used to graze grass and pick up small prey. The mallard can also filter tiny animals from the water by means of the tooth-like membranes, known as lamellae, that line the inside of its bill.

FEET
Webbed feet enable the mallard to paddle efficiently and half-submerge itself to reach aquatic plants.

SPECULUM
Male and female alike have a bright blue flash, known as a speculum, on each wing. The specula are much more visible in flight.

CREATURE COMPARISONS

From a distance, the northern shelduck (Tadorna tadorna) seems to have a striking black-and-white patterned plumage, as the species' bottle-green head and orange-chestnut breast-band are apparent only at close range. The male shelduck has a prominent 'knob' on the bill, giving him a quite different head profile to the female.

A bird of Eurasia's coastal mudflats and estuaries, the northern shelduck is rarely found far inland. It has a more specialized diet than the mallard, feeding by picking small shellfish, snails and worms from the mud.

Mallard (male)

Northern shelduck (male)

WHERE IN THE WORLD?

Found in a huge range that includes nearly all of the northern hemisphere's temperate zone, with introduced populations in Australia and New Zealand.

RELATED SPECIES

The mallard is 1 of 36 species of surface-feeding, or dabbling, duck in the genus Anas, which also includes the Eurasian wigeon, Anas penelope, and the pintails, shovelers and teals. Ducks belong to the family Anatidae within the order Anseriformes, which includes geese and swans.

• **ORDER** • *Anseriformes* • **FAMILY** • *Anatidae* • **GENUS & SPECIES** • *Anser anser*

GREYLAG GOOSE

As a grazer, the greylag goose needs to eat large amounts of food to gain sufficient energy, and so is adapted for a life mainly spent feeding on land.

KEY FEATURES

- Similar in colour, the male and female maintain a pair-bond throughout their lives.
- Small feet and a long neck are adaptations for spending long periods walking and grazing on dry land.
- Moving from northern breeding grounds to milder climates in winter, migrating flocks are a familiar sight on farmlands near the coast.

VITAL STATISTICS

WEIGHT	2.5–4.1kg (5.5–9lb)
LENGTH	76–89cm (29.9–35in)
WINGSPAN	1.47–1.8m (4ft 8in–5ft 9in)
SEXUAL MATURITY	3 years
BREEDING SEASON	March to August
NUMBER OF EGGS	3 to 12, usually 4 to 6
INCUBATION PERIOD	27–28 days
FLEDGING PERIOD	50–60 days
BREEDING INTERVAL	1 year
TYPICAL DIET	Grass, roots, leaves, seeds, and fruits of a wide variety of plants
LIFESPAN	About 10 years in the wild

BILL
A reinforced shield-shaped plate, called the nail, at the tip of the upper half of the bill is designed for digging up roots, snipping grass, and pecking at seeds and berries. The bill edges are serrated to help cut through vegetation.

DIGESTIVE TRACT
While the goose feeds, food is stored in a sac-like extension of the oesophagus called the crop (A). The food then enters the muscular gizzard (B), which grinds up hard food, such as seeds, with the help of particles of grit that the goose has swallowed, before it enters the intestine. Faeces are excreted through the anus via the cloaca (C) — the opening through which waste and genital products pass.

FOOT
Typical of many aquatic birds, the greylag goose has webbed feet for swimming. However, unlike those species that spend a lot of time on water the feet are relatively small, enabling the greylag to walk about more easily.

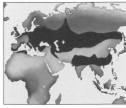

JUVENILE PLUMAGE
A young greylag looks similar to an adult but its plumage is duller, lacking the distinctive, sharply defined bars on the upperparts and the dark blotches on the belly.

CREATURE COMPARISONS

The closely related bar-headed goose, *Anser indicus*, is one of the most distinctive-looking geese. The white head crossed by two black bands is unique, as is the vertical neck stripe. It is a high altitude species breeding on a variety of plateaux wetlands at 4000–5000m (13,120–16,400ft) in central Asia. It winters farther south on lowland marshes and lakes in northern India, Bangladesh, Pakistan and Burma (Myanmar). Like the greylag goose, it is mainly vegetarian, feeding on grasses, sedges and plant roots. Its future in China, where there are about 10,000 breeding pairs, is threatened by direct human persecution in the form of egg-collecting, hunting and habitat destruction.

Bar-headed goose

Greylag goose

WHERE IN THE WORLD?

Breeds in Iceland, Britain, Scandinavia, central Europe and Russia to northeastern China. Winters in parts of coastal Europe and southern Asia from northern India to southern China.

RELATED SPECIES

Geese are members of the family Anatidae, which has 148 species and includes swans and ducks. Geese are generally bulkier and longer-necked than ducks and spend a lot of time feeding on land, whereas ducks tend to feed in water. There are 10 species in the genus Anser and the greylag goose is one of 6 species in this genus known as grey geese; the others are the pink-footed, white-fronted, lesser white-fronted, bar-headed, and bean goose.

SNOW GOOSE

• **ORDER** • *Anseriformes* • **FAMILY** • *Anatidae* • **GENUS & SPECIES** • *Anser caerulescens*

KEY FEATURES

- Exists in two colour forms, white and blue, and two races: the greater and the lesser snow goose.
- One of the world's most abundant species of goose, with populations numbering in millions.
- Annual migrations to southerly wintering grounds are among the greatest of all wildlife spectacles.

VITAL STATISTICS

WEIGHT	2.5–3.3kg (5.5–7.3lb)
LENGTH	66–84cm (26–33.1in)
WINGSPAN	1.32–1.65m (4ft 3in–5ft 4in)
SEXUAL MATURITY	2 years, but does not usually breed until 3–4 years old
BREEDING SEASON	June –September
NUMBER OF EGGS	2 to 10, but usually 4 or 5
INCUBATION PERIOD	23–25 days
FLEDGING PERIOD	40–50 days
BREEDING INTERVAL	1 year
TYPICAL DIET	Wide variety of vegetation
LIFESPAN	Up to 17 years

With its robust body, muscular neck and sharply serrated bill, the snow goose is perfectly adapted to digging up a wide variety of plants and vegetables.

WINGS
The snow goose has black wingtip feathers, which are highly resistant to wear and tear. These tough plumes prove their worth when the bird makes its long twice-yearly migrations.

BLUE FORM
As well as the white form, there is a blue form of snow goose (above). Its colour results from silvery-grey feathers overlying brown feathers. The blue form is common in the lesser snow goose, but rare in the greater race. There are intermediate colours between the two forms.

FEET & LEGS
The snow goose's broadly webbed feet provide it with a powerful swimming stroke. Its legs are more centrally positioned on its body than in ducks, providing the snow goose with improved agility and balance when walking and feeding on land and in shallow water.

BILL
The thickened cutting edges of the snow goose's sturdy bill are lined with serrations, perfect for digging out and cutting up plant roots and tubers. The black serrations form a distinctive 'grin' on the pink bill.

CREATURE COMPARISONS

Like the snow goose, the red-breasted goose (Branta ruficollis) breeds on the Arctic tundra. Much smaller than the snow goose, it belongs to the group of geese known as 'black geese' (genus Branta) rather than to the 'grey geese' (genus Anser). As well as beautiful plumage, it has a rounded head, a short neck and an extremely short bill for grazing short grass and vegetation.

Unlike the snow goose, the red-breasted goose nests in small colonies of up to five pairs, often within 5–10m (16ft 4in–32ft 8in) of nesting peregrines, buzzards and large gulls. As these aggressive birds drive predatory Arctic foxes from the breeding colony, the red-breasted goose benefits from the association.

Red-breasted goose

Snow goose

WHERE IN THE WORLD?

Breeds mostly inside the Arctic Circle, from Baffin Island and Greenland west across Canada. Migrates south to spend winter in warmer parts of the USA.

RELATED SPECIES

The lesser snow goose, Anser caerulescens caerulescens, and the greater snow goose, A. c. atlanticus, share the genus Anser with 10 other species, including the bar-headed goose, A. indicus. All geese and swans are members of the tribe Anserini.

• **ORDER** • *Anseriformes* • **FAMILY** • *Anatidae* • **GENUS & SPECIES** • *Aythya fuligula*

TUFTED DUCK

The flamboyant crest and striking colouring of the male tufted duck make it one of the most easily recognized birds, but they are not permanent features.

KEY FEATURES

- Now a common and widespread species as a result of a huge expansion that began only 150 years ago.
- Dives for its natural food to the bottom of lakes, but is tame enough to take bread from humans in parks.
- Named after its 'pigtail' of long feathers, its old country name of magpie diver is equally descriptive.

MALE PLUMAGE
The male (below) sports bold plumage for the breeding season. He later moults and enters the flightless eclipse phase, with dull plumage for better camouflage.

EYES
The male's eyes change from their juvenile brown to bright yellow during his first winter.

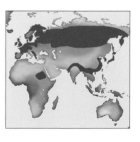

WINGS
Narrow wings give fast, direct flight. The white wing feathers create a distinctive pattern.

BILL
The adult male's bill becomes more bluish in the breeding season. It is greyer during his eclipse period but usually remains paler than that of females and juveniles.

CREST
The male's drooping crest is at its longest in the breeding season. In eclipse plumage, it is no longer than that of the female.

VITAL STATISTICS

WEIGHT	Male 750–770g (26.4–27.2oz); female 700–720g (24.7–25.4oz)
LENGTH	40–47cm (15.7–18.5in)
WINGSPAN	67–73cm (26.4–28.7in)
SEXUAL MATURITY	1–2 years
BREEDING SEASON	May to August
NUMBER OF EGGS	8 to 11
INCUBATION PERIOD	23–28 days
FLEDGING PERIOD	45–50 days
BREEDING INTERVAL	2 clutches in a year in south of range; otherwise 1 year
TYPICAL DIET	Molluscs, crustaceans, insects, seeds, plants
LIFESPAN	Up to 14 years

CREATURE COMPARISONS

The scaup (*Aythya marila*) is very similar in appearance to the tufted duck and overwinters on some of the same British waters, although it more often frequents coasts and estuaries, whereas the tufted duck prefers freshwater. Both feed by diving and dabbling beneath the surface and, in estuarine areas at least, both take molluscs. Several features distinguish the two: the scaup is around ten per cent larger and lacks a crest. They are hardest to distinguish when tufted duck males are in eclipse plumage and their crest is diminished. Hybrids of the two species are not uncommon.

Scaup

Tufted duck

WHERE IN THE WORLD?

Occupies a broad range extending from Iceland across western and northern Europe, through Siberia to Japan. Overwinters in Africa and southeastern Asia.

RELATED SPECIES

Hybridization sometimes occurs between the 12 closely related species in the genus Aythya, which includes the tufted duck; its North American counterpart the ring-necked duck A. collaris; the hardhead, A. australis, an Australian species; the ferruginous duck, A. nyroca; and the pochard, A. ferina — a familiar chestnut-headed duck often found with the tufted duck on British lakes and ponds. All belong to the order Anseriformes.

CANADA GOOSE

• ORDER • *Anseriformes* • FAMILY • *Anatidae* • GENUS & SPECIES • *Branta canadensis*

KEY FEATURES

- Stages one of nature's great spectacles as thousands fill the flyways on their journey south in autumn.
- Travels in wavering V-formations, creating slipstreams to minimize the effort of migratory flight.
- Has a built-in compass to aid navigation when clouds obscure landmarks and hide the stars.

VITAL STATISTICS

WEIGHT	1.35–5kg (3–11lb)
LENGTH	56–110cm (22–43.3in)
WINGSPAN	1.22–1.83m (4–6ft)
SEXUAL MATURITY	2–3 years
BREEDING SEASON	March to July
NUMBER OF EGGS	Usually 4 to 7
INCUBATION PERIOD	24–30 days
FLEDGING PERIOD	6–12 weeks
BREEDING INTERVAL	1 year
TYPICAL DIET	Grasses, grain and aquatic vegetation
LIFESPAN	Up to 23 years

Warmed by dense plumage in the cold skies, the high-flying Canada goose travels thousands of kilometres or miles each year on migration.

BILL
Tooth-like serrations along the edges of the upper and lower mandibles of the bill help the goose to grip the plants on which it grazes.

NECK
The long neck enables the Canada goose to reach down for food underwater, when it upends like a duck or a swan.

PLUMAGE
Insulating plumage keeps the bird warm in northern latitudes and while flying at high altitudes. The Canada goose sheds all its primary (wingtip) feathers simultaneously, and so becomes flightless during its annual moult.

SIZE
The largest subspecies and largest goose in the world, the giant Canada goose of the northern USA (Branta canadensis maxima) towers over the smallest, the cackling Canada goose of Alaska (B. c. minima).

FEET
Typical of most waterfowl, the three front toes are connected by webbing to provide power while swimming.

CREATURE COMPARISONS

The Canada goose's close relatives bear distinctive plumage, particularly on the face. The black brant is a black-faced subspecies of the brant goose. The red-breasted goose has a black face boldly marked with white and rusty-brown. The barnacle goose has a bold white face against a dark crown, neck and breast, while the Canada goose bears only a white bib against its dark facial plumage.

Black brant goose

Red-breasted goose

Barnacle goose

Canada goose

WHERE IN THE WORLD?

Breeds across northern North America. Winters farther south in the USA and in Mexico. Introduced into Britain, Scandinavia and New Zealand.

RELATED SPECIES

The Canada goose is one of 15 so-called 'true' geese in a family of 147 species, which also contains ducks and swans. The Canada goose is the largest of five species in the genus Branta, which are known collectively as black geese. Along with the swans, the whistling ducks, the Cape Barren goose and the freckled duck, the true geese are classified in the subfamily Anserinae. Geese and swans are classified together in the tribe Anserini.

• **ORDER** • *Anseriformes* • **FAMILY** • *Anatidae* • **GENUS & SPECIES** • *Cygnus olor*

MUTE SWAN

KEY FEATURES

- One of the world's heaviest flying birds, celebrated for its pure white plumage and effortless elegance.
- A notoriously aggressive bird that has the power to inflict serious injuries.
- Quieter than other swans, but still hisses and snorts loudly when agitated.

VITAL STATISTICS

WEIGHT	7–14kg (15.4–30.9lb)
LENGTH	1.2–1.6m (3ft 9in–5ft 2in)
WINGSPAN	2–2.4m (6ft 6in–7ft 9in)
SEXUAL MATURITY	3 years
BREEDING SEASON	Spring
NUMBER OF EGGS	3 to 12, but usually 5 to 7
INCUBATION PERIOD	About 36 days
FLEDGING PERIOD	120–150 days
BREEDING INTERVAL	1 year
TYPICAL DIET	Water plants, grasses and small aquatic animals
LIFESPAN	Up to 20 years

The pristine plumage and balletic beauty of the mute swan mask its true nature as a bird of enormous weight and power.

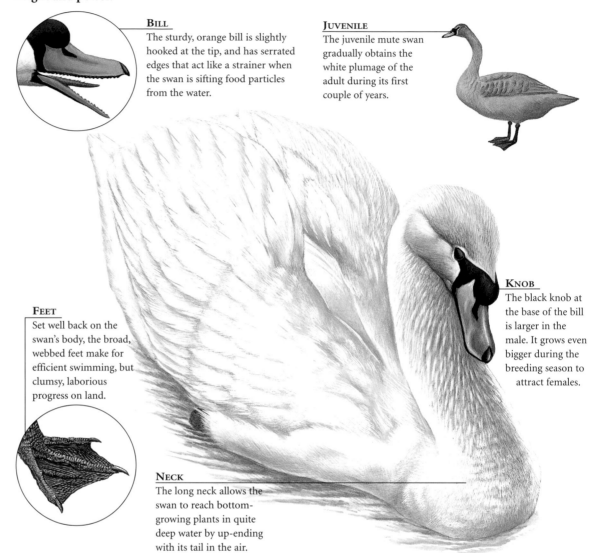

BILL
The sturdy, orange bill is slightly hooked at the tip, and has serrated edges that act like a strainer when the swan is sifting food particles from the water.

JUVENILE
The juvenile mute swan gradually obtains the white plumage of the adult during its first couple of years.

KNOB
The black knob at the base of the bill is larger in the male. It grows even bigger during the breeding season to attract females.

FEET
Set well back on the swan's body, the broad, webbed feet make for efficient swimming, but clumsy, laborious progress on land.

NECK
The long neck allows the swan to reach bottom-growing plants in quite deep water by up-ending with its tail in the air.

CREATURE COMPARISONS

Named for its powerful, trumpeting call, the whooper swan (Cygnus cygnus) breeds on northern wetlands up near the Arctic Circle, migrating south into Europe for the winter. Much the same size as the mute swan, the whooper swan holds its neck erect like a goose, in contrast to the mute swan's gentle curve, and has a more wedge-shaped, yellow bill. The whooper swan has similar feeding habits to those of the mute swan, dabbling for water plants or grazing on wet pastures near rivers and estuaries. Like the mute swan, the whooper swan also has audible wingbeats, but the sound is more of a whistle than a throb.

Whooper swan   Mute swan

WHERE IN THE WORLD?

A native of Eurasia, found in scattered populations from Britain to China. Introduced to North America, South Africa, Japan, Australia and New Zealand.

RELATED SPECIES

The mute swan is 1 of 6 species of swan in the genus Cygnus, which also includes the trumpeter swan, Cygnus buccinator, of North America, and the black swan, C. atratus, of Australia. It belongs to the family Anatidae which contains 147 species of swan, goose and duck.

TORRENT DUCK

• **ORDER** • *Anseriformes* • **FAMILY** • *Anatidae* • **GENUS & SPECIES** • *Merganetta armata*

Powerfully webbed feet, a streamlined body and stiff tail feathers equip the torrent duck to live in fast-flowing waters.

KEY FEATURES

- Unusual among ducks in its preference for fast-flowing mountain streams with numerous waterfalls.
- Slimly built, long-tailed and short-legged, it dives into boulder-strewn waters to find insects on the riverbed.
- One of the most attractive of all ducks, the male has a striking black-and-white head and orange bill.

VITAL STATISTICS

WEIGHT	300–400g (10.6–14oz)
LENGTH	43–46cm 16.8–18.1in)
WINGSPAN	55cm (21.6in)
SEXUAL MATURITY	1 year
BREEDING SEASON	Variable, according to locality; usually between November and June
NUMBER OF EGGS	3 to 4
INCUBATION PERIOD	43–44 days
FLEDGING PERIOD	Unknown
BREEDING INTERVAL	Probably 1 year
TYPICAL DIET	Aquatic insects and their larvae, molluscs and occasionally small fish
LIFESPAN	Unknown

FEMALE
Lacks the striking black-and-white head pattern of the male. Her grey wings, neck and head contrast with orange underparts.

WING-SPUR
Both sexes have a small bony spur, like a thumb, at the outer joint of the wing. This spur is used as a weapon in territorial disputes.

PLUMAGE
The male (below) has a white head with black stripes over the crown and from the eye.

TAIL
The stiff tail feathers are pressed down against the riverbed to brace the bird when it is standing in fast-flowing water.

FOOT
Extremely large webbed feet help propel the duck through fast currents and also provide a sturdy base when it stands feeding in the shallows. A sharp hindclaw enables the bird to grip slippery rocks.

CREATURE COMPARISONS

The blue duck (Hymenolaimus malacorhynchus), which takes its name from its uniformly blue-grey colouring, is found only in New Zealand, and like the torrent duck is an inhabitant of fast-flowing mountain streams. Standing about 55cm (21.6in) high, the blue duck is slightly taller than the torrent duck but it is a more dumpy-looking bird than its relative. Like the torrent duck, the blue duck is mainly sedentary, feeding and breeding along the same stretch of river for most of its adult life. An increasingly rare bird, the blue duck also feeds in a similar way to the torrent duck, probing among rocks, diving, and upending in shallow waters for aquatic invertebrates, including insect larvae.

Torrent duck

Blue duck

WHERE IN THE WORLD?

Resident in three separate areas of the Andes Mountains of western South America: Venezuela to southern Colombia; Ecuador to Peru; and south through Bolivia and Chile to Argentina.

RELATED SPECIES

The torrent duck is the only species in the genus Merganetta. This genus belongs to the family Anatidae, which contains ducks, geese and swans. The 147 members of this diverse family are found worldwide, except on the continent of Antarctica, and range in size from the massive whooper swan, Cygnus cygnus, which weighs in at over 12kg (26.5lb), to the tiny African pygmy goose, Nettapus auritus, which tips the scales at just 260–285g (9.2–10oz).

• **ORDER** • *Anseriformes* • **FAMILY** • *Anatidae* • **GENUS & SPECIES** • *Mergus albellus*

SMEW

KEY FEATURES

- The smallest duck to have a saw-edged bill — a useful tool for catching insects and small fish.
- Nests in tree-holes in the forests of the far north, flying farther south to spend the winter.
- In late winter, small groups indulge in courtship displays and pair off before migrating north.

VITAL STATISTICS

WEIGHT	515–935g (18.2–33oz)
LENGTH	35–44cm (13.8–17.3in)
WINGSPAN	55–69cm (21.6–27.2in)
SEXUAL MATURITY	2 years
BREEDING SEASON	Spring and early summer
NUMBER OF YOUNG	Usually 7 to 9
INCUBATION PERIOD	26–28 days
FLEDGING PERIOD	About 4 weeks
BREEDING INTERVAL	Once a year
LIFESPAN	Unknown: probably a few years

The serrated edges of the bill and the clawed, webbed feet of the smew enable it to lead a lifestyle of fishing in waters near its woodland nesting site.

BILL
The serrated edges allow the bird to grip fish and give rise to the term 'sawbilled duck'.

MALE
The male smew in breeding plumage is distinguished from other wildfowl by his striking white head and neck, and a black eye-mask. His crest of white feathers serves in breeding displays.

FEMALE
Characterized by white cheek-flashes, the female (above) keeps the same ginger-red head plumage all year round. The immature smew has similar plumage to the female.

FOOT
The feet are grey in colour. The three forward-facing toes are webbed, and the hindtoe is strongly clawed to help the bird grip branches.

CREATURE COMPARISONS

Like the smew, the goosander (Mergus merganser) is a sawbilled duck. It is about twice the size of the smew, and its bill is more pointed. In common with the smew, it nests in tree-holes and breeds in northern Europe, although it is more widespread, also occurring in America. The male goosander has a glossy-green head and neck, while females and immature males have a ginger-red head and neck. The female has a small white patch at the base of her bill, compared to the much larger white mask of the female smew. Outside of the breeding season, the male smew is difficult to distinguish from the female and immatures since they all have a ginger-red head and nape.

Goosander

Smew

WHERE IN THE WORLD?

Breeds in the far north of Europe and Asia. Migrates south in winter to western and central Europe, Russia, the Middle East and eastern China, Korea and Japan.

RELATED SPECIES

The smew is one of 6 species of sawbill duck. The other 5 species are the hooded merganser, Mergus cucullatus, the Brazilian merganser, M. octosetaceus, the red-breasted merganser, M. serratob, the Chinese merganser, M. squamatus, and the goosander. Sawbills are all fish-eating birds and belong to the subfamily of ducks — the Anatinae. This subfamily belongs to the family Anatidae, which also includes the many species of geese and swans.

• **ORDER** • *Anseriformes* • **FAMILY** • *Anatidae* • **GENUS & SPECIES** • *Oxyura jamaicensis*

RUDDY DUCK

KEY FEATURES

- Feeds by swimming along the bottom of lakes and pools while straining the silt with its bill.
- A superbly skilled diver that can sink beneath the water surface like a stone and rise again like a cork.
- Both sexes are aggressive during the breeding season, when males fight bill and claw for territories.

VITAL STATISTICS

WEIGHT	Male 550–800g (19.4–28.2oz); female 300–650g (10.6–22.9oz)
LENGTH	35–43cm (13.8–16.9in)
WINGSPAN	53–62cm (20.9–24.4in)
SEXUAL MATURITY	1–2 years
BREEDING SEASON	Spring in North America and Europe; all year round in South America
NUMBER OF EGGS	6 to 14
INCUBATION PERIOD	25–26 days
FLEDGING PERIOD	50–55 days
TYPICAL DIET	Insects, seeds and leaves of aquatic plants
LIFESPAN	About 8 years

The ruddy duck's sturdy legs, waterproof plumage and stocky, naturally buoyant body enable it to swim and dive with masterful ease.

FLIGHT
The ruddy duck flies low on rapidly beating, whirring wings. It rarely leaves water other than to migrate.

TAIL
The long, stiffened tail feathers help the duck to steer underwater, by acting as a rudder. At the surface, the ruddy duck often holds its tail vertically.

BILL
The heavy, rather spatula-shaped bill is bright blue in the male (left) and steel-grey in the female and young.

FEMALE
The female, or duck, is fractionally smaller than the male, or drake. She is also much drabber, to camouflage her when sitting on the nest.

CREATURE COMPARISONS

The teal family includes many of the world's smallest ducks. The green-winged teal (Anas crecca) — one of the most abundant and widespread teals — is slightly smaller than the ruddy duck, with much shorter tail feathers. The teal belongs to the tribe known as the surface-feeding, or dabbling, ducks, whereas the ruddy duck belongs to the stiff-tailed, diving ducks.

Bill shape is the most important difference between these species. The green-winged teal's slender, flattened bill is adapted to grazing along the shore, nibbling plants and skimming from the water surface. The ruddy duck's broad, saw-toothed bill allows it to filter insects and seeds from the muddy bottom.

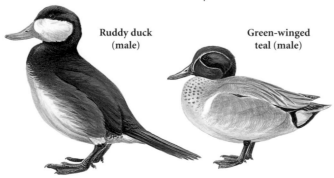

Ruddy duck (male)

Green-winged teal (male)

WHERE IN THE WORLD?

One race occurs in much of North America, and two other races are found along the coastal strip of western South America.

Introduced to Britain in the 1950s, from where it has spread to mainland Europe.

RELATED SPECIES
The ruddy duck is 1 of 8 species in the stifftail tribe, Oxyurini. Stifftails are among 140 or so species in the order Anseriformes, including the pintail, Anas acuta. Anseriforms, which also include swans, geese and screamers, have short, strong legs, webbed feet and oily plumage.

• **ORDER** • *Anseriformes* • **FAMILY** • *Anatidae* • **GENUS & SPECIES** • *Somateria mollissima*

COMMON EIDER DUCK

Cold-cheating down feathers insulate the common eider duck against icy seas, and a powerful, shell-cracking bill helps it exploit abundant shellfish.

KEY FEATURES

- A hardy bird that spends most of its life at sea, living on cold, storm-tossed waters.
- Expert diving skills and a hefty bill enable the eider to feed on shellfish on the seabed.
- Uses its own soft, down feathers plucked from its breast to make a snug lining for its nest. The down is 'harvested' by humans for use in quilts and sleeping bags.

FEMALE
In contrast to the drake's bold, black-and-white breeding plumage, the female is a uniform brown with blackish stripes and bars all year round. This colouration provides camouflage when the female is nesting.

BILL
The large, triangular bill is employed for cracking open mussels, crabs, whelks and other shellfish.

FEET
The feet are large and broadly webbed, providing the eider with the thrust needed to dive down to the seabed to feed.

DOWN FEATHER
Under the outer body feathers is a thick layer of down. These small, soft and loosely structured feathers help trap a layer of air close to the skin, giving the eider duck excellent protection against the cold.

VITAL STATISTICS

WEIGHT	1.9–2.2kg (4.2–4.8lb)
LENGTH	50–71cm (19.7–27.9in)
WINGSPAN	80–108cm (31–42.5in)
SEXUAL MATURITY	2–3 years
BREEDING SEASON	April to July
NUMBER OF EGGS	1 to 8, but usually 4 to 6
INCUBATION PERIOD	25–28 days
FLEDGING PERIOD	60–75 days
BREEDING INTERVAL	1 year
TYPICAL DIET	Mainly shellfish; occasionally fish and plant matter
LIFESPAN	5–6 years

CREATURE COMPARISONS

In the breeding season, the drakes of all four species of eider duck are strikingly patterned, but the most spectacular, hence its scientific name, is the king eider (*Somateria spectabilis*) when it becomes resplendent in its velvety-black body and rose-tinged white breast. The pale green and pearl-grey head is also adorned by a remarkable bright-orange 'shield' outlined in black at the base of the red bill.

The common eider lacks the king eider's colourful head and adornments, and has a white back, making it appear much cleaner cut than the king eider. After breeding, both species moult into a dark, drab 'eclipse' plumage, looking quite unlike the smart livery of their courtship dress.

Common eider duck

King eider duck

WHERE IN THE WORLD?

Found on coasts from Alaska, across northern Canada and northeastern USA, to southern Greenland, Great Britain, Scandinavia and eastern Siberia. Birds in the High Arctic and Baltic areas migrate south in winter.

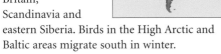

RELATED SPECIES

The common eider is a member of the family Anatidae, a large group containing over 140 species. The majority of these species are ducks, including the Magellanic flightless steamer duck, *Tachyeres pteneres*. However, geese and swans also belong to the same family.

EURASIAN TOAD

• **ORDER** • *Anura* • **FAMILY** • *Bufonidae* • **GENUS & SPECIES** • *Bufo bufo*

KEY FEATURES

- The largest toad in Europe, it is an extremely effective controller of slugs and other garden pests.
- Breeds 'explosively' in spring, when several hundred toads may arrive en masse at one spawning site.
- Secretes pungent venom from glands on its thick skin which it uses to deter predators.

VITAL STATISTICS

WEIGHT	Male 20–30g (0.7–1.1oz); female 30–50g (1.1–1.8oz)
LENGTH	Male 8–10cm (3.1–3.9in); female up to 15cm (5.9in)
SEXUAL MATURITY	Male 2–3 years; female 3–4 years
BREEDING SEASON	February to April
NUMBER OF EGGS	600 to 4000
HATCHING PERIOD	About 10 days
BREEDING INTERVAL	1 year
TYPICAL DIET	A variety of invertebrates and occasionally small mammals
LIFESPAN	5 years average; up to 40 years in captivity

Unable to leap to safety when danger threatens, the chunky Eurasian toad finds protection instead with special glands that emit powerful toxins.

SKIN
The colour of the skin varies, ranging from pale yellow to black, depending on the toad's age, its mood, the humidity, the season and moulting activity. Dark patches regularly occur over the upper body.

PAROTID GLANDS
The Eurasian toad has a large gland behind each eye that releases a white, toxic fluid when the toad senses danger. The secretion is powerful enough to paralyze a dog but is used mainly as a deterrent.

HINDFEET
The hindfeet are webbed to aid movement in the water when mating.

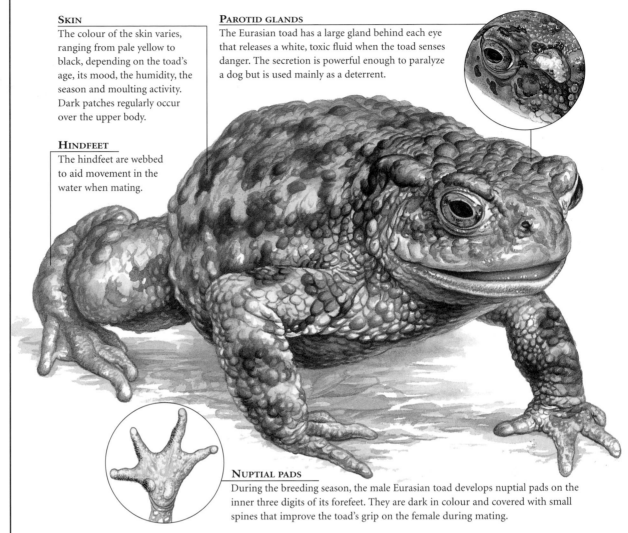

NUPTIAL PADS
During the breeding season, the male Eurasian toad develops nuptial pads on the inner three digits of its forefeet. They are dark in colour and covered with small spines that improve the toad's grip on the female during mating.

CREATURE COMPARISONS

Counterparts of the Eurasian toad live throughout the world and often differ only slightly in appearance. The Sonoran Desert toad (Bufo alvarius), for instance, is only fractionally bigger than its Eurasian cousin, with a smoother skin. It is the largest toad in western North America and is found in many types of habitat, including deserts and grasslands and even in Mexico's tropical forests. Another North American species, the great plains toad (Bufo cognatus) is slightly smaller than the Eurasian toad and is marked with large, bold blotches. As its name implies, it is primarily a grassland species, but it also inhabits scrubby desert.

Eurasian toad

Sonoran Desert toad

Great plains toad

WHERE IN THE WORLD?

The Eurasian toad is found throughout most of Europe, east across central Asia to Japan. It also occurs in northwestern Africa from Morocco to Tunisia.

RELATED SPECIES

There are about 250 species of toad in the genus Bufo. They range in size from the tiny North American oak toad, which is just 3cm (1.2in) long, to the giant South American marine toad, or cane toad, Bufo marinus, which grows to a massive 25cm (9.8in).

• **ORDER** • *Anura* • **FAMILY** • *Bufonidae* • **GENUS & SPECIES** • *Bufo marinus*

MARINE TOAD

The marine toad's large size, menacing appearance, venomous glands and tough, warty skin are enough to deter most predators.

KEY FEATURES

- A large, heavily built amphibian that secretes extremely venomous fluid to deter enemies.
- Highly adaptable: it has a varied diet and is often found close to human dwellings, especially in parks and gardens.
- Released into many regions by sugar cane growers to control insect pests, now a pest itself and a danger to native animals including amphibians.

COLOURATION
The marine toad is olive-brown to reddish-brown and speckled with white spots. Its underside is creamy-yellow flecked with brown. The female has smoother skin than the male.

PAROTID GLAND
The toad's parotid glands are large, triangular sacs located behind each ear. If the toad is attacked, the glands exude a milky-white, highly venomous toxin, squirting it up to 1m (3ft 3in).

SKIN
As with all toads, the thick, leathery skin is covered in small glands and warts that secrete toxins, making the toad distasteful to any predator.

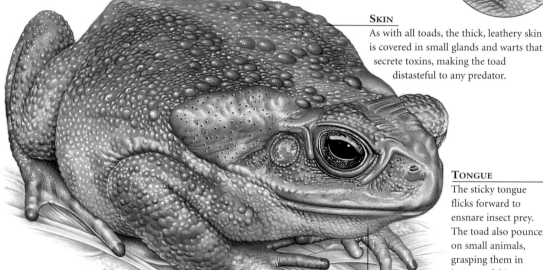

TONGUE
The sticky tongue flicks forward to ensnare insect prey. The toad also pounces on small animals, grasping them in its powerful jaws.

HINDLEGS
The muscular hindlegs allow the toad to hop and crawl long distances, rather than spring rapidly like a frog. The toes are only slightly webbed for swimming as the toad spends much of its time on land.

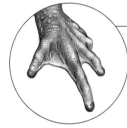

VOCAL SAC
The toad swells and deflates its vocal sac to produce its distinctive call. It makes a rhythmical trill, said to sound like a telephone dialling tone or a distant tractor.

VITAL STATISTICS

WEIGHT	Up to 1.8kg (4lb)
LENGTH	10–24cm (3.9–9.4in), female larger than male
SEXUAL MATURITY	Possibly 1 year
MATING SEASON	All year, except dry season
NUMBER OF EGGS	Up to 20,000
HATCHING PERIOD	3–7 days
LARVAL STAGE	45–60 days
BREEDING INTERVAL	Several spawnings per year
TYPICAL DIET	Mainly insects; also small mammals, amphibians and reptiles
LIFESPAN	10–15 years; up to 40 years in captivity

CREATURE COMPARISONS

The black toad (Bufo exsul) of the USA is only about a third of the length of its more widespread cousin, the marine toad. As its name suggests, it is mainly black in colour, although it may possess scattered whitish flecks and lines on its upperparts. It has a narrow white strip along its back and markings on its belly. Unlike the nocturnal marine toad, the black toad is mostly active during the day, when, like most small amphibians, it forages for invertebrates. At night it burrows into moist, sandy soil to hide. Listed as endangered, it is far more dependent on water than is the marine toad, and its range is strictly limited to the marshes and ponds of Deep Springs Valley, California.

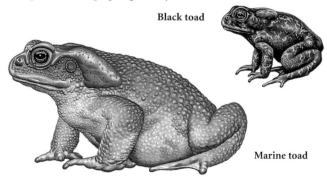

Black toad

Marine toad

WHERE IN THE WORLD?

Native to South America from Patagonia northwards, as well as Central America and parts of southern USA. Introduced to Florida, the Caribbean islands, Hawaii, New Guinea and Australia.

RELATED SPECIES

Also known as the cane toad, the neotropical toad, the giant toad or the aga toad, the marine toad is 1 of 339 species in the genus Bufo, the largest of the 25 genera in the family Bufonidae. 20 families of frogs and toads, totalling 3500 species, make up the order Anura. The class Amphibia contains 4000 species in total; salamanders and newts, order Urodeles, and caecilians, order Gymnophiona, make up the remainder of the class.

• ORDER • *Anura* • FAMILY • *Dendrobatidae* • GENUS & SPECIES • *Dendrobates pumilio*

POISON-ARROW FROG

A living jewel in the forest gloom, the strawberry poison-arrow frog is a deadly mouthful for any animal rash enough to make a meal of it.

KEY FEATURES

- Produces a powerful toxin that oozes from its skin, making it one of the most poisonous animals on Earth.
- Adorned with brilliant colours to warn of its deadly nature — and so stop predators from striking before it becomes too late to save predator or prey.

VITAL STATISTICS

LENGTH	2.5cm (1in)
MATING SEASON	All year
NUMBER OF EGGS	4 to 6; tadpoles develop in tiny pools of water in tree-growing plants, where they are fed unfertilized eggs
INCUBATION PERIOD	Varies according to the temperature
BIRTH INTERVAL	12 months
TYPICAL DIET	Ants, other small insects and spiders
LIFESPAN	3–5 years

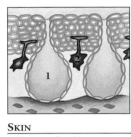

MOUTH AND TONGUE
The frog's mouth can open wide to engulf prey. The sticky tongue is attached to the front of the mouth, so it flips out a long way to snare insects and spiders.

SKIN
As long as the skin stays moist, it can absorb oxygen from the air and the frog can retain water. Above, glands in the skin produce poison (1) and mucus (2).

BODY
Many of the spine bones are fused into a single bone, the urostyle, to cope with the force exerted by the legs when leaping.

EYES
The eyes are relatively big to gather the dim light of the forest floor. Each pupil contracts to a horizontal slit in bright light to protect the sensitive retina.

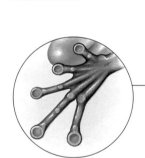

FEET
Each toe ends in a disc that acts like a sucker, so the frog can cling to glossy leaves and climb high into trees to reach its tadpoles.

LEGS
The hindlegs have powerful muscles for leaping, although poison-arrow frogs are not as athletic as some frogs.

CREATURE COMPARISONS

Frogs of the Dendrobates genus are all small-to-medium-sized species, found in the tropical American forests. They are distinguished by their brilliant skin colours that, across the genus, represent all the colours of the rainbow. The examples below include some of the most spectacular. They are similar to the strawberry poison-arrow frog in that they all raise their tadpoles in nursery pools and are highly toxic.

Dendrobates auratus

D. lehmanni

D. terribilis

D. azureus

WHERE IN THE WORLD?

Found throughout the humid rainforests of Costa Rica and parts of Nicaragua and Panama, in Central America. Many other species live in the rainforests of Amazonia.

RELATED SPECIES

The strawberry poison-arrow frog's family, Dendrobatidae, contains at least 116 species in three genera. Many more may yet be discovered in the rainforests of Central and South America. Half of these frogs are brightly coloured, poisonous species from the genera Dendrobates and Phyllobates. The third genus, Colosthetus, includes frogs that are less colourful — most are dull brown — but still share many of their relatives' habits.

• **ORDER** • *Anura* • **FAMILY** • *Pipidae* • **GENUS & SPECIES** • *Pipa spp.*

PIPA TOAD

KEY FEATURES

- Spends almost all of its life underwater.
- Uses antenna-like fingers to detect prey in murky water.
- During mating, male and female cling to each other while somersaulting through the water.
- In an extraordinary breeding cycle, female carries eggs and young on her back, snuggled in pits in her skin.

The pipa toad's camouflaged colouring enables it to ambush prey in the clouded waters of rainforest streams, ponds and marshes.

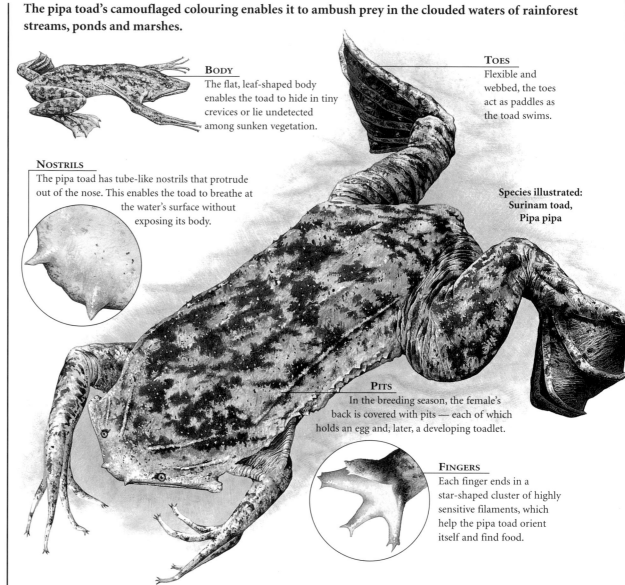

BODY
The flat, leaf-shaped body enables the toad to hide in tiny crevices or lie undetected among sunken vegetation.

TOES
Flexible and webbed, the toes act as paddles as the toad swims.

NOSTRILS
The pipa toad has tube-like nostrils that protrude out of the nose. This enables the toad to breathe at the water's surface without exposing its body.

Species illustrated: Surinam toad, Pipa pipa

PITS
In the breeding season, the female's back is covered with pits — each of which holds an egg and, later, a developing toadlet.

FINGERS
Each finger ends in a star-shaped cluster of highly sensitive filaments, which help the pipa toad orient itself and find food.

VITAL STATISTICS

LENGTH	4–18cm (1.6–7.1in)
SEXUAL MATURITY	Unknown
MATING SEASON	December to May depending on location
NUMBER OF EGGS	40 to 100
PERIOD OF DEVELOPMENT	2–4 months
BREEDING INTERVAL	1 year
TYPICAL DIET	Small invertebrates, such as insects, crustaceans and molluscs
LIFESPAN	Unknown

CREATURE COMPARISONS

Members of the same family, the African clawed toad (Xenopus laevis) and the pipa toad share a similar body plan — a flattened head and torso with heavily muscled hindlegs ending in broadly webbed toes. However, the clawed toad, which is found throughout southern Africa, has an added feature: its skin oozes a foul-smelling, slimy substance, which deters predators. Almost entirely aquatic like the pipa toad, the African clawed toad is found in ponds, lakes and rivers.

It is an exceptional swimmer and can even move backwards at speed. Unlike its South American relative, the clawed toad plays no part in rearing its offspring, although it lays many thousands of eggs to ensure that some young survive to adulthood.

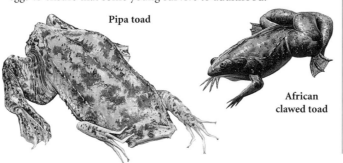

Pipa toad

African clawed toad

WHERE IN THE WORLD?

Occurs in northern and central South America east of the Andes. Also found on the island of Trinidad and parts of Central America.

RELATED SPECIES

There are 5 species in the genus Pipa: the Surinam toad, P. Pipa; Arrabal's Surinam toad, P. arrabali; Carvalho's Surinam toad, P. carvalhoi; the Sabana Surinam toad, P. parva; and the Utinga Surinam toad, P. snethlageae. The pipa toads of Central and South America share the family Pipidae with 20 species of frog, all of which are found in Africa. Like the pipa toads, these frogs are all tongueless. Frogs and toads belong to the order Anura.

• ORDER • *Anura* • FAMILY • *Ranidae* • GENUS & SPECIES • *Rana catesbeiana*

AMERICAN BULLFROG

KEY FEATURES

- The largest frog in North America, it attempts to eat any creature that fits into its enormous mouth.

- Deep, croaky bellow of the male is said to sound like jug-o'-rum — an alternative name for the bullfrog.

- Male aggressively defends his breeding territory, even wrestling with rivals.

VITAL STATISTICS

WEIGHT	200–500g (7–17.6oz)
LENGTH	Head & Body; 8.5–20cm (3.3–7.9in) Legs; Up to 25cm (9.8in)
SEXUAL MATURITY	3–5 years
BREEDING SEASON	Between February and October, according to location
NUMBER OF EGGS	10,000–20,000
HATCHING TIME	Up to 1 week
BREEDING INTERVAL	1 year
TYPICAL DIET	Insects and other invertebrates; larger prey includes frogs, reptiles and fish
LIFESPAN	Up to 15 years

Equipped with powerful legs, a wide mouth and camouflage colouring, the bullfrog is a feared predator of freshwater ponds and lakes in North America.

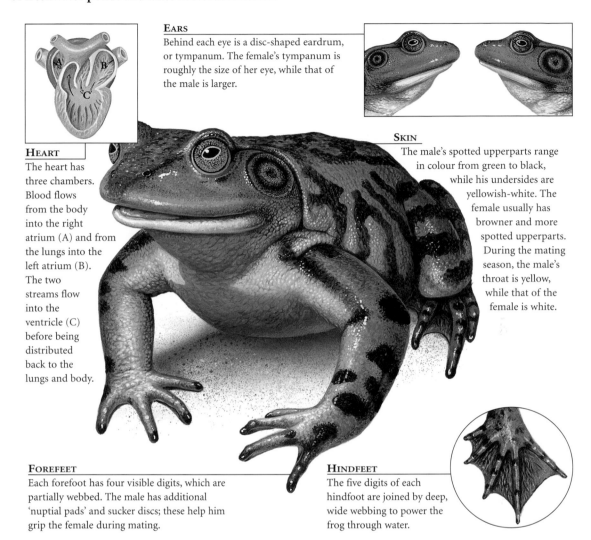

EARS
Behind each eye is a disc-shaped eardrum, or tympanum. The female's tympanum is roughly the size of her eye, while that of the male is larger.

HEART
The heart has three chambers. Blood flows from the body into the right atrium (A) and from the lungs into the left atrium (B). The two streams flow into the ventricle (C) before being distributed back to the lungs and body.

SKIN
The male's spotted upperparts range in colour from green to black, while his undersides are yellowish-white. The female usually has browner and more spotted upperparts. During the mating season, the male's throat is yellow, while that of the female is white.

FOREFEET
Each forefoot has four visible digits, which are partially webbed. The male has additional 'nuptial pads' and sucker discs; these help him grip the female during mating.

HINDFEET
The five digits of each hindfoot are joined by deep, wide webbing to power the frog through water.

CREATURE COMPARISONS

Like the American bullfrog, the African bullfrog (Pyxicephalus adspersus) is a ferocious predator, often catching rodents and birds. However, whereas the American bullfrog hibernates for the winter in the cooler parts of its range, the African bullfrog endures a period of aestivation (summer dormancy) during the hottest months of the year, as the ponds it lives in dry out. The frog burrows into the mud at the bottom of the pond and surrounds itself with a watertight sac that it secretes from its skin. When the rains return, soaking the soil, the frog wakes up, eats its sac and digs its way to the surface.

African bullfrog

American bullfrog

WHERE IN THE WORLD?

Native to eastern USA from the Great Lakes in the north to Florida in the south. Introduced to western states and other parts of the world, including Japan and Italy.

RELATED SPECIES

The bullfrog is one of more than 600 species in the family Ranidae. All frogs and toads belong to the order Anura, which means 'without tails' and is divided into 6 suborders and 20 families. The 3500 anuran species form by far the largest part of the class Amphibia. Other amphibians include more than 350 species of the order Urodela (newts and salamanders), and 150 species of the little-known order Gymnophiona (caecilians).

• **ORDER** • *Anura* • **FAMILY** • *Ranidae* • **GENUS & SPECIES** • *Rana temporaria*

COMMON FROG

The common frog has a range of special adaptations for life both on land and in the water, catering for all its needs from feeding to breeding.

KEY FEATURES

- A secretive amphibian that preys on slugs, worms and insects on warm, dark nights.
- Spends much of its time on land, but spawns in traditional breeding pools.
- Threatened in some areas by pollution and wetland drainage, but common in garden ponds.

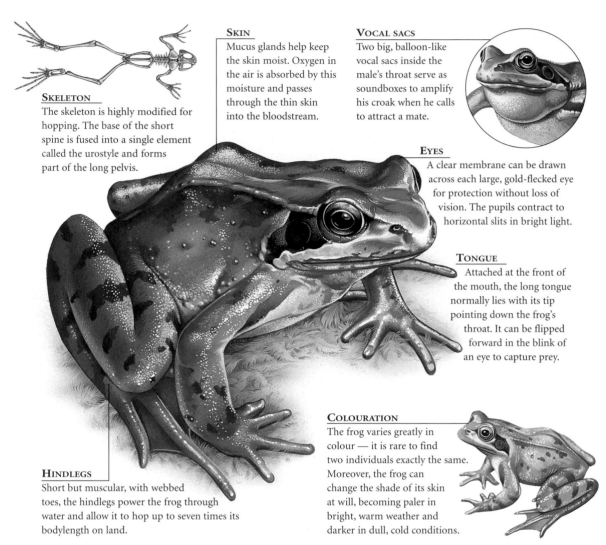

SKELETON
The skeleton is highly modified for hopping. The base of the short spine is fused into a single element called the urostyle and forms part of the long pelvis.

SKIN
Mucus glands help keep the skin moist. Oxygen in the air is absorbed by this moisture and passes through the thin skin into the bloodstream.

VOCAL SACS
Two big, balloon-like vocal sacs inside the male's throat serve as soundboxes to amplify his croak when he calls to attract a mate.

EYES
A clear membrane can be drawn across each large, gold-flecked eye for protection without loss of vision. The pupils contract to horizontal slits in bright light.

TONGUE
Attached at the front of the mouth, the long tongue normally lies with its tip pointing down the frog's throat. It can be flipped forward in the blink of an eye to capture prey.

COLOURATION
The frog varies greatly in colour — it is rare to find two individuals exactly the same. Moreover, the frog can change the shade of its skin at will, becoming paler in bright, warm weather and darker in dull, cold conditions.

HINDLEGS
Short but muscular, with webbed toes, the hindlegs power the frog through water and allow it to hop up to seven times its bodylength on land.

VITAL STATISTICS

WEIGHT	10–20g (0.3–0.7oz)
LENGTH	6–8cm (2.4–3.1in); female larger than male
SEXUAL MATURITY	3 years
BREEDING SEASON	January –March
NUMBER OF EGGS	1000 to 4000, laid in water
HATCHING TIME	10–21 days, depending on temperature
BREEDING INTERVAL	1 year
LARVAL STAGE	10–12 weeks
TYPICAL DIET	Insects, slugs and worms
LIFESPAN	Up to 12 years

CREATURE COMPARISONS

Found in many parts of Europe, the marsh frog (Rana ridibunda) is bigger and more aquatic than the common frog. It lives in large colonies by ponds, streams and slow rivers and feeds on a range of prey, from insects to fish, mice and other frogs. Indeed, wherever the marsh frog colonizes, the common frog declines, largely as a result of predation. The male marsh frog has a large external vocal sac and a much louder croak than the purring grook-grook of the common frog. The marsh frog was introduced to England in 1935, to Romney Marsh in Kent. It has since spread to the Pevensey Levels and other marshy areas in Sussex, and been introduced to other southern counties.

Marsh frog

Common frog

WHERE IN THE WORLD?

Found throughout Europe from northern Spain, northern Italy, Bulgaria and the whole of Scandinavia east through central Asia as far as Japan.

RELATED SPECIES

The common frog is 1 of approximately 250 species in the genus Rana. Found almost everywhere apart from Australia and New Zealand, the genus includes the leopard frog, R. pipiens, of North America, and the tiger frog, R. tigrina, of southeastern Asia. Rana is 1 of nearly 50 genera in the family Ranidae, the true frogs, which includes more than 600 species. The order Anura comprises 20 families of frogs and toads, with a total of some 3500 species.

• ORDER • *Apodiformes* • FAMILY • *Apodidae* • GENUS & SPECIES • *Apus apus*

EURASIAN SWIFT

The swift's scythe-like wings help it twist and turn after prey, and its wide gape forms an efficient scoop for flying insects.

KEY FEATURES

- When not nesting, spends all of its time in the air — even mating on the wing.
- Feeds by trawling through swarms of insects.
- Gathers in huge, screaming flocks when feeding and before migration.
- Sleeps in the air at altitudes of up to 1800m.

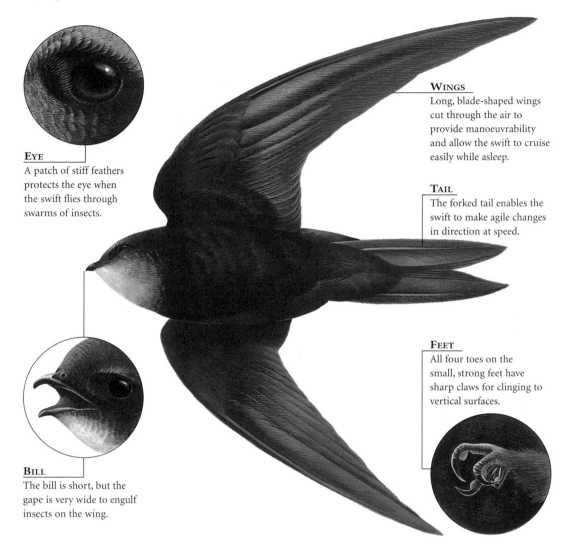

EYE
A patch of stiff feathers protects the eye when the swift flies through swarms of insects.

WINGS
Long, blade-shaped wings cut through the air to provide manoeuvrability and allow the swift to cruise easily while asleep.

TAIL
The forked tail enables the swift to make agile changes in direction at speed.

FEET
All four toes on the small, strong feet have sharp claws for clinging to vertical surfaces.

BILL
The bill is short, but the gape is very wide to engulf insects on the wing.

VITAL STATISTICS

WEIGHT	37–50g (1.3–1.8oz)
LENGTH	16–17cm (6.3–6.7in)
WINGSPAN	41–47.5cm (16.1–18.7in)
SEXUAL MATURITY	1–2 years, but probably does not breed until 4 years old
BREEDING SEASON	Late April to early August
NUMBER OF EGGS	1 to 4; usually 2 or 3
INCUBATION PERIOD	19–27 days, usually 20 days
FLEDGING PERIOD	5–8 weeks
BREEDING INTERVAL	Annual
TYPICAL DIET	Flying insects; spiders
LIFESPAN	Up to 21 years

CREATURE COMPARISONS

Swifts are found throughout the world in temperate and tropical regions. Although broadly similar in appearance, the species differ dramatically in size. The tiny pygmy palm swift (*Tachornis furcata*), which barely reaches 10cm (3.9in) in length, is native to northeastern Colombia in South America. It is most commonly seen near palm trees, and its flight is rapid but erratic.

Measuring more than 20cm (7.9in) in length, the brown spine-tailed swift (*Hirundapus giganteus*) lives mainly in woodlands. It has an extensive range across Asia from western India east to Java, Bali and Sumatra. This giant among swifts makes up for its lack of agility with a terrific turn of speed.

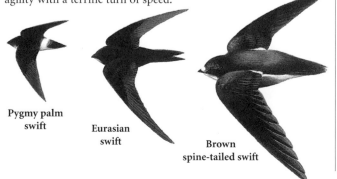

Pygmy palm swift

Eurasian swift

Brown spine-tailed swift

WHERE IN THE WORLD?

Breeds throughout Europe, parts of North Africa and the Middle East to central Asia, extending as far east as northern China. Many birds migrate to Africa in winter.

RELATED SPECIES

Although they look like swallows and martins, swifts are not related to them. The swift family Apodidae is placed in the order Apodiformes, along with the 4 species of tree swift in the family Hemiprocnidae, and the 330 or more hummingbirds in the family Trochilidae. The 82 species within the swift family are further classified in 3 subfamilies: the Apodinae (including the Eurasian swift), the Cypseloidinae and the Chaeturinae.

• ORDER • *Apodiformes* • FAMILY • *Trochilidae* • GENUS & SPECIES • *Archilochus colubris*

HUMMINGBIRD

KEY FEATURES

- A tiny bird with big performance, capable of astonishing feats of flight and endurance.
- Able to hover and fly backward, sideways — and even upside-down.
- Brilliant colours sparkle like jewels in the sun as it sips nectar from the throats of flowers.
- Beats its wings at an incredibly fast rate to produce the 'hum.'

VITAL STATISTICS

WEIGHT	5.5–7g (0.19–0.25oz)
LENGTH	9–9.5cm (3.5–3.7in)
WINGSPAN	10–12cm (3.9–4.7in)
SEXUAL MATURITY	1 year
MATING SEASON	Mainly May to June, but from March in the south to July in the north
NUMBER OF EGGS	2
INCUBATION PERIOD	16 days
FLEDGING PERIOD	22–24 days
NUMBER OF BROODS	1, often 2, occasionally 3 per year
TYPICAL DIET	Nectar, insects and spiders
LIFESPAN	Up to 5 years in the wild

Whether hovering or accelerating vertically like a nectar-fuelled rocket, the ruby-throat is a master of the air, aided by some unique features.

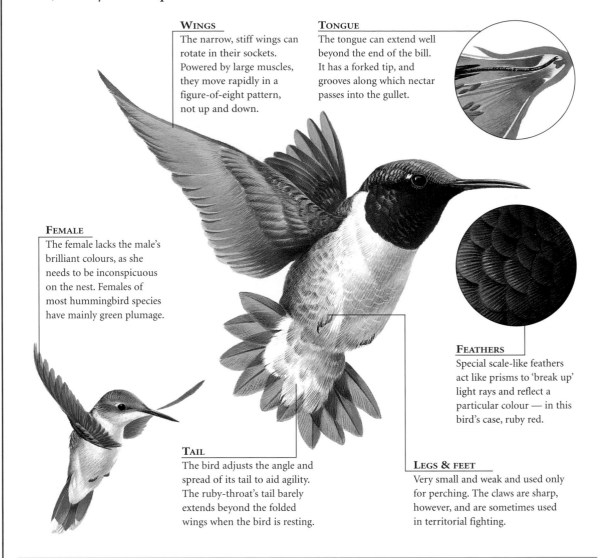

WINGS
The narrow, stiff wings can rotate in their sockets. Powered by large muscles, they move rapidly in a figure-of-eight pattern, not up and down.

TONGUE
The tongue can extend well beyond the end of the bill. It has a forked tip, and grooves along which nectar passes into the gullet.

FEMALE
The female lacks the male's brilliant colours, as she needs to be inconspicuous on the nest. Females of most hummingbird species have mainly green plumage.

FEATHERS
Special scale-like feathers act like prisms to 'break up' light rays and reflect a particular colour — in this bird's case, ruby red.

TAIL
The bird adjusts the angle and spread of its tail to aid agility. The ruby-throat's tail barely extends beyond the folded wings when the bird is resting.

LEGS & FEET
Very small and weak and used only for perching. The claws are sharp, however, and are sometimes used in territorial fighting.

CREATURE COMPARISONS

Hummingbirds have a variety of bill shapes designed for feeding from different flower species. The sword-billed hummingbird has the longest bill, in proportion to body size, of any bird. The ruby-throat can reach into comparatively smaller blooms, while the white-tipped sicklebill can reach the nectar of flowers whose petals have a curved neck. By feeding from flowers in this way, hummingbirds are important pollinators of many flower species.

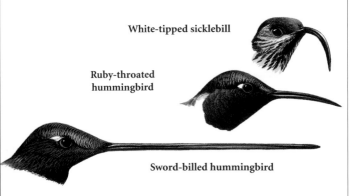

White-tipped sicklebill

Ruby-throated hummingbird

Sword-billed hummingbird

WHERE IN THE WORLD?

A migratory species that breeds east of the Rocky Mountains in the United States and southern Canada, and flies south to spend the winter

months in warmer habitats in Mexico and Central America, as far south as Panama.

RELATED SPECIES

The ruby-throat is one of more than 300 species of hummingbird found in the Americas, from Alaska to Tierra del Fuego. These include what is probably the world's smallest bird, the five-centimetre-long (2in) bee hummingbird, a rare species native to Cuba.

WOLF SPIDER

• ORDER • *Araneae* • FAMILY • *Lycosidae* • GENUS & SPECIES • *Various*

The wolf spider is an active hunter that seeks prey with its excellent eyesight, then nimbly pursues it before pouncing to inject a fatal venom.

KEY FEATURES

- Does not spin a web to catch prey, instead it hunts actively, pouncing on small insects or other spiders.
- Male courts female with flagging movements of his sex organs to avoid being mistaken as prey.
- Female keeps her eggs in a sac on her abdomen, and later carries up to 200 spiderlings on her body.

SPINNERETS
Although the wolf spider does not spin a web to catch prey, it can produce silk from spinneret organs located at the rear of the abdomen. When hunting, it often trails a line of silk so that it can abseil to safety if it misjudges a tricky leap. The female also uses the silk to spin a protective bag for her eggs.

MOUTHPARTS
The fangs (a) are part of appendages called chelicerae (B). The fangs are hollow and inject venom to kill or subdue prey.

Species illustrated: Pardosa palustris

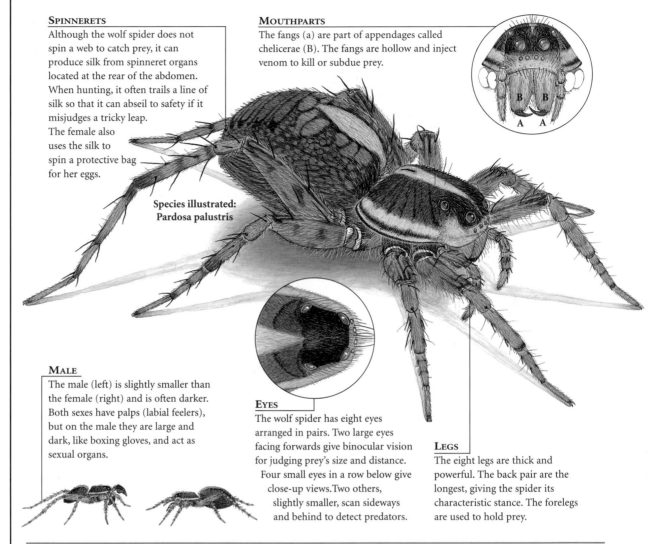

MALE
The male (left) is slightly smaller than the female (right) and is often darker. Both sexes have palps (labial feelers), but on the male they are large and dark, like boxing gloves, and act as sexual organs.

EYES
The wolf spider has eight eyes arranged in pairs. Two large eyes facing forwards give binocular vision for judging prey's size and distance. Four small eyes in a row below give close-up views. Two others, slightly smaller, scan sideways and behind to detect predators.

LEGS
The eight legs are thick and powerful. The back pair are the longest, giving the spider its characteristic stance. The forelegs are used to hold prey.

VITAL STATISTICS

LENGTH	4–35mm (0.2–1.4in)
LEGSPAN	15–100mm (0.6–3.9in)
SEXUAL MATURITY	9–15 months
BREEDING SEASON	Summer in temperate climates; all year round in tropical regions
NUMBER OF EGGS	50 to 200
INCUBATION PERIOD	1–2 weeks
BREEDING INTERVAL	Each female usually rears 2 to 4 sacs of eggs in her lifetime
TYPICAL DIET	Small insects and spiders
LIFESPAN	Up to 2 years

CREATURE COMPARISONS

Belonging to the same order as wolf spiders, the huge Mexican red-kneed spider (Brachypelma smithi), with a head and body length of 75–100mm (2.9–3.1in), is many times the size of most wolf spider species. Found in scrubby regions of southwestern Mexico, the Mexican red-kneed spider feeds on a variety of insects. But whereas a wolf spider uses its excellent eyesight to seek out prey, the Mexican red-kneed spider uses its extremely sensitive leg hairs to detect changes in air currents caused by moving prey. Like a wolf spider, this species pounces on its victims.

Wolf spider

Mexican red-kneed spider

WHERE IN THE WORLD?

Found throughout the world in a wide range of habitats, from deserts and dunes to grasslands and tropical forests. Absent only from polar regions.

RELATED SPECIES

Worldwide, there are over 2000 species of wolf spider in the order Araneae. Orb-web spiders, such as Micrathena gracilis, are also members of this order but, unlike wolf spiders, they catch prey in their impressively intricate orb webs.

• **ORDER** • *Araneae* • **FAMILY** • *Theraphosidae* • **GENUS** • *Brachypelma smithi*

MEXICAN RED-KNEED SPIDER

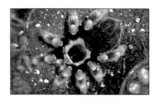

KEY FEATURES

- Poor eyesight does not deter this nocturnal predator — it relies instead on its sensitivity to noise and vibration.
- A sit-and-wait predator, ambushing its prey at or near its burrow entrance and dragging it inside to devour it.
- Endowed with a lethal reputation fuelled by lurid movies, although its deep bite is very rarely fatal to human victims.

VITAL STATISTICS

WEIGHT	57g (2oz)
BODY LENGTH	7.5–10cm (2.9–3.9in)
LEGSPAN	Up to 18cm (7.1in)
SEXUAL MATURITY	5–7 years
NUMBER OF EGGS	Up to 400
HATCHING TIME	2 to 3 months
BIRTH INTERVAL	1 year
TYPICAL DIET	Large insects; possibly small lizards and small rodents
LIFESPAN	Up to 30 years

The Mexican red-kneed spider is a highly specialized predator, equipped with needle-like fangs to inject poison and powerful jaws to crush prey.

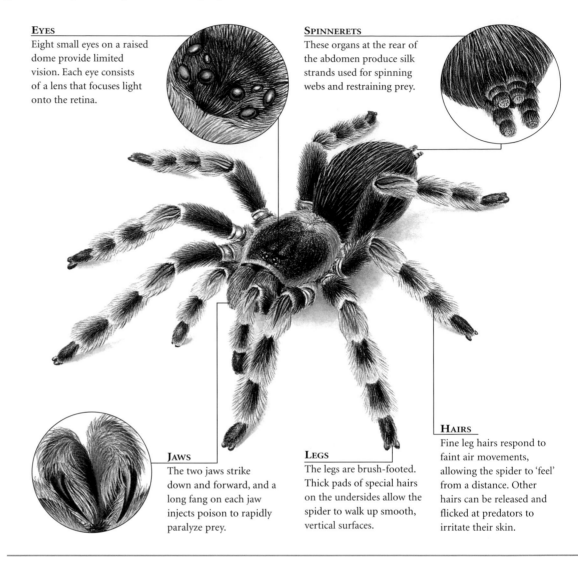

EYES
Eight small eyes on a raised dome provide limited vision. Each eye consists of a lens that focuses light onto the retina.

SPINNERETS
These organs at the rear of the abdomen produce silk strands used for spinning webs and restraining prey.

JAWS
The two jaws strike down and forward, and a long fang on each jaw injects poison to rapidly paralyze prey.

LEGS
The legs are brush-footed. Thick pads of special hairs on the undersides allow the spider to walk up smooth, vertical surfaces.

HAIRS
Fine leg hairs respond to faint air movements, allowing the spider to 'feel' from a distance. Other hairs can be released and flicked at predators to irritate their skin.

CREATURE COMPARISONS

The term tarantula is generally applied to any large, hairy spider, including the red-kneed spider. The huge tarantulas of the genera Lasiodora and Grammostola from the Brazilian jungles prey on small snakes, lizards and frogs. Avicularia avicularia, from Brazil, Guyana and Trinidad, lives in trees, where it spins tubular silk retreats attached to branches. It feeds on lizards and nestling birds. The largest of all the tarantulas is the goliath spider of Guyana, which has a legspan of nearly 30cm (11.8in).

Red-kneed spider   Avicularia   Goliath spider

WHERE IN THE WORLD?

Found in southwestern Mexico, west of the mountainous Sierra Madre Occidental, between Jalisco and Oaxaca states. Most abundant in Guerrero state, situated roughly in the middle of this range.

RELATED SPECIES

The Mexican red-kneed spider belongs to the suborder Orthognatha: this includes large, tropical species, such as funnel-web spiders, bird-eating spiders and the tarantulas, including the true tarantula, Lycosa tarantula, that is found in southern Europe.

BLACK WIDOW SPIDER

• **ORDER** • *Araneae* • **FAMILY** • *Theridiidae* • **GENUS & SPECIES** • *Latrodectus mactans*

The female black widow spider is surprisingly small, given the extreme potency of her venom — and the harmless male is tinier still.

KEY FEATURES

- Ensnares insects with a sticky, tangled web, and subdues or kills them with extremely potent venom.
- Responsible for several deaths among humans in the USA, although only a small fraction of bites are fatal.
- Female is much larger than the male; she alone bites humans, but is aggressive only when provoked.

VITAL STATISTICS

LENGTH	Female up to 1.25cm (0.5in); male much smaller
LEGSPAN	1.9cm (0.7in)
SEXUAL MATURITY	1 year
MATING SEASON	During the warmest months of the year
NUMBER OF EGGS	50 to 100
HATCHING PERIOD	4–6 weeks
BREEDING INTERVAL	1 year
TYPICAL DIET	Arthropods, such as beetles, cockroaches and scorpions, as well as other species of spider
LIFESPAN	Up to 2 years

BODY
The cephalothorax (head and thorax) contains the brain, mouthparts, venom glands, leg muscles and a sucking stomach. The abdomen contains the heart, lungs, and reproductive organs, as well as the digestive system and silk spinnerets.

LEGS
The eight legs have hairs and bristles sensitive to vibration. Barbed hairs and a hook on the claws allow the spider to move around on, and hang from, its web.

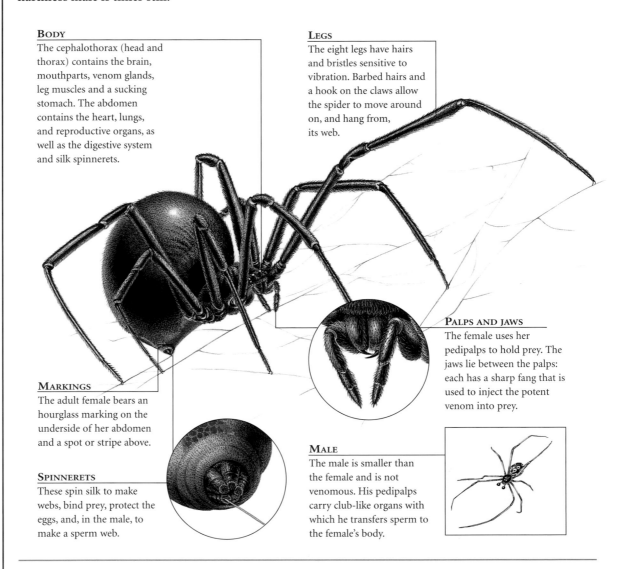

MARKINGS
The adult female bears an hourglass marking on the underside of her abdomen and a spot or stripe above.

SPINNERETS
These spin silk to make webs, bind prey, protect the eggs, and, in the male, to make a sperm web.

PALPS AND JAWS
The female uses her pedipalps to hold prey. The jaws lie between the palps: each has a sharp fang that is used to inject the potent venom into prey.

MALE
The male is smaller than the female and is not venomous. His pedipalps carry club-like organs with which he transfers sperm to the female's body.

CREATURE COMPARISONS

Only a few spiders are dangerous to humans, and most live in warmer parts of the world. In South Africa, Sicarius hahnii rarely bites humans, but is among the most toxic of all spiders. The male Sydney funnelweb spider, common in Sydney, Australia, is more deadly than the female. Another venomous Australian spider is the redback, a close relative of the black widow spider. The Loxosceles recluse spiders occur in the USA and other parts of the world: their bites can cause skin blisters leading to gangrene. (Spiders not drawn to scale.)

Sicarius hahnii

Sydney funnelweb spider

Australian redback spider

Recluse spider

WHERE IN THE WORLD?

Found in North America, from Massachusetts south to Florida and west through Texas, Oklahoma, Kansas and California. Also found in Mexico and Panama.

RELATED SPECIES

The 30 or so species in the genus Latrodectus are distributed widely across the world's warm regions. The European widow spider, L. tredecimguttatus, is probably the real culprit of a plague of bites two to three centuries ago in Italy and France that were once attributed to tarantulas.

• **ORDER** • *Araneae* • **FAMILY** • *Theridiidae* • **GENUS & SPECIES** • *Theridion sisyphium*

MOTHERCARE SPIDER

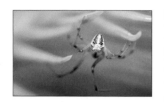

KEY FEATURES

- Most spiders abandon their newly hatched young, but the female mothercare spider guards hers for up to five weeks to protect them from predators.

- Female feeds a nutritious milk, mouth to mouth, to her spiderlings. As a result, they grow much faster than the young of other spider species.

VITAL STATISTICS

LENGTH	Female up to 4.7mm (0.18in); male slightly smaller
LEGSPAN	11mm (0.4in)
SEXUAL MATURITY	About 9 months
BREEDING SEASON	Late May to early July
NUMBER OF EGGS	25 to 35
HATCHING PERIOD	3–5 weeks
BREEDING INTERVAL	Each female produces one brood in her lifetime
TYPICAL DIET	Invertebrates, such as beetles, flies, ants, other spiders
LIFESPAN	Up to 15 months

The mothercare spider is one of the 'comb-footed' spiders, named after the bristles on its hindlegs with which it cleans its spinnerets.

PEDIPALPS AND JAWS
The female uses her pedipalps (feelers) for holding prey. The jaws bear a pair of curved fangs able to inject a powerful venom into victims.

MALE
The male has a smaller abdomen than the female. He uses his pedipalps to transfer sperm to the female.

ABDOMEN
The female's black-and-white abdomen has a reddish-brown marking. Spinnerets at the rear end pay out silk for making webs and trapping prey.

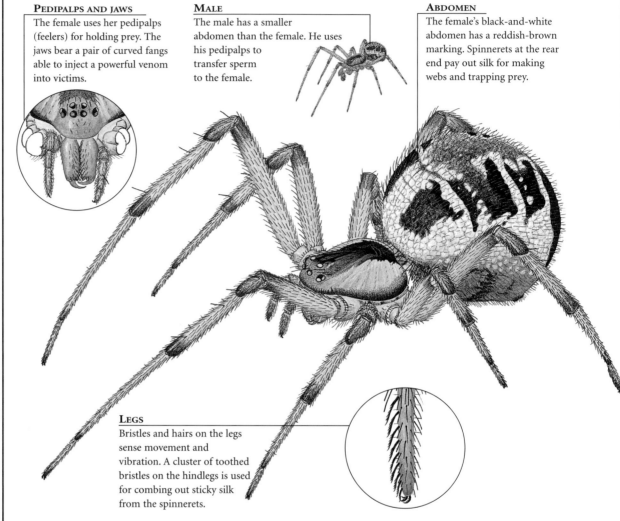

LEGS
Bristles and hairs on the legs sense movement and vibration. A cluster of toothed bristles on the hindlegs is used for combing out sticky silk from the spinnerets.

CREATURE COMPARISONS

Some other spiders care for their young, although few are as diligent as the mothercare spider. Achaearanea riparia from Europe plucks her web to bring her spiderlings down to feed on a trapped insect. A. tepidariorum makes a succession of egg-sacs over a short period but does not nurture her young. Enoplognatha ovata stands guard over her eggs until she dies at her post, before the spiderlings hatch.

Mothercare spider

Achaearanea riparia

A. tepidariorum

Enoplognatha ovata

WHERE IN THE WORLD?

Widespread across warm temperate zones of much of Eurasia, from Britain and Spain east across Europe and Central Asia as far as eastern China.

RELATED SPECIES

Worldwide, there are about 2200 species in the family Theridiidae, several of which look broadly similar to the mothercare spider; some also feed their young. Many species build a scaffold web near the ground, complete with vertical sticky lines for catching crawling insects. Theridion bimaculatum trails her large egg-sac behind her on a silken thread. In T. pallens, the egg-sacs are larger even than the adult spider.

PRONGHORN

• **ORDER** • *Artiodactyla* • **FAMILY** • *Antilocapridae* • **GENUS & SPECIES** • *Antilocapra americana*

KEY FEATURES

- Swifter than a thoroughbred racehorse, it can reach and sustain speeds of over 80km/h (49.7mph).
- Flourishes in the scorching heat of the desert and the freezing temperatures of high-altitude plains.
- Sole member of its family, displaying a unique combination of goat- and antelope-like features.

VITAL STATISTICS

WEIGHT	36–70kg (79.4–154.3lb)
LENGTH	Head & Body: 1–1.5m (3ft 3in–4ft 9in) Tail: 7.5–18cm (2.9–7.1in)
HORNS	Male 43cm (16.9in); female 4cm (1.6in)
SHOULDER HEIGHT	81–104cm (31.9–40.9in)
SEXUAL MATURITY	15–16 months
MATING SEASON	July to early October
GESTATION PERIOD	252 days
NUMBER OF YOUNG	1 for initial birth, then 2, rarely 3, subsequently
BIRTH INTERVAL	1 year
TYPICAL DIET	Shrubs, grasses, herbs and cacti
LIFESPAN	6–8 years

Exceptional eyesight and long legs enable the pronghorn to detect danger and escape at speeds unmatched by any other land animal in the New World.

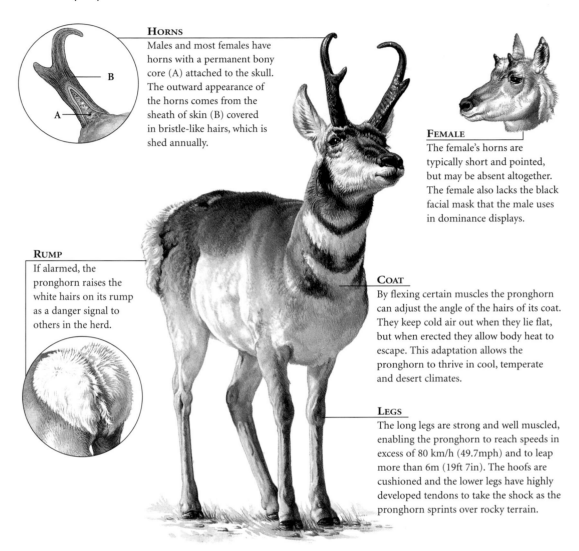

HORNS
Males and most females have horns with a permanent bony core (A) attached to the skull. The outward appearance of the horns comes from the sheath of skin (B) covered in bristle-like hairs, which is shed annually.

FEMALE
The female's horns are typically short and pointed, but may be absent altogether. The female also lacks the black facial mask that the male uses in dominance displays.

RUMP
If alarmed, the pronghorn raises the white hairs on its rump as a danger signal to others in the herd.

COAT
By flexing certain muscles the pronghorn can adjust the angle of the hairs of its coat. They keep cold air out when they lie flat, but when erected they allow body heat to escape. This adaptation allows the pronghorn to thrive in cool, temperate and desert climates.

LEGS
The long legs are strong and well muscled, enabling the pronghorn to reach speeds in excess of 80 km/h (49.7mph) and to leap more than 6m (19ft 7in). The hoofs are cushioned and the lower legs have highly developed tendons to take the shock as the pronghorn sprints over rocky terrain.

CREATURE COMPARISONS

The pronghorn's unusual horns have been the subject of intensive study — their uniqueness providing the reason for the animal's exclusion from either the Cervidae (deer) or Bovidae (antelope, cattle, goats and sheep) family. The roe deer (Capreolus capreolus), for example, a member of the family Cervidae, has antlers resembling the pronghorn's, but they have no permanent bony core. Likewise, the horns of the bushbuck (Tragelaphus scriptus), a member of the family Bovidae, are slightly larger, but they are not shed annually like those of the pronghorn.

Pronghorn   Roe deer   Bushbuck

WHERE IN THE WORLD?

Ranges over western North America, from southwestern Canada through the USA, especially the Rocky Mountain states, south into northern Mexico.

RELATED SPECIES

The pronghorn belongs to the order Artiodactyla, which includes all grazing mammals with an even number of toes. Its habits, behaviour and appearance persuaded some experts to classify it within the family Bovidae, which includes antelope, cattle and sheep. However, the differences in horn structure now seem to be conclusive physiological evidence that the pronghorn should be placed as the sole member of its own family: the Antilocapridae.

• ORDER • *Artiodactyla* • FAMILY • *Bovidae* • GENUS & SPECIES • *Hippotragus niger*

SABLE ANTELOPE

Big-boned, powerfully built and armed with a spectacular set of horns, the sable antelope is one of the most imposing animals of the African savannahs.

KEY FEATURES

- Mature males live solitary lives, while females gather in herds with strict hierarchical structures.
- Long, pointed horns are deadly enough to deter predators — unlike those of most antelopes.
- Almost horse-like in appearance with sturdy legs and a thick neck capped with a short, stiff mane.

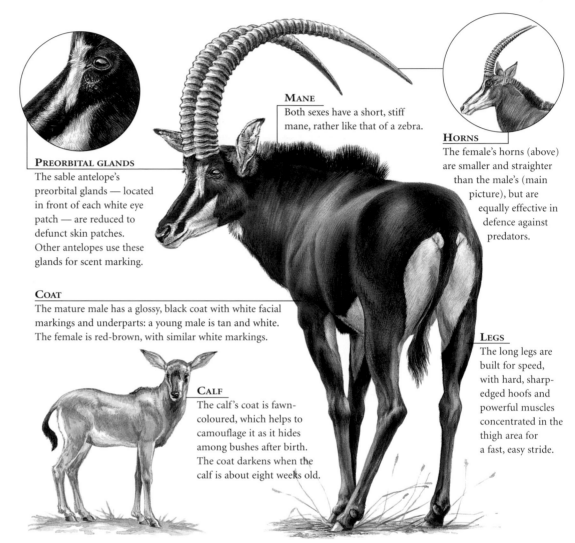

MANE
Both sexes have a short, stiff mane, rather like that of a zebra.

HORNS
The female's horns (above) are smaller and straighter than the male's (main picture), but are equally effective in defence against predators.

PREORBITAL GLANDS
The sable antelope's preorbital glands — located in front of each white eye patch — are reduced to defunct skin patches. Other antelopes use these glands for scent marking.

COAT
The mature male has a glossy, black coat with white facial markings and underparts: a young male is tan and white. The female is red-brown, with similar white markings.

CALF
The calf's coat is fawn-coloured, which helps to camouflage it as it hides among bushes after birth. The coat darkens when the calf is about eight weeks old.

LEGS
The long legs are built for speed, with hard, sharp-edged hoofs and powerful muscles concentrated in the thigh area for a fast, easy stride.

VITAL STATISTICS

WEIGHT	Male 216–263kg (476.2–579.8lb) female 204–232kg (449.7–511.5lb)
LENGTH	Head & Body: 1.9–2.1m (6ft 2in–6ft 9in) Tail: 37–76cm (14.6–29.9in)
SHOULDER HEIGHT	1.2–1.4m (3ft 9in–4ft 6in)
SEXUAL MATURITY	Male 6 years; female 2 years
MATING SEASON	Varies according to location; births timed to occur in the rainy season
GESTATION PERIOD	8–9 months
NUMBER OF YOUNG	1
BIRTH INTERVAL	1 year
TYPICAL DIET	Mainly grass; some leaves
LIFESPAN	Up to 10 years

CREATURE COMPARISONS

The sable antelope's closest relative is the roan antelope (Hippotragus equinus). Unlike the sable antelope there is no difference in colouration between the male and female — both sexes are sand-coloured. The roan antelope is slightly larger than the sable antelope, but otherwise is very similar in its appearance and habits. Although the roan antelope is widely distributed throughout the savannahs of southern and central Africa, it is rare and even endangered in many parts of its range as a result of poaching and loss of habitat.

Roan antelope

Sable antelope

WHERE IN THE WORLD?

Found in wooded savannah grasslands in parts of Africa, from southeastern Kenya south to South Africa. An isolated population also occurs in Angola.

RELATED SPECIES

There are four subspecies of sable antelope: Hippotragus niger roosevelti, from Kenya and Tanzania, has the shortest horns, while H. n. varianii, or giant sable antelope of Angola, has the longest. H. n. kirkii lacks cheek stripes and has the largest range, and H. n. niger is the most distinctive subspecies — with females nearly as dark as the males. H. n. niger is found south of the Zambezi River in Zimbabwe and Mozambique.

ADDAX

KEY FEATURES

- Impressively horned antelope that inhabits one of the harshest environments on Earth: the Sahara Desert.
- Survives by minimizing fluid loss, gaining almost all of its moisture from the plants it eats.
- Hunted heavily in the past; classified as endangered by the IUCN (World Conservation Union).

VITAL STATISTICS

WEIGHT	60–125kg (132.3–275.6lb)
SHOULDER HEIGHT	95–110cm (37.4–43.3in)
LENGTH	Head & Body: 1.5–1.7m (4ft 9in–5ft 6in) Tail: 25–35cm (9.8–13.8in)
SEXUAL MATURITY	2–3 years
MATING SEASON	Peaks in hottest and coldest months
GESTATION PERIOD	257–264 days
NUMBER OF YOUNG	1
BREEDING INTERVAL	1 year
TYPICAL DIET	Desert grasses and shrub foliage
LIFESPAN	20 years

Heavily built and with an ambling gait, the addax is designed for stamina and endurance rather than nimble sprinting.

SKULL
The skull is very thick all over to absorb the shock as males head-butt each other to gain dominance. The bone is thickest at the forehead where the impact is greatest.

SUMMER COAT
In the summer the addax grows an almost white coat, which helps to reflect much of the sun's life-sapping heat. In addition, predators find the animal harder to spot against the bleached terrain.

HORNS
Both sexes possess the large, striking horns, which have up to three twists.

FACIAL PATTERN
Some experts believe that the yellow, white and chestnut pattern on the addax's face is a form of camouflage to confuse desert predators.

TAIL
The tail has a tassel at the tip — a useful swatter to discourage the constant swarms of flies.

HOOF
The hoofs are widely splayed and flatten further when in contact with the ground. This helps the addax walk on loose sand and gravel.

CREATURE COMPARISONS

The scimitar-horned oryx (Oryx dammah), so called because its long straight horns resemble a curved sword or scimitar, shares parts of its range with the addax. However, it rarely ventures as deeply into the Sahara Desert as does its hardy cousin, and is found mainly in the semi-desert Sahel region to the south, and from there through Nigeria to the Atlantic coast. The scimitar-horned oryx is slightly larger than the addax and has more colour patches on its body. Like the addax, it has declined heavily across its range and now teeters on the brink of extinction in the wild. Its survival depends on the success of captive-breeding programmes.

Addax

Scimitar-horned oryx

WHERE IN THE WORLD?

Patchy distribution in northern, western and central Sahara Desert with small concentrations in Niger, Mali, Chad, Sudan and Mauritania.

RELATED SPECIES

The addax is the sole member of its genus. Its closest relatives are the sable antelope, the roan antelope and the 3 members of the genus Oryx. These species are adapted to live in semi-arid habitats, but none so well as the addax. All antelopes belong to the family Bovidae, which also includes cattle, bison, goats and sheep. The family Bovidae is 1 of 9 families in the order Artiodactyla, or even-toed hoofed mammals.

• ORDER • *Artiodactyla* • FAMILY • *Bovidae* • GENUS & SPECIES • *Aepyceros melampus*

IMPALA

KEY FEATURES

- Performs an unusual defence strategy when startled by a predator, involving a series of stiff, high leaps that triggers the rest of the herd to 'explode' in the same way.
- Outside the breeding season, lives in herds of up to 100 animals.
- Both a grazer and a browser, it adjusts its diet of vegetation according to the time of year and the type of habitat.

VITAL STATISTICS

WEIGHT	Male 60–65kg (132.3–143.3lb) female 40–45kg (88.2–99.2lb)
LENGTH	Head & Body: 1–1.4m (3ft 3in– 4ft 6in) Tail: 20–40cm (7.9–15.7in)
SHOULDER HEIGHT	80–100cm (31–39.4in)
SEXUAL MATURITY	13 months, but female rarely breeds before 2 years and male before 4 years
MATING SEASON	March to June; September to November
GESTATION PERIOD	195–200 days
NUMBER OF YOUNG	1
BIRTH INTERVAL	1 year
TYPICAL DIET	Leaves, short grasses, fruit
LIFESPAN	12–13 years

A graceful build and long, powerful legs mean that the impala is always quick off the mark. This enables it to evade sudden attacks by predators.

FEMALE
Female impala lack horns and are smaller than males, but in other respects are similar, with a long muzzle and pointed ears. Both sexes have excellent senses of sight, hearing and smell.

HORNS
The male's horns are a symbol of maturity and dominance. Rings are added with age and some males have as many as 25 rings.

BACK
The straight back, a characteristic feature of the species, is very strong and helps the impala absorb the landing shock of its 3m (9ft 8in)-high jumps.

FOREHEAD
A gland on the male's forehead produces a scent that tells other males of his status. Within a male herd, individuals may signal group ties by rubbing heads and exchanging scents.

GLAND
Male and female impala have tufts of black hair that cover glands on their hindlegs just above the ankles. These glands, unique among antelopes, lay a scent trail, which an individual can follow back to its herd if it becomes lost.

LEGS AND BODY
The impala is a medium-sized antelope with a lightweight frame. It is built for speed and agility, and is especially nimble among the scrub and trees of the savannah's light woodlands. It can run at approximately 50 km/h (31.1mph) on its long, slender legs.

CREATURE COMPARISONS

The springbok and Thomson's gazelle are exceptional as members of the family Bovidae in that the does (females) as well as the bucks (males) have horns. These two species, like the impala, have horns that curve outward and end in inward-pointing tips. The impala's graceful, lyre-shaped horns, though, which may grow to 90cm (35.4in), are especially distinctive.

Springbok   Thomson's gazelle   Impala

WHERE IN THE WORLD?

Found in sandy bush country, open woodlands and acacia savannahs of central and southern Africa, ranging from Kenya to South Africa. Range also extends to a coastal strip of Angola.

RELATED SPECIES

The impala is the only species within the genus Aepyceros. Although in the past the impala has been grouped with gazelles, kobs and, most recently, hartebeests, it is so different from all other antelopes that it is also classed in a tribe of its own. There is also no evidence that more than one species has ever existed. There are, however, six subspecies, including the black-faced impala, found in southwest Angola.

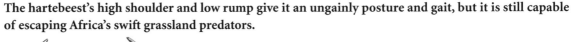

The hartebeest's high shoulder and low rump give it an ungainly posture and gait, but it is still capable of escaping Africa's swift grassland predators.

KEY FEATURES

- Shows distinct local variations in horn shape and coat colouring across the different parts of its African grassland range.
- Females live in herds that may be hundreds strong; males hold individual territories.
- Faces competition from domestic cattle. Two subspecies are currently listed as endangered by the IUCN (World Conservation Union).

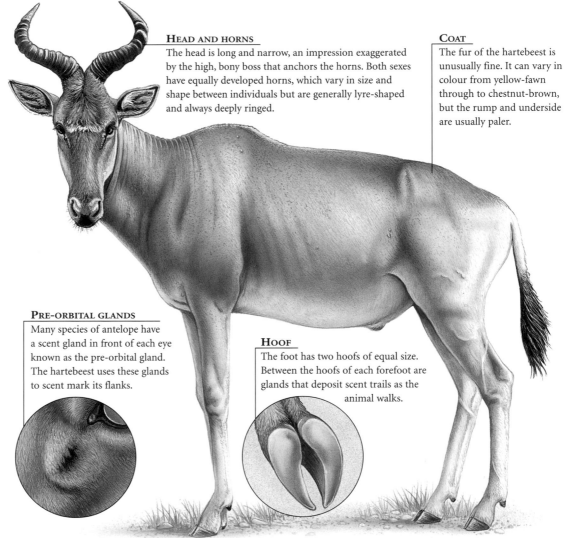

HEAD AND HORNS
The head is long and narrow, an impression exaggerated by the high, bony boss that anchors the horns. Both sexes have equally developed horns, which vary in size and shape between individuals but are generally lyre-shaped and always deeply ringed.

COAT
The fur of the hartebeest is unusually fine. It can vary in colour from yellow-fawn through to chestnut-brown, but the rump and underside are usually paler.

PRE-ORBITAL GLANDS
Many species of antelope have a scent gland in front of each eye known as the pre-orbital gland. The hartebeest uses these glands to scent mark its flanks.

HOOF
The foot has two hoofs of equal size. Between the hoofs of each forefoot are glands that deposit scent trails as the animal walks.

VITAL STATISTICS

WEIGHT	Male 125–218kg (275.6–480.6lb); female 116–185kg (255.7–407.9lb)
LENGTH	Head & Body: 1.07–2.15m (3ft 5in–7ft) Tail: 30–70cm (11.8–27.6in))
SHOULDER HEIGHT	1.1–1.5m (3ft 6in–4ft 9in)
SEXUAL MATURITY	2–2.5 years
MATING SEASON	February–June
GESTATION PERIOD	240 days
NUMBER OF YOUNG	1, rarely twins
BREEDING INTERVAL	1 year
TYPICAL DIET	Mainly grasses
LIFESPAN	Up to 20 years

CREATURE COMPARISONS

A close relative of the hartebeest is the bontebok (*Damaliscus dorcas*). This is a much smaller African antelope — only half the weight of the hartebeest and much shorter at the shoulder. Its coat shows greater contrast, being a dark brown on the back and neck with startling white rump, underside and stockings, and a wide, white blaze down the face.

Today the bontebok survives mainly as a domesticated species, having been hunted almost to extinction by European settlers in the 19th century. In 1931 a Bontebok National Park was established in Cape Province, South Africa, with a second park added 30 years later.

Bontebok

Hartebeest

WHERE IN THE WORLD?

Found across much of sub-Saharan Africa where there is suitable coarse grassland and open woodland. From Senegal in the west to Ethiopia in the east, and from Sudan to South Africa.

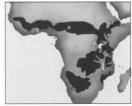

RELATED SPECIES
Several subspecies of hartebeest are recognized. Along with other antelope, such as the topi, *Damaliscus lunatus*, the hartebeest belongs to the family Bovidae, which also contains gazelles and cattle.

41

• ORDER • *Artiodactyla* • FAMILY • *Bovidae* • GENUS & SPECIES • *Antidorcas marsupialis*

SPRINGBOK

Using its sleek build to outsprint predators, the springbok lives on arid grasslands, grazing the tough vegetation with its specially adapted teeth.

KEY FEATURES

- Name stems from the young springbok's habit of making spectacular leaps into the air when excited.
- Able to survive in some of the hottest and driest regions of Africa with little or no drinking water.
- Male aggressively defends his breeding territory, using his long, pointed horns to wrestle with rivals.

HORNS
Both sexes have the robust, lyre-shaped and ridged horns. Gazelles and duikers have solid horns, but the springbok — like goats and impala — has hollow horn cores.

EARS
Long, mobile ears pick up the faintest sounds and give early warning of predators.

PRE-ORBITAL GLAND
This gland at the corner of each eye produces a pungent, oily secretion. The male uses it to mark his breeding territory.

CREST
The white dorsal crest runs along the lower spine, hidden between two folds of scent-secreting skin. The crest is raised during leaps.

COAT
The smooth, short coat allows the springbok to stay cool in the hot, semi-arid regions of southern Africa. The rich chestnut-brown upperparts sport near-black arcs on the mid flanks.

SKULL AND TEETH
A boss above the eye sockets supports the horns. The lower incisors crop vegetation against an upper palate, then the molars (cheek teeth) grind the food.

VITAL STATISTICS

WEIGHT	Male 30–60kg (66.1–132.3lb) female 20–45kg (44.1–99.2lb)
LENGTH	Head & Body: 1.2–1.5m (3ft 9in–4ft 9in) Tail: 15–30cm (5.9–11.8in)
SHOULDER HEIGHT	70–90cm (27.6–35.4in)
SEXUAL MATURITY	Female 6–7 months, male about 2 years
MATING SEASON	Varies due to location
GESTATION PERIOD	167–171 days
NUMBER OF YOUNG	1, rarely 2
BIRTH INTERVAL	1 year, some females breed twice a year
TYPICAL DIET	Grass, herbs, leaves, roots and bulbs
LIFESPAN	7–10 in wild; up to 20 in captivity

CREATURE COMPARISONS

Found on the open plains and plateaus of northeastern Africa, Speke's gazelle (Gazella spekei) has similar markings and colouring to the springbok. However, it has a more delicate build, with neither sex topping 25kg (55.1lb) in weight.

Like the springbok, Speke's gazelle is a grazer and a browser. But whereas the springbok spends most of its time in large mixed herds, Speke's gazelle is less sociable, living in family groups of 5 to 10 individuals. When excited or alarmed, Speke's gazelle inflates a bulbous pouch of skin on top of its snout; this helps amplify the gazelle's snorts of alarm.

Speke's gazelle

Springbok

WHERE IN THE WORLD?

Found in the Namib and Kalahari deserts of southwestern Africa, spanning the countries of Angola, Namibia, Botswana and South Africa.

RELATED SPECIES
The springbok is the only species in the genus Antidorcas, which is 1 of 12 genera in a group known as the dwarf antelopes. The largest of these is the genus Gazella, whose 11 species include Thomson's gazelle, G. thomsoni, of Tanzania, Kenya and Sudan.

AMERICAN BISON

• **ORDER** • *Artiodactyla* • **FAMILY** • *Bovidae* • **GENUS & SPECIES** • *Bison bison*

The bison's bulk enables it to withstand the fierce winters of the American high plains and to defeat rivals in breeding battles.

KEY FEATURES

- Dramatic breeding battles between the bulls ensure that weaker males are denied a chance to reproduce.
- Uses the thick mat of coarse hair on its head to sweep away deep snow and uncover vegetation for grazing.
- Adult males and females remain separate except during seasonal migrations, breeding and when under attack.

BODY
Bison bulls have huge, bulky forequarters and a massive head. This battering-ram physique is employed in battles for superiority during the breeding season. The leaner hindquarters help give a good turn of speed when running.

HUMP
The distinctive shoulder hump is a thick pad of body tissues covering bony outgrowths from the spine.

HORNS
Both sexes have stout, sharp, upturned horns. They are used as weapons by bulls in rivalry fights.

COAT
A woolly 'cape' covers the head, neck and forelegs. The dark, shaggy winter coat falls off in patches in spring and is replaced by a light, short summer coat.

HOOF
The hoof is cloven and splays to spread the animal's great weight on soft ground and snow. Two large central toes form each basic hoof — the two outer toes are much smaller.

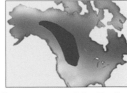

VITAL STATISTICS

WEIGHT	Male 1000kg; (2205lb) female 600kg (1323lb)
LENGTH	Head & Body 2.1–3.5m (6ft 9in–11ft 5in); Tail 50–60cm (19.7–23.6in)
SHOULDER HEIGHT	1.5–2m (4ft 9in–6ft 6in)
SEXUAL MATURITY	2–3 years
MATING SEASON	August
GESTATION PERIOD	270–300 days
NUMBER OF YOUNG	1
BIRTH INTERVAL	2 years
TYPICAL DIET	Prairie grasses, herbs; leaves, shoots, bark in north of range
LIFESPAN	25 years

CREATURE COMPARISONS

The African buffalo (Syncerus caffer) has much larger horns than the North American bison and, on average, is slightly smaller in all-round dimensions. However, it shares the American bison's preference for grazing on extensive, open grasslands. The African buffalo, found south of the Sahara on the broad savannahs, is also known as the Cape buffalo. Whatever its habitat, the African buffalo always remains near water to wallow in mud, which keeps it cool and rids its skin of parasites. It feeds mainly at night, resting in dense cover during the day. The American bison is often, wrongly, called a buffalo: the two animals are not closely related.

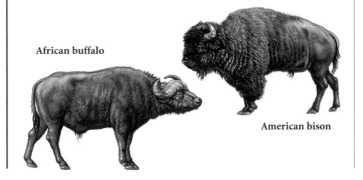

African buffalo

American bison

WHERE IN THE WORLD?

Once ranged widely across North America's prairies and high plains, from Alaska in the north south through Canada into the USA, east of the Rocky Mountains. Now confined to a few reserves within its natural range.

RELATED SPECIES

The European bison (Bison bonasus) is the only other member of the genus Bison. Some authorities recognize two subspecies of the American bison — B. b. athabascae, or wood bison, from Canada in the north of the traditional range and B. b. bison, or plains bison, from the USA in the south.

• **ORDER** • *Artiodactyla* • **FAMILY** • *Bovidae* • **GENUS & SPECIES** • *Bos gaurus*

GAUR

Weighing up to a tonne, with sleek, muscular flanks, the gaur is one of the world's most spectacular grazing and browsing animals.

KEY FEATURES

- The world's largest species of cattle.
- Despite its great bulk, it is a shy and retiring animal that lives in grassy clearings deep in the forest.
- Bulls roar for hours on end to establish dominance.
- Outside the few national parks and nature reserves where it thrives, the gaur now faces extinction.

BULL
The bull weighs at least 150kg (330.7lb) more than the cow, or female (below), and has larger shoulders that bulge to form a prominent ridge.

DEWLAP
A loose fold below the neck, known as a dewlap, helps the male keep cool. It increases the surface area over which bodyheat can be lost.

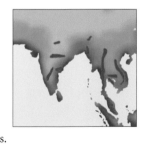

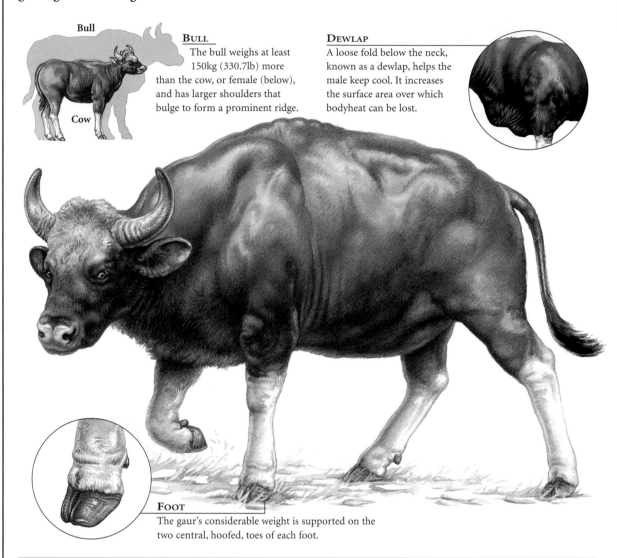

FOOT
The gaur's considerable weight is supported on the two central, hoofed, toes of each foot.

VITAL STATISTICS

WEIGHT	Male 600–940kg (1323–2072lb) female up to about 800kg (1764lb)
LENGTH	Head & Body 2.5–3.3m (8ft 2in–10ft 8in) Tail 70–100cm (27.6–39.4in)
SHOULDER HEIGHT	1.5–2.2m;(4ft 9in–7ft 2in) female shorter than male
SEXUAL MATURITY	At least 30 months
MATING SEASON	All year
GESTATION PERIOD	270 days
NUMBER OF YOUNG	1
TYPICAL DIET	Grasses, fresh leaves, fruits, twigs and bark
LIFESPAN	24–30 years

CREATURE COMPARISONS

Although still enormous, the banteng (Bos javanicus) tends to be smaller than the gaur, as its bulls do not exceed 1.7m (5ft 6in) at the shoulder and weigh 900kg (1984lb) at most. The two species of cattle look very similar, with rather stubby horns, a brown, muscle-packed body and contrasting, white 'stockinged' legs. However, the banteng has a most distinctive white patch on its hindquarters and a shield-like area of bare, hardened skin between its horns, both features that are lacking in the gaur. The banteng also favours more open, grassier habitats.

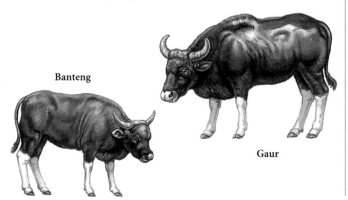

Banteng

Gaur

WHERE IN THE WORLD?

Once common throughout southern and Southeast Asia, but now restricted to a rapidly declining number of small herds in the region's upland areas.

RELATED SPECIES

The gaur is the largest species in the genus Bos, or oxen, which has 4 other members: the banteng, yak, kouprey and domestic cattle. The kouprey, Bos sauveli, was not discovered until 1937 and is considered to be one of the rarest large mammals.

YAK

• **ORDER** • *Artiodactyla* • **FAMILY** • *Bovidae* • **GENUS & SPECIES** • *Bos grunniens*

Surviving a Tibetan winter is no easy task, but the yak manages with the help of its remarkably warm coat, and by using its horns to dig for food under snow.

KEY FEATURES

- Highly adapted to living in harsh, barren lands among some of the world's highest mountains.
- Domesticated yaks are widely used as dairy animals and as cargo transporters in the Himalayas.
- Has such a thick, woolly coat that it may spend the summer above the snow-line to avoid overheating.

VITAL STATISTICS

WEIGHT	Male 300–550kg (661.4–1213lb) female 180–350kg (396.8–771.6lb)
LENGTH	Up to 3.3m (10ft 8in)
SHOULDER HEIGHT	1–1.35m (3ft 3in–4ft 4in)
SEXUAL MATURITY	6–8 years
MATING SEASON	Autumn
GESTATION PERIOD	270–280 days
NUMBER OF YOUNG	1
BIRTH INTERVAL	2 years
TYPICAL DIET	Grass, herbs and lichens
LIFESPAN	Up to 25 years

FEMALE
Smaller than the bull (male) and weighing about a third as much, the cow (female) has smaller horns and a less bulky shoulder hump — a symbol of strength among bulls.

HORNS
The male's horns grow up to 95cm (37.4in) long and are used in breeding fights with other males; the female's are smaller at about 50cm (19.7in) long. Both sexes use their horns to dig beneath the snow to find food.

DIGESTIVE SYSTEM
The digestive system doubles as a form of 'central heating'. Vegetation in the rumen ferments at 40ºC (104ºF), helping to keep the yak warm.

COAT
Long, shaggy outer hair provides waterproofing and a dense underfur retains heat. The wild yak has a black-brown coat with touches of white; the domestic yak tends to be red, mottled, brown or black.

HOOF
Each foot bears a split hoof formed from two enlarged toes. The hoofs are broad to help spread the yak's weight when moving over deep snow and also help the animal keep its grip on bare, rocky slopes.

NOSE
The wild yak uses its keen sense of smell to find food, detect enemies and recognize other herd members.

CREATURE COMPARISONS

The gaur (Bos gaurus), like the yak is a species of wild ox. It is about the same length as the yak, but stands up to 2.2 (7ft 2in) metres tall at the shoulder and weighs up to a tonne. It lives in the tropical forests of India, Burma (Myanmar) and Malaysia, so has no need for a woolly coat. A male gaur stays with a herd of females and young throughout the year, unlike bull yaks, which spend most of the year in male herds. The gaur has suffered from habitat destruction and is classified as vulnerable by the IUCN — World Conservation Union.

Yak

Gaur

WHERE IN THE WORLD?

The wild yak is found only on the Tibetan Plateau of Central Asia. Domesticated animals are widespread in Kashmir, Nepal, Bhutan, Tibet, Mongolia and China.

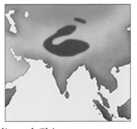

RELATED SPECIES

The yak belongs to the family Bovidae, which contains 138 species of cattle, antelopes, goats and sheep. As one of the 5 species of wild oxen in the genus Bos, the yak is related to the banteng, Bos javanicus, which is found in the forests of Southeast Asia.

• **ORDER** • *Artiodactyla* • **FAMILY** • *Bovidae* • **GENUS & SPECIES** • *Boselaphus tragocamelus*

NILGAI

KEY FEATURES

- A stocky grazer and browser, one of India's biggest herbivores and the largest of all antelopes to live outside Africa.
- Sexes spend most of the year apart, males living in small separate herds and females grouping together with calves and juveniles.
- Traditionally protected in India because it resembles the sacred cow of the Hindu religion.

VITAL STATISTICS

WEIGHT	Up to 300kg (661.4lb)
LENGTH	Head & Body 1.8–2.1m (5ft 9in–6ft 9in) Tail 45–54cm (17.7–21.2in)
SHOULDER HEIGHT	1.2–1.5m (3ft 9in–4ft 9in)
SEXUAL MATURITY	Female 3 years, male 5 years
MATING SEASON	December to March
GESTATION PERIOD	243–247 days
NUMBER OF YOUNG	1 to 3, usually twins
BIRTH INTERVAL	1 year
TYPICAL DIET	Grasses, twigs, leaves and fruit
LIFESPAN	Up to 22 years in captivity, around 10 years in the wild

With its muscular chest and sloping back, the nilgai is one of the most powerful of all antelopes, and the largest in its native India.

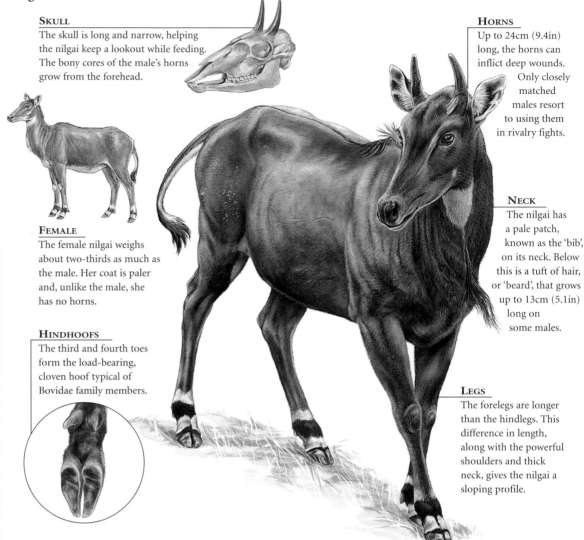

SKULL
The skull is long and narrow, helping the nilgai keep a lookout while feeding. The bony cores of the male's horns grow from the forehead.

FEMALE
The female nilgai weighs about two-thirds as much as the male. Her coat is paler and, unlike the male, she has no horns.

HINDHOOFS
The third and fourth toes form the load-bearing, cloven hoof typical of Bovidae family members.

HORNS
Up to 24cm (9.4in) long, the horns can inflict deep wounds. Only closely matched males resort to using them in rivalry fights.

NECK
The nilgai has a pale patch, known as the 'bib', on its neck. Below this is a tuft of hair, or 'beard', that grows up to 13cm (5.1in) long on some males.

LEGS
The forelegs are longer than the hindlegs. This difference in length, along with the powerful shoulders and thick neck, gives the nilgai a sloping profile.

CREATURE COMPARISONS

The topi lives on the open plains south of the Sahara in Africa. It is one of a number of antelope species known as sassabies. The topi is almost as long as the nilgai, but its build is much lighter — on average a topi weighs only about half as much as a nilgai. Avoiding dense woodlands, the topi chooses instead to move from one rich source of grass to another. It gets a lot of moisture from its grassy diet, and if needs be it can survive for up to a month without water.

Despite its longer horns, the male topi shares the nilgai's preference for asserting dominance with posture and ritual sparring, and it only fights rivals in earnest as a last resort.

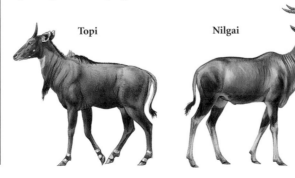

Topi   **Nilgai**

WHERE IN THE WORLD?

Found in eastern Pakistan and throughout Nepal and India except for the highest mountain regions, deserts and the densest forests. Introduced to Texas in the USA, where it now flourishes.

RELATED SPECIES

The sole member of its genus, the nilgai belongs to the family Bovidae, which includes cattle, goats and sheep. It is actually more closely related to buffaloes and bison than to most antelopes. Only a few other large antelope species, including elands, kudu and nyalas, share the subfamily Bovinae to which it and all cattle species belong. Bovidae is 1 of 9 families in the order Artiodactyla, or even-toed hoofed mammals.

IBEX

• **ORDER** • *Artiodactyla* • **FAMILY** • *Bovidae* • **GENUS & SPECIES** • *Capra ibex*

KEY FEATURES

- An agile mountain goat that lives at high altitude, just below the permanent snowline.
- Males fight for mating rights by sparring with their horns, often on the brink of a sheer precipice.
- Once very rare in Europe, but now increasing thanks to protection and reintroduction programmes.

VITAL STATISTICS

WEIGHT	35–150kg (77.2–330.7lb); male substantially heavier than female
LENGTH	1.3–1.7m; (4ft 3in–5ft 6in) male one-third larger than female
SEXUAL MATURITY	18–24 months
MATING SEASON	October to February
GESTATION PERIOD	150–180 days
NUMBER OF YOUNG	1, rarely 2
BIRTH INTERVAL	1 year
TYPICAL DIET	Grass, leaves, flowers, mosses and lichens
LIFESPAN	15 years

The magnificently horned male ibex is one of the most impressive of all the mountain-dwelling wild goats.

SKULL AND TEETH
The male's skull is thickened to protect his brain from damage during horn-clashing combat. Huge molar (cheek) teeth give the ibex the grinding power to pulp tough, fibrous grass.

Male

Female

SEXES
The female is smaller and lighter than the male. Her finely ridged horns, though much smaller, serve as deadly stabbing weapons when she is defending young.

COAT
The grey-brown coat gives good camouflage among the rocks of the high peaks. The pale belly offsets the natural shadow that forms beneath the ibex's body, so its rounded shape is not so obvious to a predator.

HOOFS
The cloven hoof of an ibex is softer than that of a sheep or goat, giving the animal an excellent grip on the rock as it leaps over the crags and negotiates narrow cliff-ledges.

HORNS
The swept-back horns of a male are flattened in front and embossed with thick, deep ridges. Growing to lengths of 1.4m (4ft 6in), the horns play a role in rivalry fights.

CREATURE COMPARISONS

The Himalayan foothills of Afghanistan, Pakistan and Tadjikistan harbour one of the most spectacular of the ibex's relatives: the markhor. In addition to a luxuriant beard, this rare animal has the most elaborate headgear of any wild goat: a pair of extravagantly spiralling horns that, in males, project up to 1.5m(4ft 9in) above the head. Like the male ibex, the markhor uses its horns to overawe its rivals, and those of the females are similarly much shorter. The markhor is usually found at lower altitudes.

Ibex

Markhor

WHERE IN THE WORLD?

Inhabits mountainous terrain in central Europe, northern Ethiopia, the Near and Middle East and an extensive region around the northwestern Himalayas.

RELATED SPECIES
The ibex is 1 of 8 species of wild goat in the genus Capra, including the Spanish ibex (C. pyrenaica), Walia ibex (C. walie) and wild goat (C. aegagrus). All Capra species share the general characteristics that have become familiar in the domestic goat. Along with tahrs and wild sheep, they make up the Caprini, 1 of 4 tribes of goat-antelope that include creatures as diverse as the chamois and the mighty musk ox of the Arctic tundra.

• **ORDER** • *Artiodactyla* • **FAMILY** • *Bovidae* • **GENUS & SPECIES** • *Connochaetes taurinus*

COMMON WILDEBEEST

KEY FEATURES

- Some populations assemble in vast numbers to trek to and from their seasonal feeding grounds.
- May mate while on the move, with some males defending territories for just a few minutes.
- Migrates with relentless urgency, even crossing broad rivers in its path: many are drowned as a result.

VITAL STATISTICS

WEIGHT	127–267kg (280–588.6lb)
LENGTH	Head & Body 1.72–2.31m (5ft 6in–7ft 6in) Tail 61–91cm (24–35.8in)
SHOULDER HEIGHT	1.2–1.45m (3ft 9in–4ft 8in)
SEXUAL MATURITY	Female 18–30 months; male 3 years or more
MATING SEASON	April to June in the Serengeti; earlier elsewhere
GESTATION PERIOD	8–8½ months
NUMBER OF YOUNG	1
BIRTH INTERVAL	1 year
TYPICAL DIET	Mainly grasses
LIFESPAN	Up to 21 years in captivity; less in wild

The male wildebeest uses his horns to fence with rivals. Faced with predators, however, both sexes rely on their fast acceleration to escape.

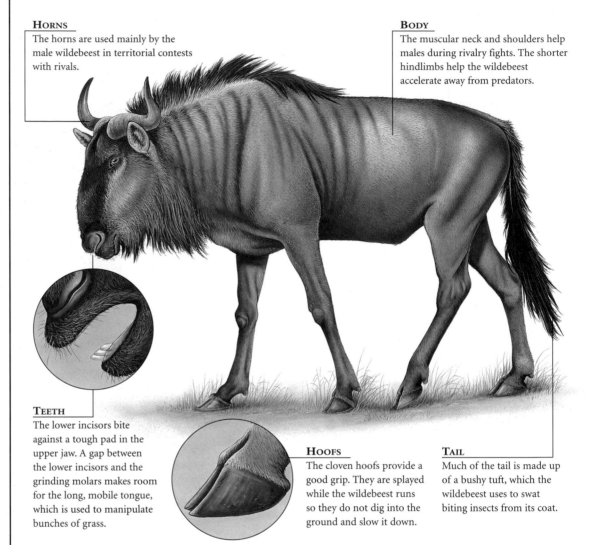

HORNS
The horns are used mainly by the male wildebeest in territorial contests with rivals.

BODY
The muscular neck and shoulders help males during rivalry fights. The shorter hindlimbs help the wildebeest accelerate away from predators.

TEETH
The lower incisors bite against a tough pad in the upper jaw. A gap between the lower incisors and the grinding molars makes room for the long, mobile tongue, which is used to manipulate bunches of grass.

HOOFS
The cloven hoofs provide a good grip. They are splayed while the wildebeest runs so they do not dig into the ground and slow it down.

TAIL
Much of the tail is made up of a bushy tuft, which the wildebeest uses to swat biting insects from its coat.

CREATURE COMPARISONS

Like the common wildebeest, the closely related black wildebeest, *Connochaetes gnou*, is a grazing migrant of Africa's savannahs. It shares the stocky forequarters and long, ox-like head of the common wildebeest, but its coat is buff-brown and the brush on its tail is white. Its muzzle also sports a brush-like tuft of upswept hairs. The black wildebeest's horns also differ from its relative in that they sweep forward and then upward, although in both species the horns serve the same purposes — as weapons during male rivalry fights and, occasionally, as a defence against predators.

Black wildebeest

Common wildebeest

WHERE IN THE WORLD?

Found on Africa's southern and eastern savannahs, south of the equator from Kenya, through Tanzania, Mozambique, Zimbabwe, Botswana and eastern Namibia, to Zambia and southern Angola.

RELATED SPECIES

The common wildebeest belongs to the subfamily Hippotraginae, a group of large grazing antelope in the family Bovidae. Its close relatives include the black wildebeest, *Connochaetes gnou*, the bontebok, *Damaliscus dorcas*, and the hartebeest, *Alcelaphus buselaphus*.

BONTEBOK

• **ORDER** • *Artiodactyla* • **FAMILY** • *Bovidae* • **GENUS & SPECIES** • *Damaliscus dorcas*

KEY FEATURES

- Once occupied a continuous range, but geographical separation has led to the evolution of two subspecies.

- Compact antelope with strong facial markings and, in some individuals, purplish-brown colouring.

- Once common on grasslands of southern Africa; now confined to ranches, reserves and national parks.

VITAL STATISTICS

WEIGHT	55–80kg (121.3–176.4lb); blesbok slightly heavier than bontebok
LENGTH	Head & Body 1.4–1.6m (4ft 6in–5ft 2in) Tail 30–45cm (11.8–17.7in)
SHOULDER HEIGHT	85–100cm (33.5–39.4)
SEXUAL MATURITY	2–3 years
BREEDING SEASON	Bontebok January–March; blesbok March–April
GESTATION PERIOD	225–240 days
NUMBER OF YOUNG	1
BREEDING INTERVAL	1 year
TYPICAL DIET	Grasses, herbs, grain
LIFESPAN	21 years in captivity

One of the most richly coloured antelopes, the bontebok has distinctive markings that it uses to communicate with herd members, mates and rivals.

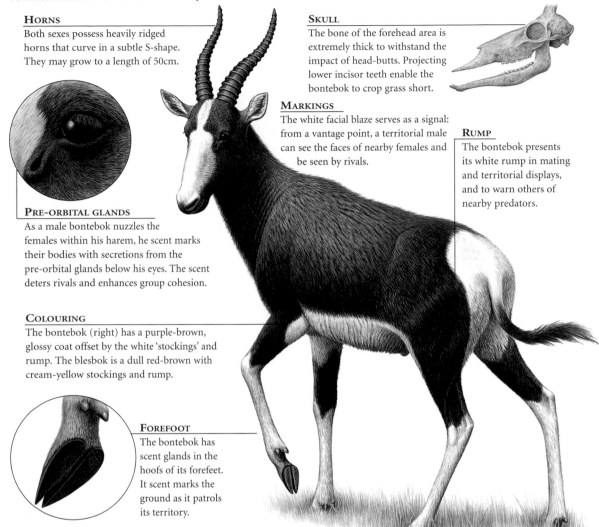

HORNS
Both sexes possess heavily ridged horns that curve in a subtle S-shape. They may grow to a length of 50cm.

SKULL
The bone of the forehead area is extremely thick to withstand the impact of head-butts. Projecting lower incisor teeth enable the bontebok to crop grass short.

MARKINGS
The white facial blaze serves as a signal: from a vantage point, a territorial male can see the faces of nearby females and be seen by rivals.

RUMP
The bontebok presents its white rump in mating and territorial displays, and to warn others of nearby predators.

PRE-ORBITAL GLANDS
As a male bontebok nuzzles the females within his harem, he scent marks their bodies with secretions from the pre-orbital glands below his eyes. The scent deters rivals and enhances group cohesion.

COLOURING
The bontebok (right) has a purple-brown, glossy coat offset by the white 'stockings' and rump. The blesbok is a dull red-brown with cream-yellow stockings and rump.

FOREFOOT
The bontebok has scent glands in the hoofs of its forefeet. It scent marks the ground as it patrols its territory.

CREATURE COMPARISONS

Taller and bulkier than the bontebok but with similar proportions, the hartebeest (Alcelaphus buselaphus) reaches a head-and-body length of 2.45m (8ft) and a weight of 225kg (496lb). It ranges in colour from sandy fawn to brownish-grey to chestnut, and lacks the bontebok's distinctive markings. Both sexes have hooked and twisted horns, which vary in shape from region to region.

The hartebeest occurs at the edge of plains and in open woodland across much of western, central and eastern Africa, in herds of up to 300 or so. It has long, slender legs that enable it to reach a top speed of 80 km/h (49.7mph), allowing it to outrun all but the swiftest of predators.

Hartebeest

Bontebok

WHERE IN THE WORLD?

There are two geographically isolated subspecies. The blesbok lives in central and eastern South Africa; the bontebok is restricted to the Cape area of South Africa.

RELATED SPECIES
The bontebok, Damaliscus dorcas dorcas, and the blesbok, D. d. phillipsi, are regarded by some experts as distinct species with the blesbok being renamed D. pygargus. Both subspecies are close relatives of the more numerous topi, D. lunatus, and the rare Hunter's hartebeest, D. hunteri. All antelopes belong to the family Bovidae, which contains a total of 138 species in 47 genera and includes cattle and goats.

• ORDER • *Artiodactyla* • FAMILY • *Bovidae* • GENUS & SPECIES • *Gazella dorcas*

DORCAS GAZELLE

The lightweight body and long, slender legs of the dorcas gazelle give it a fragile profile, yet only the fastest predators can catch this speedster.

KEY FEATURES

- Roams across some of the world's driest terrain, gaining most of its moisture from plant matter.
- Second smallest of all the gazelles, relying on speed and sure-footedness to elude predators.
- Male becomes territorial in the breeding season, performing an elaborate scent-marking ritual.

VITAL STATISTICS

WEIGHT	12–17kg (26.5–37.5lb)
LENGTH	Head & Body 90–110cm (35.4–43.3in) Tail 15–17cm (5.9–6.7in)
SHOULDER HEIGHT	55–65cm (21.6–25.6in)
SEXUAL MATURITY	Male 18 months; female 9 months to 1 year
MATING SEASON	April to June
GESTATION PERIOD	180 days
NUMBER OF YOUNG	1
BIRTH INTERVAL	1 year (occasionally 2)
TYPICAL DIET	Mainly the leaves and shoots of acacia plants; also grasses and locusts
LIFESPAN	12–15 years

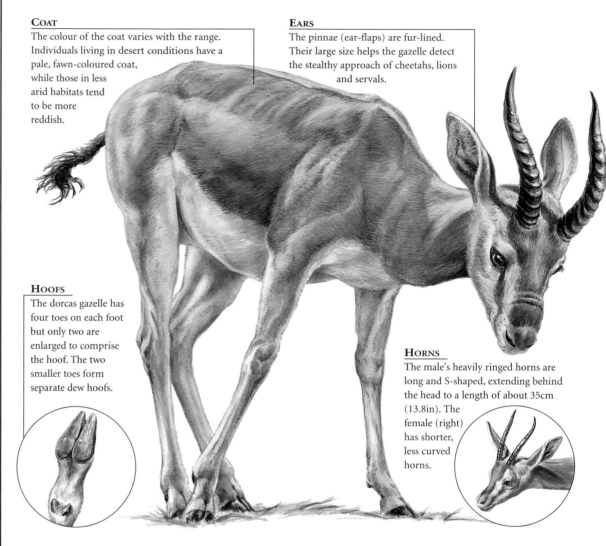

COAT
The colour of the coat varies with the range. Individuals living in desert conditions have a pale, fawn-coloured coat, while those in less arid habitats tend to be more reddish.

EARS
The pinnae (ear-flaps) are fur-lined. Their large size helps the gazelle detect the stealthy approach of cheetahs, lions and servals.

HOOFS
The dorcas gazelle has four toes on each foot but only two are enlarged to comprise the hoof. The two smaller toes form separate dew hoofs.

HORNS
The male's heavily ringed horns are long and S-shaped, extending behind the head to a length of about 35cm (13.8in). The female (right) has shorter, less curved horns.

CREATURE COMPARISONS

The gerenuk (Litocranius walleri) lives in the deserts and dry bushland of northeastern Africa, ranging from Somalia to Tanzania. It has a very long neck and stilt-like legs, and with a shoulder height of over 1m (3ft 3in) is much larger than the dorcas gazelle. The gerenuk is reddish-fawn in colour and has a dark band extending down its neck, back and rump. Unlike the dorcas gazelle, only the male gerenuk has horns.

By standing on its hindlegs and stretching with its long neck for high-level leaves, the gerenuk avoids competing with smaller herbivores for food. In this way it occupies a similar niche to the giraffe — indeed, the name gerenuk means giraffe in Somali.

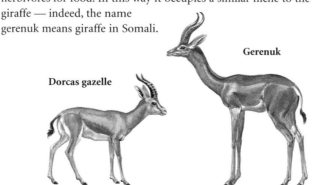

Dorcas gazelle

Gerenuk

WHERE IN THE WORLD?

Distributed across northern Africa from the Ivory Coast to Somalia, across much of the Middle East and east as far as northern India.

RELATED SPECIES

The dorcas gazelle is 1 of the 19 species in the Antilopini tribe. These species are categorized in 8 genera, the most widely distributed being the genus Gazella. Its members are found in countries as far afield as South Africa (Soemmering's gazelle) and China (the goitred gazelle). Gazelles are members of the family Bovidae, whose 121 grazing or browsing species include antelope, cattle, duikers and the pronghorn.

• **ORDER** • *Artiodactyla* • **FAMILY** • *Bovidae* • **GENUS & SPECIES** • *Gazella thomsoni*

THOMSON'S GAZELLE

KEY FEATURES

- The fastest-running gazelle species, it uses its speed to escape from predators, such as cheetahs and wild dogs.

- Specially equipped to graze the grasses that are too short to be eaten by other grazing animals.

- Joins in the mass migration of African animals in search of new feeding grounds when the winter dry season shrivels up its food supply.

Living on the open savannah, Thomson's gazelle is exposed to attack by predators, so its keen eyesight and terrific speed are essential survival aids.

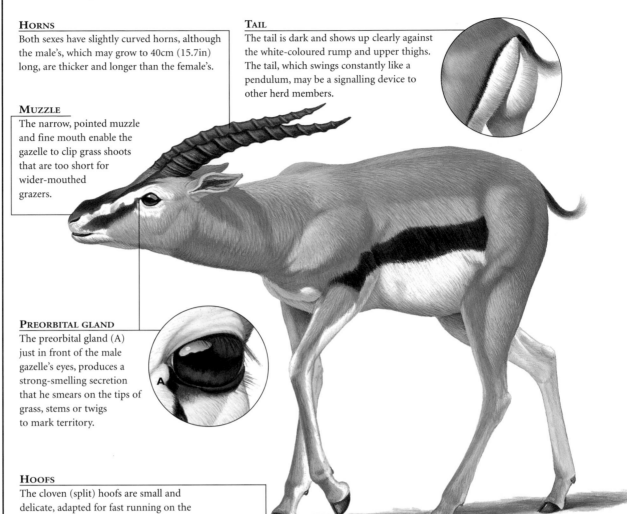

HORNS
Both sexes have slightly curved horns, although the male's, which may grow to 40cm (15.7in) long, are thicker and longer than the female's.

MUZZLE
The narrow, pointed muzzle and fine mouth enable the gazelle to clip grass shoots that are too short for wider-mouthed grazers.

TAIL
The tail is dark and shows up clearly against the white-coloured rump and upper thighs. The tail, which swings constantly like a pendulum, may be a signalling device to other herd members.

PREORBITAL GLAND
The preorbital gland (A) just in front of the male gazelle's eyes, produces a strong-smelling secretion that he smears on the tips of grass, stems or twigs to mark territory.

HOOFS
The cloven (split) hoofs are small and delicate, adapted for fast running on the firm ground of the African savannah.

VITAL STATISTICS

WEIGHT	13–29kg (28.7–63.9lb)
LENGTH	Head & Body 85–100cm (33.5–39.4in) Tail 20–25cm (7.9–9.8in)
HORNS	Male 25–43cm (9.8–16.9in); female 8–15cm (3.1–5.9in)
SHOULDER HEIGHT	60–65cm (23.6–25.6in)
SEXUAL MATURITY	1–2 years
MATING SEASON	Throughout the year (some wet season peaks)
GESTATION PERIOD	160–180 days
NUMBER OF YOUNG	1
BIRTH INTERVAL	6–7 months or 1 year
TYPICAL DIET	Grasses; buds and foliage in dry season
LIFESPAN	10–15 years

CREATURE COMPARISONS

Although similar in colouring and marking, Grant's gazelle, Gazella granti, is much larger than Thomson's gazelle, and has much larger horns, which can reach 80cm (31in) long in males. Also, in contrast to Thomson's gazelle's dark tail, Grant's gazelle has a whitish tail, which blends in with the rump and thigh colouration when the animal is seen from behind. Although Grant's gazelle's range overlaps with that of Thomson's, it also extends farther north into drier areas and, unlike Thomson's gazelle, Grant's gazelle rarely, if ever, drinks. Another major difference between these two species is that Thomson's gazelle is mainly a grazer, while Grant's gazelle is a browser.

Grant's gazelle

Thomson's gazelle

WHERE IN THE WORLD?

A native of the East African savannah. Moves seasonally northwards from Tanzania into southern Kenya during the winter dry season. Isolated population also found in southern Sudan.

RELATED SPECIES

There are 15 other species of gazelle inhabiting a range that extends from Morocco and Senegal across North and East Africa. Several species are native to the Middle East and south-central Asia and one, G. subgutturosa, lives in northern China. The genus is usually subdivided into three subgenera, Gazella, Trachelocele and Nanger, with the Thomson's gazelle and most other African species belonging to the subgenera Gazella.

• **ORDER** • *Artiodactyla* • **FAMILY** • *Bovidae* • **GENUS & SPECIES** • *Hippotragus equinus*

ROAN ANTELOPE

KEY FEATURES

- Classed within a tribe of large grazers known as 'horse-antelopes' on account of their build.
- Males try to use ritual displays to establish social rank: an acknowledgment of the damage that their powerful curved horns can do to each other.
- Depends on regular access to water — a factor that limits its capacity to roam widely in search of food on Afrcan savannahs.

VITAL STATISTICS

WEIGHT	223–300kg (491.6–661.4lb)
LENGTH	Head & Body 1.9–2.4m (6ft 2–7ft 9in) Tail 37–48cm (14.6–18.9)
SEXUAL MATURITY	Female 2 years; male first breeds at 5–6 years old
MATING SEASON	Year round
GESTATION PERIOD	268–280 days
NUMBER OF YOUNG	1
BIRTH INTERVAL	10–10.5 months
TYPICAL DIET	Mainly grass and other ground plants
LIFESPAN	Unknown

Fourth-largest of all antelopes, this heavily horned grazer poses a challenge to all but the most determined predators on the African savannah.

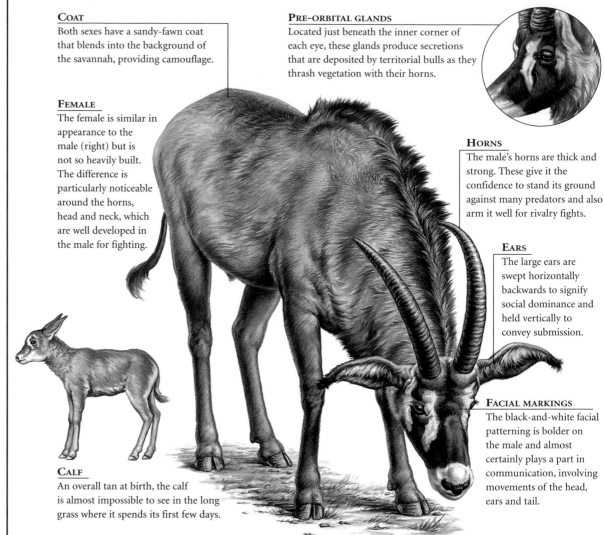

COAT
Both sexes have a sandy-fawn coat that blends into the background of the savannah, providing camouflage.

PRE-ORBITAL GLANDS
Located just beneath the inner corner of each eye, these glands produce secretions that are deposited by territorial bulls as they thrash vegetation with their horns.

FEMALE
The female is similar in appearance to the male (right) but is not so heavily built. The difference is particularly noticeable around the horns, head and neck, which are well developed in the male for fighting.

HORNS
The male's horns are thick and strong. These give it the confidence to stand its ground against many predators and also arm it well for rivalry fights.

EARS
The large ears are swept horizontally backwards to signify social dominance and held vertically to convey submission.

FACIAL MARKINGS
The black-and-white facial patterning is bolder on the male and almost certainly plays a part in communication, involving movements of the head, ears and tail.

CALF
An overall tan at birth, the calf is almost impossible to see in the long grass where it spends its first few days.

CREATURE COMPARISONS

Smaller than the roan antelope, the rhebok (Pelea capreolus) is today found on the rocky slopes and plateaus of South Africa. It probably once ranged through the grassy upland valleys in the area.

The rhebok looks and acts more like a goat than an antelope, although it is quite closely related to the roan antelope. Covered with a woolly coat of hair and possessed of striking agility and speed, it navigates its high-altitude home with similar grace to its European equivalent, the chamois. Unlike the male roan antelope, which wanders in attendance of small herds of females and their young, the male rhebok holds a year-round territory. The better his territory the more females he can attract to it to feed and breed.

Rhebok

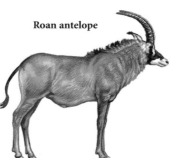

Roan antelope

WHERE IN THE WORLD?

Found only in Africa; occupies a patchy distribution within a vast overall range from Senegal in West Africa, east to Kenya and as far south as Mozambique.

RELATED SPECIES

The roan antelope shares its genus with the sable antelope, Hippotragus niger. It belongs to the family Bovidae, which includes other large cattle, antelopes, sheep and goats. Bovids belong to the order Artiodactyla, or even-toed hoofed mammals.

WATERBUCK

• **ORDER** • *Artiodactyla* • **FAMILY** • *Bovidae* • **GENUS & SPECIES** • *Kobus ellipsiprymnus*

KEY FEATURES

- A robust, heavily built antelope that secretes a foul-smelling scent from skin glands beneath its long, shaggy coat.

- Lives on the savannahs of Africa always close to water, which it needs to visit at least once a day to quench its thirst.

- Males are equipped with a handsome pair of pointed horns with which they can gore a predator or see off a rival.

With its bulky build and long, spiralled horns, the waterbuck presents a commanding sight on Africa's savannahs.

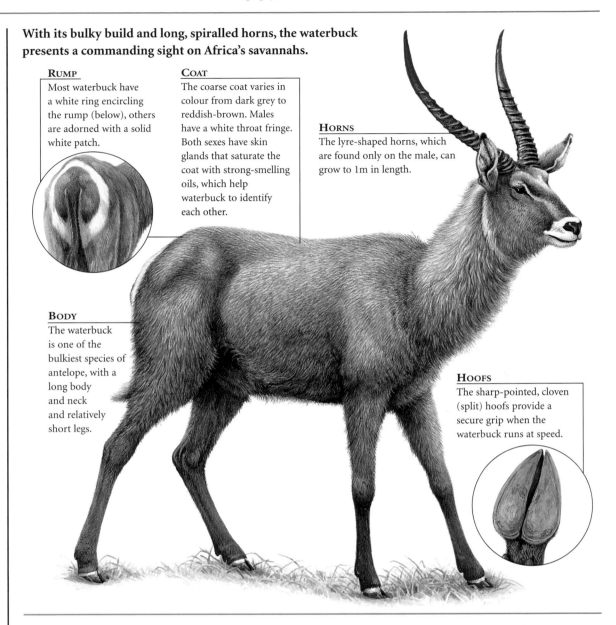

RUMP
Most waterbuck have a white ring encircling the rump (below), others are adorned with a solid white patch.

COAT
The coarse coat varies in colour from dark grey to reddish-brown. Males have a white throat fringe. Both sexes have skin glands that saturate the coat with strong-smelling oils, which help waterbuck to identify each other.

HORNS
The lyre-shaped horns, which are found only on the male, can grow to 1m in length.

BODY
The waterbuck is one of the bulkiest species of antelope, with a long body and neck and relatively short legs.

HOOFS
The sharp-pointed, cloven (split) hoofs provide a secure grip when the waterbuck runs at speed.

VITAL STATISTICS

WEIGHT	170–270kg (374.8–595.2lb)
LENGTH	Head & Body 1.8–2.3m (5ft 9in–7ft 5in) Tail 33–40cm (13–15.7in)
SHOULDER HEIGHT	1.2–1.4m (3ft 9in–4ft 6in)
SEXUAL MATURITY	Male 3 years, but does not breed until 6 years; female 18 months, but rarely breeds before 3 years
MATING SEASON	All year with peaks in the rainy season
GESTATION PERIOD	8–9 months
NUMBER OF YOUNG	1, twins rare
BIRTH INTERVAL	1 year
TYPICAL DIET	Grasses, reeds and rushes
LIFESPAN	14–16 years

CREATURE COMPARISONS

The waterbuck and its close relative the lechwe differ in size and form. The lechwe has a more delicate build, with males weighing up to 128kg (282.2lb) and females no more than 97kg (213.8lb). The lechwe's chestnut-coloured coat has a sleek quality compared with the waterbuck's shaggy, grey-brown hairs. The female lechwe, like the female waterbuck, does not have horns. Found on the floodplains of southern Africa, the lechwe is the most aquatic member of the genus Kobus. Unlike the waterbuck, which enters water only occasionally to feed and drink, the lechwe specializes in feeding on the grasses growing in water plains, and is frequently seen up to its shoulders in water.

Waterbuck

Lechwe

WHERE IN THE WORLD?

Found in sub-Saharan Africa, from Senegal in the west to Ethiopia and southern Somalia in the east, and to northern parts of South Africa in the south.

RELATED SPECIES

There are 2 subspecies of waterbuck: Kobus ellipsiprymnus ellipsiprymnus and K. e. defassa, which are similar in appearance and behaviour. The 4 other species of antelope in the genus Kobus are the Nile lechwe, K. megaceros, the lechwe, K. leche, the kob, K. kob, and the puku, K. vardoni. Found only in Africa, these 4 species and the waterbuck share the subfamily Hippotraginae with 19 other species of grazing antelope.

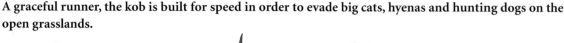

KOB

KEY FEATURES

- A grazing antelope that inhabits tracts of short-grass savannah close to water.

- Forms large herds, which regularly undertake long journeys to find productive feeding grounds.

- In some areas, rival males jostle for territory and mates in traditional breeding arenas known as leks.

VITAL STATISTICS

WEIGHT	65–95kg (143.3–209.4lb)
SHOULDER HEIGHT	80–100cm (31–39.5in)
LENGTH	Head & Body 1.6–1.8m (5ft 2in–5ft 9in) Tail 10–15cm (3.9–5.9in)
HORN LENGTH	40–70cm (15.7–27.6in)
SEXUAL MATURITY	Female 1 year; male older
MATING SEASON	Year-round or seasonal, depending on region
NUMBER OF YOUNG	1
GESTATION PERIOD	240–270 days
BIRTH INTERVAL	1 year
TYPICAL DIET	Grass
LIFESPAN	18 years

A graceful runner, the kob is built for speed in order to evade big cats, hyenas and hunting dogs on the open grasslands.

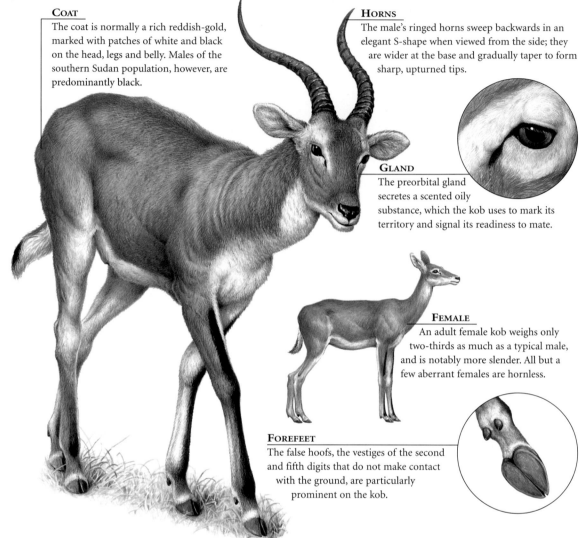

COAT
The coat is normally a rich reddish-gold, marked with patches of white and black on the head, legs and belly. Males of the southern Sudan population, however, are predominantly black.

HORNS
The male's ringed horns sweep backwards in an elegant S-shape when viewed from the side; they are wider at the base and gradually taper to form sharp, upturned tips.

GLAND
The preorbital gland secretes a scented oily substance, which the kob uses to mark its territory and signal its readiness to mate.

FEMALE
An adult female kob weighs only two-thirds as much as a typical male, and is notably more slender. All but a few aberrant females are hornless.

FOREFEET
The false hoofs, the vestiges of the second and fifth digits that do not make contact with the ground, are particularly prominent on the kob.

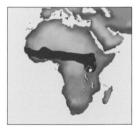

CREATURE COMPARISONS

The kob shares much of its geographical range with the common reedbuck (*Redunca arundinum*), another savannah antelope from a closely related genus. Distinctly smaller and more golden in colour than the kob, the reedbuck can be best distinguished by its horns, which tend to grow straight and then curve markedly forward at the tip. The reedbuck also favours a slightly different habitat, preferring a covering of grasses of medium height rather than the short-grass savannah associated with the kob — but both species rely heavily on a permanent water supply. Whereas the kob is a gregarious animal, the reedbuck lives in monogamous pairs accompanied by one or two offspring.

Common reedbuck

Kob

WHERE IN THE WORLD?

Scattered over a belt of African savannah that runs from Senegal in the west to Sudan, Uganda and western Ethiopia in the east.

RELATED SPECIES

The kob is 1 of 5 species within the genus Kobus, including the waterbuck, *K. ellipsiprymnus*; lechwe, *K. leche*; Nile lechwe, *K. megaceros*; and puku, *K. vardoni*. The genus forms part of the large mammal family Bovidae.

GERENUK

• ORDER • *Artiodactyla* • FAMILY • *Bovidae* • GENUS & SPECIES • *Litocranius walleri*

KEY FEATURES

- Balances on its hindlegs and stretches to feed on leaves beyond the reach of most mammals.
- Superbly efficient at retaining water from its food, enabling it to populate areas farther from permanent water supplies than almost any other browser.
- Uses its acute hearing to detect approaching predators, since it cannot outrun them.

VITAL STATISTICS

WEIGHT	30–52kg (66.1–114.6lb)
LENGTH	Head & Body 1.4–1.6m (4ft 6in–5ft 2in) Tail 20–35cm (7.9–13.8in)
SHOULDER HEIGHT	85–105cm (33.5–41.3in)
SEXUAL MATURITY	Male 18 months; female 12 months
MATING SEASON	Most births occur in the rainy season from October to December
GESTATION PERIOD	195–210 days
NUMBER OF YOUNG	1
BIRTH INTERVAL	8 months
TYPICAL DIET	Leaves and shoots of thorny bushes and trees
LIFESPAN	10–12 years

The gerenuk's form is stretched to the extreme to give it a feeding advantage. Although it looks fragile, the long neck is impressively muscled in the male.

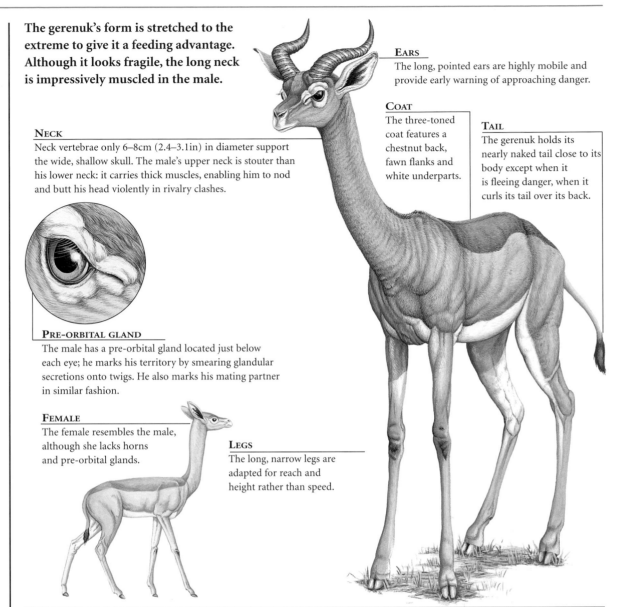

EARS
The long, pointed ears are highly mobile and provide early warning of approaching danger.

COAT
The three-toned coat features a chestnut back, fawn flanks and white underparts.

TAIL
The gerenuk holds its nearly naked tail close to its body except when it is fleeing danger, when it curls its tail over its back.

NECK
Neck vertebrae only 6–8cm (2.4–3.1in) in diameter support the wide, shallow skull. The male's upper neck is stouter than his lower neck: it carries thick muscles, enabling him to nod and butt his head violently in rivalry clashes.

PRE-ORBITAL GLAND
The male has a pre-orbital gland located just below each eye; he marks his territory by smearing glandular secretions onto twigs. He also marks his mating partner in similar fashion.

FEMALE
The female resembles the male, although she lacks horns and pre-orbital glands.

LEGS
The long, narrow legs are adapted for reach and height rather than speed.

CREATURE COMPARISONS

The dibatag (*Ammodorcas clarkei*) is the antelope that most closely resembles the gerenuk, and the two share a similar East African range. Like the gerenuk, the dibatag has a graceful appearance and a long, slender neck. It has white underparts, but its upperparts lack the two-tone colouration of the gerenuk. The dibatag has dark tips on its ears, and shorter, forward-angled horns. It also has a black, well furred tail.

The main difference between the two species is their size, with the dibatag standing about 10cm (3.9in) shorter at the shoulder and about 30cm (11.8in) shorter in length. The dibatag weighs about 10kg (22lb) less than the gerenuk.

Gerenuk

Dibatag

WHERE IN THE WORLD?

Found in scattered populations in the semi-arid thornbush country of northeastern Africa, from central and southern Ethiopia, through Djibouti, Somalia and Kenya, as far as northeastern Tanzania.

RELATED SPECIES

The gerenuk is the only member of its genus, Litocranius (which means stone-skull, in reference to the species' reinforced braincase). It is a member of the family Bovidae, which also contains the royal antelope, Neotragus pygmaeus. Weighing less than 9kg (19.8lb), the royal antelope is the smallest hoofed mammal. The family Bovidae contains 138 species, including cattle, goats and sheep. The family is placed in the order Artiodactyla.

• ORDER • *Artiodactyla* • FAMILY • *Bovidae* • GENUS & SPECIES • *Madoqua spp.*

DIK-DIK

Using its specially modified nostrils as a set of bellows, the dik-dik survives the hottest conditions by snorting rapidly to cool down.

KEY FEATURES

- Delicately built dwarf antelopes that rarely stray far from the safety of dense cover.
- Wary and secretive, owing to the constant threat of attack from a host of enemies.
- Each species possesses a highly adapted snout that allows excess heat to escape from the body.

RUMP
Both sexes expose the white hair on their haunches as a form of communication, particularly during mating.

FEMALE
The female dik-dik is slightly longer and roughly 1kg (2.2lb) heavier than her male counterpart, but she lacks the male's pair of short, ringed horns.

COAT
The coat, which is made up of fine soft hairs, is grey or brown, concealing the animal in dense thickets. Some species may have reddish underparts.

AIR CONDITIONING
The dik-dik cools itself by panting, which draws air in and out of its nasal cavity (A) rapidly. Dry, incoming air causes moisture within the cavity to evaporate, drawing heat from the blood vessels beneath (B).

Species illustrated:
Kirk's dik-dik,
Madoqua kirkii

VITAL STATISTICS

WEIGHT	3–7kg, (6.6–15.4lb) depending on species
LENGTH	Head & Body 52–72cm (20.5–28.3in) Tail 3–6cm (1.2–2.4in)
SHOULDER HEIGHT	34–43cm (13.4–16.9)
SEXUAL MATURITY	10 months
MATING SEASON	Year-round, but with birth peaks in the rainy season
GESTATION PERIOD	150–180 days
NUMBER OF YOUNG	1
BIRTH INTERVAL	1 or 2 young each year
TYPICAL DIET	Leaves, stems, buds, fruit and flowers
LIFESPAN	10 years

CREATURE COMPARISONS

The beira (Dorcatragus megalotis) is about 40 per cent larger than Kirk's dik-dik. Confined to the rocky uplands of northern Somalia, its range overlaps with those of several dik-dik species. An exceptionally long-legged antelope, the beira is perfectly adapted for running and leaping among bare rocks, where agility rather than pure speed is vital for survival. The dik-dik, by contrast, is more at home among dense thickets. A wary animal, the beira relies on its huge ears to give it advance warning of danger. Its secretive nature is probably the reason for its continuing survival in a region heavily exploited by farmers and their herds of cattle, although its numbers are declining.

Kirk's dik-dik

Beira

WHERE IN THE WORLD?

The four species have overlapping ranges across eastern Africa, from northeastern Sudan to central Tanzania. One species has a second, separate population in Namibia and southwestern Angola.

RELATED SPECIES

There are 4 closely related species of dik-dik: Swayne's dik-dik, Madoqua saltiana, the silver dik-dik, M. piacentinii, Guenther's dik-dik, M. guentheri and Kirk's dik-dik, M. kirkii. Dik-diks are commonly grouped together with other dwarf antelopes, such as the beira, klipspringer and royal antelope, in the subfamily Antilopinae. These animals are part of the largest and most diverse family of hoofed mammals, the Bovidae.

MOUNTAIN GOAT

• **ORDER** • *Artiodactyla* • **FAMILY** • *Bovidae* • **GENUS & SPECIES** • *Oreamnos americanus*

KEY FEATURES

- Sure-footed 'goat-antelope' that grazes on rocky and often snowbound peaks in North America.
- Agile enough to negotiate the narrowest of ledges, even in the icy depths of winter.
- Male has extra-thick skin on his rump to protect him during rivalry contests in the breeding season.

VITAL STATISTICS

WEIGHT	45–136kg (99.2–299.8lb)
LENGTH	Head & body 1.2–1.75m (3ft 9in–5ft 7in) Tail 10–20cm (3.9–7.9in)
SHOULDER HEIGHT	90–120cm (35.4–47.2in)
SEXUAL MATURITY	30 months
MATING SEASON	November to January
GESTATION PERIOD	186 days
NUMBER OF YOUNG	1 or 2
BIRTH INTERVAL	1 year
TYPICAL DIET	Grasses, woody plants, mosses, lichens, herbaceous plants
LIFESPAN	Male 14 years, female 18 years

With its woolly coat, sharp-edged hoofs and pointed horns, the mountain goat is well equipped to graze and defend itself on the icy slopes.

HORNS
Both sexes have sharp horns that curve slightly backwards. The male's horns are longer and reach about 30cm (11.8in) in length.

SIZE
The female is about 30 per cent smaller than the male.

TEETH
The mountain goat can crop grass closely because its incisor teeth project slightly forwards.

COAT
The woolly, yellowish-white fur becomes longer in winter. A ridge of especially long, soft fur extends halfway down the back.

HOOF
With a sharp rim and rubber-like sole, the mountain goat's hoof is well adapted for rugged slopes.

CREATURE COMPARISONS

The closely related serow (Capricornis sumatraensis) is found mainly in southern China, the Himalayas, and Southeast Asia. Like the mountain goat, the serow is a sure-footed ungulate (hoofed mammal) that grazes in mountainous regions. The serow is similar in size to its North American cousin and has similar horns.

Colouration and coat thickness are the obvious differences: the mainly brown serow does not have such a pronounced beard and lacks the woolly fur or 'pantaloons' that cover the legs of the mountain goat.

Serow

Mountain goat

WHERE IN THE WORLD?

Found in North America, from southeastern Alaska, British Columbia and Alberta south to northern Idaho, Montana and parts of Oregon and Washington State.

RELATED SPECIES

This species belongs to the tribe Rupricaprini, or goat-antelopes — 1 of 3 tribes in the subfamily Caprinae. The other 2 tribes are the Caprini (sheep and goats) and the Ovibonini, which includes the takin, Budorcas taxicolor, and musk ox. All belong to the family Bovidae.

• ORDER • *Artiodactyla* • FAMILY • *Bovidae* • GENUS & SPECIES • *Oreotragus oreotragus*

KLIPSPRINGER

A combination of muscle power, agility and specialized hoofs enables the klipspringer to move confidently and gracefully over rocky slopes.

KEY FEATURES

- Small, agile antelope found in steep, rocky terrain in the African highlands and savannah.
- Lives in a small family group and aggressively defends a territory against intruders.
- Gives birth in secluded spot where offspring hides for two or three months.
- Marks territory with dung and secretions from facial glands.

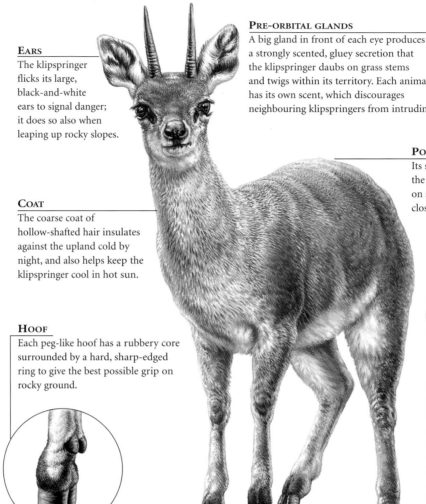

EARS
The klipspringer flicks its large, black-and-white ears to signal danger; it does so also when leaping up rocky slopes.

PRE-ORBITAL GLANDS
A big gland in front of each eye produces a strongly scented, gluey secretion that the klipspringer daubs on grass stems and twigs within its territory. Each animal has its own scent, which discourages neighbouring klipspringers from intruding.

COAT
The coarse coat of hollow-shafted hair insulates against the upland cold by night, and also helps keep the klipspringer cool in hot sun.

POSTURE
Its strongly arched back helps the klipspringer stand securely on small ledges, with its hoofs close together.

HOOF
Each peg-like hoof has a rubbery core surrounded by a hard, sharp-edged ring to give the best possible grip on rocky ground.

FEMALE
Female klipspringers lack horns, except those of the race Oreotragus oreotragus schillingsi. These females occupy small territories in Kenya and Tanzania and often clash with their klipspringer neighbours while defending their patch.

VITAL STATISTICS

WEIGHT	Male 9–11.5kg (19.8–25.3lb); female 5–16kg (11–35.3lb)
LENGTH	Head & Body 77–115cm (30.3–45.3in) Tail 5–13cm (2–5.1in)
SHOULDER HEIGHT	45–60cm (17.7–23.6in)
SEXUAL MATURITY	Female 1 year; male a little later
MATING SEASON	Year round
GESTATION PERIOD	214–225 days
NUMBER OF YOUNG	1
BIRTH INTERVAL	1 year
TYPICAL DIET	Leaves, shoots, berries, fruits, seed-pods, herbs, flowers and grass
LIFESPAN	Up to 12 years in captivity

CREATURE COMPARISONS

The suni (Neotragus moschatus) is slightly smaller than the klipspringer, with a longer, constantly flicking tail. Its horns are ringed for most of their length, while those of its relative are ringed only at the base. The suni is found from Kenya to eastern South Africa and lives in broken woodland at the bottom of mountains, rather than on the slopes themselves. Like its relative, the suni is strongly territorial, laying claim to a small tract of food-rich terrain and defending it against intruders with its short, sharp horns. In addition to scent marking the vegetation with its big pre-orbital glands, as its relative does, the male suni scars tree-trunks with its horns as a visible sign of ownership. Both species eat herbs and shoots and feed during the cooler hours of the day.

Suni   Klipspringer

WHERE IN THE WORLD?

Found from Ethiopia in the east, southwards to South Africa. Isolated populations in northern Nigeria, Central African Republic, Sudan and southwestern Africa.

RELATED SPECIES

The klipspringer is the sole species in the genus Oreotragus. It is 1 of 13 species of dwarf antelope, including the dik-dik, the beira and the royal antelope, the smallest of all hoofed animals, that live in the forests and scrublands of Africa. Together with the gazelles they make up the subfamily Antelopinae, 1 of 5 subfamilies in the family Bovidae. The family Bovidae contains all antelopes, bison, cattle, buffalo, goats and sheep.

GEMSBOK

The gemsbok skilfully wields its deadly horns in fierce contests with rivals and only rarely inflicts injuries.

KEY FEATURES

- Nomadic antelope with special adaptations that enable it to survive in some of the most arid regions of Africa.
- Both sexes possess long, curved horns, which are used to establish dominance within a herd or defend territory.
- Divided into two groups — one large population in southern Africa and two smaller groups in eastern Africa.

SKULL
The eye sockets are high up on the skull to enable the animal to watch for predators while grazing short grass.

COAT
The coat is thick enough to provide warmth at night, but in very hot conditions the hairs can be erected to allow heat to escape from the skin.

TAIL
A large male's tail, which the animal uses as a fly swat, may reach over 50cm (19.7in) in length.

HORNS
The slender, ridged and sharp horns are curved slightly backwards. They range in length from 60–120cm (23.6–47.2in).

HOOFS
The gemsbok is an even-toed ungulate (hoofed grazer). The two hoofs on each foot splay as the animal walks, spreading its weight and enabling it to walk on soft sand. False hoofs are visible at the back of each leg, just above the foot.

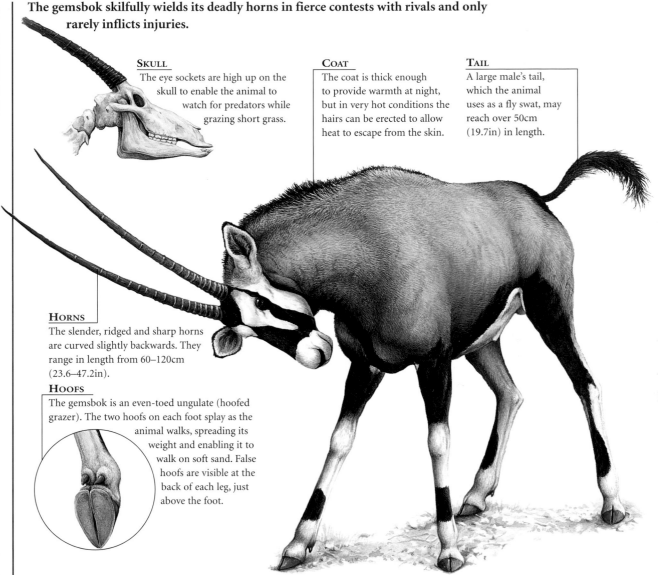

VITAL STATISTICS

WEIGHT	Male 165–209kg (363.8–460.8lb); female 116–188kg (255.7–414.5lb)
LENGTH	153–170cm (60.2–66.9in)
SHOULDER HEIGHT	115–125cm (45.3–66.9in)
SEXUAL MATURITY	Male 5 years; female 2 years
MATING SEASON	All year
GESTATION PERIOD	265 days
NUMBER OF YOUNG	1
BIRTH INTERVAL	1 year
TYPICAL DIET	Grass, herbs, tubers
LIFESPAN	20 years

CREATURE COMPARISONS

The Arabian oryx, which lives in the deserts of Arabia, is closely related to the gemsbok. A quarter of the weight of its African cousin, the Arabian oryx shares many of the gemsbok's adaptations for coping with extremes of temperature and scarcity of water. Both animals are active at night and during the cooler hours of the day, when they make the most of any food. Hunted to extinction in the wild in 1972, the Arabian oryx is now most commonly found in zoos. However, captive-breeding programmes have enabled conservationists to reintroduce the animal to parts of Oman and Saudi Arabia.

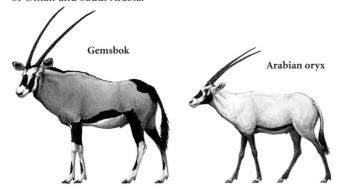

Gemsbok

Arabian oryx

WHERE IN THE WORLD?

Found in parts of Angola, Namibia, South Africa and Botswana. Subspecies occur in eastern Africa from Somalia and Kenya to Uganda and Tanzania.

RELATED SPECIES
The gemsbok and its subspecies, the fringe-eared oryx, Oryx gazella callotis, and the beisa, O. g. beisa, belong to the same genus as 2 rare species — the Arabian oryx, O. leucoryx, and the scimitar-horned oryx, O. dammah.

• ORDER • *Artiodactyla* • FAMILY • *Bovidae* • GENUS & SPECIES • *Ourebia ourebi*

ORIBI

KEY FEATURES

- A small, delicately built antelope that lives in herds, usually made up of a male and his harem of up to four females.
- Lives in a dangerous, open habitat but is an expert at concealing itself from predators on the ground and in the air.
- Uses a variety of scent glands to communicate to other members of the herd and to mark its ownership of territory.

VITAL STATISTICS

WEIGHT	14–21kg (30.9–46.3lb)
LENGTH	Head & Body 92–140cm (36.2–55.1in) Tail 6–15cm (2.4–5.9in)
SHOULDER HEIGHT	50–70cm (19.7–27.6in)
SEXUAL MATURITY	Male 14 months; female 12 months
MATING SEASON	All year
GESTATION PERIOD	210 days
NUMBER OF YOUNG	1
BIRTH INTERVAL	1 year
TYPICAL DIET	Grasses
LIFESPAN	Unknown in wild; 14 years in captivity

Communication by smell is highly important among oribis — the male has no fewer than six scent glands located on many different parts of the body.

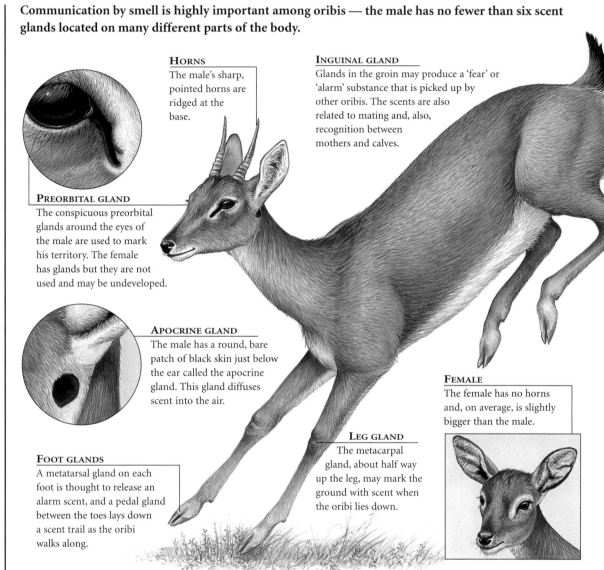

HORNS
The male's sharp, pointed horns are ridged at the base.

INGUINAL GLAND
Glands in the groin may produce a 'fear' or 'alarm' substance that is picked up by other oribis. The scents are also related to mating and, also, recognition between mothers and calves.

PREORBITAL GLAND
The conspicuous preorbital glands around the eyes of the male are used to mark his territory. The female has glands but they are not used and may be undeveloped.

APOCRINE GLAND
The male has a round, bare patch of black skin just below the ear called the apocrine gland. This gland diffuses scent into the air.

FEMALE
The female has no horns and, on average, is slightly bigger than the male.

LEG GLAND
The metacarpal gland, about half way up the leg, may mark the ground with scent when the oribi lies down.

FOOT GLANDS
A metatarsal gland on each foot is thought to release an alarm scent, and a pedal gland between the toes lays down a scent trail as the oribi walks along.

CREATURE COMPARISONS

The build of the oribi and its relative the klipspringer (Oreotragus oreotragus) reflects their quite different lifestyles. For example, the klipspringer browses mainly among mountain ranges and rocky outcrops, predominantly in eastern Africa. As an adaptation to rock climbing it has huge hindquarters, relatively short legs and hoofs that seem to be cut off at the tips, which gives it the appearance of standing on tiptoe. The relatively long-legged oribi, on the other hand, is a grazer, built for running on flat open grasslands.

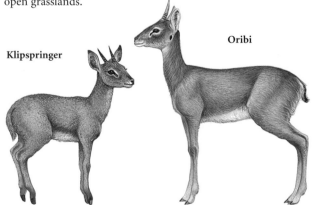

Oribi

Klipspringer

WHERE IN THE WORLD?

Patchily distributed over parts of sub-Saharan Africa, from Senegal and Guinea in the west, eastwards to Ethiopia and northern Somalia, and south through East Africa and Zaire to northern South Africa.

RELATED SPECIES

The oribi antelope is one of the dwarf antelopes, of which there are 12 species in 6 genera living in very different habitats. For example, the pygmy antelope (Neotragus spp.) hides in the dense forests of central Africa; the dik-diks (Madoqua spp.) are found in African bush; the beira (Dorcatragus megalotis) is confined to the rocky crags of northern Somalia and Ethiopia; and the steenbuck and grysbucks (Raphicerus spp.) inhabit wooded plains.

MUSK OX

• **ORDER** • *Artiodactyla* • **FAMILY** • *Bovidae* • **GENUS & SPECIES** • *Ovibos moschatus*

KEY FEATURES

- Survives on the sparse vegetation of the bleak Arctic tundra.
- Lives farther north and in colder conditions than any other hoofed animal.
- Huddles together in herds for warmth and for defence against predators.
- Waterproof coat has 60cm (23.6in) -long hairs and resists frost. Beneath it, a fine, woolly undercoat provides insulation.

VITAL STATISTICS

WEIGHT	180–400kg (396.8–881.8lb). Male much heavier than female
LENGTH	1.9–2.2m (6ft 2in–7ft 2in)
SEXUAL MATURITY	Male 5 years; female 2 years
BREEDING SEASON	July to August
GESTATION PERIOD	About 240 days
NUMBER OF YOUNG	Usually 1
BIRTH INTERVAL	1–2 years
TYPICAL DIET	Grasses and sedges in summer, leaves and twigs of shrub-like trees in winter
LIFESPAN	Up to 24 years

The hardy musk ox, with its sturdy build and double coat, is well equipped for its life foraging on the freezing Arctic tundra.

HORNS
The male's broad horns are flattened at the base; they almost meet on the head, forming a solid 'boss'. The female's horns (above) are narrower at the base and smaller overall.

COAT
The musk ox's coat is composed of two layers. An outer layer of coarse guard hairs, which reach almost to the ground, helps rain and snow fall straight off the body. A very soft, dense inner coat keeps out cold and frost.

HOOFS
The two toes on each foot each bear a hoof, with sharp inner edges that bite firmly into the icy ground.

CREATURE COMPARISONS

The musk ox, the bighorn and the ibex all have formidable horns. The males of each of these species use their horns to spar with rival males during the breeding season. In the case of the bighorn and the ibex that is the sole use of the horns. Because these species live on mountain ranges, they can respond to any danger by fleeing to ever-higher and more remote regions, so their horns are not needed for self-defence. By contrast, the tundra-dwelling musk ox has nowhere to flee from fleet-footed wolves. So the musk ox herd forms a defensive wall, and their great horns, lowered in a shield, become deadly weapons.

Musk ox

Bighorn sheep

Ibex

WHERE IN THE WORLD?

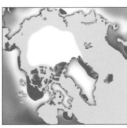

Found in isolated pockets, mainly in northern mainland Canada and its northern islands, and Greenland. Musk ox have also become established in Alaska, Norway, Sweden and Siberia.

RELATED SPECIES
The musk ox belongs to the family Bovidae, and is the only species in the genus Ovibos. Despite its cattle-like appearance, the musk ox is more closely related to sheep. Its nearest relation is the takin, Budorcas taxicolor, which resembles a goat.

• **ORDER** • *Artiodactyla* • **FAMILY** • *Bovidae* • **GENUS & SPECIES** • *Ovis canadensis*

BIGHORN SHEEP

A nimble and sure-footed animal, the bighorn sheep is built for survival in the high, remote mountains of its North American home.

KEY FEATURES

- Equally at home in the mountains or desert areas, but always in wild places away from humans.
- Named after the male's massive horns, which are as thick as a human arm and often curve forwards.
- In the summer rut, the air resounds with the din of epic battles as the males clash in breeding displays.

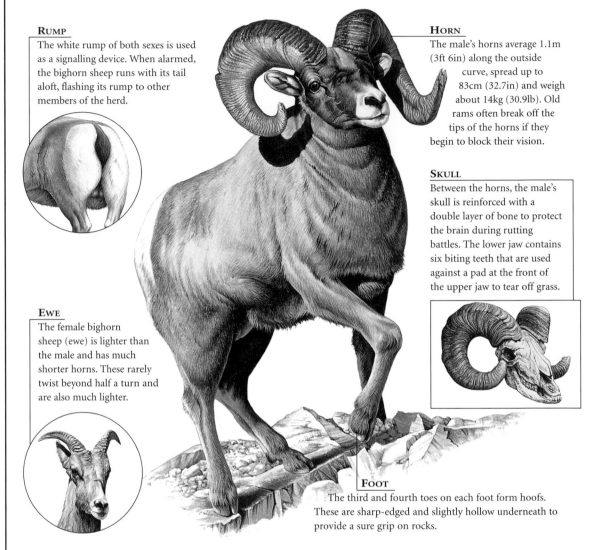

RUMP
The white rump of both sexes is used as a signalling device. When alarmed, the bighorn sheep runs with its tail aloft, flashing its rump to other members of the herd.

EWE
The female bighorn sheep (ewe) is lighter than the male and has much shorter horns. These rarely twist beyond half a turn and are also much lighter.

HORN
The male's horns average 1.1m (3ft 6in) along the outside curve, spread up to 83cm (32.7in) and weigh about 14kg (30.9lb). Old rams often break off the tips of the horns if they begin to block their vision.

SKULL
Between the horns, the male's skull is reinforced with a double layer of bone to protect the brain during rutting battles. The lower jaw contains six biting teeth that are used against a pad at the front of the upper jaw to tear off grass.

FOOT
The third and fourth toes on each foot form hoofs. These are sharp-edged and slightly hollow underneath to provide a sure grip on rocks.

VITAL STATISTICS

WEIGHT	Male 53–143kg (116.8–315.3lb) female 34–91kg (75–200.6lb). Southern sheep smaller than northern sheep
LENGTH	Male 1.6–1.8m (5ft 2in–5ft 9in); female 1.3–1.6m (4ft 3in–5ft 2in)
SHOULDER HEIGHT	94–110cm (37–43.3in)
SEXUAL MATURITY	2–3 years
MATING SEASON	Autumn and early winter
GESTATION PERIOD	50–180 days
NUMBER OF YOUNG	1 to 4
BIRTH INTERVAL	1 year
TYPICAL DIET	Grasses, herbs, leaves
LIFESPAN	Usually 9 years; up to 24

CREATURE COMPARISONS

The Dall sheep (Ovis dalli) is found in remote, rocky regions from northern British Columbia to Alaska. The most obvious distinction from the bighorn sheep is its colour: this is the only species of completely white sheep in the world. The Dall sheep can also be found on cliffs, but, at up to 90kg (198.4lb), has a lighter build than the bighorn. The Dall sheep's horns are also thinner than those of its relation and curve in a more open spiral. This has given rise to this sheep's alternative name — the thinhorn sheep. The female Dall is similar to the female bighorn sheep in having smaller, straighter horns.

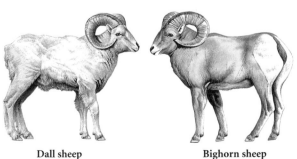

Dall sheep   Bighorn sheep

WHERE IN THE WORLD?

Found in remote parts of the Rocky Mountains of North America, from southern Canada to Colorado. A subspecies lives in dry upland deserts from Nevada and California west to Texas and south into Mexico.

RELATED SPECIES
There are 8 species of true sheep in the genus Ovis. The bighorn sheep's relations in the same genus include the mouflons of Europe and Asia, the snow sheep of Siberia, the urial of central Asia, the argalis of Mongolia and Tibet, the Dall sheep of western North America and the domestic sheep. All sheep belong to the subfamily Caprinae, or goat antelopes. The precise relationships between members of this group are still uncertain.

MOUFLON

• ORDER • *Artiodactyla* • FAMILY • *Bovidae* • GENUS & SPECIES • *Ovis musimon*

KEY FEATURES

- The wild ancestor of all domestic sheep, found in the mountainous regions of islands in the Mediterranean.
- Highly social, with well developed instincts for avoiding its enemies of both land and air.
- Males indulge in spectacular battles to achieve social status and the right to mate.

VITAL STATISTICS

WEIGHT	Male 25–55kg (55.1–121.3lb) female 17–40kg (37.5–88.2lb)
LENGTH	1.1–1.3m (3ft 6in–4ft 3in)
SHOULDER HEIGHT	65–75cm (25.6–29.5in)
SEXUAL MATURITY	Male 18 months; female 12 months
MATING SEASON	October to December
GESTATION PERIOD	150–160 days
NUMBER OF YOUNG	1 or 2
BIRTH INTERVAL	1 year
TYPICAL DIET	Grass, moss, herbs, heather and young leaves
LIFESPAN	Up to 15 years

Small and agile, yet armed with a magnificent set of horns, the mouflon ram is built for bruising battle and fast footwork among rocky terrain.

HORNS
The size of the ram's curved, spiral horns determines his status within a group. Females are attracted to the rams with the biggest horns.

TEETH
The mouflon crops grass by nipping it between the front incisor teeth in its lower jaw and a hard horny pad in its palate. Broad, ridged cheek teeth then grind the grass. These teeth gradually wear down, and many old mouflon die because they can no longer chew food.

HOOFS
The cloven (split) hoofs are rounded at both ends. They give the mouflon a sure grip on the loose rocks of mountain slopes.

FEMALE
Lighter and smaller than the ram, the ewe (female) also has thinner and shorter horns. In fact, some ewes have no horns at all.

COAT
In winter the mouflon grows a thick, woolly undercoat. This lining provides excellent insulation against driving winds and freezing temperatures, and is shed as temperatures increase in spring.

CREATURE COMPARISONS

Largest of all wild sheep, the argali tips the scales at 180kg (396.8lb) — more than three times the weight of a mouflon — and its horns can reach 1.9m (6ft 2in) in length. It is suited to the icy slopes of the Himalayas and the Tibetan plateau, where its large size in relation to surface area helps it conserve bodyheat.

The mouflon is the smallest of wild sheep. Living in temperate parts of Europe, where it shelters below the treeline, it does not need an especially large body to keep warm. A nimble footing on unstable ground is important to the mouflon, so small is best.

WHERE IN THE WORLD?

Lives in small populations in the mountains of Corsica, Sardinia and Cyprus. It has also been introduced to many other places in Europe.

RELATED SPECIES

The mouflon is 1 of 8 species of sheep in the genus Ovis. They include the American bighorn sheep, O. canadensis, found from southwestern Canada south to northern Mexico, and the domestic sheep, believed to be a direct descendant of the mouflon.

Argali

Mouflon

• **ORDER** • *Artiodactyla* • **FAMILY** • *Bovidae* • **GENUS & SPECIES** • *Rupicapra rupicapra*

CHAMOIS

KEY FEATURES

- Incredibly agile: able to scale apparently sheer rock faces in its mountainous habitat.

- Females and young live sociably in large herds; adult males lead a mostly solitary life among the highest crags.

- Male aggressively defends his territory, occasionally fatally goring rivals with upward thrusts of his sharply hooked horns.

VITAL STATISTICS

WEIGHT	Male 30–60kg (66.1–88.2lb); female 25–40kg (55.1–88.2lb)
LENGTH	Head & Body 1–1.3m (3ft 3in–4ft 3in) Tail 10–15cm (3.9–5.9in)
SEXUAL MATURITY	4 years, though 2-year-old females can conceive
MATING SEASON	October–December; shorter in warmer climates
GESTATION PERIOD	160–170 days
NUMBER OF YOUNG	1, rarely 2
BIRTH INTERVAL	1 year
TYPICAL DIET	Alpine plants and grasses in summer; lichen, tree bark, pine needles in winter
LIFESPAN	15–22 years

A striking sight with its bold facial markings and hooked horns, the chamois moves with agility and sure-footed grace over rocky terrain.

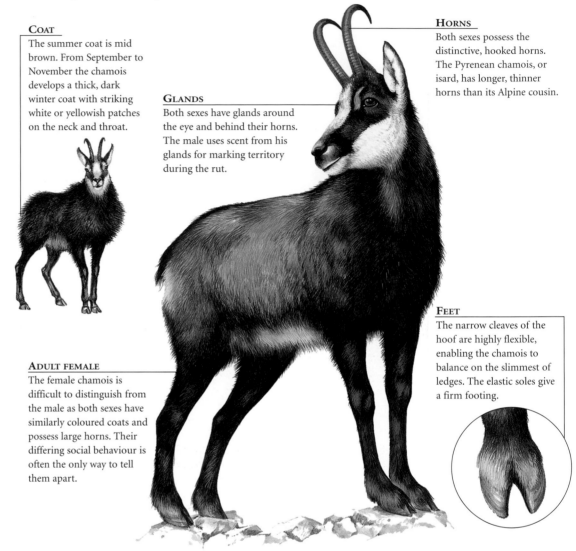

COAT
The summer coat is mid brown. From September to November the chamois develops a thick, dark winter coat with striking white or yellowish patches on the neck and throat.

GLANDS
Both sexes have glands around the eye and behind their horns. The male uses scent from his glands for marking territory during the rut.

HORNS
Both sexes possess the distinctive, hooked horns. The Pyrenean chamois, or isard, has longer, thinner horns than its Alpine cousin.

ADULT FEMALE
The female chamois is difficult to distinguish from the male as both sexes have similarly coloured coats and possess large horns. Their differing social behaviour is often the only way to tell them apart.

FEET
The narrow cleaves of the hoof are highly flexible, enabling the chamois to balance on the slimmest of ledges. The elastic soles give a firm footing.

CREATURE COMPARISONS

Like the chamois, the American mountain goat (Oreamnos americanus), also known as the rocky mountain goat, is adapted for snowy mountains. The mountain goat is a much larger, heavier animal, and clambers slowly over rock-faces, in sharp contrast to the supple agility of its European cousin. Whereas the female chamois is a very sociable animal, the mountain goat only congregates in numbers in the winter, and during the rest of the year is seldom seen in groups of more than four animals. Lacking the distinctive markings of the chamois, the mountain goat is the only member of the family Bovidae to keep a white coat the whole year round.

Chamois   **American mountain goat**

WHERE IN THE WORLD?

Found in the high mountains of central and southern Europe, including the Alps and Pyrenees, and ranging as far north as Czechoslovakia's Tatra Mountains and east to the Caucasus.

RELATED SPECIES

The chamois was thought to comprise between 8 and 10 subspecies, but the Spanish, Pyrenean and Apennine chamois have now been reclassified separately as the isard, Rupicapra pyrenaica. This species is smaller than the chamois, with slightly different colouring. The chamois belongs to the family Bovidae, which includes cattle and antelope and belongs to the order Artiodactyla, or even-toed hoofed mammals.

SAIGA

• **ORDER** • *Artiodactyla* • **FAMILY** • *Bovidae* • **GENUS & SPECIES** • *Saiga tatarica*

The saiga's unusually inflated nose enables it to scent danger from a distance, while its powerful legs help it run faster than a horse to escape its enemies.

KEY FEATURES

- Outsized, proboscis-like nose provides keen sense of smell and helps moisten and warm dry, icy air.
- Once hunted to near extinction, it has made a remarkable recovery over the past 70 years.
- Able to sprint at up to 80 km/h (49.7mph)over the treeless, open plains of Central Asia.

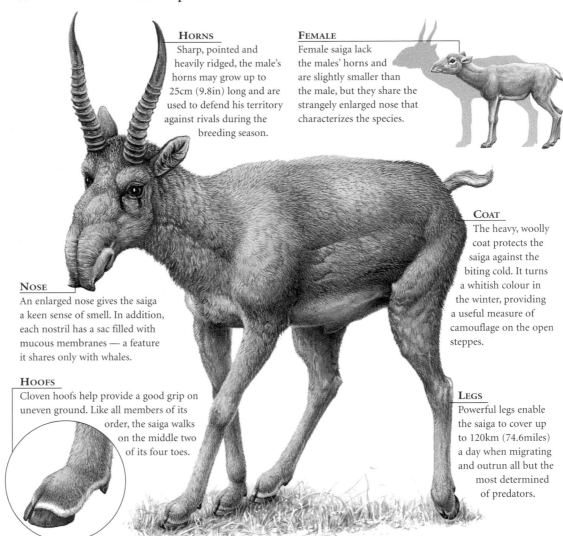

HORNS
Sharp, pointed and heavily ridged, the male's horns may grow up to 25cm (9.8in) long and are used to defend his territory against rivals during the breeding season.

FEMALE
Female saiga lack the males' horns and are slightly smaller than the male, but they share the strangely enlarged nose that characterizes the species.

NOSE
An enlarged nose gives the saiga a keen sense of smell. In addition, each nostril has a sac filled with mucous membranes — a feature it shares only with whales.

HOOFS
Cloven hoofs help provide a good grip on uneven ground. Like all members of its order, the saiga walks on the middle two of its four toes.

COAT
The heavy, woolly coat protects the saiga against the biting cold. It turns a whitish colour in the winter, providing a useful measure of camouflage on the open steppes.

LEGS
Powerful legs enable the saiga to cover up to 120km (74.6miles) a day when migrating and outrun all but the most determined of predators.

VITAL STATISTICS

WEIGHT	25–70kg (55.1–154.3lb)
LENGTH	Head & Body 1–1.4m (3ft 3in–4ft 6in) Tail 6–12cm (2.4–4.7in)
SHOULDER HEIGHT	60–80cm (23.6–31in)
SEXUAL MATURITY	Female 10–12 months; males 19–20 months
MATING SEASON	December to January
GESTATION PERIOD	140–152 days
NUMBER OF YOUNG	Usually 2, sometimes 1
BIRTH INTERVAL	1 year
TYPICAL DIET	Grasses, shrubs and herbs
LIFESPAN	10–12 years

CREATURE COMPARISONS

Sharing part of its range with the saiga, the zeren, or Mongolian gazelle, inhabits the dry, high altitude grasslands and the semi-desert areas of Mongolia, northern China and southern Siberia. Like the saiga, the male zeren has short, ridged horns, differing only in that they curve backwards. Although the zeren lacks the bizarre enlarged nose of the saiga, males have a strangely distended throat that enlarges during the mating season. Both species undertake seasonal migrations and at this time are highly gregarious. Herds of up to 8000 zeren once gathered for the trek north each spring but overhunting has now severely reduced numbers.

Saiga

Zeren

WHERE IN THE WORLD?

Native to the steppes of central Asia, it now ranges from the republics of Kazakhstan and Uzbekistan to the western regions of Mongolia.

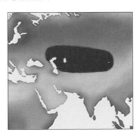

RELATED SPECIES

The saiga, together with its closest relative the chiru, *Pantholops hodgsoni*, of Kashmir, Tibet and China, are two of 26 species in the subfamily Caprinae: the goat antelopes. This includes the takin, *Budorcas taxicolor*, a native of the Himalayan foothills and the steppes of western China.

• **ORDER** • *Artiodactyla* • **FAMILY** • *Bovidae* • **GENUS & SPECIES** • *Sylvicapra grimmia*

BUSH DUIKER

Camouflaged by its sandy, pale brown coat, the tiny bush duiker exploits food and habitats unavailable to larger antelopes.

KEY FEATURES

- A diminutive browsing antelope that eats a wide variety of food — including meat.
- Hardy and adaptable, occurring in open habitats from remote mountain slopes to the fringes of towns.
- Runs fast into cover when disturbed, disappearing into thickets with a characteristic plunging leap.

MALE
The male is slightly smaller than the female, but only he possesses the short, backward-sloping horns. The female is hornless, but has a pronounced tuft of hair between the ears.

COAT VARIATION
Across its vast range, the bush duiker's different subspecies and populations show variations in colour, from grey-buff to yellowish or reddish-brown.

EYE GLAND
Black grooves in front of the eyes identify the pre-orbital glands. They exude a scented substance that the male, in particular, rubs against objects to signal his presence.

TEETH
Incisors at the front of the lower jaw are used to pluck leaves or tear meat. The food is then crushed by the molars.

FOREFOOT
The hoof is made up of the enlarged toenails of the central toes. The outer toes are absent. The duiker has scent glands on each forefoot.

VITAL STATISTICS

WEIGHT	12–25kg (26.5–55.1lb)
LENGTH	80–115cm (31–45.3in)
SHOULDER HEIGHT	45–70cm (17.7–27.6in)
SEXUAL MATURITY	Female 9 months; male up to 20 months
MATING SEASON	All year, with some regional variation
GESTATION PERIOD	210 days
NUMBER OF YOUNG	1
BREEDING INTERVAL	1 year
TYPICAL DIET	Leaves, fruit, flowers, roots; some animal matter
LIFESPAN	15 years in captivity

CREATURE COMPARISONS

The bush duiker lives in more open habitats than other duiker species, such as the threatened zebra duiker (Cephalophus zebra). Confined to densely vegetated habitats, the zebra duiker relies on its reddish coat and bold stripes to camouflage it from enemies. It has smaller ears and — in the male — short horns, which are almost absent in some adults. Long horns would risk entanglement as it plunges through thick undergrowth. The bush duiker, by contrast, has duller, more uniform colours to blend in with its open savannah haunts. It has a slender build for speed, and large, mobile ears to detect predators.

Female zebra duiker

Female bush duiker

WHERE IN THE WORLD?

Widespread throughout sub-Saharan Africa, except in areas of dense forest or true desert. Absent from the Horn of Africa and Madagascar.

RELATED SPECIES

The bush duiker is the sole member of the genus Sylvicapra, but it is divided into 8 subspecies. The other 16 duiker species are forest-dwellers and belong to the genus Cephalophus. They include the black-fronted duiker, Cephalophus nigrifrons.

CAPE BUFFALO

KEY FEATURES

- Huge weight, fearsome horns and a short temper make this animal one of the most dangerous in Africa.
- Spends most of its time grazing but often stops to take a midday wallow in cool mud.
- Often gathers in large, wandering herds on the African plains and wooded savannahs.

VITAL STATISTICS

WEIGHT	250–850kg (551.2–1874lb)
LENGTH	Head & Body 1.7–3.4m (5ft 6in–11ft 1in) Tail 50–80cm (19.7–31in)
SHOULDER HEIGHT	1–1.7m (3ft 3in–5ft 6in)
SEXUAL MATURITY	3–5 years
MATING SEASON	February to March
GESTATION PERIOD	340 days
NUMBER OF YOUNG	1
BIRTH INTERVAL	2 years
TYPICAL DIET	Grasses; swamp plants; twigs, leaves, and young shoots in forested areas
LIFESPAN	Up to 26 years

Muscular, bulky and armed with a pair of lethally hooked horns, the Cape buffalo is powerful enough to stand its ground even against lions.

MALE HORNS
The massive horns of the male become flatter, wider and thicker towards the base, forming a protective boss over the top of the skull. This prevents males from damaging their heads when they clash during breeding battles.

FEMALE HORNS
The horns of the female are more upward-curving than those of the male, and lack the bony flattened boss of the male's.

MUZZLE
The flattened, square muzzle allows the buffalo to reach close to the ground to crop grass efficiently.

TEETH
Like all cattle, the Cape buffalo has only lower incisor (biting) teeth at the front of its mouth. These teeth project slightly forward for grazing. The molar (chewing) teeth behind have ridges to grind tough grasses.

FOOT
As an even-toed ungulate (hoofed mammal), the buffalo has four digits on each foot, two of which are developed into broad, evenly-sized hoofs. The other two are vestigial (remnant) and no longer have any use.

CREATURE COMPARISONS

Large though the Cape buffalo is, it is significantly lighter than the huge water buffalo (Bubalus arnee), which is found locally from India to Malaysia. The water buffalo may stand up to 1.9m (6ft 2in) at the shoulder and weigh in at up to 1.2 tonnes. Its long horns have less of a thickened boss on the head than the Cape buffalo.

The water buffalo lives in wet grasslands, swamps and densely vegetated river valleys. A semi-domesticated form has been widely introduced to North Africa, southern Europe, South America and even northern Australia.

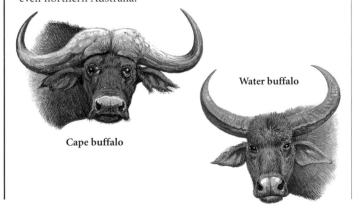

Cape buffalo

Water buffalo

WHERE IN THE WORLD?

Found south of the Sahara, mainly on open plains and in open woodland. Avoids forested areas and is absent in some regions as a result of hunting and disease.

RELATED SPECIES

There are three subspecies of buffalo: the Cape buffalo, Syncerus caffer caffer, the forest buffalo, S. c. nana, and the western buffalo, S. c. brachyceros. The forest buffalo is smaller than the Cape buffalo, usually standing under 1.2m (3ft 9in) high at the shoulder and weighing about 320kg (705.5lb), which makes it better suited to a life in dense woodland. It has a reddish coat, with a dark mane, and backward-pointing horns.

• **ORDER** • *Artiodactyla* • **FAMILY** • *Bovidae* • **GENUS & SPECIES** • *Taurotragus oryx*

ELAND

KEY FEATURES

- A massive, ox-like antelope with a pronounced dewlap (fold of skin) between its throat and chest.
- Females live in herds on open plains; males are more solitary, keeping closer to woodland.
- Both males and females have long horns twisted into a tight spiral.

Rugged and powerfully built, the eland is well adapted to survive on Africa's often parched open plains and scattered woodlands.

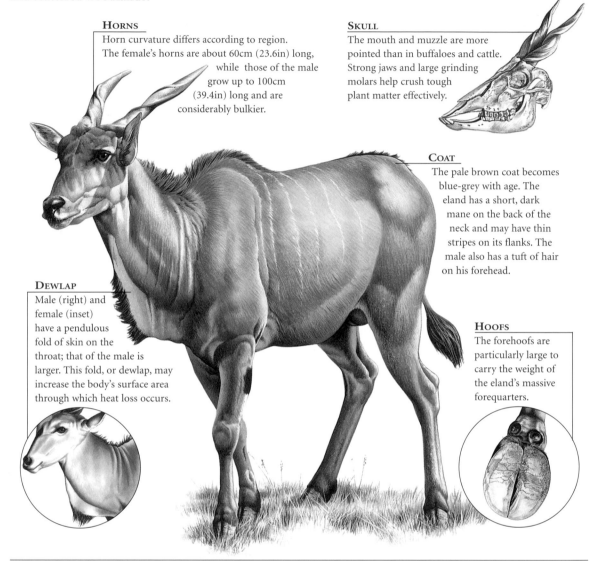

HORNS
Horn curvature differs according to region. The female's horns are about 60cm (23.6in) long, while those of the male grow up to 100cm (39.4in) long and are considerably bulkier.

SKULL
The mouth and muzzle are more pointed than in buffaloes and cattle. Strong jaws and large grinding molars help crush tough plant matter effectively.

COAT
The pale brown coat becomes blue-grey with age. The eland has a short, dark mane on the back of the neck and may have thin stripes on its flanks. The male also has a tuft of hair on his forehead.

DEWLAP
Male (right) and female (inset) have a pendulous fold of skin on the throat; that of the male is larger. This fold, or dewlap, may increase the body's surface area through which heat loss occurs.

HOOFS
The forehoofs are particularly large to carry the weight of the eland's massive forequarters.

VITAL STATISTICS

WEIGHT	Male 500–1000kg (1102–2205lb) female 450–595kg (992.1–1312lb)
LENGTH	Head & Body 2–3.4m (6ft 6in–11ft 1in) Tail 50–90cm (19.7–35.4)
SHOULDER HEIGHT	1.25–1.8m (4.1–5ft 9in)
SEXUAL MATURITY	Male 4 years; female 3 years
MATING SEASON	Varies according to region
GESTATION PERIOD	254–277 days
NUMBER OF YOUNG	1
BIRTH INTERVAL	1 year
TYPICAL DIET	Leaves, fruit, twigs, seeds, grasses
LIFESPAN	Up to 25 years

CREATURE COMPARISONS

The greater kudu (Tragelaphus strepsiceros) is a supremely agile antelope with a lighter build and smaller dewlap than the eland. Its long neck enables it to browse higher than most other plant-eating mammals. Both sexes have long, dramatic horns more loosely spiralled than those of the eland, and much sought after by trophy hunters. The greater kudu is found in small groups in eastern and southern Africa in areas of thicket and woodland that offer plenty of food and cover. Whereas the eland remains in herds during the wet season, the greater kudu scatters widely to take advantage of the abundant browse.

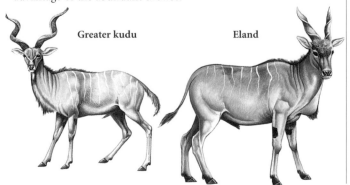

Greater kudu · Eland

WHERE IN THE WORLD?

Occurs in Africa, from southern Ethiopia, southern Sudan, Zaire and Angola south to South Africa.

RELATED SPECIES

The eland is 1 of 2 species in the genus Taurotragus. The other is the giant or Derby eland, T. derbianus, which has 2 subspecies: the eastern and the western. The western eland is considered endangered, and the eastern eland seriously threatened. Elands belong to the family Bovidae, which includes all antelopes, cattle, goats, deer, pigs and sheep. Bovids belong to the order Artiodactyla, or even-toed hoofed mammals.

• ORDER • *Artiodactyla* • FAMILY • *Bovidae* • GENUS & SPECIES • *Tetracerus quadricornis*

FOUR-HORNED ANTELOPE

KEY FEATURES

- The males are the only members of the bovid family that have a double set of horns.
- A solitary inhabitant of thick woodland and open forests.
- One of only two survivors of a primitive tribe of animals from which all wild cattle are descended.
- Threatened by the loss of its forest habitat.

VITAL STATISTICS

WEIGHT	17–21kg (37.5–46.3lb)
LENGTH	Head & Body 80–100cm (31–39.4in) Tail 13cm (5.1in)
SHOULDER HEIGHT	60cm (23.6in)
SEXUAL MATURITY	Unknown
MATING SEASON	July to September
GESTATION PERIOD	225–240 days
NUMBER OF YOUNG	1 to 3
BIRTH INTERVAL	1 year
TYPICAL DIET	Leaves, bulbs, shoots, grasses, herbs and fruits
LIFESPAN	Up to 10 years

Sporting unique headgear, the four-horned antelope is a delicately built and agile animal, able to move nimbly on thickly vegetated ground.

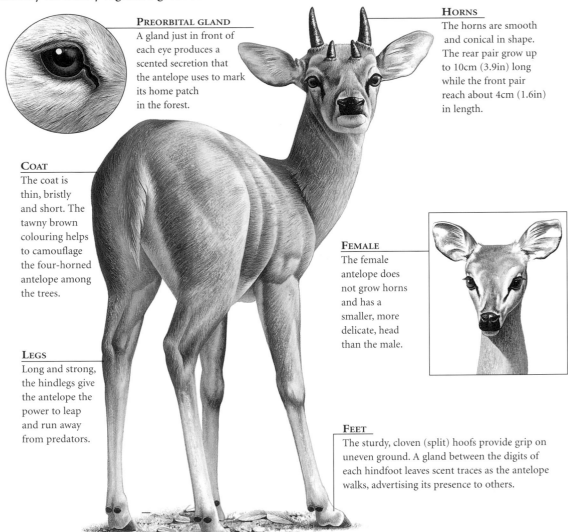

PREORBITAL GLAND
A gland just in front of each eye produces a scented secretion that the antelope uses to mark its home patch in the forest.

HORNS
The horns are smooth and conical in shape. The rear pair grow up to 10cm (3.9in) long while the front pair reach about 4cm (1.6in) in length.

COAT
The coat is thin, bristly and short. The tawny brown colouring helps to camouflage the four-horned antelope among the trees.

FEMALE
The female antelope does not grow horns and has a smaller, more delicate, head than the male.

LEGS
Long and strong, the hindlegs give the antelope the power to leap and run away from predators.

FEET
The sturdy, cloven (split) hoofs provide grip on uneven ground. A gland between the digits of each hindfoot leaves scent traces as the antelope walks, advertising its presence to others.

CREATURE COMPARISONS

The closest living relative of the four-horned antelope is the nilgai (Boselaphus tragocamelus). About twice the size of the four-horned antelope, the nilgai is found in the woodlands and grasslands of India, Nepal and eastern Pakistan.

Rather horse-like in appearance, the nilgai is anatomically similar to the four-horned antelope. It is more sociable, though, and the females usually live in small herds with their young. Mature males are generally solitary, except in the breeding season when, like the four-horned antelope, they use their horns to fight each other for territory and gather females into breeding harems.

Nilgai

Four-horned antelope

WHERE IN THE WORLD?

Found in the hilly and highly mountainous regions of India and Nepal, from the foothills of the Himalayas to the southern parts of the Western Ghats — the coastal mountains of southwestern India.

RELATED SPECIES
The four-horned antelope is a member of the wild cattle subfamily, the Bovinae, which is divided into three tribes. The four-horned antelope and the nilgai are the last survivors of the tribe Boselaphini from which the wild cattle (tribe Bovini) are descended. There are 12 species of wild cattle, including the yak, American bison and African buffalo. The tribe Strepsicerotini contains nine species of spiral-horned antelope.

• **ORDER** • *Artiodactyla* • **FAMILY** • *Bovidae* • **GENUS & SPECIES** • *Tragelaphus angasi*

NYALA

KEY FEATURES

- Distinguished from other large, spiral-horned antelopes by the luxuriant growth of shaggy hair on the male's underparts.
- Male and female have differently patterned coats, but both sexes are well camouflaged in their scrubland habitat.
- Less sociable than most antelopes, it relies heavily on the scent made by its hindfeet glands for communication.

VITAL STATISTICS

WEIGHT	Male 100–140kg (220.5–308.6lb); female 62–90kg (136.7–198.4lb)
LENGTH	Head & Body 1.35–1.95m (4ft 4in–6ft 4in) Tail 36–55cm (14.2–21.6in)
SHOULDER HEIGHT	80–115cm (31–45.3in)
SEXUAL MATURITY	18 months, males do not breed until 3–5 years old
MATING SEASON	All year; births peak in spring and autumn
GESTATION PERIOD	220 days
NUMBER OF YOUNG	1
BIRTH INTERVAL	10 months
TYPICAL DIET	Leaves, grass, roots and fruit
LIFESPAN	16 years plus

Striking differences between the male and female nyala mean that the sexes of this impressive antelope could be mistaken for different species.

COAT
The female is a rich russet or tan, with a dark stripe along the spine. Each flank is marked with up to 18 white stripes, which break up the outline among vegetation.

EARS
The large ears move independently to pick up the quietest of sounds.

CALF
Calves resemble adult females. A young male's horns start to bud at five or six months old, and his coat colour changes gradually to that of an adult male.

MALE
The much larger male has a chocolate to slate-grey coat, fewer distinct stripes and a long white crest running along the ridge of his back. He also has shaggy underparts and sports spiralling horns, which are the colour of burnt toast.

HINDFOOT
On each hindfoot, a pair of 'false hoofs' sits just above the two real hoofs. These nubs are fringed with short hairs that conceal scent glands used in communication.

CREATURE COMPARISONS

Like the nyala, the greater kudu (Tragelaphus strepsiceros) is a spiral-horned antelope. It has well muscled forequarters and weighs about twice as much as the nyala. The male greater kudu's spectacular horns — the largest of any antelope — can grow as long as 1.8m (5ft 9in) along the outermost curve. Unlike the water-dependent nyala, the greater kudu has adapted to the arid conditions found in its huge range stretching from South Africa to the Ethiopian highlands. It favours thornbush savanna and thrives even on stony uplands, where it displays great agility.

Like its smaller relative, the greater kudu feeds on every part of plants, obtaining all the water it needs from leaves and fruits.

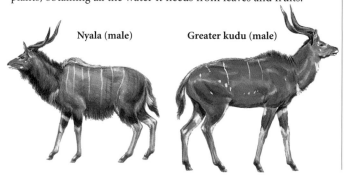

Nyala (male)   Greater kudu (male)

WHERE IN THE WORLD?

Its isolated populations are scattered throughout Mozambique, especially on the coastal plain and along major river valleys, plus adjacent countries in southeastern Africa.

RELATED SPECIES

The nyala is a member of the genus Tragelaphus, which also contains the mountain nyala, bushbuck, sitatunga, greater kudu, lesser kudu and bongo. All 7 species in Tragelaphus have spiral horns in the male, a feature also found in the eland and Derby's eland, the only members of the genus Taurotragus. The 9 species in Tragelaphus and Taurotragus are known collectively as spiral-horned antelopes and belong to the large family Bovidae.

BONGO

KEY FEATURES

- Africa's largest and most colourful forest antelope.
- Both sexes have long, spiralled horns up to 1m (3ft 3in) long.
- Browses soft herbs and foliage, and roams widely to obtain the choicest items.
- Listed as near-threatened by the IUCN (World Conservation Union).

VITAL STATISTICS

WEIGHT	Male 240–405kg (529.1–892.9lb); female 210–253kg (463–557.8lb)
LENGTH	Head & Body 1.7–2.5m (5ft 6in–8ft 2in) Tail 24–65cm (9.4–25.6in)
SHOULDER HEIGHT	1.1–1.3m (3ft 6in–4ft 3in)
HORN LENGTH	60–100cm (23.6–39.4in)
SEXUAL MATURITY	30 months
MATING SEASON	Year-round, with seasonal peaks
NUMBER OF YOUNG	1
GESTATION PERIOD	270 days
TYPICAL DIET	Shoots, buds, leaves, roots
LIFESPAN	Up to 20 years

In the dense foliage and dappled forests of central Africa, the bongo's richly coloured coat conceals it from predators.

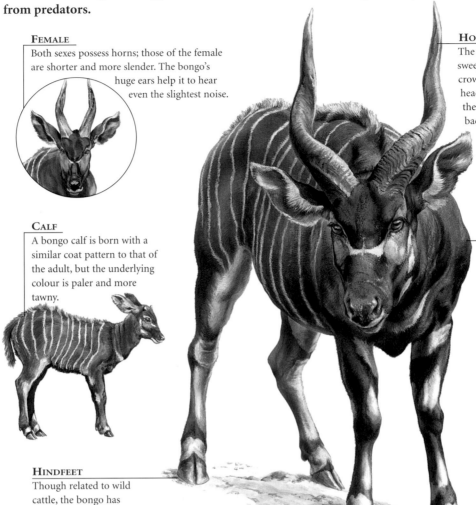

FEMALE
Both sexes possess horns; those of the female are shorter and more slender. The bongo's huge ears help it to hear even the slightest noise.

HORNS
The gently twisting horns sweep back from the crown. The bongo lifts its head when it runs, laying the horns flat along its back. This keeps the horns free of dense vegetation as the bongo dashes through the forest.

CALF
A bongo calf is born with a similar coat pattern to that of the adult, but the underlying colour is paler and more tawny.

COAT
In shady conditions, the bongo's bold white markings serve as visual signals, helping herd members keep in touch. They also break up the animal's outline, camouflaging it. The male bongo darkens with age until nearly black.

HINDFEET
Though related to wild cattle, the bongo has markedly different hoofs. They are much more delicate and leave tracks that are oval in outline.

CREATURE COMPARISONS

The mountain nyala (Tragelaphus buxtoni), found in the highlands of Ethiopia, has much in common with the bongo, though it has a smaller range. Only discovered in 1908, the nyala has declined substantially due to hunting and habitat loss. The vegetation of the nyala's alpine forest home is also dense, and it too is a selective browser that forages alone or in small groups. About the same height as the bongo, the nyala has similarly shaped horns and similar white face and neck markings. The transverse stripes on its back, however, are greatly reduced or, in many cases, absent. It differs most in its coat, which is not only greyish-brown but shaggy, as an adaptation to the chill of high altitude.

Mountain nyala

Bongo

WHERE IN THE WORLD?

Discontinuous range through the main rainforest zones of West and Central Africa, from Sierra Leone in the west to the highlands of Kenya in the east.

RELATED SPECIES
The genus Tragelaphus contains 7 species of spiral-horned antelope. In addition to the bongo, these are the mountain nyala, nyala, sitatunga, bushbuck, lesser kudu and greater kudu, Tragelaphus strepsiceros.

• ORDER • *Artiodactyla* • FAMILY • *Bovidae* • GENUS & SPECIES • *Tragelaphus scriptus*

BUSHBUCK

Slender-legged yet sturdy enough to push through thickets, this antelope is an elusive resident of the African bush.

KEY FEATURES

- Lacks the speed of other antelopes, remaining concealed in dense vegetation during the day.
- Forms informal associations with primates for security and to gain more food.
- Regarded as a threat to cattle in some areas because it can infect them with a fatal disease.

SKULL
The male's horns reach lengths of 25–60cm (9.8–23.6in). Like many bovids, the bushbuck crops food between lower incisors and a hard upper palate.

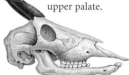

MANE
The male has a crest of hair running down the spine. During courtship displays and disputes with other males, the hair becomes erect.

COAT
Both sexes have white spots and stripes that help to break up their bodyshape in the undergrowth. Mountain and forest bushbuck are darker, while those living in drier areas are yellowish.

FEMALE
Like the male, the female has an elongated head with well developed, mobile ears, but she lacks horns.

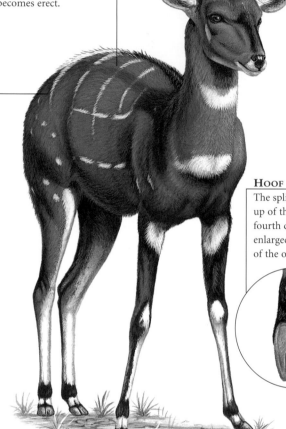

HOOF
The split hoof is made up of the third and fourth digits, which are enlarged at the expense of the other digits.

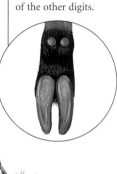

VITAL STATISTICS

WEIGHT	Male 40–80kg (88.2–176.4lb) female 25–60kg (55.1–132.3lb)
LENGTH	Head & Body Male 1.2–1.5m (3ft 9in–4ft 9in); female 1.1–1.3cm Tail 20–25cm
SHOULDER HEIGHT	Male 70––100cm (27.6–39.4in); female 65–85cm (25.6–33.5in)
SEXUAL MATURITY	1 year
MATING SEASON	All year; peaks in rainy season
GESTATION PERIOD	180 days
NUMBER OF YOUNG	1
BIRTH INTERVAL	8–10 months
TYPICAL DIET	Leaves, twigs and flowers
LIFESPAN	12 years in captivity

CREATURE COMPARISONS

One of the bushbuck's larger antelope relatives is the nyala (Tragelaphus angasi). The male nyala can weigh 140kg (308.6lb), while the female is less bulky, approaching 90kg (198.4lb). Whereas the male and female bushbuck have similar coat colouration, the nyala sexes differ markedly. The female is hornless, slender in build, reddish in colour, and marked with 18 bold, white stripes down her flanks. The male nyala undergoes dramatic changes as he reaches adulthood. A young buck has a sandy-grey coat with a few tufts of hair on the chin, throat and belly. A mane running the length of his back grows longer and more prominent; his coat becomes darker, and the horns grow to an impressive 80cm (31in) or so.

Nyala (adult male)

Bushbuck (adult male)

WHERE IN THE WORLD?

Found across much of sub-Saharan Africa but absent from Somalia in East Africa and the arid regions of the southwest, such as the Kalahari Desert.

RELATED SPECIES
The bushbuck is 1 of 7 species in the genus Tragelaphus. The other 6 species are the mountain nyala, T. buxtoni, the sitatunga, T. spekei, the nyala, T. angasi, the greater kudu, T. strepsiceros, the lesser kudu, T. imberis, and the bongo, T. euryceros. They belong to the family Bovidae, which includes cattle, goats and sheep. This family is 1 of 9 in the order Artiodactyla, which contains hoofed plant-eaters with an even number of toes.

GREATER KUDU

• **ORDER** • *Artiodactyla* • **FAMILY** • *Bovidae* • **GENUS & SPECIES** • *Tragelaphus strepsiceros*

The greater kudu is an extremely wary antelope with acute senses, but it is also one of the best equipped to deter predators with its long, spiral horns.

KEY FEATURES

- One of the largest of the African antelopes, yet nimble enough to leap over obstacles up to 2.5m (8ft 2in) high.
- Males bear a huge set of spiralled horns that are the longest of any species of antelope.
- Unlike most large mammals, it can inhabit settled land as long as there is enough cover to conceal it from its human neighbours.

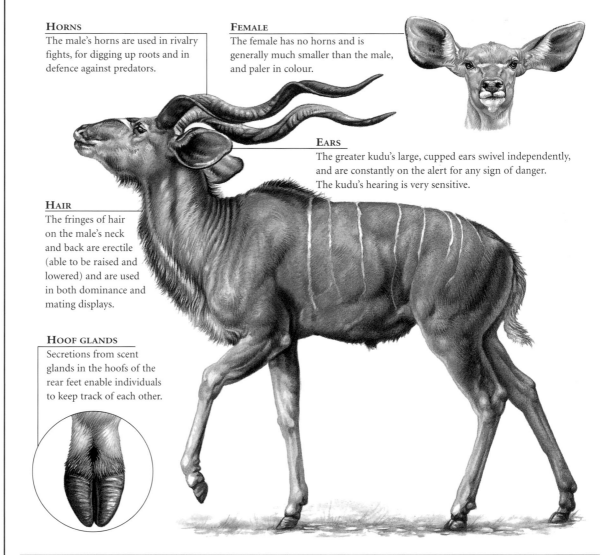

HORNS
The male's horns are used in rivalry fights, for digging up roots and in defence against predators.

FEMALE
The female has no horns and is generally much smaller than the male, and paler in colour.

EARS
The greater kudu's large, cupped ears swivel independently, and are constantly on the alert for any sign of danger. The kudu's hearing is very sensitive.

HAIR
The fringes of hair on the male's neck and back are erectile (able to be raised and lowered) and are used in both dominance and mating displays.

HOOF GLANDS
Secretions from scent glands in the hoofs of the rear feet enable individuals to keep track of each other.

VITAL STATISTICS

WEIGHT	Male 190–315kg (418.9–694.5lb); female 120–215kg (264.6474lb)
LENGTH	Head & Body 1.95–2.45m (6ft 4in–8ft) Tail 37–48cm (14.6–18.9in)
HORNS	1.2m (3ft 9in)
SHOULDER HEIGHT	1–1.5m (3ft 3in–4ft 9in)
SEXUAL MATURITY	Male 5 years; female 3 years
MATING SEASON	Varies due to location; young born in rainy season
GESTATION PERIOD	240–250 days
NUMBER OF YOUNG	1 (rarely 2)
BIRTH INTERVAL	1 year
TYPICAL DIET	Mixed vegetation
LIFESPAN	10–12 years

CREATURE COMPARISONS

The chestnut-red bongo (Tragelaphus euryceros), a member of the same genus as the kudu, resembles its relation, with its white-striped body and spiralling horns. Unlike the kudu, though, both male and female bongos have horns, and these have only one twist, as opposed to the kudu's two, along their 84cm (33.1in) (length.The bongo lives in forests in Africa, remaining hidden in the most thickly vegetated areas and relying on its barred flanks for camouflage. It is very shy and bolts at full speed through even the most tangled undergrowth when disturbed. It is the largest of the forest-dwelling antelopes, with the bulls weighing up to 300kg ((661.4lb).

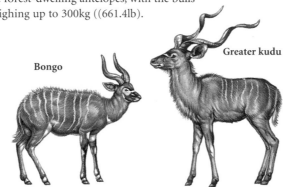

Bongo

Greater kudu

WHERE IN THE WORLD?

Found in scattered areas of sub-Saharan Africa from Chad, Ethiopia and Somalia in the north, south through East Africa to Botswana, Angola and South Africa.

RELATED SPECIES

The greater kudu is one of seven spiral-horned antelopes in the genus Tragelaphus. The others are the sitatunga, T. spekei; the nyala, T. angasi; the bushbuck T. scriptus; the mountain nyala, T. buxtoni; the lesser kudu, T. imberbis; and the bongo, T. euryceros. All are found in Africa.

• ORDER • *Artiodactyla* • FAMILY • *Camelidae* • GENUS & SPECIES • *Camelus dromedarius*

DROMEDARY CAMEL

The dromedary's hump serves as a food supply, while its fur insulates it against the cold desert nights and scorching daytime heat.

KEY FEATURES

- Able to lose up to 40 per cent of its bodyweight in water without risking permanent damage.
- Uses its familiar hump to store body fats. These can be converted into energy with the minimum of water loss.
- Its kidneys are so efficient that they can process brackish (salty) water — often the only source of water available in the desert.

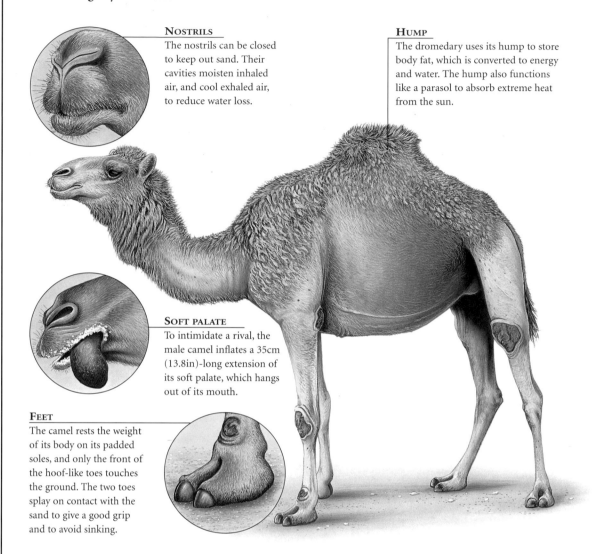

NOSTRILS
The nostrils can be closed to keep out sand. Their cavities moisten inhaled air, and cool exhaled air, to reduce water loss.

HUMP
The dromedary uses its hump to store body fat, which is converted to energy and water. The hump also functions like a parasol to absorb extreme heat from the sun.

SOFT PALATE
To intimidate a rival, the male camel inflates a 35cm (13.8in)-long extension of its soft palate, which hangs out of its mouth.

FEET
The camel rests the weight of its body on its padded soles, and only the front of the hoof-like toes touches the ground. The two toes splay on contact with the sand to give a good grip and to avoid sinking.

VITAL STATISTICS

WEIGHT	450–635kg (992.1–1400lb)
LENGTH	Head & Body 2.1–3.3m (6ft 9in–10ft 8in) Tail 51cm (20.1in)
SHOULDER HEIGHT	2m (6ft 6in)
SEXUAL MATURITY	2–4 years
MATING SEASON	Year round, but births peak to coincide with plant regrowth from February to May
GESTATION PERIOD	390–420 days
NUMBER OF YOUNG	1
BIRTH INTERVAL	2 years
TYPICAL DIET	Leaves, grasses, thorny shrubs and herbs
LIFESPAN	12–15 years

CREATURE COMPARISONS

The Bactrian camel, the only other species of the genus Camelus, is the dromedary's closest relative. It is distinguished by its long, shaggy winter coat and by its two humps. The two species can interbreed, and the offspring have a single, elongated hump. Some scattered populations of Bactrian camels still live in their original range: the Gobi Desert of China and Mongolia.

Dromedary camel   Bactrian camel

WHERE IN THE WORLD?

Now domesticated in its native deserts and semi-arid grasslands of North Africa and the Middle East. Introduced in the 1800s to other regions, including Australia, where some wild populations have become established.

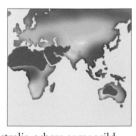

RELATED SPECIES
The non-camel species within the Camelidae family include the llama and alpaca, which are both domesticated species.

GUANACO

• ORDER • *Artiodactyla* • FAMILY • *Camelidae* • GENUS & SPECIES • *Lama guanicoe*

The guanaco is a high-altitude specialist, with a thick coat to keep it warm in the thin air and a modified snout for nibbling the wind-stunted vegetation.

KEY FEATURES

- Wild ancestor of the South American alpaca and llama, and still able to breed with these species.
- Survives for long periods without water in the Atacama Desert, the driest place on Earth.
- Thrives at altitudes that would exhaust most mammals of a similar size.

VITAL STATISTICS

WEIGHT	100–120kg (220.5–264.6lb)
LENGTH	Head & Body 1.5–2m (4ft 9in–6ft 6in) Tail 18–25cm (7.1–9.8in)
SHOULDER HEIGHT	90–130cm (35.4–51.2in))
SEXUAL MATURITY	1–2 years
MATING SEASON	August to September
GESTATION PERIOD	340–360 days
NUMBER OF YOUNG	1
BIRTH INTERVAL	2 years
TYPICAL DIET	Grasses, herbs and mosses
LIFESPAN	Up to 28 years in captivity

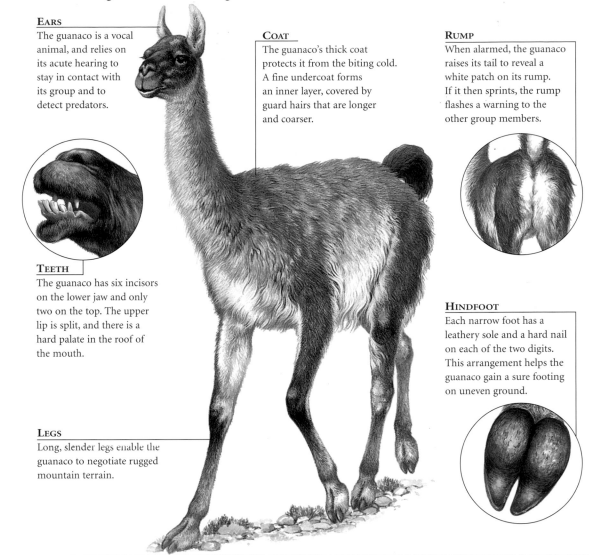

EARS
The guanaco is a vocal animal, and relies on its acute hearing to stay in contact with its group and to detect predators.

COAT
The guanaco's thick coat protects it from the biting cold. A fine undercoat forms an inner layer, covered by guard hairs that are longer and coarser.

RUMP
When alarmed, the guanaco raises its tail to reveal a white patch on its rump. If it then sprints, the rump flashes a warning to the other group members.

TEETH
The guanaco has six incisors on the lower jaw and only two on the top. The upper lip is split, and there is a hard palate in the roof of the mouth.

HINDFOOT
Each narrow foot has a leathery sole and a hard nail on each of the two digits. This arrangement helps the guanaco gain a sure footing on uneven ground.

LEGS
Long, slender legs enable the guanaco to negotiate rugged mountain terrain.

CREATURE COMPARISONS

The alpaca (Lama pacos) is a domesticated animal of southern Peru and western Bolivia. It is believed to be descended from the guanaco, having been bred by native South Americans 4000–5000 years ago. Although the two species share a similar bodyplan, the alpaca is more compact, weighing just 55–65kg (121.3–143.3lb). Its distinctly paler coat, containing hairs up to 50cm (19.7in) long, is renowned for its luxuriantly soft and thick wool. Like the guanaco, the alpaca lives at high altitude, but whereas the guanaco grazes and browses, the alpaca is strictly a grazer.

Alpaca

Guanaco

WHERE IN THE WORLD?

Native to South America, ranging from the Andes Mountains of Peru in the north, through Chile and western Argentina, as far as the islands of Tierra del Fuego at the southern tip of the continent.

RELATED SPECIES

The guanaco is 1 of 3 species in the genus Lama. The llama, L. glama, and the alpaca, L. pacos, are the 2 other members. They belong to the family Camelidae, which contains 2 other genera: Vicugna, which has a single member in the vicuña, and the Camelus, which contains the dromedary and the Bactrian camel. The Camelidae differ from all other mammals in the shape of their red blood corpuscles, which are oval instead of circular.

• **ORDER** • *Artiodactyla* • **FAMILY** • *Camelidae* • **GENUS & SPECIES** • *Lama pacos*

ALPACA

The alpaca's dense coat of luxurious, wind-cheating wool allows it to eke out a living with little competition in the biting cold of the Andes mountains.

KEY FEATURES

- A domestic animal first bred 5000 years ago, it occurs only as semi-wild stock, farmed for its thick coat of supersoft wool.
- Grazes some of the world's highest mountain grasslands in huge herds.
- Extremely efficient digestive and circulation systems enable it to survive on poor quality grasses and in the thin, oxygen-starved air of its high-altitude habitat.

VITAL STATISTICS

WEIGHT	55–65kg (121.3–143.3lb)
LENGTH	Head & Body 1.2–2.25m (3ft 9in–7ft 4in)) Tail 12–25cm (4.7–9.8in)
SHOULDER HEIGHT	94–104cm (37–40.9in)
SEXUAL MATURITY	Male 2–3 years; female 1 year
MATING SEASON	August to September in South America
GESTATION PERIOD	320–376 days
NUMBER OF YOUNG	1 (rarely 2)
BIRTH INTERVAL	Every other year
TYPICAL DIET	Grasses, sedges and other hardy alpine plants
LIFESPAN	15–25 years

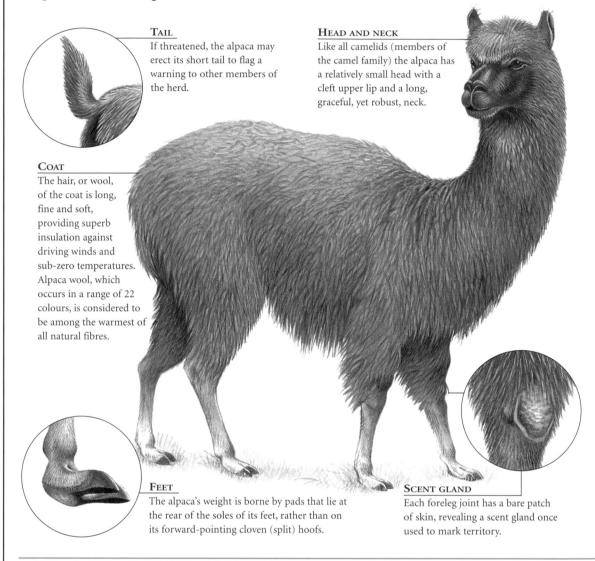

TAIL
If threatened, the alpaca may erect its short tail to flag a warning to other members of the herd.

HEAD AND NECK
Like all camelids (members of the camel family) the alpaca has a relatively small head with a cleft upper lip and a long, graceful, yet robust, neck.

COAT
The hair, or wool, of the coat is long, fine and soft, providing superb insulation against driving winds and sub-zero temperatures. Alpaca wool, which occurs in a range of 22 colours, is considered to be among the warmest of all natural fibres.

FEET
The alpaca's weight is borne by pads that lie at the rear of the soles of its feet, rather than on its forward-pointing cloven (split) hoofs.

SCENT GLAND
Each foreleg joint has a bare patch of skin, revealing a scent gland once used to mark territory.

CREATURE COMPARISONS

The alpaca and the llama (Lama glama) occur only as semi-wild domestic animals. Both are thought to be descended from the truly wild guanaco (L. guanicoe). A recent theory, however, suggests that the alpaca is the result of a cross between the llama and the vicuña (Vicugna vicugna).

The long, thick coat of the alpaca makes it appear to be a similar size to the llama. In fact, the llama is much the larger of the two, standing up to 1.19m (3ft 9in) at the shoulder and weighing up to 155kg (341.7lb). It feeds on lower, less wind-buffeted slopes and, unlike the alpaca, browses on shrubs as well as grazing on grasses.

Alpaca

Llama

WHERE IN THE WORLD?

Ranges over South American alpine meadows in the Andes mountains, from central Peru east to western Bolivia and south to northern Chile. Introduced to parts of New Zealand, Australia and the USA.

RELATED SPECIES
The alpaca is one of 6 species in the family Camelidae. It shares the genus Lama with the llama and guanaco. The other species are the vicuña of the genus Vicugna, and the dromedary camel and Bactrian camel of the genus Camelus.

VICUNA

• ORDER • *Artiodactyla* • FAMILY • *Camelidae* • GENUS & SPECIES • *Vicugna vicugna*

KEY FEATURES

- Wild relative of the llama that inhabits the bleak, dry grassy plateaux of the high Andes.
- Family groups commute daily between firmly established resting and feeding territories.
- Wild population is now protected, but demands for its soft, fine fleece nearly caused the species' demise.

VITAL STATISTICS

WEIGHT	35–65kg (77.2–143.3lb)
LENGTH	Head & Body 1.2–1.9m (3ft 9in–6ft 2in) Tail 15–25cm (5.9–9.8in)
SHOULDER HEIGHT	70–110cm (27.6–43.3in)
SEXUAL MATURITY	2 years
MATING SEASON	March to April
GESTATION PERIOD	330–350 days
NUMBER OF YOUNG	1
BIRTH INTERVAL	16 months
TYPICAL DIET	Coarse grasses
LIFESPAN	Up to 16 years in the wild; up to 24 years in captivity

Despite its delicate appearance, the vicuña is a hardy creature with feet, teeth and coat all specially adapted to its high-altitude habitat.

COAT
The extremely dense, soft coat traps a layer of warm air next to the body to provide protection against freezing night temperatures.

TEETH
Unique among the Artiodactyla, the vicuña's lower incisors grow continuously, like those of rodents, to cope with its diet of tough grasses.

NIPPLES
The female has two pairs of nipples that supply her offspring with a supply of rich milk enabling it to grow quickly.

LEGS
During the day, the vicuña sometimes risks overheating in the strong mountain sunshine. To cool down it stands with its long legs apart, allowing cool air to flow around the thinly furred insides of its thighs.

NECK
The vicuña cranes its long neck to scan its open habitat for signs of danger.

FEET
The vicuña walks on the soles of its feet rather than on its hoofs. By flexing its two slender toes it can improve its grip when climbing over rocky terrain and scrambling down gravel-strewn slopes.

CREATURE COMPARISONS

The Andes mountain range is also home to the guanaco, Lama guanicoe, the closest wild relative of the vicuña. Both are long-necked herbivores that graze on poor vegetation in an arid environment. However, the guanaco ranges farther south than the vicuña, even inhabiting parts of Tierra del Fuego, the southernmost tip of Argentina.

The guanaco is larger and more robust than the vicuña, having a head and body length of 1.2–2m (3ft 9in–6ft 6in) and a shoulder height of 90–130cm (35.4–51.2in). Both creatures live in family groups that are controlled by a dominant male, but the guanaco's family members are less tightly knit, tending to spread out more over their grazing and sleeping territories.

Vicuña

Guanaco

WHERE IN THE WORLD?

A native of South America, found along the Andes mountain range from southern Peru to northern Chile and into adjacent parts of Bolivia and Argentina.

RELATED SPECIES

The vicuña is one of six species in the family Camelidae. Apart from the vicuña, which is the only representative of the genus Vicugna, members of the camelid family are divided into two genera. Lama contains the guanaco, the domesticated llama, L. glama, and the alpaca, L. pacos, while Camelus includes both the dromedary camel, C. dromedarius, and the Bactrian camel, C. bactrianus.

• **ORDER** • *Artiodactyla* • **FAMILY** • *Cervidae* • **GENUS & SPECIES** • *Alces alces*

MOOSE

The male moose's spectacular antlers are formidable tools for his aggressive annual campaign to win a mate.

MUZZLE
The upper jaw and lip droop over the lower jaw, helping the moose tear foliage delicately from thorny twigs.

ANTLERS
Restricted to males, the lobed antlers can have more than a dozen 'points,' and span about 2m (6ft 6in). They are shed each December, with replacements growing in the spring.

DEWLAP
Both sexes have a large dewlap — a fold of loose skin and hair — called a 'bell,' hanging from the neck. The dewlap helps make the male look more imposing to breeding rivals.

HOOFS
The hoofs splay out as the moose walks, forming broad, secure bases that support it on soft mud or deep snow.

KEY FEATURES

- Solitary for most of the year, gathering with others only in the mating season.
- In noisy mating displays, the male bellows and crashes around through the undergrowth.
- Female attracts potential mates with moaning calls and a powerful sexual scent.

VITAL STATISTICS

WEIGHT	360–800kg (793.7–1764lb)
LENGTH	2.15–3m (7ft 1in–9ft 8in)
SHOULDER HEIGHT	1.52–2.13m (5ft–7ft)
SEXUAL MATURITY	2 years
MATING SEASON	Autumn
GESTATION PERIOD	240–250 days
NUMBER OF YOUNG	1 or 2 (rarely, 3)
BIRTH INTERVAL	1 year
TYPICAL DIET	Leaves, twigs and tree bark; aquatic plants
LIFESPAN	Up to 27 years

CREATURE COMPARISONS

As the largest member of the deer family, the moose makes a striking contrast with the smallest deer, the southern pudu, which stands just 38cm (15in) high. However, the extinct Irish elk would have looked down on the moose, bearing huge antlers that could span nearly 4m (13ft 1in). Moose are called elk in Europe, whereas in North America the name elk is used to describe a smaller species, the wapiti, which is so closely related to the European red deer that the two are sometimes classified as a single species.

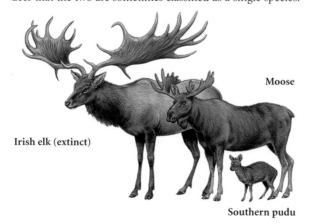

Irish elk (extinct)

Moose

Southern pudu

WHERE IN THE WORLD?

Inhabits northern woodlands right around the world, from Alaska and Canada to Siberia. Small populations in New England and central Rocky Mountains.

RELATED SPECIES

There is only one species of moose, but six subspecies have been recognized in various parts of its range. Relatives include the mule deer and white-tailed deer of North America, the European roe deer, and the caribou, or reindeer, of the Arctic.

AXIS DEER

• ORDER • *Artiodactyla* • FAMILY • *Cervidae* • GENUS & SPECIES • *Axis axis*

KEY FEATURES

- Graceful, spotted deer of medium build; male possesses large antlers.
- Lives in the monsoon-fed grasslands and woodlands of southern Asia.
- One of the most sociable deer, commonly found in large, loose herds of several hundred animals.

VITAL STATISTICS

WEIGHT	50–110kg (110.2–242.5lb)
LENGTH	Head & Body 95–175cm (37.4–69in) Tail 12–38cm (4.7–15in)
SHOULDER HEIGHT	60–100cm (23.6–39.4in)
SEXUAL MATURITY	14–17 months in female, longer in male
MATING SEASON	Year-round but peaks March to June
NUMBER OF YOUNG	1, rarely 2
GESTATION PERIOD	240–254 days
BREEDING INTERVAL	Usually 1 year
TYPICAL DIET	Grass, herbs, leaves, twigs, fruit, flowers
LIFESPAN	14 years

A lithe and elegant animal, the axis deer has long, slender limbs to help it sprint away from attacking tigers and other predators.

TAIL
The tail is unusually long for a deer, reaching up to 38cm in the largest stags. The deer signals danger by raising the tail and revealing its white rump.

COAT
The attractive white-spotted upperparts vary in hue from region to region. In many populations, the ground colour is reddish; in others it is browner or tinged with yellow.

FAWN
The young axis deer is born with a spotted coat, which it retains throughout its life.

EYES
Set to the sides of the head, the eyes give the deer a wide field of vision as it watches for predators.

HOOF
The hoof is formed from the enlarged nails of the third and fourth toes. The second and fifth digits are tiny by comparison, and the first digit is missing entirely.

STAG
A full-grown male sports a pair of three-pronged antlers. The first prong points forwards from the brow; the main stem arcs back, ending in a wide fork.

CREATURE COMPARISONS

Like the axis deer, the pampas deer (Ozotoceros bezoarticus) is generally found within the tropics, though its home is on the other side of the world in the open grasslands, or pampas, of South America. Roughly three-quarters the height of its Indian counterpart, it has much shorter and more upright antlers, though they are similarly three-pronged. In common with most deer, the adult pampas deer does not have a spotted coat, and the overall hide colour is more yellowish-brown than is typical of the axis deer. The pampas deer was once South America's most abundant deer, but has been heavily hunted and is declining rapidly.

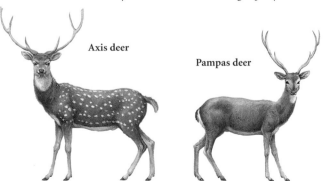

Axis deer

Pampas deer

WHERE IN THE WORLD?

Natural range encompasses almost the whole of the Indian subcontinent, with a separate subspecies occupying the island of Sri Lanka.

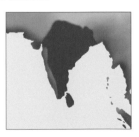

RELATED SPECIES

As well as the axis deer, the genus Axis contains the hog deer, Kuhl's deer and the Calamian deer. These closely related animals belong to the subfamily Cervinae, 1 of 4 subdivisions of the main deer family, Cervidae. The subfamily contains 4 genera and 14 species. The largest genus, Cervus, comprises 8 species including the red deer, while the genera Dama and Elaphurus contain only the fallow deer and Père David's deer respectively.

• **ORDER** • *Artiodactyla* • **FAMILY** • *Cervidae* • **GENUS & SPECIES** • *Capreolus capreolus*

ROE DEER

While sharing the pointed ears and slender build of the deer family, the male roe deer can be identified by his small stature and stunted antlers.

KEY FEATURES

- Europe's smallest native deer usually leads a solitary life or lives in a small, loose herd.
- Widespread in wooded habitats, but is adaptable enough to survive in open areas lacking in trees.
- Has a reddish coat and yellow rump in the summer, which moults to grey with a white rump in winter.

VITAL STATISTICS

WEIGHT	15–50kg (33.1–110.2lb)
LENGTH	Head & Body 95–135cm (37.4–53.1in) Tail 2–4cm (0.8–1.6in)
SHOULDER HEIGHT	65–90cm (25.6–35.4in)
SEXUAL MATURITY	16 months
MATING SEASON	June to August
GESTATION PERIOD	294 days (includes 150 days delayed implantation)
NUMBER OF YOUNG	1 to 3, usually 2
TYPICAL DIET	Grasses, herbs, shoots, leaves, cereal crops
LIFESPAN	12 years, usually less in captivity because of delicate nature

ANTLERS
The male roe deer has a pair of erect, three- or four-pronged antlers that have knobbly lower parts and a well developed 'coronet' at the base. The male sheds his antlers between October and early January. By March, they are fully regrown and covered in velvet that is shed during April by mature adults and May by juveniles.

FEMALE
As in almost all species of deer, the female roe deer does not normally possess antlers, although occasionally a doe appears with knob-like stumps or even small versions of male antlers.

COAT
Both sexes are greyish-fawn in winter. Between March and June, the roe deer moults, and becomes a rusty-red with a yellowish rump.

RUMP
In its winter coat, the roe deer has a prominent patch of white fur on its rump. These hairs become flared and still more prominent when the animal is excited or alarmed.

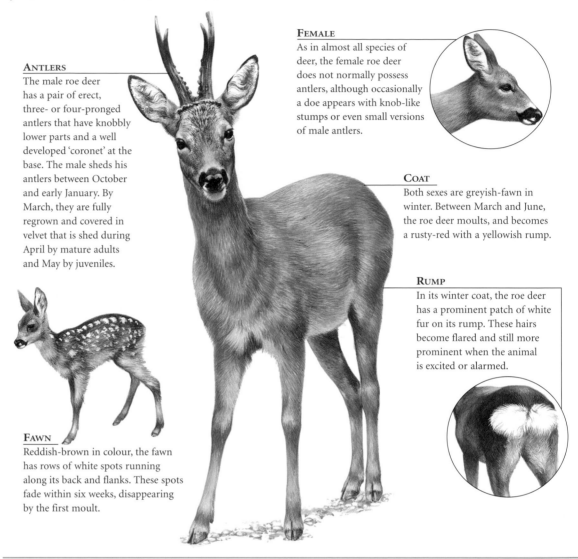

FAWN
Reddish-brown in colour, the fawn has rows of white spots running along its back and flanks. These spots fade within six weeks, disappearing by the first moult.

CREATURE COMPARISONS

Also a member of the deer family, Reeve's muntjac (Muntiacus reevesi) lives in areas of dense forest in China. With a shoulder height of about 50cm (19.7in), the muntjac is much smaller than the roe deer. As with the roe deer, the muntjac male has antlers, which are absent in the female. By contrast, however, he also has long, tusk-like upper canines.

The muntjac is more vocal than the roe deer, and together with five other species forms a genus known as the barking deer. If the muntjac spots a predator, it 'barks' for an hour or more, and in doing so identifies itself to other members of its species and betrays the presence of the unwelcome visitor.

Reeve's muntjac

Roe deer

WHERE IN THE WORLD?

Distributed across Eurasia, as far as the Volga River and northern Iran. Absent from the Mediterranean islands, Iceland, Ireland and much of Norway and Sweden.

RELATED SPECIES

The roe deer is 1 of 2 species in the genus **Capreolus**, which belongs to the family Cervidae. The family members are found throughout the world, and include Père David's deer, *Elaphurus davidianus*, native to lowland regions of China.

RED DEER

• ORDER • *Artiodactyla* • FAMILY • *Cervidae* • GENUS & SPECIES • *Cervus elaphus*

Highly alert and built for speed, the red deer has a legendary ability to vanish into the distance, betrayed only by a fleeting glimpse of its white rump.

KEY FEATURES

- Mature males bellow loudly and lock antlers in push-and-shove battles to claim a mating territory and attract females to it.
- Antlers are shed by the adult male, or stag, in early spring and regrow in midsummer, becoming more elaborate each year.
- Outside the mating season, stags stay in small bachelor groups, while females and young live in herds up to 1000 strong.

VITAL STATISTICS

WEIGHT	75–340kg (165.3–749.6lb)
LENGTH	Head & Body 1.6–2.6m (5ft 2in–8.5in) Tail 10–27cm (3.9–10.6in))
SHOULDER HEIGHT	75–150cm (29.5–59.1in)
SEXUAL MATURITY	Male 2 years, but rarely breeds before 5 years; female 28 months
MATING SEASON	Autumn
GESTATION PERIOD	235–265 days
NUMBER OF YOUNG	1; rarely, twins
BIRTH INTERVAL	1 year
TYPICAL DIET	Grasses and other plants, shoots, leaves, heather, fungi, twigs and bark
LIFESPAN	12–15 years

FEMALE
The female, or hind, lacks the impressive antlers of the stag, but like him has a gland in front of each eye for marking territory.

COAT
The red deer's coat is chestnut-red in summer, or occasionally brown or golden. In autumn, it grows a denser, greyer coat with longer, waterproof 'guard' hairs. At this time, the stag also develops a thick mane (right) to enhance his appearance in mating rituals.

HOOFS
The cloven (split) hoofs are rounded at both ends so that they provide grip without digging in when running.

RUMP
At the first sign of danger, the red deer lifts its tail to reveal its creamy-white rump (right), flagging a warning to the rest of the herd.

ANTLERS
A symbol of his age, the male's antlers are shed in March or April and take about 100 days to regrow. In his first year, he has prong-like horns, to which new branches are added every year.

CREATURE COMPARISONS

The antlers of the red deer stag have up to 16 points, known as tines. Those of the male brow-antlered deer (*Cervus eldi*) have a maximum of three—uniquely among members of its genus, they form a continuous curve from brow to tip. In mature males the antlers of both species may grow over 1m (3ft 3in) long.

Unlike the red deer, the brow-antlered deer avoids areas of dense woodland, and is primarily a grazer of open ground. It is found in low-lying, swampy land from the state of Assam in northeast India to Indochina, and also on the island of Hainan off the southern coast of China.

Red deer

Brow-antlered deer

WHERE IN THE WORLD?

Found over much of Europe, parts of North Africa and through central Asia. Scattered populations occur in southern Canada and the USA. Introduced to parts of Australia, New Zealand and Argentina.

RELATED SPECIES

There are 10 species of deer in the genus Cervus. Most are native to Asia except for the fallow and red deer, which are native to the Mediterranean. All are rusty or grey-brown, but the fallow, axis and sika deer, C. nippon, also have overlying white spots.

• **ORDER** • *Artiodactyla* • **FAMILY** • *Cervidae* • **GENUS & SPECIES** • *Cervus unicolor*

SAMBAR DEER

The male sambar's magnificent antlers are formidable weapons, used in sparring matches during the mating season to stave off rivals.

KEY FEATURES

- The largest species of deer in southern Asia.
- Mature males bellow loudly and lock antlers in 'wrestling' matches to claim a mating territory and attract members of the opposite sex.
- Exhibits the solitary nature typical of many large forest-dwelling mammals, and lacks the ritualized posturing and herding behaviour of more social deer species.

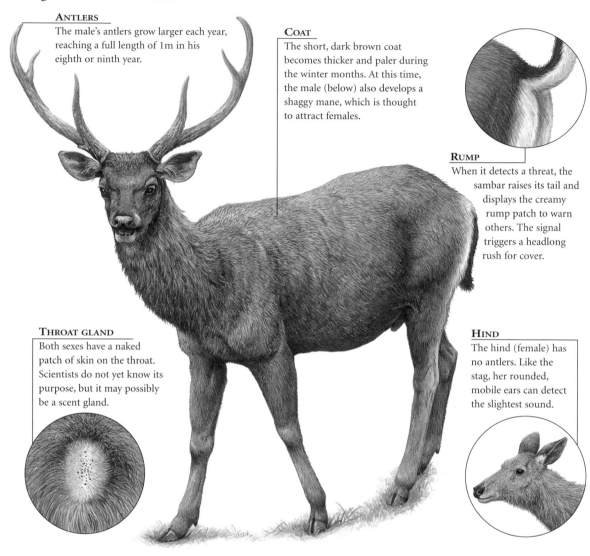

ANTLERS
The male's antlers grow larger each year, reaching a full length of 1m in his eighth or ninth year.

COAT
The short, dark brown coat becomes thicker and paler during the winter months. At this time, the male (below) also develops a shaggy mane, which is thought to attract females.

RUMP
When it detects a threat, the sambar raises its tail and displays the creamy rump patch to warn others. The signal triggers a headlong rush for cover.

THROAT GLAND
Both sexes have a naked patch of skin on the throat. Scientists do not yet know its purpose, but it may possibly be a scent gland.

HIND
The hind (female) has no antlers. Like the stag, her rounded, mobile ears can detect the slightest sound.

VITAL STATISTICS

WEIGHT	109–260kg (240.3–573.2lb)
LENGTH	Head & Body 1.6–2.5m (5ft 2in–8ft 2in) Tail 25–30cm (9.8–11.8in)
SHOULDER HEIGHT	1–1.6m (3ft 3in–5ft 2in)
SEXUAL MATURITY	2 years
MATING SEASON	Mainly September to January
GESTATION PERIOD	About 240 days
NUMBER OF YOUNG	1
BIRTH INTERVAL	1 year
TYPICAL DIET	Leaves, buds, fruits and grasses
LIFESPAN	Up to 20 years

CREATURE COMPARISONS

A close relative of the sambar is the Sunda sambar or rusa deer (*Cervus timorensis*), which is found on the islands of Java, Bali, Sulawesi, Timor and many smaller Indonesian islands. They are similar in appearance, but the Sunda sambar is smaller with a head-and-body length of 1.4–1.8m (4ft 6in–5ft 9in) and weighing 50–115kg (110.2–253.5lb). It also has a coarser coat.

While the sambar is found mainly in wooded areas, the Sunda sambar occurs in a variety of habitats including forests, plantations and grasslands. An island creature, it has been known to wade into the sea for a swim and to feed on seaweed and other marine plants.

Sunda sambar

Sambar

WHERE IN THE WORLD?

Found throughout southern and Southeast Asia, from India and Sri Lanka in the west to the Philippines in the east.

Introduced populations have gone feral in Australia, New Zealand and the USA.

RELATED SPECIES

The sambar is 1 of 10 species in the genus Cervus, which includes the red deer, C. elaphus, of Europe, Asia and North America (where it is called the wapiti). Other cervids include the sika deer, C. nippon, of Southeast Asia and Japan, and Schomburgk's deer, C. schomburgki, of Thailand. Cervus is one of 17 genera in the family Cervidae, which contains 45 species. All deer belong to the order Artiodactyla, or even-toed hoofed mammals.

FALLOW DEER

• ORDER • *Artiodactyla* • FAMILY • *Cervidae* • GENUS & SPECIES • *Dama dama*

KEY FEATURES

- Has a coat that can change colour to reflect the seasons, providing excellent camouflage.
- Males mark out territories during the autumn breeding season and often clash in fierce battles over females.
- Thrives in captive herds in places where it has been introduced, but numbers of wild fallow deer have been greatly reduced.

VITAL STATISTICS

WEIGHT	40–100kg (88.2–220.5lb)
LENGTH	Head & Body 1.3–1.75m (4ft 3in– 5ft 7in) Tail 15–23cm (5.9–9in)
SHOULDER HEIGHT	80–105cm (31–41.3in)
SEXUAL MATURITY	Male 17 months; female 16 months
MATING SEASON	September to October
GESTATION PERIOD	About 230 days
NUMBER OF YOUNG	1 (occasionally twins)
BIRTH INTERVAL	1 year
TYPICAL DIET	Grasses, foliage, nuts, berries
LIFESPAN	15–20 years

The fallow deer's coat varies with the seasons and its habitat, and the male is distinguished by his magnificent palm-shaped antlers.

COAT
The are four main varieties of coat colour: common (brown with white spots in summer, dark greyish brown in winter); menil (pale fawn with white spots year-round); white (almost albino); and black (dark, with grey-brown spots).

FEMALE
Like most deer, the female fallow deer has no antlers, and her head is much more delicate and finely boned than the male's.

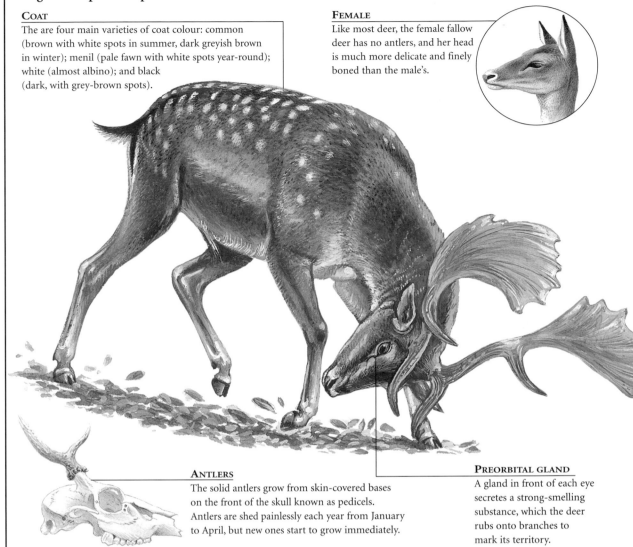

ANTLERS
The solid antlers grow from skin-covered bases on the front of the skull known as pedicels. Antlers are shed painlessly each year from January to April, but new ones start to grow immediately.

PREORBITAL GLAND
A gland in front of each eye secretes a strong-smelling substance, which the deer rubs onto branches to mark its territory.

CREATURE COMPARISONS

A relative of the fallow deer, the axis deer (Axis axis) is a native of India and Sri Lanka. It is one of four species in the genus Axis. Although a little smaller than the fallow deer, the axis deer is a similar shape, and the colour of its coat can also vary from season to season. Both species, however, have different antler arrangements. The fallow deer is easily recognized by its broad, flattened antlers; a shape described as palmate because it resembles an open palm with fingers extended. The axis deer has slender antlers with three distinct branches, the lowest of which extends forwards almost at a right angle to the base.

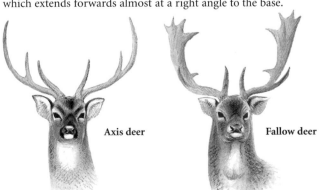

Axis deer   **Fallow deer**

WHERE IN THE WORLD?

A native of the Mediterranean region, although introduced as wild herds across most of Europe as far north as southern Scandinavia. Captive herds occur in parts of all continents except Antarctica.

RELATED SPECIES
The fallow deer belongs to the family Cervidae, which contains 4 subfamilies containing 17 genera and 45 species. A close relation is the red deer, Cervus elaphus, which is found in Europe, Asia and North America.

• **ORDER** • *Artiodactyla* • **FAMILY** • *Cervidae* • **GENUS & SPECIES** • *Elaphurus davidianus*

PÈRE DAVID'S DEER

The splayed feet and long legs of Père David's deer enabled it to exploit the swamp habitats of its native home in China.

KEY FEATURES

- A large deer that retains the adaptations it needed when it once roamed the lowland swamps of China.
- Rescued from certain extinction by the missionary and naturalist Père Armand David in the late 19th century.
- Thrives today in an English park, with a few other individuals found in zoos around the world.

COAT
The coat is tawny red with a dark dorsal stripe in summer, growing coarser and turning buff-grey in winter.

FAWN
Long legs give the fawn a coltish appearance. It has the distinctive tasselled tail of the species.

HOOF
Each hoof is splayed to increase its surface area, enabling the deer to walk on soft, muddy ground.

MALE
The male (above) has antlers. Shed annually after the rut, they take six months to grow again. Each antler has two main shafts, the forward having more tines (small branches).

LEGS
Long legs enable the deer to wade in water and pick its way through tall grass.

VITAL STATISTICS

WEIGHT	Male 200kg (440.9lb); female 115kg (253.5lb)
LENGTH	Head & Body 1.5m (4ft 9in) Tail 50cm (19.7in)
SHOULDER HEIGHT	1.2m (3ft 9in)
SEXUAL MATURITY	2–3 years
MATING SEASON	June to August in Britain
GESTATION PERIOD	8 months
NUMBER OF YOUNG	1 or 2
BIRTH INTERVAL	1 year
TYPICAL DIET	Grass and water plants
LIFESPAN	20–25 years

CREATURE COMPARISONS

The largest deer in South America, the marsh deer (Blastocerus dichotomus) lives in the wetlands and grasslands of southern Brazil and Argentina. It has a shoulder height of up to 1.2m (3ft 9in), and a coarse coat that moults to a reddish-brown in summer. Unlike Père David's deer, the marsh deer has black lower limbs and a black-tipped snout. The male has antlers, too, and they are more heavily branched than those of Père David's deer.

The marsh deer lives alone or in groups of up to six individuals, and does not appear to have a rutting season where males take control of females. Nor does it have a definite season when it drops its antlers, which in Père David's deer occurs in autumn.

Marsh deer **Père David's deer**

WHERE IN THE WORLD?

Originated in eastern China, but now extinct in the wild. The deer park of Woburn Abbey, England, is home to the world's largest captive population.

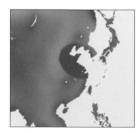

RELATED SPECIES

Père David's deer is the sole member of its genus, Elaphurus. It is related to the red deer, Cervus elaphus, and is part of the deer family Cervidae, which contains 36 species and is 1 of 10 families in the order Artiodactyla: the even-toed hoofed mammals.

MUSK DEER

• **ORDER** • *Artiodactyla* • **FAMILY** • *Cervidae* • **GENUS & SPECIES** • *Moschus moschiferus*

KEY FEATURES

- Males produce a strongly scented secretion called musk, which is highly valued as a perfume base.
- An extremely cautious creature that spends most of the day resting in secluded hiding places.
- Both sexes lack antlers, but males are equipped with a pair of unusually long, fang-like teeth.

VITAL STATISTICS

WEIGHT	7–17kg (15.4–37.5lb)
LENGTH	Head & Body 80–100cm (31–39.4in) Tail 4–6cm (1.6–2.4in)
SHOULDER HEIGHT	50–70cm (19.7–27.6in)
SEXUAL MATURITY	About 18 months
MATING SEASON	November to December
GESTATION PERIOD	185–198 days
NUMBER OF YOUNG	1 or 2, but usually 2
BIRTH INTERVAL	1 year
TYPICAL DIET	Leaves, flowers, young shoots, grasses, twigs, mosses, lichens
LIFESPAN	13 years in the wild; up to 20 years in captivity

With long legs and large, sturdy hoofs the musk deer is well equipped for climbing and leaping on rocky mountainsides.

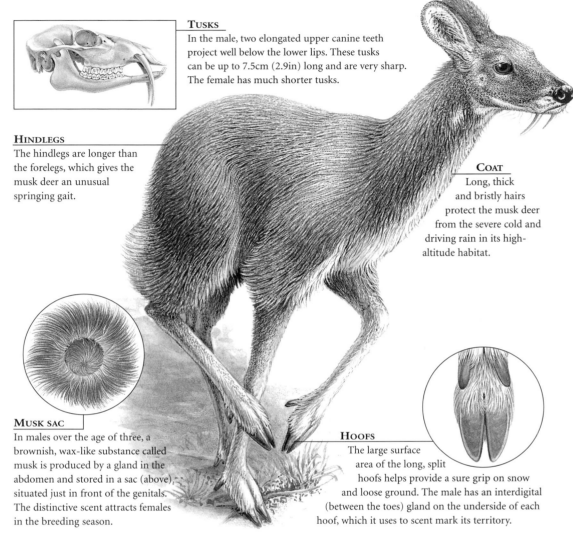

TUSKS
In the male, two elongated upper canine teeth project well below the lower lips. These tusks can be up to 7.5cm (2.9in) long and are very sharp. The female has much shorter tusks.

HINDLEGS
The hindlegs are longer than the forelegs, which gives the musk deer an unusual springing gait.

COAT
Long, thick and bristly hairs protect the musk deer from the severe cold and driving rain in its high-altitude habitat.

MUSK SAC
In males over the age of three, a brownish, wax-like substance called musk is produced by a gland in the abdomen and stored in a sac (above), situated just in front of the genitals. The distinctive scent attracts females in the breeding season.

HOOFS
The large surface area of the long, split hoofs helps provide a sure grip on snow and loose ground. The male has an interdigital (between the toes) gland on the underside of each hoof, which it uses to scent mark its territory.

CREATURE COMPARISONS

The five species of musk deer and the Chinese water deer (Hydropotes inermis) are the only species of deer without antlers. However, all these species are equipped with tusks. As with musk deer, it is the male Chinese water deer that grows the longest tusks.

Although the musk deer and Chinese water deer are similar in size, the latter stands out with its reddish-brown face colouring. Found in China and in Korea, the Chinese water deer has been known to produce eight young at a time: more than any other species of deer.

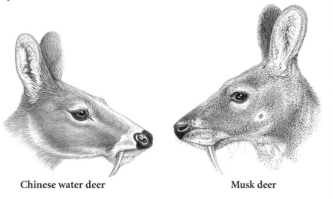

Chinese water deer   Musk deer

WHERE IN THE WORLD?

Found in mountainous regions up to 3600m (11,810ft) in central and northeastern Asia, from Siberia and Mongolia in the north, south through much of China to North and South Korea.

RELATED SPECIES
There are 5 species of musk deer. Although classed in the deer family Cervidae, which includes Père David's deer, Elaphurus davidianus, many authorities believe that musk deer, because of their tusks, belong in a family of their own — Moschidae.

• **ORDER** • *Artiodactyla* • **FAMILY** • *Cervidae* • **GENUS & SPECIES** • *Muntiacus muntjac*

INDIAN MUNTJAC

A compact body and short, neat antlers are assets to this furtive deer, which spends most of its life slipping through trails in dense undergrowth.

KEY FEATURES

*   Small, aggressive species of deer that is active both day and night, relying on vegetation for concealment.
*   Male possesses short antlers and protruding upper canines that serve as effective weapons against other deer and attacking predators.
*   Its eerie call, similar to a dog's bark, warns other deer of a predator in the vicinity.

VITAL STATISTICS

WEIGHT	Up to 18kg (39.7lb); male heavier than female
SHOULDER HEIGHT	Male 57cm (22.4in); female 49cm (19.3in)
SEXUAL MATURITY	At least 1 year
MATING SEASON	Throughout the year
GESTATION PERIOD	180 days
NUMBER OF YOUNG	1, rarely 2
BIRTH INTERVAL	Variable, but females can give birth twice a year
TYPICAL DIET	Bark, leaves, mushrooms, fruit, herbs
LIFESPAN	19 years in captivity

ANTLERS
The antlers are often no longer than 17cm (6.7in) and have a single, short tine (branch) off the main stem.

MALE'S SKULL
The antlers grow from long pedicels (bases), which continue as ridges down the facial region.

TUSKS
The male uses his 2.5cm (1in)-long upper canines against rivals or predators.

FEMALE
Considerably smaller than the male, the female lacks tusks and has small, virtually hidden knobs in place of antlers.

LIMBS
The limbs are dainty but muscular. When threatened, the muntjac makes bounding leaps into the undergrowth. If the deer is cornered, its small, cloven hoofs can deliver a powerful blow.

CREATURE COMPARISONS

The tufted deer (Elaphodus cephalophus) is a forest-dweller of northern Burma and China. It has a coarse, brown coat and white underparts. At up to 50kg (19.7in) in weight, it is larger than the muntjac, but is similar. In both species the males have upper tusks and antlers, although in the tufted deer the tiny antlers are almost hidden in the tufted hair of the crown. In addition, the tufted deer lacks the forehead ridges of the muntjac. Like the muntjac, the tufted deer usually lives in dense vegetation, but it can be found at higher altitudes, sometimes up to 4500m (14,760ft).

Tufted deer

Indian muntjac

WHERE IN THE WORLD?

Found throughout the Indian subcontinent, as well as Sri Lanka. Also present in Borneo, Java, Malaysia, Sumatra, Thailand, Vietnam, Burma, Tibet and southwestern China.

RELATED SPECIES

The Indian muntjac is 1 of 7 species in the genus Muntiacus. Fea's muntjac, M. feae, is the most endangered species: until 1977 there were only 2 recorded specimens. In 1994 a new, giant species of muntjac, Megamuntiacus vuquangensis, was found in the highlands of Vietnam, Laos and Cambodia. It is twice the weight of the Indian muntjac. Muntjacs are also known as barking deer on account of their dog-like calls.

MULE DEER

• ORDER • *Artiodactyla* • FAMILY • *Cervidae* • GENUS & SPECIES • *Odocoileus hemionus*

Ever alert and fleet of foot, the mule deer races to safety at the slightest hint of danger, moving swiftly with powerful leaps and bounds.

KEY FEATURES

- A highly adaptable species of deer found in a wide range of habitats, from mountains to hot desert and tropical forest.
- Named after its large, mule-like ears that seem to twitch constantly.
- Mature male stays loyal to one female at a time, unlike most deer.
- Escapes from its predators in a series of powerful bounds.

FEMALE
The doe (female) has a smaller, lighter build, emphasized by her lack of antlers.

ANTLERS
The stag's antlers begin to grow in April or May each year, lose their velvet covering in August and September, and finally fall off between January and March.

EARS
The ears are unusually large and very mobile, twisting from side to side to assess unfamiliar sounds.

CALF
Weighing just 1.5–3.5kg (3.3–7.7lb), the newborn calf is soon on its feet. Its white-spotted coat mimics dappled light falling on vegetation.

COAT
The thick, wind-cheating coat is greyish-brown in winter and reddish-brown in summer. Its hollow hairs trap air, greatly improving insulation.

RUMP
When the mule deer retreats into cover to hide from a predator, the white rump patch helps break up the animal's tell-tale outline.

VITAL STATISTICS

WEIGHT	Male 75–150kg (165.3–330.7lb) female 45–70kg (99.2–154.3lb)
LENGTH	Head & Body: 85–210cm (33.5–82.7in); Tail: 10–35cm (3.9–13.8in)
SHOULDER HEIGHT	Up to 1m (3ft 3in)
SEXUAL MATURITY	1–2 years
MATING SEASON	October –January
GESTATION PERIOD	195–215 days
NUMBER OF YOUNG	1 to 4; usually 2
BIRTH INTERVAL	1 year
TYPICAL DIET	Grasses, leaves, lichen, seeds, nuts, acorns, berries, twigs, mushrooms
LIFESPAN	Up to 20; usually less than 10 years

CREATURE COMPARISONS

Up to 1.25m (4ft 1in) tall at the shoulders, the swamp deer (*Cervus duvauceli*) of India is larger than the mule deer, weighing around 175kg (385.8lb). The swamp deer has an appearance more typical of the deer family, thanks to its brown coat and small ears. The swamp deer's Indian name, barasingha, means 'twelve horns'; it refers to the numerous tines (prongs) branching off each antler stem, although only the most mature stags carry such a number.

Once found in large numbers across the damp grasslands of northern India, the swamp deer is now endangered, with a total population of fewer than 5000 individuals. Unlike its North American relative, it has been unable to adapt to changes in its habitat, especially the spread of agriculture.

Mule deer stag

Swamp deer stag

WHERE IN THE WORLD?

Ranges throughout the western half of North America, from southern Saskatchewan in Canada south as far as western Texas. Also found in northernmost Mexico.

RELATED SPECIES

The mule deer shares the genus Odocoileus with just 1 other species, the white-tailed deer, which is found from Canada south to northeastern Brazil. The 2 species can interbreed and produce hybrid offspring. There are 16 other genera in the deer family, Cervidae, containing a total of 43 species including the musk and fallow deer, elk, reindeer and red deer. Deer belong to the large order Artiodactyla, or even-toed hoofed mammals.

• **ORDER** • *Artiodactyla* • **FAMILY** • *Cervidae* • **GENUS & SPECIES** • *Odocoileus virginianus*

WHITE-TAILED DEER

The white-tailed deer has a built-in signalling system to warn other deer of danger — it raises its white tail to flash the white underside.

KEY FEATURES

- Flashes a warning of danger to other deer with the white underside of its tail.
- The newborn young is so well camouflaged that it is left largely on its own for the first month of its life.
- Adaptable to a wide range of habitats — from northern woodlands to tropical forests.

ANTLERS
The male's antlers, which reach full size by about four or five years old, grow and drop off annually.

EYES
The eyes are large and are also set high on the head, which gives the deer almost all-round vision. This makes it very difficult for predators to approach undetected.

FEMALE
The female white-tailed deer is generally smaller than the male and lacks antlers.

TAIL
The deer raises, or 'flags', its tail when it is alarmed, exposing the white underside and rump area as a warning to other white-tailed deer. 'Hightailing' also makes it easier for a fawn to follow its mother in flight.

CAMOUFLAGE
The newborn young's brown and pale-spotted coat provides excellent camouflage in the dappled light of the forest.

VITAL STATISTICS

WEIGHT	50–200kg (110.2–440.9lb)
LENGTH	Head & Body 85–210cm (33.5–82.7in) Tail 10–35cm (3.9–13.8in)
SHOULDER HEIGHT	80–100cm (31–39.4in)
SEXUAL MATURITY	Male 2 years; female 1–2
MATING SEASON	Oct to Jan in North America; Feb to May South America; non-seasonal in tropical areas
GESTATION PERIOD	195–212 days
NUMBER OF YOUNG	1 at first birth; 2 (sometimes 3 or 4) after
BIRTH INTERVAL	1 year
TYPICAL DIET	Grasses, leaves, shoots
LIFESPAN	10–20 years

CREATURE COMPARISONS

The white-tailed deer is a relative of the fallow deer, *Dama dama*, which is more slightly built, weighing only about half as much as the white-tailed deer. The male fallow deer's antlers are also quite different in shape, being broad and palmate (shaped like an open hand). For this reason, the fallow deer is placed in its own genus in the family Cervidae. Both deer shed their antlers in late winter. The fallow deer's coat has four main colour varieties — more than any other deer — and, unlike the white-tailed deer, some mature fallow deer retain a spotted coat all their lives.

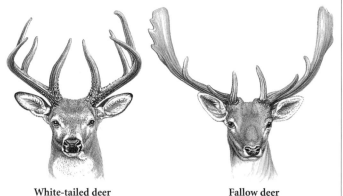

White-tailed deer   Fallow deer

WHERE IN THE WORLD?

Found in North, Central and South America, from southern Canada south to Bolivia and northeastern Brazil. Occurs throughout most of the USA, except in the more arid regions of the southwest.

RELATED SPECIES

There are 45 species of deer in the family Cervidae. Across their enormous range — from Arctic tundra to tropical forest — deer vary greatly in size. The Southern pudu (*Pudu pudu*) is the smallest, weighing only 6–8kg (13.2–17.6lb). The largest is the moose, *Alces alces*, weighing up to 825kg (1819lb).

PUDU

• ORDER • *Artiodactyla* • FAMILY • *Cervidae* • GENUS & SPECIES • *Pudu pudu, P. mephistophiles*

The minuscule but powerful pudu is small enough to weave its way through the thick tangles and dense undergrowth of its forest home.

KEY FEATURES

- The smallest two species of deer in the world, with a compact build and superb agility.
- Males use their territories — with accompanying food resources and safe resting sites — to attract mates.
- Living at low densities in isolated areas, both species are classified as threatened by the IUCN (World Conservation Union).

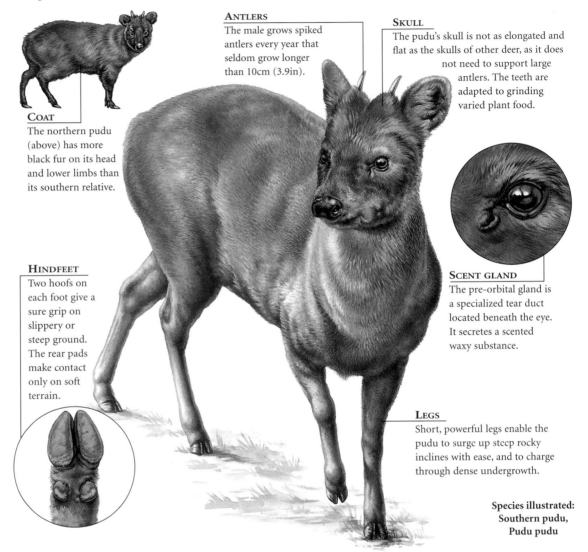

COAT
The northern pudu (above) has more black fur on its head and lower limbs than its southern relative.

ANTLERS
The male grows spiked antlers every year that seldom grow longer than 10cm (3.9in).

SKULL
The pudu's skull is not as elongated and flat as the skulls of other deer, as it does not need to support large antlers. The teeth are adapted to grinding varied plant food.

HINDFEET
Two hoofs on each foot give a sure grip on slippery or steep ground. The rear pads make contact only on soft terrain.

SCENT GLAND
The pre-orbital gland is a specialized tear duct located beneath the eye. It secretes a scented waxy substance.

LEGS
Short, powerful legs enable the pudu to surge up steep rocky inclines with ease, and to charge through dense undergrowth.

Species illustrated:
Southern pudu,
Pudu pudu

VITAL STATISTICS

WEIGHT	5.8–13.4kg (12.8–29.5lb)
LENGTH	Head & Body: 60–83cm (23.6–32.7in); Tail: 2.5–4.5cm (1–1.8in)
SHOULDER HEIGHT	25–43cm (9.8–16.9in)
SEXUAL MATURITY	Male 18 months; female 6 months
MATING SEASON	P. pudu: April to June; P. mephistophiles: year round
GESTATION PERIOD	202–223 days
NUMBER OF YOUNG	1
BIRTH INTERVAL	1 year
TYPICAL DIET	Wide variety of vegetation
LIFESPAN	12.5 years in captivity

CREATURE COMPARISONS

The moose (Alces alces) lives in the pine forests of northern Europe, Asia and Canada. The largest deer in the world, it is five times the size of a pudu. Some individuals reach a weight of more than 800kg (1764lb) and a height of 2.3m (7ft 5in). The distance across the moose's antlers can exceed 2m (6ft 6in).

The moose and the pudu both eat vegetation, but the larger animal relies far more on woody plants, especially during the long, cold winters. It also submerges itself completely in rivers to feed on bottom-growing plants. Some moose populations make long-distance seasonal migrations of up to 200km (124.3miles) to exploit food sources, whereas the pudu remains in its home range throughout the year.

Moose

Pudu

WHERE IN THE WORLD?

Found in three regions of South America. The southern pudu is found in the lower Andes of Chile and Argentina. The northern pudu occurs in separate ranges of the Andes in Ecuador, Peru and Colombia.

RELATED SPECIES

The genus Pudu contains 2 species: the northern pudu, P. mephistophiles, and the southern pudu, P. pudu. It is 1 of 16 genera in the deer family Cervidae. Pudus are closely related to the red brocket deer, Mazama americana, which lives in thickets in Central and South America.

• **ORDER** • *Artiodactyla* • **FAMILY** • *Giraffidae* • **GENUS & SPECIES** • *Giraffa camelopardalis*

GIRAFFE

KEY FEATURES

- The tallest of all living land animals.
- Remains standing most of the time, as lying down makes it vulnerable to attack by predators.
- Moves in loose herds, ambling gracefully across the African savannah.
- Can see over greater distances than any other land animal, which helps it to detect predators from a long way off.

VITAL STATISTICS

WEIGHT	Male 800–1930kg (1764–4255lb) female 550–1180kg (1213–2601lb)
LENGTH	Head & Body 3.8–4.7m (12ft 5in–15ft 4in) Tail 80–100cm (31–39.4in)
SHOULDER HEIGHT	To tip of horns: male 4.7–5.3m (15ft 4in–17ft 4in); female 3.9–4.5m (12.8–14.8in)
SEXUAL MATURITY	Male 4 years; female 3 years
MATING SEASON	All year
GESTATION PERIOD	400–465 days
NUMBER OF YOUNG	1 (2 is rare)
BIRTH INTERVAL	2 years
TYPICAL DIET	Shoots, leaves, grasses
LIFESPAN	20–25 years

Sometimes described as an animal 'assembled from spare parts', the giraffe's extraordinary height is a great advantage both for feeding and defence.

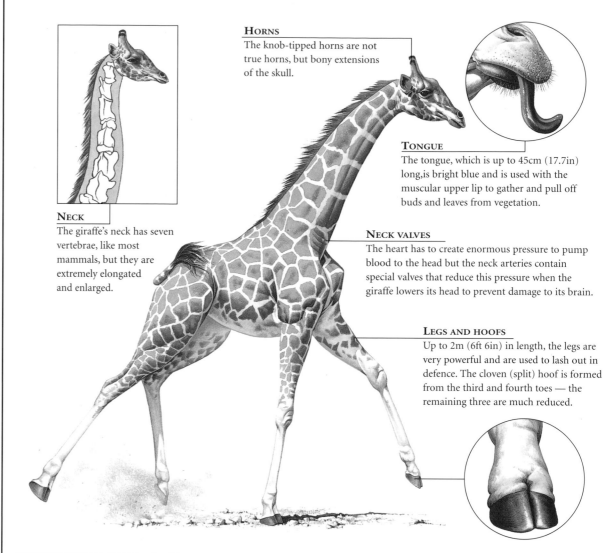

NECK
The giraffe's neck has seven vertebrae, like most mammals, but they are extremely elongated and enlarged.

HORNS
The knob-tipped horns are not true horns, but bony extensions of the skull.

TONGUE
The tongue, which is up to 45cm (17.7in) long, is bright blue and is used with the muscular upper lip to gather and pull off buds and leaves from vegetation.

NECK VALVES
The heart has to create enormous pressure to pump blood to the head but the neck arteries contain special valves that reduce this pressure when the giraffe lowers its head to prevent damage to its brain.

LEGS AND HOOFS
Up to 2m (6ft 6in) in length, the legs are very powerful and are used to lash out in defence. The cloven (split) hoof is formed from the third and fourth toes — the remaining three are much reduced.

CREATURE COMPARISONS

Each giraffe's coat markings are unique, and there is great variation across the giraffe's natural range. The different subspecies of giraffe, grouped according to location, are identified by the general patterns and colouring of their markings. For instance, some giraffes have chestnut-coloured blocks divided by narrow, white lines while others have jagged patches that may be dark brown or pale orange. All other characteristics among subspecies are identical. However, identification through markings can prove difficult if subspecies have interbred.

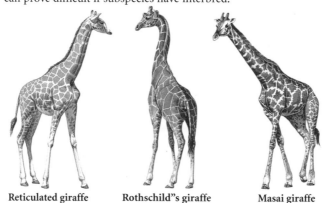

Reticulated giraffe   Rothschild"s giraffe   Masai giraffe

WHERE IN THE WORLD?

Distributed throughout sub-Saharan Africa. Prefers open woodlands and grasslands on the African savannah, but occasionally wanders in semi-arid country well away from water.

RELATED SPECIES

There are seven living races of giraffe. The only other member of the family Giraffidae is the okapi, from the rainforests of the Democratic Republic of Congo (Zaire). When first discovered by western science about 100 years ago, it was thought to be related to the zebra.

OKAPI

• ORDER • *Artiodactyla* • FAMILY • *Giraffidae* • GENUS & SPECIES • *Okapia johnstoni*

In the open, the okapi stands out in its velvety-brown, boldly striped livery. In its forest home, however, it melts invisibly into the background.

KEY FEATURES

- Secretive forest-dwelling herbivore that was first discovered by naturalists less than 100 years ago.

- Female has such a long gestation period that she can breed only every other year.

- Strips the leaves off twigs using an enormous tongue, which also doubles as a grooming brush.

VITAL STATISTICS

WEIGHT	200–250kg (440.9–551.2lb)
LENGTH	Head & Body: 1.9–2.2m (6ft 2in–7ft 2in); Tail: 30–42cm (11.8–16.5in)
SHOULDER HEIGHT	1.5–1.7m (4ft 9in–5ft 6in)
SEXUAL MATURITY	20–36 months
MATING SEASON	June to August
GESTATION PERIOD	425–491 days
NUMBER OF YOUNG	1
BIRTH INTERVAL	2 years
TYPICAL DIET	Leaves, buds, shoots, fruit and fungi
LIFESPAN	Not known in wild; over 15 years in captivity

FEMALE & MALE
Unusually among mammals, the female is larger than the male. Both sexes vary slightly in colour ranging from an almost purple-black through chocolate to chestnut-brown.

HORNS
The male's stumpy, hair-covered horns are used to butt rivals when competing for females. The female is hornless but sometimes bears hollow horn sheaths.

NECK AND HEAD
The 1m (3ft 6in) -long neck allows the okapi to reach high vegetation, and the soft, mobile lips help it to manipulate leaves while browsing.

TONGUE
The long, black tongue is prehensile: the okapi uses it not only to grasp twigs to pluck off the leaves but also to clean its eyes and coat.

FOOT
Each foot has a cloven (split) hoof. Glands under the hoofs mark the okapi's territory with scent as it walks about.

STRIPES
Striped legs and hindquarters help break up the okapi's shape against the green backdrop of the forest and reduce the chance of a predator spotting it while it has its back turned.

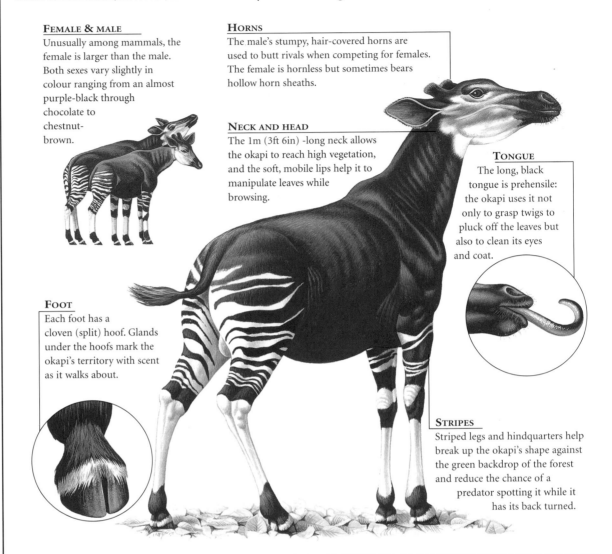

CREATURE COMPARISONS

The giraffe is a relation of the okapi and these animals have some clear similarities. For example, they are browsers and have extended necks and long, mobile tongues for stripping leaves from trees. Also, both are taller at the shoulders than at the rump, and have a coat pattern that is designed to provide camouflage by breaking up the body outline. The male okapi even has stumpy horns like the giraffe's. Both species also share an unusually long gestation period of about 15 months.

Beyond these common features, though, the giraffe stands apart from the okapi, and every other land animal, in its immense height — 3.9–5.3m (12ft 8in–17ft 4) infrom ground to horn tip. This allows it to feed at a higher level than any other browser.

Giraffe

Okapi

WHERE IN THE WORLD?

Found only in the dense, damp rainforests of northern, central and eastern parts of the Democratic Republic of Congo (Zaire).

RELATED SPECIES

The family Giraffidae contains just 2 species in 2 genera: the okapi, *Okapia johnstoni*, and the giraffe, *Giraffa camelopardalis*. The Giraffidae belong to the order Artiodactyla, which contains 211 species in all and includes antelopes, such as the African bushbuck, *Tragelaphus scriptus*.

• **ORDER** • *Artiodactyla* • **FAMILY** • *Hippopotamidae* • **GENUS & SPECIES** • *Choeropsis liberiensis*

PYGMY HIPPOPOTAMUS

The pygmy hippo may seem at first sight like a scaled-down hippopotamus, but a closer look reveals special adaptations for living in moist rainforest.

KEY FEATURES

- Leads a secretive and solitary existence beside rivers and swamps in dense rainforest.
- Lies in muddy wallows or hides under riverbanks by day, emerging at night to feed on the forest floor.
- Much less aquatic than its larger and more familiar relative, the hippopotamus.

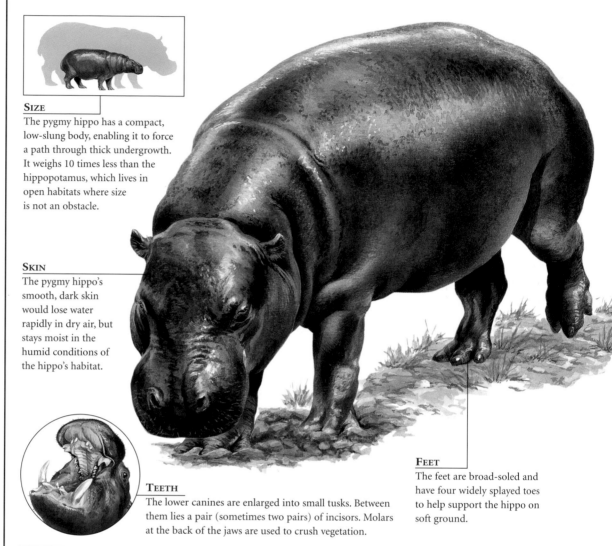

SIZE
The pygmy hippo has a compact, low-slung body, enabling it to force a path through thick undergrowth. It weighs 10 times less than the hippopotamus, which lives in open habitats where size is not an obstacle.

SKIN
The pygmy hippo's smooth, dark skin would lose water rapidly in dry air, but stays moist in the humid conditions of the hippo's habitat.

TEETH
The lower canines are enlarged into small tusks. Between them lies a pair (sometimes two pairs) of incisors. Molars at the back of the jaws are used to crush vegetation.

FEET
The feet are broad-soled and have four widely splayed toes to help support the hippo on soft ground.

VITAL STATISTICS

WEIGHT	180–270kg (396.8–595.2lb)
LENGTH	Head & Body 1.7–1.95m (5ft 6in–6ft 4in) Tail 75–100cm (29.5–39.4in)
SEXUAL MATURITY	3–5 years
MATING SEASON	November to December
GESTATION PERIOD	180–210 days
NUMBER OF YOUNG	1
BIRTH INTERVAL	2 years
TYPICAL DIET	Aquatic plants, algae, leaves, fallen fruit, roots, tubers and grasses
LIFESPAN	Up to 35 years

CREATURE COMPARISONS

A close examination of the heads of the pygmy hippo and the hippopotamus (Hippopotamus amphibius) reveals a number of structural differences. High-set eyes, ears and nostrils enable the hippopotamus to see, hear and breathe while almost fully submerged. The pygmy hippo lives mainly on land, and its facial features sit lower on the skull. In both species, the muscular nostrils can be sealed to keep out water. The huge, wide jaws of the highly social hippopotamus are used by males to threaten and fight each other, but the docile and solitary pygmy hippo has a small, bullet-shaped head.

Hippopotamus

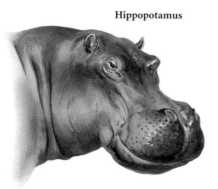

Pygmy hippopotamus

WHERE IN THE WORLD?

Found in a much reduced range along the West African coastline, in Guinea, Sierra Leone, Liberia and the Ivory Coast. Now extremely rare outside national parks.

RELATED SPECIES

There is 1 species in each of the 2 genera in the family Hippopotamidae. Choeropsis contains the pygmy hippo, while the hippopotamus is placed in Hippopotamus. Hippos belong to the order Artiodactyla, or even-toed ungulates, which includes the hippos' only close relatives — the pigs. A subspecies of pygmy hippo, C. liberiensis heslopi, may still survive in the Niger Delta in Nigeria but is most likely extinct.

HIPPOPOTAMUS

• ORDER • *Artiodactyla* • FAMILY • *Hippopotamidae* • GENUS & SPECIES • *Hippopotamus amphibius*

KEY FEATURES

- Spends more than 18 hours a day in the water, only emerging at night to feed on grassy shores.
- Equipped with enormous canine teeth that can inflict fatal wounds on predators and even fellow hippos.
- Excretes a pink, oily fluid from glands, which acts as a sunblock on its sun-sensitive skin.

VITAL STATISTICS

WEIGHT	Male 1000–4500kg (2205–9921lb) female 1000–1700kg (2205–3748lb)
LENGTH	Head & Body 2.9–5m (9ft 5in–16ft 4in) Tail 40–56cm (15.7–22in)
SHOULDER HEIGHT	1.5–1.65m (4ft 9in–5ft 4in)
SEXUAL MATURITY	Male 6–13 years; female 7–15 years
MATING SEASON	Dry season, which varies according to location
GESTATION PERIOD	227–240 days
NUMBER OF YOUNG	1 (2 is rare)
BIRTH INTERVAL	About 2 years
TYPICAL DIET	Grass, aquatic vegetation
LIFESPAN	35–50 years

The hippo's enormous bulk and short, stocky legs make it cumbersome on land — yet it is surprisingly agile in the water, swimming with graceful ease.

TAIL
The tail is very short in relation to body size. A male marks his territory by whirling his tail and defecating at the same time to spray dung at the boundaries.

TUSKS
The hippo's formidable tusks are elongated incisor and canine teeth. The lower outer tusks (canine teeth) may protrude 30cm (11.8in) above gum level in male hippos, and to display them in threat displays, the jaws can open to an angle of 150°.

SKIN GLANDS
Glands located just beneath the hippo's sensitive, almost hairless skin continuously exude drops of pink, oily mucus. The mucus sets hard, lacquering the skin to form a screen against sunburn, insect bites and the entry of germs into wounds.

FEET
The hippo's broad feet make excellent paddles for swimming and the four, thick toes spread its enormous weight on land to stop it sinking in soft ground.

CREATURE COMPARISONS

The pygmy hippo, Choeropsis liberiensis, as its name suggests, is much smaller than its relative the hippo, weighing only 160–270kg (352.7–595.2lb). Head to tail, it is also much shorter than the hippo, reaching only about one-third the length.

Although found along swamps and rivers in the lowland forests of West Africa, the pygmy hippo lives mainly on land. It seeks water only to take refuge when it is threatened, or to feed. Accordingly, its eyes are set lower on its head than the hippo's, as it does not spend much time submerged in the water.

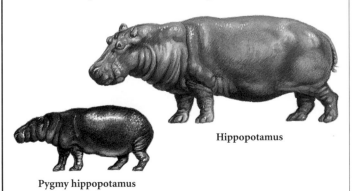

Hippopotamus

Pygmy hippopotamus

WHERE IN THE WORLD?

Occurs over much of sub-Saharan Africa, from Senegal in the west, east to Ethiopia and south to northern Namibia, Botswana and South Africa.

RELATED SPECIES

The hippo is the only member of the genus Hippopotamus and there are just two genera in the family Hippopotamidae — the other being Choerpsis. This genus also contains a single species: the pygmy hippo, Choeropsis liberiensis. Hippos' closest relatives are members of the family Suidae — the pigs. Pigs and hippos have the distinction of being the only non-ruminating (non-cud-chewing) members of the order Artiodactyla.

• **ORDER** • *Artiodactyla* • **FAMILY** • *Suidae* • **GENUS & SPECIES** • *Babyrousa babyrousa*

BABIRUSA

The babirusa would look rather like a dainty-legged farmyard pig, were it not for the extraordinary pair of tusks that grow through the male's snout.

KEY FEATURES

- A secretive member of the pig family found only on a handful of tropical islands in southeastern Asia.

- In a bizarre twist of nature, the male's upper canines grow upwards — through the very skin of his snout.

- Listed by the IUCN (World Conservation Union) as threatened with extinction, as a result of habitat loss.

VITAL STATISTICS

WEIGHT	Up to 100kg (220.5lb)
LENGTH	Head & Body 87–106cm (34.2–41.7in) Tail 27–32cm (10.6–12.6in)
SHOULDER HEIGHT	65–80cm (25.6–31in)
SEXUAL MATURITY	1–2 years
MATING SEASON	Year round
GESTATION PERIOD	125–150 days
NUMBER OF YOUNG	1 or 2
BIRTH INTERVAL	Unknown
TYPICAL DIET	Foliage, roots, snails, worms, small birds and mammals
LIFESPAN	24 years in captivity; around 10 years in the wild

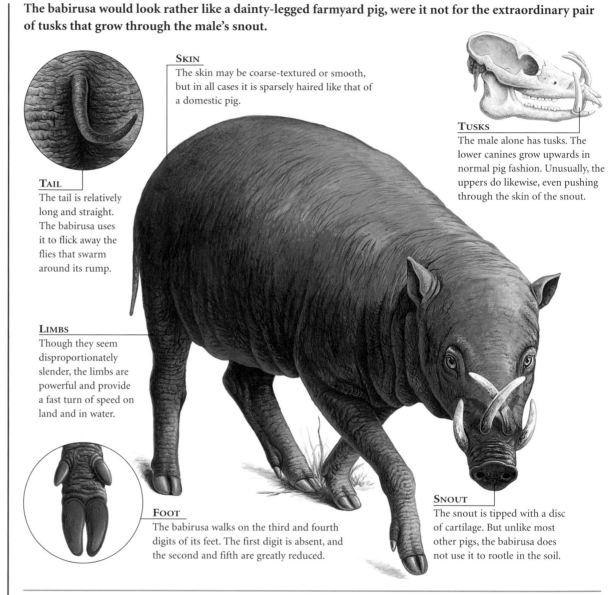

SKIN
The skin may be coarse-textured or smooth, but in all cases it is sparsely haired like that of a domestic pig.

TAIL
The tail is relatively long and straight. The babirusa uses it to flick away the flies that swarm around its rump.

TUSKS
The male alone has tusks. The lower canines grow upwards in normal pig fashion. Unusually, the uppers do likewise, even pushing through the skin of the snout.

LIMBS
Though they seem disproportionately slender, the limbs are powerful and provide a fast turn of speed on land and in water.

FOOT
The babirusa walks on the third and fourth digits of its feet. The first digit is absent, and the second and fifth are greatly reduced.

SNOUT
The snout is tipped with a disc of cartilage. But unlike most other pigs, the babirusa does not use it to rootle in the soil.

CREATURE COMPARISONS

Like the babirusa, the white-lipped peccary (Tayassu pecari) of Central and South America is found in thick rainforest, where it lives in tight-knit family groups. Active night and day, the peccary forages for hard nuts and seeds but eats almost anything if necessary. Its upper canines, which grow downwards, are much shorter than those of the babirusa, at only 4cm (1.6in) long. However, it readily uses these stout, sharp tusks to defend its young against coyotes and bobcats.

At up to 1.2m (3ft 9in) long, the peccary is a little larger than its Asian relative, although its tail is much smaller. Its hide, covered in thick grey to dark brown bristles, contrasts with that of the sparsely haired babirusa.

White-lipped peccary

Babirusa

WHERE IN THE WORLD?

Confined to parts of Sulawesi in Indonesia, as well as the nearby island groups of Buru, Togian and Sula.

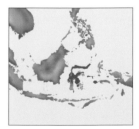

RELATED SPECIES

The babirusa is the sole member of its genus. Other members of the family Suidae are the warthog, giant forest hog, African bushpig, wild boar or pig, bearded pig, Sulawesi wild boar and Javan warty pig. In the Americas, the 3 species of peccary, family Tayassuidae, occupy a similar ecological niche to the African and Eurasian pigs. Pigs and peccaries are members of the order Artiodactyla, or even-toed hoofed mammals.

GIANT FOREST HOG

• **ORDER** • *Artiodactyla* • **FAMILY** • *Suidae* • **GENUS & SPECIES** • *Hylochoerus meinertzhageni*

KEY FEATURES

- Male is the largest of all the world's wild pigs and arguably the most fearsome, regularly fighting rivals for the possession of territory.

- Several generations of offspring live with their parents in an extended family group.

- Unusually for a wild pig, it is primarily a grazer.

VITAL STATISTICS

WEIGHT	Male 145–275kg (319.7–606.3l b); female 130–204kg (286.6–449.7lb)
LENGTH	Head & Body 130–210cm (51.2–82.7in)) Tail 30–45cm (11.8–17.7in)
SHOULDER HEIGHT	76–110cm (29.9–43.3in)
SEXUAL MATURITY	1 year, most males do not mate until 3
MATING SEASON	Year-round, peaks towards the end of the rainy season in some areas
GESTATION PERIOD	125 days
NUMBER OF YOUNG	2 to 11
BIRTH INTERVAL	1 year or less
TYPICAL DIET	Grass, foliage
LIFESPAN	Not known

The goliath of all swine, a giant forest hog makes a terrifying sight as it gallops from cover, brandishing its swollen face and menacing tusks.

TUSKS
The upper canines grow outwards from the jaw to form tusks, which may be up to 30cm (11.8in) long in the male. The female has much smaller tusks.

PREORBITAL GLANDS
Prominent swellings just in front of the male's eyes contain preorbital glands. These exude scent secretions that send a potent signal of the male's presence.

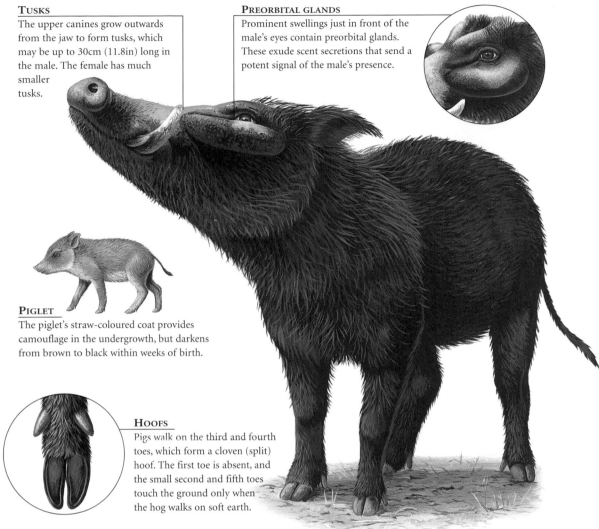

PIGLET
The piglet's straw-coloured coat provides camouflage in the undergrowth, but darkens from brown to black within weeks of birth.

HOOFS
Pigs walk on the third and fourth toes, which form a cloven (split) hoof. The first toe is absent, and the small second and fifth toes touch the ground only when the hog walks on soft earth.

CREATURE COMPARISONS

One of the giant forest hog's strangest-looking cousins lives in Indonesia, in the tropical forests of Sulawesi and neighbouring islands. The babirusa (Babyrousa babyrussa) is a little over half the size of its African relative and lacks the giant forest hog's mantle of long, coarse hair. The babirusa's face is free of the fleshy warts common to most hogs, but instead has a double set of tusks. The lower tusks flare outwards and upwards from the mouth in the conventional manner, but the upper pair grow straight up through the muzzle. The babirusa uses these tusks to grapple with an opponent's lower tusks.

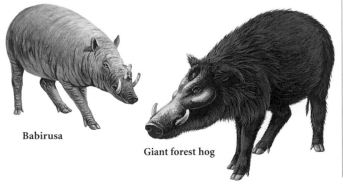

Babirusa

Giant forest hog

WHERE IN THE WORLD?

Found mainly in the humid, forested regions of central Africa, but scattered populations stretch from Liberia in the west to southwestern Ethiopia, Kenya and northern Tanzania in the east.

RELATED SPECIES

The pig family, Suidae, contains 5 genera and 9 species. The wild boar, pygmy hog, Javan pig, bearded pig and Celebes wild boar all belong to the genus Sus. Each of the remaining species — the African bushpig, warthog, babirusa and giant forest hog — is placed in its own separate genus. The pig family belongs to the large order of even-toed grazing mammals, Artiodactyla, which also includes deer, cattle and camels.

• **ORDER** • *Artiodactyla* • **FAMILY** • *Suidae* • **GENUS & SPECIES** • *Potamochoerus porcus*

AFRICAN BUSHPIG

KEY FEATURES

- Rich colouration, tasselled ears and hairy mane distinguish this widespread pig of the African bush.
- Uses its powerful snout, tipped with a tough disc of gristle, to rootle in soft soil for tubers and grubs.
- Compact in form and fast on its trotters; can use its tusks to deadly effect when cornered or wounded.

VITAL STATISTICS

WEIGHT	46–130kg (101.4–286.6lb)
LENGTH	1.3–2m (4ft 3in–6ft 6in)
SHOULDER HEIGHT	59–96cm (23.2–37.8in)
MATING SEASON	In rainy season (November to February in south; June to September farther north)
GESTATION PERIOD	120 days
NUMBER OF YOUNG	1 to 6, usually 3 or 4
BIRTH INTERVAL	3 years
TYPICAL DIET	Organic matter, including roots, berries, fruit, birds, mammals, eggs, carrion
LIFESPAN	20 years in captivity; 10–12 in wild

Colourful and whiskered, the bushpig is built like a sturdy slab of muscle, and barges through the thickest undergrowth on deceptively dainty limbs.

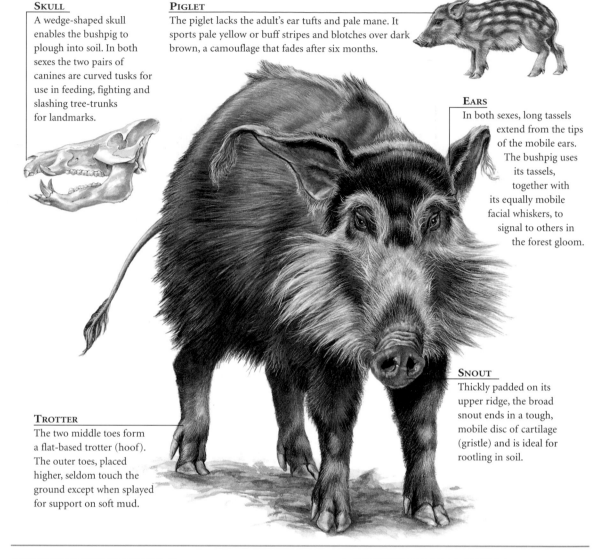

SKULL
A wedge-shaped skull enables the bushpig to plough into soil. In both sexes the two pairs of canines are curved tusks for use in feeding, fighting and slashing tree-trunks for landmarks.

PIGLET
The piglet lacks the adult's ear tufts and pale mane. It sports pale yellow or buff stripes and blotches over dark brown, a camouflage that fades after six months.

EARS
In both sexes, long tassels extend from the tips of the mobile ears. The bushpig uses its tassels, together with its equally mobile facial whiskers, to signal to others in the forest gloom.

SNOUT
Thickly padded on its upper ridge, the broad snout ends in a tough, mobile disc of cartilage (gristle) and is ideal for rootling in soil.

TROTTER
The two middle toes form a flat-based trotter (hoof). The outer toes, placed higher, seldom touch the ground except when splayed for support on soft mud.

CREATURE COMPARISONS

The wild boar (Sus scrofa), a close relative of the bushpig, can be found across Europe and Asia to the Malay Peninsula. For as long as 10,000 years, humans have been farming and selectively breeding the wild boar, a process that has given creation to dozens of domestic pig breeds.

Like its wild relatives, the domestic pig can eat almost anything. The process of selection, however, has made domestic breeds stockier and more fertile, while also removing their tusks and taming their aggressiveness. The pot-bellied pig, a popular domestic breed from southeastern Asia, is an extreme example of this trait.

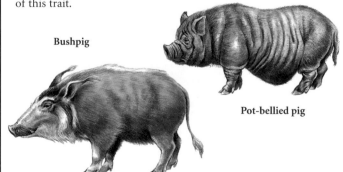

Bushpig

Pot-bellied pig

WHERE IN THE WORLD?

Found in a broad band across sub-Saharan Africa, as far as the coastal fringe of South Africa. Absent from the driest regions.

RELATED SPECIES

The many localized races of bushpig include the red river hog, Potamochoerus porcus larvatus. The family Suidae contains 9 species including the wild boar, Sus scrofa, and 4 other species of wild pig; the warthog, Phacochoerus aethiopicus; the giant forest hog, Hylochoerus meinertzhageni, and the uniquely tusked babirusa of Sulawesi, S. celebensis. All suids belong to the order Artiodactyla, or even-toed hoofed mammals.

WILD BOAR

• ORDER • *Artiodactyla* • FAMILY • *Suidae* • GENUS & SPECIES • *Sus scrofa*

Built for fighting, the male wild boar is armed with fearsome slashing tusks and has tough, thickened skin to help protect it during battles with rivals.

KEY FEATURES

- Strong and fearless in self-defence, the powerfully built male boar is a formidable adversary.
- Curved tusks protruding from the lower jaw are used as digging tools and as lethal weapons.
- Dark, shaggy-coated and nimble, it contrasts sharply with its familiar descendant — the domestic pig.

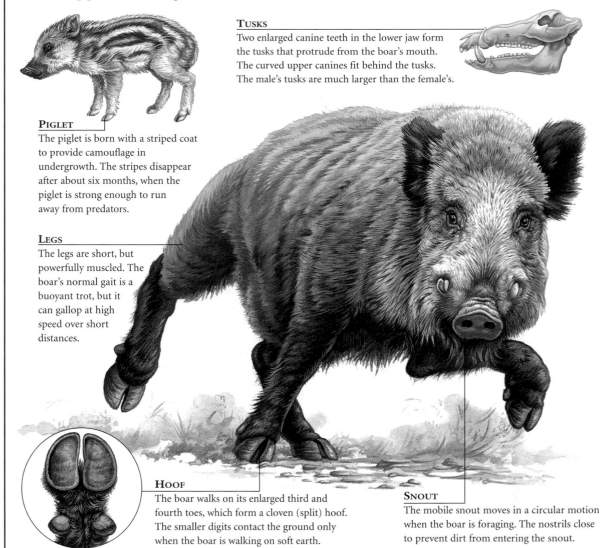

PIGLET
The piglet is born with a striped coat to provide camouflage in undergrowth. The stripes disappear after about six months, when the piglet is strong enough to run away from predators.

TUSKS
Two enlarged canine teeth in the lower jaw form the tusks that protrude from the boar's mouth. The curved upper canines fit behind the tusks. The male's tusks are much larger than the female's.

LEGS
The legs are short, but powerfully muscled. The boar's normal gait is a buoyant trot, but it can gallop at high speed over short distances.

HOOF
The boar walks on its enlarged third and fourth toes, which form a cloven (split) hoof. The smaller digits contact the ground only when the boar is walking on soft earth.

SNOUT
The mobile snout moves in a circular motion when the boar is foraging. The nostrils close to prevent dirt from entering the snout.

VITAL STATISTICS

WEIGHT	50–350kg (110.2–771.6lb)
LENGTH	Head & Body 90–180cm (35.4–70.9) Tail 30–40cm (11.8–15.7in)
SHOULDER HEIGHT	55–110cm (21.6–43.3in)
SEXUAL MATURITY	8–10 months. Females breed at 18 months, males at about 5 years
MATING SEASON	All year round in the tropics; Oct to Dec in temperate areas
GESTATION PERIOD	100–140 days
NUMBER OF YOUNG	1 to 12, but usually 4 to 8
BIRTH INTERVAL	1 year
TYPICAL DIET	Vegetable and animal material
LIFESPAN	15–20 years

CREATURE COMPARISONS

The wart hog (Phacochoerus aethiopicus), which is found over most of Africa south of the Sahara, is a close relative of the wild boar, but is smaller with a prominent mane that runs along its neck and back.

The wart hog prefers an open, grassy habitat to forest and, unlike most members of the pig family, including the wild boar, it is active during the day rather than at night. It is also the only pig that moves about on its knees when looking for food. The wart hog is further distinguished by its enormous tusks — its two upper canines curve sharply upwards to a point and may grow to 63cm. Young wart hogs also differ from wild boar piglets in that they have no stripes.

Wild boar

Wart hog

WHERE IN THE WORLD?

Found in small, scattered populations in Europe, through North Africa and south and central Asia. Introduced to many other parts of the world.

RELATED SPECIES

The wild boar is one of 9 species of pig in the family Suidae, which includes the babyrousa and giant forest hog. The domestic pig is the same species as the wild boar, but through selective breeding by humans has lost the thick coat, leaner build and long tusks of its wild relation.

• **ORDER** • *Artiodactyla* • **FAMILY** • *Tayassuidae* • **GENUS & SPECIES** • *Tayassu tajacu*

COLLARED PECCARY

KEY FEATURES

- Forages for all kinds of plant matter in habitats ranging from semi-desert to thick forest.
- Covered by a tough, bristly coat which protects it as it roams through deep undergrowth.
- Related to the pig, but more sociable, travelling in groups of up to 20 animals.

Individuals range in size and colour, from the small, grey scrub-dwellers to the large, black rainforest hogs — but all bear a distinctive, pale collar.

SKULL AND TEETH
The upper canines are straight, unlike a pig's curved tusks. The jaws work up and down, in contrast to the side-to-side action of most hoofed mammals.

YOUNG
At birth the piglet-like young peccary is the size of a rabbit. Its reddish-brown coat darkens as it matures.

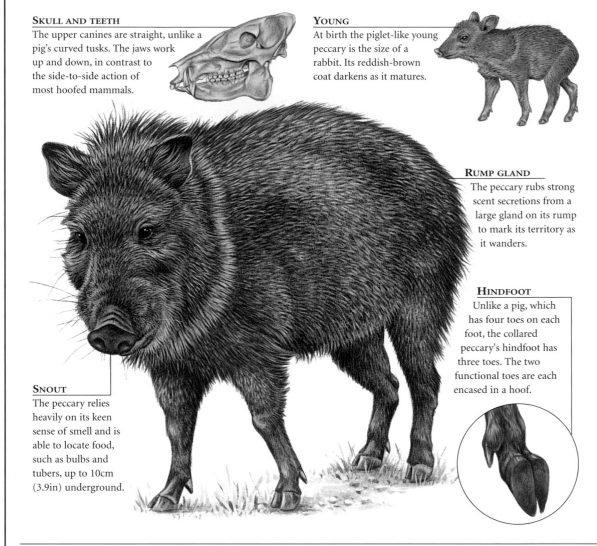

RUMP GLAND
The peccary rubs strong scent secretions from a large gland on its rump to mark its territory as it wanders.

HINDFOOT
Unlike a pig, which has four toes on each foot, the collared peccary's hindfoot has three toes. The two functional toes are each encased in a hoof.

SNOUT
The peccary relies heavily on its keen sense of smell and is able to locate food, such as bulbs and tubers, up to 10cm (3.9in) underground.

VITAL STATISTICS

WEIGHT	14–35kg (30.9–77.2lb)
LENGTH	Head & Body 75–98cm (29.5–38.6in) Tail 3.5–4.5cm (1.4–1.8in)
SHOULDER HEIGHT	44–58cm (17.3–22.8in)
SEXUAL MATURITY	Male 46–47 weeks; female 33–34 weeks
MATING SEASON	All year
GESTATION PERIOD	142 days
NUMBER OF YOUNG	1 to 4
BIRTH INTERVAL	1 year
TYPICAL DIET	Roots, fruit and seeds; also insects, small mammals and reptiles
LIFESPAN	8–10 years

CREATURE COMPARISONS

Thought to have been extinct since the last Ice Age, the Chacoan peccary (Catagonus wagneri) was discovered in 1974 living in the semi-arid Gran Chaco area of northern Argentina, western Paraguay and southeastern Bolivia. Larger than the collared peccary, and with a grizzled grey-brown coat, the Chacoan peccary also has a longer snout and ears. Because of its restricted range, the Chacoan peccary is even more susceptible to habitat destruction and hunting than its relative. Since 1983, a conservation project has been operating in the Chaco Basin in an attempt to preserve the animal, but it is now classified as vulnerable.

Collared peccary

Chacoan peccary

WHERE IN THE WORLD?

Found from southwestern USA through Central America, south to western Ecuador, Brazil and northeastern Argentina.

RELATED SPECIES
The family Tayassuidae contains 3 species in 2 genera. The genus Tayassu comprises the collared peccary and the white-lipped peccary, T. pecari, while the genus Catagonus contains the Chacoan peccary.

STINGRAY

• ORDER • *Batiformes* • FAMILY • *Dasyatidae* • GENUS & SPECIES • *Taeniura, Urolophus, etc.*

KEY FEATURES

- Flattened relatives of the sharks, armed with a sharp, barbed, and venomous tail sting.
- Spend most of their life hidden in the seabed sediment, rising to prey on bottom-living creatures.
- Flap like graceful, stately birds over the seabed, but are also capable of powerful acceleration.

With a flattened body, shell-crushing teeth and a venomous tail sting, a stingray is perfectly adapted to hunting armoured prey on the seabed.

Species shown:
blue-spotted stingray,
Taeniura lymma

TAIL
The tail is used to steer, and some species have a fringe-like tail fin to increase efficiency. The tail also provides the momentum behind the sting.

PECTORAL FINS
The 'wings' are highly modified pectoral fins that have fused to the body along the flanks. Powered by strong muscles, they provide impressive acceleration.

STING
Long and sharp, with hook-like barbs, the sting is a modified, grooved spine with glandular tissue on its underside that produces a potent venom. Some species have more than one sting.

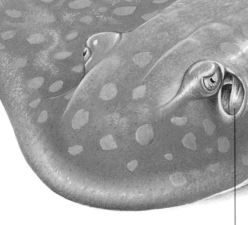

SENSES
Stingrays have good eyesight and a superb sense of smell. Water is absorbed through spiracles (vents) behind the eyes and receptors sample it for any taste of prey.

MOUTH
The mouth lies on the underside of the body, perfectly placed to scoop up crustaceans and molluscs from the seabed. Powerful jaws are lined with rows of flat-topped teeth for crushing shells.

VITAL STATISTICS

WEIGHT	Up to 340kg (749.6lb)
LENGTH	Up to 4.5m (14ft 8in) including tail
SEXUAL MATURITY	Unknown
MATING SEASON	Late spring to early summer
GESTATION PERIOD	Unknown
NUMBER OF YOUNG	Up to 12
BIRTH INTERVAL	Unknown
TYPICAL DIET	Crustaceans (especially crabs), molluscs and occasionally small fish
LIFESPAN	Unknown

CREATURE COMPARISONS

Although all stingrays have a flattened body, they vary widely in shape. Some are 'square stingrays', with pronounced corners at the tip of each fin, while others are 'round stingrays' with a disc-shaped body.

The blue-spotted stingray (Taeniura lymma) is strikingly colourful; its spots help advertise its venomous capabilities. The banded stingaree (Urolophus cruciatus) of Australian waters is better suited to camouflaging itself. It has a flexible, fleshy tail, which it thrusts forward in defence if provoked.

Banded stingaree

Blue-spotted stingray

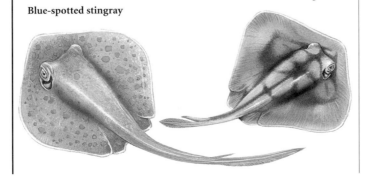

WHERE IN THE WORLD?

Found around the world in tropical and subtropical seas. Some species migrate into the temperate waters around Britain and Spain in the summer.

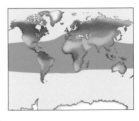

RELATED SPECIES

Stingrays are closely related to sharks. Species in these groups have a skeleton made of cartilage, which is lighter than bone and enhances buoyancy in the water. The blue-spotted stingray belongs to the Indo-Pacific stingray genus Taeniura. This genus is 1 of 19 comprising the family Dasyatidae. There are about 100 species in Dasyatidae, which is 1 of 7 families of skates and rays in the order Batiformes.

• ORDER • *Blattaria* • FAMILY • *Blattidae* • GENUS & SPECIES • *Periplaneta americana*

AMERICAN COCKROACH

KEY FEATURES

- Infests houses, restaurants, bakeries and warehouses.
- Scavenges spilled and stored food, but eats almost any animal or vegetable matter.
- Contaminates human food and household surfaces with dirt and disease.
- Has developed resistance to many insecticides.

VITAL STATISTICS

LENGTH	Up to 4.4cm (1.7in)
SEXUAL MATURITY	10–20 days after final moult
MATING SEASON	All year round
INCUBATION PERIOD	1–3 weeks
NYMPHAL PERIOD	5–23 months, depending on temperature
NUMBER OF YOUNG	6 to 28 eggs in each egg-case; on average 13 or 14 hatch
BIRTH INTERVAL	First egg-case 1 week after mating, others every 4–12 days
TYPICAL DIET	Almost any organic matter
LIFESPAN	Up to about 22 months

Little changed in 250 million years, the primitive cockroach owes its success to its opportunism and its unspecialized body form.

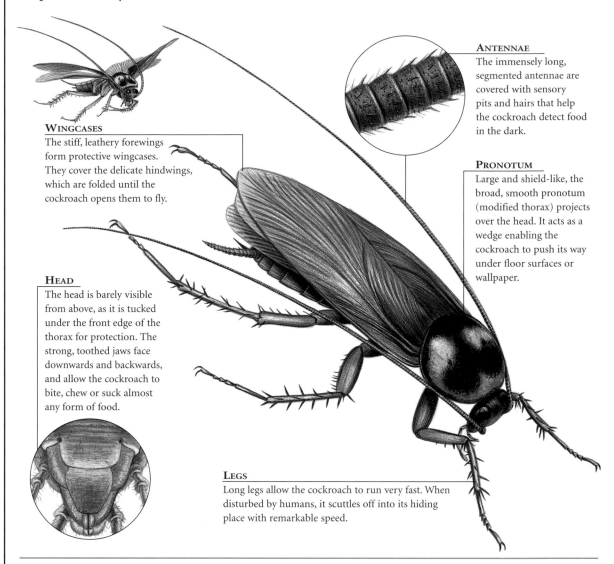

WINGCASES
The stiff, leathery forewings form protective wingcases. They cover the delicate hindwings, which are folded until the cockroach opens them to fly.

HEAD
The head is barely visible from above, as it is tucked under the front edge of the thorax for protection. The strong, toothed jaws face downwards and backwards, and allow the cockroach to bite, chew or suck almost any form of food.

ANTENNAE
The immensely long, segmented antennae are covered with sensory pits and hairs that help the cockroach detect food in the dark.

PRONOTUM
Large and shield-like, the broad, smooth pronotum (modified thorax) projects over the head. It acts as a wedge enabling the cockroach to push its way under floor surfaces or wallpaper.

LEGS
Long legs allow the cockroach to run very fast. When disturbed by humans, it scuttles off into its hiding place with remarkable speed.

CREATURE COMPARISONS

Four cockroach species account for most infestations, and have all been carried throughout the world from their homelands by the movements of humans.

The oriental cockroach (Blatta orientalis) originated in Asia. A flightless species, it reaches 2.85cm (1.1in) in length. The Australian cockroach (Periplaneta australasiae) is roughly the same length. The German cockroach (Blatella germanica) reaches a length of 1.58cm (0.6in)and is often brought into the home in grocery bags or food crates. The German, Australian and American cockroaches all originated in Africa.

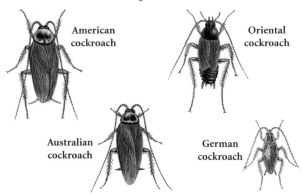

American cockroach

Oriental cockroach

Australian cockroach

German cockroach

WHERE IN THE WORLD?

Completely cosmopolitan, despite its common name, occurring in almost every part of the world that has been settled by humans.

RELATED SPECIES

There are about 4000 known species of cockroach, with probably a similar number awaiting discovery. Fewer than 20 of these — less than half of 1 per cent — are reported as pests. The wingless hissing cockroach lives in the wild, eating fallen fruit and other plant debris.

TAWNY FROGMOUTH

• ORDER • *Caprimulgiformes* **• FAMILY •** *Podargidae* **• GENUS & SPECIES •** *Podargus strigoides*

The tawny frogmouth is an odd-looking bird, but its short-necked profile and patterned plumage are key elements in its superb disguise.

KEY FEATURES

- A nocturnal hunter and daytime rooster that thrives in a number of different habitats throughout its range.
- Equipped with excellent camouflage that enables it to hunt or hide undetected by either prey or predator.
- Feeds on a variety of food, ranging from insects and frogs to small mammals and even cultivated citrus fruits.

VITAL STATISTICS

WEIGHT	75–110g (2.6–3.9lb)
LENGTH	35–50cm (13.8–19.7in)
WINGSPAN	45–60cm (17.7–23.6in)
SEXUAL MATURITY	1 year
BREEDING SEASON	Varies across range
NUMBER OF EGGS	Usually 2
INCUBATION PERIOD	30 days
FLEDGING PERIOD	30 days
BREEDING INTERVAL	As short as 2 months, though usually annual
TYPICAL DIET	Large insects, small mammals, fruit
LIFESPAN	Unknown

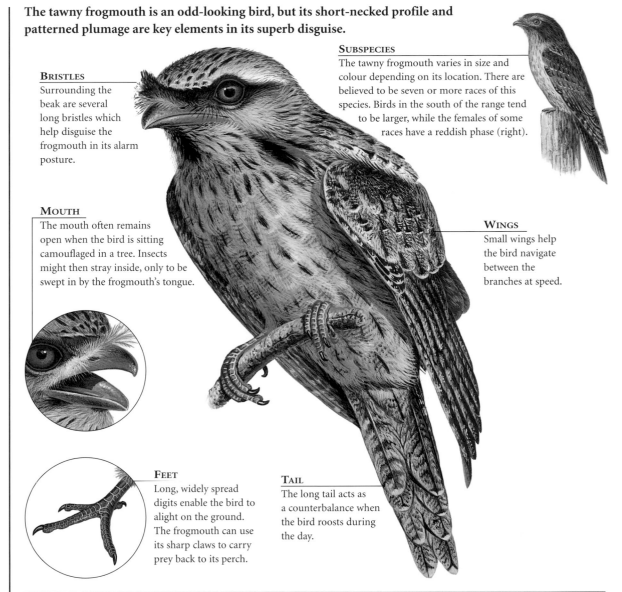

BRISTLES
Surrounding the beak are several long bristles which help disguise the frogmouth in its alarm posture.

MOUTH
The mouth often remains open when the bird is sitting camouflaged in a tree. Insects might then stray inside, only to be swept in by the frogmouth's tongue.

SUBSPECIES
The tawny frogmouth varies in size and colour depending on its location. There are believed to be seven or more races of this species. Birds in the south of the range tend to be larger, while the females of some races have a reddish phase (right).

WINGS
Small wings help the bird navigate between the branches at speed.

FEET
Long, widely spread digits enable the bird to alight on the ground. The frogmouth can use its sharp claws to carry prey back to its perch.

TAIL
The long tail acts as a counterbalance when the bird roosts during the day.

CREATURE COMPARISONS

The common potoo (Nyctibus griseus) is found in the West Indies and from western Mexico to Uruguay. Roughly the same size as the frogmouth, the potoo has similar grey, mottled and streaked plumage. It, too, is found in wooded environments, relying on its plumage for camouflage. It has a smaller bill with a sharper, more pronounced hook, but similarly has protective bristles above the bill. Both birds catch insects on the wing, but the larger bill of the frogmouth enables it to take prey of greater size. Like the frogmouth, the potoo roosts during the day, perched motionless on a branch. It springs into action at night, but unlike the tawny frogmouth it never lands on the ground. The potoo owes its name to its melancholy call: a descending poh-o oh oh oh oh.

Common potoo

Tawny frogmouth

WHERE IN THE WORLD?

Found throughout the mainland of Australia and Tasmania. Also occurs on New Guinea and the Solomon Islands.

RELATED SPECIES

The tawny frogmouth is 1 of 3 species in the genus Podargus. The Papuan frogmouth, P. papuensis, and the marbled frogmouth, P. ocellatus, are the other members. They belong to the order Caprimulgiformes, which includes the European nightjar, Caprimulgus europaeus.

• **ORDER** • *Carcharhiniformes* • **FAMILY** • *Carcharhinidae* • **GENUS & SPECIES** • *Galeocerdo cuvier*

TIGER SHARK

The sleek profile and muscular tail of the tiger shark combine to give speed and agility, while its menacing teeth produce a deadly bite.

KEY FEATURES

- One of the most dangerous of all sharks; tears large prey to pieces by rolling and twisting rapidly.
- Feeds alone in shallow water, and detects prey using highly sensitive pores in its skin.
- Indiscriminate feeder, often lurking near discharge pipes and swallowing inedible items of refuse.

VITAL STATISTICS

WEIGHT	300–1000kg (661.4–2205lb)
LENGTH	4–6m (13ft 1in–19ft 7in)
SEXUAL MATURITY	Reached at around 3m (9ft 8in)
MATING SEASON	Probably early summer
GESTATION PERIOD	16 months (eggs hatch internally)
NUMBER OF YOUNG	Normally 10 to 40; up to 80
BIRTH INTERVAL	Thought to be 2 years
TYPICAL DIET	Fish, seabirds, sea mammals, molluscs, sea turtles, carrion, items of refuse
LIFESPAN	40–50 years

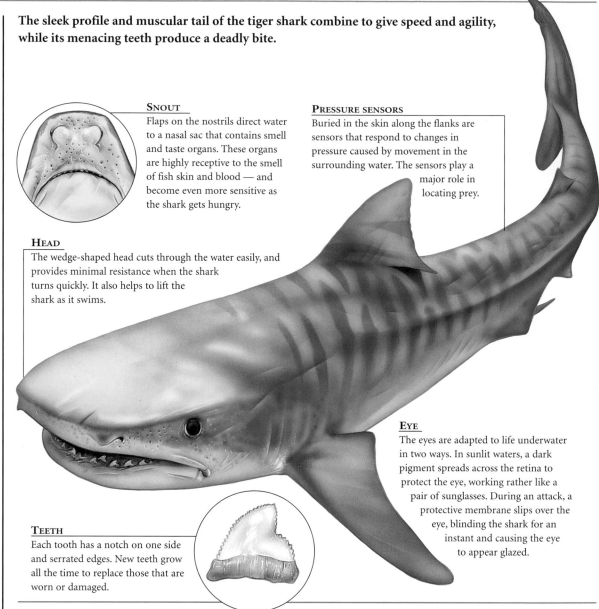

SNOUT
Flaps on the nostrils direct water to a nasal sac that contains smell and taste organs. These organs are highly receptive to the smell of fish skin and blood — and become even more sensitive as the shark gets hungry.

PRESSURE SENSORS
Buried in the skin along the flanks are sensors that respond to changes in pressure caused by movement in the surrounding water. The sensors play a major role in locating prey.

HEAD
The wedge-shaped head cuts through the water easily, and provides minimal resistance when the shark turns quickly. It also helps to lift the shark as it swims.

EYE
The eyes are adapted to life underwater in two ways. In sunlit waters, a dark pigment spreads across the retina to protect the eye, working rather like a pair of sunglasses. During an attack, a protective membrane slips over the eye, blinding the shark for an instant and causing the eye to appear glazed.

TEETH
Each tooth has a notch on one side and serrated edges. New teeth grow all the time to replace those that are worn or damaged.

CREATURE COMPARISONS

The Port Jackson shark (Heterodontus portjacksoni) is on average less than half the length of the tiger shark.

It is more richly coloured, however, sporting black markings on a sandy background. Its head, much blunter than that of the tiger shark, has two ridges running along the top, giving it the appearance of having horns. Found mainly in the tropical waters of the Pacific Ocean, the Port Jackson shark is a bottom-dweller. Its back teeth are flattened plates that crush its shellfish prey.

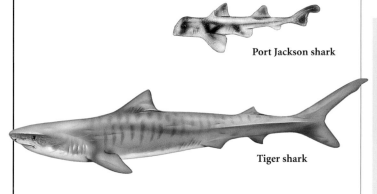

Port Jackson shark

Tiger shark

WHERE IN THE WORLD?

Most common along the coastlines of tropical oceans, especially around coral reefs. On occasion, has been spotted as far north as Greenland.

RELATED SPECIES

The tiger shark is the sole species in the genus Galeocerdo, which belongs to the family Carcharhinidae along with 9 other genera. This family of about 100 species includes the blacktip shark, Carcharhinus melanopterus, and is placed in the order Carcharhinoidiformes.

• ORDER • *Carcharhiniformes* • FAMILY • *Sphyrnidae* • GENUS & SPECIES • *Sphyrna mokarran*

HAMMERHEAD SHARK

KEY FEATURES

* The largest species of hammerhead shark, growing to nearly 5m long.
* Has a bizarre, wing-like head with eyes and nostrils at the tips of the 'wings.'
* An active killer that regularly catches and kills large fish, including other sharks.

VITAL STATISTICS

WEIGHT	225–900kg (496–1984lb)
LENGTH	Up to 4.8m (15ft 7in)
SEXUAL MATURITY	About 5 years
MATING SEASON	Varies with location
GESTATION PERIOD	Probably about 10 months
NUMBER OF YOUNG	10 to 30
BIRTH INTERVAL	Unknown
TYPICAL DIET	Fish, squid and crabs
LIFESPAN	20–30 years

The hammerhead shark is a highly specialized marine hunter, with a horizontally flattened head equipped with a battery of prey sensors.

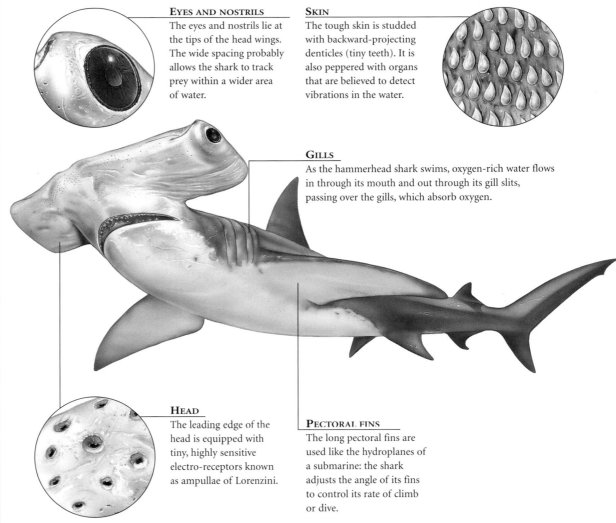

EYES AND NOSTRILS
The eyes and nostrils lie at the tips of the head wings. The wide spacing probably allows the shark to track prey within a wider area of water.

SKIN
The tough skin is studded with backward-projecting denticles (tiny teeth). It is also peppered with organs that are believed to detect vibrations in the water.

GILLS
As the hammerhead shark swims, oxygen-rich water flows in through its mouth and out through its gill slits, passing over the gills, which absorb oxygen.

HEAD
The leading edge of the head is equipped with tiny, highly sensitive electro-receptors known as ampullae of Lorenzini.

PECTORAL FINS
The long pectoral fins are used like the hydroplanes of a submarine: the shark adjusts the angle of its fins to control its rate of climb or dive.

CREATURE COMPARISONS

All members of the hammerhead shark genus share an odd-looking, flattened head. The shape is believed to enhance the senses and also gives a lift effect when the shark swims forward. The size and shape of the head varies widely among the species, and ranges from the narrow and rounded kidney shape of the small bonnethead shark to the extreme span of the winghead shark.

Bonnethead shark

Mallethead shark

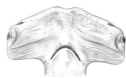

Great hammerhead shark

Winghead shark

WHERE IN THE WORLD?

Widespread in the tropical oceans, and often seen in the shallows around remote oceanic islands.

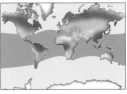

Often migrates great distances across the oceans.

RELATED SPECIES

The great hammerhead shark is one of nine similar species in the genus Sphyrna. The hammerheads belong to the group known as the requiem sharks, which includes many active hunters, such as the tiger and lemon sharks. The hammerhead sharks form a highly successful group, possibly as a consequence of their unusual features: they colonized the world's oceans from as early as 50 million years ago.

• **ORDER** • *Carcharhinoidiformes* • **FAMILY** • *Carcharhinidae* • **GENUS & SPECIES** • *Triaenodon obesus* WHITETIP REEF SHARK

The whitetip reef shark's slender, flexible body is admirably suited for twisting and turning through the labyrinth of a coral reef.

KEY FEATURES

- Common, shallow-water shark of tropical seas, named for the prominent spots on its dorsal fins.
- Unusual among sharks in that it has a habit of resting motionless in shaded sites on the seabed.
- Supple and agile, it hunts for small prey among the crevices and caves of coral reefs.

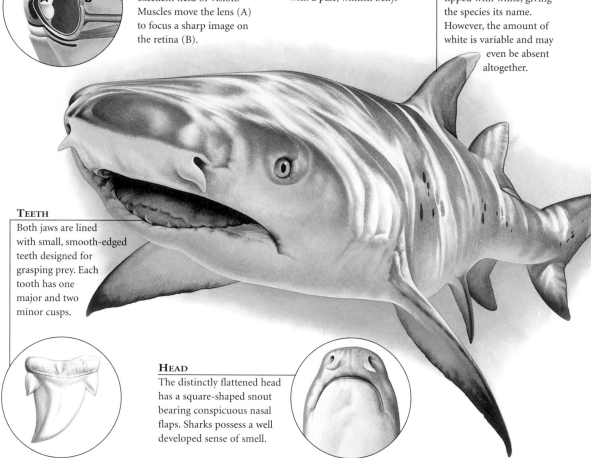

EYES
The eyes are located on the sides of the head and give an excellent field of vision. Muscles move the lens (A) to focus a sharp image on the retina (B).

COLOUR
The shark's basic body colouring is grey upperparts with a pale, whitish belly.

DORSAL AND TAIL FIN
The front dorsal fin and the upper tail-fin lobe are tipped with white, giving the species its name. However, the amount of white is variable and may even be absent altogether.

TEETH
Both jaws are lined with small, smooth-edged teeth designed for grasping prey. Each tooth has one major and two minor cusps.

HEAD
The distinctly flattened head has a square-shaped snout bearing conspicuous nasal flaps. Sharks possess a well developed sense of smell.

VITAL STATISTICS

WEIGHT	Up to 80kg (176.4lb)
LENGTH	1.5–2.1m (4ft 9in–6ft 9in)
SEXUAL MATURITY	5 years
BREEDING SEASON	Varies according to region
NUMBER OF YOUNG	1 to 5
GESTATION PERIOD	5 months
BREEDING INTERVAL	1 year
TYPICAL DIET	Fish, octopus, crustaceans
LIFESPAN	25 years

CREATURE COMPARISONS

The coral reefs of the Indian and Pacific oceans are also home to the blacktip reef shark (Carcharhinus melanopterus), a relative of the whitetip reef shark. The blacktip has a similar shape to the whitetip, but is slightly shorter and, as its name suggests, has fins decorated with dabs of black rather than white. It swims much closer to the shore than its cousin, and is the most common shark species to visit the clear lagoons that lie on the landward side of reefs, a habitat usually too shallow for the larger whitetip reef shark. The blacktip hunts fish in open waters and cruises shallow seabeds searching for octopus, cuttlefish, crabs and even shrimps.

Whitetip reef shark

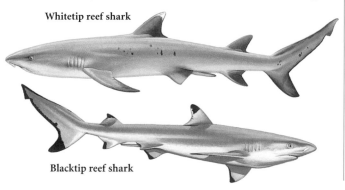

Blacktip reef shark

WHERE IN THE WORLD?

Widely distributed throughout the warmer zones of the Indian and Pacific oceans, especially along reef-bearing coasts and around oceanic islands.

RELATED SPECIES

The whitetip reef shark is 1 of about 85 species in 22 genera that together comprise the large and diverse family of requiem sharks, the Carcharhinidae. Other requiem sharks include the grey sharks, blacktip reef shark and bull shark of the genus Carcharhinus; the lemon shark, genus Negaprion; blue shark, genus Prionace; and tiger shark, genus Galeocerdo. The family is the largest within the order Carcharhinoidiformes.

• ORDER • *Carnivora* • FAMILY • *Canidae* • GENUS & SPECIES • *Alopex lagopus*

ARCTIC FOX

The Arctic fox possesses an array of heat-saving adaptations, equipping it to combat the worst that freezing Arctic conditions can throw at it.

KEY FEATURES

- Has enormous resistance to the cold and can survive temperatures of below -70°C (-94°F)
- Nearly 70 percent of its winter coat is made up of a thick, insulating underfur
- When food is plentiful, the fox hides it in the snow and retrieves it in times of hardship

EARS
Ears are small compared to most other foxes and are lined with fur to help retain heat.

SUMMER COAT
Most Arctic foxes are white in winter, but darken in summer to a bluish-brown. In less snowbound parts of its range, the fox is this darker color year round.

HEAD
The head is short and blunt, which helps reduce heat loss.

PAWS
The paws have woolly hair on the soles to provide insulation and grip. They are relatively large to help stop the fox from sinking in soft snow.

TAIL
The tail is short, but extremely thick and bushy. When sleeping, the Arctic fox wraps it around its feet and legs to keep warm.

VITAL STATISTICS

WEIGHT	2.7–3.6kg (6–8 lb); male is heavier than female
LENGTH	Head/Body: 45.7–66cm (18–26in) Tail 25.4–40.6cm (10–16in)
SEXUAL MATURITY	About 1 year
MATING SEASON	February to May
GESTATION PERIOD	About 52 days
NUMBER OF YOUNG	6 to 20; average 7
BIRTH INTERVAL	1 year, but may not breed when food is scarce
TYPICAL DIET	Anything it can catch or find, such as birds, lemmings, eggs, mammals and berries
LIFESPAN	Up to 15 years

CREATURE COMPARISONS

Many wild dogs are related to the Arctic fox. The biggest, the gray wolf, shares its range with the smaller coyote. They're able to live close together because each hunts different prey. The smaller red fox is adept at exploiting human habitats and food sources. The Arctic fox, although tiny, thrives in places that would not provide enough food for its bigger cousins.

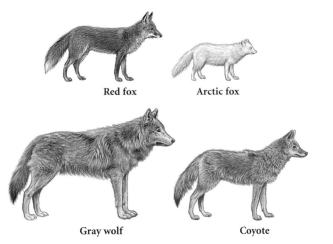

Red fox

Arctic fox

Gray wolf

Coyote

WHERE IN THE WORLD?

Found across the polar regions of mainland North America and northern Scandinavia east to Siberia and northward almost to the North Pole.

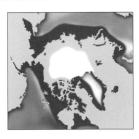

RELATED SPECIES

The Arctic fox is the only species in its genus, but is in the family Canidae and is related to wolves, including the Arctic wolf, jackals, wild dogs, coyotes and other foxes. Its closest relative is the North American swift fox.

• ORDER • *Carnivora* • FAMILY • *Canidae* • GENUS & SPECIES • *Canis adustus*

SIDE-STRIPED JACKAL

KEY FEATURES

- A slender and stealthy relative of the wolf that lives an opportunistic life on Africa's savannahs.

- Usually portrayed as a scavenger, it actually eats more or less anything from fallen fruit to live prey.

- A cautious creature that is more nocturnal and less predatory than other species of jackal.

VITAL STATISTICS

WEIGHT	6.5–14kg (14.3–30.9lb); male slightly heavier than female
LENGTH	Head & Body: 65–81cm ((25.6–31.9in) Tail; 30–41cm (11.8–16.1in)
SHOULDER HEIGHT	41–50cm (16.1–19.7in)
SEXUAL MATURITY	6–8 months
MATING SEASON	Varies according to region, occurs in rainy season
GESTATION PERIOD	57–70 days
NUMBER OF YOUNG	3 to 6
BIRTH INTERVAL	1 year
TYPICAL DIET	Small mammals, reptiles, insects, plant material
LIFESPAN	10–12 years

Equipped with acute senses, the side-striped jackal rarely misses the chance of a meal — catching tiny insects and small mammals in the dark of night.

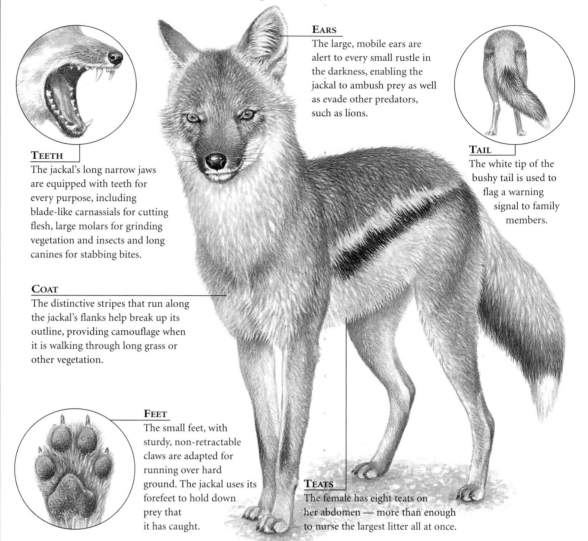

EARS
The large, mobile ears are alert to every small rustle in the darkness, enabling the jackal to ambush prey as well as evade other predators, such as lions.

TEETH
The jackal's long narrow jaws are equipped with teeth for every purpose, including blade-like carnassials for cutting flesh, large molars for grinding vegetation and insects and long canines for stabbing bites.

TAIL
The white tip of the bushy tail is used to flag a warning signal to family members.

COAT
The distinctive stripes that run along the jackal's flanks help break up its outline, providing camouflage when it is walking through long grass or other vegetation.

FEET
The small feet, with sturdy, non-retractable claws are adapted for running over hard ground. The jackal uses its forefeet to hold down prey that it has caught.

TEATS
The female has eight teats on her abdomen — more than enough to nurse the largest litter all at once.

CREATURE COMPARISONS

Less widespread than the side-striped jackal, but perhaps more widely familiar, the black-backed jackal, Canis mesomelas, is very similar to its side-striped cousin in build and habits. It prefers drier habitats, though, so it is more common on the arid grasslands of savannahs such as the Serengeti. The black-backed jackal is also a more efficient hunter of big game than the side-striped jackal, and is capable of killing an antelope either alone or while hunting in a group. In fact, the black-backed jackal is a target of farmers as it is considered to be a serious predator of sheep.

Side-striped jackal

Black-backed jackal

WHERE IN THE WORLD?

Widespread throughout Africa south of the Sahara, from Senegal to Somalia, and south to northern Namibia and Botswana and eastern South Africa. Absent from the equatorial rainforests.

RELATED SPECIES

The side-striped jackal is one of 4 species of jackal in the genus Canis. The others are the Simien jackal, Canis simensis, the golden jackal and the black-backed jackal. Canis also contains 4 other species: the red and grey wolves, the coyote and the domestic dog.

• **ORDER** • *Carnivora* • **FAMILY** • *Canidae* • **GENUS & SPECIES** • *Canis aureus*

KEY FEATURES

- An opportunistic hunter that employs its acute hearing, smell and vision to find prey.
- Male and female form a long-lasting partnership, which is the core of a close-knit family group.
- Ably exploits human settlements, scavenging for scraps around towns and villages.

VITAL STATISTICS

WEIGHT	7–15kg (15.4–33.1lb)
LENGTH	Head & Body: 38–106cm (15–3.5in) Tail; 20–30cm (7.9–11.8in)
SHOULDER HEIGHT	38–50cm (15–19.7in)
SEXUAL MATURITY	11 months
MATING SEASON	All year in tropical Asia; April to May north of Asian range; January to February in Africa
GESTATION PERIOD	63 days
NUMBER OF YOUNG	1 to 9, but usually 2 to 4
BIRTH INTERVAL	1 year
TYPICAL DIET	Small mammals, birds, reptiles, fruit, insects and carrion
LIFESPAN	Up to 13 years

The lean and wiry golden jackal is a crafty opportunist. Wary yet wily, this nimble predator is equipped to make a meal of almost anything.

MALE AND FEMALE
The male golden jackal is larger and heavier than the female.

EARS
The large ears help to gather sounds and focus the jackal's highly acute sense of hearing. The set of the ears also indicates the jackal's mood to others of its kind.

NOSE
In high temperatures the jackal regularly licks its nose so that the evaporating moisture draws out heat from its body and helps it cool off.

LEGS
The long legs, allied to a lean build, enable the golden jackal to sprint rapidly and to maintain a steady, jogging pace.

CREATURE COMPARISONS

Part of the golden jackal's range in Asia overlaps with another member of the family Canidae: the dhole (Cuon alpinus). Slightly larger than the jackal, the dhole ranges from southern Siberia to India and the Malay Peninsula. Similar in shape to the jackal, it is a richer, rusty red colour.

Unlike the golden jackal, its range includes tropical forests and mountainous areas. Hunting in packs, the dhole is often bolder than the jackal, sometimes driving predators as large as tigers and bears away from their kills to feed on carcasses.

Golden jackal

Dhole

WHERE IN THE WORLD?

Over North Africa, from Morocco south to northern Tanzania, through the Middle East and the Balkans, and east through central and southern Asia to Thailand.

RELATED SPECIES

The golden jackal is one of four species of jackal belonging to the large and diverse family Canidae. This family contains a total of 36 species, which include foxes, wolves, coyotes, jackals and dogs. Although many members of this family are familiar, there are some less known examples. One such is the raccoon dog, Nyctereutes procyonoides, a native of Asia, which, as its name implies, looks like a raccoon. This dog is the only canid that hibernates.

• **ORDER** • *Carnivora* • **FAMILY** • *Canidae* • **GENUS & SPECIES** • *Canis latrans*

COYOTE

The quick and clever coyote uses its keen senses to find and follow its prey over long distances, if necessary, waiting for the precise moment to attack.

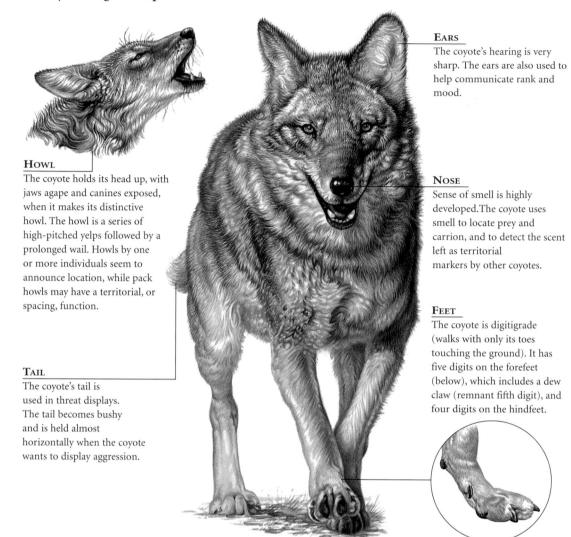

KEY FEATURES

- One of the most adaptable of all mammals, found in a variety of habitats ranging from deserts and grasslands to mountains and city suburbs.
- Has a complex, constantly changing social structure.
- An expert, opportunist hunter that uses its sharp senses to locate a wide variety of prey.

EARS
The coyote's hearing is very sharp. The ears are also used to help communicate rank and mood.

HOWL
The coyote holds its head up, with jaws agape and canines exposed, when it makes its distinctive howl. The howl is a series of high-pitched yelps followed by a prolonged wail. Howls by one or more individuals seem to announce location, while pack howls may have a territorial, or spacing, function.

NOSE
Sense of smell is highly developed. The coyote uses smell to locate prey and carrion, and to detect the scent left as territorial markers by other coyotes.

FEET
The coyote is digitigrade (walks with only its toes touching the ground). It has five digits on the forefeet (below), which includes a dew claw (remnant fifth digit), and four digits on the hindfeet.

TAIL
The coyote's tail is used in threat displays. The tail becomes bushy and is held almost horizontally when the coyote wants to display aggression.

VITAL STATISTICS

WEIGHT	7–20kg (15.4–44lb)
LENGTH	Head & Body: 75–100cm (29.5–39.4in) Tail; 30–40cm (11.8–15.7in)
SHOULDER HEIGHT	38–50cm (15–19.7in)
SEXUAL MATURITY	1–2 years
MATING SEASON	January to March
GESTATION PERIOD	58–65 days
NUMBER OF YOUNG	2 to 12, but usually 6
BIRTH INTERVAL	1 year
TYPICAL DIET	Mainly small mammals, such as rodents; also reptiles, insects, carrion and fruit
LIFESPAN	Up to 15 years

CREATURE COMPARISONS

The grey fox, *Urocyon cinereoargenteus* shares the same range as the coyote and belongs to the family Canidae. Its fur is silver-grey with rusty and yellow shades on the underside, while the coyote has a buff-grey coat with tawny on its muzzle, back, outer side of the ears, forelegs and feet. The grey fox is smaller than the coyote, with a body length of 48–69cm (18.9–27.9in) and weight of 2.5–7kg. (5.5–15.4lb) Unlike the coyote, the grey fox climbs trees, to escape predators and to rest: resting hollows have been found up to 9m (29ft 5in) high.

Coyote

Grey fox

WHERE IN THE WORLD?

Has a widespread distribution extending through most of North and Central America from Alaska east to Nova Scotia and south to Panama.

RELATED SPECIES

The coyote is one of eight species in the genus Canis. Four of these species are jackals: the golden jackal, C. aureus, which lives in southeastern Europe, North Africa, Asia and Southeast Asia; the black-backed jackal, C. mesomelas, the side-striped jackal, C. adustus, and the simien jackal, C. simensis, are all from parts of Africa. Other members of the genus are the grey wolf, C. lupus, the red wolf, C. rufus, and the domestic dog, C. familiaris.

• ORDER • *Carnivora* • FAMILY • *Canidae* • GENUS & SPECIES • *Canis lupus*

GREY WOLF

KEY FEATURES

- Lives in a pack that has a complex social order, dominated by an adult male and female.
- Hunts cooperatively to improve its success against prey as large as moose.
- Tasks, such as caring for nursing females and their pups, are shared by pack members.

VITAL STATISTICS

WEIGHT	18–80kg (39.7–176.4lb) Male heavier than female
LENGTH	Head & Body: 1–1.47m (3ft 3in–4ft 8in) Tail 33–50cm (13–19.7in)
SHOULDER HEIGHT	66–96cm (26–37.8in)
SEXUAL MATURITY	Female 1 year; male 2 years
MATING SEASON	Typically, January to March
GESTATION PERIOD	60–63 days
NUMBER OF YOUNG	Usually 5 or 6
BIRTH INTERVAL	1 year
TYPICAL DIET	Mainly large grazing mammals, but some smaller mammals
LIFESPAN	Up to 17 years

The grey wolf's long legs, large paws and great stamina enable it to cover distances of 30km (18.6miles) or more at an energy-efficient 6–10 km/h (3.7–6.2mph) trot.

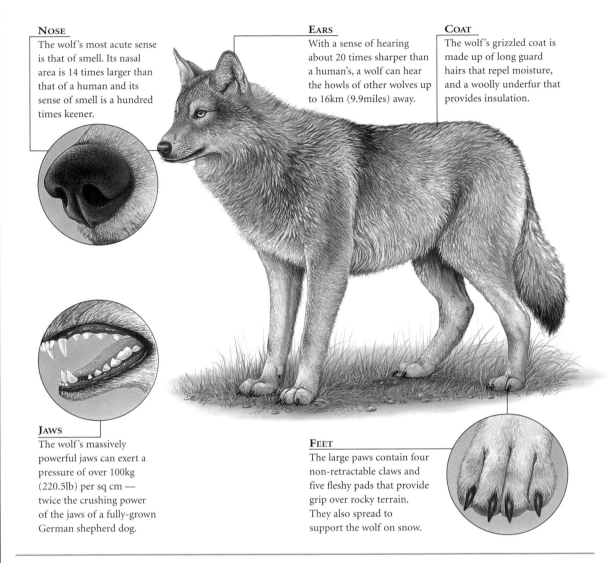

NOSE
The wolf's most acute sense is that of smell. Its nasal area is 14 times larger than that of a human and its sense of smell is a hundred times keener.

EARS
With a sense of hearing about 20 times sharper than a human's, a wolf can hear the howls of other wolves up to 16km (9.9miles) away.

COAT
The wolf's grizzled coat is made up of long guard hairs that repel moisture, and a woolly underfur that provides insulation.

JAWS
The wolf's massively powerful jaws can exert a pressure of over 100kg (220.5lb) per sq cm — twice the crushing power of the jaws of a fully-grown German shepherd dog.

FEET
The large paws contain four non-retractable claws and five fleshy pads that provide grip over rocky terrain. They also spread to support the wolf on snow.

CREATURE COMPARISONS

The wolf shows considerable variation in coat colour. Black wolves, in particular, are common, although there are no records of albino wolves. In North America 16 subspecies have been recognized, including the white-coated Arctic wolf, Canis lupus arctos. In Eurasia there are about eight subspecies, including the Iberian wolf of Spain and Portugal, C. l. signatus. A further 12 subspecies worldwide are extinct.

Grey wolf

Arctic wolf

Black wolf

Iberian wolf

WHERE IN THE WORLD?

Found in North America, Europe, Africa and Asia, from Alaska and Canada east to Greenland, and from Central Europe east to eastern China.

RELATED SPECIES

Of the 35 or so species in the family Canidae, eight belong to the genus Canis, which includes the wolf. Of these, the wolf's closest relatives are the red wolf, C. rufus, and the coyote, C. latrans. The domestic dog, C. familiaris, is widely believed to be descended from the wolf.

• **ORDER** • *Carnivora* • **FAMILY** • *Canidae* • **GENUS & SPECIES** • *Canis mesomelas*

BLACK-BACKED JACKAL

KEY FEATURES

- Adaptable, aggressive dog species that hunts a wide range of prey and boosts its diet with plant material and carrion

- Forms a long-lasting pair-bond and defends a communal territory

- A mated pair is often assisted in caring for pups by offspring from an earlier litter; this reduces the mortality rate of the vulnerable infants

VITAL STATISTICS

WEIGHT	(7–13.6kg (15.4–30lb)
LENGTH	Head & Body: 68.6–76.2cm (27–30in); Tail; 30.5–38.1cm (12–15in)
SHOULDER HEIGHT	30.5–48.3cm (2–19in)
SEXUAL MATURITY	10–11 months
MATING SEASON	May to August
GESTATION PERIOD	About 60 days
NUMBER OF YOUNG	1 to 8
BIRTH INTERVAL	1 year
TYPICAL DIET	Invertebrates, reptiles, amphibians, mammals and birds
LIFESPAN	Up to 14 years in captivity

Although long-legged and rangy, the black-backed jackal has a deep chest and large lungs that give it the stamina to cover up to 19.3 km (12 miles) a night.

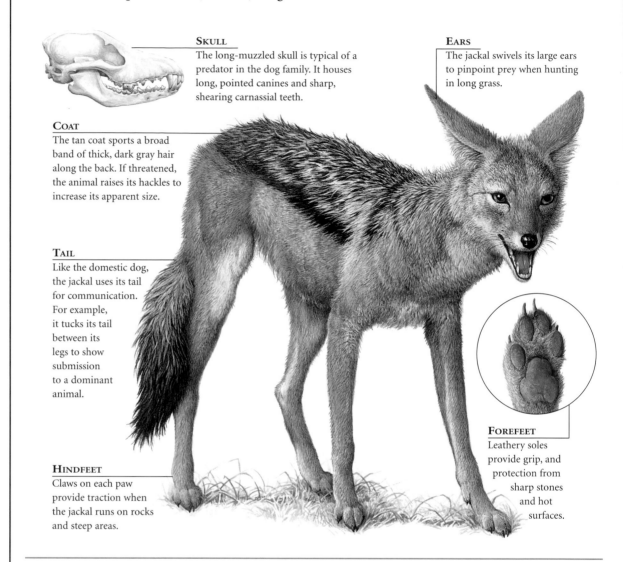

SKULL
The long-muzzled skull is typical of a predator in the dog family. It houses long, pointed canines and sharp, shearing carnassial teeth.

EARS
The jackal swivels its large ears to pinpoint prey when hunting in long grass.

COAT
The tan coat sports a broad band of thick, dark gray hair along the back. If threatened, the animal raises its hackles to increase its apparent size.

TAIL
Like the domestic dog, the jackal uses its tail for communication. For example, it tucks its tail between its legs to show submission to a dominant animal.

HINDFEET
Claws on each paw provide traction when the jackal runs on rocks and steep areas.

FOREFEET
Leathery soles provide grip, and protection from sharp stones and hot surfaces.

CREATURE COMPARISONS

The Ethiopian wolf (Canis simensis) is found only in the Ethiopian highlands. Its range overlaps with that of the black-backed jackal. Unlike its relative, it lives in packs of two or more adult females and about five adult males, who are often brothers.

The Ethiopian wolf hunts alone by day, but pack members meet up to rest together. It is an expert at catching giant mole-rats, which constitute about 40% of its diet.

Today, farmers with livestock have encroached on the wolf's habitat, and the species is on the brink of extinction.

Ethiopian wolf   **Black-backed jackal**

WHERE IN THE WORLD?

One population in Somalia and eastern Ethiopia through Kenya to northern Tanzania; the other in the southern quarter of Africa apart from the Namib Desert

RELATED SPECIES

The black-backed jackal shares its genus with 7 other species, like the side-striped jackal, Canis adustus. The dog family, Canidae, belongs to the order Carnivora along with bears, weasels, cats, mongooses and raccoons.

• ORDER • *Carnivora* • FAMILY • *Canidae* • GENUS & SPECIES • *Chrysocyon brachyurus*

Described as looking like a fox on stilts, the maned wolf has evolved long legs that enable it to forage successfully in South America's grasslands.

KEY FEATURES

- Stands high on its unusually long legs to peer over the grasses of its native plains habitat.

- Erects the long, dark mane along its spine and shoulders to enlarge its profile when threatened by rivals.

- Now very rare as a result of persecution and widespread habitat loss. Classified as vulnerable by the IUCN (World Conservation Union).

VITAL STATISTICS

WEIGHT	20–25kg (44–55.5lb)
LENGTH	Head & Body: 74–87cm (29.1–34.2in)
SHOULDER HEIGHT	28–45cm (11–17.7in)
SEXUAL MATURITY	1 year, but rarely breeds until second year
MATING SEASON	April to July, peaking in May and June
GESTATION PERIOD	62–66 days
NUMBER OF YOUNG	2 to 5
BIRTH INTERVAL	1 year
TYPICAL DIET	Small rodents, birds, insects, fruit and other plant matter
LIFESPAN	13 years in captivity

EARS
Large ears and acute hearing locate food in the grass.

MANE
The species is named for the long, usually dark hair on the nape and shoulders. The wolf bristles its mane in threat postures.

JAWS AND TEETH
The narrow jaws enable the maned wolf to seize small prey. Carnassial (shearing) teeth slice through animal prey, while broad molars grind up the plant element in the wolf's diet.

FEET
The maned wolf walks with only its toes making contact with the ground. It can splay these toes to spread its weight while crossing marshy ground.

LIMBS
The maned wolf is not a fast runner; its long limbs instead help it see over tall grasses. The wolf moves by pairing the limbs on one side, then those on the other, except when making abrupt turns (above).

CREATURE COMPARISONS

The maned wolf is the largest South American member of the family Canidae; second largest is the colpeo fox (Pseudalopex culpaeus). The colpeo fox is more dog-like in appearance, and is one of several closely related species of South American fox. Inhabiting highland plains in the Andes from Ecuador to Patagonia, the colpeo fox has dense underfur to keep it warm in low temperatures — a feature lacking in the maned wolf, which has no need for such heavy insulation. The colpeo fox's fur is much sought after, and this has led to widespread hunting of the species. Both the maned wolf and the colpeo fox share a broad, opportunistic diet that includes both animal and vegetable matter.

Maned wolf

Colpeo fox

WHERE IN THE WORLD?

Until recently, found across much of central South America including parts of Bolivia and Paraguay. Now confined to northeastern Brazil and northern Argentina.

RELATED SPECIES

The maned wolf is the sole species in the genus Chrysocyon. It belongs to the family Canidae, which includes wolves, foxes and jackals. In appearance and habits, the maned wolf is much closer to a fox than to a true wolf, such as the increasingly endangered red wolf, Canis rufus.

• **ORDER** • *Carnivora* • **FAMILY** • *Canidae* • **GENUS & SPECIES** • *Cuon alpinus*

DHOLE

KEY FEATURES

- Wild dog of Asia that hunts in cooperative, tight-knit packs and shares the rearing of the young.
- Fearsome predator of a range of animals including mammals up to 30 times its own weight.
- Widely persecuted by humans, and now listed as vulnerable by the IUCN (World Conservation Union).

VITAL STATISTICS

WEIGHT	Male 15–21kg (33.1–46.3lb); female 10–17kg (22–37.5lb)
LENGTH	Head & Body: 80–115cm (31–45.3in) Tail; 42–55cm (16.5–21.6in)
SHOULDER HEIGHT	40–50cm (15.7–19.7in)
SEXUAL MATURITY	1 year
MATING SEASON	Varies according to region
GESTATION PERIOD	60–63 days
NUMBER OF YOUNG	4 to 9
BIRTH INTERVAL	1 year
TYPICAL DIET	Large and small mammals
LIFESPAN	15 years in captivity

Built for stamina when tracking its prey, the dhole has a lean body, long legs and a strong jaw capable of delivering a fatal bite at the end of the pursuit.

TAIL
The thickly furred, expressive tail is usually darker than the rest of the body and ends in a conspicuous black tip. In some individuals, however, the tail tip may be white or grey.

SKULL
Compared with many dog species, the dhole has a broad skull with a short, but wide, muzzle. The four canines on the upper and lower jaws can rip through thick hide.

COAT
Colouration can vary throughout its range, but the dhole usually has rust upperparts with whitish underparts. In the northern parts of its range, it develops long, soft fur with a dense undercoat in winter.

TEATS
The dhole produces large litters of pups, a trait reflected in the number of mammae, or teats, present on females. Most dog species have 10 mammae, but dholes may have as many as 16.

FOOT
The claws on each foot are non-retractile, enabling the dhole to maintain its grip when chasing prey over rugged terrain.

CREATURE COMPARISONS

At first glance the dingo (Canis familiaris dingo) closely resembles its cousin the dhole. The two species have a rust-red coat with patches of white on the underparts, and stand at a similar height. However, the dingo is longer and heavier with a shorter, less bushy tail. The dingo lives in arid central Australia, usually alone but sometimes in loose family groups. Although, like the dhole, it often hunts in packs, it lacks the dhole's intensely social nature. The dingo is almost certainly descended from domesticated strains of the Indian wolf, a species that overlaps in range with the dhole. Neither the dhole nor the dingo can bark like a domestic dog, but the dhole makes a whistling sound to keep the pack together.

Dingo

Dhole

WHERE IN THE WORLD?

Scattered across southern, central and eastern Asia, from southern Siberia and Mongolia to India, Malaysia, China and Korea, and the islands of Sumatra and Java.

RELATED SPECIES

The dhole is the sole member of the genus Cuon. It belongs to the dog family, Canidae, which contains 36 species in 16 genera. The vulpine foxes form the largest genus, Vulpes, with 10 species including the red fox, V. vulpes, and the sand fox, V. rueppellii, which lives in the desert zone from Morocco to Afghanistan. Jackals and wolves, together with the coyote, dingo and domestic dog, make up the 8 species in the genus Canis.

FENNEC FOX

• ORDER • *Carnivora* • FAMILY • *Canidae* • GENUS & SPECIES • *Fennecus zerda*

KEY FEATURES

- Dense, pale coat keeps the fox warm during the cold desert nights, and provides camouflage.

- Its huge ears are larger in relation to its size than those of any other fox. They help it to keep cool in the desert by radiating surplus body heat.

- Paws have fully furred soles to protect pads from the burning surface and to provide a secure grip while running on sand.

VITAL STATISTICS

WEIGHT	1–1.5kg (2.2–3.3lb)
LENGTH	Head & Body: 33–40cm Tail (13–15.7in) 16.5–30cm (6.5–11.8in)
SEXUAL MATURITY	About 1 year
MATING SEASON	January to February
GESTATION PERIOD	About 51 days
NUMBER OF YOUNG	1 to 5
BIRTH INTERVAL	1 year, but a second litter may be produced if the first is lost
TYPICAL DIET	Mainly insects and small rodents; birds and their eggs; plant matter
LIFESPAN	About 10 years in captivity; much less in the wild

The fennec fox makes up for its tiny stature with its huge ears: they act as heat-regulators in a habitat where, above ground, shade is very scarce.

EARS
The ears make up about 20 per cent of the fox's total body surface area. Richly supplied with blood vessels, they help radiate surplus body heat, and are vital aids in detecting prey by sound.

COAT
The dense, long and soft fur insulates the fox against the cold desert nights. The pale colouration reflects excess daytime heat and provides camouflage against sand.

TAIL
On cold nights, the fox fluffs up its thick, bushy tail and wraps it like a scarf over its feet to prevent them from releasing body heat.

PAWS
The broad paws have fully furred soles to protect the pads from hot surfaces, and to give a better grip on loose sand. Blood vessels on the paws' upper surfaces dissipate excess heat.

CREATURE COMPARISONS

Several other foxes are specialized for arid lands, including Blanford's fox, which is almost as tiny as the fennec and also has large ears. These foxes have a small body to cope with temperature extremes and a diet of small prey. By contrast, the red fox is a generalist feeder able to eat almost anything, and its larger body size suits it to a much wider range of habitats.

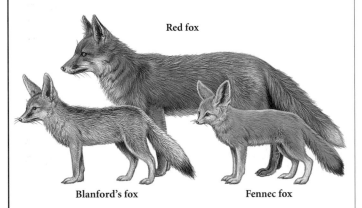

Red fox

Blanford's fox

Fennec fox

WHERE IN THE WORLD?

Found across desert areas of North Africa and the Middle East — from Morocco in the west, east across the Sahara Desert to arid parts of the Middle East as far east as the Arabian Desert.

RELATED SPECIES
There are 21 species of fox. These include the Cape fox, which inhabits dry areas of southern Africa. The fennec fox is the only member of its genus.

• ORDER • *Carnivora* • FAMILY • *Canidae* • GENUS & SPECIES • *Lycaon pictus*

AFRICAN WILD DOG

The lean and sinewy African wild dog is built for the chase. The only heavily built part of its frame is the powerful jaw.

KEY FEATURES

- A highly efficient hunter that attacks large animals by hunting in a closely cooperating pack.
- Has a unique social system in which males stay with their natal pack and females leave to breed elsewhere.
- Driven to near-extinction by a combination of habitat loss, hunting and disease.

VITAL STATISTICS

WEIGHT	20–30kg (44–66.1lb)
LENGTH	Head & Body: 75–100cm (29.5–39.4in) Tail; 30–40cm (11.8–15.7in)
SHOULDER HEIGHT	60–75cm (23.6–29.5in)
SEXUAL MATURITY	12–18 months
MATING SEASON	Variable; when prey becomes abundant
GESTATION PERIOD	70–75 days
NUMBER OF YOUNG	2 to 19; average 7 to 10
BIRTH INTERVAL	About 1 year
TYPICAL DIET	Carnivorous; prefers big game, but will prey on hares, rodents and other small animals
LIFESPAN	10 years

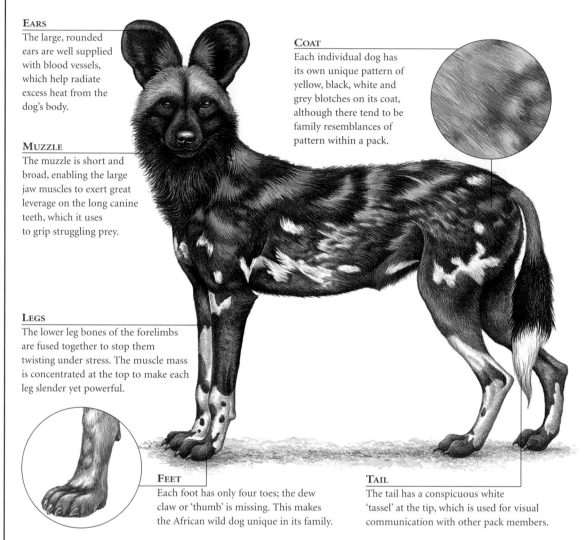

EARS
The large, rounded ears are well supplied with blood vessels, which help radiate excess heat from the dog's body.

MUZZLE
The muzzle is short and broad, enabling the large jaw muscles to exert great leverage on the long canine teeth, which it uses to grip struggling prey.

LEGS
The lower leg bones of the forelimbs are fused together to stop them twisting under stress. The muscle mass is concentrated at the top to make each leg slender yet powerful.

COAT
Each individual dog has its own unique pattern of yellow, black, white and grey blotches on its coat, although there tend to be family resemblances of pattern within a pack.

FEET
Each foot has only four toes; the dew claw or 'thumb' is missing. This makes the African wild dog unique in its family.

TAIL
The tail has a conspicuous white 'tassel' at the tip, which is used for visual communication with other pack members.

CREATURE COMPARISONS

The African wild dog has a similar build to a greyhound, with a lightweight frame and long, strong, slim legs. Yet, unlike the greyhound, which can reach speeds of about 65 km/h (40.4 mph), it is no sprinter. The greyhound's extra-deep chest accommodates huge lungs to supply its muscles with plenty of oxygen, but its energy reserves quickly give out. The wild dog employs its energy in a different way, running more slowly but for much greater distances.

African wild dog   Greyhound

WHERE IN THE WORLD?

Once widespread across Africa south of the Sahara, but now found only in scattered localities in eastern and southern Africa — from southern Ethiopia south through Tanzania to Zimbabwe and Botswana.

RELATED SPECIES

The African wild dog is a member of the Canidae, or dog family, which includes all dogs, wolves, jackals and foxes. It is classified in a genus of its own, Lycaon, but its closest relatives are probably the Asiatic dhole and the little-known bush dog of Central and South America, which are both forest dwellers. All three are highly carnivorous pack hunters, and all share the same distinctive adaptation of meat-slicing carnassial teeth.

BAT-EARED FOX

• ORDER • *Carnivora* • FAMILY • *Canidae* • GENUS & SPECIES • *Otocyon megalotis*

Most foxes are opportunists, able to exploit a wide range of food, but the bat-eared fox is adapted for a single purpose — to track and catch insects.

KEY FEATURES

- A unique African fox that specializes in eating a range of insects.
- The only fox with a habitat defined by its diet. Since it feeds almost exclusively on grassland insects, it lives only on open savannahs.
- Enormous ears have a dual function: they help to control body temperature and also gather and focus the faint sounds of insects moving in the ground.

VITAL STATISTICS

WEIGHT	3–5kg (6.6–11lb)
LENGTH	Head & Body: 46–66cm (18.1–26in) Tail; 23–34cm (9–13.4in)
SHOULDER HEIGHT	30–40cm (11.8–15.7in)
SEXUAL MATURITY	6–8 months
MATING SEASON	September to February
GESTATION PERIOD	60–70 days
NUMBER OF YOUNG	2 to 6
BIRTH INTERVAL	1 year
TYPICAL DIET	Mainly termites and other insects; occasionally small mammals, young birds and plant matter
LIFESPAN	Up to 10 years

JAW
The bat eared-fox has four to eight more molar teeth than other foxes enabling it to mince its insect prey before swallowing it. A step-like protrusion on the rear of the lower jaw anchors an extra-large muscle adapted for rapid chewing.

EARS
The huge ears are highly sensitive and help focus the faintest sounds, enabling the fox to pinpoint insects feeding underground. They are also rich in blood vessels, which helps the fox to lose heat in the hot sun.

TAIL
The large, bushy tail is used as a rudder when running to escape from predators. With a flick of its tail, the fox can change direction without losing speed. The tail, along with the ears, is also used for signalling to other bat-eared foxes.

FOREPAWS
The forepaws have four toes and a tiny dew (remnant) claw higher up the foot. Long claws on the middle two toes are designed for digging.

CREATURE COMPARISONS

A relative of the bat-eared fox, the dhole (Cuon alpinus) is found from southern Siberia to India and the Malay Peninsula and on the islands of Sumatra and Java. It is twice the size of the bat-eared fox, with a head and body length of 88–113cm (34.6–44.5in), and stands 42–55cm (16.5–21.6in) at the shoulder.

Although superficially similar, these animals represent two extremes of dog evolution. While the bat-eared fox is specialized to eat insects, the dhole hunts in an organized pack and preys on animals larger than itself, such as deer, wild pigs and antelope. The bat-eared fox has many small teeth for chewing tiny items of food, while the dhole has a reduced number of big, blade-like teeth adapted for shearing through skin, flesh and sinew.

Bat-eared fox   Dhole

WHERE IN THE WORLD?

Once more widespread across Africa, it now occurs as two separate populations: one from Ethiopia, Somalia and southern Sudan to Tanzania, and another from Angola and Zambia to South Africa.

RELATED SPECIES

The bat-eared fox is a member of the dog family, the Canidae, which consists of 16 genera and 36 species and includes wolves, coyotes, jackals and foxes. Members of the Canidae are usually grouped into 3 subfamilies on the basis of their teeth structure: the Simocyoninae, Caninae and Otocyoninae. The bat-eared fox is the only member of the Otocyoninae and is believed to have evolved along a separate line from the common ancestor of other dogs and foxes.

• ORDER • *Carnivora* • FAMILY • *Canidae* • GENUS & SPECIES • *Speothos venaticus*

BUSH DOG

With its short legs and relatively long body, the bush dog is the ideal shape for pushing through thick undergrowth in pursuit of prey.

KEY FEATURES

- Small South American dog that lives and hunts cooperatively in a family-based pack.
- Elusive, and seldom seen — even by the villagers that share its rainforest habitat.
- Thought to be very rare; classed as vulnerable by the IUCN (World Conservation Union).

TEETH
While most members of the Canidae family have 42 teeth, the bush dog has only 38, but they are ideally suited to eating meat.

COAT
A short, dense coat suits the bush dog's semi-aquatic lifestyle.

TAIL
The tail is short, so as not to impede the dog's progress.

MUZZLE
The short muzzle delivers a powerful bite. The moist snout provides a keen sense of smell.

LIMBS
Legs are short and stocky, but very strong.

FEET
Four webbed toes on each paw enable the bush dog to swim and dive efficiently.

VITAL STATISTICS

WEIGHT	5–7kg (11–15.4lb)
LENGTH	Head & Body: 57–75cm (22.4–29.5in) Tail; 12–15cm (4.7–5.9in)
SHOULDER HEIGHT	About 30cm ((11.8in)
SEXUAL MATURITY	10 months
MATING SEASON	Probably all year round
GESTATION PERIOD	1 to 6; usually 3 or 4
NUMBER OF YOUNG	At least 67 days
BIRTH INTERVAL	8–9 months
TYPICAL DIET	Small deer, large rodents
LIFESPAN	Unknown in wild; 10 years in captivity

CREATURE COMPARISONS

Native to the Amazon, the small-eared dog (Atelocynus microtis) is a little larger and longer-tailed than the bush dog. Short-coated and stocky, these are the only two canids found mainly in dense forests.

Although the small-eared dog depends less than the bush dog on water sources, it is more restricted in habitat. It is found only in undisturbed rainforest, whereas the bush dog also exploits forest–savannah margins.

The dogs have different hunting strategies. As a lone forager, the small-eared dog can only capture small animals such as spiny rats, so it eats little and often. The pack-hunting bush dog, by contrast, tackles much larger prey.

Bush dog

Small-eared dog

WHERE IN THE WORLD?

Isolated populations occur in forests and forest-border marshland in Panama, Colombia, Venezuela, French Guiana, Guyana, eastern Peru, Brazil, eastern Bolivia, Paraguay and northern Argentina.

RELATED SPECIES

The bush dog is the sole member of the genus Speothos. On the basis of its tooth arrangement, the species is often placed in a subfamily, Simocyoninae, along with the dhole, Cuon alpinus, of India and the African hunting dog, Lycaon pictus. There are a total of 36 species in the dog family, Canidae, which is represented in all the world's major land masses and environments, from tropical rainforests to the Arctic pack ice.

GREY FOX

KEY FEATURES

- Much more colourful than its name suggests, but is a far from common sight in the wild.
- The only canid in the world that regularly climbs trees, it takes advantage of the fruit and protection on offer in the branches.
- Lacking the stamina typical of most canids, this night hunter relies on stealth and keen senses to outwit its quarry.

VITAL STATISTICS

WEIGHT	2.5–7kg (5.5–15.4lb)
LENGTH	50–70cm (19.7–27.6in)
SHOULDER HEIGHT	25–45cm (9.8–17.7in)
SEXUAL MATURITY	Male unknown; female 1 year
MATING SEASON	Late December to March in southern USA; mid January to late May in the north
GESTATION PERIOD	51–63 days
NUMBER OF YOUNG	1 to 10, but 4 to 6 on average
BIRTH INTERVAL	One year
TYPICAL DIET	Small vertebrates, fruits and insects
LIFESPAN	Up to 14 years

The grey fox specializes in using its agility, camouflage and an acute sense of hearing, rather than speed and stamina, to catch its prey.

MOUTH AND TEETH
The jaws are packed with pin-sharp canines, cutting incisors, shearing premolars and crushing molars.

SCENT GLANDS AND BRUSH (TAIL)
The grey fox uses anal scent glands to spray vegetation or coat droppings when marking its territory. With a black line down its ridge, the brush has a 2cm (0.8in)-wide black spot, known as the 'violet gland', at its tip. The function of this gland is unknown.

COAT
The coarse grey fur on the upperparts gives way to buff areas around the neck, belly and underside of the brush.

HINDFOOT
The toe-pads are larger than those of most foxes. Like other species, the grey fox has scent glands between its toes.

CREATURE COMPARISONS

With a head-and-body length of up to 50cm (19.7in), the kit fox (Vulpes macrotis) is much smaller than its grey neighbour. Its pale coat has a yellow tinge along the back, orange-shaded flanks and shoulders, and white underparts.

The kit fox cannot climb trees like the grey fox, but it can run fast — faster even than the so-called swift fox (V. velox), its closest relative. The kit fox's ears, proportionally the largest of any North American canid, are sensitive 'radar' for detecting rodents and rabbits in its steppe and desert habitat. Like the grey fox, the kit fox hunts under the cover of darkness, and it may cover several kilometres in a night. In both species, breeding pairs share parental duties through the summer months.

Kit fox   Grey fox

WHERE IN THE WORLD?

Found in the Americas from southern Canada south to northern Venezuela. Within this range, absent only from the mountains and plains of northwestern USA and a few pockets of Central America.

RELATED SPECIES

There are 2 species of grey fox in North America: the mainland grey fox and the island grey fox, Urocyon littoralis, a smaller species found on the Channel Islands off California's coast. Despite its name, the North American grey fox is not closely related to the Argentine grey fox, Pseudalopex griseus, of Argentina and Chile. Foxes are among the 36 species in the family Canidae, which also includes dogs, wolves, coyotes and jackals.

• ORDER • *Carnivora* • FAMILY • *Canidae* • GENUS & SPECIES • *Vulpes macrotis*

KIT FOX

No bigger than a domestic cat, the kit fox survives in its desert home by using guile and speed to evade its enemies and catch a meal.

KEY FEATURES

- The smallest fox in North America and the second smallest in the world, after the fennec fox of North Africa.

- Escapes enemies such as coyotes, golden eagles and red-tailed hawks by zigzagging faster than the human eye can follow.

- A dedicated parent, the dog fox brings food back to the vixen while she stays underground for a month, suckling her cubs.

SKULL
The skull is long and narrow. At the front are sharply pointed canines, while cusped cheek teeth in the upper and lower jaws interlock to slice off flesh.

NOSE
Mucus secretions keep the nose permanently moist, heightening the kit fox's extremely keen sense of smell.

EARS
The ears are large and lined with a network of veins to radiate away excess heat. Inside each ear-flap, a covering of fine hairs prevents sand blowing into the inner ear.

COAT
The coat varies from orange to grizzled grey, with paler underparts. The coarse guard hairs are tipped with black or black and white, while dense underfur insulates the fox on cold nights.

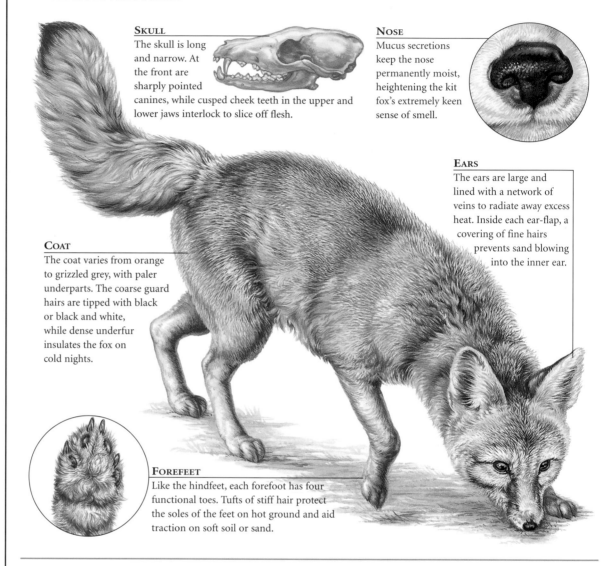

FOREFEET
Like the hindfeet, each forefoot has four functional toes. Tufts of stiff hair protect the soles of the feet on hot ground and aid traction on soft soil or sand.

VITAL STATISTICS

WEIGHT	Male 2.2kg (4.8lb); female 1.9kg (4.2lb)
LENGTH	35–50cm (13.8–19.7in)
SHOULDER HEIGHT	22–32cm (–12.6in)
SEXUAL MATURITY	1–2 years
MATING SEASON	December to February
GESTATION PERIOD	49–55 days
NUMBER OF YOUNG	2 to 6, usually 4 or 5
BIRTH INTERVAL	12 months
TYPICAL DIET	Rodents, rabbits and hares, plus some insects and plants
LIFESPAN	About 7 years in the wild, but up to 20 years in captivity

CREATURE COMPARISONS

While the kit fox is small and slight, the bat-eared fox (*Otocyon megalotis*) of Africa is stocky and can weigh 5kg (11lb). Like the kit fox, it lives in arid habitats. Big ears are typical of desert foxes, and this species has a huge pair. Uniquely for a member of the dog family, the bat-eared fox is an insectivore. Its forelegs are powerful for digging out termites, and relatively short to help it sniff for insects along the ground. Both species are nocturnal, but in parts of its range the bat-eared fox varies its daily routine according to the changing seasons.

Kit fox

Bat-eared fox

WHERE IN THE WORLD?

Found in the western USA, from Oregon and Idaho south to parts of California, Nevada, Utah, Arizona and New Mexico. Also present in Baja California and northern-central Mexico.

RELATED SPECIES

The kit fox is 1 of 10 species in the genus Vulpes, but some authorities regard it as a subspecies of the swift fox, V. velox. All foxes, including the widespread red fox, V. vulpes, are members of the Canidae family, along with wolves, dogs, jackals and coyotes.

RED FOX

• **ORDER** • *Carnivora* • **FAMILY** • *Canidae* • **GENUS & SPECIES** • *Vulpes vulpes*

With its extra-sharp senses and keen intelligence, the red fox is ideally equipped to eke out a living alongside the human race.

KEY FEATURES

- A supreme opportunist, able to live in a wide variety of natural and human habitats.
- Flourishes in city centres, where it survives on scraps and makes its den under garden sheds, or even in cellars.
- Populations virtually unaffected by methods employed by humans to control them, such as shooting, hunting, poisoning and gassing.

VITAL STATISTICS

WEIGHT	5.4–6.3kg (11.9–13.9lb)
LENGTH	Head & Body: 56–76cm (22–29.9in) Tail: 28–48cm (11–18.9in)
SHOULDER HEIGHT	35.5–40.5cm (14–15.9in)
SEXUAL MATURITY	8–9 months
MATING SEASON	Late winter
GESTATION PERIOD	53 days
NUMBER OF YOUNG	1 to 13, but usually 5
BIRTH INTERVAL	1 year
TYPICAL DIET	Small mammals, birds, insects and fruit; carrion, such as road kills; scraps and waste
LIFESPAN	Up to 10 years

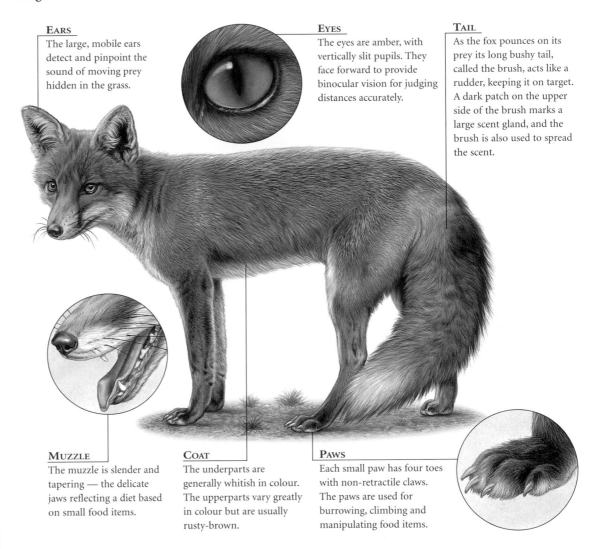

EARS
The large, mobile ears detect and pinpoint the sound of moving prey hidden in the grass.

EYES
The eyes are amber, with vertically slit pupils. They face forward to provide binocular vision for judging distances accurately.

TAIL
As the fox pounces on its prey its long bushy tail, called the brush, acts like a rudder, keeping it on target. A dark patch on the upper side of the brush marks a large scent gland, and the brush is also used to spread the scent.

MUZZLE
The muzzle is slender and tapering — the delicate jaws reflecting a diet based on small food items.

COAT
The underparts are generally whitish in colour. The upperparts vary greatly in colour but are usually rusty-brown.

PAWS
Each small paw has four toes with non-retractile claws. The paws are used for burrowing, climbing and manipulating food items.

CREATURE COMPARISONS

The red fox does not always live up to its name: there are races with distinct colour variations. The species is most common in its reddish-brown coat, but about 25 per cent of red foxes are called cross foxes because they have a black stripe down the back and another intersecting it across the shoulders. About 10 per cent of red foxes are not red at all. The so-called silver fox varies from silver to near-black, depending upon the proportion of white to black hairs in its coat.

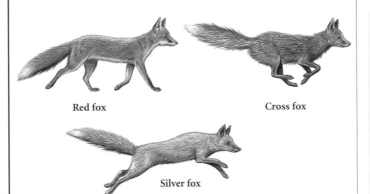

Red fox

Cross fox

Silver fox

WHERE IN THE WORLD?

Has one of the widest distributions of any land mammal, extending through most of North

America and Eurasia. Introduced into Australia, but otherwise absent from the greater part of the southern hemisphere.

RELATED SPECIES

The red fox is one of 10 species in the genus Vulpes, which includes the swift fox, V. velox, of the North American Great Plains; the Bengal fox, V. bengalensis, of the Indian subcontinent; the pale fox, V. pallida, of the northern African savannahs; and the Cape fox, V. chama, of southern Africa. The tiny fennec fox, Fennecus zerda, of the African desert and the Middle East is the only species of its genus, as is the snow-white Arctic fox, Alopex lagopus.

• **ORDER** • *Carnivora* • **FAMILY** • *Felidae* • **GENUS & SPECIES** • *Acinonyx jubatus*

CHEETAH

KEY FEATURES

- Fastest land mammal on Earth: over short distances it can reach a speed of up to 100 km/h (62.1mph).
- Can accelerate from a standing start to its top speed in just three seconds.
- At full stretch in pursuit of prey, it can cover almost 10m (32ft 8in) in a single stride.

VITAL STATISTICS

WEIGHT	34–68kg (75–150lb)
LENGTH	Head & Body: 1.3–1.5m (4ft 3in–4ft 9in) Tail 60–80cm (23.6–31in)
SHOULDER HEIGHT	71–84cm (27.9–33.1in)
SEXUAL MATURITY	20–24 months
MATING SEASON	Throughout the year
GESTATION PERIOD	90–95 days
NUMBER OF YOUNG	Up to 8, but usually 2 to 5
BIRTH INTERVAL	17–20 months
TYPICAL DIET	Gazelles and other antelope species; also, hares, rodents and gamebirds
LIFESPAN	Up to 12 years in the wild

The cheetah's anatomy is highly adapted for high speed hunting allowing it to compete with the many other predators of the savannah.

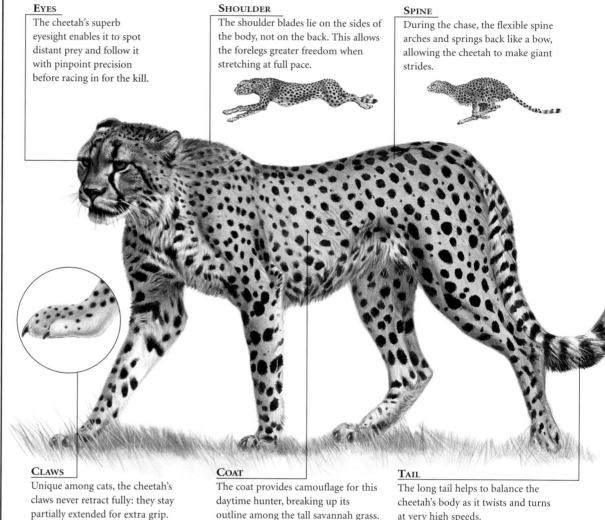

EYES
The cheetah's superb eyesight enables it to spot distant prey and follow it with pinpoint precision before racing in for the kill.

SHOULDER
The shoulder blades lie on the sides of the body, not on the back. This allows the forelegs greater freedom when stretching at full pace.

SPINE
During the chase, the flexible spine arches and springs back like a bow, allowing the cheetah to make giant strides.

CLAWS
Unique among cats, the cheetah's claws never retract fully: they stay partially extended for extra grip.

COAT
The coat provides camouflage for this daytime hunter, breaking up its outline among the tall savannah grass.

TAIL
The long tail helps to balance the cheetah's body as it twists and turns at very high speeds.

CREATURE COMPARISONS

The cheetah, leopard and jaguar all have spotted coats. They appear similar, but a closer look reveals differences. The spots of the leopard and jaguar form a rosette pattern, and the jaguar's rosettes have a central dot. These patterns provide camouflage in low light conditions, when these animals usually hunt.

The cheetah's spots also break up the body outline, helping it to creep unseen to within sprinting range of its victim. Because the cheetah hunts by day and does not stalk prey to the same extent as its relatives, it cannot rely on camouflage as a hunting aid.

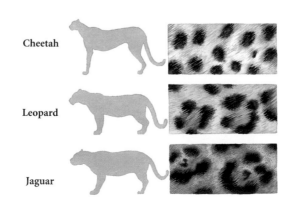

Cheetah

Leopard

Jaguar

WHERE IN THE WORLD?

Widely distributed across the savannah grasslands and semi-deserts of western, eastern and southern Africa. An Asian subspecies still survives in Iran.

RELATED SPECIES
The cheetah is classed as one of the 'big cats'. However, the other five —the lion, tiger, snow leopard, leopard and jaguar — all belong to a separate genus: Panthera.

A subspecies of cheetah (Acinonyx jubatus venaticus) is found in the Middle East and South Asia.

CARACAL

• **ORDER** • *Carnivora* • **FAMILY** • *Felidae* • **GENUS & SPECIES** • *Felis caracal*

KEY FEATURES

- A solitary hunter that can leap up to 3m (9ft 8in) in the air to catch birds as they rise in flight.

- The most widespread of Africa's small cats, it is also the fastest — thanks to its long and immensely powerful hindlimbs.

- Long, black tufts on the tips of its outsized, mobile ears empha size facial expressions — vital for communication between individuals.

VITAL STATISTICS

WEIGHT	13–19kg (28.7–41.9lb)
LENGTH	Head & Body: 60–91cm (23.6–35.8in) Tail: 23–31cm (9–12.2in)
SHOULDER HEIGHT	38–50cm (15–19.7in)
SEXUAL MATURITY	Male 12–15 months; female 14–16 months
MATING SEASON	Year round
GESTATION PERIOD	69–78 days
NUMBER OF YOUNG	1 to 6, usually 3
BIRTH INTERVAL	1 year
TYPICAL DIET	Birds, small mammals, young antelope
LIFESPAN	Up to 17 years in captivity

With massively powerful hindquarters providing an electrifying turn of speed, the caracal can bring down prey up to twice its own weight.

EARS
Black on the outside and pale on the inside, the ears have black tufts of hair up to 4.5cm (1.8in) long on their tips. The tufts and striking colouration exaggerate the cat's facial movements and expressions.

COAT
The fur is short but dense, varying in colour from tawny-brown to reddish-grey and even wine-red, with white underparts. Melanistic (dark form) individuals are also known.

SKULL
A short, compact muzzle and powerful jaw muscles provide the caracal with devastating biting power.

FEET
Large paws help in batting or hooking birds from the air. The claws are retractile.

LIMBS
The well muscled hindlimbs are longer than the forelimbs, accounting for the caracal's distinctive, high-rumped profile.

CREATURE COMPARISONS

Similar in size and weight to the caracal is the African golden cat (*Felis aurata*). It occurs in the rainforests of tropical Africa, from lowland areas to montane forest. The golden cat has a background coat colour of rust-red, yellow or grey, with white cheeks, chin and dark-spotted underparts. Its relatively small ears are probably an adaptation to a life spent pushing through thorny forest undergrowth.

Like the caracal, the golden cat is solitary and nocturnal. It hunts mostly on the ground but also climbs well, preying on small deer as well as domestic animals.

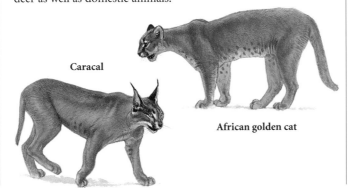

Caracal

African golden cat

WHERE IN THE WORLD?

Occurs in arid areas and dry savannah scrubland throughout Africa except the Sahara and tropical rainforest. Also found in eastern Mediterranean countries, coastal areas of the Arabian Peninsula and southwestern Asia.

RELATED SPECIES
The caracal is closely related to the serval, *Felis serval* , a slightly larger African cat with a spotted coat. The serval occupies a similar ecological niche in wetter areas where there is more ground cover. Both species are members of the cat family, Felidae.

PUMA

The puma's stocky, muscular body is at odds with its classification as a 'small cat'. Pound for pound, this cat is more powerful than a tiger.

KEY FEATURES

- A solitary hunter that patrols large territories in some parts of its range.
- Has a vast distribution encompassing habitats from tropical rainforest and swamp to arid scrub and mountain ranges.
- Effortlessly agile and graceful, with prodigious leaping power.
- Capable of killing prey many times its own bodyweight.

VITAL STATISTICS

WEIGHT	Male 65–105kg (143.3–231.5lb); female 35–60kg (77.2–132.3lb)
LENGTH	Head & Body: 50–80cm (19.7–31in) Tail: 60–70cm (23.6–27.6in)
SHOULDER HEIGHT	Male 1–1.9m; female (3ft 3in–6ft 2in) 0.9–1.5m (2ft 9in–4ft 9in)
SEXUAL MATURITY	2–3 years
MATING SEASON	Varies with habitat
GESTATION PERIOD	90–95 days
NUMBER OF YOUNG	1 to 4
BIRTH INTERVAL	2 years
TYPICAL DIET	Mammals, birds, insects
LIFESPAN	20 years

LIMBS
Rippling with muscle, the hindlimbs are proportionately the longest in the cat family, giving the puma phenomenal leaping power: it can reach a height of about 5m (16ft 6in) in a single bound.

HEAD
The long head is small relative to the body. The ears are highly sensitive, and the large, amber eyes give binocular vision to enable deadly accurate leaps.

MOUTH
Long canines stab into prey and hold it fast; ridges on the palate provide extra grip. Lining the jaws are carnassial teeth for shearing flesh.

TAIL
The tail is long with a black tip. It gives the puma balance and agility, allowing it to make lightning-quick turns or leap sure-footedly among boulders or branches.

CREATURE COMPARISONS

Like the puma, the pampas cat (Felis colocolo) occurs in many habitats. It is found in the South American grasslands known as pampas, but also enters humid forests and uplands. Dwarfed by the puma, the pampas cat has a long coat varying from cream to brown or pale grey. Dark bands pattern its flanks and ring its bushy tail, and two black bars mark its cheeks.

The pampas cat is nocturnal, like the puma, but is mainly terrestrial. It lacks the climbing skills of its cousin, but matches it in feline stealth as it stalks small prey including ground-nesting birds and cavies.

Pampas cat

Puma

WHERE IN THE WORLD?

Has the greatest natural distribution of any mammal in the western hemisphere, except humans. Found through the Americas from northwestern Canada to the southernmost tip of Argentina.

RELATED SPECIES

The puma is 1 of 30 species of small cat in the genus Felis. Other members of its genus include the domestic cat, F. catus, and the Iberian lynx, F. pardina, of Spain and Portugal. Felis belongs to the cat family Felidae, which includes three other genera: Neofelis, which has the clouded leopard as its sole member; Acinonyx, which also claims a single species, the cheetah; and Panthera — the genus of the big cats, including the lion, jaguar and tiger.

GEOFFROY'S CAT

• **ORDER** • *Carnivora* • **FAMILY** • *Felidae* • **GENUS & SPECIES** • *Felis geoffroyi*

KEY FEATURES

- Similar in size to a domestic cat, with a black-spotted coat ranging from silver-grey to yellow-ochre.
- A prodigious hunter that readily climbs trees or swims rivers to catch elusive prey.
- Extensively hunted in the past by fur-trappers; now protected by international law.

VITAL STATISTICS

WEIGHT	2–3.5kg (4.4–7.7lb)
LENGTH	Head & Body: 45–75cm (17.7–29.5in) Tail: 24–38cm (9.4–15in)
SHOULDER HEIGHT	15–25cm (5.9–9.8cm)
SEXUAL MATURITY	Female 18 months; male 24 months
MATING SEASON	Peaks in early spring
GESTATION PERIOD	74–76 days
NUMBER OF YOUNG	2 to 3
BIRTH INTERVAL	1 year
TYPICAL DIET	Mammals, birds reptiles, insects
LIFESPAN	10–15 years

Disguised by its cryptic colouring, the Geoffroy's cat stalks and kills small mammals and birds in the upland forests and scrub of South America.

SKULL
The rounded skull provides anchorage for powerful jaw muscles. Long canine teeth serve in holding and killing prey.

COAT
Colouration is extremely variable. In the north of its range the coat is pale yellow-brown, while in the south it is silver-grey. The round black spots sometimes merge to make indistinct stripes.

EARS
Large ears enable the cat to pinpoint the movements of prey in thick cover at night.

CLAWS
Long, razor-sharp, retractile claws give the cat a firm grip when climbing. They are also used to stab and hold prey.

BLACK CAT
All-black specimens are not unusual and occur because of an excess of melanin (black pigment) in the cat's skin or fur.

CREATURE COMPARISONS

The rusty-spotted cat (Felis rubiginosa) is roughly half the size of Geoffroy's cat. As its name suggests, it has a reddish tinge to its fur and brown spots in lines along its flanks and back. It is native to India and Sri Lanka. Like Geoffroy's cat, the rusty-spotted cat prefers to avoid dense forest, although the Sri Lankan subspecies favours the humid jungles in the south of the island. The discovery of other Indian populations thriving in abandoned houses in densely populated areas suggests that the rusty-spotted cat may be even more adaptable in its habits than Geoffroy's cat.

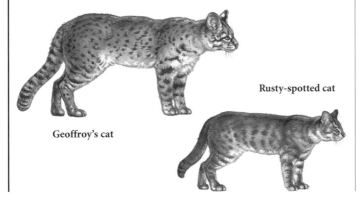

Rusty-spotted cat

Geoffroy's cat

WHERE IN THE WORLD?

Found in the southern portion of South America, from the Bolivian Andes, Paraguay and Uruguay, south through Argentina and Chile to Patagonia. Absent from Tierra del Fuego.

RELATED SPECIES

Geoffroy's cat is 1 of 28 species of small cat within the genus Felis, which includes the puma and the African wild cat, as well as the rare margay, Felis weidii, an inhabitant of South American rainforests. There are 4 genera and a total of 37 species of cat in the family Felidae.

• **ORDER** • *Carnivora* • **FAMILY** • *Felidae* • **GENUS & SPECIES** • *Felis lynx*

NORTHERN LYNX

The long-legged lynx, looking akin to a large domestic cat heavily dressed for winter weather, is a stealthy and agile predator of cold northern habitats.

KEY FEATURES

- Conspicuous ear tufts, furry jowls and large, hairy feet make the northern lynx one of the most easily recognizable of all cats.
- An agile and stealthy predator that feeds on a wide range of prey, it is capable of killing animals as large as deer.
- Solitary and adaptable, it thrives, unlike most cats, in the cold latitudes of the far north.

VITAL STATISTICS

Weight	5–38kg (11–83.8lb)
Length	Head & Body: 80–130cm (31–51.2in) Tail: 5–25cm
Shoulder Height	60–75cm (23.6–29.5in)
Sexual Maturity	Male 33 months; female 21 months
Mating Season	February–March
Gestation Period	9–10 weeks
Number of Young	1 to 5, usually 2 to 3
Birth Interval	1 year
Typical Diet	Mainly hares and rabbits, but also rodents, birds, deer, carrion and fish
Lifespan	15 years

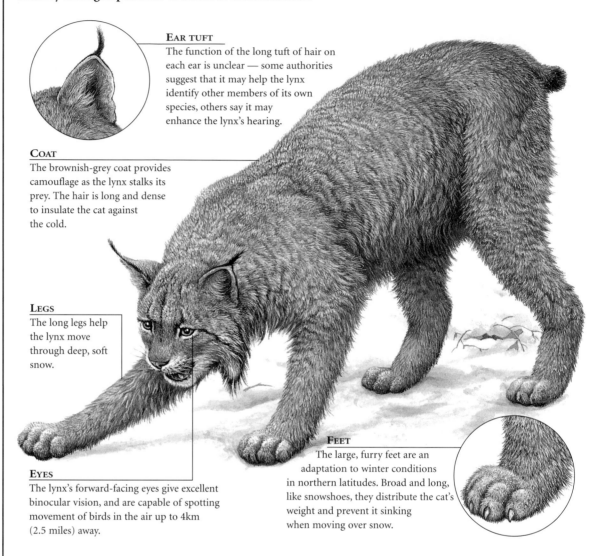

EAR TUFT
The function of the long tuft of hair on each ear is unclear — some authorities suggest that it may help the lynx identify other members of its own species, others say it may enhance the lynx's hearing.

COAT
The brownish-grey coat provides camouflage as the lynx stalks its prey. The hair is long and dense to insulate the cat against the cold.

LEGS
The long legs help the lynx move through deep, soft snow.

EYES
The lynx's forward-facing eyes give excellent binocular vision, and are capable of spotting movement of birds in the air up to 4km (2.5 miles) away.

FEET
The large, furry feet are an adaptation to winter conditions in northern latitudes. Broad and long, like snowshoes, they distribute the cat's weight and prevent it sinking when moving over snow.

CREATURE COMPARISONS

Belonging to the same family and subgenus as the northern lynx, is the endangered Spanish lynx, *Felis pardina*. With a total population of no more than 1500 animals, it is now restricted to a few mountainous areas in the Iberian Peninsula and the Guadalquivir Delta, Spain. The Spanish lynx is a similar size to its northern relative and has tufts of long hair on the tips of the ears and long cheek fur, but it has yellowish-red fur with dark spots. Its numbers fell dramatically when rabbits, its main prey, were decimated by the disease myxomatosis during the 1950s and 1960s.

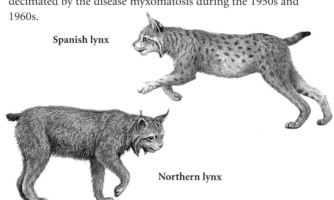

Spanish lynx

Northern lynx

WHERE IN THE WORLD?

Found across most of Canada, Alaska and northern USA. Also occurs in fragmented populations from parts of Europe, across northern and central Asia to Siberia, and south as far as Tibet.

RELATED SPECIES

The lynx's family, Felidae, is made up mainly of small-to-medium sized cats in the genus Felis, which contains 30 species. The caracal, F. caracal, is a smaller relation of the northern lynx found in dry regions of Asia and Africa. It can run faster than any cat of its size.

SAND CAT

• ORDER • *Carnivora* • FAMILY • *Felidae* • GENUS & SPECIES • *Felis margarita*

KEY FEATURES

- The only member of the cat family that lives almost exclusively in sandy desert habitats.
- Digs burrows for shelter from the daytime heat and is mainly active at night or during twilight hours.
- Uses keen senses to detect rodents and other small prey, which are thinly distributed in the desert.

VITAL STATISTICS

WEIGHT	3–4kg (6.6–8.8lb)
LENGTH	Head & Body: 48–58cm (18.9–22.8in) Tail: 28–35cm (11–13.8in)
SEXUAL MATURITY	14 months
MATING SEASON	January–October depending on location
GESTATION PERIOD	60–63 days
NUMBER OF YOUNG	Usually 2 to 5
BIRTH INTERVAL	1 to 2 litters per year
TYPICAL DIET	Mainly small rodents; also birds, lizards, locusts
LIFESPAN	Up to 8 years in the wild

This diminutive predator has a range of adaptations that enable it to survive among the harsh desert sands of Africa and Asia.

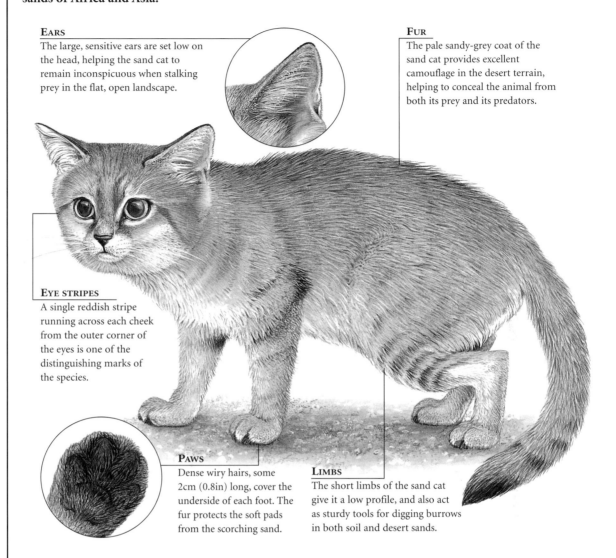

EARS
The large, sensitive ears are set low on the head, helping the sand cat to remain inconspicuous when stalking prey in the flat, open landscape.

FUR
The pale sandy-grey coat of the sand cat provides excellent camouflage in the desert terrain, helping to conceal the animal from both its prey and its predators.

EYE STRIPES
A single reddish stripe running across each cheek from the outer corner of the eyes is one of the distinguishing marks of the species.

PAWS
Dense wiry hairs, some 2cm (0.8in) long, cover the underside of each foot. The fur protects the soft pads from the scorching sand.

LIMBS
The short limbs of the sand cat give it a low profile, and also act as sturdy tools for digging burrows in both soil and desert sands.

CREATURE COMPARISONS

The sand cat is tiny when compared with its relative the African lion, Panthera leo. The lion is 50 times bigger, making it perhaps surprising that they belong to the same family.

Despite their difference in stature, they share the same body plan of a lithe, compact build, deep chest and rounded head. Long, sharp claws and teeth, combined with great agility make these cats highly effective hunters, although the sand cat would be dwarfed by even a part of a lion's typical meal.

African lioness

Sand cat

WHERE IN THE WORLD?

The sand cat lives in the northwestern Sahara, the Arabian Peninsula and the central Asian deserts,

which extend across Kazakhstan to Pakistan.

RELATED SPECIES

There are about 30 species of small cat in the genus Felis. One of the sand cat's closest relatives is the black-footed cat, Felis nigripes, of southwest Africa. It is the smallest of all the cats and dwells in dry, sandy or grassy habitats in Namibia, Botswana and South Africa.

• ORDER • *Carnivora* • FAMILY • *Felidae* • GENUS & SPECIES • *Felis pardalis*

OCELOT

With its keen senses, supple build, lethal armoury and camouflaged appearance, the ocelot displays the classic hallmarks of feline hunters.

KEY FEATURES

- The largest of several small cats living in the forests of South and Central America.

- Hunts most of its prey on the ground, making stealthy use of vegetation as ground cover.

- Long hunted by the fur trade for its beautifully patterned coat, and now listed on Appendix 1 of CITES (Convention on International Trade in Endangered Species).

SKULL
The rounded, short-snouted skull has pronounced cavities to house the ocelot's large eyes. The teeth feature long canines for stabbing, and razor-sharp carnassials for slicing.

EARS
The ocelot's forward-facing ears are large and cupped to provide excellent hearing for pinpointing prey.

FUR
The dark spots and streaks over the ocelot's body serve to break up its outline amid the shaded vegetation of a forest. Ocelots living in dry scrubland usually have a greyer shade of background fur.

HINDFEET
The ocelot has extremely flexible joints to make climbing easier. All cats except the cheetah and the flat-headed cat have fully retractile claws.

TAIL
Unlike the big cats, small cats such as the ocelot normally sit with their tail curled around their body rather than extended straight out behind.

VITAL STATISTICS

WEIGHT	11–16kg (24.2–35.3lb)
LENGTH	Head & Body: 60–100cm (23.6–39.4in) Tail: 30–45cm (11.8–17.7in)
SHOULDER HEIGHT	38–50cm (15–19.7in)
SEXUAL MATURITY	Up to 2 years
MATING SEASON	All year in most regions
GESTATION PERIOD	70 days
NUMBER OF YOUNG	1 to 4
BIRTH INTERVAL	2 years
TYPICAL DIET	Vertebrate prey including mammals, birds, reptiles and fish
LIFESPAN	7–10 years in the wild; up to 20 years in captivity

CREATURE COMPARISONS

Although they both occur in South America, the ocelot never meets its diminutive close relative, the little known kodkod (Felis guigna). The kodkod lives only in central and southern Chile and an adjacent part of Argentina, far to the southwest of the ocelot's range.

A little over half the length of the ocelot and scarcely one-quarter its weight, the kodkod has duller background fur but is similarly patterned with spots and streaks, and it too has a ringed tail. Also a forest-dweller, the kodkod reportedly hunts small mammals and birds at night.

Kodkod   Ocelot

WHERE IN THE WORLD?

Ranges from the USA–Mexico border region south through Central America and across most of tropical South America — except the central Andes — to northern Uruguay and northeastern Argentina.

RELATED SPECIES

The ocelot is a member of the subgenus Leopardus, along with the kodkod, the little spotted cat, Geoffroy's cat and the margay, Felis wiedii. The genus Felis comprises 30 species of small cat, most of which live among ground cover in forest or scrub habitats.

BOBCAT

• ORDER • *Carnivora* • FAMILY • *Felidae* • GENUS & SPECIES • *Felis rufus*

The stocky, powerful bobcat is a dedicated predator, using the power in its clawed paws to topple its prey before finishing it off quickly and efficiently.

KEY FEATURES

- The most successful species of wild cat in North America.
- Unsociable and elusive, marking out and guarding a territory that it may hold for life.
- A master of the surprise attack, it hunts alone at night, stealthily stalking its quarry before attacking in a swift leap.
- Still widely hunted for its luxuriant coat.

VITAL STATISTICS

WEIGHT	5–15kg (2–5.9lb)
LENGTH	Head & Body: 65–105cm (25.6–41.3in) Tail: 10–20cm (3.9–7.9in)
SEXUAL MATURITY	9 months
MATING SEASON	February to June
GESTATION PERIOD	60 days
NUMBER OF YOUNG	1 to 6, usually 2 or 3
BIRTH INTERVAL	Annual, but some females may raise a second litter if the first fails
TYPICAL DIET	Rabbits, rodents and other small mammals; large, ground-nesting birds
LIFESPAN	12–15 years

EARS
The bobcat's ears swivel like radar scanners to pick up the slightest rustle in ground cover. Short tufts at their tips may improve hearing efficiency.

TAIL
The black-tipped tail is unusually short for a cat and accounts for the bobcat's name.

COAT
Blotches on the dense coat provide camouflage, concealing the bobcat from its prey and enabling it to hide from larger predators.

TEETH
The short muzzle means that the jaw muscles exert terrific force on the long, stabbing canine teeth. Farther back, scissor-like carnassial teeth can slice through flesh and sinew.

CLAWS
The sharp, retractile claws are used for climbing and dragging down prey. The foot pads are naked, unlike those of the cold-adapted lynx, which are covered in dense fur.

CREATURE COMPARISONS

The bobcat is one of many species of small cat found throughout the world. One of the most distinctive is the slightly larger serval. This lean, long-legged cat has a small head with very large ears that it uses to locate rats and similar prey in the savannah grasslands of Africa. Like the bobcat, the serval hunts at dawn or dusk, using stealth to creep up on its prey, before pouncing with deadly precision. It also makes leaps 1m (3ft 6in) or so above the ground to bring down birds. The victims are often killed by the impact, but if not the serval soon dispatches them with a stab from its canine teeth.

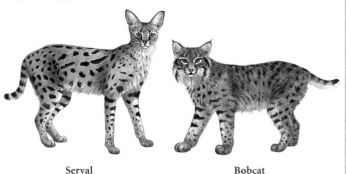

Serval   Bobcat

WHERE IN THE WORLD?

The bobcat is found throughout most of the USA. Its range extends from southern Mexico northwards into southern Canada, where it overlaps with that of the closely related Canadian lynx.

RELATED SPECIES

The bobcat is usually placed with 27 other small cats in the genus Felis, including Pallas' cat, F. manul. Some zoologists group the bobcat with the lynxes in the genus Lynx, calling it L. rufus to reflect its closer affinities with the larger cats in the family Felidae.

• **ORDER** • *Carnivora* • **FAMILY** • *Felidae* • **GENUS & SPECIES** • *Felis serval*

SERVAL

KEY FEATURES

- An adaptable member of the cat family, hunting a wide variety of prey and even catching birds in flight.
- Extremely long legs enable it to see above the tall grasses of its native African savannah.
- Hunts small mammals by sound, using its large ears to pinpoint prey movements.

VITAL STATISTICS

WEIGHT	9–18kg (19.8–39.7lb)
LENGTH	Head & Body: 54–62cm (21.2–24.4in) Tail: 70–100cm (27.6–39.4in)
SHOULDER HEIGHT	24–45cm (9.4–17.7in)
SEXUAL MATURITY	2 years
MATING SEASON	Variable
GESTATION PERIOD	65–75 days
NUMBER OF YOUNG	1 to 4
BIRTH INTERVAL	1 or 2 litters a year
TYPICAL DIET	Small mammals, birds, lizards, snakes and large insects
LIFESPAN	Up to 20 years

Its long legs, small head and large, mobile ears make the serval instantly recognizable as it prowls the African savannah in search of small animals.

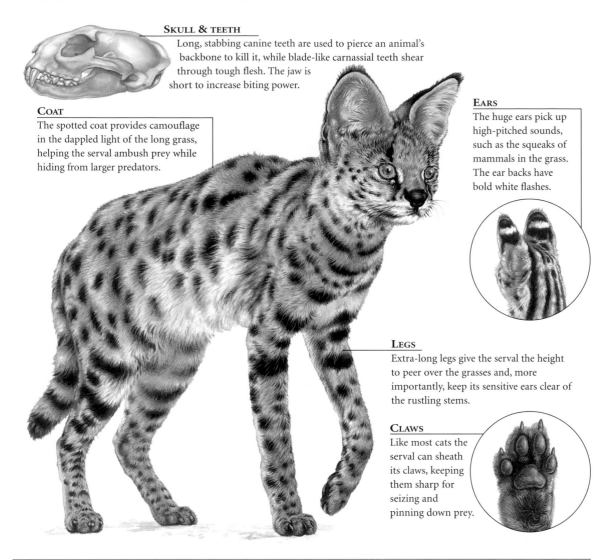

SKULL & TEETH
Long, stabbing canine teeth are used to pierce an animal's backbone to kill it, while blade-like carnassial teeth shear through tough flesh. The jaw is short to increase biting power.

COAT
The spotted coat provides camouflage in the dappled light of the long grass, helping the serval ambush prey while hiding from larger predators.

EARS
The huge ears pick up high-pitched sounds, such as the squeaks of mammals in the grass. The ear backs have bold white flashes.

LEGS
Extra-long legs give the serval the height to peer over the grasses and, more importantly, keep its sensitive ears clear of the rustling stems.

CLAWS
Like most cats the serval can sheath its claws, keeping them sharp for seizing and pinning down prey.

CREATURE COMPARISONS

The serval is sometimes regarded as a small pantherine cat — a miniature leopard or tiger — although it is classed as a small cat. The small cats include the African wild cat (Felis silvestris), which closely resembles the domestic cat. More compact than the serval and with much shorter legs, the wild cat is common across Africa, with at least 11 regional subspecies. Rats and mice make up most of its diet. Unlike its spotted cousin, the wild cat hunts almost exclusively at night, working in thick cover rather than on open grassland. It steals up on its prey, hugging the ground, before pouncing and delivering a fatal bite.

Serval

African wild cat

WHERE IN THE WORLD?

Widespread on the sub-Saharan grasslands of Africa, as far south as Botswana and northern South Africa. Also found in Morocco and Tunisia.

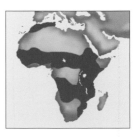

RELATED SPECIES

Although the serval's relationship to other cats is debated, it is currently classified as 1 of 28 species of small cat in the genus Felis, grouped on the basis of their size, feeding habits and ability to purr, rather than roar. As part of the family Felidae, the small cats are related to lions and tigers. Felidae is 1 of 8 families in the order Carnivora, which includes a wide range of predatory animals such as dogs, weasels and hyenas.

EUROPEAN WILDCAT

• **ORDER** • *Carnivora* • **FAMILY** • *Felidae* • **GENUS & SPECIES** • *Felis silvestris silvestris*

KEY FEATURES

- A small but fierce predator, it is extremely shy and rarely seen by humans.
- Leads a solitary life, holed up in a den by day and searching for prey at night with its sharp eyesight.
- Along with its various subspecies, the most widely distributed of all the world's small cats.

A stealthy hunter of the night, the European wildcat tracks its prey with its highly sensitive sight and pounces to the attack with slashing claws and teeth.

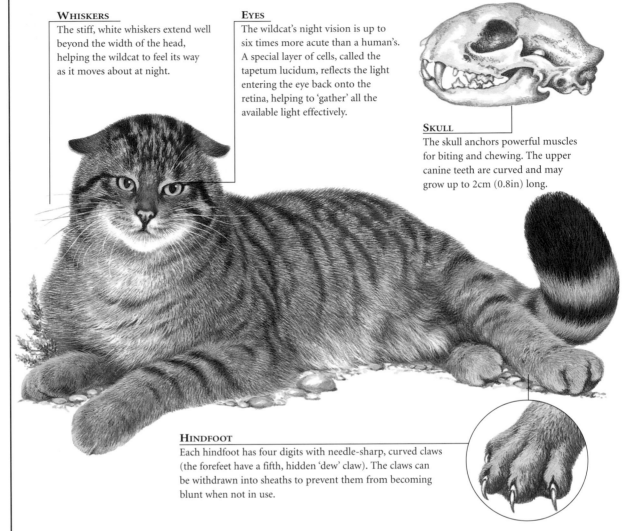

WHISKERS
The stiff, white whiskers extend well beyond the width of the head, helping the wildcat to feel its way as it moves about at night.

EYES
The wildcat's night vision is up to six times more acute than a human's. A special layer of cells, called the tapetum lucidum, reflects the light entering the eye back onto the retina, helping to 'gather' all the available light effectively.

SKULL
The skull anchors powerful muscles for biting and chewing. The upper canine teeth are curved and may grow up to 2cm (0.8in) long.

HINDFOOT
Each hindfoot has four digits with needle-sharp, curved claws (the forefeet have a fifth, hidden 'dew' claw). The claws can be withdrawn into sheaths to prevent them from becoming blunt when not in use.

VITAL STATISTICS

WEIGHT	3–8kg (6.6–17.6lb)
LENGTH	Male 52–75cm (20.5–29.5in); female 48–58cm (18.9–22.8in)
SHOULDER HEIGHT	21–35cm (8.3–13.8in)
SEXUAL MATURITY	1 year
MATING SEASON	March
GESTATION PERIOD	63–69 days
NUMBER OF YOUNG	1 to 8, usually 4
BIRTH INTERVAL	1 litter (occasionally 2) per year
TYPICAL DIET	Rabbits and other small mammals, birds, insects, some reptiles and amphibians
LIFESPAN	10–15 years

CREATURE COMPARISONS

Members of the same genus, the domestic tabby cat (Felis catus) and the European wildcat are very similar in appearance. In fact, it is very difficult to distinguish between some domestic tabbies that have become feral (reverted to the wild) and the wildcat. In general, though, the European wildcat is about one-third larger than the domestic cat and has longer legs, a broader head and a bushier tail, with a few dark rings and a distinctly 'cut-off' black tip. The wildcat's fur is also longer and softer than that of a domestic cat. The domestic cat is descended from the African wildcat subspecies and was first domesticated as a pet by the Egyptians in 2000BC. Two thousand years later the domestic cat began to be introduced into Europe.

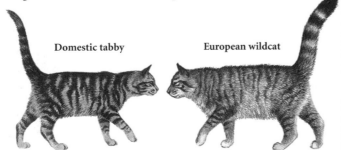

Domestic tabby　　　　**European wildcat**

WHERE IN THE WORLD?

European subspecies is found in highly localized populations throughout much of Europe. The other two subspecies are found in western Asia and Africa.

RELATED SPECIES

There are 3 subspecies of Felis silvestris: the European wildcat F. s. silvestris, the Asiatic wildcat, F. s. ornata, and the African wildcat, F. s. libyca. The genus Felis contains 30 species of small cat and includes the margay, F. weidii, of Central and South America.

• **ORDER** • *Carnivora* • **FAMILY** • *Felidae* • **GENUS & SPECIES** • *Felis wiedii*

MARGAY

The margay is perfectly equipped for life in the trees. It has especially large eyes to judge distances at night, allowing it to leap with confidence.

KEY FEATURES

- One of the best climbers in the cat family, spending most of its life high in the trees.
- Highly flexible joints in its ankles, a slender build and a long tail provide it with fluid balance and agility.
- Solitary creature that ambushes birds, mammals and reptiles at night.

SENSES
The margay's ears are long and flexible. A reflex action aims them at any source of noise. Its large eyes provide night vision six times more acute than that of humans.

COAT
The margay's beautiful coat is covered with black-ringed rosettes. The colouring mimics the effect of dappled moonlight in the forest.

SKULL
Typical of cats, the skull features large eye sockets. The short jaws hold long canines for stabbing and carnassials for shearing.

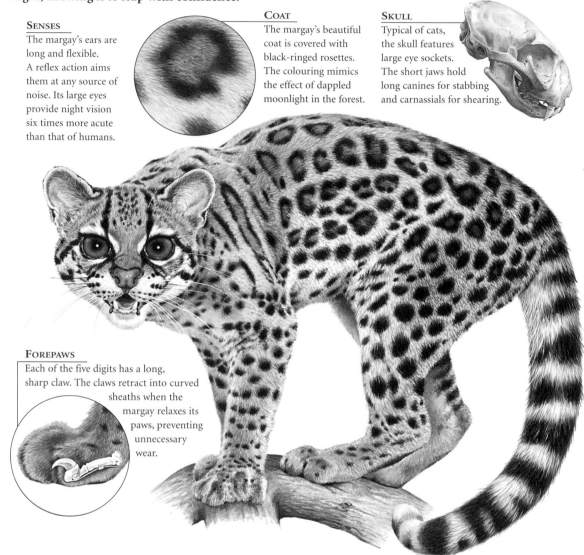

FOREPAWS
Each of the five digits has a long, sharp claw. The claws retract into curved sheaths when the margay relaxes its paws, preventing unnecessary wear.

VITAL STATISTICS

WEIGHT	3–9kg (6.6–19.8lb)
LENGTH	Head & Body: 45–80cm (17.7–31in) Tail: 32–51cm (12.6–20.1in)
SHOULDER HEIGHT	30–35cm (11.8–13.8in)
SEXUAL MATURITY	14–15 months
MATING SEASON	Year round
GESTATION PERIOD	60–80 days
NUMBER OF YOUNG	1 or 2
BIRTH INTERVAL	10–12 months
TYPICAL DIET	Birds, mammals, reptiles, amphibians; fruit
LIFESPAN	20 years in captivity

CREATURE COMPARISONS

The little spotted cat (Felis tigrina) shares parts of its range with the margay, occurring in Central and South America from Costa Rica to northern Argentina. It is more rust-coloured than the margay, and its spots are smaller and darker. Both species live primarily in rainforests, but the little spotted cat spends more time on the ground. It also has larger ears than the margay, suggesting that sound is more important in its lifestyle, while the margay's larger eyes reflect the greater importance of sight. The little spotted cat is slightly smaller than the margay, reaching a maximum head-and-body length of 55cm (21.6in) and weighing no more than 3kg (6.6lb). It also has a shorter tail.

Little spotted cat

Margay

WHERE IN THE WORLD?

Found in the rainforests of Central and South America, ranging from northern Mexico south through much of northern South America to Uruguay, northern Chile and northern Argentina.

RELATED SPECIES
The margay is classified in the genus Felis, which contains 30 species of cat including the ocelot, F. pardalis, with which it shares some of its range. Members of the genus vary in size from the domestic cat to the puma, which can reach 2m (6ft 6in) in length and weigh 100kg (220.5lb).

• ORDER • *Carnivora* • FAMILY • *Felidae* • GENUS & SPECIES • *Felis yagouaroundi*

KEY FEATURES

- Low-slung, long-bodied cat that is adept at catching a wide variety of prey on the ground, in the trees and in the water.

- One of the few cats that is active by day, occurring at forest edges and in lowland scrub-covered habitats.

- Lives alone or in pairs and roams over a vast area to satisfy its formidable appetite.

VITAL STATISTICS

WEIGHT	4.5–9kg (9.9–19.8lb)
LENGTH	Head & Body: 55–77cm (21.6–30.31in) Tail: 33–60cm (13–23.6in)
SHOULDER HEIGHT	30–35cm (11.8–13.8in)
SEXUAL MATURITY	About 2 years
MATING SEASON	Year round in the tropics; spring and late summer elsewhere
GESTATION PERIOD	63–70 days
NUMBER OF YOUNG	2 to 4
BIRTH INTERVAL	1 year
TYPICAL DIET	Birds, small mammals, reptiles, amphibians and fish
LIFESPAN	Up to 18 years

Often mistaken for a weasel or an otter, the jaguarundi has an elongated body and short legs that enable it to scamper through dense vegetation.

MOUTH
The cat stabs and kills prey with its dagger-like canines and uses its carnassials to tear flesh. Its tongue is covered with papillae (rough bumps) to rasp flesh from bone.

COAT
The jaguarundi occurs in various colour forms: black to brownish-grey and fox-red to chestnut. Darker forms are common in dense forests, while paler forms usually thrive in sparse habitats.

EARS
The small ears are equipped with highly mobile flaps that focus sounds and greatly enhance hearing.

FOREFEET
With soft pads surrounded by thick hair on their undersides, the paws provide grip and enable the cat to move silently.

HINDFEET
Each hindpaw has five claws that retract into protective sheaths. This adaptation enables the jaguarundi to keep its claws razor-sharp for holding prey and climbing trees.

CREATURE COMPARISONS

The flat-headed cat (Felis planiceps) is a member of the same genus as the jaguarundi. A native of Southeast Asia, it occurs along riverbanks in the forests of the Malay Peninsula, Sumatra and Borneo. Unlike the jaguarundi, the flat-headed cat hunts at night, taking mainly aquatic prey such as fish and frogs. It is smaller than its American cousin, weighing about 2kg (4.4lb) and reaching a maximum head-and-body length of 50cm (19.7in). Its tail is proportionately shorter, too, at only 15cm (5.9in).

The flat-headed cat has a golden-brown coat marked with darker spots, and a silver-white belly splashed with brown. It also has white face stripes. The reason for its distinctively flat skull is not documented.

Flat-headed cat

Jaguarundi

WHERE IN THE WORLD?

Found in the Americas from southern Texas and Mexico south to southern Brazil and northern Argentina.

RELATED SPECIES

The jaguarundi belongs to the genus Felis, along with 29 other species of small cat. Two unusual members of this genus are the Chinese desert cat, F. bieti, which is found in southern Mongolia and central China, and the kodkod, F. guigna, which lives in the forests of Chile and Argentina. A more familiar relative is the domestic cat, F. catus. The family Felidae contains 37 species which are placed in 4 genera.

• **ORDER** • *Carnivora* • **FAMILY** • *Felidae* • **GENUS & SPECIES** • *Neofelis nebulosa*

CLOUDED LEOPARD

A luxuriantly patterned coat enables this nimble-footed predator to steal like a wraith through the forest foliage and take its prey wholly by surprise.

TEETH
The very long canines have unusually sharp hind edges. A large gap between the canines and carnassials (slicing cheek teeth) enables this cat to take big bites out of prey.

TAIL
Equal in length to the head and body, the tail provides balance in the trees. It is thick, plushly furred and marked with black rings.

KEY FEATURES

- A highly elusive cat of the tropical rainforest, whose stocky limbs, tenacious paws and long tail give it superb agility in the trees.
- Takes its name from its large, rather cloud-like coat markings.
- Has characteristics of big and small cats.
- Tusk-like canine teeth are relatively the longest of any cat species.

COAT
The irregular markings have blurred edges and pale centres. The base colour ranges from yellow ochre to silver-grey on the upperparts; the underbelly is paler.

PAWS
Broad, strong paws have strong muscles and ligaments for running along branches, holding acrobatic postures and capturing prey. With the claws retracted, soft pads ensure the silent approach essential for stalking.

VITAL STATISTICS

WEIGHT	Male 15–23kg (33.1–lb) female 11–14kg (24.2–30.9in)
LENGTH	Head & Body: 62–106cm (24.4–41.7in) Tail: 55–91cm (21.6–35.8in)
SHOULDER HEIGHT	50–55cm (19.7–21.6in)
SEXUAL MATURITY	Average 26 months
MATING SEASON	All year round
GESTATION PERIOD	87–99 days
NUMBER OF YOUNG	1 to 5
BIRTH INTERVAL	From 8 months
TYPICAL DIET	Primates, birds, squirrels, small deer, snakes; some domestic stock
LIFESPAN	11–17 years

CREATURE COMPARISONS

The clouded leopard shares the dense rainforests of southern and southeastern Asia with the Asiatic golden cat (Felis temmincki). As its name suggests, the golden cat has a rich coat colour ranging from honey to chestnut-brown. It generally lacks distinctive markings — except in its striped face — although a few individuals in the north of its range are spotted overall. The golden cat also has a shorter body and tail than its relative.

Unlike the clouded leopard, the golden cat usually lives at ground level, where it captures less bulky prey such as hares, reptiles and young deer.

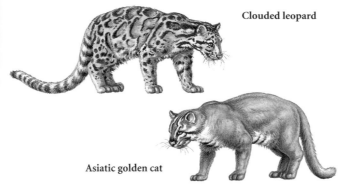

Clouded leopard

Asiatic golden cat

WHERE IN THE WORLD?

Found on the hills of Nepal, Sikkim and Bhutan, east to south China and Taiwan, and into Myanmar (formerly Burma), Thailand, Laos and Malaysia, as well as the islands of Borneo and Sumatra.

RELATED SPECIES

Most authorities give the clouded leopard its own genus, Neofelis, although some have placed it with the big cats, genus Panthera, on account of its diverse characteristics. It is one of 37 species in the cat family, Felidae. Other felids include the leopard cat, Felis bengalensis.

ASIATIC LION

• ORDER • *Carnivora* • FAMILY • *Felidae* • GENUS & SPECIES • *Panthera leo persica*

KEY FEATURES

- Has a shorter mane than the African lion, and a distinctive fold of skin along its belly. Also lives in smaller, looser prides.
- Eats mainly small deer and antelope, but also takes domestic cattle.
- After years of hunting and forest clearance, only 300 survive in the wild in one part of India. Species is listed as endangered by the IUCN (World Conservation Union).

VITAL STATISTICS

WEIGHT	Male 150–250kg; (330.7–551.2lb) female 120–185kg (264.6–407.9lb)
LENGTH	Head & Body: Male 1.7–2.5m; (5ft 6in–8ft 2in) female 1.4–1.75m (4ft 6in–5ft 7in) Tail: 70–105cm (27.6–41.3in)
SHOULDER HEIGHT	Male 1–1.23m; (3ft 3in–4ft) female 80–107cm (31–42.1in)
SEXUAL MATURITY	Male 5 years; female 4 years
MATING SEASON	All year round
GESTATION PERIOD	100–119 days
NUMBER OF YOUNG	1 to 6
BIRTH INTERVAL	18–26 months
TYPICAL DIET	Goat, cattle, boar, antelope
LIFESPAN	16–18 years

Superbly camouflaged for stalking, the Asiatic lion combines sleekness and strength to burst out from cover and bring down unsuspecting prey.

COAT
Whitish underneath and sandy to reddish-brown above, the lion is almost invisible as it steals through long, dry grass.

MANE
The male Asiatic lion has a smaller mane than his counterpart in Africa.

LIONESS
An Asiatic lioness looks almost identical to an African lioness. Both are smaller than males and have no mane.

JAWS
The Asiatic lion has short jaws operated by powerful muscles. The jaws do not move from side to side, so the animal cannot chew. Instead, its tongue is coated with sharp studs for rasping flesh from a carcass.

ELBOW
A male Asiatic lion has much thicker elbow tufts than a male African lion.

TAIL
All lions also have a tail tuft — the only big cats to do so. A tail tuft may help swish away flies or serve a signalling purpose.

CREATURE COMPARISONS

The genetic difference between Asiatic and African lions is small, indicating that they became isolated only 100,000 years ago. The Asiatic lion differs mainly in usually having a fold of skin along its belly, and a short mane. However, there are so few Asiatic lions, all in one small, particular environment, that it is hard to say how typical such features are. Individual lions vary. A short mane may simply be an adaptation to allow easier passage through the thick forest in Gir — Asiatic lions in zoos in temperate countries often grow long manes. Or it may be that, because male lions in Gir do not compete for dominance of prides, they do not need a long, showy mane.

Male Asiatic lion

Male African lion

WHERE IN THE WORLD?

Found only in the Gir Wildlife Sanctuary and adjacent National Park, known collectively as the Gir Protected Area, at the southern tip of the Kathiawar peninsula in the state of Gujarat, northwestern India.

RELATED SPECIES

Some scientists classify all African lions as **Panthera leo**, with the Asiatic lion the only subspecies. Other experts divide African lions into various subspecies as well. There are 4 other species in the genus Panthera: the tiger, P. tigris, of Asia; the snow leopard, P. uncia, of Asia; the jaguar, P. onca, of South America; and the leopard, P. pardus, of Asia and Africa. The cat family Felidae includes a further 30 or so species, most of them small.

• ORDER • *Carnivora* • FAMILY • *Felidae* • GENUS & SPECIES • *Panthera onca*

JAGUAR

KEY FEATURES

- Looks like a massively muscled, heavyweight leopard.

- Stalks or ambushes a wide range of animals by night, killing its prey with a stabbing bite to the throat.

- Rosetted coat provides excellent camouflage by breaking up the jaguar's outline among the moonlight-dappled vegetation of the forest.

VITAL STATISTICS

WEIGHT	Male 90–120kg; (198.4–264.6lb) female 60–90kg (132.3–198.4lb)
LENGTH	Head & Body: 1.1–1.8m (3ft 6in–5ft 9in) Tail: 45–75cm (17.7–29.5in)
SHOULDER HEIGHT	68–76cm (26.8–29.9in)
SEXUAL MATURITY	2–4 years
MATING SEASON	Tropics all year, seasonal peaks elsewhere
GESTATION PERIOD	93–107 days
NUMBER OF YOUNG	1 to 4; usually 2
BIRTH INTERVAL	About 2 years
TYPICAL DIET	Mammals; also turtles, fish, caimans and farm livestock
LIFESPAN	Up to 22 years in captivity

The largest carnivore in South America, the jaguar has a lithe, muscle-packed body for overpowering large prey and a spotted coat for camouflage.

HYOID BONE
The jaguar makes a sound like a coughing grunt rather than a true roar, yet it has the same vocal apparatus as other big cats. This consists of a two-part hyoid bone (A), supporting the tongue, linked by cartilage (B). The elasticity of the cartilage allows the hyoid bone to vibrate in a 'roar'. In small cats the hyoid is solid, which is why they can only purr.

COAT
The jaguar's coat varies from off-white to black, but is usually yellow-brown, becoming paler on the chest and belly. Its black rosettes are wider-spaced than the leopard's and, unlike its relative, often have one or more dark spots in the centre.

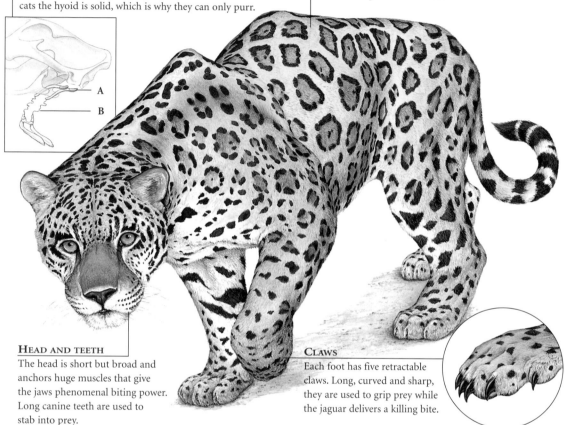

HEAD AND TEETH
The head is short but broad and anchors huge muscles that give the jaws phenomenal biting power. Long canine teeth are used to stab into prey.

CLAWS
Each foot has five retractable claws. Long, curved and sharp, they are used to grip prey while the jaguar delivers a killing bite.

CREATURE COMPARISONS

The jaguar shares most of its range with the margay, or tree ocelot (Felis wiedii), a smaller but similar-looking cat of mixed forest and scrubland. The margay's leaner physique and proportionately longer tail contribute to its climbing ability as it clambers and leaps in pursuit of birds, tree squirrels and monkeys.

The secret of the margay's climbing skill lies in its hindfeet, however, which can rotate through 180° to help it manoeuvre. In addition, all four feet are broad and soft-soled, spreading around branches to give a sure grip. A tree-dwelling lifestyle enables the margay to share the jaguar's range without competing for food, as the larger cat hunts mainly on the ground. Like the jaguar the margay is now equally rare or even extinct in many areas.

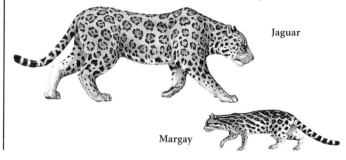

Jaguar

Margay

WHERE IN THE WORLD?

Formerly ranged from southern USA through Central America to northern Argentina. Now extremely rare in most regions, and probably extinct in Uruguay, El Salvador, Nicaragua and southwestern USA.

RELATED SPECIES

There are 4 genera in the cat family, Felidae: Panthera, the 'big cats', which includes the jaguar, leopard, snow leopard, lion and tiger; Felis, containing the 28 species of 'small cats', including the jaguarundi; Neofelis containing the clouded leopard; and Acinonyx, containing the cheetah.

LEOPARD

• ORDER • *Carnivora* • FAMILY • *Felidae* • GENUS & SPECIES • *Panthera pardus*

KEY FEATURES

- The leopard relies on the advantages of stealth and surprise to catch prey up to twice its own size and weight.

- The mottled coat pattern conceals the leopard as it rests by day, and provides superb camouflage while the cat hunts in dim light.

- Possesses excellent hearing and night vision, as well as touch-sensitive whiskers on the muzzle.

VITAL STATISTICS

WEIGHT	27–90kg (59.5–198.4lb)
LENGTH	Head & Body: 1–1.9m (3ft 3in–6ft 2in) Tail 61–94cm (24–37in)
SHOULDER HEIGHT	46–79cm (18.1–31in)
SEXUAL MATURITY	2½–3 years
BREEDING SEASON	At any time of year in the tropics; spring elsewhere
GESTATION PERIOD	90–105 days
NUMBER OF YOUNG	1 to 6, usually 2 to 4
BIRTH INTERVAL	2 years
TYPICAL DIET	Grazing mammals, pigs, primates, dogs, insects, fish and birds
LIFESPAN	Up to 23 years

The living embodiment of stealth, grace and power, the leopard is a deadly hunter that pounces on its victims under cover of the night.

EYES
Like all cat species, the leopard has excellent eyesight: its night vision may be six times better than that of humans.

COAT
The spots are bold, dark rosettes upon a paler base colour. Coat patterns and colours vary widely among leopards from different regions.

TAIL
The tail provides balance. The leopard walks with the tip raised, showing the white underside. This may help to marshal the cubs.

TEETH
As in other cat species, the leopard's short but well muscled jaws give it great biting power, helping the long, pointed canines to stab through flesh.

PAWS
The leopard walks silently on its padded paws. The retractable claws grip prey and are also used for scratching trees to define territorial boundaries.

CREATURE COMPARISONS

The familiar term 'black panther' actually refers to true leopards that have a melanistic (dark-pigmented) coat. The silvery, smudged coat of the snow leopard (Panthera uncia) resembles that of the rare Amur leopard (P. pardus orientalis) of Asia. The spotted and rosetted coat of the jaguar (P. onca) closely resembles that of the leopard, although the jaguar occurs only in Central and South America.

Leopard

Melanistic leopard

Snow leopard

Jaguar

WHERE IN THE WORLD?

Still very widespread, but with an increasingly patchy distribution over most of sub-Saharan Africa, parts of Arabia,

Afghanistan, India and Sri Lanka, and northern China south through Southeast Asia.

RELATED SPECIES

The leopard is related to the other big cats in the Panthera genus; the lion, tiger, jaguar and snow leopard. The cheetah, also a big cat, belongs to a separate genus, while the clouded leopard, is the bridge between the big and small cat groups.

• **ORDER** • *Carnivora* • **FAMILY** • *Felidae* • **GENUS & SPECIES** • *Panthera tigris altaica*

SIBERIAN TIGER

One of the world's deadliest predators, the massive Siberian tiger is a muscle-packed powerhouse that strikes prey with awesome strength.

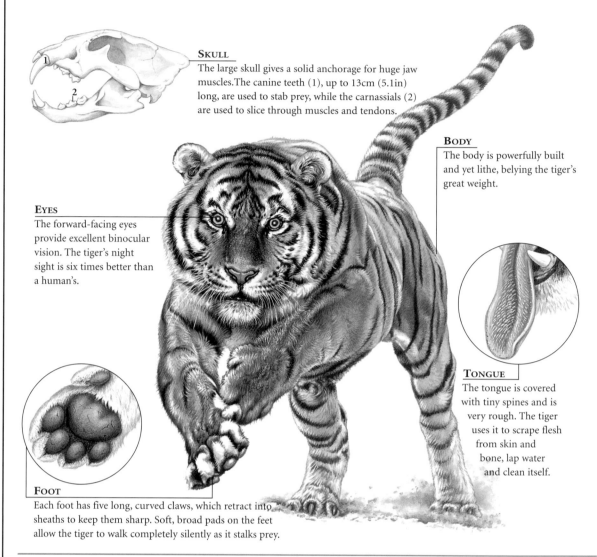

KEY FEATURES

- Largest member of the cat family, weighing nearly 70 times as much as a domestic cat.
- Has an extra layer of body fat to keep it warm in the Siberian winters.
- Often travels hundreds of kilometres over harsh terrain in search of food.
- Able to pounce more than three times its own length in order to catch and despatch prey.

SKULL
The large skull gives a solid anchorage for huge jaw muscles. The canine teeth (1), up to 13cm (5.1in) long, are used to stab prey, while the carnassials (2) are used to slice through muscles and tendons.

EYES
The forward-facing eyes provide excellent binocular vision. The tiger's night sight is six times better than a human's.

BODY
The body is powerfully built and yet lithe, belying the tiger's great weight.

TONGUE
The tongue is covered with tiny spines and is very rough. The tiger uses it to scrape flesh from skin and bone, lap water and clean itself.

FOOT
Each foot has five long, curved claws, which retract into sheaths to keep them sharp. Soft, broad pads on the feet allow the tiger to walk completely silently as it stalks prey.

VITAL STATISTICS

WEIGHT	Male 180–300kg; (396.8–661.4lb) female 100–165kg (220.5–363.8lb)
LENGTH	Head & Body: 1.6–2.8m (5ft2in–9ft 2in) Tail: 60–95cm ((23.6–37.4in)
SHOULDER HEIGHT	1–1.1m (3ft 3in–3ft 6in)
SEXUAL MATURITY	Male 4–5 years; female 3–4 years
MATING SEASON	November to April
GESTATION PERIOD	104–106 days
NUMBER OF YOUNG	1 to 6
BIRTH INTERVAL	2–2.5 years
TYPICAL DIET	Pigs, deer, bears, small birds and fish
LIFESPAN	15 in the wild; 26 in captivity

CREATURE COMPARISONS

The puma (Felis concolor), also known as the cougar or the mountain lion, is the largest member of the cat family in the western hemisphere. Averaging about two-thirds the length of the Siberian tiger, it weighs considerably less but is remarkably agile and enormously strong for its size: it can make single vertical leaps of over 5m (16ft 4in) into a tree and is powerful enough to kill a horse. Although now endangered throughout most of its range it has the largest natural distribution of any mammal — except humans — in the Americas.

Siberian tiger

Puma

WHERE IN THE WORLD?

Thinly distributed across the northeastern part of China (often referred to as Manchuria), south towards North and South Korea. Recently reintroduced to a river region of Russia, north of Vladivostok.

RELATED SPECIES

The Siberian tiger is the largest member of the cat family, Felidae. The closely related snow leopard, Uncia uncia, is another big cat that, like the Siberian tiger, lives in an extremely cold environment. It is found in the Himalayas at altitudes of up to about 5500m (18,040ft).

• ORDER • *Carnivora* • FAMILY • *Felidae* • GENUS & SPECIES • *Panthera tigris tigris*

BENGAL TIGER

The tiger's powerful muscles and massive build are the keys to its hunting success: in seconds, it can knock down and kill prey that weighs a ton.

KEY FEATURES

- Solitary cat that kills by stealth and ambush.
- Strong enough to kill a water buffalo weighing more than a ton—twice the tiger's own weight.
- Most water-loving of the big cats: it will even chase prey into water.
- Uses its long canine teeth to kill its victim with a deadly bite to the neck or throat.

EYES
The tiger's night vision is six times better than our own, aided by a mirror-like layer at the back of the eye which reflects extra light.

EARS
Hearing is the tiger's sharpest sense. The white spots behind the ears help tigers to identify one another in the dark jungle.

COAT
Every tiger has a unique pattern of black stripes on a deep-orange coat. This breaks up the outline of the body in dense cover.

TEETH
The tiger uses its long canine teeth to stab and kill prey. The molars behind them act like scissors, slicing strips of flesh from a carcass.

CLAWS
The claws are used to grip prey and to scratch trees. They retract when the tiger walks, to remain sharp and to allow it to stalk prey silently.

VITAL STATISTICS

WEIGHT	181.4–263.1kg (400–580lb).
LENGTH	Head & Body: 190.5–221cm (75–87in); Tail 81.3–88.9cm (32–35in)
SHOULDER HEIGHT	88.9–94cm (35–37in)
SEXUAL MATURITY	Female 3–4 years; male 4–5 years
MATING SEASON	Winter to spring
GESTATION PERIOD	95–112 days
NUMBER OF YOUNG	2 to 4
TYPICAL DIET	Sambar deer, chital deer, buffalo, wild pigs, gaur, and monkeys
LIFE SPAN	Up to 26 years in the wild

CREATURE COMPARISONS

The Siberian tiger is the world's largest cat: adult males may reach more than 3.6m (12ft) in length. The coat is shaggier and paler than that of the Bengal tiger, equipping the tiger for its icy northeast Asian habitat. The Siberian tiger occupies a vast territory and preys mainly on wild pig. There may be no more than 150 left in the wild.

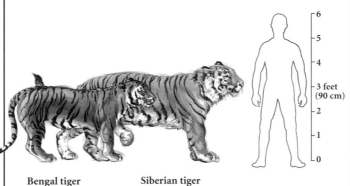

Bengal tiger   Siberian tiger

WHERE IN THE WORLD?

Isolated populations found across India, but most numerous in the mangrove swamps of the Sundarbans region that lies in Bangladesh and the northeastern Indian state of West Bengal. Scattered populations also found in neighboring countries of Nepal, Bhutan, and Burma (now Myanmar).

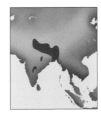

RELATED SPECIES
There were once eight subspecies of tiger. Today, only five remain: the Bengal, the Siberian, the Sumatran, the Indochinese, and the Caspian. The tiger's closest relatives are the other 'big cats'—the lion, the leopard, the jaguar, and the snow leopard (genus Panthera).

• **ORDER** • *Carnivora* • **FAMILY** • *Felidae* • **GENUS & SPECIES** • *Panthera uncia*

SNOW LEOPARD

The snow leopard's soft, warming coat provides camouflage among the rocks and snow, and its thickly padded paws conceal a battery of deadly claws.

KEY FEATURES

- Capable of killing prey up to three times its own size and weight.

- Has a luxuriant, silvery coat, with fur 12cm (4.7in) thick on its belly to protect it from the extreme cold in its high homelands.

- Now on the brink of extinction as a result of illegal trade in its coat and bodyparts, and listed as endangered by the IUCN (World Conservation Union).

VITAL STATISTICS

WEIGHT	25–75kg (55.1–165.3lb)
LENGTH	Head & Body: 1–1.3m (3ft 3in–4ft 3in) Tail: 80–100cm (31–39.4in)
SHOULDER HEIGHT	60cm (23.6in)
SEXUAL MATURITY	2–3 years
MATING SEASON	January to April
GESTATION PERIOD	90–103 days
NUMBER OF YOUNG	1 to 5, but usually 2 or 3
BIRTH INTERVAL	More than 2 years
TYPICAL DIET	Mammals and birds
LIFESPAN	Up to 20 years

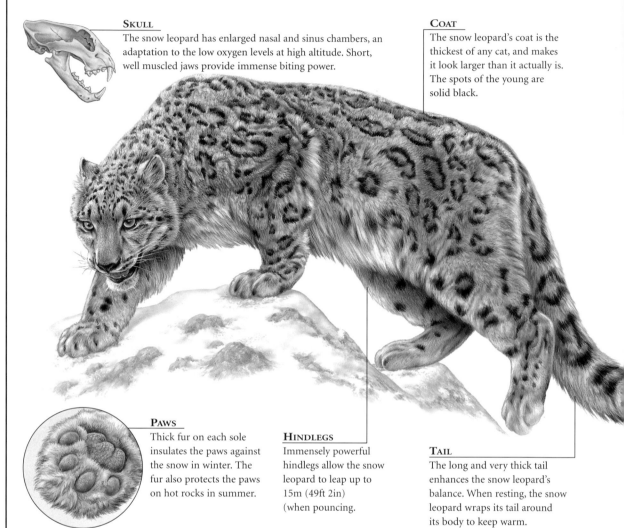

SKULL
The snow leopard has enlarged nasal and sinus chambers, an adaptation to the low oxygen levels at high altitude. Short, well muscled jaws provide immense biting power.

COAT
The snow leopard's coat is the thickest of any cat, and makes it look larger than it actually is. The spots of the young are solid black.

PAWS
Thick fur on each sole insulates the paws against the snow in winter. The fur also protects the paws on hot rocks in summer.

HINDLEGS
Immensely powerful hindlegs allow the snow leopard to leap up to 15m (49ft 2in) (when pouncing.

TAIL
The long and very thick tail enhances the snow leopard's balance. When resting, the snow leopard wraps its tail around its body to keep warm.

CREATURE COMPARISONS

Considered to be the most elusive of all the big cats, the clouded leopard (Neofelis nebulosa) is found in dense, tropical forests from Nepal to southeastern China and the Malay Peninsula.

Like the snow leopard, and indeed, most cats, the clouded leopard is solitary and nocturnal. Living in a warmer climate, the clouded leopard has a thinner coat, but both cats have shortened limbs to lower their centre of gravity. The snow leopard has short limbs as an adaptation to enhance its agility on the rocky terrain of its mountain home, whereas a low profile helps its arboreal relative steal swiftly along branches while tracking prey.

Clouded leopard

Snow leopard

WHERE IN THE WORLD?

Found in scattered populations throughout the mountains of central Asia, from Afghanistan east to Russia and northern Mongolia, and through parts of southern China, into India, Nepal, Tibet and Bhutan.

RELATED SPECIES

The snow leopard is usually placed in the genus Panthera with the tiger, leopard, jaguar and lion, but is sometimes given a genus of its own: Uncia. It is seen as a 'bridge' between the small cats of the genus Felis and its larger relatives. Other Panthera species have a flexible hyoid bone in the larynx that enables them to roar. The snow leopard, like the small cats, has a rigid hyoid and so cannot roar. There are 35 species in the cat family, Felidae.

LION

• ORDER • *Carnivora* • FAMILY • *Felidae* • GENUS & SPECIES • *Panthera leo*

The lion's immense physical strength places it at the top of the savannah food chain, whether hunting alone or as a team.

KEY FEATURES

- Lives in a family group called a pride, in which duties are strictly divided: while the lionesses hunt, the males stay back to defend the territory and young.
- Individual lions can hunt effectively, but they are more than twice as successful at catching large prey, such as zebra, when they work as a team.

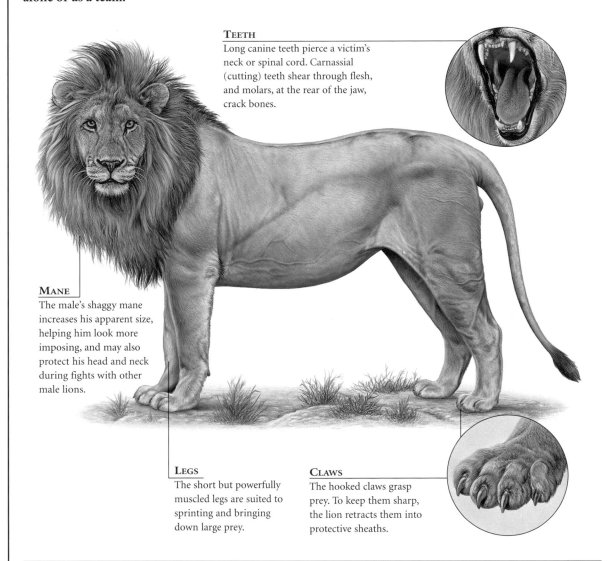

TEETH
Long canine teeth pierce a victim's neck or spinal cord. Carnassial (cutting) teeth shear through flesh, and molars, at the rear of the jaw, crack bones.

MANE
The male's shaggy mane increases his apparent size, helping him look more imposing, and may also protect his head and neck during fights with other male lions.

LEGS
The short but powerfully muscled legs are suited to sprinting and bringing down large prey.

CLAWS
The hooked claws grasp prey. To keep them sharp, the lion retracts them into protective sheaths.

VITAL STATISTICS

WEIGHT	150–250kg (330.7–551.2lb)
LENGTH	Head & Body: 1.65–2.5m (5ft 4in–8ft2in) Tail 89–102cm (35–40.2in)
SHOULDER HEIGHT	1.2m. (3ft 9in) Male can be up to 50 per cent larger than female
SEXUAL MATURITY	18 months
MATING SEASON	Throughout the year
GESTATION PERIOD	102–113 days
NUMBER OF YOUNG	1 to 4
BIRTH INTERVAL	18–26 months
TYPICAL DIET	Zebra, antelope, giraffe, other mammals; also carrion
LIFESPAN	Up to 16 years

CREATURE COMPARISONS

On the African savannah, the lion includes its relative the leopard among its neighbours. The leopard is only about 60 per cent of the size of the lion, and hunts correspondingly smaller prey, such as wild goats, wild pigs and small antelope. It will even switch to preying on rodents, rabbits and invertebrates when larger prey is scarce. Like the lion, the leopard hunts by creeping up stealthily on prey and executing the attack in a final rush or spring. It does not hunt in a team, however, except on the rare occasions when a breeding pair cooperates to provide for its cubs.

Lion

Leopard

WHERE IN THE WORLD?

Found in open savannah and desert areas of Africa south of the Sahara. A small population also exists in the Gir Forest National Park in northwest India.

RELATED SPECIES

There is an Asiatic subspecies of lion, Panthera leo persica, with a population of about 300. In addition to the lion, the 'big cats' of the genus Panthera also include the jaguar of South America, the tiger of Asia, the leopard of Africa and Asia and the snow leopard of Asia. A further 30 species are classified in the family Felidae, including the cougar, three species of lynx and 26 species of 'small cat', such as the ocelot.

MEERKAT

The meerkat's characteristic upright stance serves it well during 'sentry duty,' when it uses its sharp eyesight to keep a lookout for predators.

KEY FEATURES

- Works as part of a tight-knit team for maximum protection against predators, using a system of 'sentry-duty.' This is a behavioural response to a life spent out in the open in semi-desert conditions.

- Pale, sand-coloured coat provides good camouflage against the soil in arid regions — a vital asset for a species exposed by day to aerial predators.

VITAL STATISTICS

WEIGHT	570–1220g (20.1–43oz) female larger than male
LENGTH	25–35cm (9.8–13.8in)
TAIL	16.5–25cm (6.5–9.8in)
SEXUAL MATURITY	About 1 year
MATING SEASON	Mainly September to October
GESTATION PERIOD	About 75 days
NUMBER OF YOUNG	2 to 5, usually 4
BIRTH INTERVAL	1 year
TYPICAL DIET	Insects, such as termites; scorpions; some small vertebrates, such as lizards; birds' eggs and plant matter
LIFESPAN	Up to 10 years

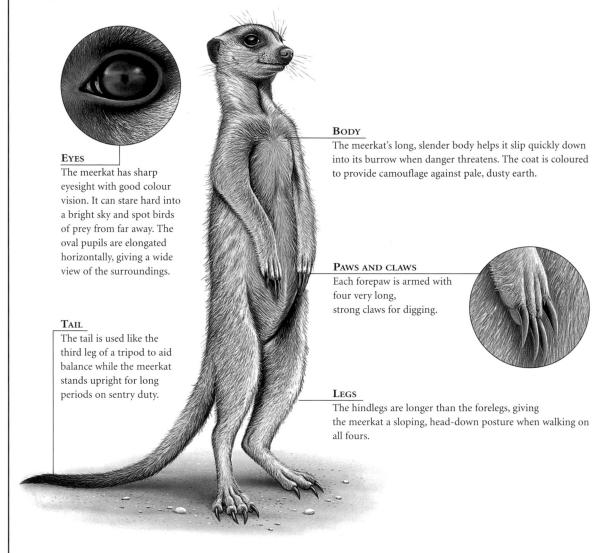

EYES
The meerkat has sharp eyesight with good colour vision. It can stare hard into a bright sky and spot birds of prey from far away. The oval pupils are elongated horizontally, giving a wide view of the surroundings.

TAIL
The tail is used like the third leg of a tripod to aid balance while the meerkat stands upright for long periods on sentry duty.

BODY
The meerkat's long, slender body helps it slip quickly down into its burrow when danger threatens. The coat is coloured to provide camouflage against pale, dusty earth.

PAWS AND CLAWS
Each forepaw is armed with four very long, strong claws for digging.

LEGS
The hindlegs are longer than the forelegs, giving the meerkat a sloping, head-down posture when walking on all fours.

CREATURE COMPARISONS

The meerkat and its relatives, the mongooses, are typically agile and active. Like the meerkat, the yellow mongoose is a social animal, living mainly in open country in southern Africa and preying on insects and small mammals. The bush-tailed mongoose is a solitary inhabitant of moist savannah and woodland in Kenya and Mozambique, where it forages for ants and termites.

Yellow mongoose

Bush-tailed mongoose

Meerkat

WHERE IN THE WORLD?

Found in the dry plains and semi-deserts of southern Africa, over a range covering parts of southwestern Angola, Namibia, Botswana and South Africa. It avoids forested areas and prefers to live on open ground.

RELATED SPECIES
The meerkat belongs to a subfamily of mongooses, Mungotinae, which includes the dwarf mongoose, a tiny species with a body length up to 25cm (9.8in).

SPOTTED HYENA

• ORDER • *Carnivora* • FAMILY • *Hyaenidae* • GENUS & SPECIES • *Crocuta crocuta*

Fleet of foot, stockily built and armed with powerful jaws, the spotted hyena is one of the most feared predators of sub-Saharan Africa.

KEY FEATURES

- Uses powerful-smelling anal secretions to signal sexual readiness or to identify itself to other hyenas.
- Curbs extreme aggression to team up in packs to hunt the large grazing animals of the African plains.
- Genitals of both sexes almost identical, which makes males and females difficult to distinguish in the field.

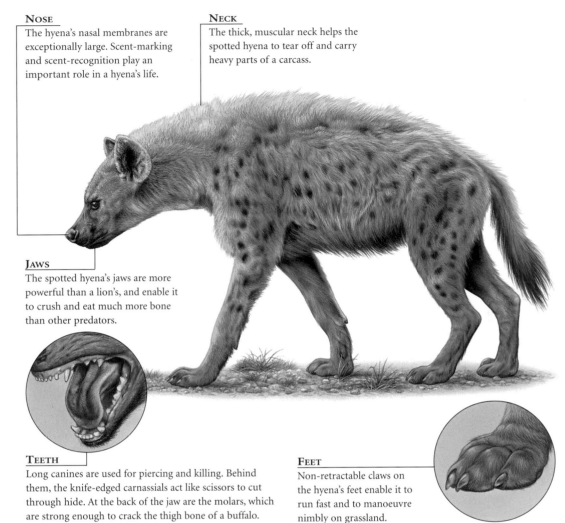

NOSE
The hyena's nasal membranes are exceptionally large. Scent-marking and scent-recognition play an important role in a hyena's life.

NECK
The thick, muscular neck helps the spotted hyena to tear off and carry heavy parts of a carcass.

JAWS
The spotted hyena's jaws are more powerful than a lion's, and enable it to crush and eat much more bone than other predators.

TEETH
Long canines are used for piercing and killing. Behind them, the knife-edged carnassials act like scissors to cut through hide. At the back of the jaw are the molars, which are strong enough to crack the thigh bone of a buffalo.

FEET
Non-retractable claws on the hyena's feet enable it to run fast and to manoeuvre nimbly on grassland.

VITAL STATISTICS

WEIGHT	50–79kg (110.2–174lb)
LENGTH	Head & Body: 1.5–1.6m (4ft 9in–5ft 2in) Tail: 25–30cm (9.8–11.8in)
SHOULDER HEIGHT	90cm (35.4in)
SEXUAL MATURITY	Male 2 years; female 3 years Mating Usually spring season
GESTATION PERIOD	About 110 days
NUMBER OF YOUNG	1 or 2
BIRTH INTERVAL	1–2 years
TYPICAL DIET	Medium-size antelope, such as wildebeest; zebra and domestic livestock; also carrion
LIFESPAN	Up to 25 years

CREATURE COMPARISONS

The aardwolf is much smaller and more lightly built than the other three hyena species. Its forelimbs are comparatively weak, as are its skull and jaws. However, the aardwolf possesses a number of adaptations that suit its exclusive diet of termites. It has a long, sticky tongue with which it licks termites from the grass, while its large ears enable it to detect the faint sounds of insect prey.

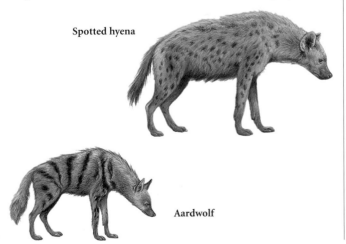

Spotted hyena

Aardwolf

WHERE IN THE WORLD?

A native of sub-Saharan Africa, covering an area ranging from semi-desert to moist savannah, and at elevations up to 3600m (11,810ft). Follows large herbivore prey in the course of seasonal migrations.

RELATED SPECIES
The family Hyaenidae contains four species, all of which occur widely across Africa. The genus Hyaena also includes the striped hyena, H. hyaena, and the brown hyena, H. brunnea. The aardwolf, Proteles cristatus, is the only member of its genus.

• ORDER • *Carnivora* • FAMILY • *Hyaenidae* • GENUS & SPECIES • *Hyaena brunnea*

BROWN HYENA

KEY FEATURES

- A robust scavenger that lives mainly off the food scraps that big cats and other predators leave behind.
- Inhabits arid areas of southern Africa, travelling 30km (18.6miles) or more each night in its search for food.
- Usually forages and rests alone, but lives in a clan that scent marks and defends a territory.

VITAL STATISTICS

WEIGHT	37–50kg (81.6–110.2lb)
LENGTH	Head & Body: 110–135cm (43.3–53.1in) Tail: 18–26cm (7.1–10.2in)
SHOULDER HEIGHT	64–88cm (25.2–34.6in)
SEXUAL MATURITY	2–3 years
MATING SEASON	All year, peaking May to August
GESTATION PERIOD	About 90 days
NUMBER OF YOUNG	2 to 5, but usually 3
BIRTH INTERVAL	12–14 months
TYPICAL DIET	Mainly the carrion of large mammals; also fruit, small mammals, insects and eggs
LIFESPAN	At least 12 years

With its keen senses and bone-cracking jaws, the brown hyena is equipped to sniff out and process even the toughest food scraps.

JAWS & TEETH
The hyena has short, deep short jaws with a mighty biting force. They are packed with huge carnassials and premolars to chop and shear through tough hide and bone.

EARS
Excess heat radiates from the large ears, keeping the hyena cool in the desert.

MANE
The brown hyena erects its long mane as a warning during hostile confrontations with other hyenas.

ANAL POUCH
Scent glands in the anal pouch produce strong-smelling secretions that are used to mark group territories. Each hyena emits its own unique scent, which helps individuals to recognize each other.

FOREPAWS
Each forepaw has four blunt, non-retractile claws, which the hyena uses to enlarge its dens and dig small rodent prey from their burrows.

CREATURE COMPARISONS

The brown hyena and striped hyena (Hyaena hyaena) are smaller than the spotted hyena (Crocuta crocuta), with smaller teeth to match. Both have the sloping back typical of hyenas. They are less dedicated to butchery than the spotted hyena, with a diet that relies more on small mammals, insects and fruit. With a more northerly distribution, the striped hyena does not cross paths with the brown hyena, but both species may be forced to yield a carcass to their powerful spotted cousin.

Striped hyena

Brown hyena

WHERE IN THE WORLD?

Found in southern Africa from Namibia's Skeleton Coast east to southern Mozambique. Has been exterminated from much of South Africa except for the northern areas of the Transvaal and Cape Province.

RELATED SPECIES

The family Hyaenidae contains 3 genera. In addition to the brown hyena, the genus Hyaena includes the striped hyena, H. hyaena. The spotted hyena, Crocuta crocuta, brings to 3 the total of so-called 'true' hyenas, which are chiefly scavengers. An unusual addition to the family is the aardwolf, Proteles cristatus, which lives solely on insects. All of these species are found in Africa, but the striped hyena also occurs in Asia.

• ORDER • *Carnivora* • FAMILY • *Hyaenidae* • GENUS & SPECIES • *Hyaena hyaena*

STRIPED HYENA

KEY FEATURES

- An aggressive, powerful hunter and scavenger that steals kills from other large predators.
- Female and young found in small family groups, while adult male is more solitary.
- Despised by humans and heavily persecuted throughout its extensive range.

Solidly built for endurance, the striped hyena roams the plains looking for animal remains, which it grinds up using its bone-crushing teeth.

NECK
A heavily muscled neck enables the striped hyena to lift and carry heavy carcasses long distances to sheltered spots, and back to its den.

SENSES
The striped hyena has a superb sense of smell, thanks to nasal membranes that are 50 times larger than those of humans. It also has acute hearing, enabling it to detect a predator making a kill several hundred metres away.

SKULL
The hyena has a short jaw that provides devastating biting power, enabling it to crack large bones. Long canines and carnassial teeth are adapted for stabbing, crushing and shearing.

CREST
The hairs on the mane or crest are 20cm (7.9in) long. The animal erects these hairs to dramatically enlarge its profile when confronting rivals.

JUVENILE
The cub has a similar colouration to the adult, but has a black dorsal stripe rather than a mane. The mane develops as the cub approaches maturity.

FEET
Heavily furred on the underside, each foot has four digits, which end in non-retractile claws. Although not exceptionally sharp, they provide grip when the hyena is running.

VITAL STATISTICS

WEIGHT	37–55kg (81.6–121.3lb)
LENGTH	Head & Body: 91–120cm (35.8–47.2in) Tail: 26–47cm (10.2–18.5in)
SHOULDER HEIGHT	60–94cm (23.6–37in)
SEXUAL MATURITY	2–3 years
MATING SEASON	All year round
GESTATION PERIOD	88–92 days
NUMBER OF YOUNG	1 to 6; usually 2 to 4
BIRTH INTERVAL	1 year
TYPICAL DIET	Carrion, insects, birds, fruit and seeds
LIFESPAN	24 years in captivity

CREATURE COMPARISONS

The striped hyena shares parts of its range with the spotted hyena, which occurs in much of sub-Saharan Africa. Varying from a reddish-brown to a tan colour, with a dark muzzle, the spotted hyena is the largest of the hyenas, weighing up to 79kg (174lb) and reaching almost 2m (6ft 6in) in length, tail included. Both hyena species live in dry scrublands and savannah, surviving largely by scavenging the kills of other predators. But, whereas the striped hyena usually loses out to lions, leopards and even spotted hyenas, the larger hyena is rarely driven from a carcass. It also hunts efficiently in packs, preying on wildebeest calves and small grazers.

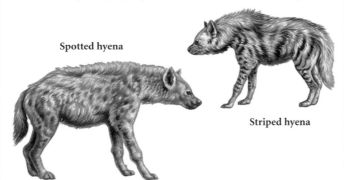

Spotted hyena

Striped hyena

WHERE IN THE WORLD?

Found in eastern and northern Africa, except the Sahara Desert. Also occurs in the Middle East and parts of Asia from southern Kazakhstan east to India.

RELATED SPECIES
The striped hyena shares its genus with the brown hyena, Hyaena brunnea, which lives in southern Africa. Along with the powerful spotted hyena, Crocuta crocuta, and the more delicately built aardwolf, Proteles cristatus, which feeds on termites, these animals make up the family Hyaenidae. The family is classified within the order Carnivora, which also includes nearly 90 genera of dogs, bears, raccoons, cats, weasels and mongooses.

• **ORDER** • *Carnivora* • **FAMILY** • *Hyaenidae* • **GENUS & SPECIES** • *Proteles cristatus*

AARDWOLF

The aardwolf uses its sharp hearing and long, sticky tongue to forage for termites, while its striped coat helps conceal it from larger predators.

KEY FEATURES

- Smallest and most specialized member of the hyena family, feeding almost exclusively on termites.
- Emerges at dusk from its den on the African plains to wander across a large home range in search of food.
- Defends its territory and discourages attackers by raising the stiff hairs of its mane and tail to enlarge its profile.

VITAL STATISTICS

WEIGHT	9–14kg (19.8–30.9lb)
LENGTH	Head & Body: 55–80cm (21.6–31in) Tail: 20–30cm (7.9–11.8in)
SHOULDER HEIGHT	45–50cm (17.7–19.7in)
SEXUAL MATURITY	2 years
MATING SEASON	Varies according to location; births peak in summer
GESTATION PERIOD	90–110 days
NUMBER OF YOUNG	1 to 5, usually 2 or 3
BIRTH INTERVAL	1 year
TYPICAL DIET	Termites
LIFESPAN	14 years in captivity

SKULL
The skull is more lightweight than those of the other three hyena species. Weak jaws contain sharp canines and widely spaced molars that are too small to crush meat but make short work of termites.

MANE
By bristling the long, stiff hairs along its spine, the aardwolf makes itself look bigger and more impressive during conflicts.

BODY
The high shoulders and low rump are a feature of all hyenas.

COAT
Pale yellow-brown fur with black stripes on the body and legs breaks up the aardwolf's outline against its desert surroundings. Soft underfur lies beneath longer, coarser guard hairs.

TONGUE
The long tongue is covered in sticky saliva, ideal for picking up termites.

HINDFOOT
The aardwolf is the only hyena species that has four toes on each hindfoot instead of five.

FOREFOOT
Each forefoot has four large toes and a greatly reduced fifth. The toepads and claws are used for opening termite mounds.

CREATURE COMPARISONS

The aardwolf bears a striking resemblance to one of its close relatives, the striped hyena (Hyaena hyaena), with which it shares the arid habitat of the Horn of Africa. However, the striped hyena is far larger than its cousin, reaching 72cm (28.3in) at the shoulder and 1.5m (4ft 9in) in length. Both species are active at dusk and by night but, while the aardwolf seeks out termites, the striped hyena tackles larger fare. Like the brown and spotted hyenas, the striped hyena has powerful jaws and huge grinding teeth that make mincemeat of anything from small reptiles to carrion and medium-sized mammals.

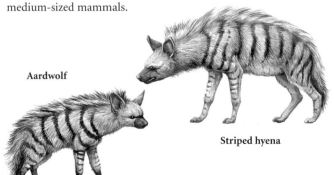

Aardwolf

Striped hyena

WHERE IN THE WORLD?

A northeastern population ranges from southern Egypt to central Tanzania, while a southern population ranges from Angola east to Zambia, and south to South Africa.

RELATED SPECIES
The family Hyaenidae includes 3 genera: Crocuta, containing the spotted hyena, C. crocuta; Hyaena (the brown and striped hyenas); and Proteles (the aardwolf). The hyenas' closest relatives are the mongooses, civets and genets in the family Viverridae.

• ORDER • *Carnivora* • FAMILY • *Mustelidae* • GENUS & SPECIES • *Eira barbara*

KEY FEATURES

- A thickset predator that lives in the forests and woodlands of the American tropics.
- Climbs trees with extraordinary agility, and often hunts birds and small mammals high in the canopy.
- More gregarious than most of its weasel and marten relatives, and is regularly found in pairs or groups.

VITAL STATISTICS

WEIGHT	4–6kg (8.8–13.2lb)
LENGTH	Head & Body: 55–65cm (21.6–25.6in) Tail: 35–45cm (13.8–17.7in)
SEXUAL MATURITY	12 months
MATING SEASON	All year
GESTATION PERIOD	63–67 days
NUMBER OF YOUNG	2 to 4
BIRTH INTERVAL	I year
TYPICAL DIET	Small mammals, lizards, birds and fruit
LIFESPAN	Up to 18 years

Sleek and agile, with long legs and a thick tail for balance, the tayra leaps from branch to branch in search of fruit and prey.

COLOURING
The tayra's head and neck usually contrast strongly with the body, and may be grey, brown or even yellow.

TEETH
Sharp canine teeth sever a victim's spinal cord or puncture its skull. Blade-like carnassials in the sides of the jaw slice through flesh.

HEAD
Keen eyes, a moist, sensitive nose and acute hearing enable the tayra to find food in the forest twilight.

TAIL
The heavy tail balances the weight of the tayra's body as the animal manoeuvres through the forest canopy.

SKULL
Long and flattened, the tayra's skull tapers towards the muzzle. Large jaws give power to the bite.

FEET
The soles of the feet have naked skin to grip bark as the tayra leaps through the branches. Sharp claws also give a firm foothold.

CREATURE COMPARISONS

The fisher (Martes pennanti) is one of the tayra's closest relatives. A powerful, solitary predator, it inhabits the temperate forests of Canada and the USA, where it preys on birds and small mammals, often high in the canopy. But the fisher is best known for its prowess in hunting porcupines. Weaving and darting to avoid a faceful of quills, the fisher skilfully subdues a porcupine with bites to its exposed head. Unlike the tayra, the fisher is much sought after for its fur and has become rare in parts of its range.

Tayra

Fisher

WHERE IN THE WORLD?

Found in Central and South America from southern Mexico to northern Argentina. Absent from High Andes and eastern Brazil.

RELATED SPECIES

The tayra closely resembles the martens of the genus Martes, such as the pine marten, M. martes, and sable, M. zibellina. However, crucial physical differences, such as its long legs and less elongated body, mean that it is classed in its own genus, Eira. The martens and the tayra belong to the family Mustelidae, which also includes weasels, skunks, otters and badgers. The family is 1 of 7 in the order Carnivora.

•ORDER • *Carnivora* • FAMILY • *Mustelidae* • GENUS & SPECIES • *Enhydra lutris*

SEA OTTER

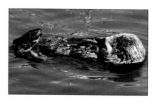

KEY FEATURES

- A fully aquatic mammal that enjoys a close relationship with the giant seaweed in its coastal habitat.
- Relies on incredibly dense fur to keep warm and grooms diligently to maintain its coat in peak condition.
- Exhibits a unique talent among sea mammals in using rocks as tools to crack open the toughest of shellfish.

VITAL STATISTICS

WEIGHT	Male 22–45kg (48.5–99.2kg); female 15–32kg (33.1–70.5lb)
LENGTH	Head & Body: 55–140cm (21.6–55.1in) Tail: 25–37cm (9.8–14.6in)
SEXUAL MATURITY	Male 5 years; female 3 years
MATING SEASON	All year round, but peaks vary according to location
GESTATION PERIOD	Around 130 days; further 240–350 days if implantation is delayed
NUMBER OF YOUNG	1
BIRTH INTERVAL	1 year
TYPICAL DIET	Sea urchins, molluscs, crabs, fish
LIFESPAN	15–20 years

Insulating fur, flipper-like hindlimbs and shell-shattering teeth equip the sea otter to thrive in an aquatic environment.

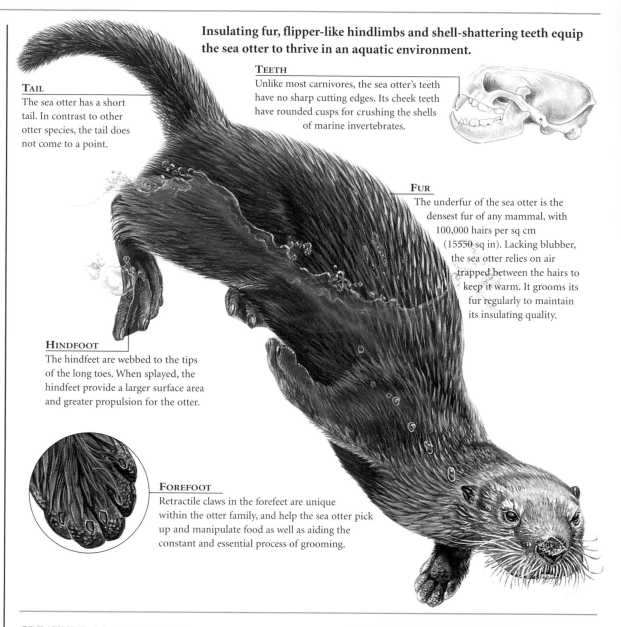

TAIL
The sea otter has a short tail. In contrast to other otter species, the tail does not come to a point.

TEETH
Unlike most carnivores, the sea otter's teeth have no sharp cutting edges. Its cheek teeth have rounded cusps for crushing the shells of marine invertebrates.

FUR
The underfur of the sea otter is the densest fur of any mammal, with 100,000 hairs per sq cm (15550 sq in). Lacking blubber, the sea otter relies on air trapped between the hairs to keep it warm. It grooms its fur regularly to maintain its insulating quality.

HINDFOOT
The hindfeet are webbed to the tips of the long toes. When splayed, the hindfeet provide a larger surface area and greater propulsion for the otter.

FOREFOOT
Retractile claws in the forefeet are unique within the otter family, and help the sea otter pick up and manipulate food as well as aiding the constant and essential process of grooming.

CREATURE COMPARISONS

While the sea otter is the heaviest of all otters, with some males topping 45kg (99.2lb), the Oriental small-clawed otter (Aonyx cinerea) is probably the lightest, with a top weight of about 5.5kg (12.1lb). Its body is 40–65cm (15.7–25.6in) long. Both are coloured reddish-to-dark brown with a creamy throat and chest, this paler fur also extends all over the sea otter's head.

The Oriental small-clawed otter finds molluscs, small crabs and tiny fish in the muddy streams, ditches and paddy-fields of its range in India, Bangladesh and Southeast Asia. Like its cousin, it uses an 'anvil' to open molluscs.

Oriental small-clawed otter

Sea otter

WHERE IN THE WORLD?

Inhabits the coastal waters of the North Pacific, extending in an arc from the Sea of Okhotsk across to the remote Aleutian Islands off Alaska, and south to the coast of California.

RELATED SPECIES

The sea otter is the only species in its genus. The genus Lutra includes 8 species of otter, including the Eurasian otter, L. lutra. The 3 small-clawed or clawless otters comprise the genus Aonyx, while the giant otter of South America, Pteronura brasiliensis, has its own genus. Together the otters form the Lutrinae, a subfamily within the Mustelidae family, which includes weasels, badgers and skunks.

WOLVERINE

• **ORDER** • *Carnivora* • **FAMILY** • *Mustelidae* • **GENUS & SPECIES** • *Gulo gulo*

KEY FEATURES

- Remarkably dense, warm fur allows the wolverine to hunt through the subzero Arctic nights.
- Tracks prey and potential mates by sense of smell.
- During the long days of the polar summer, it forgoes its nocturnal lifestyle in favour of short periods of activity and rest.

VITAL STATISTICS

WEIGHT	7–34kg (15.4–75lb)
LENGTH	Head & Body: 66–104cm (26–40.9in) Tail: 16.5–25cm (6.5–9.8in)
SEXUAL MATURITY	2–3 years
MATING SEASON	Late April to July
GESTATION PERIOD	About 9 months, including time for delayed implantation
NUMBER OF YOUNG	1 to 5, usually 2 to 4
BIRTH INTERVAL	2–3 years
TYPICAL DIET	Carrion, birds and their eggs, lemmings, wild sheep, caribou, nuts, fruit
LIFESPAN	Up to 17 years in captivity; 13 in the wild

This compact and powerful creature is built for a life of hunting and scavenging in the frozen wastes of northern latitudes.

HEAD
The head is thickset and muscular, with an almost bear-like face. Most of the wolverine's relatives, such as weasels and martens, have a more slender, wedge-shaped head.

COAT
The long, coarse and dense fur accumulates frost less readily than other animal furs. Native northern peoples use the fur for lining coats.

ANAL GLANDS
Like those of skunks, the wolverine's anal glands can spray a smelly, yellow-green liquid over a distance of 1m (3ft 3in) or more.

TEETH
The heavily muscled jaws give the wolverine a bite of bone-cracking power. The stout canines and rows of incisors are used to grab and tear flesh, while the other teeth slice and chew.

FEET
Each foot has five toes armed with long, stout, sharp claws. The broad feet act like snowshoes and allow the wolverine to run easily over deep snow without sinking in.

CREATURE COMPARISONS

The wolverine is a member of the weasel family, which typically includes highly active predators with a slender body, short legs, sharp claws and potent anal glands. The different species vary greatly in size and weight. Smallest is the least weasel, which weighs 28–70g (1–2.5oz). The American marten is about the same length as a domestic cat and weighs up to 1.25kg (2.7lb). The heaviest is the wolverine, at up to 34kg (75lb), and the sea otter, which can tip the scales at around 45kg (99.2lb).

Sea otter

Wolverine

American marten

Least weasel

WHERE IN THE WORLD?

Found in northern North America, the northern sub-Arctic islands, and northern Eurasia from Scandinavia east to Siberia. Also found in Greenland.

RELATED SPECIES

There are two races, or subspecies, of wolverine: **Gulo gulo gulo**, of Europe and Asia, and **G. gulo luscus**, of North America. The wolverine belongs to the weasel family, Mustelidae, which includes the American badger, but it is most closely related to true martens and the tayra.

• **ORDER** • *Carnivora* • **FAMILY** • *Mustelidae* • **GENUS & SPECIES** • *Ictonyx striatus*

ZORILLA

With a low-slung body and short, muscular legs, the zorilla is equipped to dig the complex burrows in which it spends the day.

KEY FEATURES

- Anal glands spray a secretion so repulsive that the zorilla is one of the smelliest animals in the world.
- Mixed blessing to African farmers — kills poultry but also preys on household pests such as rodents.
- Relies on its very acute sense of smell to locate its prey on nocturnal hunting expeditions.

SCENT GLANDS
Flanking the anus, and opening into it, are two glands that produce a devastatingly pungent scent secretion.

TEETH
The zorilla has short but strong canines, carnassials adapted for shearing and broad molars for crushing and grinding.

COAT
The zorilla has white markings on its face, several white stripes down its back and a mostly white tail. Its underparts are black. Face markings vary between regions and may indicate the existence of several subspecies. The bold coat pattern warns potential predators that the zorilla makes a distasteful meal.

TAIL
The zorilla raises its tail when alarmed, giving it an even bushier appearance; the coat is longest on the tail.

FEET
Non-retractile claws on each of five digits enable the zorilla to dig effectively.

VITAL STATISTICS

WEIGHT	400–1400g (14–49.4oz); male larger than female
LENGTH	Head & Body: 28–38cm (11–15in) Tail: 20–30cm (7.9–11.8in)
SHOULDER HEIGHT	10–13cm (3.9–5.1in)
SEXUAL MATURITY	Male 33 months; female 9 months
MATING SEASON	March to August
GESTATION PERIOD	36 days
NUMBER OF YOUNG	1 to 3
BIRTH INTERVAL	1 year
TYPICAL DIET	Small to medium-sized vertebrates; invertebrates
LIFESPAN	5–7 years in the wild

CREATURE COMPARISONS

Weighing no more than 350g (771.6lb), the African striped weasel (Poecilogale albinucha) resembles a smaller and much more slender version of the zorilla. It has sleeker fur, with less pronounced white markings on the face and tail but with similar white stripes over a black back. Its tail is far less bushy than that of the zorilla.

The striped weasel occurs across Africa south of the Equator. It favours thick woodland areas and generally avoids the open grasslands in which the zorilla thrives. Like the zorilla, the weasel is an expert killer of small vertebrates, but instead of eating victims on the spot it takes them back to its burrow.

Zorilla

African weasel

WHERE IN THE WORLD?

Found through much of sub-Saharan Africa in savannah, scrubland and upland areas. Absent from equatorial rainforest and the eastern tip of Somalia.

RELATED SPECIES

The zorilla is the sole member of Ictonyx, 1 of 23 genera in the family Mustelidae. Most mustelids have short legs and a long, sinuous body. They include the grison, Galictis vittata, of tropical Central and South America. The family Mustelidae belongs to the order Carnivora.

•ORDER • *Carnivora* • FAMILY • *Mustelidae* • GENUS & SPECIES • *Lutra canadensis*

NORTH AMERICAN OTTER

The sleek, powerful North American river otter swims with the speed and agility to rival that of the fish it preys upon.

KEY FEATURES

- Relative of the weasels and polecats that is adapted for life both in water and on land.
- Graceful fish hunter that also finds time to indulge in boisterous play.
- Threatened by habitat destruction and the contamination of its fish prey with pesticides.

SKULL AND TEETH
The extremely flattened, streamlined skull is armed with sharp incisor and canine teeth to hold a struggling fish, and carnassial teeth to slice it up.

COAT
The coat has a layer of dense waterproof underfur, protected by long guard hairs that trap air for insulation in the cold water.

TAIL
The powerful, muscular tail helps propel the otter swiftly through the water.

HINDFOOT
Larger than the forefoot, the hindfoot is also more extensively webbed.

FOREFEET
The feet are webbed for fast swimming, and equipped with unusually long, sturdy claws for digging dens and gripping slippery fish.

NOSE
The distinctive peaked shape of the moist, hairless nose is unique among otters. The otter seals its nostrils tightly when swimming underwater.

VITAL STATISTICS

WEIGHT	7–10kg (15.4–22lb)
LENGTH	Head & Body: 65–105cm (25.6–41.3in) Tail: 30–45cm (11.8–17.7in)
SEXUAL MATURITY	2 years
MATING SEASON	March–April
GESTATION PERIOD	10–12 months, including delayed implantation
NUMBER OF YOUNG	Up to 5, usually 2 to 3
BIRTH INTERVAL	1–2 years
TYPICAL DIET	Fish, frogs, crayfish, small mammals and ducklings
LIFESPAN	Up to 15 years

CREATURE COMPARISONS

While the river otter is a freshwater hunter, it has a close relative that spends much of its time at sea, the marine otter (*Lutra felina*). Found along the rocky Pacific shoreline of South America, as far south as Tierra del Fuego, this tiny otter, weighing only about 5kg (11lb), appears too fragile to survive the turbulent waters of the Humboldt Current, which flows north from Antarctica. Like all otters, it is an agile hunter, expertly catching fish, but also taking shellfish, which it cracks open with its powerful molars. It often hunts in pairs, unlike its more solitary relative. Declining across its range, the marine otter is persecuted by shellfish farmers and fur hunters.

North American river otter

Marine otter

WHERE IN THE WORLD?

Found in many parts of North America, particularly in Florida, Alaska and northern Canada. Absent from much of western and central USA.

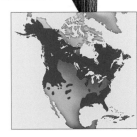

RELATED SPECIES

Closely related to the Eurasian otter, *Lutra lutra*, the North American river otter is classified in the same genus, along with 6 other species. The genus is part of the otter subfamily Lutrinae, which has 12 otter species in all, including the sea otter, *Enhydra lutris*, and giant otter, *Pteronura brasiliensis*. Along with mink, weasels, badgers and skunks, otters are members of the family Mustelidae, 1 of 7 families within the order Carnivora.

• **ORDER** • *Carnivora* • **FAMILY** • *Mustelidae* • **GENUS & SPECIES** • *Lutra lutra*

EURASIAN OTTER

Well equipped for life in the water as well as on land, the otter enjoys the best of both worlds, but it is an especially efficient aquatic predator.

KEY FEATURES

- A powerful swimmer, its lithe, streamlined body provides speed and agility when hunting in the water.
- Leaves conspicuous scent-marked droppings to tell other otters its sex, age and readiness to mate.
- Maintains its outer layer of waterproof fur by frequent daily grooming sessions.

VITAL STATISTICS

WEIGHT	10kg (22lb)
LENGTH	Head & Body: 57–70cm (22.4–27.6in) Tail: 35–40cm (13.8–15.7in)
SEXUAL MATURITY	2 years
MATING SEASON	February to March; non-seasonal in southern range
GESTATION PERIOD	62–63 days
NUMBER OF YOUNG	Usually 2
BIRTH INTERVAL	1 year
TYPICAL DIET	Mainly fish, but will also take crustaceans, shellfish, snails, beetles, amphibians, and small mammals
LIFESPAN	8 years in wild; up to 12 years in captivity

NOSTRILS
Located high on the nose, the otter's nostrils allow it to breathe while most of its body remains submerged. The nostrils close automatically when the otter dives.

COAT
The otter has two types of fur. An outer layer of thick guard-hairs is coated with oil to repel water, and an under layer of short, dense fur provides insulation in cold water.

WEBBED FEET
All four feet are webbed, to give forward thrust when the otter swims. The large hindfeet, which have proportionately more webbing, provide most of the power.

WHISKERS
The sensitive whiskers pick up underwater vibrations, such as those made by the movement of a fish.

TEETH
Long, sharp canines are used to grab slippery fish, while the carnassials (premolars) are used to slice through bone and flesh.

SPRAINT
Spraint — an otter's droppings — is strongly scented with musk. Since the spraint is a message to other otters, it is usually deposited in a conspicuous place.

TAIL
More than half as long as the body, the robust tail provides both propulsion and steering when the otter is swimming. It also acts as a prop when the otter stands on its hindlegs.

CREATURE COMPARISONS

The Eurasian otter is dwarfed by the giant otter, a native of the northern and central river systems of South America. The largest of all otters, although second to the sea otter in weight, the giant otter is almost twice as long as the Eurasian otter.

Like other otter species, the giant otter is threatened by habitat disturbance and it is also hunted for its skin, which is highly prized on the world fur market. The giant otter is protected by conservation laws in some South American countries, but the laws are difficult to enforce in the remote areas of its range.

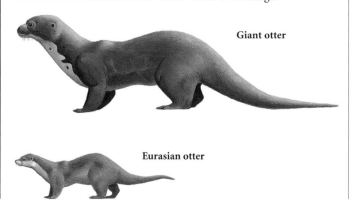

Giant otter

Eurasian otter

WHERE IN THE WORLD?

Ranges from the British Isles in the west, eastwards through other parts of Europe, North Africa and much of Central and Southeast Asia.

RELATED SPECIES
There are probably eight other species of otter — the exact number is open to debate — in the family Mustelidae, which includes weasels and skunks. Scent plays an important role among Mustelids, especially in the case of the striped skunk (Mephitis mephitis) of North America.

• ORDER • *Carnivora* • FAMILY • *Mustelidae* • GENUS & SPECIES • *Martes martes*

EURASIAN PINE MARTEN

The size of a cat, the Eurasian pine marten has the lithe build of a dedicated hunter, and is adept at climbing, sprinting and slipping ferret-like into holes.

KEY FEATURES

- A mainly nocturnal predator that hunts down small mammals and birds, storing any excess prey in grisly larders.

- Extremely agile both on the ground and in the upper branches of its forest home.

- Leads a solitary existence, seeking out companions only during the mating season, when noisy, vicious fights sometimes break out.

TEETH
Pointed canines and sharp carnassial teeth lining both jaws are used for stabbing into and slicing up prey.

COAT
The luxuriant winter coat is composed of long, silky hairs to insulate the pine marten from the cold. In spring the long hairs moult and a shorter, darker coat grows.

TAIL
The Eurasian pine marten's long, bushy tail aids balance when the animal is moving swiftly along slender branches. It also acts as a rudder when the marten leaps across gaps between the trees.

FEET
Large feet with long, partially retractable claws give the pine marten a sure grip as it scales tree-trunks and runs along branches.

GLANDS
Anal glands produce a strong musky scent. Rubbed on prominent objects, such as tree stumps, the scent is used to define a territory and so deter neighbours from trespassing.

VITAL STATISTICS

WEIGHT	800–1800g (28.2–63.5oz)
LENGTH	Head & Body: 45–58cm (17.7–22.8in) Tail: 16–28cm (6.3–11in)
SEXUAL MATURITY	2 years
MATING SEASON	July to August
GESTATION PERIOD	230–275 days
NUMBER OF YOUNG	2 to 8, but usually 3 to 5
BIRTH INTERVAL	1 year
TYPICAL DIET	Small mammals, birds and birds' eggs, insects, fruit, honey and carrion
LIFESPAN	Up to 17 years

CREATURE COMPARISONS

The yellow-throated marten, Martes flavigula, of East and Southeast Asia matches the Eurasian pine marten in general appearance and in its remarkable agility in the trees. It is larger than its western cousin, growing to twice the weight. Its coat is also lighter and has a distinct yellow 'bib' from the chin to the chest.

A forest dweller like the Eurasian pine marten, the yellow-throated marten's daily life differs markedly. It is primarily active by day rather than by night, and is more sociable, often hunting in pairs or family groups. Although both animals have a broadly similar diet, the yellow-throated marten has been known to hunt prey as large as young musk deer.

Yellow-throated marten

Eurasian pine marten

WHERE IN THE WORLD?

Occurs across most of central and northern Europe westwards through Russia to western Siberia. Absent from most parts of Ireland, England and Wales, but more widespread in Scotland.

RELATED SPECIES

There are 8 species of marten in a single genus, **Martes**, within the family Mustelidae. Along with the Eurasian pine marten these are: the American pine marten, the Japanese marten, the beech marten, the Nilgiri marten, the yellow-throated marten, the sable and the fisher.

• **ORDER** • *Carnivora* • **FAMILY** • *Mustelidae* • **GENUS & SPECIES** • *Martes pennanti*

FISHER

The fisher may be a small predator but it is highly agile and nimble, equipped to scale trees to find prey and to dash in pursuit on the ground.

KEY FEATURES

- One of the few creatures that is daring enough, and skilled enough, to attack and kill a porcupine.
- Lives in coniferous forests and forages for food in the trees as well as on the ground.
- Female delays the implantation of the fertilized eggs so that her young are born in the summer months.

TEETH
Razor-sharp teeth in powerful jaws can despatch a hare with one bite to the neck.

BODY COLOUR
Most fishers are dark brown to blackish on the back with a lighter-coloured throat patch. Some individuals have a light brown, almost creamy, underside with white spots. Male and female are similarly coloured.

EARS
The short, rounded ears help limit heat loss.

FUR
A dense, warm layer of fur underlies a longer outer coat.

PAWS
The large paws on both the forelegs and hindlegs have hairy soles and sharp, semi-retractile claws for climbing and hunting.

HINDFEET
The hindfeet can swivel backwards, allowing the fisher to grip as it descends trees.

TAIL
The fisher's long, bushy tail is used as a balance when negotiating branches and jumping from tree to tree.

VITAL STATISTICS

WEIGHT	Males up to 5.5kg (12.1lb); females up to 3.2kg (7lb)
LENGTH	Head & Body: Up to 75cm (29.5in) Tail: Up to 43cm (16.9in)
SEXUAL MATURITY	1–2 years
MATING SEASON	March to May
GESTATION PERIOD	11–12 months (including 9–10 months delayed implantation
NUMBER OF YOUNG	1 to 6
BIRTH INTERVAL	1 year
TYPICAL DIET	Small and medium-sized mammals, such as rodents and hares; also birds, carrion, occasional fish
LIFESPAN	10–15 years

CREATURE COMPARISONS

The fisher is the largest and most heavily built of the martens, with males reaching over 5kg (11lb). The yellow-throated marten (Martes flavigula) is one of the larger martens but is lighter than the fisher, reaching a maximum of about 3kg (6.6lb). Both hunt in the trees and on the ground, but the fisher is solitary, while the yellow-throated marten may hunt in pairs or groups.

Like the fisher, the yellow-throated marten hunts birds, small mammals and carrion, but also eats frogs, insects, honey and fruit. In the northern part of its range, mainly in the mountain forests of Southeast Asia, the yellow-necked marten preys on the diminutive musk deer.

Fisher

Yellow-throated marten

WHERE IN THE WORLD?

Found in the forests of Canada, from British Columbia in the west eastwards to Quebec. Also occurs in parts of the northern USA.

RELATED SPECIES

There are 8 species of marten in the genus **Martes**, including the American marten, **Martes americana**, or American pine marten. As members of the family **Mustelidae**, their relations include weasels and otters.

• **ORDER** • *Carnivora* • **FAMILY** • *Mustelidae* • **GENUS & SPECIES** • *Meles meles*

EURASIAN BADGER

KEY FEATURES

- A social animal that lives in well defined groups of a dozen or more individuals.
- Digs a complex burrow system, or sett, consisting of numerous tunnels and chambers.
- Rests in the sett during the daylight hours, emerging at night to forage in its forest abode.
- Spends days on end underground in winter.

VITAL STATISTICS

WEIGHT	10–16kg (22–35.3lb)
LENGTH	Head & Body: 56–90cm (22–35.4in) Tail: 12–20cm (4.7–7.9in)
SEXUAL MATURITY	1 year
MATING SEASON	All year
GESTATION PERIOD	6–8 weeks, not including variable delayed implantation
NUMBER OF YOUNG	2 to 6, but usually 3 or 4
BIRTH INTERVAL	1 year
TYPICAL DIET	Earthworms, small mammals, insects, fruit, plants, cereals and roots
LIFESPAN	7–10 years

A muscular, thick-set body and powerful claws help make the Eurasian badger an expert tunneller — and a formidable opponent if cornered.

SKULL
The large skull houses massive jaw muscles, which give the badger a powerful bite. Teeth are deeply rooted and sharp, although the molars wear down as the badger ages.

COAT
Thicker in winter than in summer, a coarse grizzled coat of longer hair lies on top of finer, dense underfur.

SCENT GLANDS
The anal and subcaudal glands (underneath the tail) are used to scent mark territory, and other badgers in a colony, with a musky secretion.

MAMMAE
Female Eurasian badgers have two sets of mammae each with three nipples (one set shown right).

CLAWS
Each foot has five strong, curved claws adapted for digging. The claws on the forefeet are twice as long as those on the hindfeet and are also used for defence.

CREATURE COMPARISONS

Lighter in colour and slightly smaller than the Eurasian badger, the American badger, Taxidea taxus, is found from southwest Canada and the northern regions of the central United States south to Mexico. Lacking the striking black-and-white facial pattern that makes the Eurasian badger so distinctive, its head is instead emblazoned with a thin white stripe that runs down to its shoulders. The American badger also has a less rounded body, covered with long, shaggy hair.

Eurasian badger

American badger

WHERE IN THE WORLD?

Occurs from Britain and Ireland eastwards across much of Europe, Russia and central Asia to northern China and Japan.
South of range bounded by Jordan, Saudi Arabia and Pakistan, east to southern China.

RELATED SPECIES

There are nine species of badger in the family Mustelidae, which also includes otters, skunks and weasels. The hog badger, Aconyx collaris, is named after its flexible, pig-like snout, with which it searches for food in the undergrowth of forests in Southeast Asia and China.

• ORDER • *Carnivora* **• FAMILY •** *Mustelidae* **• GENUS & SPECIES •** *Mellivora capensis*

RATEL

KEY FEATURES

- Can defend itself against almost any predator, including lions, with a ferocity that belies its size.

- Able to manoeuvre within its loose, tough skin to turn aggressively back on an attacker.

- Forms a partnership with an African bird in order to locate beehives, which it raids for honey and larvae.

VITAL STATISTICS

WEIGHT	7–13kg (15.4–28.7lb)
LENGTH	Head & Body: 60–77cm (23.6–30.31in) Tail: 20–30cm (7.9–11.8in)
SHOULDER HEIGHT	25–30cm (9.8–11.8in)
SEXUAL MATURITY	Unknown
MATING SEASON	All year in parts; autumnal peak in other areas
GESTATION PERIOD	About 6 months
NUMBER OF YOUNG	1 to 4, usually 2
BIRTH INTERVAL	Unknown
TYPICAL DIET	Insects, small mammals, reptiles, fish, honey, fruit
LIFESPAN	Up to 26 years in captivity; unkown in wild

A fearless, fearsome fighter, the ratel is armed with sharp teeth and claws and protected by a tough hide that is impervious to the fangs of a cobra.

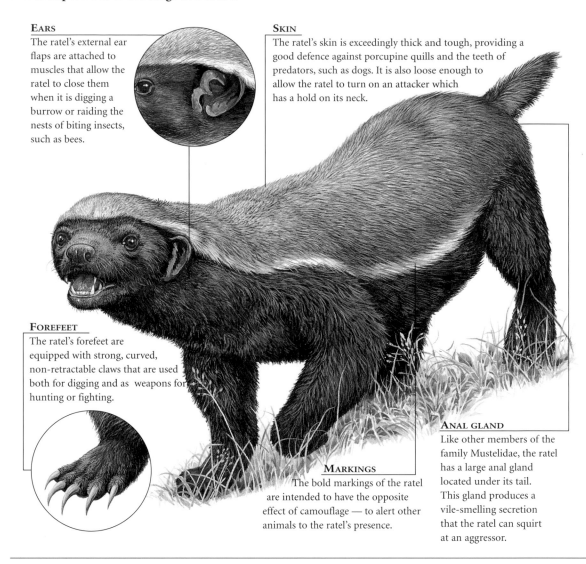

EARS
The ratel's external ear flaps are attached to muscles that allow the ratel to close them when it is digging a burrow or raiding the nests of biting insects, such as bees.

SKIN
The ratel's skin is exceedingly thick and tough, providing a good defence against porcupine quills and the teeth of predators, such as dogs. It is also loose enough to allow the ratel to turn on an attacker which has a hold on its neck.

FOREFEET
The ratel's forefeet are equipped with strong, curved, non-retractable claws that are used both for digging and as weapons for hunting or fighting.

MARKINGS
The bold markings of the ratel are intended to have the opposite effect of camouflage — to alert other animals to the ratel's presence.

ANAL GLAND
Like other members of the family Mustelidae, the ratel has a large anal gland located under its tail. This gland produces a vile-smelling secretion that the ratel can squirt at an aggressor.

CREATURE COMPARISONS

The stink badger (Mydaus javanensis), a native of Sumatra, Java, Borneo and the Natuna Islands, bears a remarkable resemblance to its relative the ratel in both overall shape and colouration. It is, however, about half the size of the ratel with a head and body length of 37–51cm (14.6–20.1in).

The stink badger is a montane species, often reported at elevations of 2100m (6890ft) or more. Like the ratel, the stink badger is nocturnal, emerging from its burrow each evening to feed on worms, insects and small animals. The stink badger's name refers to its anal secretions, which are as powerful as those of the skunk and can temporarily blind an attacker.

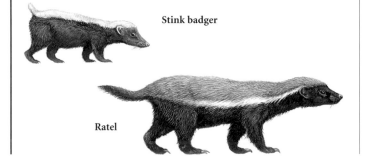

Stink badger

Ratel

WHERE IN THE WORLD?

Most numerous on African savannah grassland but ranges from Morocco to the Cape and as far east as India, Nepal and the southern borders of Russia.

RELATED SPECIES

The ratel is the only species in the genus Mellivora. It is, however, one of 65 species in the family Mustelidae, which includes weasels, badgers, skunks and otters. The smallest member of the family is the least weasel, Mustela nivalis, which has a head and body length of 11–26cm (4.3–10.6in) and is approximately a quarter of the size of the largest mustelids — the otters in the genera Pteronura and Enhydra, which grow to a length of 1m or more.

STRIPED SKUNK

• ORDER • *Carnivora* • FAMILY • *Mustelidae* • GENUS & SPECIES • *Mephitis mephitis*

With its thick, black fur streaked with bands of white, the striped skunk is a walking warning sign, telling other animals to keep away.

KEY FEATURES

- A boldly patterned relative of badgers and weasels that lives on a broad range of foods, from small mammals to seeds and fruit.
- Spends the day hidden in a burrow or among vegetation before emerging at night to feed.
- Defends itself with a spray of powerful-smelling musk, which burns attackers' eyes and induces nausea.

VITAL STATISTICS

WEIGHT	3–6kg (6.6–13.2lb)
LENGTH	Head & Body: 28–38cm (11–15in) Tail: 19–43cm (7.5–16.9in)
SEXUAL MATURITY	1 year
MATING SEASON	February to April
GESTATION PERIOD	59–77 days
NUMBER OF YOUNG	1 to 10, usually 4
BIRTH INTERVAL	1 year
TYPICAL DIET	Rodents and other small vertebrates; insects, fruit, seeds and green vegetation
LIFESPAN	Up to 13 years; 6 years on average

TEETH
The canines and carnassials are powerful enough to kill small animals. Overall, however, the skunk's teeth reflect its omnivorous nature and are also adapted for grinding up fruit and seeds.

MUSK GLANDS
If attacked, the skunk sprays its assailant with jets of fetid, oily musk from two anal glands. As well as its offensive odour, the musk causes intense pain and temporary blindness if sprayed into the eyes.

FEET
The feet have five toes, each of which ends in a sharp, non-retractile claw. The claws are used for digging up buried insects.

TAIL
The tail is raised at the first sign of danger, and its hairs spread out to signal the skunk's agitation. This is usually enough to deter most predators from attacking.

FUR
Thick fur keeps the skunk warm and grows particularly luxuriantly in the colder northern parts of its range.

CREATURE COMPARISONS

Found in Mexico and southwestern USA, the hog-nosed skunk (Conepatus mesoleucus) is similar in size to its more widespread relative, the striped skunk. However, it is easily distinguished by its pure, silver-white crown, back and tail. Its long, hairless muzzle also helps to differentiate it from the other skunk species that share its range, and is an adaptation for sniffing out and rooting up the ground- and soil-living insects that are its main food. Long claws on its forepaws also help it dig up its prey. As well as insects, the hog-nosed skunk relishes spiders, snails, worms, lizards, small mammals and, like the striped skunk, also consumes vegetation.

Hog-nosed skunk

Striped skunk

WHERE IN THE WORLD?

Distributed from southern Canada through the USA to northern Mexico. Absent from eastern California and western Arizona.

RELATED SPECIES

The striped skunk shares its genus with the hooded skunk. There are also 2 species of spotted skunk and 5 species of hog-nosed skunk, including the Patagonian skunk, Conepatus humboldtii. Skunks belong to the family Mustelidae.

• ORDER • *Carnivora* • FAMILY • *Mustelidae* • GENUS & SPECIES • *Mustela erminea*

STOAT

Long, lean and short-legged, the stoat's sinuous body allows it to pursue its prey deep into underground burrow systems.

KEY FEATURES

- Voracious predator that is able to catch and kill prey very much larger than itself.
- Black-tipped tail distinguishes it from similar-looking relatives, such as the weasel and polecat.
- In the far north, changes its largely brown summer coat for a white one — known as ermine — in winter.

WINTER WHITE
In northern parts of its range, the stoat moults its summer coat to white between October and November and retains this until the following April or May.

TEETH
The stoat has 34 teeth set in a long triangular skull that anchors powerful jaw and neck muscles. The canines are sharp for stabbing and the upper carnassials (slicing teeth) are pointed and sharp edged.

SPINE
The long, very flexible spine along with the short legs give the stoat its distinctive gait — known as the 'marten run'. It pushes off with the hindfeet, stretching its spine, lands on its forefeet and quickly brings its hindfeet forward again by arching its spine into a tight loop.

FOOT
Each foot has five toes bearing long, sharp claws, which are used mainly for digging. The hindfeet are much larger than the forefeet. The legs are short, enabling the stoat to move easily in confined spaces.

COAT
The upperparts are a rich chestnut brown while the bib and belly are a creamy white. In the southern parts of its range, the stoat wears these colours all year.

VITAL STATISTICS

WEIGHT	42–365g (1.5–12.9oz)
LENGTH	Head & Body: 17–33cm (6.7–13in) Tail: 4–12cm (1.6–4.7in)
SEXUAL MATURITY	Males 12 months; females about 2 months
MATING SEASON	Late spring to midsummer
GESTATION PERIOD	About 11 months, including delayed implantation lasting 9–10 months
NUMBER OF YOUNG	3 to 18; average 6 to 9
BIRTH INTERVAL	1 year
TYPICAL DIET	Rabbits, rodents, birds, eggs, insects amphibians
LIFESPAN	About 2 years

CREATURE COMPARISONS

The stoat and its relation the European polecat (Mustela putorius) share many features typical of their family, although the polecat is larger at 21–46cm (8.3–18.1in) and is distinguished by its face mask and white-tipped ears. The polecat's year-round coat is much darker than the stoat's summer outfit, ranging from dark brown to almost black. The habits of both animals are generally similar except that the European polecat is exclusively nocturnal while the stoat often hunts during the day.

As the ancestor of the domestic ferret (M. p. furi), the polecat breeds freely with escaped ferrets and the hybrids that result show an enormous variety of colours and markings.

Stoat

European polecat

WHERE IN THE WORLD?

Widespread in Canada, many Arctic islands and northwestern USA. Also across Europe and Asia from Ireland in the west, east to the Bering Sea.

RELATED SPECIES

The stoat belongs to the genus Mustela, which contains 17 species and includes 10 species of weasel, 3 species of mink, 2 species of polecat and the black-footed ferret. Mustela falls within the family Mustelidae, which has 65 species distributed in 23 genera. The stoat's relations in this family include the wolverine, badgers, martens, skunks and otters. All mustelids are small- to medium-sized animals with long bodies and short legs.

With the physique of a pipe-cleaner and a set of teeth designed for efficient butchery, the tiny weasel is one of the deadliest predators for its size.

KEY FEATURES

- The smallest living carnivore, able to kill an animal three times its own bodyweight.
- Extremely adaptable, living in a variety of habitats across a large range.
- Burns energy fast to maintain its bodyheat, so cannot go more than a day without food.

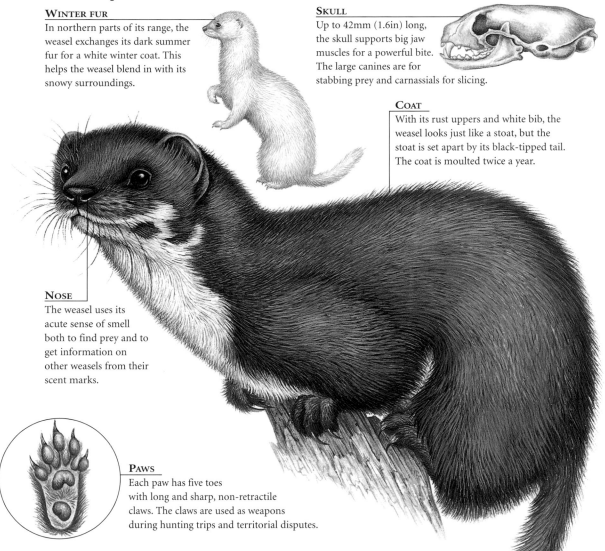

WINTER FUR
In northern parts of its range, the weasel exchanges its dark summer fur for a white winter coat. This helps the weasel blend in with its snowy surroundings.

SKULL
Up to 42mm (1.6in) long, the skull supports big jaw muscles for a powerful bite. The large canines are for stabbing prey and carnassials for slicing.

COAT
With its rust uppers and white bib, the weasel looks just like a stoat, but the stoat is set apart by its black-tipped tail. The coat is moulted twice a year.

NOSE
The weasel uses its acute sense of smell both to find prey and to get information on other weasels from their scent marks.

PAWS
Each paw has five toes with long and sharp, non-retractile claws. The claws are used as weapons during hunting trips and territorial disputes.

VITAL STATISTICS

WEIGHT	Male 50–250g (1.8–8.8oz); female 25–125g (0.6oz–4.4oz)
LENGTH	Head & Body: 11–26cm (4.3–10.2in) Tail: 17–78mm (0.7–3.1in)
SEXUAL MATURITY	3–4 months
MATING SEASON	Spring and summer
GESTATION PERIOD	35–37 days
NUMBER OF YOUNG	3 to 10
BIRTH INTERVAL	Usually 1, but sometimes 2 litters a year
TYPICAL DIET	Mainly small rodents, but occasionally birds, frogs, eggs and lizards
LIFESPAN	About 1 year

CREATURE COMPARISONS

Whereas the weasel is found on four continents, the Patagonian weasel (Lyncodon patagonicus) is restricted to the pampas (temperate grasslands) of Chile and Argentina. It is much larger than its cosmopolitan relative, with a head-and-body length of 30–35cm (11.8–13.8in). Both species have the typical bodyplan of the family Mustelidae. The weasel has a dot of colour below either ear, whereas the Patagonian weasel can be identified by a white 'bandanna' that extends over its ears.

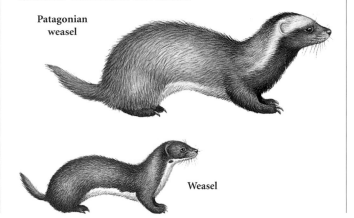

Patagonian weasel

Weasel

WHERE IN THE WORLD?

Found throughout Europe (except Ireland), North Africa, Asia, Siberia and the Far East. Also occurs from Alaska and Canada south into the USA.

RELATED SPECIES

The weasel is 1 of 17 species in the genus Mustela, which includes the stoat, minks, ferrets and polecats. The stoat, Mustela erminea, can hunt in rabbit holes, but grows too large to raid the small rodent burrows visited by the weasel.

• **ORDER** • *Carnivora* • **FAMILY** • *Mustelidae* • **GENUS & SPECIES** • *Mustela putorius*

EUROPEAN POLECAT

The sinuous, low-slung polecat is built like an overgrown weasel, and has the same deadly blend of speed, agility, enterprise and giant-killing ferocity.

KEY FEATURES

- A larger relative of the weasel that hunts by night for mice, rats and rabbits, killing them with a single bite.
- Has a notoriously powerful scent, which it can spray from its anal glands to defend itself, like a skunk.
- Wiped out by gamekeepers in England and Scotland, but now spreading again from its Welsh strongholds.

SKULL
The elongated skull is equipped with powerful jaws that are armed with a battery of sharp teeth for killing and butchering prey. The canines pierce like daggers, while the molars shear like scissors through skin and flesh.

COAT
The polecat is kept warm by a thick layer of cream-coloured underfur, protected by long, dark guard hairs. As it moves, the pale underfur shows through.

KITTEN
A baby polecat is helpless at birth, but soon grows a protective coat of silky hair. It learns to hunt by following its mother, but its urge to kill is instinctive.

SCENT GLANDS
Pea-sized anal glands produce a pungent, persistent scent, used mainly for marking the borders of a territory.

HINDFEET
Sharp, non-retractaile claws on the long hindfeet give good grip as the polecat works its way over rocks and fallen logs in search of prey.

MASK
The dark mask may be a signal to other predators to stay clear, warning them of the polecat's chemical defences.

VITAL STATISTICS

WEIGHT	Female 450–800g (15.9–28.2oz); male 800–1500g (28.2–52.9oz)
LENGTH	Head & Body: Female 21–38cm (8.3–15in); male 30–46cm (11.8–18.1in) Tail: Female 7–14cm (2.7–5.5in); male 9–11cm (3.5–4.3in)
SEXUAL MATURITY	9–12 months
MATING SEASON	March–May
GESTATION PERIOD	40–43 days
NUMBER OF YOUNG	2 to 12, usually 3 to 7
BIRTH INTERVAL	1 year
TYPICAL DIET	Small mammals, birds, fish, frogs, lizards
LIFESPAN	Up to 6 years

CREATURE COMPARISONS

On the arid steppes of central Asia the European polecat is replaced by the marbled polecat (Vormela peregusna), a smaller but similar animal that sports an elegant coat of pale fur blotched with chocolate-brown. In the mating season, male marbled polecats become more vividly coloured as they become increasingly excited, and in any encounter between two rivals the male with the boldest colours always wins. Like its European relative, the marbled polecat is a specialist at hunting small mammals, often pursuing them into their burrows like a poacher's ferret.

Marbled polecat

European polecat

WHERE IN THE WORLD?

Found throughout most of Europe, except Greece, the former Yugoslavia and most of Britain. Its range extends east to the Urals and north to southern Scandinavia.

RELATED SPECIES

The European polecat's closest relative is the domestic ferret, Mustela furo. European polecats and escaped ferrets often breed to produce fertile hybrids. The 17 species in the genus Mustela include several polecats, minks and the rare black-footed ferret, M. nigripes, of the USA.

• ORDER • *Carnivora* **• FAMILY •** *Mustelidae* **• GENUS & SPECIES •** *Mustela vison*

AMERICAN MINK

A swift runner and an agile swimmer, the mink is a deadly hunter, using its sharp teeth and claws to tackle surprisingly large prey.

KEY FEATURES

- An opportunistic hunter that resembles a cross between a small otter and a weasel.
- Inhabits a wide variety of aquatic habitats, including coastal regions.
- Colonies of escaped animals thrive in countries where the animal is farmed for its sleek, lustrous fur.

VITAL STATISTICS

WEIGHT	Female 570–1090g (20.1–38.4oz); male 680–1350g (23.9–47.6oz)
LENGTH	Head & Body: 30–43cm (11.8–16.9in) Tail: 18–23cm (7.1–9in)
SEXUAL MATURITY	Female 12 months; male 18 months
MATING SEASON	February–March
GESTATION PERIOD	27–33 days
NUMBER OF YOUNG	4 to 6
BIRTH INTERVAL	1 year
TYPICAL DIET	Fish, mammals, birds, crayfish
LIFESPAN	12 years in captivity

WINTER COAT
In the extreme north of its range, the mink grows a white coat in winter to help it blend in with snow-covered ground.

TEETH
The long canines are vital for holding and killing prey. Behind them are carnassials for shearing flesh into manageable pieces.

FUR
Long guard hairs protect the soft underfur from water. The thick black, or occasionally white, winter coat is shed in spring.

TAIL
The sturdy, furred tail acts as a rudder as the mink swims underwater after prey such as muskrats.

HINDFOOT
Partial webbing on the hindfeet helps the mink when swimming. Sharp claws enable the small hunter to grasp slippery prey firmly.

CREATURE COMPARISONS

A close relative of the American mink, and one that shares much of its natural range in North America, is the long-tailed weasel (*Mustela freneta*). This predator shares the same basic bodyshape of the mink but is far smaller and has paler brown fur, yellowish-white underparts and a less bushy tail. It hunts similar prey to that of its relative, such as small mammals and birds and their eggs, and searches for these in fields and woods near water. Like the mink, the long-tailed weasel grows a white coat in winter in the north of its range, which has led to it being extensively targeted by fur hunters.

American mink

Long-tailed weasel

WHERE IN THE WORLD?

Native to North America from the Gulf of Mexico north to Alaska and Labrador. Feral mink have become established in Iceland, Ireland, Scandinavia, Spain, Britain, the Netherlands and Russia.

RELATED SPECIES

The American mink belongs to the genus Mustela, which includes other small, sinuous predators, such as stoats, weasels and polecats, and includes the smallest of all predatory mammals, the least weasel, M. nivalis. Mustela is 1 of 26 genera, containing a total of 65 species, in the family Mustelidae. Mustelids, which also include otters, badgers, skunks and the wolverine, are placed within the order Carnivora.

• ORDER • *Carnivora* • FAMILY • *Mustelidae* • GENUS & SPECIES • *Pteronura brasiliensis*

GIANT OTTER

The giant otter's sleek, torpedo-shaped body, strongly webbed feet and muscular tail help it surge forwards after fleeing prey.

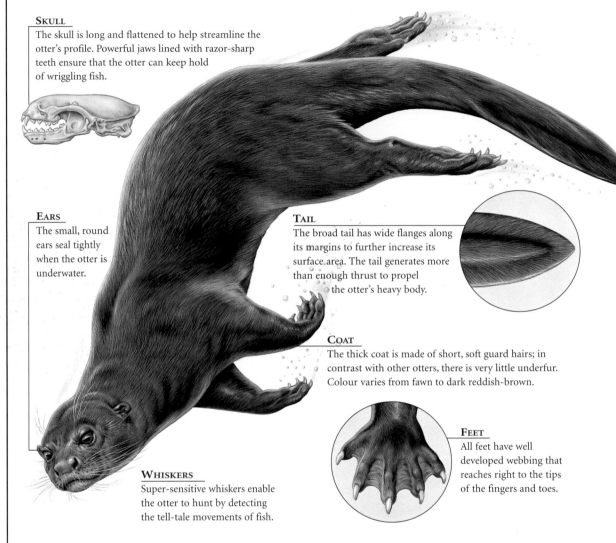

SKULL
The skull is long and flattened to help streamline the otter's profile. Powerful jaws lined with razor-sharp teeth ensure that the otter can keep hold of wriggling fish.

EARS
The small, round ears seal tightly when the otter is underwater.

TAIL
The broad tail has wide flanges along its margins to further increase its surface area. The tail generates more than enough thrust to propel the otter's heavy body.

COAT
The thick coat is made of short, soft guard hairs; in contrast with other otters, there is very little underfur. Colour varies from fawn to dark reddish-brown.

FEET
All feet have well developed webbing that reaches right to the tips of the fingers and toes.

WHISKERS
Super-sensitive whiskers enable the otter to hunt by detecting the tell-tale movements of fish.

KEY FEATURES

- A muscular heavyweight among otters and an expert hunter of freshwater fish.
- Swims strongly, using its broad tail and webbed feet.
- Lives in large but close-knit family groups.
- Listed as threatened by the IUCN (World Conservation Union).

VITAL STATISTICS

WEIGHT	Male 26–32kg (57.3–70.5lb); female 22–26kg (48.5–57.3lb)
LENGTH	Head & Body: Male 1–1.2m (3ft 3in–3ft 9in); female 0.9–1.1m (2ft 9in–3ft 6in) Tail: Male 50–60cm (19.7–23.6in); female 45–50cm (17.7–19.7in)
SEXUAL MATURITY	2 years
MATING SEASON	All year
GESTATION PERIOD	52–79 days
NUMBER OF YOUNG	1 to 5, but usually 2
BIRTH INTERVAL	9 months
TYPICAL DIET	Fish, crabs, frogs. Also snakes and caimans
LIFESPAN	Unknown

CREATURE COMPARISONS

Although they occupy widely separated ranges, the world's otters all have a basic bodyplan optimized for aquatic hunting, and differ very little other than in size. One of the more subtle ways in which they have diversified lies in the appearance of their nose-pads.

The giant otter is the only species with a fully furred nose-pad. The spot-necked otter (Hydrictis maculicollis) of Africa resembles its larger South American relative but has a hairless, narrow nose-pad — in addition to creamy blotches on the throat and neck. The North American river otter (Lutra canadensis) has a large, naked nose-pad resembling the ace of spades. The Eurasian river otter (L. lutra, not pictured) has a narrow pad with a central peak.

Spot-necked otter

Giant otter

River otter

WHERE IN THE WORLD?

Lives in South America, where it is widespread along the waterways of the Orinoco, Amazon and La Plata river basins. Also found in the rivers of Guyana, French Guiana and Surinam.

RELATED SPECIES

The giant otter is the sole member of its genus, Pteronura. 12 other species occupy 3 more genera in the subfamily Lutrinae, including the closely related African spot-necked otter and the European river otter. Most otters are fish-eaters. They all belong to the family Mustelidae, which also includes the land-bound weasels, martens, polecats, minks, badgers, grisons and skunks. Mustelids belong to the order Carnivora.

SPOTTED SKUNK

• ORDER • *Carnivora* • FAMILY • *Mustelidae* • GENUS & SPECIES • *Spilogale putorius*

KEY FEATURES

- Defends itself with a pungent, sulphurous liquid sprayed from its anal glands.
- Striking coat colouration warns larger predators not to attack it.
- Hides away in a den by day, coming out at night to hunt under the cover of darkness.

VITAL STATISTICS

WEIGHT	227–900g (8–31.7oz)
LENGTH	Head & Body: 35.5–40.5cm (14–15.9in) Tail 18–23cm (7.1–9in)
SEXUAL MATURITY	11 months
MATING SEASON	September to October in the west of its range; March to April in the east
GESTATION PERIOD	Actual gestation about 50–65 days; longer with delayed implantation
NUMBER OF YOUNG	2 to 9, usually 3 to 6
BIRTH INTERVAL	2 years
TYPICAL DIET	Vegetation, insects, small mammals
LIFESPAN	Up to 10 years in captivity

The skunk's bold black-and-white markings inform other animals that it is not an easy target. Would-be attackers ignore the warning at their peril!

EYES
Forward-facing eyes give the spotted skunk good binocular vision, a feature typical of carnivores. Binocular vision helps an animal to judge distances.

TAIL
The tail is fluffed up and erected during defensive and courtship displays. The long white hairs flag a 'keep away' warning message to other predators.

TEETH
The spotted skunk has proportionally larger carnassial teeth than other skunks: carnassials are used to slice through flesh.

COAT
Each skunk has a unique coat pattern, which helps individuals recognize each other. The pattern also helps predators to spot, and avoid, the skunk.

ANAL GLANDS
Two glands (1) in the anal tract (2) produce the spray fluid. When a skunk sprays, the glands are squeezed, and the fluid shoots out through nozzle-like openings.

CREATURE COMPARISONS

The common, or striped, skunk is larger than the spotted skunk. The spotted skunk is the more active hunter, while the striped skunk prefers a wider diet, including insects, larvae and plant matter. The striped skunk has larger claws (for digging up grubs) and smaller carnassial teeth than its smaller relative.

Spotted skunk   Striped skunk

WHERE IN THE WORLD?

Found in North and Central America, from British Columbia in the north, through most of the USA and Mexico, to Costa Rica in the south.

RELATED SPECIES

Skunks are related to weasels, badgers and otters. The nine skunk species, all found in the Americas, comprise two species of spotted skunk, five species of hog-nosed skunk, and the hooded skunk and striped skunk, Mephitis mephitis.

• **ORDER** • *Carnivora* • **FAMILY** • *Mustelidae* • **GENUS & SPECIES** • *Taxidea taxus*

AMERICAN BADGER

With fearsome claws and a bulldog grip, the American badger is a dangerous enemy for the burrow-dwelling animals of the prairies and deserts.

KEY FEATURES

- A burrowing heavyweight that specializes in hunting prairie dogs and ground squirrels.
- More carnivorous than the Eurasian badger, and probably only a distant relative.
- Driven from the prairies by the plough, it is becoming a common sight in the suburbs.

EARS
The badger's ears are short and rounded, so they are no hindrance underground. Its hearing is not outstanding, but probably a lot better than ours.

FUR
The soft undercoat is protected by long, coarse guard hairs that shed the soil easily and prevent the fur from becoming matted.

TEETH
The American badger has broad cheek teeth for grinding tough food, but not as broad as those of the omnivorous badgers of Africa and Eurasia.

CLAWS
The long, powerful claws on the forefeet make very effective shovels for burrowing, and also serve as useful weapons during territorial disputes.

TAIL
The well furred tail has no obvious function. Its short length is typical of burrowing mammals.

VITAL STATISTICS

WEIGHT	4–12kg (8.8–26.5lb)
LENGTH	Head & Body: Male 52–72cm (20.5–28.3in); female 42–64cm (16.5–25.2in) Tail: 10–15cm (3.9–5.9in)
SEXUAL MATURITY	5–12 months
MATING SEASON	August to September
GESTATION PERIOD	Up to 8 months (including delayed implantation)
NUMBER OF YOUNG	1 to 5, usually 2
BIRTH INTERVAL	1 year
TYPICAL DIET	Small mammals, lizards, snakes, insects and carrion
LIFESPAN	Up to 20 years

CREATURE COMPARISONS

The American badger is a heavyweight compared to the Chinese ferret badger (*Melogale moschata*), a relatively slender creature resembling a polecat which is light and agile enough to climb trees.

Like other Old World badgers, the ferret badger has a broad diet, feeding on fruit and nuts as well as insects, worms and other small animals. It is most active at night, lying concealed in a burrow or crevice by day, and is notorious for the pungent scent released by its anal glands.

Chinese ferret badger

American badger

WHERE IN THE WORLD?

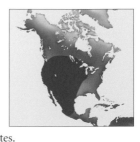

Has a wide range extending from southwest Canada, through the central and western states of the USA to central Mexico. Absent from the eastern American states.

RELATED SPECIES

The sole species in its genus, the American badger is probably only distantly related to the other 7 badgers that make up the subfamily Melinae. This subfamily is 1 of 5 in the weasel family Mustelidae, which consists of the badgers, honey badger, weasels, otters and skunks.
The Mustelidae is 1 of 7 families in the order Carnivora, which also includes the dogs, cats, bears, hyenas, mongooses and civets.

•ORDER • *Carnivora* •FAMILY • *Procyonidae* •GENUS & SPECIES • *Ailurus fulgens*

Something of a zoological puzzle, the small, compact red panda shares characteristics of two families: the raccoons and the bears.

JAW
The red panda has strong jaw muscles to help it chew bamboo. Like most members of the order Carnivora it has large canines for tearing meat, but its molar teeth are flattened for grinding vegetation.

EARS
Large ears suggest that hearing is well developed and is used to detect predators, such as leopards.

FEET
Hairy soles and semi-retractile claws make the red panda an adept climber. Each forepaw also has an elongated wrist bone, which forms a horny pad that is used as a 'thumb' to grasp vegetation.

TAIL
The long, bushy tail is not prehensile (capable of grasping), but is used as a balancing aid when the red panda climbs in the trees.

KEY FEATURES

· Lives a solitary life high in the Himalayas.

· Equipped with soft, dense fur to survive the cold winter months of its high-altitude habitat.

· An agile climber, able to move quickly through trees.

· Its big namesake, the giant panda, was once placed in the same family but is now classed with the bears.

VITAL STATISTICS

WEIGHT	3–6kg (6.6–13.2lb)
LENGTH	Head & Body: 51–63cm (20.1–24.8in) Tail: 28–48cm
SEXUAL MATURITY	18–20 months
MATING SEASON	January to March
GESTATION PERIOD	90–145 days
NUMBER OF YOUNG	1 to 4, but usually 2
BIRTH INTERVAL	1 year
TYPICAL DIET	Mainly bamboo shoots, fruit, roots, acorns and grasses, but sometimes insects, eggs, nestlings and small rodents
LIFESPAN	Unknown in wild; Up to 14 years in captivity

CREATURE COMPARISONS

Members of the same family, the ringtail, or cacomistle (*Bassariscus astutus*), and the red panda have a similar bodyplan. However, the ringtail, which is found from southwestern Oregon and eastern Kansas south to Mexico, is about half the size of its relative. An able climber like the red panda, the ringtail occurs mainly in rocky areas, where it clambers over cliffs and ledges with great agility.

The biggest difference between these species lies in their diets. Whereas the red panda feeds mainly on plant matter, the ringtail is more predatory, seeking out lizards, small mammals and insects.

Red panda

Ringtail

WHERE IN THE WORLD?

Found in Nepal, Bhutan, northern Burma, southern Tibet and Yunnan and Sichuan provinces of China. May still occur in the Indian states of Sikkim and Assam.

RELATED SPECIES

The red panda belongs to the Procyonidae, or raccoon family, which is made up of 19 species in 7 genera and includes the olingo, *Bassaricyon gabbi*, and the kinkajou, *Potos flavus*. The giant panda was once part of the Procyonidae but is now placed in the bear family, Ursidae.

• **ORDER** • *Carnivora* • **FAMILY** • *Procyonidae* • **GENUS & SPECIES** • *Nasua nasua*

COATI

The powerful limbs, sharp claws and extremely long tail of the coati enable it to negotiate the tangled obstacle course of the rainforest.

KEY FEATURES

- Long-tailed, flexible-snouted relative of the raccoons, equally at home on the ground and in the trees.
- Forages during daylight hours and feasts on animals and plants from various levels of the forest.
- Females and young live in close-knit bands, admitting males for brief periods during the breeding season.

TAIL
The coati holds its tapering, banded tail out as a counterbalance when climbing. On the ground, its tail sways erect and aloft.

SNOUT
Extended and pointed, the coati's snout ends in a highly flexible and sensitive nose, perfect for poking in cavities and snuffling through leaf litter in search of edible morsels.

COAT
Thickly furred, the coati has dark brown or rust-coloured upperparts, with white patches around the throat and eyes.

HINDFOOT
The long, muscular hindlimbs provide most of the power for running and climbing. When scurrying down a trunk head-first, the coati brakes its descent by rotating its ankle backwards and then gripping with its claws.

VITAL STATISTICS

WEIGHT	3–6kg (6.6–13.2lb)
LENGTH	Head & Body: 40–67cm (15.7–26.4in) Tail: 32–69cm (12.6–27.2in)
SEXUAL MATURITY	2 years
MATING SEASON	Varies according to region
GESTATION PERIOD	77 days
NUMBER OF YOUNG	2 to 7
BIRTH INTERVAL	1 year
TYPICAL DIET	Invertebrates, fruit
LIFESPAN	7 years

CREATURE COMPARISONS

The bushy-tailed olingo (Bassaricyon gabbii) of Central America and northern South America shares some of its forest haunts with the coati, but it is more elusive and more confined to the treetops than its semi-arboreal cousin. Smaller in size and with no facial markings, the olingo has a slimmer body but slightly shorter limbs and a much shorter snout. Like the coati, its tail is banded and at least as long as its combined head and body length. Nocturnal, with large eyes giving superb vision, the olingo is by no means as sociable as the coati and usually lives alone or in pairs.

Coati

Olingo

WHERE IN THE WORLD?

Ranges through tropical and subtropical America, from the extreme southern USA to South America east of the Andes, as far as Uruguay and northeastern Argentina.

RELATED SPECIES

The genus Nasua also includes the Cozumel coati, N. nelsoni. A white-nosed subspecies of coati is sometimes described as a separate species: Nasua narica. There are 6 other genera in the raccoon family, Procyonidae, in the order Carnivora.

• ORDER • *Carnivora* • FAMILY • *Procyonidae* • GENUS & SPECIES • *Potos flavus*

KEY FEATURES

- Uses its prehensile tail like a fifth limb, wrapping it around branches to aid balance and as a safety device when climbing in the forest trees.

- Soft and cuddly-looking, but capable of inflicting serious wounds with its sharp canines.

- Equipped with a long, extensible tongue that is ideal for licking up and extracting food from difficult-to-reach places.

VITAL STATISTICS

WEIGHT	1.4–4.6kg (3.1–10.1lb)
LENGTH	Head & Body: 41–76cm (16.1–29.9in) Tail: 39–57cm (14.6–22.4in)
SHOULDER HEIGHT	Up to 25cm (9.8in)
SEXUAL MATURITY	Male 1.5 years; female 2 years and 3 months
MATING SEASON	Year round
GESTATION PERIOD	112–118 days
NUMBER OF YOUNG	1, rarely 2
BIRTH INTERVAL	1 year
TYPICAL DIET	Fruit, nectar, honey and insects
LIFESPAN	Over 23 years in captivity

The kinkajou gets another of its common names — honey bear — from the golden lustre of its dense, soft and woolly fur.

TONGUE
Nearly 12cm (5in) long, the slender tongue is used for licking up nectar, honey, fruit pulp and ants.

TAIL
The kinkajou uses its prehensile (grasping) tail as a fifth limb, to leave its forefeet free for selecting food. The tail also acts as a braking device when the kinkajou descends a tree head-first.

FOREFEET
The forefeet have sharp claws for gripping branches when climbing and can manipulate objects skilfully.

HINDFEET
Each hindfoot has five digits tipped with stout claws. The naked sole provides a firm grip on branches.

CREATURE COMPARISONS

The kinkajou shares the American tropics with several raccoon-like relatives. These include the mountain coati (*Nasuella olivacea*), which lives at altitudes of 2000–3000m (6562–9843ft) in the Andes of Venezuela, Colombia and Ecuador. It favours damp forests near the treeline and open mountain pastures. Several physical features distinguish the coati. A little smaller than the kinkajou, it has a markedly pointed snout, and its non-prehensile tail is boldly ringed. Unlike the kinkajou, the mountain coati is active by day, and it readily descends to forage on the ground for favourite foods, which include insects, fruit and small vertebrates.

Mountain coati

Kinkajou

WHERE IN THE WORLD?

Found in rainforests and woodland from southern Tamaulipas, in eastern Mexico, through Central America and south to the Mato Grosso of central Brazil.

RELATED SPECIES

The sole representative of the genus Potos, the kinkajou belongs to the raccoon family, Procyonidae, which contains 19 species in 7 genera. Members of this family have a wide diet, with long, sharp canine teeth and broad crushing molars. They are good tree climbers. Other members of the Procyonidae family include the coatimundi, *Nasua nasua*, found in South America and the red or lesser panda, *Ailurus fulgens*, of eastern Asia.

• ORDER • *Carnivora* • FAMILY • *Procyonidae* • GENUS & SPECIES • *Procyon lotor*

RACCOON

The raccoon's keen senses and dextrous hands, which equip it so well for its natural forested habitat, also suit it to life in the urban jungle.

KEY FEATURES

- One of the most adaptable of all North American mammals, its range and population have spread alongside human settlement.

- Uses its long-fingered, dextrous forepaws to prise lids from rubbish bins and open discarded food containers.

- Readily makes its den in haystacks, wood piles or even abandoned car and lorry bodies.

VITAL STATISTICS

WEIGHT	5.4–15.8kg (11.9–34.8lb)
LENGTH	Head & Body: 41–71cm (16.1–27.9in) Tail: 20–41cm (7.9–16.1in)
SHOULDER HEIGHT	23–30cm (9–11.8in)
SEXUAL MATURITY	1 year
MATING SEASON	February to March
GESTATION PERIOD	60–73 days
NUMBER OF YOUNG	3 to 6
BIRTH INTERVAL	1 year
TYPICAL DIET	Small mammals, eggs, frogs, insects, spiders, worms, crayfish, birds, fruit, nuts and scraps
LIFESPAN	Up to 16 years

TEETH
The raccoon's unspecialized incisor teeth, long canines, small, sharp premolars and broad, low-crowned molars are adaptations to an omnivorous diet.

FUR
The raccoon's dense, 'salt and pepper' fur enables it to thrive in cold climates. Soft but durable, the pelt is also prized by trappers and fur traders who fashion it into warm hats and coats.

MASK
The dark mask across the raccoon's pointed face probably helps to aid night vision: white fur would cause glare.

FEET
The raccoon can use the long fingers of its dextrous forepaws to empty cans and operate latches.

TAIL
The bushy tail provides balance when the raccoon climbs, and acts as a prop when the animal is sitting upright to feed.

CREATURE COMPARISONS

Members of the raccoon family display diverse feeding methods. While the raccoon uses its paws to gather almost any item, from berries to crayfish, the ring-tailed coati uses its paws and long, mobile snout to grub up insects and reptile eggs from the leaf litter in its South American forest home. The kinkajou, however, which lives in forests from Mexico to Brazil, uses its very long tongue for lapping flower nectar.

Raccoon

Coati

Kinkajou

WHERE IN THE WORLD?

Traditionally associated with wooded or swampy areas, its range has spread across southern Canada and mainland USA, and as far south as Panama. Can survive in open plains or in urban areas as long as there is water nearby.

RELATED SPECIES

The raccoon is one of seven species in the genus Procyon. The genus also includes the crab-eating raccoon of eastern South America, and five species found only on islands in the West Indies. The raccoon family, Procyonidae, includes the kinkajou, two species of ringtail or cacomistle, three species of coati and five species of olingo. All are found only in the Americas. Also included in the family is the red or lesser panda, Ailurus fulgens, of Asia.

• ORDER • *Carnivora* • FAMILY • *Ursidae* • GENUS & SPECIES • *Ailuropoda melanoleuca*

Isolated in its cool, damp, mountain strongholds, the giant panda has developed thick fur and a bulky build to help it conserve energy.

KEY FEATURES

- Newborn cub is 1/900th the weight of its mother.
- Spends almost all of its waking hours eating nutritionally poor bamboo leaves and stems.
- Acknowledged as a National Treasure by China in 1949, this very rare species is now the symbol of the World Wide Fund for Nature. It is listed as endangered by the IUCN (World Conservation Union).

VITAL STATISTICS

WEIGHT	100–125kg (220.5–275.6lb)
LENGTH	Head & Body: 1.22–1.52m (4–5ft) Tail: 12–15cm (4.7–5.9in)
SHOULDER HEIGHT	51–64cm (20.1–25.2in)
SEXUAL MATURITY	5–7 years
MATING SEASON	April to May
GESTATION PERIOD	90–165 days
NUMBER OF YOUNG	1 (1 usually dies if twins are born)
BIRTH INTERVAL	2 years
TYPICAL DIET	Almost exclusively bamboo stems; occasionally small animals, including fish
LIFESPAN	25–30 years

EYES
The Chinese call the panda xiongmao — 'giant cat bear'. This refers to its eyes, which have vertical slit pupils like those of a cat.

TEETH
The giant panda has few of the cutting teeth typical of carnivores. Instead, it uses a battery of broad molars to grind up its bamboo food.

COAT
The springy, oily coat protects the panda from cold and damp. The colours give excellent camouflage, particularly against snow and in dappled light.

PAW
The paws point inwards. Each has five partially retractile claws. On each forepaw, a claw-like wrist bone serves as a 'thumb' to aid grasping.

CREATURE COMPARISONS

The giant panda possesses the basic bodyplan common to all bears (family Ursidae): squat limbs with a flat-footed stance; a barrel-like torso, and a massive skull with long jaws. It is, however, dwarfed by the grizzly bear (Ursus arctos) of North America, which weighs in at up to 780kg (1720lb). The grizzly's diet includes protein-rich salmon, nuts and berries, which may account for its mighty size. Unlike the panda, the grizzly sleeps through the winter, living on reserves of body fat.

Giant panda   Grizzly bear

WHERE IN THE WORLD?

Found only in the Xifan Mountains in Sichuan Province of southwestern China. Prefers steep terrain ranging from semi-tropical bamboo forests to snowy mountains. More than half of all wild pandas now live in reserves.

RELATED SPECIES

The giant panda was once classed with the 18 members of the raccoon family, Procyonidae, which include the red panda, Ailurus fulgens. Most zoologists now place it in the bear family, Ursidae, and some give it its own subfamily: Ailuropodinae.

• ORDER • *Carnivora* • FAMILY • *Ursidae* • GENUS & SPECIES • *Tremarctos ornatus*

SPECTACLED BEAR

KEY FEATURES

- The only bear native to South America, its ancestors arrived two million years ago from North America.
- Name refers to its distinctive facial markings, which vary considerably between individuals.
- Threatened by habitat clearance and hunting to supply products used in traditional medicine.

VITAL STATISTICS

WEIGHT	Male 100–170kg (220.5–374.8lb); female 60–62kg
LENGTH	Head & Body: 1.2–1.8m (3ft 9in–5ft 9in) Tail: 7cm (2.7in)
SHOULDER HEIGHT	70–80cm (27.6–31in)
SEXUAL MATURITY	Male unknown, probably 5–6 years; female 4–7 years
MATING SEASON	April to June
GESTATION PERIOD	195–255 days
NUMBER OF YOUNG	1 to 3
BIRTH INTERVAL	2 years
TYPICAL DIET	Fruit and other vegetation; some animal matter
LIFESPAN	Up to 36 years

The spectacled bear gets its unusual name from the white markings that surround its eyes. It is thought these 'glasses' are used in staring matches.

MARKINGS
The bear's creamy 'spectacles' usually ring the eyes entirely, but sometimes only form semicircles. On some bears they may appear on the throat or chest, while other individuals may have no markings at all.

BODY
The spectacled bear is relatively compact and light, which enables it to climb onto the thinner limbs of fruit-bearing trees when feeding, and to exploit a wide range of den sites.

SKULL
The massive skull supports large masseter (chewing) muscles that give terrific biting power. The 40 teeth include much-reduced carnassials (shearing teeth) and broad molars. These teeth reveal how the bear has evolved away from a carnivorous diet to one comprising mainly fruit and vegetation.

PAWS
Hairy soles provide grip on the ground (hindpaw, right); while the long, sharp claws help the bear to climb trees with ease.

CREATURE COMPARISONS

Like the spectacled bear, the sloth bear (Ursus ursinus) of the Indian subcontinent is among the smaller species of bears. However, the sloth bear is larger with a shoulder height of 61–91cm (24–35.8in) and is usually a little heavier. Its thicker, shaggier coat, though, makes it appear much bigger.

Whereas the spectacled bear feeds mainly on vegetation, the sloth bear is a specialist insect eater. Its inner pair of upper incisors are missing, forming a gap in the front teeth. This adaptation allows it to suck up teeming insects, such as termites.

Spectacled bear   Sloth bear

WHERE IN THE WORLD?

Found mainly in cloud forests on the slopes of the Andes in western Venezuela, Colombia, Ecuador, Peru and northwestern Bolivia. Unconfirmed sightings in eastern Panama and northern Argentina.

RELATED SPECIES

The spectacled bear is one of 8 species of bear in the family Ursidae. The other 7 are: the Malayan sun bear, U. malayanus; the sloth bear, U. ursinus; the Asiatic black bear, U. thibetanus; the brown bear, U. arctos; the American black bear, U. americanus; the polar bear, U. maritimus; and the recently reclassified giant panda, Ailuropoda melanoleuca. This endangered species was formerly placed, along with the red panda, in the family Procyonidae.

• ORDER • *Carnivora* • FAMILY • *Ursidae* • GENUS & SPECIES • *Ursus americanus*

AMERICAN BLACK BEAR

The American black bear's powerful build and thick coat help it negotiate the tangled undergrowth of its favoured forest habitat with ease.

KEY FEATURES

- The most widespread and numerous bear in North America, with a total population of up to 500,000.

- A carnivore with a very broad-based diet — even scavenges scraps from humans whenever possible.

- May spend more than half the year in hibernation with its heart and metabolic rate slowed dramatically.

VITAL STATISTICS

WEIGHT	Male 115–270kg (253.5–595.2lb) female 100–140kg (220.5–308.6lb)
LENGTH	Head & Body: 1.5–1.8m (4ft 9in–5ft 9in) Tail: 12cm (4.7in)
SHOULDER HEIGHT	80–95cm (31–37.4in)
SEXUAL MATURITY	Female 4–5 years; male 5–6 years
MATING SEASON	June to mid July
GESTATION PERIOD	220 days, includes delayed implantation
NUMBER OF YOUNG	1 to 5
BIRTH INTERVAL	2 years, even 3–4 years
TYPICAL DIET	Grasses, fruits, nuts, also fish, insects and mammals
LIFESPAN	Up to 25 years

WHITE PHASE BEAR
The cream-coloured Kermodes bear is a rare subspecies of the American black bear that lives on the Pacific Coast of British Columbia. Its black nose and brown eyes show that it is not simply an albino race.

FUR
The name 'black bear' is deceptive as fur colour ranges from black to chocolate-brown and cinnamon-brown.

TEETH
Like most omnivores, the American black bear has relatively underdeveloped canines and broad molars. The molars are used for grinding the vegetable matter that forms the majority of its diet.

FEET
The black bear's feet are padded and have long, curved claws at the end of each of the five toes. As with humans, both heel and toe make contact with the ground when walking — which is known as plantigrade locomotion.

CREATURE COMPARISONS

The Asiatic black bear is slightly smaller than the American black bear, although the bushier fur ruff around its neck gives it a bulkier appearance than its weight would suggest.

The Asiatic black bear is also distinguished by its prominent ears. It is an excellent climber, and inhabits forests and scrubland up to altitudes of 3600m (11,810ft) across a range from Afghanistan eastwards to coastal Siberia and Japan.

Like the American black bear, the Asiatic black bear is largely vegetarian — however, it is more than capable of catching and killing animals as large as deer and domestic cattle.

Asiatic black bear

American black bear

WHERE IN THE WORLD?

Found over much of North America apart from central areas. Range extends north to the Alaskan and Canadian tundra and south into northern Mexico.

RELATED SPECIES

There are six species of bear in the genus Ursus: U. thibetanus, the Asiatic black bear, U. ursinus, the brown bear, U. arctos, the sloth bear, U. maritimus, the polar bear and the Malayan sun bear, U. malayanus. The family Ursidae contains two other species, the spectacled bear and the recently added giant panda. Scientists formerly included the panda in the raccoon family, Procyonidae, but new genetic techniques have led to its reclassification.

• ORDER • *Carnivora* **• FAMILY •** *Ursidae* **• GENUS & SPECIES •** *Ursus arctos horribilis*

GRIZZLY BEAR

KEY FEATURES

- Combines immense physical strength with surprising speed over short distances, enabling it to attack large or fleet-footed prey.
- Able to knock a fully grown bison off its feet — but prefers to eat berries and roots.
- Powerful and aggressive enough to drive away predators, such as wolves and pumas, from their kills.

VITAL STATISTICS

WEIGHT	225–320kg (496–705.5lb)
LENGTH	1.5–2.5m (4ft 9in–8ft 2in)
SHOULDER HEIGHT	90–105cm (35.4–41.3in)
SEXUAL MATURITY	2–3 years
MATING SEASON	Spring to early summer
GESTATION PERIOD	About 225 days
NUMBER OF YOUNG	1 to 4, usually 2
BIRTH INTERVAL	2–3 years
TYPICAL DIET	Greatly varied; includes nuts, berries, roots, insects, small vertebrates, fish and carrion
LIFESPAN	Up to 25 years

The grizzly's bulky body enables it to survive some of the world's coldest winters. Its sturdy limbs give it great strength and speed.

TEETH
Like other bears, the grizzly lacks carnassial (shearing) teeth to slice into flesh. Instead, it has broad molars to grind up plant material.

COAT
The shaggy, brown hair helps keep out the winter cold. The greyish tips give the bear a 'grizzled' look, and provide it with its common name.

SNOUT
The moist nose on the snout provides the grizzly bear's most important tool: a superb sense of smell.

PAWS
The broad, flat, five-toed feet have long, sharp claws. Like other bears, the grizzly walks on the full soles of its feet.

LIMBS
The grizzly can manage brief bursts of speed on its short, powerful limbs. The sturdy hindlegs can support the full weight of the bear when standing.

CREATURE COMPARISONS

The grizzly bear is one of many subspecies of brown bear found across Europe, Asia and North America. These subspecies increase in size from east to west. Those found in the Alps and Apennines of western Europe weigh only about one-quarter as much as the grizzly bear; the Kodiak, the grizzly's northern neighbour, is larger still.

American black bear   Grizzly bear   Polar bear

WHERE IN THE WORLD?

Found in western North America, mainly in mountainous regions and national parks, but large populations occur only in Alaska and western Canada. Widespread hunting since the pioneer days has reduced numbers dramatically.

RELATED SPECIES

There are seven species of bear (family Ursidae), including the American black bear, U. americanus. Evolved from meat-eating, dog-like ancestors, bears have developed a far more varied diet. This versatility has contributed to their wide distribution.

MALAYAN SUN BEAR

• ORDER • *Carnivora* **• FAMILY •** *Ursidae* **• GENUS & SPECIES •** *Ursus malayanus*

KEY FEATURES

- Smallest of all bears, it is an agile climber that spends most days high above the forest floor in a rough 'tree house'.
- Equipped with an extremely long tongue to capture bees and other insects from hard-to-reach places.
- Threatened by loss of habitat and hunting. Listed as vulnerable by the IUCN (World Conservation Union).

VITAL STATISTICS

WEIGHT	27–65kg (59.5–143.3lb)
LENGTH	1–1.4m (3ft 3in–4ft 6in)
SHOULDER HEIGHT	70cm (27.6in)
SEXUAL MATURITY	About 2 years
MATING SEASON	All year round
GESTATION PERIOD	95–240 days, including delayed implantation
NUMBER OF YOUNG	1 or 2
BIRTH INTERVAL	Usually 1 year
TYPICAL DIET	Insects, honey, fruit and other vegetation; some small mammals, reptiles and birds
LIFESPAN	Up to 25 years

The Malayan sun bear is a highly successful forager equipped with powerful claws, a prodigious tongue and exceptional climbing skills.

COAT
The fur is shorter and smoother than that of other bears — probably an adaptation to its tropical habitat. Colouration is usually very dark.

TEETH AND TONGUE
The very long tongue is used to probe tree holes and termite mounds for food. The bear's cheek teeth are broad and flat — suitable for crushing insects and chewing tough plant matter.

MARKINGS
The crescent mark on the bear's chest can vary greatly in colour, position and shape.

NOSE
Like all bears, the Malayan sun bear has a permanently wet nose, a characteristic that enhances its highly developed sense of smell.

PAWS
Naked soles and long, powerful claws provide grip when the bear climbs. The claws, measuring up to 15cm (6in) long, are also used to strip the bark from trees and to rip open bees' nests.

CREATURE COMPARISONS

The South American spectacled bear (Tremarctos ornatus), the only member of the bear family living on that continent, is almost twice the size of the sun bear. Like the sun bear it is an opportunistic feeder and forages among the trees of its forested mountain habitat. The spectacled bear is more dependent on seasonably variable plants than is the sun bear, and therefore has a much wider foraging range. It lacks the sun bear's long tongue but has an exceptionally strong jaw which enables it to tackle tough plant foods, such as bromeliads, that few other local animals can exploit.

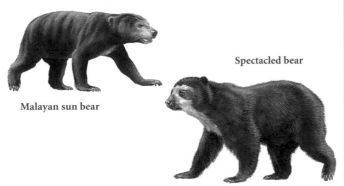

Malayan sun bear

Spectacled bear

WHERE IN THE WORLD?

Found throughout southeastern Asia, from Burma (Myanmar), south through the Malay Peninsula, to the islands of Sumatra and Borneo. May also still survive in Yunnan Province, southern China.

RELATED SPECIES

The Malayan sun bear is 1 of 6 species in the genus Ursus. The others are the Asiatic black bear, the American black bear, the brown bear, the polar bear and the sloth bear. These 6 bears, along with the spectacled bear, Tremarctos ornatus, and the giant panda, Ailuropoda melanoleuca, make up the bear family, Ursidae. Despite their largely vegetarian diet, all members of Ursidae are classified as part of the order Carnivora.

• ORDER • *Carnivora* • FAMILY • *Ursidae* • GENUS & SPECIES • *Ursus maritimus*

POLAR BEAR

Clad in insulating fur and fat, the polar bear is able to sleep through biting blizzards, or plunge into the Arctic's near-freezing waters.

KEY FEATURES

- Dense, waterproof coat enables it to survive some of the lowest temperatures on Earth. Polar bear tracks have been seen just a few kilometres from the North Pole.
- Large and powerful; its substantial body volume helps it to retain heat in its cold surroundings.
- Preys mainly on blubber-rich seals, which it kills with a bite to the head or a blow from its large, heavy paws.

VITAL STATISTICS

WEIGHT	Male up to 725kg (1598lb); female up to 249kg (549lb).
LENGTH	2.4–3m (7ft 9in–6ft 6in)
SEXUAL MATURITY	Usually 4–5 years. Most males do not mate until 8–10 years old
MATING SEASON	Mainly April to May
GESTATION PERIOD	195–265 days which includes a period of delayed implantation
NUMBER OF YOUNG	1 to 4, usually 2
BIRTH INTERVAL	3–4 years
TYPICAL DIET	Mainly sealsl
LIFESPAN	Up to 30 years, but usually 15–18

TEETH
The polar bear has 42 teeth, including long, sharp canines for piercing flesh.

BODY
The bear's large size and rotund shape help minimize heat loss. A 10cm (4in) layer of fat lies under the skin, which is black to absorb heat.

COAT
The polar bear's coat is a key to its survival. Long guard hairs lie over a dense underfur. The guard hairs become matted when wet to help keep the skin dry.

HEAD
The polar bear's head is long and tapering, with small ears and powerful jaws. The bear's sense of smell is acute, but its eyesight is not especially good for a carnivore.

PAWS
In the water the large, rounded forepaws help the bear to swim strongly. On land, the paws spread the bear's weight like snowshoes. Each paw has five claws.

CREATURE COMPARISONS

The polar bear shares its range with the Arctic fox — another carnivore with similar nomadic habits. But the two animals have adapted to the intense cold in very different ways. The polar bear's immense size helps it to keep warm, but the Arctic fox is tiny and relies instead on incredibly efficient insulation. Its coat is thick and fluffy, and all its extremities are well protected. It has small, fur-lined ears and a short head. Its paws are large and have woolly hair on the soles. When sleeping, the Arctic fox wraps its bushy tail around its legs and feet to reduce heat loss.

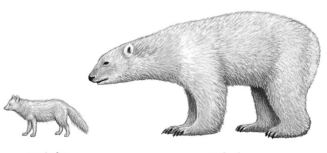

Arctic fox   **Polar bear**

WHERE IN THE WORLD?

Found off the northern coasts of North America, northern Russia east to Siberia, and around Greenland and other islands in the Arctic

Ocean, to the southern limits of the pack ice.

RELATED SPECIES

The polar bear is one of eight species of bear in three genera. It is so closely related to the brown bear, Ursus arctos, that the two species can interbreed and produce fertile hybrid offspring. Unlike the mainly carnivorous polar bear, the brown bear has a very mixed diet, a large part of which is made up of berries, nuts and fruit. One coastal subspecies of the brown bear, the Kodiak, closely matches the polar bear in size.

ASIAN BLACK BEAR

• **ORDER** • *Carnivora* • **FAMILY** • *Ursidae* • **GENUS & SPECIES** • *Ursus thibetanus*

The short-sighted, shambling Asian black bear has opted for a sleepy, unambitious approach to life, but is perfectly capable of looking after itself.

KEY FEATURES

- A tough, resourceful native of the mountain forests of Asia, it survives in some of the most rugged terrain on Earth.
- Primarily vegetarian, despite its carnivorous ancestry, it feeds mainly on fruit and nuts.
- Threatened by habitat loss and the trade in its body parts for medicine. Classed as vulnerable by the IUCN (World Conservation Union).

TEETH
The cheek teeth are adapted for chewing a largely vegetable diet. The male uses his long canine teeth when fighting.

FUR
Fur around the neck and shoulders is particularly long, forming a mane like that of a male lion.

MUZZLE
The bear's long muzzle contains efficient scenting apparatus, but its eyesight and hearing are relatively poor.

MARKINGS
The coat is usually jet black with a white, crescent-shaped marking across the chest.

FOOT
The bear walks flat on the soles of its feet, which turn inwards and give it a slightly clumsy gait. Its five long, hooked claws cannot be retracted and are exellent for climbing.

VITAL STATISTICS

WEIGHT	Male 50–120kg (110.2–264.6lb); female 42–70kg (92.6–154.3lb)
LENGTH	Male 1.4–1.7m (4ft 6in–5ft 6in); female 1.1–1.4m (3ft 6in–4ft 6in)
SEXUAL MATURITY	3 years
MATING SEASON	June to July
GESTATION PERIOD	Up to 220 days (including delayed implantation)
NUMBER OF YOUNG	Usually 2
BIRTH INTERVAL	2–3 years
TYPICAL DIET	Succulent vegetation, fruit, nuts, insects and carrion
LIFESPAN	Up to 25 years

CREATURE COMPARISONS

The Asian black bear has a smaller counterpart across the Pacific in South America: the spectacled bear (Tremarctos ornatus). Named for the pale markings around its eyes, this small, agile climbing bear is descended from a predatory species that entered South America about two million years ago. Today, it is the only bear living on the continent. Like the Asian black bear, the spectacled bear is an opportunistic feeder and lives in a variety of habitats ranging from lush forests to the grassland slopes of the Andes at altitudes up to 4200m (13,780ft).

Spectacled bear

Asian black bear

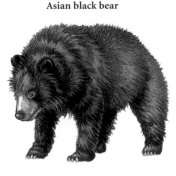

WHERE IN THE WORLD?

Found in the mountain forests of southern Asia, from Iran in the west, through the Himalayas and Tibet to China, Southeast Asia and Japan in the east.

RELATED SPECIES

The Asian black bear is a close relative of the American black bear, Ursus americanus. They are among 8 species in the family Ursidae, which is broken down into 3 subfamilies. The subfamily Ursinae contains both black bears, the sun and sloth bears, the polar bear and the brown bear or grizzly. The subfamilies Tremarctinae and Ailuropodinae cover the South American spectacled bear and the giant panda respectively.

• **ORDER** • *Carnivora* • **FAMILY** • *Ursidae* • **GENUS & SPECIES** • *Ursus ursinus*

SLOTH BEAR

KEY FEATURES

- Special adaptations enable it to excavate termite mounds and suck up hordes of insects.
- A plant- and insect-eater, but considered by locals to be one of the deadliest animals in the forest.
- A shy and solitary animal threatened by the continued destruction of its habitat.

VITAL STATISTICS

WEIGHT	55–145kg (121.3–319.7lb)
LENGTH	1.5–1.9m (4ft 9in–6ft 2in)
SHOULDER HEIGHT	60–90cm (23.6–35.4in)
SEXUAL MATURITY	3–4 years
MATING SEASON	June in north of range; all year in south
GESTATION PERIOD	180–210 days
NUMBER OF YOUNG	Usually 2
BIRTH INTERVAL	2–3 years
TYPICAL DIET	Termites, insect larvae, honey, fruit, carrion
LIFESPAN	35–40 years in captivity; unknown in wild

Some remarkable adaptations enable the sloth bear to take advantage of a variety of foods found in its forest habitat.

CRESCENT MARK
A crescent-shaped marking on the chest is typical. It may vary in colour from near-white to chestnut-brown.

MOUTH
A long snout, flexible lips and a gap between the upper incisors enable the bear to suck termites from their nests.

FOOT
The broad, naked-soled feet turn inwards and are ideal for climbing trees. The long, sickle-shaped claws are powerful digging tools and also help the bear to grip when climbing.

CREATURE COMPARISONS

The sloth bear is found mainly in India's forests, while the Malayan sun bear (*Ursus malayanus*) ranges across the moister forests from Burma (Myanmar) to Vietnam and along the Malay Peninsula to Sumatra. The sun bear, smallest of all bear species, is little more than half the size of the sloth bear and weighs only 27–65kg (59.5–143.3lb).

Like the sloth bear, the sun bear feeds mainly on fruit and insects. Both species of bear commonly have a distinctive, crescent-shaped marking on the chest, but the sloth bear's coat is much shaggier.

Sloth bear

Sun bear

WHERE IN THE WORLD?

Found only in India, Nepal and Sri Lanka, where it is confined to the last few lowland forests. Does not live farther east than Assam in the northeast of India.

RELATED SPECIES

The sloth bear is 1 of 6 species in Ursinae, a subfamily of the family Ursidae. Also in Ursinae are the 2 other Asian bears — the sun bear and the Asian black bear — as well as the American black bear, the brown bear and the polar bear. The giant panda and the South American spectacled bear are classified under separate subfamilies within Ursidae. All bears are classed as carnivores, despite their mainly plant-based diet.

BINTURONG

•ORDER• *Carnivora* •FAMILY• *Viverridae* •GENUS & SPECIES• *Arctictis binturong*

The chunky binturong is not the most agile of climbers, but its prehensile tail gives it an advantage over most other tree-dwelling carnivores.

KEY FEATURES

- A shaggy-haired, rainforest tree-dweller belonging to one of the most diverse carnivore families.

- Large and cumbersome, but moves with sure-footed skill among the trees thanks to its prehensile tail.

- Raises its young in small social groups, but otherwise lives a solitary life.

SKULL
In common with other members of the family Viverridae, the binturong's skull is almost identical to fossil specimens of the earliest carnivores, the Miacoidea, which lived more than 38 million years ago. A primitive array of small crushing and piercing teeth suits the binturong's varied diet.

HEAD
Small, round and tufted ears, along with the white whiskers, give the binturong an appearance somewhere between a cat and a bear — indeed it is also known as the bear cat.

TAIL
The long, heavy tail fulfils two roles: its prehensile tip enables the animal to grip branches for extra stability, while the muscular base aids balance.

COAT
The fur is long and coarse, and made up of dark hairs with pale tips.

PAWS
Bare soles on the feet and sharp, non-retractile claws provide an excellent climbing grip. The binturong places its foot flat on the ground when it walks — a characteristic of species that spend much of their time clinging to tree limbs.

VITAL STATISTICS

WEIGHT	9–14kg (19.8–30.9lb)
LENGTH	Head & Body: 60–97cm (23.6–38.2in) Tail: 50–90cm (19.7–35.4in)
SEXUAL MATURITY	Male 27 months; female 30 months
MATING SEASON	Throughout the year, but peaking in March to April and October to November
GESTATION PERIOD	84–99 days
NUMBER OF YOUNG	Usually 1 or 2, but up to 6
BIRTH INTERVAL	2 litters a year
TYPICAL DIET	Leaves and fruit, insects, small birds, mammals, fish
LIFESPAN	22 years in captivity

CREATURE COMPARISONS

The binturong looks unlike any other member of the family Viverridae. A more typical viverrid is the masked palm civet (Paguma larvata), with its characteristic long body and snout. This civet shares the binturong's southeastern Asian forest home. Like its relative, the civet forages in the trees by night, taking a range of insect and reptile prey, as well as fruit and shoots. Being smaller and lighter than the binturong, the civet is also much more agile in the branches.

Masked palm civet

Binturong

WHERE IN THE WORLD?

Found in southeastern Asia from Nepal in the north west through Burma (Myanmar) and along the Malay Peninsula to Sumatra, Java and Borneo.

RELATED SPECIES

As a member of the family Viverridae the binturong has among its close relatives 65 species of civet, mongoose, linsang and genet. These include the meerkat, Suricata suricatta, and the common palm civet, Paradoxurus hermaphroditus.

• **ORDER** • *Carnivora* • **FAMILY** • *Viverridae* • **GENUS & SPECIES** • *Civettictis civetta*

AFRICAN CIVET

Small but powerfully built, the African civet stalks through tall grasses by night and seizes animals — even venomous snakes — in its jaws.

KEY FEATURES

- Looks like a cross between a dog and a small spotted cat, but is more closely related to mongooses.
- Glands secrete a strong-smelling, greasy substance that it uses to mark its territory.
- Hunts snakes and small mammals, killing them by shaking them violently in its jaws.

VITAL STATISTICS

WEIGHT	7–20kg (15.4–44lb)
LENGTH	Head & Body: 68–95cm (26.8–37.4in) Tail: 40–53cm (15.7–20.9in)
SEXUAL MATURITY	1 year
MATING SEASON	Year round
GESTATION PERIOD	60–72 days
NUMBER OF YOUNG	1 to 4
BIRTH INTERVAL	Up to 3 litters a year
TYPICAL DIET	Small mammals, invertebrates, reptiles, birds and their eggs, grass, leaves, fruit, vegetables
LIFESPAN	Up to 28 years in captivity

TAIL
The fur on the tail is long, thick and coarse.

SCENT GLANDS
Glands under the tail secrete an oily, musky substance with which the civet marks its territory. Once applied to a tree-trunk, the secretion gradually hardens and darkens.

SKULL
The skull is robustly built. Long canines and big carnassial (shearing) teeth reflect the civet's wide diet.

COAT
Dark blotches on a yellow-white base break up the civet's outline as it hunts.

FOREFEET
The soles of the feet are covered with thick hair. Each forefoot has five digits.

HINDFEET
Five non-retractile claws on each hindfoot provide grip when running and climbing.

CREATURE COMPARISONS

The African palm civet (Nandinia binotata) is closely related to the African civet, and shares much of its range, occurring in the dense equatorial forests of central and western Africa. Whereas the African civet forages on the ground, the palm civet makes its home in the trees. Smaller than its cousin, the palm civet lacks the African civet's strong markings and is mostly a dull olive-brown colour, with softer rings on its tail. The palm civet has a muscular tail that improves its balance, helping it hunt arboreal animals such as squirrels and raid birds' nests high in the canopy.

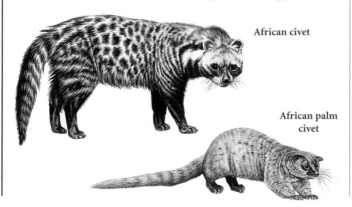

African civet

African palm civet

WHERE IN THE WORLD?

Widespread throughout much of sub-Saharan Africa. Absent from the Horn of Africa, southern South Africa, Namibia and the island of Madagascar.

RELATED SPECIES

The African civet is the sole member of Civettictis, 1 of 7 genera of oriental civets, genets and linsangs in the subfamily Viverrinae. It is closely related to the common palm civet, Paradoxurus hermaphroditus, a nocturnal forest-dweller that lives in southeastern Asia.

COMMON GENET

• **ORDER** • *Carnivora* • **FAMILY** • *Viverridae* • **GENUS & SPECIES** • *Genetta genetta*

The black-spotted markings of the common genet help to conceal this agile predator as it stalks through the forests under the cover of darkness.

KEY FEATURES

- A nocturnal predator that hunts a variety of prey both on the ground and in the trees.
- Bold enough to build a den alongside human settlements but is often regarded as a pest.
- Feline-looking, with the short legs, long tail and muzzle typical of its family, but is quite unrelated to cats.

HEAD
The head is cat-like with large eyes, mobile ears and long whiskers. White facial markings on the cheeks, muzzle and above the eyes are probably unique to each individual.

TEETH
The four canine teeth are small but very sharp. As in other carnivores, the carnassials (cheek teeth) are used to shear off chunks of meat.

FOOT
The common genet has short legs and small paws each with five toes. The claws are retractile so they remain sharp until needed for hunting and climbing.

SPINAL CREST
A line of black hairs runs along the spine from the shoulder to the base of the tail. When threatened, the genet erects these hairs to form a distinctive spinal crest.

COAT
The coarse yellow-grey fur of the common genet has black spots in irregular rows along each side of the body and black rings on the tail.

VITAL STATISTICS

WEIGHT	Up to 2.25kg (5lb); female smaller than the male
LENGTH	Head & Body: 40–63cm (15.7–24.8in) Tail: 40–51cm (15.7–20.1in)
SHOULDER HEIGHT	15–20cm (5.9–7.9in)
SEXUAL MATURITY	2 years
MATING SEASON	January to March in Europe; all year in Africa, peaks during seasonal rains
GESTATION PERIOD	10–11 weeks
NUMBER OF YOUNG	1 to 4
BIRTH INTERVAL	1 year; 6 months in West Africa
TYPICAL DIET	Birds, reptiles, insects, carrion
LIFESPAN	14 years in captivity

CREATURE COMPARISONS

The common genet spends much of its active time climbing through trees and bushes, unlike most other members of its family, which tend to be more terrestrial. The African civet, for example, climbs trees only to escape predators. Although larger than the common genet, this civet resembles its relation in many ways. The animals share a similar body plan and wear a camouflaged coat for concealment. Both have a crest of fur along the spine, although the civet's is longer, especially over the tail. The African civet has a scent-releasing gland, producing large amounts of musk — as much as 19g (0.7oz) per week from captive animals. Civet musk is used as the base for many perfumes.

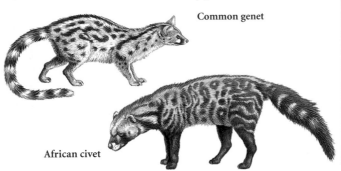

Common genet

African civet

WHERE IN THE WORLD?

Found in Africa, the Middle East and parts of Europe from Spain, the Balearic Islands, and southwestern France as far north as the River Loire.

RELATED SPECIES

There are nine species of genet in the family Viverridae. The common genet and the large-spotted genet are the most common species. Many other genets are rare or mysterious. For example, very little is known of the Abyssinian and Johnston's genet. The giant, pardine, servaline and Angolan genets are forest dwellers, while the hausa genet prefers savannah. Relations of the genets in the same order include civets, mongooses and fossas.

• ORDER • *Carnivora* • FAMILY • *Viverridae* • GENUS & SPECIES • *Helogale parvula*

DWARF MONGOOSE

KEY FEATURES

- A miniature hunter that forages for insects and small animals on the open, grassy plains of Africa.
- Always found in packs, it has developed an unusual social life in which only one pair in a group breeds.
- Wary and alert, pack members take turns keeping watch for danger while others feed.

The dwarf mongoose is a small, but efficient hunter equipped with long claws for digging up insects and a slender body for slipping into narrow holes.

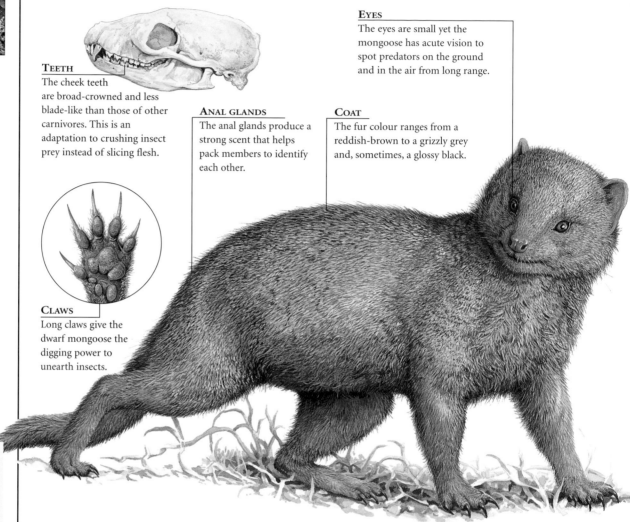

TEETH
The cheek teeth are broad-crowned and less blade-like than those of other carnivores. This is an adaptation to crushing insect prey instead of slicing flesh.

CLAWS
Long claws give the dwarf mongoose the digging power to unearth insects.

ANAL GLANDS
The anal glands produce a strong scent that helps pack members to identify each other.

EYES
The eyes are small yet the mongoose has acute vision to spot predators on the ground and in the air from long range.

COAT
The fur colour ranges from a reddish-brown to a grizzly grey and, sometimes, a glossy black.

VITAL STATISTICS

WEIGHT	315–326g (11.1–11.5oz)
LENGTH	Head & Body: 16–23cm (6.3–9in) Tail: 14–18cm (5.5–7.1in)
SEXUAL MATURITY	As early as 3.5 months, but does not normally mate until at least 3 years of age
MATING SEASON	All year with peaks in the rainy season
GESTATION PERIOD	49–56 days
NUMBER OF YOUNG	1 to 7, but usually 4
BIRTH INTERVAL	2–3 litters per year; more if young die
TYPICAL DIET	Mainly insects, also birds, small mammals, reptiles
LIFESPAN	Up to 10 years

CREATURE COMPARISONS

Nearly twice the size of the dwarf mongoose, the yellow mongoose, *Cynictis penicillata*, of southern Africa has a distinctive golden coat. However, after a spring moult, the fur turns reddish for summer. Although quite different in size and colour, these two species have similar habits. Like its cousin, the yellow mongoose lives in packs that hunt for insects by day. However, unlike the more territorial dwarf mongoose, the yellow mongoose shares its night-time burrows with other species of mongoose.

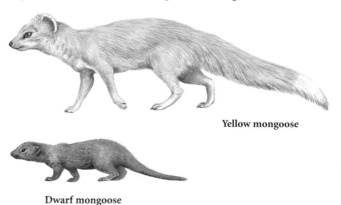

Yellow mongoose

Dwarf mongoose

WHERE IN THE WORLD?

Found in sub-Saharan Africa, from southern Ethiopia south through East Africa to northeastern South Africa. Also through Zambia west to Angola and northern Namibia.

RELATED SPECIES

The dwarf mongoose is one of 31 species of mongoose in the family Viverridae. It shares this family with other small carnivores, such as civets and cusimanses. There are 4 species of cusimanse, including *Crossarchus obscurus*, which is found in West Africa.

MONGOOSE

• **ORDER** • *Carnivora* • **FAMILY** • *Viverridae* • **GENUS & SPECIES** • *Herpestes*

Bold and tenacious, the mongoose has the agility and armoury to subdue even the most venomous of snakes in its savannah and woodland habitats.

KEY FEATURES

- Slender, low-slung carnivores that seize their prey — even venomous snakes — with a sudden short-range lunge.
- May perform acrobatic antics to lure curious victims to within easy striking distance.
- Use scent to mark the borders of home ranges.
- Active by day, foraging either alone or in small, extended family groups.

TEETH
Large canines on the upper and lower jaw are used to seize prey, while the carnassial teeth (just behind the canines) cut into flesh and crush tough bodyparts.

NOSE
A strong sense of smell helps the mongoose forage for food, locate family members, and detect the territorial boundaries of other mongoose groups.

**Species illustrated:
African grey mongoose,
Herpestes ichneumon**

TAIL
The long, tapering black-tipped tail provides the mongoose with a valuable balancing aid.

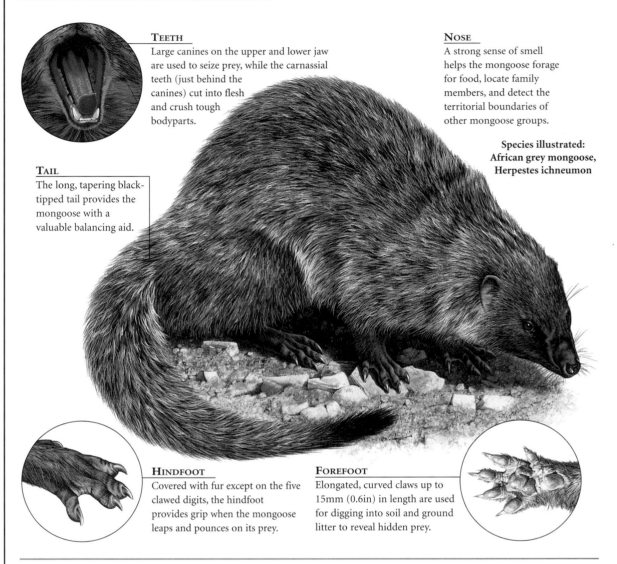

HINDFOOT
Covered with fur except on the five clawed digits, the hindfoot provides grip when the mongoose leaps and pounces on its prey.

FOREFOOT
Elongated, curved claws up to 15mm (0.6in) in length are used for digging into soil and ground litter to reveal hidden prey.

VITAL STATISTICS

WEIGHT	1.7–4kg (3.7–8.8lb)
LENGTH	Head & Body: 48–60cm (18.9–23.6in) Tail: 33–54cm (13–21.2in)
SEXUAL MATURITY	1–2 years
MATING SEASON	Varies according to region
GESTATION PERIOD	42–84 days
NUMBER OF YOUNG	1 to 4
TYPICAL DIET	Small mammals, birds, reptiles, invertebrates and frogs
LIFESPAN	12 years (in captivity)

CREATURE COMPARISONS

Like the African grey mongoose, the slender mongoose (*Herpestes sanguines*) is a widespread resident of sub-Saharan Africa. Both species have a typical mongoose build — a lengthy body and short legs — with a long, bushy tail that has a black tip. However, the slender mongoose is much smaller in size, and while its coat is often a grizzled grey, it may also be dark-brown, reddish-brown or yellowish in colour.

The slender mongoose is much more solitary in habit than the African grey mongoose, living alone or in a pair. Unlike the other species, it frequently climbs, rests and hunts in trees.

African grey mongoose

Slender mongoose

WHERE IN THE WORLD?

Members of the genus are found from southern Europe, throughout the African continent, eastwards across India and Sri Lanka, to Southeast Asia and as far east as Taiwan.

RELATED SPECIES

The genus Herpestes comprises 14 mongoose species. It is one of 36 genera in the family Viverridae, which contains another 14 mongoose species. The family also includes civets and genets, such as the African civet, Viverra civetta.

• ORDER • *Carnivora* • FAMILY • *Viverridae* • GENUS & SPECIES • *Mungos mungo*

BANDED MONGOOSE

KEY FEATURES

- Close-knit groups collectively defend territories, look after young and ward off predators
- Social ties are reinforced by play-fighting and scent-marking of one another's fur
- Forages in a pack: members follow each other closely in line and wind along like a huge snake

VITAL STATISTICS

WEIGHT	1–2kg (2.2–4.4lb)
LENGTH	Head/Body: 33–40.6cm (13–16in) Tail: 17.8–27.9cm (7–11in)
SEXUAL MATURITY	9–10 months
BREEDING SEASON	Varied; in some areas year 'round
GESTATION PERIOD	2 months
NUMBER OF YOUNG	2 to 6
BIRTH INTERVAL	Minimum 10 weeks
TYPICAL DIET	Insects, other invertebrates; lizards, small snakes, ground birds, rodents, eggs, fruit
LIFESPAN	Up to 10 years

The banded mongoose shuffles briskly along in fits and starts, hunched over the ground with its keen senses ever alert for prey.

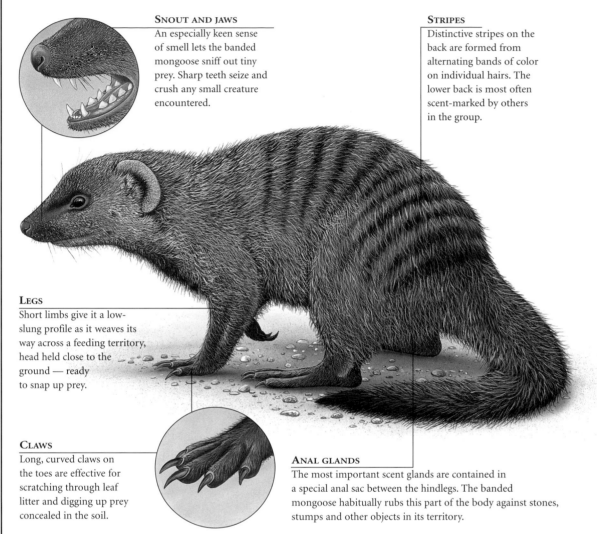

SNOUT AND JAWS
An especially keen sense of smell lets the banded mongoose sniff out tiny prey. Sharp teeth seize and crush any small creature encountered.

STRIPES
Distinctive stripes on the back are formed from alternating bands of color on individual hairs. The lower back is most often scent-marked by others in the group.

LEGS
Short limbs give it a low-slung profile as it weaves its way across a feeding territory, head held close to the ground — ready to snap up prey.

CLAWS
Long, curved claws on the toes are effective for scratching through leaf litter and digging up prey concealed in the soil.

ANAL GLANDS
The most important scent glands are contained in a special anal sac between the hindlegs. The banded mongoose habitually rubs this part of the body against stones, stumps and other objects in its territory.

CREATURE COMPARISONS

The Indian gray mongoose is the best known Asian species. The latter was the model for Rudyard Kipling's character Rikki-tikki-tavi in *The Jungle Book*. Longer, but more slender than the banded mongoose, the Indian gray preys largely on rodents and birds and, like Rikki-tikki-tavi, sometimes engages in lethal duels with snakes. But it's a loner, never forming the social ties central to the life of the banded mongoose.

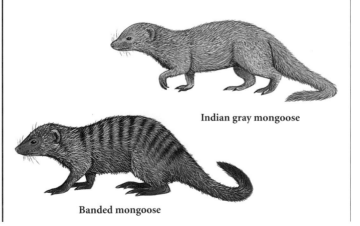

Indian gray mongoose

Banded mongoose

WHERE IN THE WORLD?

Occurs widely throughout Africa south of the Sahara Desert; absent only from the rainforest zones of West and Central Africa, the Ethiopian Highlands and the arid lands of southwestern Africa

RELATED SPECIES

The Gambian mongoose, *Mungos gambianus*, of West Africa, is the closest relative of the banded mongoose. Though similar in build, the Gambian lacks the distinctive back stripes of the banded. There are 31 species of mongoose distributed widely across Africa and southern Asia. The mongooses 40 relatives in the family Viverridae include the civets, genets, linsangs and the single species of fossa.

• **ORDER** • *Casuariiformes* • **FAMILY** • *Casuariidae* • **GENUS** • *Casuarius casuarius*

DOUBLE-WATTLED CASSOWARY

KEY FEATURES

- Though flightless and heavy, it can sprint at 50 km/h (31mph) and jump into the air to its own head-height.

- Female mates several times a year, leaving each partner to tend her eggs and young single-handed.

- Lashes out with the dagger-like claws of its huge feet when in danger.

- Adorned with bizarre tassels of bare skin, and a hard 'helmet' on its head.

VITAL STATISTICS

WEIGHT	Male 29–45kg (63.9–99.2in); female 58kg (127.9lb)
LENGTH	1.3–1.7m (4ft 3in–5ft 6in)
SEXUAL MATURITY	3 or 4 years
BREEDING SEASON	June to October
NUMBER OF EGGS	3 to 5
INCUBATION PERIOD	About 50 days
FLEDGING PERIOD	About 36 weeks
BREEDING INTERVAL	Probably 1 year
TYPICAL DIET	Fallen fruit; also fungi, insects, snails, small mammals and birds; occasionally carrion
LIFESPAN	At least 12–19 years

Massive legs enable the double-wattled cassowary to rush across the forest floor and kill prey as well as acting as formidable defensive weapons.

CASQUE
The function of the cassowary's horn-like casque is not known for certain. It grows as the bird becomes older, so may serve as a highly visible symbol of its dominance and age. It has also been suggested that the casque helps the cassowary to force a path through dense vegetation.

PLUMAGE
Coarse, tough feathers protect the cassowary's skin from damage by thorns, twigs and tangled undergrowth. They also form a cloak, keeping the cassowary dry in the high humidity of the rainforest.

WATTLES
This cassowary is named after the two loose folds of naked skin, or wattles, that hang from its neck. Their function is unclear, but the bold colours, which can be red, yellow, blue, purple or white, may help communication in the dark forests. The female is brighter than the male.

JUVENILE
The juvenile is considerably drabber than the adult, and has a smaller casque.

TOES
When threatened, the double-wattled cassowary uses its 10cm (3.9in)-long inner toes as slashing weapons, sometimes inflicting fatal wounds.

CREATURE COMPARISONS

The dwarf cassowary (Casuarius bennetti), despite being smaller than the double-wattled cassowary, is even more aggressive when cornered, and is often considered to be the world's most dangerous bird. It raises its body and kicks out with its muscular legs, or charges towards its aggressor while flailing its legs and slashing with its claws. A single blow can kill a dog-sized animal.

The dwarf cassowary has a more thickly feathered neck than the double-wattled cassowary, and its casque is both smaller and darker. It occurs at up to 3000m (9843ft) in the mountains of Papua New Guinea, where it is known as the moruk. Like the double-wattled cassowary, it feeds mainly on fruit, often plucking it off shrubs.

Dwarf cassowary

Double-wattled cassowary

WHERE IN THE WORLD?

Once more widespread, it now ranges over two areas in northeastern Queensland, Australia, and most of lowland New Guinea. Also found on the island of Seram and the Aru Islands, off New Guinea's western coast.

RELATED SPECIES

The order Casuariiformes consists of just two families: the Dromaiidae, of which the Australian emu is the sole member, and the Casuariidae, to which the double-wattled cassowary and 2 other species belong: these are the northern, or single-wattled cassowary, and the dwarf, or Bennett's, cassowary. Casuariiformes cannot fly, and walk or run on outsized legs — like their relatives the rheas of South America, the kiwis of New Zealand, and the ostrich of Africa.

• **ORDER** • *Casuariiformes* • **FAMILY** • *Dromaiidae* • **GENUS & SPECIES** • *Dromaius novaehollandiae*

EMU

The long, powerful legs of the emu compensate for its heavy body, small wings and shaggy plumage, which prevent it from flying.

PARTING
As if styled by a heavy-duty comb, the emu's coarse plumage has a prominent middle parting running down the hindneck and along the bird's back.

MALE
The male emu is about10 per cent smaller than the female (main picture). The light-blue skin that shows through the sparse neck feathers is paler in males.

FEATHERS
The emu's double-shafted feather structure is unique among birds. A secondary plume sprouts from the base of the shaft, equal in length to the main feather.

WINGS
The small, claw-tipped wings are useless for flight and hang limply at the emu's sides.

LEGS AND FEET
Long and sturdy, the legs give the emu a good turn of speed, while the long-clawed toes provide grip and allow it to deliver flying kicks in defence.

KEY FEATURES

- Distributed widely across Australia, the emu occurs in a diverse range of habitats.
- Second in size only to the ostrich, which lives in Africa, this huge bird is similarly flightless and relies on its ability to run fast when threatened.
- Unusually among birds, the male incubates the eggs and rears the brood, without assistance from the female.

VITAL STATISTICS

WEIGHT	35–50kg (77.2–110lb)
HEIGHT	To top of head 1.5–1.9m (4ft 9in–6ft 2in); to top of back 1–1.3m (3ft 3in–4ft 3in)
SEXUAL MATURITY	2 years
BREEDING SEASON	April to June
NUMBER OF EGGS	7 to 11
INCUBATION PERIOD	8 weeks
BREEDING INTERVAL	Usually 1 year
TYPICAL DIET	Seeds, fruits, flowers, shoots, and insects
LIFESPAN	6 years

CREATURE COMPARISONS

The greater rhea (Rhea americana), from South America, has much in common with the emu. Shorter in stature and of slimmer build, the greater rhea remains a giant among birds even though its bodyweight is about half that of its Australian counterpart. Like the emu, it is a flightless bird, built for walking. It has long legs and a neck designed for foraging at ground level in the open terrain that it favours. Like the emu, the greater rhea male takes sole responsibility for the incubation and the upbringing of its offspring.

Emu

Greater rhea

WHERE IN THE WORLD?

Occurs throughout much of the Australian continent, the emu is found in a wide variety of habitats from coastal flats,

woodlands and grassy plains to the uplands of the Great Dividing Range.

RELATED SPECIES

The emu is the only member of its family but is related to the strikingly coloured double-wattled cassowary (Casuarius casuarius) in the order Casuariiformes. Standing 1m high to the top of its back, it is Australia's only other large flightless bird. Although their ranges overlap in places the two species are unlikely to meet as the cassowary is confined to a habitat that the emu avoids — the tropical forests of northeastern Australia.

HUMPBACK WHALE

• **ORDER** • *Cetacea* • **FAMILY** • *Balaenopteridae* • **GENUS & SPECIES** • *Megaptera novaeangliae*

Easily identified, the humpback whale has long flippers, a small 'hump' in front of the dorsal fin, and distinctive marks on the tail flukes and flippers.

KEY FEATURES

- Spends the summer feeding in polar seas and migrates to warm, equatorial waters in winter to breed.
- Feeds on krill and small fish, filtering them from the sea using sieve-like plates of baleen in the mouth.
- 'Songs' sung by the male in the breeding season are among the most complex sounds made by any animal.

VITAL STATISTICS

WEIGHT	35–45 tonnes (34.3–44.3 tons)
LENGTH	Male up to 17m (55.8ft); female up to 19m (62.3ft). Average about 12m (39.4ft)
SEXUAL MATURITY	4–5 years
MATING SEASON	October to March in northern hemisphere; and April to September in the southern hemisphere
GESTATION PERIOD	11–12 months
NUMBER OF YOUNG	1
BIRTH INTERVAL	Usually every two years
TYPICAL DIET	Krill, fish (cod, herring, sand eels, anchovies, salmon)
LIFESPAN	Up to 70 years

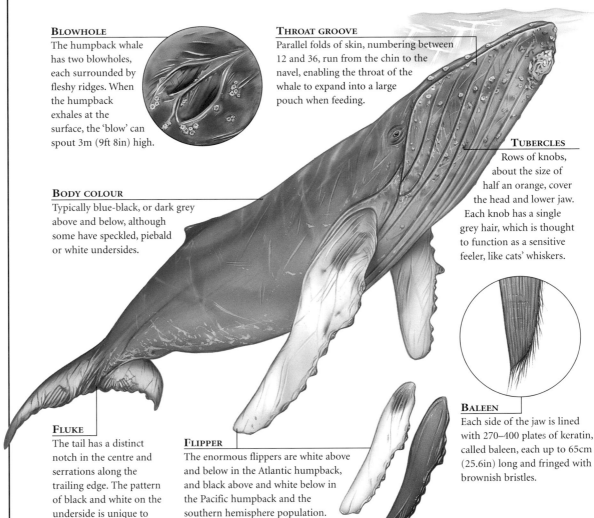

BLOWHOLE
The humpback whale has two blowholes, each surrounded by fleshy ridges. When the humpback exhales at the surface, the 'blow' can spout 3m (9ft 8in) high.

THROAT GROOVE
Parallel folds of skin, numbering between 12 and 36, run from the chin to the navel, enabling the throat of the whale to expand into a large pouch when feeding.

TUBERCLES
Rows of knobs, about the size of half an orange, cover the head and lower jaw. Each knob has a single grey hair, which is thought to function as a sensitive feeler, like cats' whiskers.

BODY COLOUR
Typically blue-black, or dark grey above and below, although some have speckled, piebald or white undersides.

BALEEN
Each side of the jaw is lined with 270–400 plates of keratin, called baleen, each up to 65cm (25.6in) long and fringed with brownish bristles.

FLUKE
The tail has a distinct notch in the centre and serrations along the trailing edge. The pattern of black and white on the underside is unique to individual whales.

FLIPPER
The enormous flippers are white above and below in the Atlantic humpback, and black above and white below in the Pacific humpback and the southern hemisphere population. The leading edge is uneven and knobbly.

CREATURE COMPARISONS

The fin whale (Balaenoptera physalus) is a larger relation of the humpback whale that can reach nearly 25m (82ft) in length and weigh up to 70 tonnes (68.9 tons). Both whales rely on their large tails for propulsion, and in the fin whale's case it powers it to speeds of over 35 km/h (21.7mph). Compared with the humpback's tail, the flukes of the fin whale are triangular with a less prominent notch between them, and have a smooth trailing edge. The flukes are also white below with no mottling. The fin whale's tail stock is thicker than the humpback's and is distinctly ridged from the dorsal fin to the fluke, lending it the alternative name of the razorback whale.

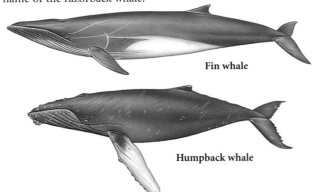

Fin whale

Humpback whale

WHERE IN THE WORLD?

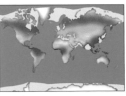

Wide-ranging but with distinct seasonal changes in distribution. Spends much of the year near mainland coasts or islands, but migrates across open seas.

RELATED SPECIES

The humpback is one of six rorqual whales. All are streamlined, have throat grooves and filter food using baleen. The family includes the largest animal known to have lived on Earth, the blue whale (Balaenoptera musculus). The other rorquals, in descending order of size, are the fast-swimming fin whale (B. physalus), the sei whale (B. borealis), Bryde's whale (B. edeni) and the smallest, the minke whale (B. acutorostrata).

• **ORDER** • *Cetacea* • **FAMILY** • *Delphinidae* • **GENUS & SPECIES** • *Delphinus delphis*

COMMON DOLPHIN

KEY FEATURES

- The most widespread and numerous of the world's cetaceans.
- Lives in an extended family group, or in a large herd that may be thousands strong.
- An intelligent and inquisitive animal that hunts cooperatively.
- Uses its advanced echolocation sense to maintain contact with the herd and track prey.

VITAL STATISTICS

WEIGHT	70–110kg (154.3–242.5lb)
LENGTH	1.7–2.6m (5ft 6in–8ft 5in)
SEXUAL MATURITY	3–5 years
MATING SEASON	Late summer
GESTATION PERIOD	10–11 months
NUMBER OF YOUNG	1
BIRTH INTERVAL	About 16 months
TYPICAL DIET	Small shoaling fish, squid, shrimp, crabs
LIFESPAN	25–30 years

Sleek, muscular and equipped with an echolocating sense that can track prey in the dark depths, the common dolphin is a highly effective predator.

ECHOLOCATION
The head contains sensitive organs that enable the dolphin to emit and receive sounds over a huge range of pitch. These are the organs used in echolocation — the method by which the dolphin locates and tracks its prey. Rapid pulses of sound produced in the animal's nasal passages are focused through a fatty deposit on the forehead known as the melon. Another fatty deposit on the jaw amplifies returning signals that have been reflected by objects in the environment and transmits them, via the jawbone, to the ears. Much of the dolphin's large brain capacity is thought to be devoted to interpreting these auditory signals.

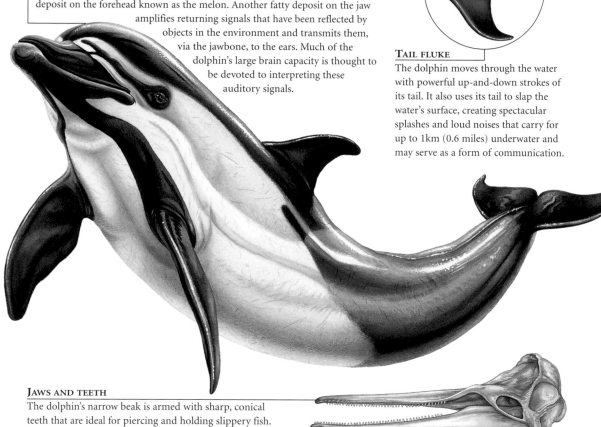

TAIL FLUKE
The dolphin moves through the water with powerful up-and-down strokes of its tail. It also uses its tail to slap the water's surface, creating spectacular splashes and loud noises that carry for up to 1km (0.6 miles) underwater and may serve as a form of communication.

JAWS AND TEETH
The dolphin's narrow beak is armed with sharp, conical teeth that are ideal for piercing and holding slippery fish.

CREATURE COMPARISONS

The harbour porpoise (Phocoena phocoena) is perhaps the most commonly seen porpoise and is frequently mistaken for the common dolphin. Although it shares the same basic torpedo bodyshape and similar colouring, the harbour porpoise is about three-quarters the length of the dolphin. Its blunt, rounded head lacks a beak, and its dorsal fin is less pronounced. The harbour porpoise hunts in much shallower waters than does the dolphin, staying close to shore. It is also found in cooler, more northerly waters than those favoured by the dolphin. While the dolphin is highly sociable, the porpoise generally lives in groups of fewer than six.

Common dolphin

Harbour porpoise

WHERE IN THE WORLD?

Inhabits a broad band of the world's oceans, from Iceland, Nova Scotia and Japan in the north to southern Chile and New Zealand in the south. The Mediterranean, the Red Sea and the Black Sea all have populations.

RELATED SPECIES
The common dolphin is 1 of 34 species that comprise the family Delphinidae, the oceanic dolphins. Some authorities recognize a variant, the long-beaked common dolphin, as a separate species. Other members of Delphinidae include the bottle-nosed dolphin, Tursiops truncatus, and, largest of all, the killer whale, Orcinus orca. All are members of the 70 species-strong suborder Odontoceti, the toothed whales.

PILOT WHALE

With powerful strokes of its tail, the streamlined pilot whale surges through the ocean, snapping up prey with its sharp teeth.

KEY FEATURES

- Dark-bodied, toothed mammal that is a common victim of mass strandings.
- Travels in tight-knit family groups through the sea, often following the migrations of its prey.
- Heavily exploited over the centuries but its populations seem to be stable.

VITAL STATISTICS

WEIGHT	Male 1.7 tonnes (1.67 tons); female 1 tonne (0.98 tons)
LENGTH	Male 5.6–5.8m (18ft 4in–19ft); female 4.5–4.8m (14ft 8in–15ft 7in)
SEXUAL MATURITY	Male 12–20 years; female 6–10 years
MATING SEASON	Peaks April to May; probably October to November in the southern hemisphere
GESTATION PERIOD	15–16 months
NUMBER OF YOUNG	1
BIRTH INTERVAL	3 years
TYPICAL DIET	Squid, octopus, fish
LIFESPAN	30–50 years

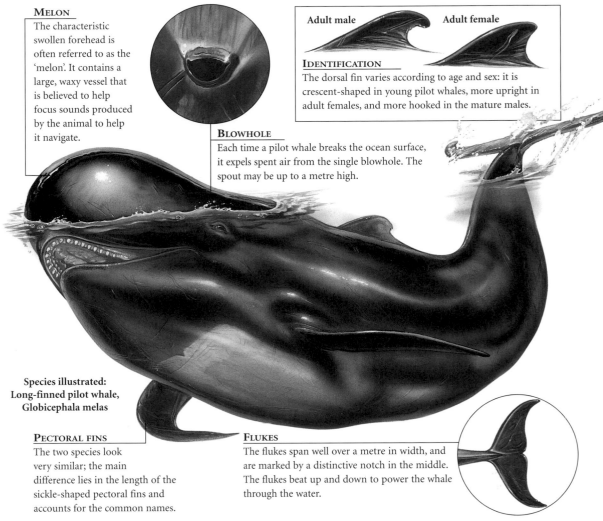

MELON
The characteristic swollen forehead is often referred to as the 'melon'. It contains a large, waxy vessel that is believed to help focus sounds produced by the animal to help it navigate.

BLOWHOLE
Each time a pilot whale breaks the ocean surface, it expels spent air from the single blowhole. The spout may be up to a metre high.

IDENTIFICATION
Adult male   Adult female
The dorsal fin varies according to age and sex: it is crescent-shaped in young pilot whales, more upright in adult females, and more hooked in the mature males.

Species illustrated: Long-finned pilot whale, Globicephala melas

PECTORAL FINS
The two species look very similar; the main difference lies in the length of the sickle-shaped pectoral fins and accounts for the common names.

FLUKES
The flukes span well over a metre in width, and are marked by a distinctive notch in the middle. The flukes beat up and down to power the whale through the water.

CREATURE COMPARISONS

The false killer whale (Pseudorca crassidens) is sometimes confused with the pilot whale. The two are of a similar size and colour and have a formidable array of teeth, but the false killer whale has a more upright, dolphin-like dorsal fin and less pointed pectoral fins. Its blunt snout lacks the bulbous shape seen in the pilot whale.

The false killer has a wide distribution, being found in deep, offshore waters in temperate and tropical latitudes. Like the pilot whale, it is susceptible to mass strandings.

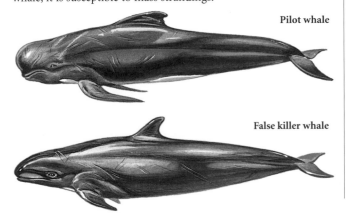

Pilot whale

False killer whale

WHERE IN THE WORLD?

The short-finned pilot whale is found in temperate and equatorial waters, while the long-finned species roams the North Atlantic and sub-Antarctic waters.

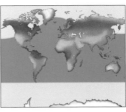

RELATED SPECIES

There are 2 species in the genus Globicephala: the short-finned pilot whale, G. macrorhynchus, and the long-finned species, G. melas. They belong to the dolphin family, Delphinidae, which is 1 of 6 families of toothed whale. The baleen whales and the toothed whales belong to the order Cetacea. Baleen whales, such as the humpback and minke, tend to be much larger and feed by filtering plankton through bristles in their mouths.

• **ORDER** • *Cetacea* • **FAMILY** • *Delphinidae* • **GENUS & SPECIES** • *Orcinus orca*

ORCA

With a sleek, powerful body and strong, sharp teeth, the fast-swimming orca is among the most deadly predators of the deep.

KEY FEATURES

- A streamlined killing machine that can weigh over 6000kg (13,230lb) and swim at over 50km/h (31mph).
- Kills animals as large as blue whale calves, and is the only whale that hunts other warm-blooded animals.
- Hunts alone and in packs, which cooperate to attack large or numerous prey.

DORSAL FIN
The male's tall, straight dorsal fin stands up to 1.8m (5ft 9in) high. The female's fin is usually half this height and curves backward.

TEETH
There are 20 to 26 conical teeth in each jaw. Each tooth curves backward and inward, and is used to seize prey and tear it into chunks.

Male

Female

TAIL
The muscular tail flukes propel the orca at high speed. The tail is also used to slap the water and produce deafening reports, with which the orca can stun whole schools of fish into immobility.

ECHOLOCATION
When hunting, the orca produces sounds from a nasal plug in its air passages, and flexes muscles in its forehead to focus the sounds into a beam. By analyzing the echoes that bounce back from objects hit by the beam, it can discover the direction and range of prey.

— Sonar pulse
----- Returning echo

VITAL STATISTICS

WEIGHT	Male up to 7.7 tonnes (7.6 tonns); female up to 5.5 tonnes (5.4 tons)
LENGTH	Male 9m (29ft 5in); female 8m (26ft 2in)
SEXUAL MATURITY	12–16 years
MATING SEASON	December –June in southern hemisphere, May–July in northern hemisphere
GESTATION PERIOD	15–17 months
NUMBER OF YOUNG	1
BIRTH INTERVAL	2–6 years
TYPICAL DIET	Fish, squid, seals, sea lions, and other whales, including minke and grey whales
LIFESPAN	30 years

CREATURE COMPARISONS

The orca is one of the 'toothed whales' (suborder Odontoceti). These whales have sharp teeth to kill and tear up their prey. Baleen whales (suborder Mysticeti), such as the minke, do not have teeth. Instead, their jaws contain flat plates of a fibrous material called baleen. These plates are used like a net to trap the plankton and fish on which these whales feed.

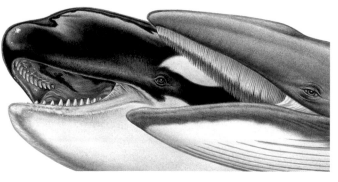

Orca

Minke whale

WHERE IN THE WORLD?

Found throughout every ocean of the world, the orca has the widest distribution of any whale. Coastal and cooler waters are its preferred habitat.

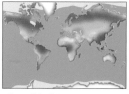

RELATED SPECIES

The orca is usually grouped with the dolphins, such as the spotted dolphin, in the family Delphinidae, but its blunt head and small number of teeth have led some scientists to place it in the family Globicephalidae. This family also includes the false and pygmy orcas.

• ORDER • *Cetacea* **• FAMILY •** *Delphinidae* **• GENUS & SPECIES •** *Stenella attenuata & S. frontalis*

SPOTTED DOLPHIN

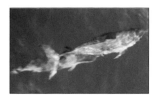

KEY FEATURES

- Two species of sleek, polka-dotted dolphins that inhabit the warmer oceans of the world.
- Hunt cooperatively and often associate with schools of tuna in the search for food.
- Powerful and high-speed swimmers; one species performs acrobatic leaps.

VITAL STATISTICS

WEIGHT	100–140kg (220.5–308.6lb)
LENGTH	2–2.6m (6ft 6on–8ft 5in)
SEXUAL MATURITY	10–15 years; female matures earlier than male
MATING SEASON	Varies according to region
GESTATION PERIOD	335–350 days
NUMBER OF YOUNG	Normally 1 but occasionally twins
BIRTH INTERVAL	2–4 years
TYPICAL DIET	Fish, octopus and squid
LIFESPAN	Up to 46 years

Streamlined and sturdy, spotted dolphins are strong yet graceful swimmers that combine their aquatic skills with intelligence to herd and capture prey.

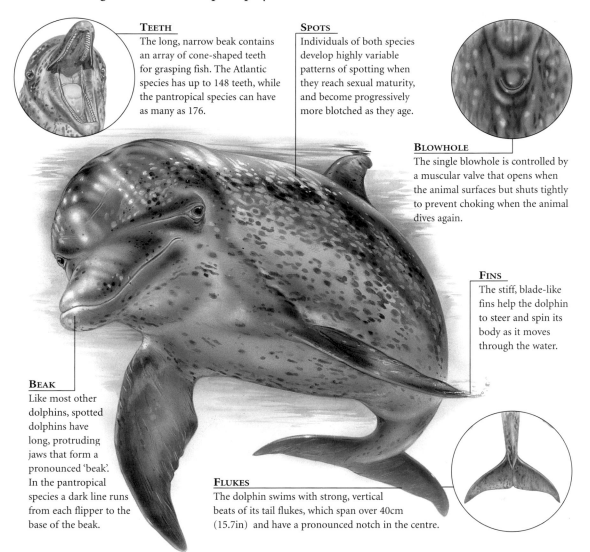

TEETH
The long, narrow beak contains an array of cone-shaped teeth for grasping fish. The Atlantic species has up to 148 teeth, while the pantropical species can have as many as 176.

SPOTS
Individuals of both species develop highly variable patterns of spotting when they reach sexual maturity, and become progressively more blotched as they age.

BLOWHOLE
The single blowhole is controlled by a muscular valve that opens when the animal surfaces but shuts tightly to prevent choking when the animal dives again.

FINS
The stiff, blade-like fins help the dolphin to steer and spin its body as it moves through the water.

BEAK
Like most other dolphins, spotted dolphins have long, protruding jaws that form a pronounced 'beak'. In the pantropical species a dark line runs from each flipper to the base of the beak.

FLUKES
The dolphin swims with strong, vertical beats of its tail flukes, which span over 40cm (15.7in) and have a pronounced notch in the centre.

CREATURE COMPARISONS

Like the spotted dolphins, the white-sided dolphins (genus Lagenorhynchus) are speedy swimmers that live in often very large groups. But unlike their speckled cousins, they avoid tropical and subtropical waters and instead inhabit the chillier waters of temperate and sub-polar latitudes. Inhabiting coastal waters and the open sea, the six species of this genus feed mainly on squid and shoaling fish. All are very acrobatic.

Similar in shape and size to the spotted dolphins, the white-sided dolphins have much shorter, stubbier beaks. They also tend to be darker, with more contrasting patches and bands.

White-sided dolphin

Spotted dolphin

WHERE IN THE WORLD?

Pantropical species (Stella attenuata) occurs in warm waters of the Atlantic, Indian and Pacific oceans; Atlantic species (S. frontalis) is confined to the Atlantic.

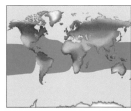

RELATED SPECIES

The genus Stenella contains 5 species. As well as the pantropical and Atlantic spotted dolphins, it includes the striped dolphin, the spinner dolphin and the Atlantic spinner dolphin. There are 15 other genera and 27 more species in the dolphin family Delphinidae.

• ORDER • *Cetacea* • FAMILY • *Delphinidae* • GENUS & SPECIES • *Tursiops truncatus*

BOTTLENOSE DOLPHIN

KEY FEATURES

- Most highly studied of all the whales and dolphins, both in the wild and in captivity.
- Possesses a remarkable acoustic sense with which it 'sees' using sound — in much the same way as bats.
- Hunts both individually and cooperatively and will even beach itself to snatch prey from the shore.

VITAL STATISTICS

WEIGHT	150–275kg (330.7–606.3lb)
LENGTH	1.9–3.9m (6ft 2in–12ft 8in)
SEXUAL MATURITY	About 6–8 years
MATING SEASON	Varies geographically but mating and calving usually occur in spring and summer
GESTATION PERIOD	10–12 months
NUMBER OF YOUNG	1
BIRTH INTERVAL	2 years
TYPICAL DIET	A wide variety of fish including capelin, anchovy and salmon. Also squid and shrimp
LIFESPAN	Typically 25–30 years

A large oceanic dolphin, the bottlenose has a long, robust body and a characteristic stubby, bottle-shaped beak.

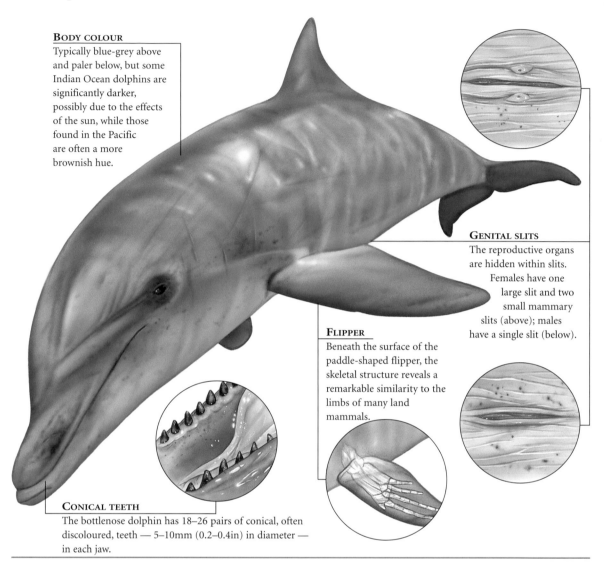

BODY COLOUR
Typically blue-grey above and paler below, but some Indian Ocean dolphins are significantly darker, possibly due to the effects of the sun, while those found in the Pacific are often a more brownish hue.

GENITAL SLITS
The reproductive organs are hidden within slits. Females have one large slit and two small mammary slits (above); males have a single slit (below).

FLIPPER
Beneath the surface of the paddle-shaped flipper, the skeletal structure reveals a remarkable similarity to the limbs of many land mammals.

CONICAL TEETH
The bottlenose dolphin has 18–26 pairs of conical, often discoloured, teeth — 5–10mm (0.2–0.4in) in diameter — in each jaw.

CREATURE COMPARISONS

The bottlenose dolphin is a member of the largest cetacean family: the oceanic, or beaked, dolphins. Powerfully built, it is superbly adapted to swimming long distances through heavy seas in search of prey. By contrast, the Amazon river dolphin, one of five species of river dolphin, is less athletic, having become adapted to life in silty, slow-flowing rivers. Unlike most river dolphins, which have poor vision, the Amazon river dolphin has good sight, but it also uses echolocation to find the bottom-dwelling fish on which it feeds.

Amazon river dolphin

Bottlenose dolphin

WHERE IN THE WORLD?

Widely distributed from cold temperate to tropical waters throughout the world, but is

particularly common in coastal waters and on the edge of continental shelves.

RELATED SPECIES
The bottlenose dolphin is one of 32 species in the family Delphinidae, which also includes the spinner dolphin. Three subspecies are recognized: a large Atlantic race T. t. truncatus, and two smaller races: T. t. gilli of the N Pacific and T. t. aduncus of the Indo-Pacific oceans.

GREY WHALE

• ORDER • *Cetacea* • FAMILY • *Eschrichtidae* • GENUS & SPECIES • *Eschrichtius robustus*

The grey whale puts on massive amounts of blubbery fat during the summer months in order to survive an exceptionally long migration.

KEY FEATURES

* Migrates twice each year, completing a round trip of nearly 20,000km (12,430 miles).

* Feeds frenziedly for six months, then eats almost nothing for the rest of the year.

* The most coastal baleen whale, providing spectacular sightings during its migrations.

BLOWHOLES
Like other baleen whales, the grey whale has two slit-shaped blowholes. Toothed whales have only one blowhole.

SKIN
The skin colour is black, or slate-grey, blotched with white. Underneath lies a layer of blubber up to 20cm (7.9in) thick, which serves as insulation and a food store.

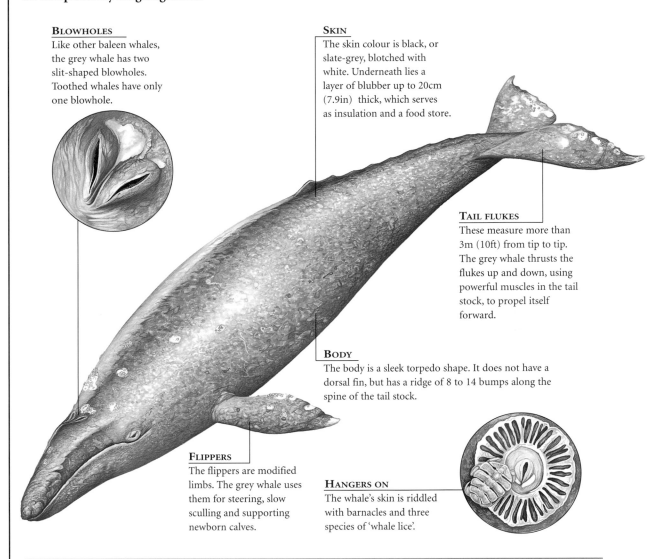

TAIL FLUKES
These measure more than 3m (10ft) from tip to tip. The grey whale thrusts the flukes up and down, using powerful muscles in the tail stock, to propel itself forward.

BODY
The body is a sleek torpedo shape. It does not have a dorsal fin, but has a ridge of 8 to 14 bumps along the spine of the tail stock.

FLIPPERS
The flippers are modified limbs. The grey whale uses them for steering, slow sculling and supporting newborn calves.

HANGERS ON
The whale's skin is riddled with barnacles and three species of 'whale lice'.

VITAL STATISTICS

WEIGHT	Male up to 22.6 tonnes (22.2 tons); female up to 31.7 tonnes (31.2 tons) when pregnant
LENGTH	Male average 13m (42ft 6in) female average 14m (45ft 9in)
SEXUAL MATURITY	5–11 years
MATING SEASON	December to February
GESTATION PERIOD	13 months
NUMBER OF YOUNG	1
BIRTH INTERVAL	Usually 2 years
TYPICAL DIET	Invertebrates, such as small shellfish and molluscs; also fish
LIFESPAN	Up to 77 years

CREATURE COMPARISONS

The grey whale takes in relatively small mouthfuls of seabed mud to filter out shellfish, and has only two or three throat grooves, which allow the throat to expand. The humpback whale swims into krill swarms and takes in huge mouthfuls and has several throat grooves to take in the watery 'soup.' The bowhead whale's cavernous mouth holds so much seawater in a single gulp that it does not need throat grooves.

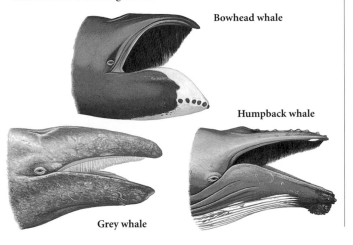

Bowhead whale

Humpback whale

Grey whale

WHERE IN THE WORLD?

Two separate populations exist in the Pacific Ocean: one on the western coast of North America, the other on the coast of Asia from Siberia south to Korea.

RELATED SPECIES
The grey whale is the only member of its family. It is most closely related to the six species of rorqual, family Balaenopteridae, and the three species of right whale, Balaenidae. The rorquals include the enormous blue whale and the highly vocal humpback whale. Like the grey whale, the rorquals and right whales all have baleen plates. All other whales, such as the orca, or killer whale, have teeth and are known as toothed whales.

• ORDER • *Cetacea* **• FAMILY •** *Monodontidae* **• GENUS & SPECIES •** *Delphinapterus leucas*

BELUGA

Supple and streamlined, the beluga powers through the open seas without tiring, while in shallow water it can perform intricate reversing manoeuvres.

KEY FEATURES

- Unique white colouration makes it one of the most easily recognized of all sea mammals.
- Lives in Arctic seas where it exploits the vast resources of fish and other marine life.
- Congregates in large numbers during the summer in shallow, coastal waters to feed and to rear young.

VITAL STATISTICS

WEIGHT	1.3–1.5 tonnes (1.27–1.47 tons)
LENGTH	3–4.6m (9ft 8in–15ft)
SEXUAL MATURITY	Female 4–7 years; male 8–9 years
MATING SEASON	Late February to May
GESTATION PERIOD	395–455 days
NUMBER OF YOUNG	1, rarely 2
BIRTH INTERVAL	2–3 years
TYPICAL DIET	Fish, squid, cuttlefish, crabs and shrimps
LIFESPAN	30–40 years

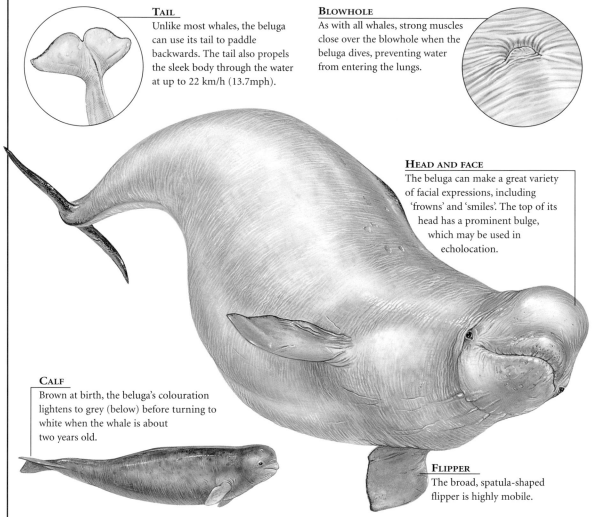

TAIL
Unlike most whales, the beluga can use its tail to paddle backwards. The tail also propels the sleek body through the water at up to 22 km/h (13.7mph).

BLOWHOLE
As with all whales, strong muscles close over the blowhole when the beluga dives, preventing water from entering the lungs.

HEAD AND FACE
The beluga can make a great variety of facial expressions, including 'frowns' and 'smiles'. The top of its head has a prominent bulge, which may be used in echolocation.

CALF
Brown at birth, the beluga's colouration lightens to grey (below) before turning to white when the whale is about two years old.

FLIPPER
The broad, spatula-shaped flipper is highly mobile.

CREATURE COMPARISONS

The little-studied North Atlantic bottle-nose whale (Hyperoodon ampullatus) shares the cold Arctic seas with the beluga, but prefers the deeper waters beyond the continental shelf where it hunts fish and squid. Much larger than its pure-white relative, the bottle-nose whale is one of 18 species of beaked whale, so called because of the protruding snout under the large, bulbous forehead. The skin of the bottle-nose whale becomes paler with age, approaching a creamy-white in the oldest individuals. However, it never becomes so white as to be confused with the ghostly beluga.

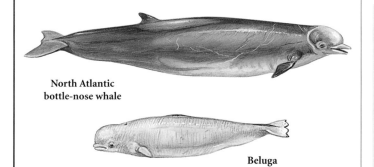

North Atlantic bottle-nose whale

Beluga

WHERE IN THE WORLD?

Found mainly in cold, shallow waters of the Arctic Ocean, Bering Sea, Sea of Okhotsk and adjoining seas.

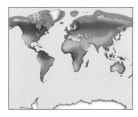

RELATED SPECIES

The beluga belongs to the family Monodontidae, which contains 1 other species, the narwhal, Monodon monoceros. Both species are part of the suborder of toothed whales, Odontoceti, which also includes porpoises, dolphins, bottle-nose whales and the sperm whale. The other suborder belonging to the whale order Cetacea is the Mysticeti, and contains the right whales, the grey whale and the rorquals, which include the blue whale.

SPERM WHALE

• ORDER • *Cetacea* • FAMILY • *Physeteridae* • GENUS & SPECIES • *Physeter macrocephalus*

A unique organ in the sperm whale's head helps control the buoyancy of this huge predator, helping it dive to greater depths than any other aquatic mammal.

KEY FEATURES

- Massive, squarish head accounts for as much as a third of its total bulk.

- Dives to tremendous depths, feeding in chasms in the ocean floor up to 3000m (9843ft) below the surface.

- Long lower jaw is lined with 20cm (7.9in)-long teeth to help the whale devour giant squid, its main prey.

- Once the most heavily hunted great whale, but fully protected since 1981.

VITAL STATISTICS

WEIGHT	Male 35–50 tonnes (34.4–49.2 tons); female 12–18 tonnes (11.8–17.7 tons)
LENGTH	Male 15–20m (5.9–7.9in); female 10–12m (3.9–4.7in)
MATING SEASON	Spring in equatorial waters
GESTATION PERIOD	14–16 months
NUMBER OF YOUNG	1
SEXUAL MATURITY	Male 18–20 years; female 10–12 years
BIRTH INTERVAL	5–7 years
TYPICAL DIET	Mainly squid, with some fish, octopus, crabs and other crustaceans
LIFESPAN	Up to 70 years

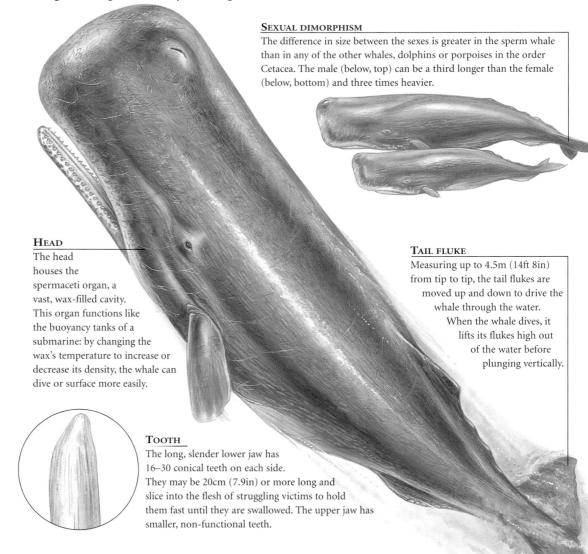

SEXUAL DIMORPHISM
The difference in size between the sexes is greater in the sperm whale than in any of the other whales, dolphins or porpoises in the order Cetacea. The male (below, top) can be a third longer than the female (below, bottom) and three times heavier.

HEAD
The head houses the spermaceti organ, a vast, wax-filled cavity. This organ functions like the buoyancy tanks of a submarine: by changing the wax's temperature to increase or decrease its density, the whale can dive or surface more easily.

TAIL FLUKE
Measuring up to 4.5m (14ft 8in) from tip to tip, the tail flukes are moved up and down to drive the whale through the water. When the whale dives, it lifts its flukes high out of the water before plunging vertically.

TOOTH
The long, slender lower jaw has 16–30 conical teeth on each side. They may be 20cm (7.9in) or more long and slice into the flesh of struggling victims to hold them fast until they are swallowed. The upper jaw has smaller, non-functional teeth.

CREATURE COMPARISONS

The pygmy sperm whale (Kogia breviceps) generally stays in warmer waters than its far larger relative, the sperm whale. Reaching a maximum length of 3.4m (11ft 1in), the pygmy sperm whale weighs up to 400kg (881.8lb): the largest bull (male) sperm whales are 125 times heavier. The two species are similar in having their functional teeth confined to the lower jaw, although the pygmy sperm whale has only 12–16 of them. Both whales eat a variety of squid, fish and crustaceans.

Little is known of the pygmy sperm whale's migratory habits or lifecycle as it is rarely seen alive. However, it strands itself fairly frequently on beaches along the coastlines of the USA, South Africa, Australia, New Zealand, India and Japan.

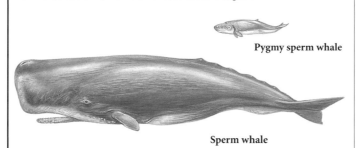

Pygmy sperm whale

Sperm whale

WHERE IN THE WORLD?

Found worldwide in deep, temperate seas, usually between 45°N and 40°S, but moves towards the poles in summer and back to the tropics in winter. Older males often swim as far as the icecaps of the Arctic and Antarctic.

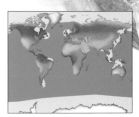

RELATED SPECIES
The sperm whale is the sole member of its genus, but shares the family Physeteridae with the pygmy sperm whale (Kogia breviceps) and the dwarf sperm whale (K. simus). All have a narrow lower jaw lined with teeth, a blowhole on the left side of the snout, and a large spermaceti organ inside the head. The latter two, however, are similar in size to larger dolphins, measuring, on average, 3m (9ft 8in) and 2.4m (7ft 9in) respectively.

• **ORDER** • *Characiformes* • **FAMILY** • *Characidae* • **GENUS & SPECIES** • *Various*

PIRANHA

Powerful jaws and deadly, razor-sharp teeth combined with a short, well-muscled body make the piranha a formidable aquatic predator.

KEY FEATURES

- Small, but powerful predator with muscular jaws and razor sharp teeth capable of cutting flesh and bone.

- An opportunistic fish that, as part of a large shoal, can tear apart and consume animals of considerable size within just a few minutes.

- Male is an attentive parent that guards his eggs.

VITAL STATISTICS

WEIGHT	1–2kg (2.2–4.4lb)
LENGTH	15–60cm (5.9–23.6in)
SEXUAL MATURITY	1–2 years
MATING SEASON	Onset of the wet season — December to May depending on location
NUMBER OF EGGS	From a few hundred up to 5000
BIRTH INTERVAL	1 year
TYPICAL DIET	Mainly fish, but also mammals and birds swimming in rivers, insects and fallen seeds, fruit and leaves; some species are vegetarian
LIFESPAN	Up to 5 years

JAWS
The protruding lower jaw anchors powerful muscles. The single row of teeth in the upper and lower jaw are periodically replaced, first on one side of the mouth then the other to allow the piranha to continue feeding.

COLOURING
Most species of piranha are olive-green or blue-black on the back with a dark to silvery-grey side and belly. An exception is the red-bellied piranha (below), which, as its name implies, has a vivid red belly.

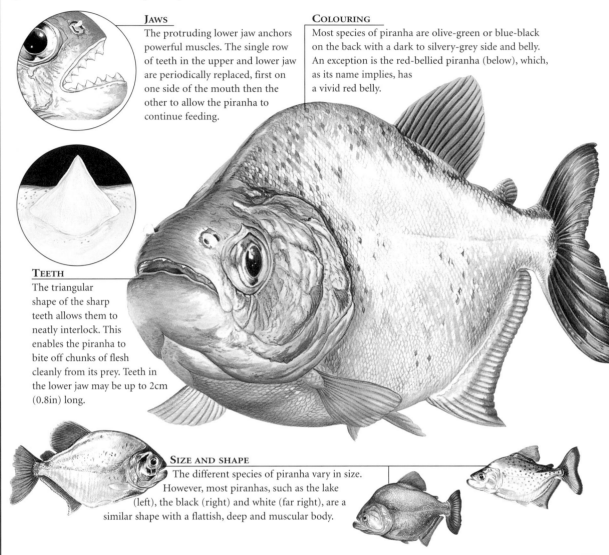

TEETH
The triangular shape of the sharp teeth allows them to neatly interlock. This enables the piranha to bite off chunks of flesh cleanly from its prey. Teeth in the lower jaw may be up to 2cm (0.8in) long.

SIZE AND SHAPE
The different species of piranha vary in size. However, most piranhas, such as the lake (left), the black (right) and white (far right), are a similar shape with a flattish, deep and muscular body.

CREATURE COMPARISONS

The Hawaiian sabre-tooth blenny (Runula goslinei), like the piranha, is a small carnivorous fish. This blenny has razor-sharp teeth but, unlike the piranha, its lower jaws bear a set of enormous fangs. However, the blenny is not a fierce predator, feeding mainly on worms, crustaceans, molluscs and some plant matter.

Its long teeth are used primarily for defence: if caught by a larger fish, for example, the blenny bites the inside of its captor's mouth and is normally spat out unharmed. Human bathers also need to beware — the sabre-tooth blenny has been known to inflict minor wounds on swimmers that disturb it.

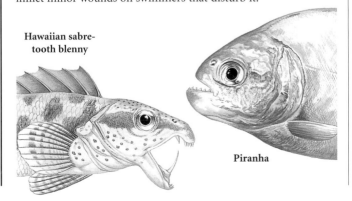

Hawaiian sabre-tooth blenny

Piranha

WHERE IN THE WORLD?

Found only in freshwaters in South America from Venezuela in the north, through much of the Amazon Basin and south to northeastern Argentina.

RELATED SPECIES

There are more than 30 species of piranha in various genera in the family Characidae. This family contains 841 species of fish, including two of the piranhas' closest cousins, the seed-eating tambaqui and the pacu toba, both of which are also found in the rivers of the Amazon Basin. While the pacu toba is similar in size and shape to the medium piranhas, the tambaqui is much larger, reaching up to 90cm (35.4in) in length and 30kg (66.1lb) in weight.

• ORDER • *Charadriiformes* • FAMILY • *Alcidae* • GENUS & SPECIES • *Alle alle*

KEY FEATURES

- A small seabird that swims around the Arctic pack-ice, where its numbers are counted in millions.

- Eats animal plankton, which it pursues underwater, powered by its wings and paddle-like feet.

- Raises its single chick in teeming, noisy colonies located on remote northern coasts.

VITAL STATISTICS

WEIGHT	140–192g (4.9–6.8oz)
LENGTH	17–19cm (6.7–7.5in)
WINGSPAN	40–48cm (15.7–18.9in)
SEXUAL MATURITY	Unknown
BREEDING SEASON	June–August
NUMBER OF EGGS	1
INCUBATION PERIOD	29 days
FLEDGING PERIOD	28–31 days
TYPICAL DIET	Animal plankton
LIFESPAN	Unknown

Dense, waterproof plumage and thick layers of body fat help to insulate the little auk from its harsh, icy environment.

BILL
The stubby bill is broad at the base for scooping up large quantities of plankton.

THROAT POUCH
The elastic skin of the throat expands to form a pouch in which the adult carries food for its chicks when returning to its nest from the sea.

WINTER PLUMAGE
Outside the breeding season, the entire underparts and lower face become white.

WINGS
The narrow wings whirr rapidly in flight, and act as flippers for propulsion underwater.

FOOT
The broad, webbed feet make efficient paddles for swimming. Like other auks, the little auk lacks hindtoes.

STANCE
The bird squats on its heels at rest. As in many swimming birds, its legs are sited close to its tail for effective paddling, but make it awkward on land.

CREATURE COMPARISONS

While the little auk feeds on plankton just below the surface in the deep ocean, its larger cousin, the black guillemot (Cepphus grylle), hunts on the seaweed-covered beds of shallower waters closer to the shore. A powerful swimmer, it catches crabs, prawns and fish, such as blennies, gobies and young cod, in its delicate slender bill. Like the little auk, the black guillemot lives in the High Arctic, although its breeding range stretches farther south to encompass northern Britain — including the Shetland Islands, where it gained its alternative name of 'tystie'. In winter, the black guillemot loses its pied plumage and its head and belly become mostly white, with upperparts speckled grey, brown and white.

Black guillemot

Little auk

WHERE IN THE WORLD?

Breeds on land within the Arctic Circle, including parts of Greenland, Iceland and northern Siberia. Winters at sea, mainly in the North Atlantic.

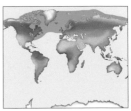

RELATED SPECIES
There are 22 species of auk in 11 genera within the family Alcidae, including the Atlantic puffin, *Fratercula arctica*, common guillemot, *Uria aalge*, and razorbill, *Alca torda*. Auks belong to the order Charadriiformes, which includes skuas, gulls, terns, plovers and waders.

• **ORDER** • *Charadriiformes* • **FAMILY** • *Alcidae* • **GENUS & SPECIES** • *Fratercula arctica*

ATLANTIC PUFFIN

KEY FEATURES

- A small, but tough and hardy seabird able to swim and dive for fish on storm-tossed high seas.
- Nests in vast clifftop or island colonies where pairs occupy a nesting burrow dug into the turf.
- Equipped with a massive and colourful bill, which is used for nibbling and wrestling during displays of affection or aggression, and also for catching fish.

VITAL STATISTICS

WEIGHT	Male 380g–550g (13.4–17.7oz); female 350–500g (12.3–17.6oz)
LENGTH	Head & Body: 26–30cm (10.2–11.8in) Bill: 3–4cm (1.2–1.6in)
WINGSPAN	47–63cm (18.5–24.8in)
SEXUAL MATURITY	5–6 years
BREEDING SEASON	April to August, depending on latitude
NUMBER OF EGGS	1 (rarely 2)
INCUBATION PERIOD	39–45 days
FLEDGING PERIOD	Very variable 35–50 days
TYPICAL DIET	Small fish, some molluscs and crustaceans particularly in Arctic waters)
LIFESPAN	10–15 years

Even with up to ten fish in its bill, the Atlantic puffin can carry on hunting and keep hold of its large catch.

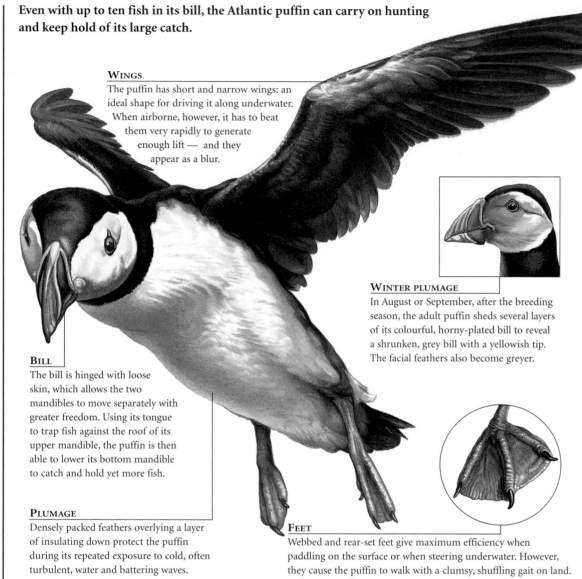

WINGS
The puffin has short and narrow wings: an ideal shape for driving it along underwater. When airborne, however, it has to beat them very rapidly to generate enough lift — and they appear as a blur.

WINTER PLUMAGE
In August or September, after the breeding season, the adult puffin sheds several layers of its colourful, horny-plated bill to reveal a shrunken, grey bill with a yellowish tip. The facial feathers also become greyer.

BILL
The bill is hinged with loose skin, which allows the two mandibles to move separately with greater freedom. Using its tongue to trap fish against the roof of its upper mandible, the puffin is then able to lower its bottom mandible to catch and hold yet more fish.

PLUMAGE
Densely packed feathers overlying a layer of insulating down protect the puffin during its repeated exposure to cold, often turbulent, water and battering waves.

FEET
Webbed and rear-set feet give maximum efficiency when paddling on the surface or when steering underwater. However, they cause the puffin to walk with a clumsy, shuffling gait on land.

CREATURE COMPARISONS

Considered one of the most striking of all the world's seabirds, the tufted puffin (Lunda cirrhata), is one of three species of puffin. During the breeding season it is adorned with a pair of flowing, pale yellow tufts of feathers, which sprout from behind its eyes and fall loosely over the back of its neck. The rest of its breeding dress is sooty black, except for the cheeks and throat, which are white. In late summer, the tufted puffin loses its colourful tassels and its cheeks become black.

Up to a third larger than the Atlantic puffin, the tufted puffin has an even more massive, red and yellow bill. It is found in the North Pacific, breeding in eastern Siberia and along North America's western seaboard as far south as California. Like its Atlantic relative, it winters far out at sea.

Atlantic puffin

Tufted puffin

WHERE IN THE WORLD?

Breeds in the Arctic and along the coasts of the North Atlantic and North Sea, from northeastern USA to northwestern France, Britain, Ireland and Scandinavia. Moves southwards and into offshore waters in winter.

RELATED SPECIES

The Atlantic puffin is one of 22 species of seabird known as auks, all of which belong to the family Alcidae. Auks are stocky, diving birds found in the oceans of the northern hemisphere and include the puffins, auklets, such as the little auk, Alle alle, guillemots, murrelets and the razorbill.

• ORDER • *Charadriiformes* • FAMILY • *Chionidae* • GENUS & SPECIES • *Chionis alba*

SNOWY SHEATHBILL

The sheathbill is essentially a wader that has adapted to spend most of its life on dry land. Luxuriantly thick plumage helps it brave the bitter winters.

KEY FEATURES

- The ultimate refuse scavenger of the Antarctic, where it survives by eating anything remotely edible.
- Lives by food-rich waters but does not swim or wade, so it has become expert at stealing from other animals.
- Usually found among penguins, timing its breeding with theirs to exploit seasonal feeding opportunities.

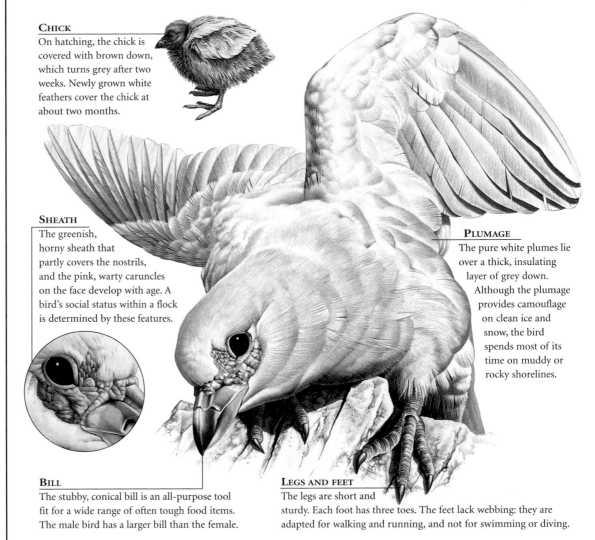

CHICK
On hatching, the chick is covered with brown down, which turns grey after two weeks. Newly grown white feathers cover the chick at about two months.

SHEATH
The greenish, horny sheath that partly covers the nostrils, and the pink, warty caruncles on the face develop with age. A bird's social status within a flock is determined by these features.

PLUMAGE
The pure white plumes lie over a thick, insulating layer of grey down. Although the plumage provides camouflage on clean ice and snow, the bird spends most of its time on muddy or rocky shorelines.

BILL
The stubby, conical bill is an all-purpose tool fit for a wide range of often tough food items. The male bird has a larger bill than the female.

LEGS AND FEET
The legs are short and sturdy. Each foot has three toes. The feet lack webbing: they are adapted for walking and running, and not for swimming or diving.

VITAL STATISTICS

WEIGHT	460–780g (16.2–27.5oz)
LENGTH	34–41cm (13.4–16.1in)
WINGSPAN	75–80cm (29.5–31in)
SEXUAL MATURITY	3–5 years
BREEDING SEASON	December to March
NUMBER OF EGGS	Usually 2 to 3
INCUBATION PERIOD	28–32 days
FLEDGING PERIOD	50–60 days
TYPICAL DIET	Any animal matter, including carrion, offal, faeces, fish, eggs and chicks. Also eats seaweed and human rubbish
LIFESPAN	Unknown

CREATURE COMPARISONS

The south polar skua (Catharacta maccormicki) is significantly heavier than the snowy sheathbill, and has a wingspan of about 1.3m (4ft 3in). Whereas the sheathbill has pure white plumage, the south polar skua varies in colour from dark brown to pale grey. Like the sheathbill, it breeds in loose colonies along the coastline of Antarctica, and is highly territorial. While the sheathbill steals food from Antarctic wildlife on land, the south polar skua does the same in the air. It chases terns and other birds relentlessly until they drop or disgorge their catches of fish. Like the sheathbill, the skua also eats penguins' eggs and chicks.

South polar skua

Snowy sheathbill

WHERE IN THE WORLD?

Breeds on the Antarctic Peninsula and nearby islands, as far north as South Georgia. Some birds overwinter in the Falkland Islands and South America.

RELATED SPECIES

The genus Chionis also includes the black-faced sheathbill, C. minor, found on a few sub-Antarctic islands in the southern Indian Ocean. Both species have white plumage, but the black-faced sheathbill has an entirely black bill and face. Sheathbills share the order Charadriiformes with several wader and seabird families. These include gulls (Laridae), terns (Sternidae), and the piratical skuas (Stercorariidae), which also live in the Southern Oceans.

• **ORDER** • *Charadriiformes* • **FAMILY** • *Glareolidae* • **GENUS & SPECIES** • *Pluvianus aegyptius*

EGYPTIAN PLOVER

Slightly hunched in appearance on the ground, the Egyptian plover reveals its stunning plumage and pointed wings in flight.

KEY FEATURES

- Attractive wading bird that uses sand to incubate its eggs, which are laid on an exposed patch of riverbed.
- Exceptionally fearless, and reputedly plucks food from the gaping mouths of crocodiles.
- A fast and nimble runner, it captures insects after a chase or stalks them with heron-like deliberation.

VITAL STATISTICS

WEIGHT	73–92g (2.6–3.2oz)
LENGTH	19–21cm (7.5–8.3in)
WINGSPAN	47–51cm (18.5–20.1in)
SEXUAL MATURITY	Probably 1 year
BREEDING SEASON	Mainly January to April, but varies across its range
NUMBER OF EGGS	2 to 3
INCUBATION PERIOD	28–31 days
FLEDGING PERIOD	30–35 days
TYPICAL DIET	Insects, worms and other invertebrates
LIFESPAN	Unknown

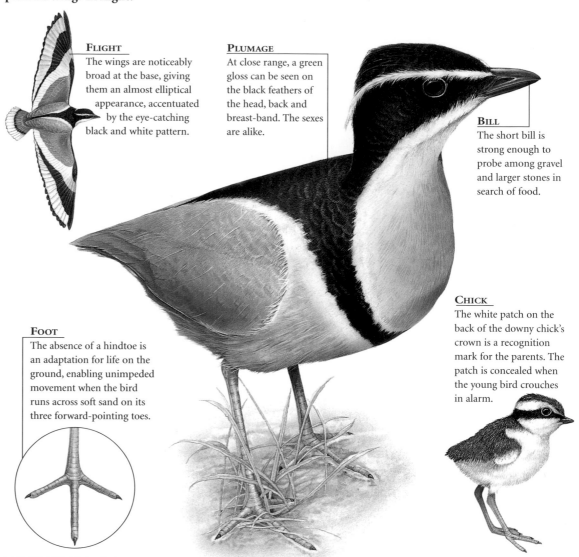

FLIGHT
The wings are noticeably broad at the base, giving them an almost elliptical appearance, accentuated by the eye-catching black and white pattern.

PLUMAGE
At close range, a green gloss can be seen on the black feathers of the head, back and breast-band. The sexes are alike.

BILL
The short bill is strong enough to probe among gravel and larger stones in search of food.

CHICK
The white patch on the back of the downy chick's crown is a recognition mark for the parents. The patch is concealed when the young bird crouches in alarm.

FOOT
The absence of a hindtoe is an adaptation for life on the ground, enabling unimpeded movement when the bird runs across soft sand on its three forward-pointing toes.

CREATURE COMPARISONS

Whereas the Egyptian plover is associated with inland waters, its relative the three-banded courser (Rhinoptilus cinctus) is found in the scrub, bushland and woodland of East Africa. Largely active from dusk till dawn, the courser uses its mottled brown upperparts to disguise itself when roosting under a bush during the day. The courser owes its common name to the three bands on its neck and breast. At the top, there is a chestnut band, then a thicker band of mottled brown with a black border, and below another chestnut band. Like the Egyptian plover, the courser feeds on the ground, either pecking at insects on the surface or probing into the soil with its bill. Its longer legs enable it to run quickly, its preferred method of escaping predators. Both birds nest in a deep scrape in the ground, partially burying their eggs at certain times during the incubation.

Three-banded courser

Egyptian plover

WHERE IN THE WORLD?

Distributed across sub-Saharan Africa, from Senegal to Ethiopia. Found mostly north of the Equator, but extends to Angola in the southern tropics. Populations in Egypt have become extinct.

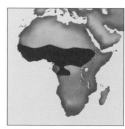

RELATED SPECIES

The Egyptian plover is the sole species in the genus Pluvianus, which is 1 of 6 genera in the family Glareolidae. This family contains the coursers and the pratincoles. The Egyptian plover is classified with the coursers — these are terrestrial birds that hawk for insects. The pratincoles are similar in size, but have a red base to the bill. The bill also has a wider gape, which helps them catch insects on the wing.

• ORDER • *Charadriiformes* • FAMILY • *Jacanidae* • GENUS & SPECIES • *Hydrophasianus chirurgus* PHEASANT-TAILED JACANA

The male pheasant-tailed jacana is smaller than the female and grows shorter, less splendid, tail plumes in the breeding season.

KEY FEATURES

- Every year, the female mates with several males, leaving each of them with a clutch of eggs to rear while she goes in search of her next breeding partner.
- Male guards his brood constantly, tucking them under his wings and carrying them whenever he goes foraging or needs to flee from predators.

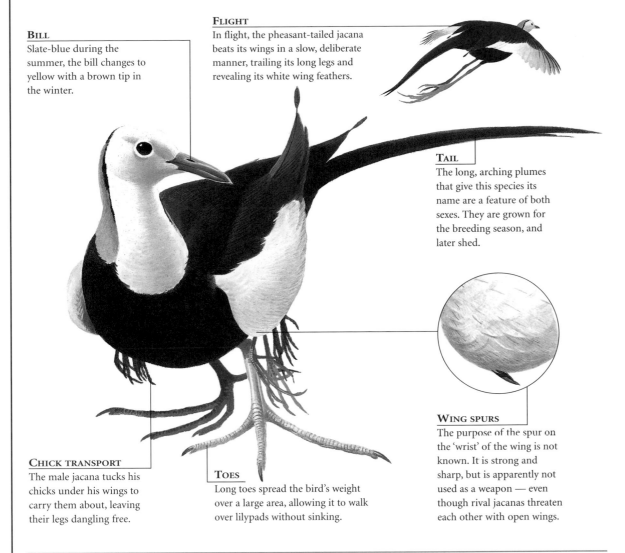

BILL
Slate-blue during the summer, the bill changes to yellow with a brown tip in the winter.

FLIGHT
In flight, the pheasant-tailed jacana beats its wings in a slow, deliberate manner, trailing its long legs and revealing its white wing feathers.

TAIL
The long, arching plumes that give this species its name are a feature of both sexes. They are grown for the breeding season, and later shed.

WING SPURS
The purpose of the spur on the 'wrist' of the wing is not known. It is strong and sharp, but is apparently not used as a weapon — even though rival jacanas threaten each other with open wings.

CHICK TRANSPORT
The male jacana tucks his chicks under his wings to carry them about, leaving their legs dangling free.

TOES
Long toes spread the bird's weight over a large area, allowing it to walk over lilypads without sinking.

VITAL STATISTICS

WEIGHT	120–184g (4.2–6.6oz)
LENGTH	58cm (22.8in), including tail plumes
WINGSPAN	63.5–68.5cm (25–27in)
SEXUAL MATURITY	2 years
BREEDING SEASON	Coincides with local rains
NUMBER OF EGGS	Usually 4 per clutch
INCUBATION PERIOD	About 26 days
FLEDGING PERIOD	50–60 days
BREEDING INTERVAL	1 to 3 broods per male; up to 10 per female
TYPICAL DIET	Molluscs, insects, seeds, roots
LIFESPAN	Not known

CREATURE COMPARISONS

Several of the pheasant-tailed jacana's relatives share some of its distinctive habits. The African jacana, or lily-trotter, also steps lightly over floating plants, as does the American purple gallinule.

The painted snipe of Africa, Asia and Australia — more closely related to jacanas than to true snipes — shares the female jacana's habit of taking several mates.

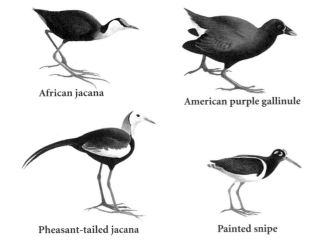

African jacana

American purple gallinule

Pheasant-tailed jacana

Painted snipe

WHERE IN THE WORLD?

Resident locally in the Middle East, across India and through Southeast Asia, including the Philippines, Taiwan and parts of Borneo. Also breeds in China.

RELATED SPECIES

The world's 8 species of jacana are found in North and South America, from the southern USA to northern Argentina, and in Africa, Australia, India, Indonesia, New Guinea and the Philippines. The jacanas' relatives include the plovers, family Charadriidae, the painted snipe, family Rostratulidae, and the oystercatchers, family Haematopodidae. The sandpipers, family Scolopacidae, are also related, but more distantly.

• ORDER • *Charadriiformes* • FAMILY • *Laridae* • GENUS & SPECIES • *Larus argentatus*

HERRING GULL

KEY FEATURES

- A versatile feeder that takes carrion and scraps as well as live prey, which it hunts with great skill and expertise.
- A bold bird prepared to take advantage of the many feeding and nesting opportunities provided by humans.
- Gregarious and lives in flocks, yet it fiercely defends a small breeding territory from unwanted intruders.

VITAL STATISTICS

WEIGHT	720–1500g (25.4–52.9oz)
LENGTH	55–67cm (21.6–26.4in)
WINGSPAN	1.35–1.45m (4ft 4in– 4ft 7in)
SEXUAL MATURITY	3–7 years, but usually 5 years
BREEDING SEASON	April to June
NUMBER OF EGGS	2 or 3
INCUBATION PERIOD	28–30 days
FLEDGING PERIOD	40–45 days
BREEDING INTERVAL	1 year
TYPICAL DIET	Fish, shellfish, worms and other invertebrates, small mammals and birds, plant matter and scraps
LIFESPAN	Up to 32 years

The large and heavily built herring gull is a versatile bird, equally equipped to soar the skies, 'sail' the seas and stroll about on the ground.

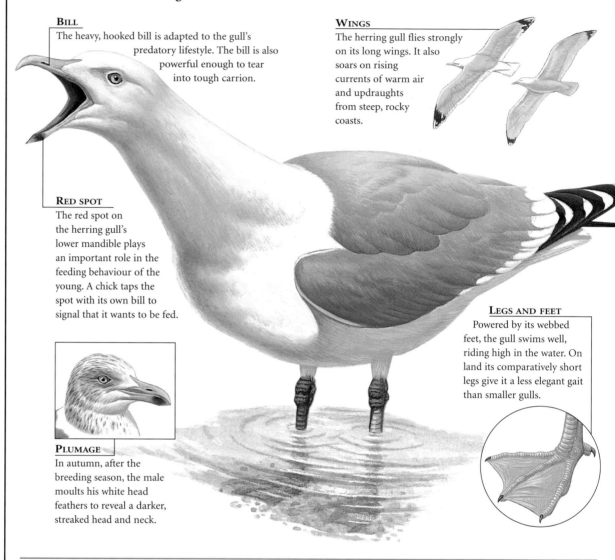

BILL
The heavy, hooked bill is adapted to the gull's predatory lifestyle. The bill is also powerful enough to tear into tough carrion.

WINGS
The herring gull flies strongly on its long wings. It also soars on rising currents of warm air and updraughts from steep, rocky coasts.

RED SPOT
The red spot on the herring gull's lower mandible plays an important role in the feeding behaviour of the young. A chick taps the spot with its own bill to signal that it wants to be fed.

LEGS AND FEET
Powered by its webbed feet, the gull swims well, riding high in the water. On land its comparatively short legs give it a less elegant gait than smaller gulls.

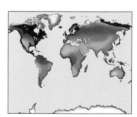

PLUMAGE
In autumn, after the breeding season, the male moults his white head feathers to reveal a darker, streaked head and neck.

CREATURE COMPARISONS

Even the larger male herring gulls are dwarfed by the great black-backed gull, *Larus marinus*, which may reach 79cm (31in) from head to tail. More powerfully built than the herring gull, the great black-backed gull's head and neck are noticeably thickset and its wingbeats are very deep and powerful.

During the breeding season, the highly predatory great black-backed gull feeds almost exclusively on seabirds and, if they are available, rabbits. Like the herring gull it also frequents rubbish dumps and scavenges around fishing ports for scraps.

Great black-backed gull   **Herring gull**

WHERE IN THE WORLD?

Breeds in North America, coastal Europe and northern Asia. Some birds remain in the north for winter, while others migrate to Iberia, the West Indies, Central America and the coasts of the South China Sea.

RELATED SPECIES

The herring gull is one of 47 species of gull in the family Laridae. Another member of this family is the striking swallow-tailed gull, *Creagrus furcatus* (below), from South America. The herring gull's relations in the order Charadriiformes include terns and skuas.

• ORDER • *Charadriiformes* • FAMILY • *Laridae* • GENUS & SPECIES • *Larus ridibundus*

BLACK-HEADED GULL

The black-headed gull has a multi-purpose body plan. Agile in the air, it is also nimble on the ground and yet quite at home paddling on the water.

KEY FEATURES

- Unlike most gulls, spends much of its life far inland.
- Adapts with ease to man-made environments, nesting and roosting on reservoirs and gravel-pits, feeding on farmland and scavenging at refuse dumps and parks.
- Sexes look identical and raise their young together, amid the din of bustling, close-packed colonies.

VITAL STATISTICS

WEIGHT	210–360g (463–793.7lb)
LENGTH	38–44cm (15–17.3in)
WINGSPAN	90–100cm (35.4–39.4in)
SEXUAL MATURITY	2 years
BREEDING SEASON	April to July
NUMBER OF EGGS	2 to 3
INCUBATION PERIOD	23–26 days
FLEDGING PERIOD	35 days
BREEDING INTERVAL	1 year
TYPICAL DIET	Invertebrates, carrion, small animal prey and scraps
LIFESPAN	Up to 30 years

BILL
The pointed bill enables the black-headed gull to catch insects in flight and to pick them off the ground or plants. It is also sturdy enough to deal with carrion and scraps.

JUVENILE
The juvenile has orange-brown areas on its back, wings, neck and head, pinkish legs and feet, and a black tip to its pale bill.

WINTER PLUMAGE
In August, the black-headed gull loses its dark 'hood'. A faint smudge behind the eye is all that remains until the hood is regained in the following February or March.

FEET
The scarlet feet are webbed, allowing the gull to paddle on the water surface and to stand on soft mud or sand.

CREATURE COMPARISONS

When seen from a distance or in poor light, the black-headed gull's chocolate-brown head appears blackish, but the great black-headed gull (*Larus ichthyaetus*) has a truly pure-black head. Both species have white 'eyelids' — actually feathers — but these are more striking in the larger great black-headed gull. Its powerful bill is yellow and red, with a narrow black band separating the two zones of colour. Its legs and feet are also bright yellow.

The great black-headed gull is far less common than the black-headed gull, breeding in scattered colonies on coastal marshes and lakes on steppes across central and southern Asia, as far west as Asian Turkey. Unlike the black-headed gull, nearly all of its populations migrate to winter on the Caspian Sea and the Indian Ocean.

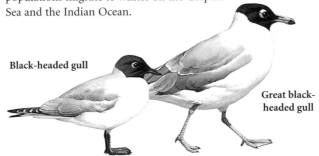

Black-headed gull

Great black-headed gull

WHERE IN THE WORLD?

Breeds across Europe and Asia, from Iceland to the far east of Russia. Some birds move south in winter, to the Middle East, western Africa and eastern North America.

RELATED SPECIES

There are 47 species of gull in the family Laridae. Most gulls generally have pale plumages that are grey above and white below, but the ivory gull (Pagophila eburnea) is all-white, and Ross's gull (Rhodostethia rosea) has pink underparts. Gulls live out at sea or in wetland habitats, and nest in noisy colonies. Close relatives of the gulls include the terns in the family Sternidae, and the skuas (also called jaegars), in the family Stercorariidae.

• **ORDER** • *Charadriiformes* • **FAMILY** • *Recurvirostridae* • **GENUS & SPECIES** • *Recurvirostra avosetta*

EURASIAN AVOCET

A delicate, upturned bill and long legs give the Eurasian avocet one the most elegant profiles of all wading birds.

KEY FEATURES

- Scythes through mud and water with its specialized upturned bill to filter out tiny aquatic organisms.
- Slim and strikingly patterned in black-and-white, it is a conspicuous inhabitant of saltwater wetlands.
- Defends its nest vigorously during the breeding season, noisily driving away intruders.

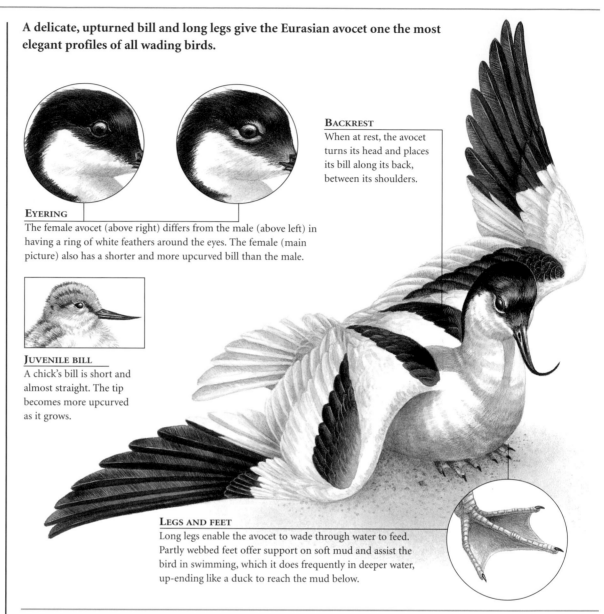

EYERING
The female avocet (above right) differs from the male (above left) in having a ring of white feathers around the eyes. The female (main picture) also has a shorter and more upcurved bill than the male.

JUVENILE BILL
A chick's bill is short and almost straight. The tip becomes more upcurved as it grows.

BACKREST
When at rest, the avocet turns its head and places its bill along its back, between its shoulders.

LEGS AND FEET
Long legs enable the avocet to wade through water to feed. Partly webbed feet offer support on soft mud and assist the bird in swimming, which it does frequently in deeper water, up-ending like a duck to reach the mud below.

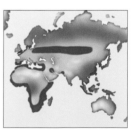

VITAL STATISTICS

WEIGHT	225–397g (7.9–14oz)
LENGTH	42–45cm (16.5–17.7in)
WINGSPAN	77–80cm (30.3–31in)
SEXUAL MATURITY	2–3 years
BREEDING SEASON	April to August in Eurasia
NUMBER OF EGGS	2 to 5, but usually 3 to 4
INCUBATION PERIOD	23–25 days
FLEDGING PERIOD	35–42 days
BREEDING INTERVAL	1 year
TYPICAL DIET	Aquatic insects, invertebrates, molluscs, worms, small fish
LIFESPAN	10–12 years

CREATURE COMPARISONS

Avocets and stilts are closely related, and birds of both families are characterized by contrasting black-and-white plumage. The black-winged stilt, *Himantopus himantopus*, has a fine, straight bill and extraordinarily long, red legs. As the muscles that operate its bill are very strong, the stilt can grip prey, such as shrimps, tightly, while its long legs enable it to wade into deep water.

Whereas the Eurasian avocet prefers saltwater habitats, the black-winged stilt favours freshwaters, such as marshes, flooded fields and lakesides, and has a virtually worldwide distribution, in both the tropics and the subtropics.

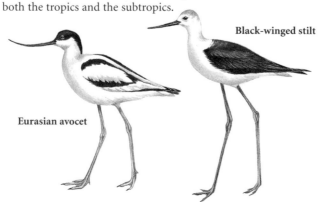

Black-winged stilt

Eurasian avocet

WHERE IN THE WORLD?

Found on wetlands from Europe across central Asia to China. Winters in North and West Africa, the Middle East and southeast China. Also occurs in East Africa.

RELATED SPECIES

There are four species of avocet and all have upturned bills and a pied plumage. Two species also share a chestnut-red head and neck: the American avocet (*Recurvirostra americana*), which occurs from Mexico to southern Canada, and the red-necked avocet (*R. novaehollandiae*), of Australia. The Andean avocet (*R. andina*), inhabits high lakes and marshes up to altitudes of 3100m (10,170ft) in South America's Andes mountain range.

• ORDER • *Charadriiformes* • FAMILY • *Scolopacidae* • GENUS & SPECIES • *Numenius arquata*

EURASIAN CURLEW

The Eurasian curlew's slender, downcurved bill is a remarkably adaptable tool that equips the bird to feed in a variety of habitats through the year.

KEY FEATURES

- Probes deep into mud or soft soil with a long, curved bill to locate and capture prey that is beyond the reach of other ground-probing birds.

- Has highly effective camouflaged plumage to help hide it when nesting on open ground.

- Moves to a different habitat with the changing seasons, migrating between inland sites and estuaries and coasts.

VITAL STATISTICS

WEIGHT	400–1300g (14–45.9oz). Female larger than male
LENGTH	50–60cm (19.7–23.6in)
WINGSPAN	80–100cm (31–39.4in)
SEXUAL MATURITY	2 years
BREEDING SEASON	April to July
NUMBER OF EGGS	2 to 5, usually 4
INCUBATION PERIOD	27–29 days
FLEDGING PERIOD	32–38 days
BREEDING INTERVAL	1 year
TYPICAL DIET	Worms, molluscs, crustaceans, invertebrates; some berries and seeds
LIFESPAN	10–15 years

FLOCK FORMATION
Outside the breeding season, curlews gather in flocks of about 25–50 birds, forming much larger flocks on migration. They may fly in a long line, but often adopt a 'V-shaped', or chevron, formation. The curlews save energy by flying in each other's wake, occasionally changing position, to take advantage of the slipstream and upwash of air produced by the wings of the birds in front.

RUMP
The Eurasian curlew has a white rump — the area above the base of the tail that extends onto its lower back in the shape of a triangle. Most visible in flight, this bold pattern helps curlews to keep track of one another when flying in flocks.

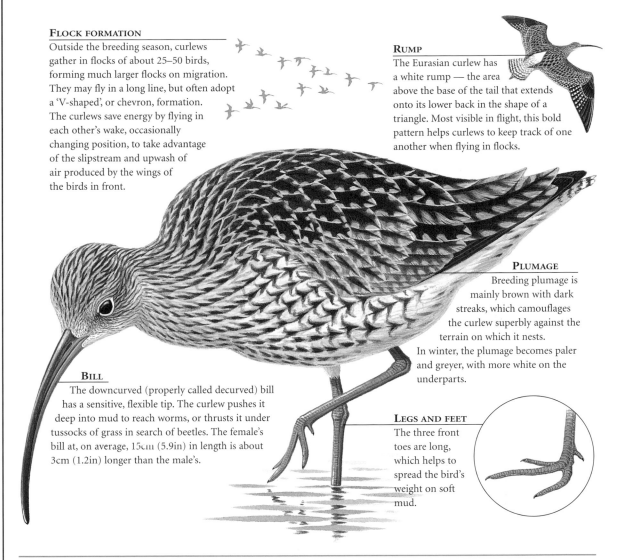

PLUMAGE
Breeding plumage is mainly brown with dark streaks, which camouflages the curlew superbly against the terrain on which it nests. In winter, the plumage becomes paler and greyer, with more white on the underparts.

BILL
The downcurved (properly called decurved) bill has a sensitive, flexible tip. The curlew pushes it deep into mud to reach worms, or thrusts it under tussocks of grass in search of beetles. The female's bill at, on average, 15cm (5.9in) in length is about 3cm (1.2in) longer than the male's.

LEGS AND FEET
The three front toes are long, which helps to spread the bird's weight on soft mud.

CREATURE COMPARISONS

The whimbrel (Numenius phaeopus), has very similar overall plumage to the closely related curlew, and at a distance is easily mistaken for it. However, the whimbrel's head is distinctively marked with a dark eyestripe and a broad brown band across the crown. The whimbrel is also smaller, at only three-quarters of the curlew's size, and it has a significantly shorter bill and legs. It feeds in a completely different way to the curlew, using its downcurved bill to snatch small prey from the surface of the ground rather than by probing into it.

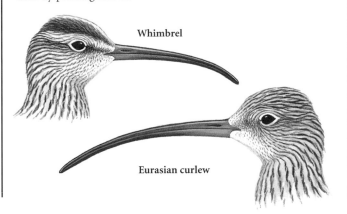

Whimbrel

Eurasian curlew

WHERE IN THE WORLD?

Breeds from Britain and Ireland across Europe, Russia and Kazakhstan, to northeast China. In winter, local populations migrate west or south to the coasts of Europe, Africa, the Gulf States, India and the Far East.

RELATED SPECIES
There are 88 species of wader in the family Scolopacidae, of which 8 are curlews. The stone-curlew, a distant relative of the curlew, belongs to the family Burhinidae (the thick-knees). It takes its name from its haunting, curlew-like calls and liking for dry, stony habitats.

• **ORDER** • *Charadriiformes* • **FAMILY** • *Scolopacidae* • **GENUS & SPECIES** • *Philomachus pugnax*

RUFF

Many male birds are brighter than their mates, but the male ruff's spring finery is exceptional. He parades in front of drab females as if in fancy dress.

KEY FEATURES

- For a few weeks in spring, each breeding male wears a uniquely patterned feather-collar, or ruff.
- Rival males compete for the right to mate by staging mock battles at communal arenas known as leks.
- Embarks on marathon migrations each year, from the Arctic tundra to southern Africa and back again.

SATELLITE MALE
Some adult males inherit white ear-tufts and ruffs (right). During the breeding season, these 'satellite males' do not compete directly with other males at the lek. Instead, they each join forces with a dominant male, which seems to help the dominant bird to attract more females. But while he is busy fighting rivals, the satellite male slyly seizes his chance to mate unnoticed.

FACE
The breeding male (below) has a featherless face, with orange or yellow skin covered in small warts.

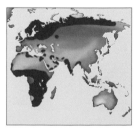

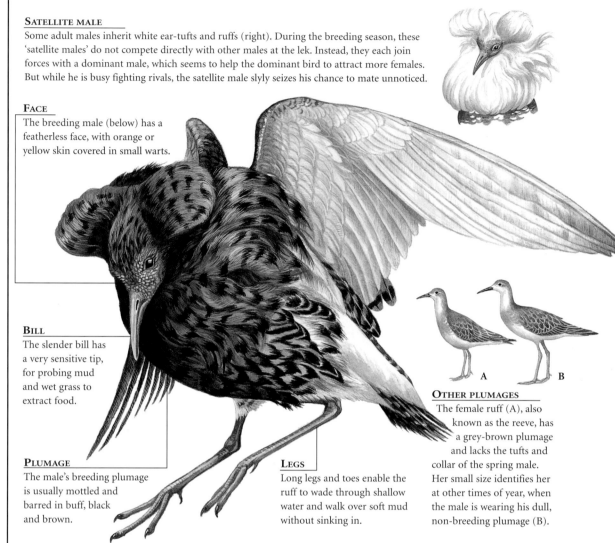

BILL
The slender bill has a very sensitive tip, for probing mud and wet grass to extract food.

PLUMAGE
The male's breeding plumage is usually mottled and barred in buff, black and brown.

LEGS
Long legs and toes enable the ruff to wade through shallow water and walk over soft mud without sinking in.

OTHER PLUMAGES
The female ruff (A), also known as the reeve, has a grey-brown plumage and lacks the tufts and collar of the spring male. Her small size identifies her at other times of year, when the male is wearing his dull, non-breeding plumage (B).

VITAL STATISTICS

WEIGHT	Male 140–230g (4.9–8.1oz); female 85–140g (3–4.9oz)
LENGTH	Male 28–30cm (11–11.8in); female 23–24cm (9–9.4in)
WINGSPAN	35–50cm (13.8–19.7in)
SEXUAL MATURITY	1–2 years
BREEDING SEASON	May to August
NUMBER OF EGGS	4 (rarely 3)
INCUBATION PERIOD	20–21 days
FLEDGING PERIOD	Chicks are independent a few days after hatching
BREEDING INTERVAL	1 year
TYPICAL DIET	Mainly insects; also molluscs, worms, seeds
LIFESPAN	Up to 10 years

CREATURE COMPARISONS

Nearly all wading birds, including the ruff, have relatively long bills with narrow points, but the spoon-billed sandpiper (Eurynorhynchus pygmeus) provides a striking exception to this rule. As its name suggests, the sandpiper has a broad, flattened bill, which gradually widens into a spatula shape at the tip. It feeds by sweeping this remarkable bill from side to side over soft mud.

Only half as large as a male ruff, or two-thirds the size of a female, the spoon-billed sandpiper has much shorter legs and a graceful, slim profile. Unlike the ruff, the sexes look identical. Only 2800 pairs of the spoon-billed sandpiper are thought to remain, breeding in northeast Siberia and wintering in India and Southeast Asia.

Ruff (breeding male; ear-tufts and collar down)

Spoon-billed sandpiper

WHERE IN THE WORLD?

Breeds from Scandinavia and the Baltic Sea region east across the Siberian Arctic. Winters in western Europe, the Mediterranean, Africa and southern Asia.

RELATED SPECIES

The male ruff's unique breeding plumage has led to the species being placed in its own genus, Philomachus, one of 23 genera in the family Scolopacidae. With 85 species, this family contains nearly half of all the world's wading birds, including the sandpipers, curlews, snipes, woodcocks, turnstones, phalaropes and godwits. Among them are the only wading birds other than the ruff to use the lek system: the great snipe and the buff-breasted sandpiper.

• ORDER • *Charadriiformes* **• FAMILY •** *Stercorariidae* **• GENUS & SPECIES •** *Stercorarius parasiticus*

ARCTIC SKUA

KEY FEATURES

- A ruthless pirate that chases and bullies weaker seabirds to make them surrender their catch of fish.

- Adaptable and agile as well as aggressive, it can also hunt small prey, rob nests and scavenge carrion.

- Migrates halfway around the world for the winter, from its Arctic nesting sites to the southern oceans.

VITAL STATISTICS

WEIGHT	350–600g (12.3–21.2oz)
LENGTH	38–48cm (15–18.9in)
WINGSPAN	1.1–1.25m (3ft 6in–4ft 1in)
SEXUAL MATURITY	4–5 years
BREEDING SEASON	May to August
NUMBER OF EGGS	2
INCUBATION PERIOD	25–28 days
FLEDGING PERIOD	25–30 days
BREEDING INTERVAL	1 year
TYPICAL DIET	Steals fish, eggs and chicks from seabirds; hunts small mammals and birds; also feeds on carrion, insects and berries
LIFESPAN	Up to 18 years

Combining a fearsome bill with the speed and manoeuvrability provided by powerful, falcon-like wings, the Arctic skua is a force to be reckoned with.

BILL
Powerful and with a strongly hooked upper mandible, the bill can rip apart flesh with ease.

PLUMAGE
The skua is seen either in the brown plumage of its dark morph (above) or the cream neck and underparts of the pale morph (below). The dark morph is common in the south of the breeding range, the pale morph prevailing in the north.

TAIL
Two of the skua's central tail feathers are long and tapering, and continue to grow throughout the bird's life.

FEET
The Arctic skua combines the webbed feet of a waterbird, such as a duck or pelican, with the sharply hooked claws of a predator, such as an eagle or hawk — a design shared by all the skuas but unique to their family.

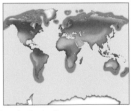

CREATURE COMPARISONS

The Arctic skua shares part of its breeding range with the great skua (*Stercorarius skua*), which prefers to nest in damper, upland habitats. Resembling a massive gull, the great skua has little of the elegant grace of its relative, and its shorter tail lacks elongated central feathers. It flies strongly on broad wings, which have distinctive white flashes on the upper and lower surfaces. Some Arctic skuas also have white wing-patches, but they are never as striking as those of the great skua, which is otherwise entirely dark-coloured.

One of the heavyweight bullies of the bird world, the great skua usually attacks larger seabirds than does the Arctic skua, and tugs at their wings and tail to make them drop or regurgitate their catch.

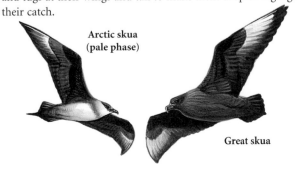

Arctic skua (pale phase)

Great skua

WHERE IN THE WORLD?

Breeds in a circumpolar ring, from Alaska around to Siberia and south as far as Scotland. Winters off southern Australia, Africa and South America.

RELATED SPECIES

The 7 species of skua in the family Stercorariidae belong to the large order Charadriiformes, which also includes 16 families of gulls, skimmers, terns, waders and auks. The Arctic, pomarine, long-tailed and great skuas nest in the far north of the northern hemisphere, while the Chilean, Antarctic and south polar skuas breed on the southernmost coasts of South America and in the sub-Antarctic and Antarctic. All the skuas are fast-flying pirates and scavengers.

• **ORDER** • *Charadriiformes* • **FAMILY** • *Sternidae* • **GENUS & SPECIES** • *Sterna paradisaea*

ARCTIC TERN

The Arctic tern's streamlined form allows it to dive for fish with masterful agility, and minimizes drag during its long migrations.

KEY FEATURES

- An elegant and agile bird with great stamina.
- Travels farther on migration than any other animal.
- Follows the sun through the seasons, experiencing more daylight in a year than any other animal.
- In its lifetime, may fly farther than the total distance to the moon and back.

BILL
The sharp edges of the bill help the tern to hold a wriggling fish. The deep red colour stimulates the chicks to beg for food; after the breeding season, the bill turns black.

WINGS
Long and pointed to allow the tern to dive with speed and agility when surface feeding.

PLUMAGE
The adult tern is pure white with a few black streaks on the forehead. In the breeding season, the head has a black cap.

FEET
The three front toes are webbed, although the tern is not a particularly good swimmer. The fourth toe is reduced to a peg at the back of the foot.

TAIL
Long tail streamers act like a rudder to help the tern adjust its angle of descent as it dives for fish. The streamers are also used for display in courtship flights.

VITAL STATISTICS

WEIGHT	100–115g (3.5–4oz)
LENGTH	33–35cm (13–13.8in)
WINGSPAN	76–84cm (29.9–33.1in)
SEXUAL MATURITY	2–5 years, usually 4
BREEDING SEASON	May to August
NUMBER OF EGGS	1 to 3
INCUBATION PERIOD	20–24 days
BREEDING INTERVAL	1 year
TYPICAL DIET	Mainly marine fish, crustaceans, small squid, insects
LIFESPAN	Up to 34 years

CREATURE COMPARISONS

A few subtle features help to distinguish the Arctic tern from other members of its family with which it shares parts of its range. The Arctic tern's bill is a deep blood red during the breeding season and black for the rest of the year, whereas the common tern, Sterna hirundo, has a black tip to its bright red bill during the breeding season. Much larger than the other two birds, the royal tern has a ragged black crest and a bright yellow-orange bill.

Arctic tern

Common tern

Royal tern

WHERE IN THE WORLD?

Breeds in the far north of Canada, Asia and Europe. Spends the rest of the year in the southern Pacific and Atlantic Oceans, chiefly on the Antarctic pack ice.

RELATED SPECIES

There are 43 species of tern in the family Sternidae. These include the common tern, Sterna hirundo, of North America, Europe and Asia. The Antarctic tern, S. vittata, which is slightly larger than the Arctic tern, was previously thought to be descended from Arctic terns that stopped migrating and stayed on to breed on islands close to the Antarctic Circle; today, though, the two birds are recognized as quite separate species.

• ORDER • *Chelonia* • FAMILY • *Cheloniidae* • GENUS & SPECIES • *Chelonia mydas*

GREEN TURTLE

The green turtle thrusts itself through the water using limbs that have been transformed by the forces of evolution into highly effective flippers.

KEY FEATURES

- A tough-shelled marine reptile that grazes on submarine meadows of sea grass.
- Undertakes awesome journeys across the oceans to mate off the shores of traditional nesting islands.
- An endangered species threatened by hunting, habitat destruction and pollution.

VITAL STATISTICS

WEIGHT	Usually 55–270kg (121.3–595.2lb), but may weigh up to 400kg (881.8lb)
LENGTH	70–150cm (27.6–59.1in)
SEXUAL MATURITY	Over 10 years
NESTING SEASON	Varies according to location, but usually late spring and early summer
NUMBER OF EGGS	75–200 per clutch, 1–8 clutches every season
INCUBATION PERIOD	Normally 6–8 weeks; depends on temperature
BREEDING INTERVAL	2–4 years
TYPICAL DIET	Marine plants
LIFESPAN	50 years or more

TEAR GLANDS
A specially adapted tear gland located next to each eye allows the green turtle to rid its body of excess salt.

FOREFLIPPERS
The turtle uses its long, powerful foreflippers for propulsion. The male has a curved claw on the leading edge of each flipper so that he can grip the female as they mate.

JAWS
Lacking teeth, the green turtle has sharp-edged, horny plates on its jaws that cut through vegetation. Like human fingernails, the plates grow continuously.

TAIL
The female (above) has a short tail, while the male's tail extends some 20cm (7.9in) beyond the upper shell. When mating, the male curls his tail around the female's rump to bring his cloaca (genital opening) into the correct position.

PLASTRON
The lower shell, or plastron, is cut away from both the foreflippers and hindflippers to allow for easy movement of the limbs.

CREATURE COMPARISONS

The green turtle shares its ocean habitat with the Pacific or olive ridley turtle (*Lepidochelys olivacea*) — a smaller species of sea turtle that ranges throughout the warmer regions of the Pacific and Indian oceans.

Unlike the green turtle, the Pacific ridley has a mainly flesh-based diet. It typically feeds on sea urchins, shellfish and jellyfish, but also takes seaweed and other marine vegetation. Like the green turtle, the Pacific ridley swims huge distances on its annual breeding migrations. The Pacific ridley is thought to be more of a bottom-dweller than other species of sea turtle.

Pacific ridley turtle

Green turtle

WHERE IN THE WORLD?

Has an enormous range, occurring in warm seas throughout the world. Cannot survive in water temperatures below 20°C (68°F).

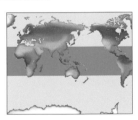

RELATED SPECIES

The green turtle is 1 of 6 species of sea turtle in the widespread family Cheloniidae. The others are the Pacific or olive ridley, the Atlantic or Kemp's ridley, the hawksbill, the loggerhead and the flatback. A seventh species of sea turtle, the leatherback, is placed in its own family, Dermochelyidae. The Cheloniidae is one of 13 families in the order Chelonia, which includes all the 240 or so species of turtle and tortoise.

• **ORDER** • *Chelonia* • **FAMILY** • *Dermochelyidae* • **GENUS & SPECIES** • *Dermochelyus coriacea*

LEATHERBACK TURTLE

On land, this turtle is so heavy that it almost crushes its own lungs. In the water, however, it is transformed into a sleek, buoyant ocean cruiser.

KEY FEATURES

- Female swims thousands of kilometres to lay her eggs on the beach where she originally hatched.
- Largest living sea turtle, with a uniquely soft shell.
- Body temperature stays several degrees above that of seawater, allowing the turtle to penetrate far into cool ocean waters.

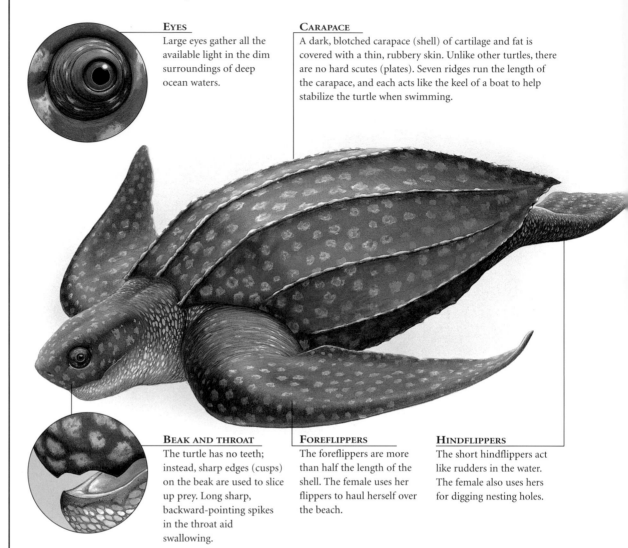

EYES
Large eyes gather all the available light in the dim surroundings of deep ocean waters.

CARAPACE
A dark, blotched carapace (shell) of cartilage and fat is covered with a thin, rubbery skin. Unlike other turtles, there are no hard scutes (plates). Seven ridges run the length of the carapace, and each acts like the keel of a boat to help stabilize the turtle when swimming.

BEAK AND THROAT
The turtle has no teeth; instead, sharp edges (cusps) on the beak are used to slice up prey. Long sharp, backward-pointing spikes in the throat aid swallowing.

FOREFLIPPERS
The foreflippers are more than half the length of the shell. The female uses her flippers to haul herself over the beach.

HINDFLIPPERS
The short hindflippers act like rudders in the water. The female also uses hers for digging nesting holes.

VITAL STATISTICS

WEIGHT	Up to about 900kg (1984lb)
LENGTH	Up to 2.7m (8ft 8in)
SEXUAL MATURITY	When carapace reaches a span of 1.3–1.45m (4ft 3in–4ft 8in)
NESTING SEASON	Dependent on location; almost any time of year
NUMBER OF EGGS	Up to 900 each season. Clutches of 80 to 90 eggs, at 10-day intervals.
INCUBATION PERIOD	55–74 days
BREEDING INTERVAL	2–3 years
TYPICAL DIET	Jellyfish, crustaceans, molluscs
LIFESPAN	Up to 100 years or more

CREATURE COMPARISONS

Most sea turtles share a similar body plan — one that has barely changed over more than 100 million years. However, the leatherback turtle is unique among sea turtles in having a soft carapace (shell). In all other sea turtles the carapace is covered with horny plates. The leatherback turtle also differs in having sharp-cutting cusps on its beak, with which it snaps up jellyfish. The green turtle, which eats eel grass, has a smooth-edged beak with no cusps.

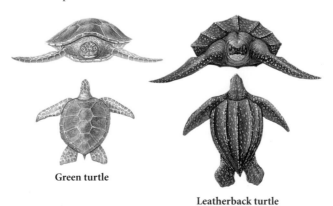

Green turtle

Leatherback turtle

WHERE IN THE WORLD?

Wanders across the Atlantic, Pacific and Indian Oceans, between latitudes 60°N and 40°S. Also found in the Mediterranean Sea. Female nests on tropical beaches.

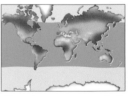

RELATED SPECIES

The leatherback is the largest of seven species of sea turtles. The others — Atlantic or Kemp's ridley, flatback, hawksbill, green, loggerhead, and Pacific or Olive ridley — are also ocean wanderers, but they are found mainly in warm waters and rarely reach temperate seas.

RED-EARED TERRAPIN

• ORDER • *Chelonia* • FAMILY • *Emydidae* • GENUS & SPECIES • *Pseudemys scripta elegans*

The red-eared terrapin is at home both in and out of the water. Its shell offers all-round protection while its webbed limbs allow it to swim and walk.

KEY FEATURES

- Takes its name from a thick, red stripe behind each eye, which looks like an ear opening.

- Shy, cautious creature that only comes out of the water to bask in the sun or to lay eggs.

- In temperatures below 10°C (50°F) or above 37°C (98.6°F), it submerges itself deep in mud to 'hibernate'.

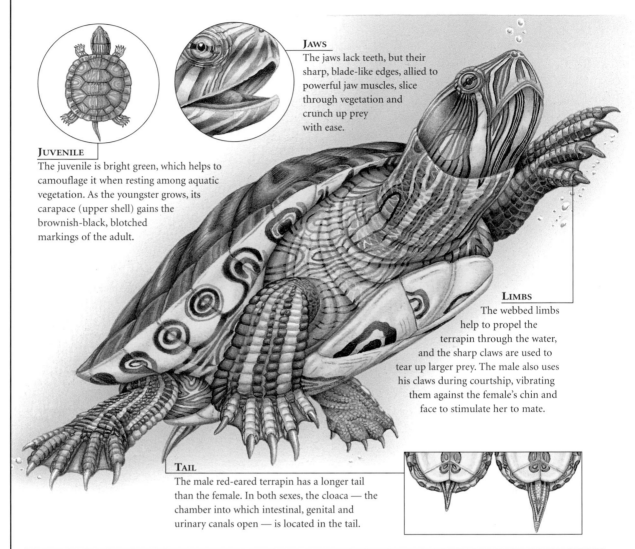

JAWS
The jaws lack teeth, but their sharp, blade-like edges, allied to powerful jaw muscles, slice through vegetation and crunch up prey with ease.

JUVENILE
The juvenile is bright green, which helps to camouflage it when resting among aquatic vegetation. As the youngster grows, its carapace (upper shell) gains the brownish-black, blotched markings of the adult.

LIMBS
The webbed limbs help to propel the terrapin through the water, and the sharp claws are used to tear up larger prey. The male also uses his claws during courtship, vibrating them against the female's chin and face to stimulate her to mate.

TAIL
The male red-eared terrapin has a longer tail than the female. In both sexes, the cloaca — the chamber into which intestinal, genital and urinary canals open — is located in the tail.

VITAL STATISTICS

LENGTH	12–25cm (4.7–9.8in) from front to rear of shell; male is smaller than the female
WEIGHT	Up to 1kg (2.2lb)
SEXUAL MATURITY	Male 1–2 years; female 3 years
BREEDING SEASON	March to June
NUMBER OF EGGS	5 to 22 per clutch; average about 10
GESTATION PERIOD	About 30 days
HATCHING PERIOD	Very variable: 2–8 months
BREEDING INTERVAL	1 to 4 clutches per year
TYPICAL DIET	Mainly aquatic plants; some small fish, molluscs, insect larvae
LIFESPAN	Over 20 years

CREATURE COMPARISONS

The Caspian pond turtle, Mauremys caspica, is a close relative of the red-eared terrapin that inhabits parts of southeastern Europe, southwestern Asia and North Africa.

The two species are about the same size and shape, but the Caspian pond turtle is brownish-grey with lighter streaks on its neck. Both creatures have similar lifestyles, although the Caspian pond turtle is more tolerant of salty and polluted water. The Caspian pond turtle is also more carnivorous than the red-eared terrapin, feeding chiefly on molluscs, amphibians and small fish.

Red-eared terrapin

Caspian pond turtle

WHERE IN THE WORLD?

Widespread through central and eastern USA, from Indiana south to New Mexico and east to northern Florida. Also occurs in northeastern Mexico.

RELATED SPECIES

There are 4 subspecies of Pseudemys scripta: the red-eared, P. s. elegans, the yellow-bellied, P. s. scripta, the Cumberland, P. s. troostii, and the Big Bend, P. s. gaigeae. All terrapins and turtles belong to the order Chelonia, which includes the snapping turtle, Chelydra serpentina.

• **ORDER** • *Chelonia* • **FAMILY** • *Testudinidae* • **GENUS & SPECIES** • *Gopherus polyphemus*

GOPHER TORTOISE

KEY FEATURES

- Withdraws its head and limbs into a thick shell, which provides excellent protection from predators.
- Each plate on the shell is ridged and each ridge represents a year's growth.
- A rapid and powerful digger — just like the gopher, a rodent, from which it takes its name.

VITAL STATISTICS

WEIGHT	Up to about 4kg (8.8lb)
LENGTH	Up to about 30cm (11.8in) (front to rear of shell)
SEXUAL MATURITY	About 10 years
BREEDING SEASON	Spring
NUMBER OF EGGS	4 to 7
INCUBATION PERIOD	80–110 days depending on temperature
BREEDING INTERVAL	1 year
DIET	Grass, leaves, berries; occasionally, carrion
LIFESPAN	Over 30 years

Armour-plated for protection, the gopher tortoise is a member of an ancient group of animals whose appearance has changed little in millions of years.

MOUTH
The tortoise has no teeth but has a sharp-edged horny beak that it uses to bite and tear pieces of vegetation.

CARAPACE
The bony shell, or carapace, that covers the soft body is made up of fused, ridged plates.

FEET
The stumpy feet are heavily scaled and have 5 short, stout claws. These help the tortoise to dig burrows in sandy soil and also shield the animal's head when it withdraws into its shell.

PLASTRON
A lower shell, the plastron, protects the belly of the tortoise from rough terrain and predators. It is concave in the male and convex in the female.

CREATURE COMPARISONS

The Texas tortoise, *Gopherus berlandieri*, is found in the southern deserts of Texas and northeastern Mexico. Slightly smaller in size than its close relative the gopher tortoise, the carapace of the Texas tortoise is more circular, its shell plates are more bulbous and their growth rings, more conspicuous.

Unlike the gopher tortoise, which is an expert burrower, the Texas tortoise normally makes a simple shallow shelter for itself by scraping away the soil at the base of a bush or clump of grass.

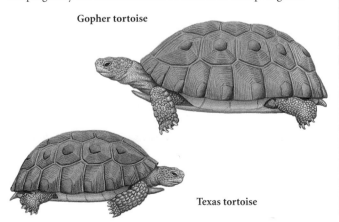

Gopher tortoise

Texas tortoise

WHERE IN THE WORLD?

Found exclusively in the southeastern United States, ranging from South Carolina across southern Georgia to eastern Louisiana and Florida.

RELATED SPECIES

There are 4 species in the genus Gopherus — all of which are the only tortoises native to the USA. They are closely related to the enormous Aldabran giant tortoise , which is found on the islands of the Seychelles in the Indian Ocean.

GHOST BAT

• ORDER • *Chiroptera* • FAMILY • *Megadermatidae* • GENUS & SPECIES • *Macroderma gigas*

One of the largest of the false vampire bats, this spectral killer is fully equipped to dispatch small mammals — including other bats.

KEY FEATURES

- Large bat that hunts prey up to its own size.
- Hunts at night like other bats, but uses sight, rather than echolocation, as the primary means of locating a potential meal.
- Swoops silently on its prey like an owl and traps it within its tough wings.
- Kills victims instantly, using its razor-sharp teeth to deliver a powerful bite to the head or neck.

VITAL STATISTICS

WEIGHT	140–170g (4.9–6oz)
LENGTH	10–12.5cm (3.9–4.9in)
WINGSPAN	Up to 67cm (26.4in)
SEXUAL MATURITY	2 years
MATING SEASON	July to August
GESTATION PERIOD	Approximately 90 days
NUMBER OF YOUNG	Usually 1
BIRTH INTERVAL	1 year
TYPICAL DIET	Insects and various other invertebrates; lizards, frogs, birds, mice, and small marsupials.
LIFESPAN	Up to 18 years

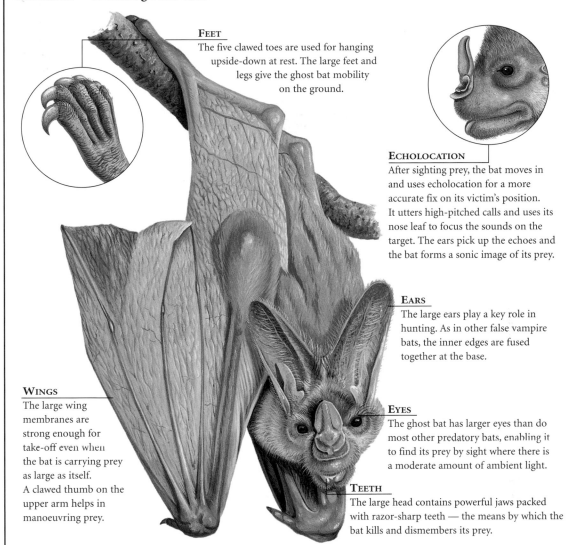

FEET
The five clawed toes are used for hanging upside-down at rest. The large feet and legs give the ghost bat mobility on the ground.

ECHOLOCATION
After sighting prey, the bat moves in and uses echolocation for a more accurate fix on its victim's position. It utters high-pitched calls and uses its nose leaf to focus the sounds on the target. The ears pick up the echoes and the bat forms a sonic image of its prey.

EARS
The large ears play a key role in hunting. As in other false vampire bats, the inner edges are fused together at the base.

EYES
The ghost bat has larger eyes than do most other predatory bats, enabling it to find its prey by sight where there is a moderate amount of ambient light.

WINGS
The large wing membranes are strong enough for take-off even when the bat is carrying prey as large as itself. A clawed thumb on the upper arm helps in manoeuvring prey.

TEETH
The large head contains powerful jaws packed with razor-sharp teeth — the means by which the bat kills and dismembers its prey.

CREATURE COMPARISONS

Most bats use echolocation to track flying insects — but there are exceptions to every rule. The ghost bat is just one of a number of bat species with unusual hunting methods and diets. The common vampire (Desmodus rotundus) is unique in its habit of biting a victim, such as a sleeping ox or horse, to make a neat incision and lapping up the seeping blood. Like the ghost bat, the bulldog or fisherman's bat (Noctilio leporinus) has very powerful legs. It flies low over rivers, using echolocation to track the ripples caused by fish. The bat lowers its feet and hooks its prey with sharp claws, then passes the slippery, struggling catch to its mouth, holding it secure with long canine teeth.

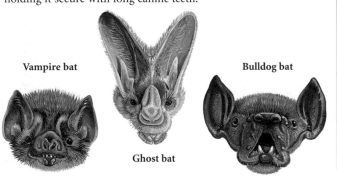

Vampire bat

Ghost bat

Bulldog bat

WHERE IN THE WORLD?

A native of northern and western Australia. Found both in the dry desert regions and in the wet northern rainforests, although its distribution is patchy.

RELATED SPECIES

The ghost bat is one of 5 species known as false vampire bats in the family Megadermatidae. They include the yellow-winged bat of Africa and the greater false vampire bat from Southeast Asia. Unlike the 3 species of true vampire bat, subfamily Desmodontinae, false vampires do not feed on the blood of living prey. Both false and true vampires belong to the suborder Microchiroptera, which contains nearly 800 species.

• **ORDER** • *Chiroptera* • **FAMILY** • *Molossidae* • **GENUS & SPECIES** • *Tadarida brasiliensis*   ## MEXICAN FREE-TAILED BAT

KEY FEATURES

- A powerful flier, flitting and swooping faster than most other species of bat.
- Sometimes roosts in immense congregations numbering millions.
- Makes spectacular mass exits from its roost at dusk, spiralling into the air in a huge, dark cloud.
- Some individuals migrate great distances to and from their summer and winter homes.

VITAL STATISTICS

WEIGHT	10–15g (0.3–0.5oz)
LENGTH	Head & Body; 4.6–6.6cm (1.8–2.6in) Tail; 2.9–4.2cm (1.1–1.6in)
SEXUAL MATURITY	18–22 months
MATING SEASON	Spring
GESTATION PERIOD	77–100 days
NUMBER OF YOUNG	1
BIRTH INTERVAL	1 year
TYPICAL DIET	Flying insects
LIFESPAN	13–18 years

Built for fast, direct flight, the Mexican free-tailed bat pursues flying insect prey with deadly accuracy under the cloak of darkness.

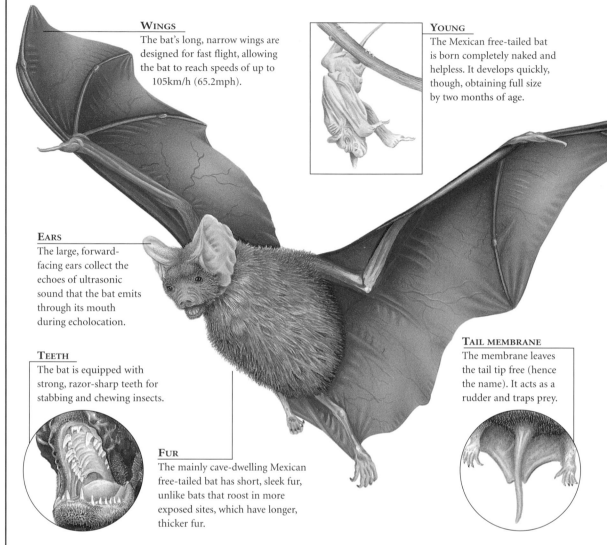

WINGS
The bat's long, narrow wings are designed for fast flight, allowing the bat to reach speeds of up to 105km/h (65.2mph).

YOUNG
The Mexican free-tailed bat is born completely naked and helpless. It develops quickly, though, obtaining full size by two months of age.

EARS
The large, forward-facing ears collect the echoes of ultrasonic sound that the bat emits through its mouth during echolocation.

TEETH
The bat is equipped with strong, razor-sharp teeth for stabbing and chewing insects.

TAIL MEMBRANE
The membrane leaves the tail tip free (hence the name). It acts as a rudder and traps prey.

FUR
The mainly cave-dwelling Mexican free-tailed bat has short, sleek fur, unlike bats that roost in more exposed sites, which have longer, thicker fur.

CREATURE COMPARISONS

The Mexican free-tailed bat, the little goblin bat (Mormopterus planiceps) and the mastiff bat (Eumops perotis) are all members of the family Molossidae. Species within this family tend to have a thick head and a broad muzzle. Their ears are also thick and, as in the case of the mastiff bat, almost touch in the middle of the forehead. The little goblin bat of Australia, which is no bigger than a human thumb, has a flat head enabling it to squeeze into small cracks and crevices. The mastiff bat, found in the USA, Mexico and South America, takes its name from its heavy, fleshy jowls.

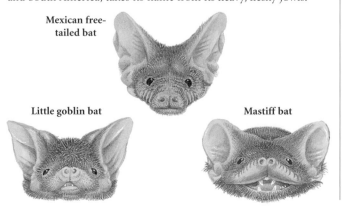

Mexican free-tailed bat

Little goblin bat

Mastiff bat

WHERE IN THE WORLD?

The Mexican free-tailed bat occurs over southern parts of the USA, south through Mexico and Central America, and into South America as far south as Chile and Argentina. It is also found in the West Indies.

RELATED SPECIES

The Mexican free-tailed bat is one of 8 species of free-tailed bat in the genus Tadarida, which are widely distributed in both the Old and New World. It shares the family Molossidae with another 85 species of small- to medium-sized, insect-eating bats, including the 2 species of naked, or hairless, bats of the genus Cheiromeles. Nearly devoid of hair, these bats are also unique since they have pouches in which they store their folded wings.

BULLDOG BAT

The bulldog bat is one of the few species of bat that is adapted to fishing. Swooping slowly over water it snatches prey with its hook-like feet.

KEY FEATURES

- Takes its name from its fleshy upper lips and hanging folds of facial skin, which give it an uncanny resemblance to a bulldog.
- An expert predator that hunts over water, emitting high-frequency sound pulses to detect prey, and using its long legs and huge feet to snatch fish from the water.
- Spends the day resting in communal roosts.

VITAL STATISTICS

WEIGHT	Male 78g (2.7oz); female 60g (2.1oz)
HEAD & BODY	9.8–13.2cm (3.8–5.2in)
WINGSPAN	28–30cm (11–11.8in)
SEXUAL MATURITY	Unknown
MATING SEASON	End of dryseason
GESTATION PERIOD	About 112 days
NUMBER OF YOUNG	1
BIRTH INTERVAL	Unknown
TYPICAL DIET	Small fish,crustaceans, amphibians and insects
LIFESPAN	About 10–12 years, but some individuals live for 20 years

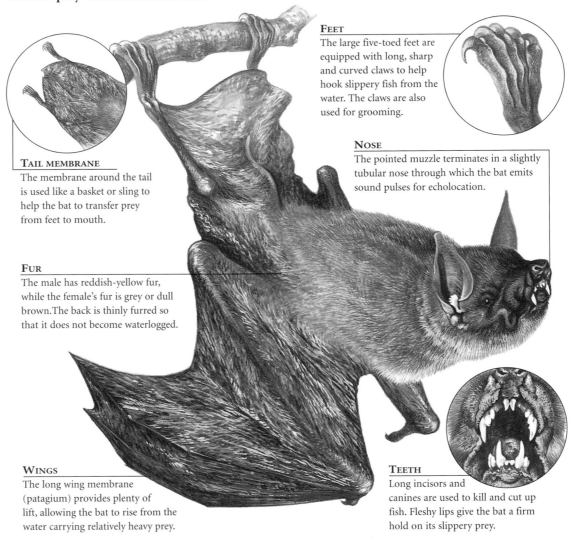

FEET
The large five-toed feet are equipped with long, sharp and curved claws to help hook slippery fish from the water. The claws are also used for grooming.

TAIL MEMBRANE
The membrane around the tail is used like a basket or sling to help the bat to transfer prey from feet to mouth.

NOSE
The pointed muzzle terminates in a slightly tubular nose through which the bat emits sound pulses for echolocation.

FUR
The male has reddish-yellow fur, while the female's fur is grey or dull brown.The back is thinly furred so that it does not become waterlogged.

WINGS
The long wing membrane (patagium) provides plenty of lift, allowing the bat to rise from the water carrying relatively heavy prey.

TEETH
Long incisors and canines are used to kill and cut up fish. Fleshy lips give the bat a firm hold on its slippery prey.

CREATURE COMPARISONS

The bulldog bat is not the only fish-eating bat. The Asian false vampire bat, Megaderma spasma, which feeds mainly on insects, such as moths and grasshoppers, also goes fishing.

With a head and body length of 6–10cm (2.4–3.9in) and weighing 23–28g (0.8–1oz), the Asian false vampire is smaller than the bulldog bat, but is an equally effective hunter, catching fish with ease and flying swiftly among trees and undergrowth to capture insect prey. It has even been known to fly into houses to pick lizards and insects off walls. Unlike the bulldog bat, which has a pointed muzzle, the false vampire bat has a blunt muzzle with skin extensions, called nose leaves, around its nostrils.These extensions help the bat direct its echolocation sound pulses.

Asian false vampire bat

Bulldog bat

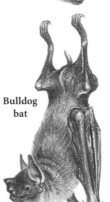

WHERE IN THE WORLD?

Ranges from central America south to northern Argentina and southeastern Brazil. Also found on many Caribbean islands, including the Bahamas and the Greater and Lesser Antilles.

RELATED SPECIES

The bulldog bat is one of 2 species in the genus Noctilio: the other is the southern bulldog bat,N. albiventris, which is found from southern Mexico to northern Argentina. Smaller than the bulldog bat it feeds mainly on insects, although it catches fish occasionally. These 2 species, along with 984 other bat species, belong to the bat suborder Microchiroptera — whose members all use echolocation to navigate and hunt prey.

• **ORDER** • *Chiroptera* • **FAMILY** • *Phyllostomidae* • **GENUS & SPECIES** • *Desmodus rotundus*

VAMPIRE BAT

KEY FEATURES

- Tiny bat found in warm climates, which feeds solely on the fresh blood of other mammals.
- Spends the day roosting with other vampire bats, with which it forms close social bonds.
- Leaves the colony at nightfall to search for a sleeping host animal.

The vampire bat has broad wings for aerial agility, and its feet and thumb hooks help it clamber over its host without waking it.

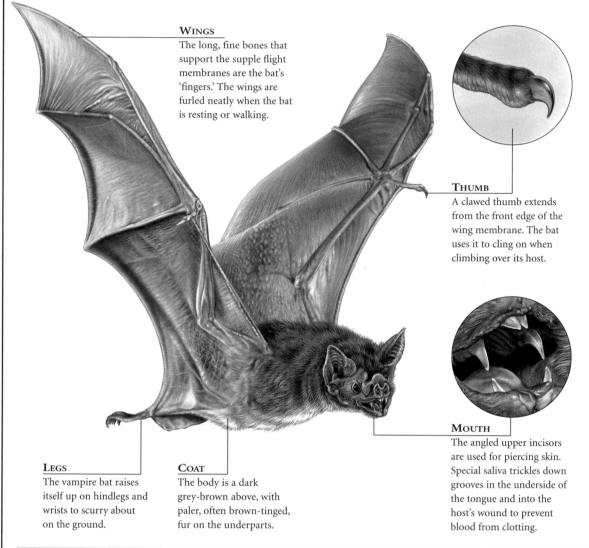

WINGS
The long, fine bones that support the supple flight membranes are the bat's 'fingers.' The wings are furled neatly when the bat is resting or walking.

THUMB
A clawed thumb extends from the front edge of the wing membrane. The bat uses it to cling on when climbing over its host.

MOUTH
The angled upper incisors are used for piercing skin. Special saliva trickles down grooves in the underside of the tongue and into the host's wound to prevent blood from clotting.

LEGS
The vampire bat raises itself up on hindlegs and wrists to scurry about on the ground.

COAT
The body is a dark grey-brown above, with paler, often brown-tinged, fur on the underparts.

VITAL STATISTICS

WEIGHT	14–50g (0.5–18oz)
LENGTH	Head & Body 7–9cm (2.7–3.5in)
WINGSPAN	20cm (7.9in)
SEXUAL MATURITY	9 months
MATING SEASON	All year round
GESTATION PERIOD	205–214 days
NUMBER OF YOUNG	1
BIRTH INTERVAL	1 year
TYPICAL DIET	Blood of grazing and other mammals, and birds
LIFESPAN	Up to 9 years in the wild; up to 19 years in captivity

CREATURE COMPARISONS

The vampire bat's features are quite different from other American bats. The bulldog bat, for example, has large feet that it uses to grab fish, while the big brown bat has large wings for enveloping insects in flight. The vampire's ears are much smaller than either of these species as its sense of echolocation is not as well developed as theirs.

Vampire bat

Bulldog bat

Big brown bat

WHERE IN THE WORLD?

Found in tropical and subtropical Central and South America, from Mexico south as far as Uruguay, central Chile and Argentina. Also found on the Caribbean islands of Margarita and Trinidad.

RELATED SPECIES

There are three species of vampire bat, of which the common vampire is the most widespread. The white-winged vampire bat, Diaemus youngi, and the hairy-legged vampire bat, Diphylla ecaudata, are also found in Central and South America, but they feed mostly on the blood of birds, not mammals. The false vampires, family Megadermatidae, of Africa, Asia and Australia, are not closely related, despite their common name.

INDIAN FLYING FOX

• ORDER • *Chiroptera* **• FAMILY •** *Pteropodidae* **• GENUS & SPECIES •** *Pteropus giganteus*

The Indian flying fox uses its keen senses of sight and smell to locate ripe fruit, and extracts the energy-rich juice with its specialized teeth.

KEY FEATURES

- Feeds on juice it obtains from tree fruit, flying up to 50km (31 miles) each night to find a ripe crop.
- Frequently flies along river courses using the clear, open channels as highways into the forest.
- Uses its soft wing membranes to protect itself from wind and rain and to regulate its body temperature.

THUMB
The flying fox uses its long, hooked thumb to hold food and to grip branches.

PATAGIUM
The patagium (wing membrane) is a soft, fine, leathery skin made up of elastic tissue and muscle fibre. This is stretched over the bat's leg bones, upper arm, forearm and the elongated fingerbones.

TEETH
The teeth are adapted for eating fruit. Canines hold the fruit firmly, while sharp incisors slice the skin and pulp. Grooved molars crush the pulp and channel juice into the throat.

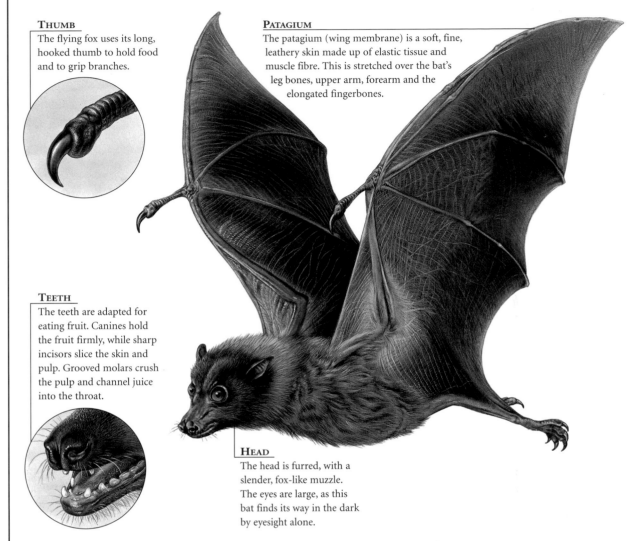

HEAD
The head is furred, with a slender, fox-like muzzle. The eyes are large, as this bat finds its way in the dark by eyesight alone.

VITAL STATISTICS

WEIGHT	Male up to 1.35kg; (3lb) female about 900g (31.7oz)
LENGTH	Up to 38cm (15in)
WINGSPAN	About 1.2m (3ft 9in)
SEXUAL MATURITY	1–2 years
MATING SEASON	Variable, but births tend to occur at the same time in any one area
GESTATION PERIOD	About 150 days
NUMBER OF YOUNG	1, very rarely 2
BIRTH INTERVAL	1 year
TYPICAL DIET	Juice of soft fruits
LIFESPAN	Up to 15 years in the wild

CREATURE COMPARISONS

Most flying foxes locate their food by sight and smell, and so they differ physically from bats that navigate and track prey by echolocation. Nearly all fruit bats have a long, pointed head, whereas insect- and flesh-eating bats possess a huge variety of muzzle and ear shapes.

The horseshoe bat (Rhinolophus ferrumequinum), for example, has a U-shaped leaf below its nose, and a slim lancet above it, to help focus sound signals. The huge ears of the long-eared bat (Plecotus auritus) assist it in navigating in darkness, although this species usually hunts by listening to the tell-tale sounds made by its prey.

Indian flying fox

Horseshoe bat

Long-eared bat

Illustrations not to scale

WHERE IN THE WORLD?

Present over much of India, eastwards through Burma (Myanmar) to the Malay Peninsula. Also found on some offshore island groups in the Indian Ocean.

RELATED SPECIES

The Indian flying fox is 1 of 17 species in the genus Pteropus and 1 of 130 species of flying fox and fruit bat in the family Pteropodidae, which are classified in a separate suborder from the other 780 or so bat species. With a wingspan of up to 1.8m (5ft 9in), the Samoan flying fox, Pteropus samoensis, is the world's largest species of bat. The smallest fruit bat, at only 6cm (2.4in) long, is the Queensland blossom bat, Syconycteris australis.

• ORDER • *Chiroptera* • FAMILY • *Rhinolophidae* • GENUS & SPECIES • *Rhinolophus ferrumequinum* GREATER HORSESHOE

The 'nose leaf' and large ears of the horseshoe bat help it find insect prey at night with a precision that equals any radar device.

KEY FEATURES

- Commonly roosts in the summer in rafters of barns and old buildings.
- Hibernates in the winter in cellars, mine tunnels or caves.
- Hunts flying insects around street lights and suburban parks.
- Seriously threatened by roof-timber treatment, renovation of houses and barns, and changes in agricultural practices.

VITAL STATISTICS

WEIGHT	14–35g (0.5–1.2oz)
LENGTH	Head & Body: 5.7–7.8cm (2.2–3in) Tail: 3.5cm (1.4in)
WINGSPAN	35.5–40cm (14–15.7in)
SEXUAL MATURITY	Female 3–4 years; male 2–3 years
BREEDING SEASON	Late autumn through spring
GESTATION PERIOD	About 6 weeks after delayed fertilization
NUMBER OF YOUNG	1
BIRTH INTERVAL	1 year
TYPICAL DIET	Large flying insects, such as beetles and moths; some prey also taken from ground
LIFESPAN	Up to 30 years

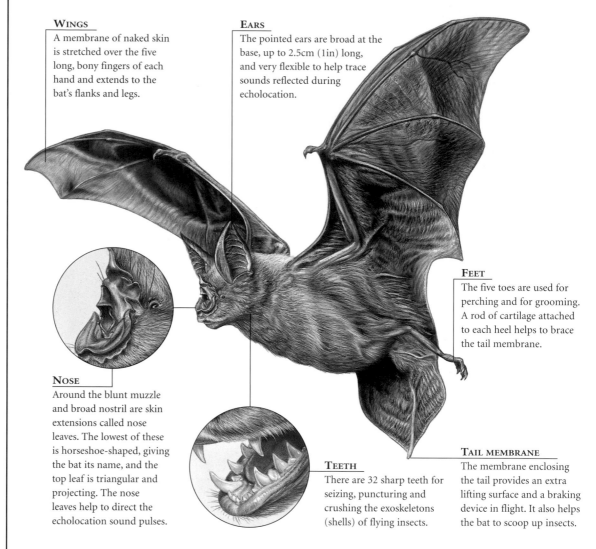

WINGS
A membrane of naked skin is stretched over the five long, bony fingers of each hand and extends to the bat's flanks and legs.

EARS
The pointed ears are broad at the base, up to 2.5cm (1in) long, and very flexible to help trace sounds reflected during echolocation.

FEET
The five toes are used for perching and for grooming. A rod of cartilage attached to each heel helps to brace the tail membrane.

NOSE
Around the blunt muzzle and broad nostril are skin extensions called nose leaves. The lowest of these is horseshoe-shaped, giving the bat its name, and the top leaf is triangular and projecting. The nose leaves help to direct the echolocation sound pulses.

TEETH
There are 32 sharp teeth for seizing, puncturing and crushing the exoskeletons (shells) of flying insects.

TAIL MEMBRANE
The membrane enclosing the tail provides an extra lifting surface and a braking device in flight. It also helps the bat to scoop up insects.

CREATURE COMPARISONS

A wide variety of bat species roosts in or around buildings. The greater horseshoe bat favours the open space of a warm loft in summer. Daubenton's bat often hangs freely in a crack behind the external shuttering of a wall, whereas the pipistrelle prefers very narrow, snug crevices.

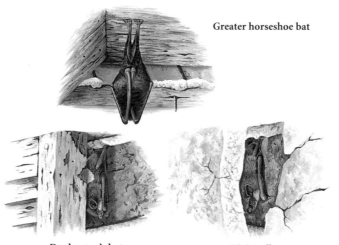

Greater horseshoe bat

Daubenton's bat

Pipistrelle

WHERE IN THE WORLD?

Found in areas of open woodland, often near old buildings, throughout the warmer parts of Europe and Central Asia, from northwest Africa and Spain in the west, east in a narrow strip through southern Asia to Japan.

RELATED SPECIES

There are 69 species of horseshoe bat, all from the Old World (outside the Americas and Australia). Together with 744 other species, the horseshoe bats belong to the bat suborder Microchiroptera, all of whose members have small eyes and use echolocation to navigate or hunt. The rest of the bat order is made up by the flying foxes, suborder Megachiroptera, which use their large eyes to find their main source of food fruit.

· ORDER · *Chiroptera* **· FAMILY ·** *Vespertilionidae* **· GENUS & SPECIES ·** *Plecotus auritus*

BROWN LONG-EARED BAT

A specialist at catching insects in confined spaces, the brown long-eared bat fields a deadly combination of super senses and agility in flight.

KEY FEATURES

- An agile night hunter equipped with super-sensitive hearing for locating elusive prey.
- Specializes in hunting in dense woodlands, where other bats are at a disadvantage.
- Hibernates in caves, or other cool damp sites, in winter when its insect prey is scarce.

VITAL STATISTICS

WEIGHT	5–10g (0.2–0.3oz)
LENGTH	Head & Body: 4.5cm (1.8in) Tail; 3.5cm (1.4in) Ears; Up to 4cm (1.6in)
WINGSPAN	25cm (9.8in)
SEXUAL MATURITY	2 years
MATING SEASON	Autumn to spring
GESTATION PERIOD	50 days after delayed implantation
NUMBER OF YOUNG	1
BIRTH INTERVAL	1 year
TYPICAL DIET	Insects; mainly moths and beetles
LIFESPAN	Up to 15 years

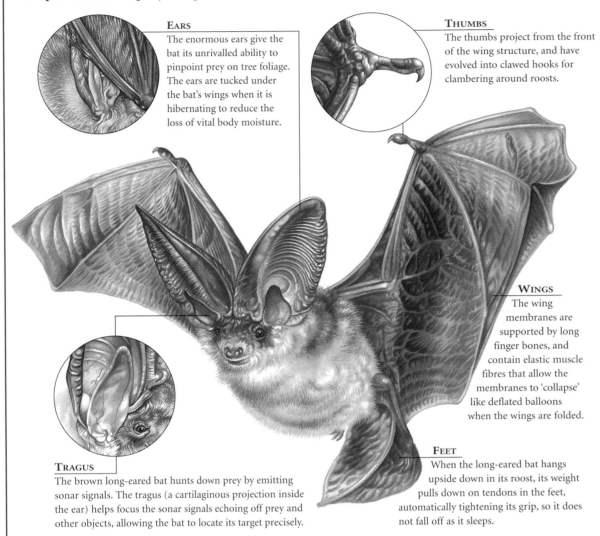

EARS
The enormous ears give the bat its unrivalled ability to pinpoint prey on tree foliage. The ears are tucked under the bat's wings when it is hibernating to reduce the loss of vital body moisture.

THUMBS
The thumbs project from the front of the wing structure, and have evolved into clawed hooks for clambering around roosts.

WINGS
The wing membranes are supported by long finger bones, and contain elastic muscle fibres that allow the membranes to 'collapse' like deflated balloons when the wings are folded.

TRAGUS
The brown long-eared bat hunts down prey by emitting sonar signals. The tragus (a cartilaginous projection inside the ear) helps focus the sonar signals echoing off prey and other objects, allowing the bat to locate its target precisely.

FEET
When the long-eared bat hangs upside down in its roost, its weight pulls down on tendons in the feet, automatically tightening its grip, so it does not fall off as it sleeps.

CREATURE COMPARISONS

Some bat species, such as the greater horseshoe bat, Rhinolophus ferrumequinum, produce calls through their nostrils — unlike the long-eared bat, which navigates and hunts by producing calls from its mouth. The horseshoe-shaped flap on the bat's nose acts as an acoustic 'lens', focusing and directing the sound waves. Its ears are big, but since the bat feeds mainly on insects flying in the open, it does not need the huge, super-efficient ears that enable the long-eared bat to distinguish insects from the foliage they are sitting on.

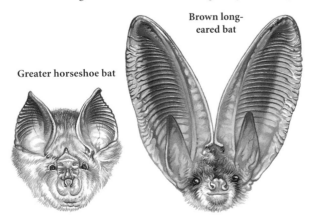

Brown long-eared bat

Greater horseshoe bat

WHERE IN THE WORLD?

Occurs in Europe from southern Scandinavia south to the Mediterranean, and east in a narrow band across central Asia to southeastern Siberia and Japan.

RELATED SPECIES

There are five species of long-eared bat in the genus Plecotus, including the grey long-eared bat, P. austriacus. Long-eared bats are 'vesper' bats — a huge family with some 350 species. It represents one of the most widespread mammalian groups after humans, and includes most of the European bats, such as the common pipistrelle, Pipistrellus pipistrellus, as well as exotic species, such as the Mexican fish-eating bat, Myotis vivesi.

• **ORDER** • *Chiroptera* • **FAMILY** • *Vespertilionidae* • **GENUS & SPECIES** • *Eptesicus fuscus*

BIG BROWN BAT

KEY FEATURES

- Common North American 'house bat' that often roosts and hibernates in lofts and buildings.

- Flies more slowly and closer to the ground than most other insect-eating bats.

- Uses its tail membrane to help pass insect food to the mouth while in flight.

The big brown bat is equipped to track down and catch its insect prey in total darkness it even eats its victims while on the wing.

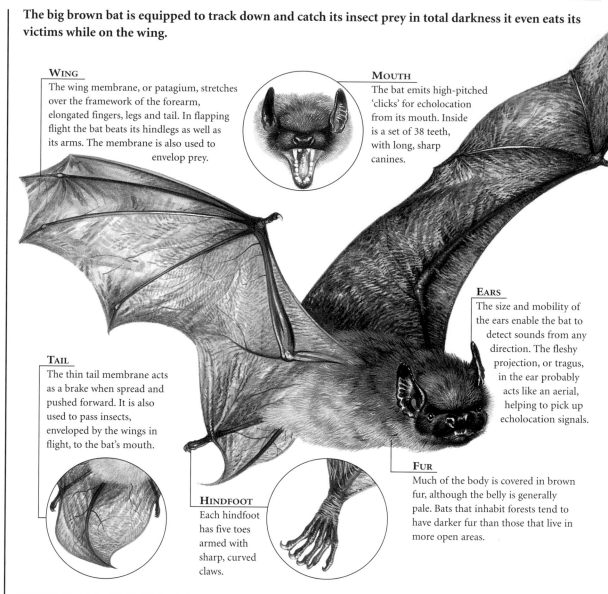

WING
The wing membrane, or patagium, stretches over the framework of the forearm, elongated fingers, legs and tail. In flapping flight the bat beats its hindlegs as well as its arms. The membrane is also used to envelop prey.

MOUTH
The bat emits high-pitched 'clicks' for echolocation from its mouth. Inside is a set of 38 teeth, with long, sharp canines.

EARS
The size and mobility of the ears enable the bat to detect sounds from any direction. The fleshy projection, or tragus, in the ear probably acts like an aerial, helping to pick up echolocation signals.

TAIL
The thin tail membrane acts as a brake when spread and pushed forward. It is also used to pass insects, enveloped by the wings in flight, to the bat's mouth.

HINDFOOT
Each hindfoot has five toes armed with sharp, curved claws.

FUR
Much of the body is covered in brown fur, although the belly is generally pale. Bats that inhabit forests tend to have darker fur than those that live in more open areas.

VITAL STATISTICS

WEIGHT	14–30g; (0.5–1.1oz) female slightly larger than male
LENGTH	Head & Body: 5.5–7.5cm (2.2–2.9in) Tail; 3.5–6cm (1.4–2.4in)
WINGSPAN	32–38cm (12.6–15in)
SEXUAL MATURITY	1–2 years
MATING SEASON	Autumn
GESTATION PERIOD	60 days, after delayed implantation
NUMBER OF YOUNG	1 or 2
BIRTH INTERVAL	1 year
TYPICAL DIET	Insects
LIFESPAN	Up to 19 years

CREATURE COMPARISONS

The head of a big brown bat displays typical bat features — flat snout, pointed ears, forward-facing eyes and a furred forehead. It shares parts of its range in Central and South America with a highly unusual-looking bat: the aptly named wrinkle-faced bat (*Centurio senex*). This species has a largely naked face and its facial skin lies in deep, loose folds. When roosting, the wrinkled-face bat stretches the extensive chin fold up and over its head and ears. A small projection on the head then anchors the fold in place. Two areas of this facial mask are, in some bats, translucent. It is thought that these allow some light to pass through and perhaps help the bat to perceive objects when its face is covered. Just why the bat does all this, though, is not fully understood.

Big brown Bat

Wrinkled-face bat

WHERE IN THE WORLD?

Ranges from southern Canada through the USA and most of Central America to northern South America. Also found in the West Indies.

RELATED SPECIES

The big brown bat is a member of the family Vespertilionidae, which contains 42 genera and 355 species of bat. There are two subgenera and 17 species of big brown bat. The single species, *Eptesicus floweri*, in the subgenus Rhinopterus lives in the arid regions of Mali and Sudan in Central Africa. Other species of big brown bat are found worldwide, although *Eptesicus fuscus* is the only species native to North America.

MOUSE-EARED BAT

• **ORDER** • *Chiroptera* • **FAMILY** • *Vespertilionidae* • **GENUS & SPECIES** • *Myotis myotis*

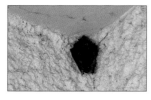

KEY FEATURES

- A nocturnal predator, this large bat takes insects on the wing and from the ground.
- Hibernates in clusters in caves and forms large summer roosting colonies.
- Increasingly rare across its range; listed by the IUCN (World Conservation Union) as endangered.

VITAL STATISTICS

WEIGHT	18–45g (0.6–1.6oz)
LENGTH	Head & Body: 65–88mm (2.6–3.5in) Tail; 35–60mm (1.4–2.4in)
WINGSPAN	35–45cm (13.8–17.7in)
SEXUAL MATURITY	Within 1 year
BREEDING SEASON	Mating occurs prior to hibernation; young born late spring to early summer
NUMBER OF YOUNG	1
GESTATION PERIOD	Up to 70 days
BREEDING INTERVAL	1 year
TYPICAL DIET	Insects and invertebrates
LIFESPAN	Up to 28 years

Large-bodied and conspicuous in flight, the mouse-eared bat is a menacing sight as it homes in on its insect prey using echolocation.

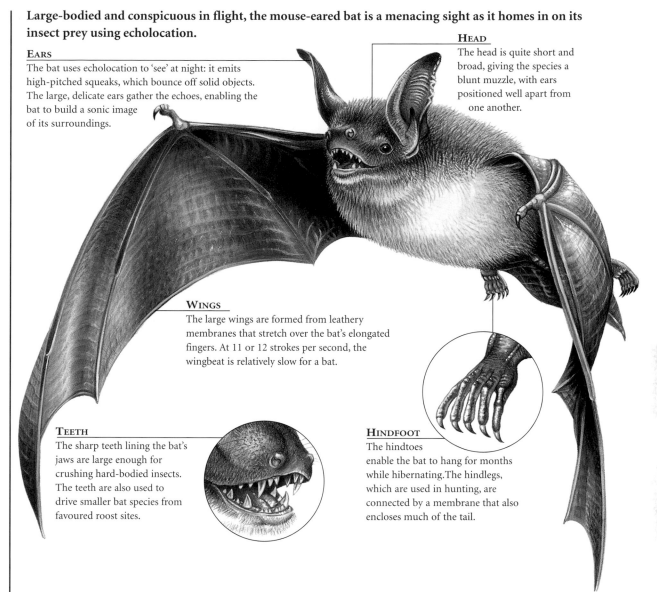

EARS
The bat uses echolocation to 'see' at night: it emits high-pitched squeaks, which bounce off solid objects. The large, delicate ears gather the echoes, enabling the bat to build a sonic image of its surroundings.

HEAD
The head is quite short and broad, giving the species a blunt muzzle, with ears positioned well apart from one another.

WINGS
The large wings are formed from leathery membranes that stretch over the bat's elongated fingers. At 11 or 12 strokes per second, the wingbeat is relatively slow for a bat.

TEETH
The sharp teeth lining the bat's jaws are large enough for crushing hard-bodied insects. The teeth are also used to drive smaller bat species from favoured roost sites.

HINDFOOT
The hindtoes enable the bat to hang for months while hibernating. The hindlegs, which are used in hunting, are connected by a membrane that also encloses much of the tail.

CREATURE COMPARISONS

Despite an overall similarity in shape, the many bat species display an enormous diversity of physical features and lifestyles. The tent-building bat (*Uroderma bilobatum*) of South America, for example, is only a little smaller than the mouse-eared bat, and looks roughly similar with an overall greyish-brown colouration. However, it is easily distinguished from the mouse-eared bat by its nose leaf, facial stripes and lack of tail.

Feeding on fruit rather than insects, the tent-building bat takes its name from its habit of constructing its own roost shelters by biting through the ribs of palm fronds so that the ends droop to form a pitched roof.

Tent-building bat

Mouse-eared bat

WHERE IN THE WORLD?

Occurs across most of southern and central Europe, and as far east as Belarus, Ukraine, Turkey and parts of the Near East.

RELATED SPECIES

The mouse-eared bat belongs to the genus *Myotis* — the vesper bats — which also includes the lesser mouse-eared bat and Bechstein's bat of Europe, as well as the grey bat and Indiana bat of the USA. Containing about 100 species, the genus *Myotis* is the largest in the family Vespertilionidae. Bats make up the order Chiroptera, which contains 18 families and roughly 1000 species — about a quarter of all known mammal species.

• **ORDER** • *Chiroptera* • **FAMILY** • *Vespertilionidae* • **GENUS & SPECIES** • *Pipistrellus pipistrellus*

PIPISTRELLE BAT

KEY FEATURES

- Britain's smallest and most common bat, it is also the one most likely to be seen around human habitation and often roosts in houses.
- Locates and tracks its flying insect prey by using echolocation and catches it in its cupped wings and tail.
- Most active on warm summer evenings; hibernates through much of winter.

VITAL STATISTICS

WEIGHT	3–8g (0.1–0.3oz)
LENGTH	Head & Body: 3.5–4.5cm (1.4–1.8in)
WINGSPAN	19–25cm (7.5–9.8in)
SEXUAL MATURITY	Male 2 years; female 1 year
MATING SEASON	September to November
GESTATION PERIOD	About 44 days, but fertilization delayed until following spring
NUMBER OF YOUNG	1, rarely 2
BIRTH INTERVAL	1 year
TYPICAL DIET	Flying insects
LIFESPAN	Up to 16 years

The pipistrelle bat's sophisticated echolocation system enables it to pinpoint and follow insects as small as mosquitoes in complete darkness.

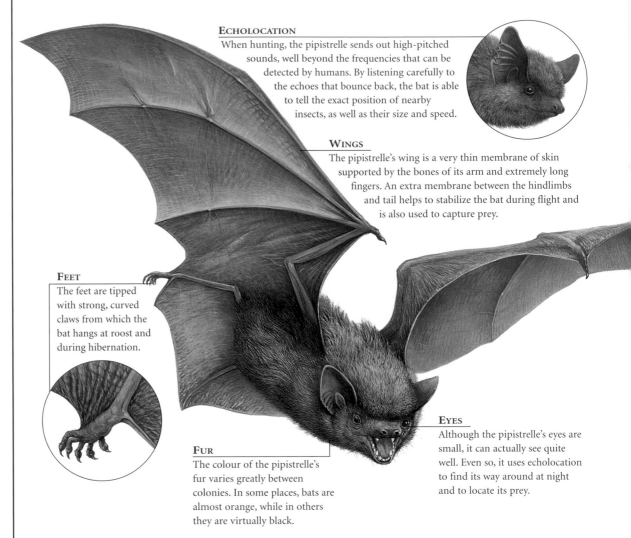

ECHOLOCATION
When hunting, the pipistrelle sends out high-pitched sounds, well beyond the frequencies that can be detected by humans. By listening carefully to the echoes that bounce back, the bat is able to tell the exact position of nearby insects, as well as their size and speed.

WINGS
The pipistrelle's wing is a very thin membrane of skin supported by the bones of its arm and extremely long fingers. An extra membrane between the hindlimbs and tail helps to stabilize the bat during flight and is also used to capture prey.

FEET
The feet are tipped with strong, curved claws from which the bat hangs at roost and during hibernation.

FUR
The colour of the pipistrelle's fur varies greatly between colonies. In some places, bats are almost orange, while in others they are virtually black.

EYES
Although the pipistrelle's eyes are small, it can actually see quite well. Even so, it uses echolocation to find its way around at night and to locate its prey.

CREATURE COMPARISONS

A native of the African continent, the butterfly bat weighs 6–14g (0.2–0.5oz), making it slightly larger than the pipistrelle. Its colouration varies — some individuals are cream or dusky brown, others are grey or even black, but almost all are patterned with white spots and stripes. Unlike the pipistrelle, the butterfly bat has very prominent veins in its wings. These may have a protective role as they give the wings the appearance of withered leaves, helping to hide the bat from predators as it roosts among bushes and other vegetation.

Like the pipistrelle, the butterfly bat feeds on insects that it catches in flight using echolocation. But while the pipistrelle is almost exclusively nocturnal, the butterfly bat also hunts during the day.

Pipistrelle bat

Butterfly bat

WHERE IN THE WORLD?

Found throughout Britain and across most of Europe except for northern Scandinavia. Also occurs in some coastal areas of northern Africa and the Middle East as well as parts of Central Asia.

RELATED SPECIES

After rodents, bats are the world's most numerous mammal species, with 355 in the family Vespertilionidae alone. Of 77 species in the genus Pipistrellus, the 2 species of pipistrelle are the only British residents. However, 14 other bats breed in Britain, including Daubenton's bat.

LEMON SHARK

• **ORDER** • *Chondrichthyes* • **FAMILY** • *Carcharhinidae* • **GENUS & SPECIES** • *Negaprion brevirostris*

KEY FEATURES

- Powerful jaws are filled with sharp, triangular teeth that are regularly replaced for maximum efficiency.
- Can detect prey from distances of over 1km (0.6 miles) using a battery of powerful sensory equipment.
- Commonly found in shallow, tropical waters, where it spends part of the day lying on the seabed.

VITAL STATISTICS

WEIGHT	120–150kg (264.6– 330.7lb)
LENGTH	Up to 3.2m (10ft 5in)
SEXUAL MATURITY	At least 12 years
BREEDING SEASON	Spring and early summer
GESTATION PERIOD	10–12 months
NUMBER OF YOUNG	5 to 19
BIRTH INTERVAL	2 years
TYPICAL DIET	Fish, including other sharks and rays, squid and crustaceans
LIFESPAN	Possibly 50 years or more

A streamlined predator, the lemon shark powers itself through the water by sweeping thrusts of its tail and steering with its large, blade-like fins.

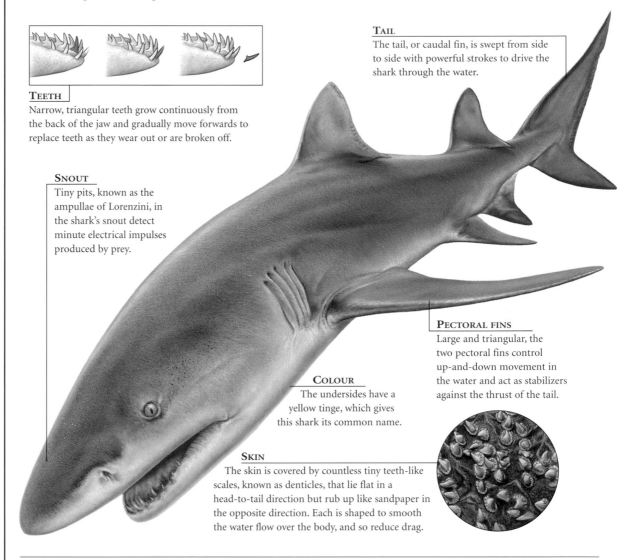

TEETH
Narrow, triangular teeth grow continuously from the back of the jaw and gradually move forwards to replace teeth as they wear out or are broken off.

TAIL
The tail, or caudal fin, is swept from side to side with powerful strokes to drive the shark through the water.

SNOUT
Tiny pits, known as the ampullae of Lorenzini, in the shark's snout detect minute electrical impulses produced by prey.

PECTORAL FINS
Large and triangular, the two pectoral fins control up-and-down movement in the water and act as stabilizers against the thrust of the tail.

COLOUR
The undersides have a yellow tinge, which gives this shark its common name.

SKIN
The skin is covered by countless tiny teeth-like scales, known as denticles, that lie flat in a head-to-tail direction but rub up like sandpaper in the opposite direction. Each is shaped to smooth the water flow over the body, and so reduce drag.

CREATURE COMPARISONS

The greater spotted dogfish (Scyliorhinus stellaris) is a small relation of the lemon shark, sharing the same basic body plan and a skeleton made of cartilage rather than bone. But whereas the lemon shark has a rounded snout, triangular teeth, large triangular dorsal fins, and a uniform colour, the greater spotted dogfish has a squat face, flat teeth, irregular spots, small dorsal fins, and, at up to 1.5m (4ft 9in) long, is dwarfed by its relative. The female lemon shark gives birth to live young, whereas the greater spotted dogfish lays leathery capsules, known as 'mermaid's purses', in which the embryos develop.

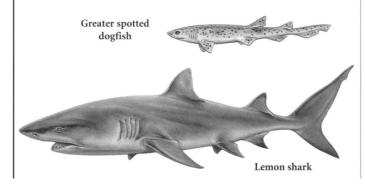

Greater spotted dogfish

Lemon shark

WHERE IN THE WORLD?

Found off parts of both coasts of North and South America, around Caribbean islands and parts of the western coast of Africa.

RELATED SPECIES

There are about 370 species of shark. The lemon shark belongs to the Carcharhinidae, or requiem sharks, a family containing about 100 species. This group of torpedo-shaped hunters includes the tiger shark (Galeocerdo cuvier), which can bite through the shell of a sea turtle, and the bull shark (Carcharhinus leucas), which enters rivers and lakes. This shark has been known to attack hippos in Africa's Zambezi River, many kilometres or miles from the sea.

• **ORDER** • *Ciconiiformes* • **FAMILY** • *Ardeidae* • **GENUS & SPECIES** • *Ardea cinerea*

GREY HERON

Standing perfectly still, the grey heron is a patient predator. Suddenly, it strikes, unleashing the whiplash power of its neck to spear prey on its bill.

KEY FEATURES

- Wades through shallow water on elegant, stilt-like legs to fish for prey.
- Hunts by standing statue-still and waiting for prey to drift into range, or by pacing slowly until it detects the slightest underwater movement.
- Shoots out its long neck like a striking snake, stabbing prey with its bill.
- Nests in noisy treetop colonies called heronries.

VITAL STATISTICS

WEIGHT	1.1–1.7kg (2.4–3.7lb)
LENGTH	90–98cm (35.4–38.6in)
WINGSPAN	1.75–1.95m (3ft 8in– 4ft 3in)
SEXUAL MATURITY	2 years
BREEDING SEASON	January to May in north; almost all year in tropics. Varies elsewhere
NUMBER OF EGGS	3 to 5
INCUBATION PERIOD	21–26 days
FLEDGING PERIOD	40–50 days
BREEDING INTERVAL	1 year
TYPICAL DIET	Fish, aquatic invertebrates and birds, amphibians, small mammals, and snakes
LIFESPAN	25 years

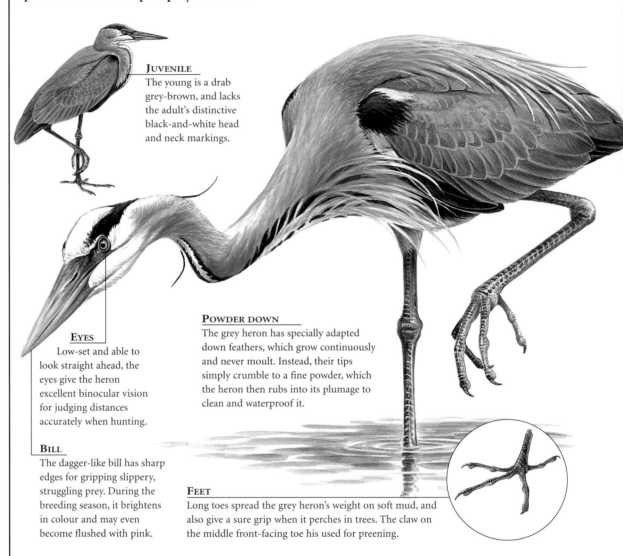

JUVENILE
The young is a drab grey-brown, and lacks the adult's distinctive black-and-white head and neck markings.

EYES
Low-set and able to look straight ahead, the eyes give the heron excellent binocular vision for judging distances accurately when hunting.

BILL
The dagger-like bill has sharp edges for gripping slippery, struggling prey. During the breeding season, it brightens in colour and may even become flushed with pink.

POWDER DOWN
The grey heron has specially adapted down feathers, which grow continuously and never moult. Instead, their tips simply crumble to a fine powder, which the heron then rubs into its plumage to clean and waterproof it.

FEET
Long toes spread the grey heron's weight on soft mud, and also give a sure grip when it perches in trees. The claw on the middle front-facing toe his used for preening.

CREATURE COMPARISONS

The long-legged, long-necked grey heron is a tall bird, but it is dwarfed by the real giant of the heron family, the goliath heron, Ardea goliath. This majestic hunter of African and Middle Eastern swamps stands almost as tall as a human, at up to 1.5m (4ft 9in) high, but stalks its prey with stealthy efficiency, so is often overlooked among the dense reedbeds and mangroves of its home. Like the grey heron, the goliath heron is intolerant of intruders. If approached, it launches itself into the air with a deep, grating croak of alarm, and flaps away over the marshes with leisurely wingbeats.

The goliath heron can wade into much deeper water than the grey heron, and fish make up a larger proportion of its diet. Its legs and bill are black, whereas those of its smaller relative are yellowish.

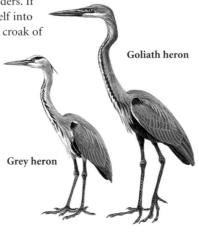

Goliath heron

Grey heron

WHERE IN THE WORLD?

Breeds further north than any other heron, from Britain and southern Scandinavia east across Russia to Japan, ranging south to India, the North African coast and other parts of Africa.

RELATED SPECIES

The 60-strong family of herons, Ardeidae, is divided into two tribes: the day-active herons, a group of 34 species that includes the grey heron, egrets and the purple heron, Ardea purpurea; and the mainly nocturnal herons — the bitterns, night herons and tiger herons.

• **ORDER** • *Ciconiiformes* • **FAMILY** • *Ardeidae* • **SPECIES** • *Nycticorax nycticorax* # BLACK-CROWNED NIGHT HERON

The black-crowned night heron feeds mainly at dawn and dusk, but also fishes during the day when it has nestlings to feed.

KEY FEATURES

- Often feeds by night, not necessarily by choice, but usually to avoid competition with other, day-active species of heron that are better adapted to hunting in aquatic habitats.
- Large eyes help it to spot prey — including aquatic creatures underwater — at dusk.
- Spends the daylight hours roosting with other herons in a large colony.

VITAL STATISTICS

WEIGHT	About 680g (23.9oz)
LENGTH	56–66cm (22–26in)
WINGSPAN	1–1.1m (3ft 3in–3ft 6in)
SEXUAL MATURITY	2–3 years
MATING SEASON	Varies according to location
NUMBER OF EGGS	Usually 3 to 5; occasionally lays two clutches
INCUBATION PERIOD	21–26 days
BREEDING INTERVAL	1 year
FLEDGING PERIOD	42–49 days
TYPICAL DIET	Mainly frogs, fish and insects; also molluscs, worms and crustaceans
LIFESPAN	Up to 25 years

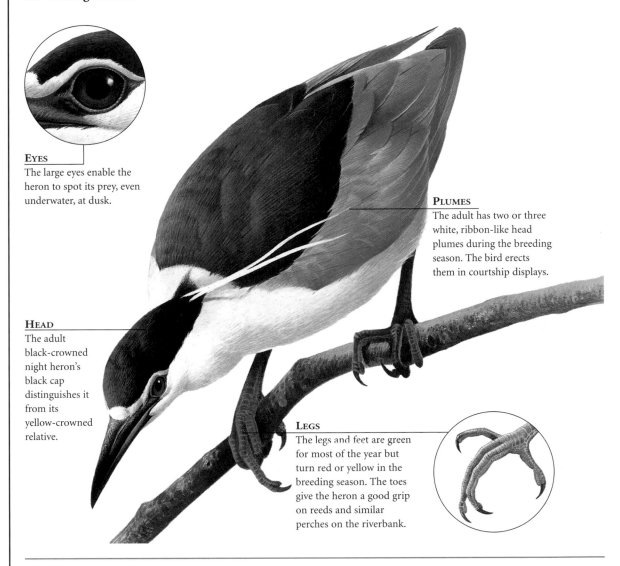

EYES
The large eyes enable the heron to spot its prey, even underwater, at dusk.

HEAD
The adult black-crowned night heron's black cap distinguishes it from its yellow-crowned relative.

PLUMES
The adult has two or three white, ribbon-like head plumes during the breeding season. The bird erects them in courtship displays.

LEGS
The legs and feet are green for most of the year but turn red or yellow in the breeding season. The toes give the heron a good grip on reeds and similar perches on the riverbank.

CREATURE COMPARISONS

An adult black-crowned night heron is not likely be mistaken for any other bird, although its young resemble those of yellow-crowned night herons or American bitterns. The boat-billed heron is one of the more unusual-looking herons due to its distinctive bill, with which it scoops fish and shrimp from the water. This species was formerly classified in a family of its own.

Black-crowned night heron

Boat-billed heron

Bittern

WHERE IN THE WORLD?

One of the most widely distributed and numerous of all herons. Found in many parts of the world, including North and South America, Europe, Asia and Africa. Also found on oceanic islands, such as Hawaii.

RELATED SPECIES

There are 60 species in the family Ardeidae, including bitterns and egrets, as well as herons. All of these medium-sized to large birds have a long neck and legs, broad wings and a slim body. The long, often dagger-like, bill, an adaptation to hunting, is also typical of many of the birds in this family. There are seven species of night heron in the family Ardeidae, including the yellow-crowned night heron, Nyctanassa violacea.

CICONIIFORMES

• **ORDER** • *Ciconiiformes* • **FAMILY** • *Balaenicipitidae* • **GENUS & SPECIES** • *Balaeniceps rex*

SHOEBILL

KEY FEATURES

- Violently thrusts its massive bill through dense aquatic vegetation to reach fish and frogs.
- On hot days, a parent uses its bill to cool its eggs and chicks by sprinkling water on them.
- Faces an uncertain future as its wetland habitat is gradually being lost to human settlement, warranting the attention of the IUCN (World Conservation Union).

VITAL STATISTICS

WEIGHT	5–6kg (11–13.2lb)
LENGTH	Up to 1.2m (3ft 9in)
WINGSPAN	2m (6ft 6in)
SEXUAL MATURITY	3–4 years
BREEDING SEASON	October to June
NUMBER OF EGGS	1 to 3, usually 2
INCUBATION PERIOD	30 days
FLEDGING PERIOD	95–105 days
BREEDING INTERVAL	1 year
TYPICAL DIET	Fish, frogs, water snakes, turtles
LIFESPAN	Up to 35 years in captivity

With its stilt-like legs and splayed feet, the shoebill can wade in shallow water, or stand on floating vegetation, ready to strike with its extraordinary bill.

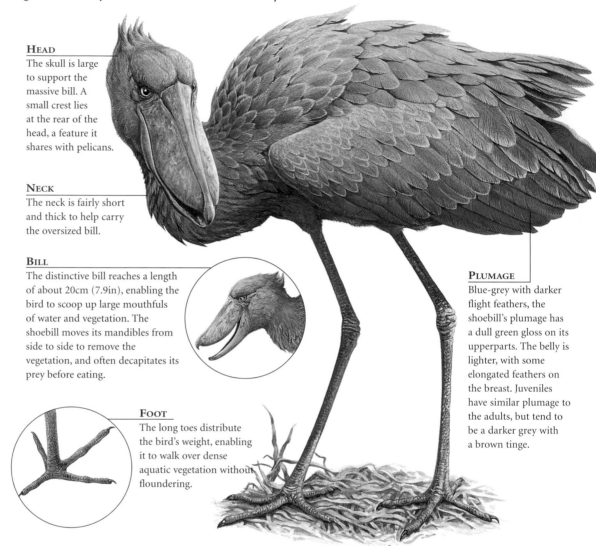

HEAD
The skull is large to support the massive bill. A small crest lies at the rear of the head, a feature it shares with pelicans.

NECK
The neck is fairly short and thick to help carry the oversized bill.

BILL
The distinctive bill reaches a length of about 20cm (7.9in), enabling the bird to scoop up large mouthfuls of water and vegetation. The shoebill moves its mandibles from side to side to remove the vegetation, and often decapitates its prey before eating.

FOOT
The long toes distribute the bird's weight, enabling it to walk over dense aquatic vegetation without floundering.

PLUMAGE
Blue-grey with darker flight feathers, the shoebill's plumage has a dull green gloss on its upperparts. The belly is lighter, with some elongated feathers on the breast. Juveniles have similar plumage to the adults, but tend to be a darker grey with a brown tinge.

CREATURE COMPARISONS

At 50cm (19.7in) in length, the hamerkop (Scopus umbretta) is dwarfed by the shoebill. It has pale brown plumage, and the back of its head sports a crest that gives rise to its name, an Africaans word meaning 'hammer-head'. Like the shoebill, the hamerkop is a waterbird. Its slender bill enables it to trap a varied diet from frogs and tadpoles to fish and small invertebrates. The hamerkop's bill has a tiny hook at the tip of the upper mandible, helping the bird pick up smaller victims and rinse them in water before eating. Although much smaller than the shoebill, the hamerkop builds one of the world's largest nests. Using sticks, reeds and grass, it builds its home in the fork of a tree or on the ground, creating a structure with an average depth of 1.5m (4ft 9in) and weighing up to 100 times more than the bird.

Hamerkop   Shoebill

WHERE IN THE WORLD?

Found in the papyrus swamps and wetlands in northeastern and Central Africa, from the Sudd swamps in southern Sudan, south through Uganda, into Zambia.

RELATED SPECIES

The shoebill is the sole member of its genus, Balaeniceps, and the only species in its family, the Balaenicipitidae. Although modern DNA analysis and the structure of its bill show it to be closely related to the pelicans, it has traditionally been thought to be most closely related to the storks and herons. With its long legs and neck it resembles a bulky stork but unlike storks or herons it seldom perches in trees, and nests on the ground.

• ORDER • *Ciconiiformes* • FAMILY • *Ciconiidae* • GENUS & SPECIES • *Ciconia ciconia*

KEY FEATURES

- A tall, stately relative of the herons.
- Strides across grassland and marshes to stab frogs and other small animals with its dagger-like bill.
- Often builds its nest on roofs, chimneys and pylons.
- Migrates in flocks thousands-strong, covering great distances with its energy-saving, soaring flight.

VITAL STATISTICS

WEIGHT	Male 2.6–4.4kg (5.7–9.7lb); female 2.3–4kg (5.1–8.8lb)
LENGTH	1–1.15m (3ft 3in–3ft 8in)
WINGSPAN	1.5–1.65m (4ft 9in–5ft 4in)
SEXUAL MATURITY	4 years
BREEDING SEASON	April to July
NUMBER OF EGGS	1 to 7; usually 3 to 5
INCUBATION PERIOD	33–34 days
FLEDGING PERIOD	58–64 days
BREEDING INTERVAL	1 year
TYPICAL DIET	Small prey: from insects and worms to frogs, snakes, lizards, birds, mammals
LIFESPAN	Up to 35 years

The white stork's resplendent plumage and graceful stride belie the fact that it is a deadly predator that kills with lightning strikes of its bill.

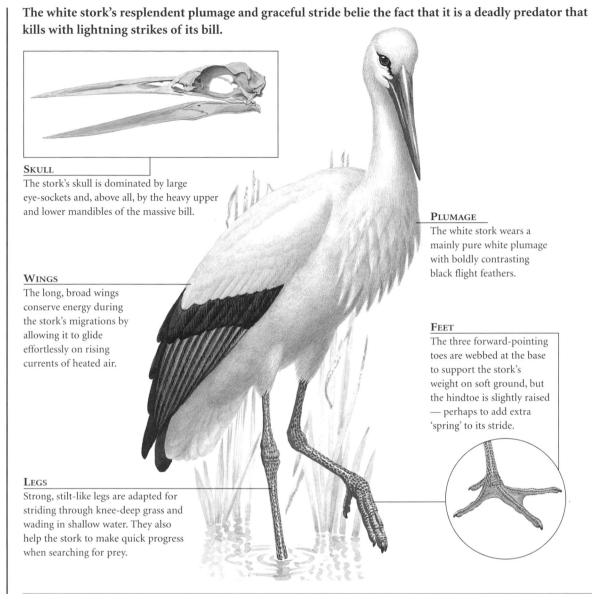

SKULL
The stork's skull is dominated by large eye-sockets and, above all, by the heavy upper and lower mandibles of the massive bill.

WINGS
The long, broad wings conserve energy during the stork's migrations by allowing it to glide effortlessly on rising currents of heated air.

LEGS
Strong, stilt-like legs are adapted for striding through knee-deep grass and wading in shallow water. They also help the stork to make quick progress when searching for prey.

PLUMAGE
The white stork wears a mainly pure white plumage with boldly contrasting black flight feathers.

FEET
The three forward-pointing toes are webbed at the base to support the stork's weight on soft ground, but the hindtoe is slightly raised — perhaps to add extra 'spring' to its stride.

CREATURE COMPARISONS

Despite its name, the black stork (Ciconia nigra) is a much more colourful bird than the marginally larger white stork. Its head, neck and upperparts appear black from a distance, but if seen at close range show their true colours — a blend of glossy greens, browns and purples. A less obvious difference between the two species is that the black stork has a red ring around its eye, whereas the white stork's eye-ring is black.

Unlike its more familiar relative, the black stork avoids all contact with humans. It nests in trees in undisturbed areas of open woodland near rivers, lakes and swamps, over a wide range from Spain to China.

Black stork

White stork

WHERE IN THE WORLD?

Breeds across Europe, from France east to Russia and south to Spain, and in North Africa, parts of central Asia and South Africa. Winters in Africa, Iran and India.

RELATED SPECIES

The white stork is one of 19 species of stork in the family Ciconiidae, which includes the Asian open-bill stork, Anastomus oscitans. Its unique bill is adapted for hunting water snails. Storks belong to the order Ciconiiformes and relatives in this order include herons, spoonbills and ibises.

• **ORDER** • *Ciconiiformes* • **FAMILY** • *Ciconiidae* • **GENUS & SPECIES** • *Ephippiorhynchus senegalensis*

SADDLE-BILL STORK

Long-necked and armed with a dagger-like bill, the saddle-bill stork is an expert fisher, relying on its bill to locate and catch its prey.

KEY FEATURES

- Tallest and most strikingly coloured of Africa's storks; broad wings allow it to soar above the plains.
- Wades through marshes and shallow water snapping up fish and other aquatic prey with its long, sharp bill.
- Builds vast nests high in the canopies of tall trees or deep within wetlands, out of the reach of predators.

FLIGHT
Like eagles and vultures, the stork possesses broad wings and specially adapted flight feathers that allow it to soar, using thermals (warm air currents) to gain height.

BILL
The gaudy, slightly upturned bill may be up to 32cm (12.6in) long. The bird takes its name from the yellow 'saddle' at the base of its bill.

WATTLES
Both sexes may develop small yellow or red fleshy wattles that dangle under the base of the bill almost like stirrups beneath the saddle.

FEET
The long, bright pink toes spread the saddle-bill stork's weight as it strides across waterlogged vegetation and soft mud.

VITAL STATISTICS

WEIGHT	6kg (13.2lb)
LENGTH	1.45–1.5m (4ft 8in–4ft 9in); male larger than female
WINGSPAN	2.4–2.7m (7ft 9in–8ft 8in)
SEXUAL MATURITY	2 years
BREEDING SEASON	During or shortly after the rainy season
NUMBER OF EGGS	1 to 5
INCUBATION PERIOD	30–35 days
FLEDGING PERIOD	70–100 days
BREEDING INTERVAL	1 year
TYPICAL DIET	Fish, frogs, aquatic invertebrates and reptiles
LIFESPAN	36 years in captivity

CREATURE COMPARISONS

The black-necked stork (*Ephippiorhynchus asiaticus*) is the Indo-Pacific counterpart of the saddle-bill stork and is found mainly in India, New Guinea and Australia. Although the two species have separate ranges, they are both birds of wetland habitats, with similar food preferences and nesting and breeding patterns. Not surprisingly, they are sometimes placed in the same genus.

However, the Asian bird is slightly smaller than its African cousin, and there are other striking physical differences. The most obvious of these is bill colour — the saddle-bill stork's spectacular weapon provides a stark contrast to the black-necked stork's black bill. The black-necked stork has coral-red legs, while the saddle-bill has pink knees and feet.

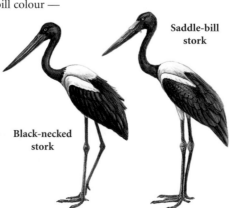

Saddle-bill stork

Black-necked stork

WHERE IN THE WORLD?

Ranges widely throughout tropical Africa, from the southern fringes of the Sahara to northern Namibia, Botswana and northeastern South Africa.

RELATED SPECIES

The saddle-bill stork is 1 of 17 species of stork in the family Ciconiidae. Of the other 5 families that make up the order Ciconiiformes, 2 contain just 1 species each: the families Balaenicipitidae and Scopidae respectively. The remaining 3 families are the Threskiornithidae with 31 species of spoonbill and ibis, the Ardeidae with 60 species of heron and bittern, and the Phoenicopteridae with 5 species of flamingo.

• ORDER • *Ciconiiformes* • FAMILY • *Scopidae* • GENUS & SPECIES • *Scopus umbretta*

With its big bill and matching crest, the hamerkop often looks large in photos, but it is much smaller than the familiar grey heron seen in Britain.

KEY FEATURES

- A strange wading bird that builds a huge nest, with a roof strong enough to support the weight of a man.
- Normally silent and solitary, it indulges in a bizarre and noisy 'false-mounting' ritual when in the company of neighbours.
- An important feature of many tales in African folklore, often appearing as a bird of ill omen.

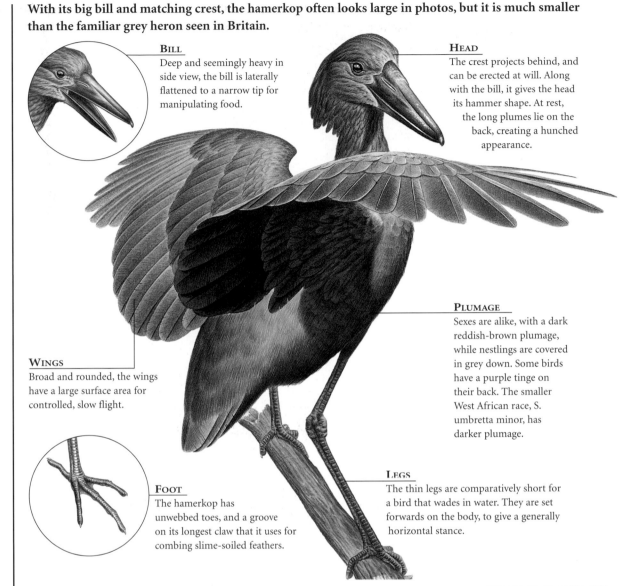

BILL
Deep and seemingly heavy in side view, the bill is laterally flattened to a narrow tip for manipulating food.

HEAD
The crest projects behind, and can be erected at will. Along with the bill, it gives the head its hammer shape. At rest, the long plumes lie on the back, creating a hunched appearance.

WINGS
Broad and rounded, the wings have a large surface area for controlled, slow flight.

PLUMAGE
Sexes are alike, with a dark reddish-brown plumage, while nestlings are covered in grey down. Some birds have a purple tinge on their back. The smaller West African race, S. umbretta minor, has darker plumage.

FOOT
The hamerkop has unwebbed toes, and a groove on its longest claw that it uses for combing slime-soiled feathers.

LEGS
The thin legs are comparatively short for a bird that wades in water. They are set forwards on the body, to give a generally horizontal stance.

VITAL STATISTICS

WEIGHT	415–470g (14.6–16.6oz)
LENGTH	50–56cm (19.7–22in)
WINGSPAN	76–82cm (29.9–32.3in)
SEXUAL MATURITY	Unknown
BREEDING SEASON	Year round, with seasonal peaks
NUMBER OF EGGS	3 to 6, rarely 7
INCUBATION PERIOD	28–32 days
FLEDGING PERIOD	44–50 days
BREEDING INTERVAL	1 year
TYPICAL DIET	Frogs, fish, crustaceans and insects
LIFESPAN	Unknown

CREATURE COMPARISONS

The boat-billed heron (Cochlearius cochlearius) of South and Central America is in many ways as unusual as the hamerkop, which it roughly matches in size. A large-eyed nocturnal bird, its most extraordinary feature is its bill, which, although less than 8cm (3.1in) long, is 5cm (2in) wide and almost the same in depth. After hiding all day in dense forest, the boat-billed heron emerges at night to scoop up fish and shrimps from mangrove swamps, coastal rivers, lakes and marshes. Unlike the hamerkop, it builds a small nest of leafy branches or uses the nest of another species. In courtship, it fans its drooping black crest, claps its bill and croaks like a frog.

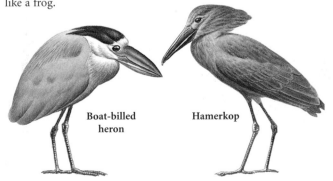

Boat-billed heron

Hamerkop

WHERE IN THE WORLD?

Resident throughout Africa, south of the Sahara Desert. Also breeds on Madagascar, and in an area of southwest Arabia bordering the southern shores of the Red Sea.

RELATED SPECIES

The hamerkop, the only member of the genus Scopus, is a 'one-off' species and is placed in its own family. It has a number of unique characteristics, and others that link it to herons, flamingos and storks, including the rare shoebill, Balaeniceps rex, of Africa. When soaring, the hamerkop extends its neck rather like a stork, but in normal flight it more closely resembles a heron with its neck partly retracted.

• **ORDER** • *Ciconiiformes* • **FAMILY** • *Threskiornithidae* • **GENUS & SPECIES** • *Threskiornis aethiopicus*

SACRED IBIS

KEY FEATURES

- A chicken-sized bird that thrives in a variety of habitats, often nesting near human settlements.
- Uses its long, curved bill to probe soft mud for invertebrates and to snap up larger prey, such as frogs, from the ground.
- Feeds and nests communally and is sometimes found in large breeding colonies alongside other species of ibis, spoonbill and heron.

VITAL STATISTICS

WEIGHT	1.5kg (3.3lb)
LENGTH	65–89cm (25.6–35in)
WINGSPAN	1.1–1.2m (3ft 6in–3ft 9in)
SEXUAL MATURITY	Unknown
BREEDING SEASON	During or shortly after rains, also during dry season in permanent marshes
NUMBER OF EGGS	Up to 5; usually 2 or 3
INCUBATION PERIOD	28–29 days
FLEDGING PERIOD	35–40 days
TYPICAL DIET	Insects, worms, crustaceans, frogs, fish, lizards, small mammals, eggs, carrion
LIFESPAN	Up to 21 years

Long legs, a naked neck and a scimitar-like bill enable the sacred ibis to hunt in water and on land for many kinds of prey.

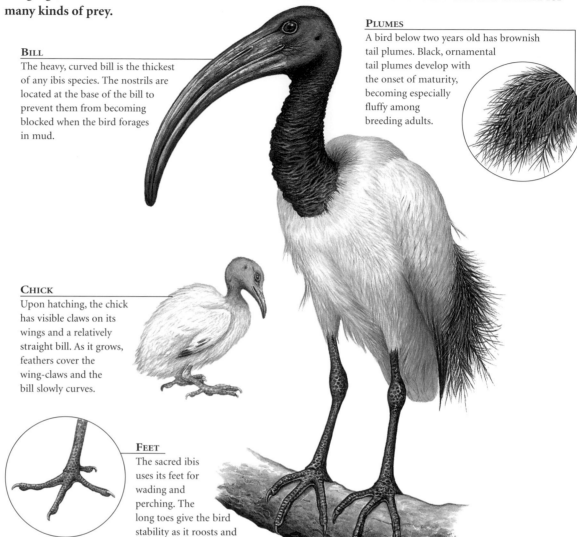

BILL
The heavy, curved bill is the thickest of any ibis species. The nostrils are located at the base of the bill to prevent them from becoming blocked when the bird forages in mud.

PLUMES
A bird below two years old has brownish tail plumes. Black, ornamental tail plumes develop with the onset of maturity, becoming especially fluffy among breeding adults.

CHICK
Upon hatching, the chick has visible claws on its wings and a relatively straight bill. As it grows, feathers cover the wing-claws and the bill slowly curves.

FEET
The sacred ibis uses its feet for wading and perching. The long toes give the bird stability as it roosts and nests in trees.

CREATURE COMPARISONS

Smaller than the sacred ibis, the strikingly coloured scarlet ibis (*Eudocimus ruber*) lives in parts of northern South America. Unlike the sacred ibis, it is restricted to wetlands where it feeds in flocks, moving rapidly through shallow water and probing the mud in search of crabs, worms and molluscs. The scarlet ibis gets its vivid colouration from its food — the red carotenoid pigments are produced by algae consumed by the ibis's invertebrate prey. The brightness of the bird's plumage depends on the abundance of the algae and varies from region to region. Like the sacred ibis, the scarlet ibis nests communally in trees and often shares its colonies with other ibises and herons. Breeding colonies may contain up to 5000 pairs.

Scarlet ibis

Sacred ibis

WHERE IN THE WORLD?

Found throughout most of sub-Saharan Africa and in the marshes of southeastern Iraq. Two separate subspecies also occur, one on Aldabra Island in the Seychelles and the other in western Madagascar.

RELATED SPECIES

The sacred ibis is 1 of 4 members in its genus. It shares its family with 22 other ibis species, including the northern bald ibis, *Geronticus eremita*, and 8 species of spoonbill. Its closest relatives are the Australian white ibis and the black-headed ibis from southeastern Asia.

GREAT DIVING BEETLE

• ORDER • *Coleoptera* **• FAMILY •** *Dytiscidae* **• GENUS & SPECIES •** *Dytiscus marginalis*

With protective armour, razor-sharp mouthparts and superb mobility in the air and underwater, the great diving beetle is a deadly predator.

FEMALE
The female has ten deep grooves on each of her wingcases, while the male has just two on each. She is also slightly smaller than the male.

LARVA
In its larval stage, the young diving beetle is long and slender. It uses its narrow and pointed mandibles (mouthparts) to catch prey.

HINDLEGS
The diving beetle propels itself through the water with its long, oar-like hindlegs.

WINGCASES
The wingcases, or elytra, are forewings that have adapted into a tough, horny covering. They protect the abdomen and the delicate hindwings, which the beetle uses to fly.

SUCTION PADS
On each foreleg (1), the male has two large suction discs surrounded by about 150 tiny suckers. When mating, he uses these suckers to grip the female's body.

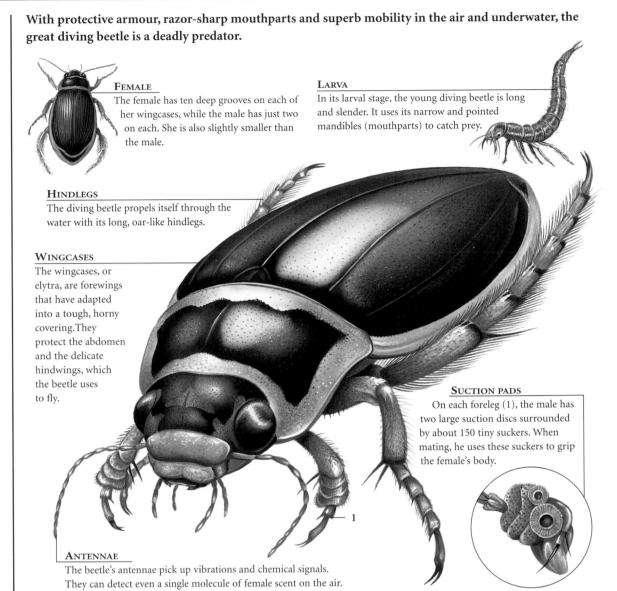

1

ANTENNAE
The beetle's antennae pick up vibrations and chemical signals. They can detect even a single molecule of female scent on the air.

KEY FEATURES

- Small but powerful aquatic predator that is capable of killing prey several times larger than itself.
- Uses its wingcases like an air tank, allowing it to stay underwater for extended periods.
- Has a complex lifecycle, involving complete metamorphosis from larva to adult form.

VITAL STATISTICS

LENGTH	2.7–3.8cm (1.1–1.5in)
BREEDING SEASON	Spring and summer
NUMBER OF EGGS	1000
HATCHING PERIOD	Unknown
LARVAL PERIOD	A few weeks
BREEDING INTERVAL	1 year
TYPICAL DIET	Small fish, tadpoles, insects and carrion
LIFESPAN	Up to 3 years in the wild; 5 years in captivity

CREATURE COMPARISONS

The great silver water beetle (Hydrophilus piceus) is a close relative of the great diving beetle. It is longer, reaching a length of 5cm (2in), and not as flattened as its streamlined cousin. Although both beetles share similar habitats, they differ markedly in behaviour.

Unlike the carnivorous great diving beetle, the silver water beetle feeds on algae and other vegetation, although its larvae are predatory. And instead of depositing her eggs in aquatic plants, the female water beetle constructs a silk capsule in which to lay her eggs. The capsule has a long funnel at one end, so the eggs receive oxygen even if the capsule is partly submerged beneath the water surface.

Great diving beetle

Great silver water beetle

WHERE IN THE WORLD?

Has a wide range extending from Western Europe, east across central and northern Asia, to Siberia and Japan.

RELATED SPECIES

The great diving beetle is 1 of about 4000 species in the family Dytiscidae, all of which are predatory diving beetles. Another predatory water beetle is the whirligig beetle, Gyrinus natator, which spends much of its time swimming in circles on the water surface. Both species belong to the order Coleoptera, which contains about 330,000 species and is the largest order in the entire animal kingdom.

• **ORDER** • *Coleoptera* • **FAMILY** • *Scarabaeidae* • **GENUS & SPECIES** • *Various*

DUNG BEETLE

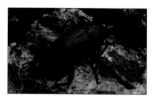

The dung beetle has a heavyweight build to cope with the effort of making proportionately enormous balls of dung, then rolling them along the ground.

KEY FEATURES

- Big, glossy beetle that lives by feeding on the dung of grazing and browsing animals.
- Unusual among invertebrates, it is an attentive parent that provides food and shelter for its offspring.
- Plays a vital role in the ecology of the world, recycling the waste material produced by other creatures.

BREEDING BURROWS
Eggs are laid in breeding burrows (above) dug mainly by females to various designs. Balls of dung are placed in the burrows and the female lays a single egg on each one. When the larvae hatch they feed on the dung.

WINGS
The majority of dung beetle species fly. Wings are long, but flight is generally slow and laboured.

WINGCASES
The strong, often ribbed, wingcases (elytra) protect the delicate folded wings that are stored beneath them.

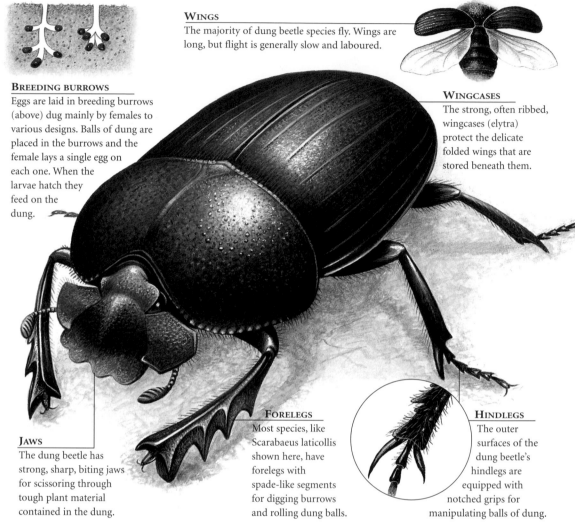

JAWS
The dung beetle has strong, sharp, biting jaws for scissoring through tough plant material contained in the dung.

FORELEGS
Most species, like Scarabaeus laticollis shown here, have forelegs with spade-like segments for digging burrows and rolling dung balls.

HINDLEGS
The outer surfaces of the dung beetle's hindlegs are equipped with notched grips for manipulating balls of dung.

VITAL STATISTICS

LENGTH	7–50mm (0.3–2in)
SEXUAL MATURITY	3–9 months
BREEDING SEASON	Early summer in temperate climates; all year round in tropical regions
NUMBER OF EGGS	5 to 10
HATCHING PERIOD	Unknown
LARVAL PERIOD	3–9 months depending on species and habitat
BREEDING INTERVAL	Breeds onlyonce
TYPICAL DIET	Dung, plus rotting plant and animal material
LIFESPAN	About 18 months

CREATURE COMPARISONS

The dung beetle is not unique in burying food for its offspring. The sexton beetle, Necrophorus vespillo, has developed a similar habit, but instead of burying dung it buries the carcasses of small animals, such as mice and birds. The male and female beetles work together to dig a burrow and then, little by little, drag the carcass down into it until it is completely hidden underground. The female lays a few eggs nearby, and when the larvae hatch she feeds them on flesh from the carcass that she has eaten and liquefied.

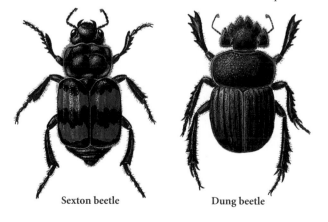

Sexton beetle   Dung beetle

WHERE IN THE WORLD?

Found wherever the concentration of grazing or browsing animals makes dung easy to find. Scarce, or absent, in deserts and the high polar latitudes.

RELATED SPECIES

There are thousands of species of dung beetle in numerous genera in the family Scarabaeidae. This family also includes some of the biggest beetles in the world, such as the Hercules beetle, Dynastes hercules, and the Goliath beetles. Some of these beetles can grow to 18cm (7.1in). In general, beetles are the most successful and numerous animals on Earth, accounting for one third of the million or so animal species known to science.

FOGSTAND BEETLE

• **ORDER** • *Coleoptera* • **FAMILY** • *Tenebrionidae* • **GENUS & SPECIES** • *Various*

The fogstand beetle's hard, domed body enables the insect to conserve water and repel heat in the desert, and in many species also aids in burrowing.

KEY FEATURES

- Shelters in a burrow during the day to escape the fierce heat of Africa's Namib Desert.
- Stands on sand dunes and collects water to drink from the sea fog that condenses on its body.
- Some species possess white wingcases to reflect the sun's heat.

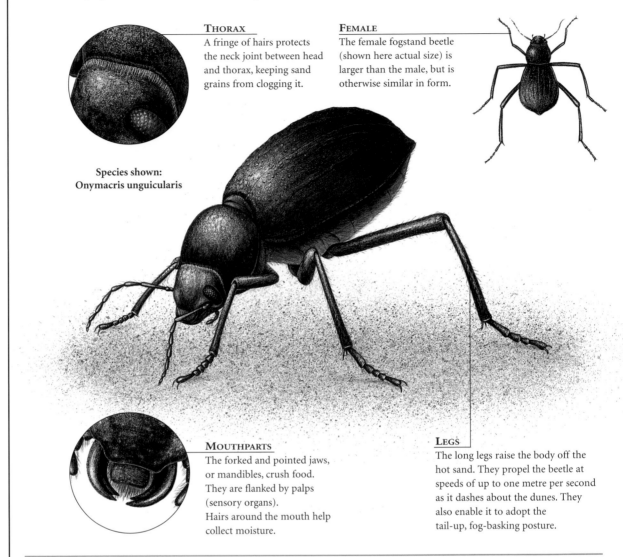

THORAX
A fringe of hairs protects the neck joint between head and thorax, keeping sand grains from clogging it.

FEMALE
The female fogstand beetle (shown here actual size) is larger than the male, but is otherwise similar in form.

Species shown:
Onymacris unguicularis

MOUTHPARTS
The forked and pointed jaws, or mandibles, crush food. They are flanked by palps (sensory organs). Hairs around the mouth help collect moisture.

LEGS
The long legs raise the body off the hot sand. They propel the beetle at speeds of up to one metre per second as it dashes about the dunes. They also enable it to adopt the tail-up, fog-basking posture.

VITAL STATISTICS

LENGTH	Up to 3.8cm (1.5in)
SEXUAL MATURITY	Not known
BREEDING SEASON	Probably all year
NUMBER OF YOUNG	Not known
BIRTH INTERVAL	Not known
TYPICAL DIET	Any available organic material, including dead and living plant matter, carrion, dung and wind-blown leaves and seeds; larvae feed on dead roots and other plant matter
LIFESPAN	Up to 9 years

CREATURE COMPARISONS

The fogstand beetles in the Namib Desert all vary in body size, leg length and wingcase design. The toothed ridges and white wingcases of Cauricara eburnea (1) help it blend in with the rough, white quartzite pebbles away from the dunes. The sleek outline of Onymacris unguicularis (2) allows the beetle almost to 'swim' into the loose sand as it burrows. The smooth, white wingcases of O. candidipennis (3) reflect some of the sun's heat.

Lepidochora discoidalis (4) uses its rounded, ridged abdomen not only to condense fog, but also to heap up ridges of sand on the dunes; these tiny ramparts trap drops of moisture as the sea breezes blow in.

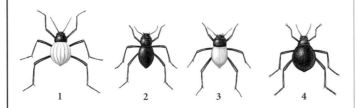

1   2   3   4

WHERE IN THE WORLD?

Found in the Namib Desert, which extends nearly 2000km (1243 miles) along the coast of Namibia in southern Africa. Distribution inland is restricted to the extent to which fogs blow in from the Atlantic Ocean.

RELATED SPECIES

There are about 200 species of fogstand beetle in the Namib Desert, including Someticus bohemani. They are among the 15,000 species of darkling beetle in the widespread family Tenebrionidae, which includes the cellar and mealworm beetles.

• **ORDER** • *Coraciiformes* • **FAMILY** • *Alcedinidae* • **GENUS & SPECIES** • *Alcedo atthis*

EURASIAN KINGFISHER

KEY FEATURES

- Bright plumage is iridescent and appears to be either blue or green, depending on the light conditions.
- Plunges into the water at great speed to catch fish in its long, pointed bill.
- Burrows deeply into a soft, sandy riverbank to build a secure nesting chamber.

VITAL STATISTICS

WEIGHT	37–44g (1.3–1.5oz)
LENGTH	16–17cm (6.3–6.7in)
WINGSPAN	24–26cm (9.4–10.2in)
SEXUAL MATURITY	1 year
BREEDING SEASON	March–July, Europe; March–April, northwest Africa; April–July, India; January–June, Southeast Asia
NUMBER OF EGGS	Up to 10 but usually 6 or 7
INCUBATION PERIOD	19–20 days
FLEDGING PERIOD	24–25 days
TYPICAL DIET	Small fish, aquatic insects and larvae
LIFESPAN	Up to 15 years

The Eurasian kingfisher is an expert fisherman, plunging like a jewelled dart at speeds of up to 45 km/h (28 mph) to catch prey in the water.

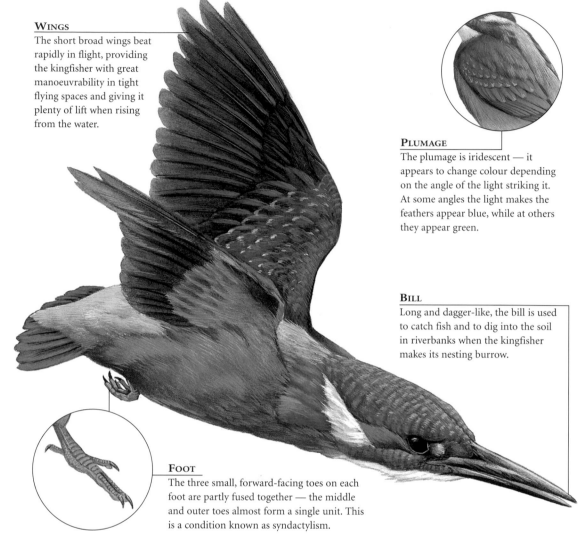

WINGS
The short broad wings beat rapidly in flight, providing the kingfisher with great manoeuvrability in tight flying spaces and giving it plenty of lift when rising from the water.

PLUMAGE
The plumage is iridescent — it appears to change colour depending on the angle of the light striking it. At some angles the light makes the feathers appear blue, while at others they appear green.

BILL
Long and dagger-like, the bill is used to catch fish and to dig into the soil in riverbanks when the kingfisher makes its nesting burrow.

FOOT
The three small, forward-facing toes on each foot are partly fused together — the middle and outer toes almost form a single unit. This is a condition known as syndactylism.

CREATURE COMPARISONS

Only about one-third of all species of kingfishers are true 'fishers': the others have somewhat varied diets of insects, snakes, earthworms, frogs, lizards, crabs and scorpions. Instead of diving into water to catch fish, they swoop down from perches in forests and woodlands to pick their prey off the ground. The laughing kookaburra (Dacelo novaeguinae) of Australia is the largest of all kingfishers, weighing up to 500g (17.6oz). Its loud, territorial call sounds like raucous human laughter. It sometimes inhabits city parks and gardens, and is a familiar bird of the dry eucalyptus forests of eastern Australia. Although not closely associated with water, it occasionally catches fish and may even raid suburban goldfish ponds. However, its diet mainly consists of snakes, lizards and rodents.

Kookaburra

Kingfisher

WHERE IN THE WORLD?

From the west of Ireland, through much of Europe, parts of Russia and Iran east to India, China, Japan and Southeast Asia. Also parts of North Africa.

RELATED SPECIES

There are over 90 species of kingfisher in 14 genera in the family Alcedinidae, including the African pygmy kingfisher, Ceyx picta; a tiny bird weighing a mere 10g (0.3oz). It inhabits Africa's savannah woodlands and hunts small insects and amphibians.

• ORDER • *Coraciiformes* • FAMILY • *Alcedinidae* • GENUS & SPECIES • *Dacelo novaeguinae*

LAUGHING KOOKABURRA

A true giant among kingfishers, the laughing kookaburra's stocky frame and sturdy bill enable it to tackle sizeable, often dangerous prey.

KEY FEATURES

- An opportunistic predator of Australia's bush, this crow-sized kingfisher grabs and stabs prey with its stout bill.
- A master reptile-killer that thrashes snakes and lizards to death, often after dropping them from high in the air to stun them first.
- Extremely noisy, with a vocabulary of loud calls that sound like chuckles and side-splitting laughs.

VITAL STATISTICS

WEIGHT	310–480g (10.9–16.9oz)
LENGTH	40–45cm (15.7–17.7in)
WINGSPAN	50–60cm (19.7–23.6in)
SEXUAL MATURITY	1 year
BREEDING SEASON	September to December
NUMBER OF EGGS	2 or 3
INCUBATION PERIOD	24–26 days
FLEDGING PERIOD	33–39 days
BREEDING INTERVAL	1 year
TYPICAL DIET	Small rodents, lizards, snakes, frogs, insects, earthworms, crayfish, nestling birds
LIFESPAN	6–10 years

BILL
To cope with a diet that includes amphibians, young birds and reptiles, the laughing kookaburra's bill is broader and thicker than those of fish-eating kingfishers. It is also tipped with a small hook for gripping struggling prey.

BODY
Heavily built, with a huge head relative to its body-size, the laughing kookaburra is the largest kingfisher in the world. The female (shown) is larger than the male.

FANNING
When making its laughing call, the kookaburra cocks and fans its tail. This displays the tail's underside, which is brown and white with grey-brown bars.

FOOT
In common with other kingfishers the kookaburra's feet are relatively small and weak, but, unlike its relatives, the toes are not fused together.

TAIL
The tail's banding breaks up the bird's outline as it swoops when hunting, helping it to take prey by surprise.

CREATURE COMPARISONS

In parts of eastern Australia, the blue-winged kookaburra (Dacelo leachii) occurs alongside the laughing kookaburra. Similar in size, both species have the dagger-like bill typical of kingfishers. The blue-winged kookaburra has noticeably paler eyes and a whiter head than its close relative, and its wings have large areas of blue feathering. Its tail and rump are also a brilliant blue.

Where the ranges of the two species overlap, the blue-winged kookaburra is found in damper habitats — in wet forests and in tall stands of trees beside watercourses. It has a wider distribution than the laughing kookaburra, occurring right across northern Australia and north to southern New Guinea, where it sometimes inhabits coastal mangrove swamps.

Blue-winged kookaburra

Laughing kookaburra

WHERE IN THE WORLD?

Found over much of eastern Australia in a broad band from Queensland in the north, south to Victoria and southwestern South Australia. Introduced to a corner of Western Australia and Tasmania.

RELATED SPECIES

The kingfisher family, or Alcedinidae, belongs to the order Coraciiformes, which also includes the bee-eater, roller and hornbill families. Alcedinidae contains 87 species of kingfisher, but only about 22 species feed exclusively on fish. There are four non-fishing species in the laughing kookaburra's genus Dacelo: the large laughing and blue-winged kookaburras, and the small rufous-bellied and spangled kookaburras (D. gaudichaud and D. tyro) of New Guinea.

• **ORDER** • *Coraciiformes* • **FAMILY** • *Bucerotidae* • **GENUS & SPECIES** • *Tockus leucomelas*

YELLOW-BILLED HORNBILL

KEY FEATURES

- Male takes total responsibility for feeding female and chicks during the breeding period.
- Female and young are sealed into their nest-hole with a wall of dried mud, to keep out predators.
- Achieves far greater fledging success than other hole-nesting birds that do not wall in their occupants.

VITAL STATISTICS

WEIGHT	140–240g (4.9–8.5oz)
LENGTH	40.5–45.7cm (15.9–18in)
WINGSPAN	61–66cm (24–26in)
SEXUAL MATURITY	1 year
BREEDING SEASON	Mainly October to February
NUMBER OF EGGS	2 to 6; usually 3 or 4
INCUBATION PERIOD	24 days
FLEDGING PERIOD	42–47 days
BREEDING INTERVAL	1 year
TYPICAL DIET	Insects, eggs, rodents, small snakes, fruit and seeds
LIFESPAN	Probably 35–40 years

The huge bill, typical of the hornbill family, serves as a trowel for walling up the nest and as surprisingly delicate tweezers for picking up food.

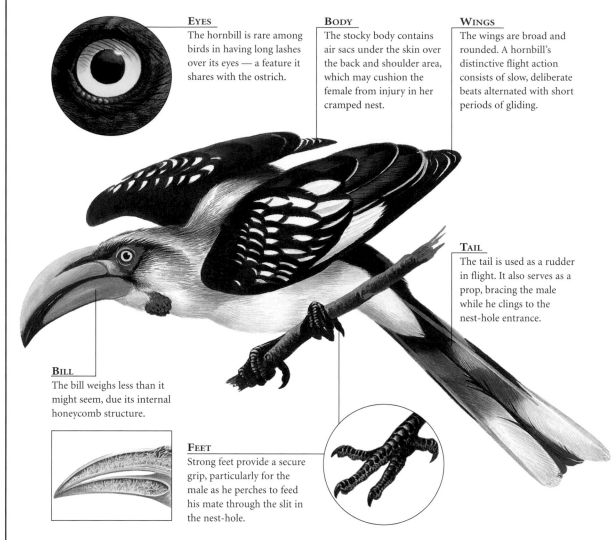

EYES
The hornbill is rare among birds in having long lashes over its eyes — a feature it shares with the ostrich.

BODY
The stocky body contains air sacs under the skin over the back and shoulder area, which may cushion the female from injury in her cramped nest.

WINGS
The wings are broad and rounded. A hornbill's distinctive flight action consists of slow, deliberate beats alternated with short periods of gliding.

TAIL
The tail is used as a rudder in flight. It also serves as a prop, bracing the male while he clings to the nest-hole entrance.

BILL
The bill weighs less than it might seem, due its internal honeycomb structure.

FEET
Strong feet provide a secure grip, particularly for the male as he perches to feed his mate through the slit in the nest-hole.

CREATURE COMPARISONS

Big, powerful curved bills for snapping up prey are a feature of the hornbill family. The southern yellow-billed hornbill eats mainly insects, plucked from the ground. The southern ground hornbill's much larger bill is a formidable weapon, capable of dealing a death blow to animals as large as hares, squirrels and snakes. The hornbills and their New World equivalents, the toucans, are unrelated, but have evolved similarly shaped bills because of their similar feeding habits.

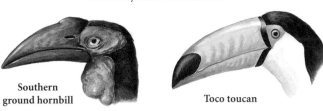

Southern yellow-billed hornbill

Southern ground hornbill

Toco toucan

WHERE IN THE WORLD?

Found from Angola through Namibia to Zambia, Malawi, Botswana, Zimbabwe, northern and eastern South Africa and southwestern Mozambique.

RELATED SPECIES

The 54 hornbill species are all found in the Old World, mostly within tropical regions. They include the 1.5m- (4ft 9in)-long great pied hornbill.

•ORDER• *Coraciiformes* • FAMILY • *Meropidae* • GENUS & SPECIES • *Merops bullockoides*

WHITE-FRONTED BEE-EATER

The white-fronted bee-eater is graceful in its aerial pursuit of insects, and robust enough to dig deep into a riverbank to make its nest.

KEY FEATURES

- A strikingly beautiful bird with a social life that in some respects seems similar to human society.
- Family groups live together, help each other with domestic chores, and visit friendly neighbours.
- Several families group together as a clan, and cooperate to protect their hunting territory.
- Plucks bees out of the air and removes the sting before eating.

VITAL STATISTICS

WEIGHT	28–38g (1–1.3oz)
LENGTH	21.5–24cm (8.5–9.4in)
WINGSPAN	30–35.5cm (11.8–14in)
SEXUAL MATURITY	1 year
BREEDING SEASON	Year-round near equator; mainly August to November elsewhere
NUMBER OF EGGS	Usually 3 or 4
INCUBATION PERIOD	19–21 days
FLEDGING PERIOD	About 28 days
TYPICAL DIET	Bees, wasps and other flying insects
LIFESPAN	Average 5–6 years, but may live to 12 years or more

BILL
The long, curved bill, used with such great dexterity in catching, killing and de-stinging bees, is strong enough to be used as a pickaxe for digging a nesting tunnel.

EYES
Acute vision enables the white-fronted bee-eater to spot its tiny prey from a great distance.

WINGS
The wings are more rounded than those of some species of bee-eater. They give the bird its characteristic buoyancy as it glides and swoops.

FEET
Bee-eaters have their middle and outer toes fused together, making their small feet more effective as shovels when excavating tunnels.

TAIL
The white-fronted bee-eater's long tail is used as a rudder as the bird twists and turns in flight. The bird also uses its tail as a brace when it clings to steep cliff-faces.

CREATURE COMPARISONS

Several species of bee-eater, including the migratory blue-cheeked bee-eater, have sharply pointed wings and long streamers projecting from the tail. The larger lilac-breasted roller is more distantly related to the bee-eaters and eats grasshoppers and lizards snatched from the ground. The African malachite sunbird, although shaped like a bee-eater, is unrelated and feeds on the nectar of flowers.

White-fronted bee-eater

Blue-cheeked bee-eater

Lilac-breasted roller

African malachite sunbird

WHERE IN THE WORLD?

The white-fronted bee-eater is found in central and southern Africa, from Gabon and Angola in the west to Kenya in the east, and in southern and eastern areas of South Africa.

RELATED SPECIES

All 24 species of bee-eater are colourful birds. Of the 18 species found in Africa, 14 live there and nowhere else, including the little bee-eater, Merops pusillus. Five other species are found in parts of Eurasia, and a single species lives in Australia.

• ORDER • *Crocodylia* • FAMILY • *Alligatoridae* • GENUS & SPECIES • *Alligator mississippiensis*

AMERICAN ALLIGATOR

KEY FEATURES

- Top aquatic predator of the southern USA, and an opportunistic feeder that will eat almost anything.
- Survives the cold winters of North America by entering a period of dormancy.
- Once almost wiped out by uncontrolled hunting, but now cherished as a lucrative tourist attraction.

VITAL STATISTICS

WEIGHT	Up to 250kg (551.2lb)
LENGTH	Male nearly 6m (7ft 9in) in the past, now 4m (13ft 1in) is considered large; female smaller
SEXUAL MATURITY	10–12 years in the wild; much sooner in captivity
BREEDING SEASON	April to May
NUMBER OF EGGS	35 to 50 per clutch
INCUBATION PERIOD	60–70 days
BREEDING INTERVAL	1 to 3 years
TYPICAL DIET	Birds, small mammals, snakes, fish, turtles
LIFESPAN	Up to 30 years

The American alligator is a near relative of the dinosaurs that has survived into the modern age as one of the most feared predators in North America.

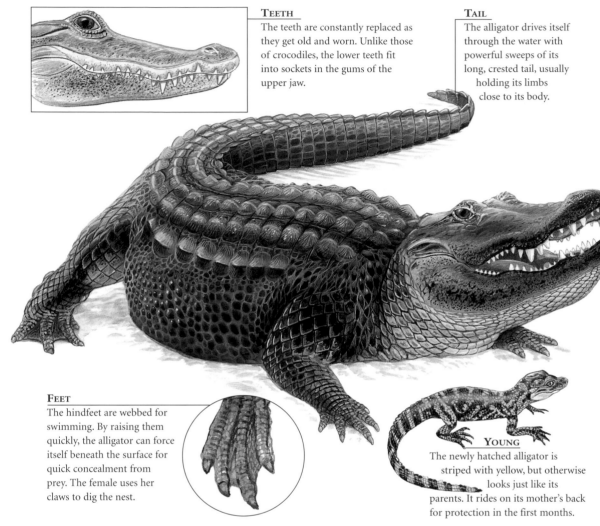

TEETH
The teeth are constantly replaced as they get old and worn. Unlike those of crocodiles, the lower teeth fit into sockets in the gums of the upper jaw.

TAIL
The alligator drives itself through the water with powerful sweeps of its long, crested tail, usually holding its limbs close to its body.

FEET
The hindfeet are webbed for swimming. By raising them quickly, the alligator can force itself beneath the surface for quick concealment from prey. The female uses her claws to dig the nest.

YOUNG
The newly hatched alligator is striped with yellow, but otherwise looks just like its parents. It rides on its mother's back for protection in the first months.

CREATURE COMPARISONS

On the shores of southern Florida, the American alligator often basks alongside the American crocodile, which is found in salt and freshwater habitats over much of the Caribbean. The crocodile is less heavily built than the alligator, with a slender snout ideally suited to catching fish (although it eats birds and mammals too) and lower teeth protruding visibly from the snout. It is now rare, as a result of the hide trade and a steady loss of suitable nesting sites through coastal development, and Florida is probably the only place where it is still flourishing.

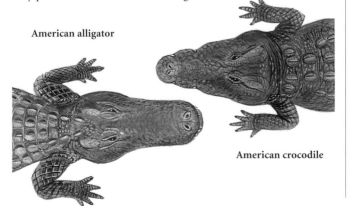

American alligator

American crocodile

WHERE IN THE WORLD?

Found in the coastal states of the southern USA from southern Virginia to eastern Texas, although it is now rare in some areas.

RELATED SPECIES

The American alligator is 1 of 7 species in the family Alligatoridae, which also includes the endangered Chinese alligator and the South American caiman. Along with 14 species of crocodile and the fish-eating gharial of India, these make up the order Crocodylia. This is the last surviving order of the subclass Archosauria, that appeared over 225 million years ago and also gave rise to the dinosaurs of the Mesozoic Era.

SPECTACLED CAIMAN

Using its muscular tail to drive it through the water, the spectacled caiman patrols the rivers and wetlands of Central and South America.

KEY FEATURES

- Pronounced bony ridges around the eyes give this species its common name.
- One of the most widely distributed crocodiles; its range and numbers are expanding in a few areas.
- Female shows strong maternal instincts, building a nest for her eggs and caring for her young when they hatch.

VITAL STATISTICS

WEIGHT	Up to 300kg (661.4lb)
LENGTH	1–3m (3ft 3in–9ft 8in)
SEXUAL MATURITY	4–7 years
BREEDING SEASON	During wet season, with nesting from August to November
NUMBER OF EGGS	14 to 40
HATCHING PERIOD	70–90 days
BREEDING INTERVAL	1 year
TYPICAL DIET	Fish, reptiles, amphibians, small mammals, waterbirds, insects, carrion
LIFESPAN	25 years or more

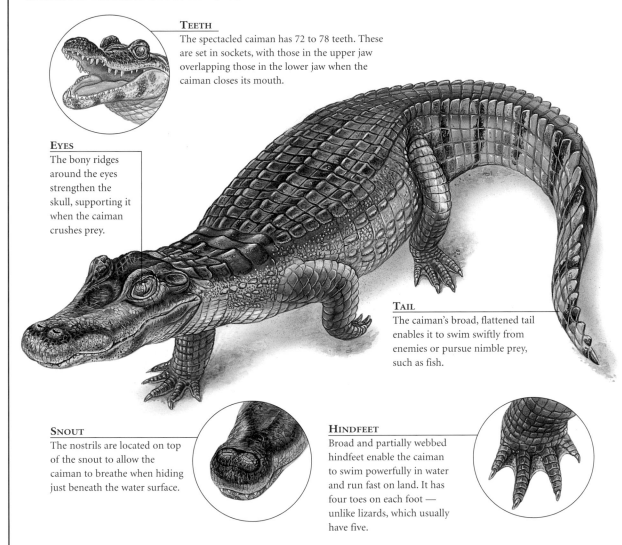

TEETH
The spectacled caiman has 72 to 78 teeth. These are set in sockets, with those in the upper jaw overlapping those in the lower jaw when the caiman closes its mouth.

EYES
The bony ridges around the eyes strengthen the skull, supporting it when the caiman crushes prey.

TAIL
The caiman's broad, flattened tail enables it to swim swiftly from enemies or pursue nimble prey, such as fish.

SNOUT
The nostrils are located on top of the snout to allow the caiman to breathe when hiding just beneath the water surface.

HINDFEET
Broad and partially webbed hindfeet enable the caiman to swim powerfully in water and run fast on land. It has four toes on each foot — unlike lizards, which usually have five.

CREATURE COMPARISONS

The gharial (Gavialis gangeticus) is one of the most distinctive members of the crocodile family, possessing a delicate, elongated, tooth-filled jaw which differs greatly from the broad, blunt, powerful jaws of animals such as the spectacled caiman. Dwarfing its South American relative, the gharial may reach 6m (19ft 7in) in length. Essentially a fish eater, its webbed feet, slender, streamlined body and narrow jaws are perfectly adapted for chasing and catching its swift prey. Like the caiman, the gharial has suffered heavily from hunters and is now restricted to a few rivers in India and Bangladesh. It is critically rare and remains in sharp decline.

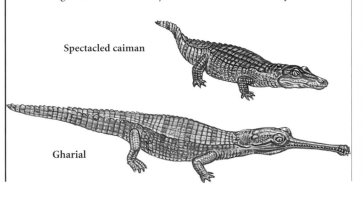

Spectacled caiman

Gharial

WHERE IN THE WORLD?

Distributed from Mexico, through Central America and south into South America as far as Peru and northern Argentina. Introduced populations survive in Florida, USA and Cuba.

RELATED SPECIES

The spectacled caiman comprises 6 subspecies. It is 1 of 2 species in the genus Caiman, the other being the broad-nosed caiman. There are 3 other closely related species in 2 genera: Paleosuchus contains the Cuvier's dwarf caiman and Schneider's smooth-fronted caiman, and Melanosuchus contains the black caiman. The 3 genera are part of the family Crocodylidae and are related to the American alligator, Alligator mississippiensis.

NILE CROCODILE

With its massive jaws, the Nile crocodile poses a deadly threat to its fellow creatures as it lurks beneath the water, waiting to snap them up.

KEY FEATURES

- Largest reptile in Africa, growing up to 6m from snout to tail and weighing over 900kg (1984lb).

- Able to remain submerged for more than an hour as it waits to ambush prey.

- Massively powerful: it can drag a fully grown zebra under water in just a few seconds.

FEET
The crocodile uses its powerful feet and claws to clamber up the riverbank with surprising speed. The female also uses her claws to dig a nest hole for her eggs.

NOSTRILS
The nostrils sit on a raised part of the snout (bottom left), enabling the crocodile to breathe when the rest of its body is submerged. Flaps seal the nostrils (bottom right) to keep out water during dives.

TEETH
The simple teeth rip huge chunks out of prey. They grow continuously, and after about two years the worn teeth (1) are forced out by sharp new ones (2) beneath them.

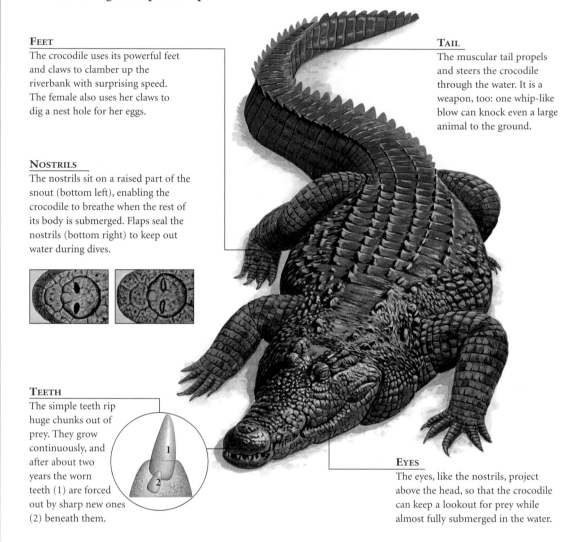

TAIL
The muscular tail propels and steers the crocodile through the water. It is a weapon, too: one whip-like blow can knock even a large animal to the ground.

EYES
The eyes, like the nostrils, project above the head, so that the crocodile can keep a lookout for prey while almost fully submerged in the water.

VITAL STATISTICS

WEIGHT	Up to 990kg (2183lb)
LENGTH	Up to 6m (19ft 7in)
SEXUAL MATURITY	7–15 years
BREEDING SEASON	Varies with latitude, but coincides with dry season
NUMBER OF EGGS	25 to 100
HATCHING PERIOD	95–100 days
BIRTH INTERVAL	Probably annual
TYPICAL DIET	Mammals, such as zebra, cattle and wildebeest, other reptiles (including other crocodiles), fish, birds, carrion; young Nile crocodiles eat frogs and insects
LIFESPAN	70–100 years

CREATURE COMPARISONS

The American alligator is a very close relative of the Nile crocodile. It grows to roughly the same length, but its snout is broader and blunter than that of the crocodile, and it can also be distinguished by its teeth. The alligator's lower teeth slot into sockets in the upper jaw, located between the teeth, so they are hidden when the mouth is closed. Some of the crocodile's lower teeth, however, are always visible.

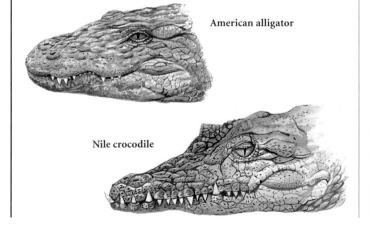

American alligator

Nile crocodile

WHERE IN THE WORLD?

Found in Africa — south of the Sahara, along the River Nile and in Madagascar. Capable of living in almost any watery place, from a ditch to the open sea.

RELATED SPECIES

The Nile crocodile is one of 13 species in the family Crocodylidae. Included in this family is the mugger crocodile, C. palustris. Close relatives include alligators and caimans. These reptiles are found throughout the tropical and subtropical areas of Asia, Australia and the Americas.

SALTWATER CROCODILE

KEY FEATURES

- The world's largest living reptile.
- A truly ocean-going species, able to live in salt water and swim huge distances between islands.
- A consummate killer, it occasionally preys on its deadliest enemy — man.
- Widely hunted, despite legal protection, for its hide. Listed as vulnerable by the IUCN (World Conservation Union).

VITAL STATISTICS

WEIGHT	Male average 500kg (1102lb); female smaller
LENGTH	Male average 4.5m (14ft 8in), maximum 7m (23ft); female a third smaller
SEXUAL MATURITY	Male at 3.2m (10ft 3in) or 14–16 years; female 2.3m (7ft 5in) or 10–12 years
BREEDING SEASON	Usually start of rainy season
NUMBER OF EGGS	25 to 90, usually 40 to 60
INCUBATION PERIOD	90 days
BREEDING INTERVAL	1 year
TYPICAL DIET	Mammals, birds, fish, reptiles, amphibians, crustaceans
LIFESPAN	40–50 years, but up to 100 or more

The saltwater crocodile is a giant among its kind, and although much of its length is taken up by its tail, its trap-like jaws are unnervingly capacious.

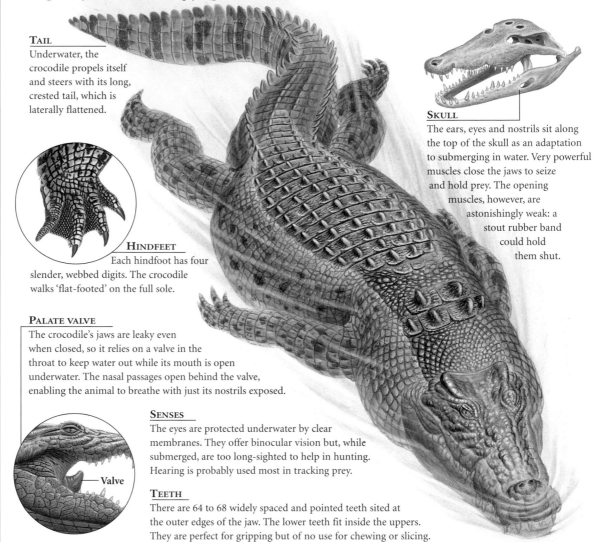

TAIL
Underwater, the crocodile propels itself and steers with its long, crested tail, which is laterally flattened.

HINDFEET
Each hindfoot has four slender, webbed digits. The crocodile walks 'flat-footed' on the full sole.

PALATE VALVE
The crocodile's jaws are leaky even when closed, so it relies on a valve in the throat to keep water out while its mouth is open underwater. The nasal passages open behind the valve, enabling the animal to breathe with just its nostrils exposed.

Valve

SENSES
The eyes are protected underwater by clear membranes. They offer binocular vision but, while submerged, are too long-sighted to help in hunting. Hearing is probably used most in tracking prey.

TEETH
There are 64 to 68 widely spaced and pointed teeth sited at the outer edges of the jaw. The lower teeth fit inside the uppers. They are perfect for gripping but of no use for chewing or slicing.

SKULL
The ears, eyes and nostrils sit along the top of the skull as an adaptation to submerging in water. Very powerful muscles close the jaws to seize and hold prey. The opening muscles, however, are astonishingly weak: a stout rubber band could hold them shut.

CREATURE COMPARISONS

One of the saltie's neighbours is the Australian freshwater crocodile or 'freshie' (Crocodylus johnsoni). Though it is no lightweight, the freshie's maximum length of 3m (9ft 8in) cannot compare with its relative.

As its name suggests, the freshwater crocodile occurs inland in river systems and swamps. Its diet, broadly similar to that of a subadult saltwater crocodile, includes all manner of aquatic prey and accounts for another common name: the fish crocodile. Its snout is narrower than that of the saltwater crocodile, which is an adaptation for catching smaller and more manoeuvrable prey.

Although less hostile than the saltie, the freshie has been known to kill humans when provoked.

Freshwater crocodile

Saltwater crocodile

WHERE IN THE WORLD?

Found in marine and freshwater habitats from India, across all of southeastern Asia, to northern Australia and New Guinea plus nearby Pacific island groups.

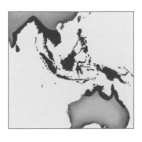

RELATED SPECIES

The genus Crocodylus contains 12 species including the American crocodile, C. acutus, and Nile crocodile, C. niloticus. It is 1 of 8 genera in the family Crocodylidae. Other crocodilians include the gharial and 7 species of alligator and caiman.

• **ORDER** • *Crocodylia* • **FAMILY** • *Gavialidae* • **GENUS & SPECIES** • *Gavialis gangeticus*

GHARIAL

With its long, narrow snout, the gharial looks even more prehistoric than its crocodilian cousins. In fact, fossil records support its ancient lineage.

KEY FEATURES

- Slender-snouted relative of crocodiles that lives in large, fast-flowing rivers.
- Catches big fish in its elongated jaws and holds them fast with its armoury of interlocking teeth.
- Classified as endangered by the IUCN (World Conservation Union).

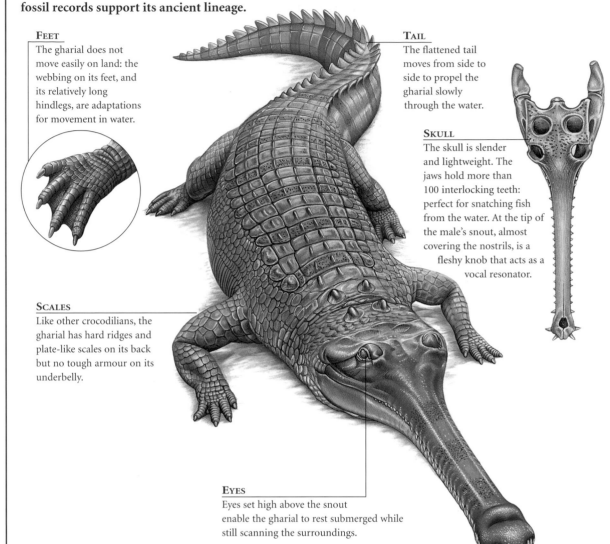

FEET
The gharial does not move easily on land: the webbing on its feet, and its relatively long hindlegs, are adaptations for movement in water.

TAIL
The flattened tail moves from side to side to propel the gharial slowly through the water.

SKULL
The skull is slender and lightweight. The jaws hold more than 100 interlocking teeth: perfect for snatching fish from the water. At the tip of the male's snout, almost covering the nostrils, is a fleshy knob that acts as a vocal resonator.

SCALES
Like other crocodilians, the gharial has hard ridges and plate-like scales on its back but no tough armour on its underbelly.

EYES
Eyes set high above the snout enable the gharial to rest submerged while still scanning the surroundings.

VITAL STATISTICS

WEIGHT	Unknown
LENGTH	Up to 7m (23ft)
SEXUAL MATURITY	At least 10 years
BREEDING SEASON	February–May
NUMBER OF EGGS	Up to 100; average 37
BREEDING INTERVAL	1 year
INCUBATION PERIOD	83–94 days
TYPICAL DIET	Juvenile eats insects and small vertebrates such as frogs; adult eats fish
LIFESPAN	Unknown

CREATURE COMPARISONS

The so-called false gharial lives to the east of the gharial's range, in the freshwater habitats of southeastern Asia. Superficially similar to its relative, the false gharial is another slender-snouted fish-eater. But scientists place it in a different genus, with closer links to the true crocodiles. On average about 1–2m (3ft 3in–6ft 6in) shorter than the gharial, the false gharial has fewer teeth — about 80 in all — and lacks the male's nasal knob. It also has a more evenly tapered skull. Unlike the gharial, the false gharial lays its eggs in a mound of vegetation and leaves its hatchlings to make their own way out of the nest and down to the water.

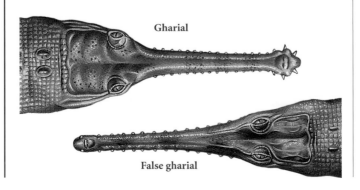

Gharial

False gharial

WHERE IN THE WORLD?

Once widely distributed in a belt south of the Himalayas in central Asia. Now has a severely fragmented range in northern India, Nepal, Bangladesh and Pakistan.

RELATED SPECIES

The crocodilians of the world may be the largest reptiles, but they form the second-smallest of the reptile orders, with a total of just 22 species. The 14 species of crocodile (including the false gharial) make up 1 family, and the 7 species of alligator and caiman make up another. The Gavialidae, the third family, today contains only the gharial. In prehistoric times it contained several species, including a number from South America.

•ORDER • *Cuculiformes* • FAMILY • *Cuculidae* • GENUS & SPECIES • *Geococcyx californianus*

GREATER ROADRUNNER

Built for life on foot, the roadrunner acquires an intimate knowledge of its territory and uses this to help it catch prey and to escape predators.

KEY FEATURES

- Conserves energy during the cold desert nights by becoming sluggish, then warms up again in the morning by exposing its dark dorsal skin to the sun.
- Uses sticks, mesquite pods, snakeskin and flakes of cattle dung to build its nest in arid, treeless regions.
- Escapes the fierce desert heat by seeking shade.

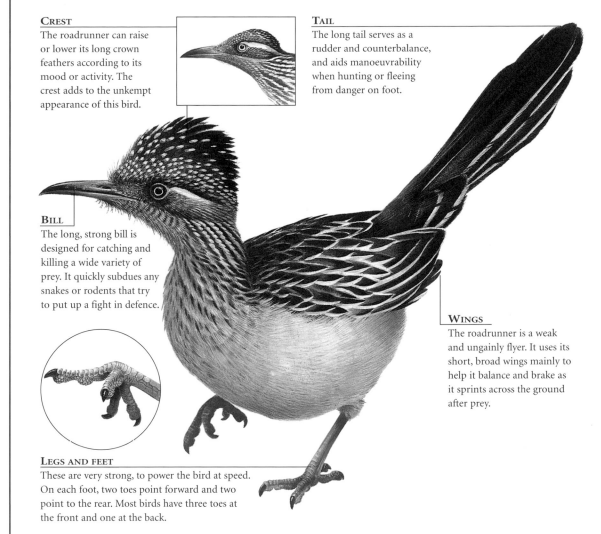

CREST
The roadrunner can raise or lower its long crown feathers according to its mood or activity. The crest adds to the unkempt appearance of this bird.

TAIL
The long tail serves as a rudder and counterbalance, and aids manoeuvrability when hunting or fleeing from danger on foot.

BILL
The long, strong bill is designed for catching and killing a wide variety of prey. It quickly subdues any snakes or rodents that try to put up a fight in defence.

WINGS
The roadrunner is a weak and ungainly flyer. It uses its short, broad wings mainly to help it balance and brake as it sprints across the ground after prey.

LEGS AND FEET
These are very strong, to power the bird at speed. On each foot, two toes point forward and two point to the rear. Most birds have three toes at the front and one at the back.

VITAL STATISTICS

WEIGHT	200–370g (7–13lb)
LENGTH	51–61cm (20.1–24in), including a 25cm (9.8in) tail
WINGSPAN	40–51cm (15.7–20.1in)
SEXUAL MATURITY	1 year
MATING SEASON	Usually April to May; second brood July to September
NUMBER OF EGGS	2 to 7; usually 3 to 5
INCUBATION PERIOD	17–20 days
NUMBER OF BROODS	1, sometimes 2
TYPICAL DIET	Insects, lizards, snakes, rodents, birds and their eggs, fruit, seeds
LIFESPAN	Up to 9 years

CREATURE COMPARISONS

The yellow-billed cuckoo, *Coccyzus americanus*, is another North American relative of the roadrunner. Unlike the roadrunner, however, it flies gracefully. The Eurasian cuckoo, *Cuculus canorus*, is a relatively strong flier travelling direct and low on rapidly beating wings and capable of covering long distances.

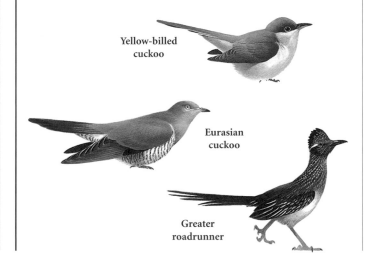

Yellow-billed cuckoo

Eurasian cuckoo

Greater roadrunner

WHERE IN THE WORLD?

Found in Mexico and the southwestern USA, throughout Arizona, New Mexico and Texas, and in parts of California, Nevada, Utah, Colorado, Kansas, Oklahoma, Arkansas and Louisiana.

RELATED SPECIES

The greater and lesser roadrunners are the only two species in their genus, *Geococcyx*, within a group of 13 species known as ground-cuckoos. The lesser roadrunner is similar to the greater, but has a more southerly range in Central America. The roadrunners are among about 130 species in the widespread cuckoo family, Cuculidae. They include the 50 species of 'true' cuckoo, all of which lay their eggs in the nests of other species.

• **ORDER** • *Cuculiformes* • **FAMILY** • *Opisthocomidae* • **GENUS & SPECIES** • *Opisthocomus hoazin*

HOATZIN

KEY FEATURES

- Unique bird of South American river and marsh edge.
- Chicks have claws on their wings, letting them scramble among the tree branches.
- Adapted to digest the tough, rubbery vegetation by swamps and rivers of the Amazon and Orinoco.
- Flies in short bursts of 30.5m (100ft) or so.

VITAL STATISTICS

WEIGHT	737.1–793.8g (26–28oz)
LENGTH	62cm (24.4in)
SEXUAL MATURITY	1–2 years
MATING SEASON	Onset of rainy season (once or twice a year)
NUMBER OF EGGS	2 to 5, usually 3
INCUBATION PERIOD	4 weeks
BIRTH INTERVAL	6 months or 1 year
TYPICAL DIET	Fruit and leaves, particularly those of arum and mangrove
LIFESPAN	Unknown

The ungainly hoatzin does not need to fly far in search of food. In fact, its wings are more useful as stabilizers than for flight.

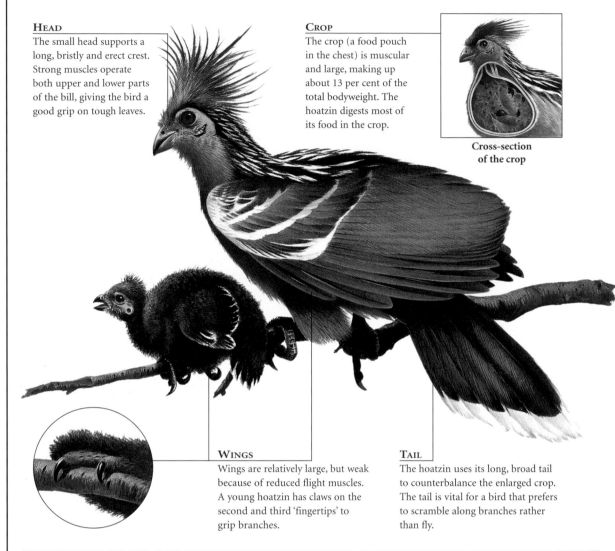

HEAD
The small head supports a long, bristly and erect crest. Strong muscles operate both upper and lower parts of the bill, giving the bird a good grip on tough leaves.

CROP
The crop (a food pouch in the chest) is muscular and large, making up about 13 per cent of the total bodyweight. The hoatzin digests most of its food in the crop.

Cross-section of the crop

WINGS
Wings are relatively large, but weak because of reduced flight muscles. A young hoatzin has claws on the second and third 'fingertips' to grip branches.

TAIL
The hoatzin uses its long, broad tail to counterbalance the enlarged crop. The tail is vital for a bird that prefers to scramble along branches rather than fly.

CREATURE COMPARISONS

Many features of the hoatzin, such as muscle attachments, skeletal structure and the chick's wing claws, resemble those of the archaeopteryx, an ancient bird that lived about 150 million years ago in the Jurassic period. Similarities such as these have helped to fuel debate about the evolution of flight in birds.

Hoatzin

Archaeopteryx

WHERE IN THE WORLD?

Found in northeastern South America, particularly in the rainforests formed by the Amazon and Orinoco rivers; forested borders of streams provide leafy food and nesting sites

RELATED SPECIES

Since 1837 the hoatzin has been linked to eight different bird orders, with birds such as pigeons, cranes, parrots and cuckoos. Placed in a family and a genus of its own, the hoatzin was then attached to the Galliformes (turkeys, pheasants, partridges and quails). The hoatzin now belongs to the order Cuculiformes, which includes coucals, cuckoos and roadrunners.

• ORDER • *Cypriniformes* • FAMILY • *Cyprinidae* • GENUS & SPECIES • *Cyprinus carpio*

CARP

Specialized for feeding on the muddy bottoms of lakes and slow-moving rivers, the muscular carp can grow to be huge in ideal conditions.

KEY FEATURES

- A toothless bottom-feeder that uses four sensitive barbels around the mouth as sensory detectors.
- Grows rapidly, with some specimens even exceeding 30kg (66.1lb) in weight and 1m (3ft 3in) in length.
- A popular fish with anglers, it is also widely kept in fish farms and ornamental lakes.

TEETH
The carp has no true teeth but instead has two bony plates in its throat called pharyngeal bones. When the fish takes in food, these plates grind it up as it is swallowed.

FINS
A long dorsal (back) fin runs along the carp's body in an elegant concave curve, while its muscular tail-stock is complemented by a broad caudal (tail) fin.

BARBELS
Two pairs of sensitive barbels, sensitive skin filaments, grow on either side of the carp's rubbery lips. They help detect food as the carp stirs up the mud on the bottom.

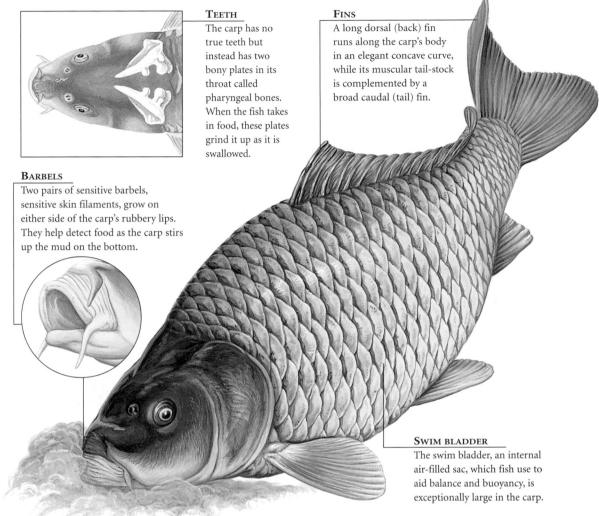

SWIM BLADDER
The swim bladder, an internal air-filled sac, which fish use to aid balance and buoyancy, is exceptionally large in the carp.

VITAL STATISTICS

WEIGHT	Up to 32kg (70.5lb) but usually less; average 8kg (17.6lb)
LENGTH	Up to 1m (3ft 3in)
SEXUAL MATURITY	2 or 3 years
BREEDING SEASON	May to June, or when the water temperature reaches 18°C (64.4°F)
NUMBER OF EGGS	Thousands
BIRTH INTERVAL	1 year
TYPICAL DIET	Invertebrates, crustaceans and plant matter from the riverbed or lake bottom
LIFESPAN	10–15 years in the wild; up to 50 years or more in captivity

CREATURE COMPARISONS

The mirror (or king) carp and the leather carp were originally bred as food fish with fewer scales from the fully scaled common carp. Today, both of these breeds are well established in the wild through much of Europe and Asia. The handsome mirror carp is named after the small number of very large, shiny scales dotted across both its back and sides. It is otherwise scaleless. The leather carp has almost no scales at all and, as its name suggests, has a thick leathery skin.

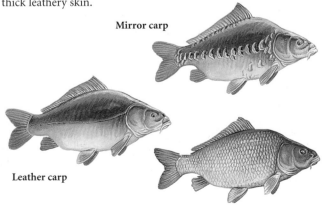

Mirror carp

Leather carp

Common carp

WHERE IN THE WORLD?

Occurs naturally from the River Danube basin and the lowland lakes of Eastern Europe eastwards to Siberia and China. Introduced to many countries worldwide.

RELATED SPECIES

Other members of the huge carp family, Cyprinidae, include the tiny minnow species and the goldfish (Carassius auratus). Every breed of goldfish is descended from the gibel carp, a fish found in Eastern Europe and Asia. Goldfish have been bred in China for at least 2000 years, while one breed of the common carp, the Koi carp, was first cultivated in Japan. Koi are large ornamental fish often patterned with stunningly bright colours.

• **ORDER** • *Cypriniformes* • **FAMILY** • *Cyprinidae* • **GENUS & SPECIES** • *Phoxinus phoxinus*

MINNOW

Sleek and swift, the minnow is shaped like a tiny torpedo and relies on sudden bursts of speed to take it away from danger.

KEY FEATURES

- A small relative of the carp that forms large breeding shoals in the shallow stretches of streams and rivers.
- An important part of the food chain in many waterways, providing food for fish, birds, aquatic invertebrates and other animals.
- Highly sensitive to changes in water quality.

VITAL STATISTICS

LENGTH	7–12cm (2.7–4.7in), female larger than male
SEXUAL MATURITY	1–2 years
BREEDING SEASON	March–July
NUMBER OF EGGS	Up to 1000
HATCHING PERIOD	5–10 days depending on water temperature
BREEDING INTERVAL	1 year
TYPICAL DIET	Aquatic invertebrates including freshwater shrimps and insect larvae; also some plant matter
LIFESPAN	Up to 5 years

MALE
In the breeding season the male's underside and parts of his lips turn bright red. Small white tubercles (bumps) appear on the top of his head, which are thought by some experts to help stimulate the female as he nuzzles her flanks during spawning. Strangely, the female also develops tubercles.

EYE
The minnow has large eyes and relies heavily on sight to find food and spot predators.

TAIL
The deeply forked tail provides the minnow with the power to swim very rapidly when attacked.

FINS
Using its tail for swimming, the minnow's other fins help it to manoeuvre and hold its position in the water.

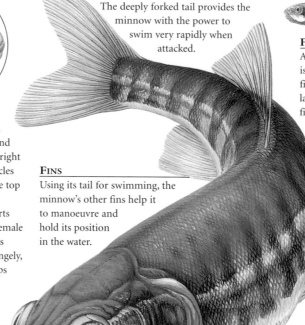

FRY
After hatching, the young minnow is only the size of an eyelash. At first, its belly is bloated with a large yolk sac that provides the first food for the tiny fish.

COLOURING
The minnow's dark upperparts camouflage it from aerial hunters, such as kingfishers. When many minnows mingle in a shoal, the cryptic flank markings of the moving fish make it difficult for predatory fish to pick out a victim.

SPECIALIZED TEETH
The minnow does not have toothed jaws. Instead it chews food in the back of its mouth using modified bones of an internal part of the gills. These bones are called pharyngeal teeth.

CREATURE COMPARISONS

The fathead minnow (Pimephalus promelas) is one of the most common fish in central North America. Although not closely related to the minnow of Europe and Asia, it occupies similar waters. However, it also survives in stagnant ponds and can tolerate high levels of pollution. In the breeding season, the male fathead minnow induces females to spawn in a protected nest site, usually near a submerged log or stone. After fertilizing the eggs, he protects them until the fry hatch — unlike the minnow, which exhibits no parental care. A short-lived fish, the fathead minnow usually dies at the end of its first breeding season, when it is about two years old.

Minnow

Fathead minnow

WHERE IN THE WORLD?

Found across much of Europe from northern Spain to Russia, and into central Asia. Absent from parts of Scandinavia, Scotland, Italy, Greece and Turkey.

RELATED SPECIES

Several members of the genus Phoxinus are found in North America and are known as dace, although they are not closely related to the European dace, Leuciscus leuciscus. Phoxinus also includes the swamp minnow of eastern Europe, P. percnurus. Like the minnow, it belongs to the carp family Cyprinidae, which has more than 1600 species, almost all of which are freshwater fish, and includes the common carp, roach, bream and goldfish.

• ORDER • *Decapoda* • FAMILY • *Coenobitoidea* • GENUS & SPECIES • *Birgus latro*

ROBBER CRAB

Despite the fact that it has taken to living on land, the massive robber crab has the same protective shell and basic bodyplan as its marine relatives.

KEY FEATURES

- Spends the majority of its life on land, often climbing trees in search of tropical fruit.
- Avoids excessive heat because it needs to keep its gills moist in order to breathe while out of the water.
- Returns to the sea to breed, and the ocean currents carry its eggs far and wide.

VITAL STATISTICS

WEIGHT	Up to 3kg (6.6lb)
LENGTH	Body: up to 60cm (32.6in) Legspan; Up to 90cm (35.4in)
SEXUAL MATURITY	Several months
BREEDING SEASON	Varies according to location
NUMBER OF EGGS	Several thousand
BREEDING INTERVAL	1 year
TYPICAL DIET	Mainly nuts, fruit and carrion (including carrion of its own species)
LIFESPAN	Unknown

SHELL
The tough shell, or carapace, is reinforced with calcium. It protects the crab and helps prevent the loss of body moisture. The colour varies according to the location and with each seasonal moult of the carapace.

EYES
Although its eyes extend on stalks, the crab has poor vision and depends on scent to find food.

PINCERS
The pincers are operated by powerful muscles anchored to the inside of the shell.

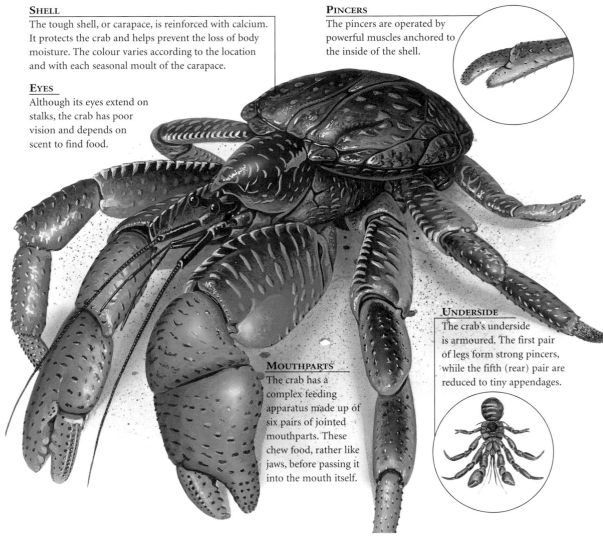

MOUTHPARTS
The crab has a complex feeding apparatus made up of six pairs of jointed mouthparts. These chew food, rather like jaws, before passing it into the mouth itself.

UNDERSIDE
The crab's underside is armoured. The first pair of legs form strong pincers, while the fifth (rear) pair are reduced to tiny appendages.

CREATURE COMPARISONS

The robber crab is a giant relative of the hermit crab (Pagurus bernhardus), which is found in rockpools on European coasts. At up to 12cm (4.7in) long, the hermit crab is much smaller than the robber crab, and also lives on land. It is best known for its habit of living in the discarded shell of another animal, such as a whelk, which protects the unusually soft rear segments of its body. As it grows, the hermit crab changes its 'home' for a larger one — if it cannot find a shell big enough, it dies. The hermit crab has one front claw larger than the other, whereas the front claws of the robber crab are about the same size.

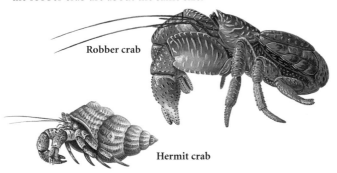

Robber crab

Hermit crab

WHERE IN THE WORLD?

Widely distributed on islands, and even small coral atolls if trees grow on them, throughout the tropical regions of the Pacific and Indian oceans.

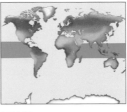

RELATED SPECIES

There are several island subspecies of the robber crab, which is the largest of the land hermit crabs in the suborder Anomura. The many species of land crab in the order of true crabs, Brachyura, include the giant land crab, Cardiosoma guanhumi, of the West Indies and West Africa.

• **ORDER** • *Decapoda* • **FAMILY** • *Lolaginidae* • **GENUS & SPECIES** • *Loligo opalescens*

OPALESCENT SQUID

KEY FEATURES

- An intelligent, jet-propelled predator with a poisonous bite and powerful suckers.
- Hunts its prey by sight in the twilit depths of the northern Pacific, rising to the surface at night.
- Releases a dense cloud of ink to screen itself as it shoots away from predators.

The opalescent squid uses its spectacular ability to change colour to communicate with others and to conceal itself from prey or predators.

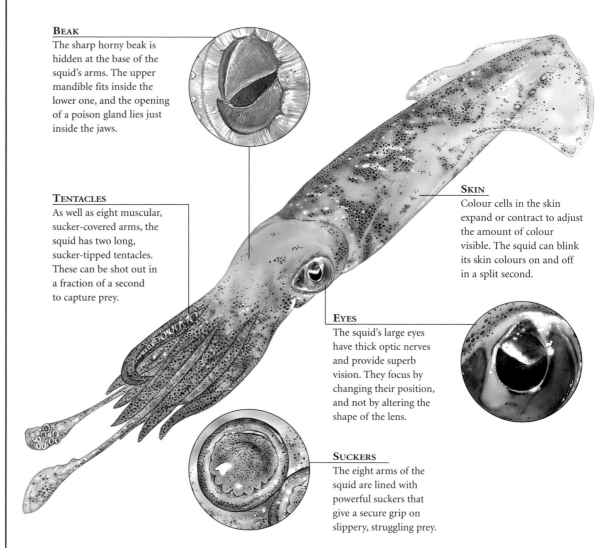

BEAK
The sharp horny beak is hidden at the base of the squid's arms. The upper mandible fits inside the lower one, and the opening of a poison gland lies just inside the jaws.

TENTACLES
As well as eight muscular, sucker-covered arms, the squid has two long, sucker-tipped tentacles. These can be shot out in a fraction of a second to capture prey.

SKIN
Colour cells in the skin expand or contract to adjust the amount of colour visible. The squid can blink its skin colours on and off in a split second.

EYES
The squid's large eyes have thick optic nerves and provide superb vision. They focus by changing their position, and not by altering the shape of the lens.

SUCKERS
The eight arms of the squid are lined with powerful suckers that give a secure grip on slippery, struggling prey.

VITAL STATISTICS

LENGTH	25cm (9.8in), plus extendable tentacles
SEXUAL MATURITY	3 years
BREEDING SEASON	March
NUMBER OF EGGS	Laid in 20 batches of 100 to 200, after being fertilized internally
HATCHING INTERVAL	3–4 weeks
BREEDING INTERVAL	Dies after breeding
TYPICAL DIET	Fish and crustaceans, such as crabs
LIFESPAN	3 years

CREATURE COMPARISONS

The opalescent squid is one of the smallest species of squid. The deep-sea squid, Architeuthis dux, regularly grows to 10m (32.8ft) or more, and the largest ever found measured more than 19m (62.3ft). It has never been seen alive, but its remains have been found in the stomachs of sperm whales, which hunt them in the ocean depths.

Giant squid

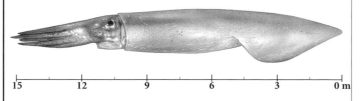

| 15 | 12 | 9 | 6 | 3 | 0 m |

WHERE IN THE WORLD?

Found throughout the eastern North Pacific Ocean, but most numerous in the food-rich waters along the coasts of California, western Mexico and Central America.

RELATED SPECIES

The opalescent squid is a mollusc — a member of a group of about 100,000 species of mainly aquatic creatures, as well as garden slugs and snails. Squid belong to the class Cephalopoda, which includes species of octopus, nautilus and cuttlefish. Cephalopods are noted for their highly developed brain and eyes. They all have the same basic body plan, but the 350 species of squid are adapted for high-speed swimming in open water.

FIDDLER CRAB

• ORDER • *Decapoda* • FAMILY • *Ocypodidae* • GENUS & SPECIES • *Uca species*

KEY FEATURES

- Fiddler crabs build burrows in wet muddy shorelines, coming to the surface to feed at low tide.
- Males have a huge fiddle-like claw, which they wave about to advertise for a mate.
- Ritualized combat takes place between males as they jostle for the attention of females.

VITAL STATISTICS

WEIGHT	Average 8g (0.3oz)
LENGTH	Carapace 2–33mm (0.08–1.3in) long; 3–47mm (0.1–1.8in) wide
MALE CLAW	1.2–10.9cm (0.5–4.3in)
SEXUAL MATURITY	1–2 years
MATING SEASON	Usually throughout the year in tropical species
NUMBER OF EGGS	Several hundred
INCUBATION PERIOD	7–10 days
TYPICAL DIET	Small particles of plant or animal matter
LIFESPAN	Unknown

The male's oversized claw looks as much like a weapon as a fiddler's instrument, but it is mainly used for communication rather than battle.

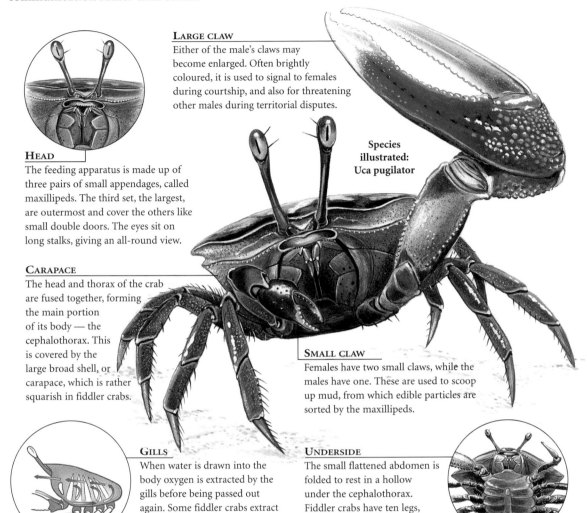

LARGE CLAW
Either of the male's claws may become enlarged. Often brightly coloured, it is used to signal to females during courtship, and also for threatening other males during territorial disputes.

HEAD
The feeding apparatus is made up of three pairs of small appendages, called maxillipeds. The third set, the largest, are outermost and cover the others like small double doors. The eyes sit on long stalks, giving an all-round view.

Species illustrated: Uca pugilator

CARAPACE
The head and thorax of the crab are fused together, forming the main portion of its body — the cephalothorax. This is covered by the large broad shell, or carapace, which is rather squarish in fiddler crabs.

SMALL CLAW
Females have two small claws, while the males have one. These are used to scoop up mud, from which edible particles are sorted by the maxillipeds.

GILLS
When water is drawn into the body oxygen is extracted by the gills before being passed out again. Some fiddler crabs extract oxygen in a special cavity and have reduced gills.

UNDERSIDE
The small flattened abdomen is folded to rest in a hollow under the cephalothorax. Fiddler crabs have ten legs, including the two modified into claws (chelipeds).

CREATURE COMPARISONS

Fiddler crabs are semi-terrestrial, living in the tidal zone. The blue land crab, Cardiosoma guanhumi, however, often spends most of its life inland, sometimes many kilometres from the coast. Females return to the sea at spring tides, though, to deposit their larvae that have hatched from eggs. Like fiddler crabs, the land crab has one particularly large claw, and although this, and the rest of its legs are drably coloured, its carapace is a distinctive blue.

The blue land crab digs deep burrows, sometimes up to 2m (6ft 6in) long, whereas fiddler crab burrows rarely exceed about 40cm (15.7in). The land crab climbs trees to nip off fruit, returning to the ground to eat it. It also scavenges for other food.

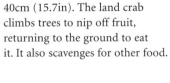

Fiddler crab

Blue land crab

WHERE IN THE WORLD?

Fiddler crabs are found mainly in the tropical and subtropical Pacific Ocean, the South Atlantic, the Indian Ocean and the seas of Southeast Asia.

RELATED SPECIES

The order Decapoda (ten-legged creatures) contains about 8500 species of crayfish, lobsters, shrimps and crabs. A close relation of the fiddler crab in the family Ocypodidae is the ghost crab. Ocypode means 'fast-footed' — the ghost crab sprints at 1.6m per second (5.2ft per second).

SPINY LOBSTER

KEY FEATURES

- Seabed-dwelling scavengers that live in rock and coral crevices.
- Some species make mass migrations over the seabed each year.
- Lack the formidable claws of other lobsters, but possess a defensive array of bristling spines.
- Several species are important food sources and support commercial and local fisheries.

VITAL STATISTICS

WEIGHT	Up to 8kg (17.6lb)
LENGTH	Body: up to 50cm (19.7in) Antennae; Up to 60cm
SEXUAL MATURITY	1 year
BREEDING SEASON	Varies according to region; March to June off the Florida coast
NUMBER OF EGGS	Probably thousands
BREEDING INTERVAL	Depends on region; annually in Florida
TYPICAL DIET	Molluscs, echinoderms (such as starfish and sea urchins), crustaceans and other marine invertebrates
LIFESPAN	At least several years

The spiny lobster's tough outer shell bristles with sharp spines and long whip-like antennae, which help to protect its soft, delicate body.

SPINES
Stiff spines protrude from the carapace (upper shell), tail and antennae. Two elongated spines or 'horns' project forwards from just above the eyes.

ANTENNAE
The spiny lobster is equipped with an outsized pair of antennae, often longer than its own body. These are used both for touch and for defence.

TAIL
The spiny lobster has a flattened tail. Curling the long abdomen and beating the spread tail up and down like a paddle, the lobster can shoot backwards when alarmed.

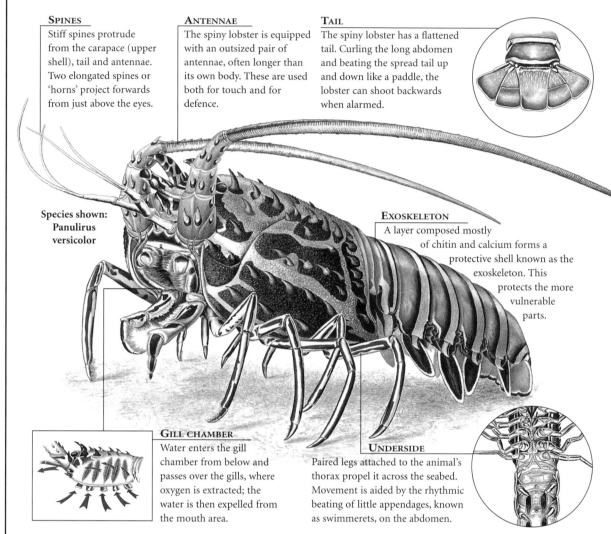

Species shown:
Panulirus versicolor

EXOSKELETON
A layer composed mostly of chitin and calcium forms a protective shell known as the exoskeleton. This protects the more vulnerable parts.

GILL CHAMBER
Water enters the gill chamber from below and passes over the gills, where oxygen is extracted; the water is then expelled from the mouth area.

UNDERSIDE
Paired legs attached to the animal's thorax propel it across the seabed. Movement is aided by the rhythmic beating of little appendages, known as swimmerets, on the abdomen.

CREATURE COMPARISONS

Though the common European lobster (Homarus gammarus) belongs to a different order (Astacidea), it is similar to a typical spiny lobster in size and overall shape. The most striking difference between these two seabed-dwelling crustaceans is in the first pair of limbs. In the European lobster, they are modified to form massive pincers that are used for killing prey and manipulating food. The European lobster lacks the sharp spines of spiny lobsters, and its shell extends at the front to form a spike (or rostrum), which gives added protection against predators.

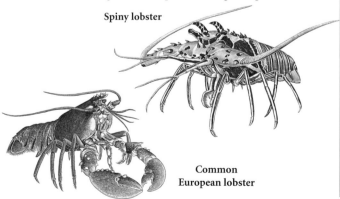

Spiny lobster

Common European lobster

WHERE IN THE WORLD?

Found in the shallow coastal waters, coral reefs and lagoons of the Pacific, Indian and Atlantic oceans, from the Americas east to Africa, India, Southeast Asia and Australasia.

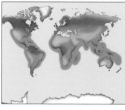

RELATED SPECIES

About a quarter of all crustaceans belong to the order Decapoda (animals with 10 legs), including crabs, shrimps, crayfish and lobsters. Within this order, there is an infraorder called Palinura, which contains 5 lobster families including the spiny lobster family, Palinuridae. The genus Palinurus (which is easily confused with the Panulirus genus) is placed in the same family as the spiny lobster and contains the European spiny lobster.

COLUGO

• **ORDER** • *Dermoptera* • **FAMILY** • *Cynocephalidae* • **GENUS & SPECIES** • *Cynocephalus*

Spreading its limbs to open an expansive membrane, the colugo transforms itself into a living kite as it glides from tree to tree.

KEY FEATURES

- An elusive creature that lives high in the treetops where it is camouflaged by a speckled coat.
- Virtually helpless on the ground, it 'sails' between the trees of its rainforest home on membranes stretched between its limbs and tail.
- Able to glide 100m (328.1ft) or more in a controlled 'flight'.

VITAL STATISTICS

WEIGHT	1–1.5kg (2.2–3.3lb)
LENGTH	Head & Body: 34–42cm (13.4–16.5in) Tail; 17–27cm (6.7–10.6in)
SEXUAL MATURITY	Unknown
MATING SEASON	Unknown, but probably all year round
GESTATION PERIOD	About 60 days
NUMBER OF YOUNG	1, rarely 2
BIRTH INTERVAL	Unknown
TYPICAL DIET	Leaves, shoots, buds, flowers; occasionally, soft, ripe fruit
LIFESPAN	Unknown in the wild. A captive individual kept in ideal conditions lived for 17 years and six months

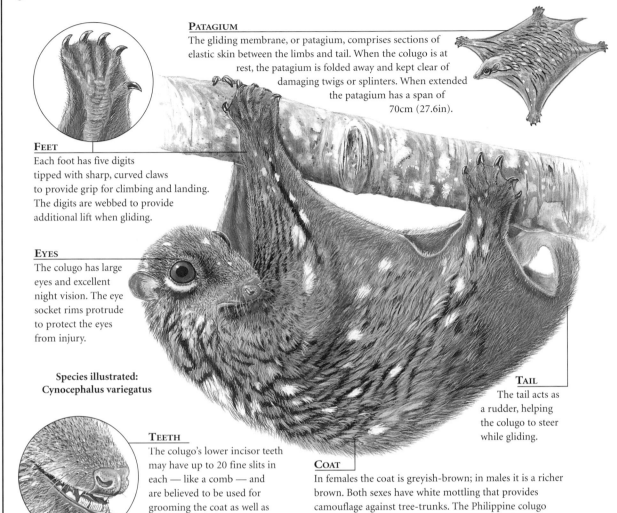

PATAGIUM
The gliding membrane, or patagium, comprises sections of elastic skin between the limbs and tail. When the colugo is at rest, the patagium is folded away and kept clear of damaging twigs or splinters. When extended the patagium has a span of 70cm (27.6in).

FEET
Each foot has five digits tipped with sharp, curved claws to provide grip for climbing and landing. The digits are webbed to provide additional lift when gliding.

EYES
The colugo has large eyes and excellent night vision. The eye socket rims protrude to protect the eyes from injury.

Species illustrated: Cynocephalus variegatus

TEETH
The colugo's lower incisor teeth may have up to 20 fine slits in each — like a comb — and are believed to be used for grooming the coat as well as stripping or straining food.

TAIL
The tail acts as a rudder, helping the colugo to steer while gliding.

COAT
In females the coat is greyish-brown; in males it is a richer brown. Both sexes have white mottling that provides camouflage against tree-trunks. The Philippine colugo is darker and less spotted than the Malayan colugo.

CREATURE COMPARISONS

Although an excellent glider, the colugo cannot match the flying abilities of bats. This is because a bat's patagium is a true wing supported by the greatly extended bones of the hand, which it beats to generate lift. The colugo, though, cannot beat its limbs and so can only glide.

Beyond this key difference, the colugo shares certain similarities with bats, especially those of the family Pteropodidae. These bats are known as flying foxes and include the Indian flying fox, Pteropus giganteus. Like the colugo, the Indian flying fox has a distinctly long muzzle with large eyes. It uses its acute night vision to fly to fruiting trees, rather than an echolocation system that is typical of insectivorous bats.

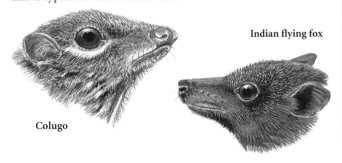

Colugo

Indian flying fox

WHERE IN THE WORLD?

The Malayan colugo is found on mainland Asia, as well as Java, Sumatra, Borneo and several smaller Indonesian islands.

The Philippine colugo occurs in the Philippines.

RELATED SPECIES

There are 2 species of colugo in a single genus, Cynocephalus: the Malayan colugo, C. variegatus, and the Philippine colugo, C. volans. The colugos are now usually placed in an order of their own — Dermoptera. However, authorities differ and some zoologists consider Dermoptera to be a suborder of Insectivora, which includes hedgehogs, shrews, tenrecs and moles. Earlier classification placed the colugos with bats

• ORDER • *Diprotodonta* • FAMILY • *Macropodidae* • GENUS & SPECIES • *Dendrolagus matschiei* HUON TREE KANGAROO

KEY FEATURES

- A highly agile kangaroo that is as much at home in the trees as it is down on the ground.
- One of the most brilliantly coloured of all the marsupials.
- Able to leap more than 10m (32.8ft) between trees and 20m (65.6m) to the ground without injury.
- Female carries her young through the trees in a pouch on her belly.

VITAL STATISTICS

WEIGHT	6–9.5kg (13.2–20.9lb)
LENGTH	Head & Body: 61–68cm (24–26.8in) Tail; 51–68cm
SEXUAL MATURITY	About 2 years
MATING SEASON	Any time of year
GESTATION PERIOD	32 days
TIME IN POUCH	11–13 months
NUMBER OF YOUNG	1
BIRTH INTERVAL	About 13 months
TYPICAL DIET	Ferns, fruit and leaves; occasionally eats meat
LIFESPAN	14 years or more in captivity

Unlike the ground-dwelling kangaroos, which have extra long hindlimbs, the Huon tree kangaroo has limbs of equal length to help it climb.

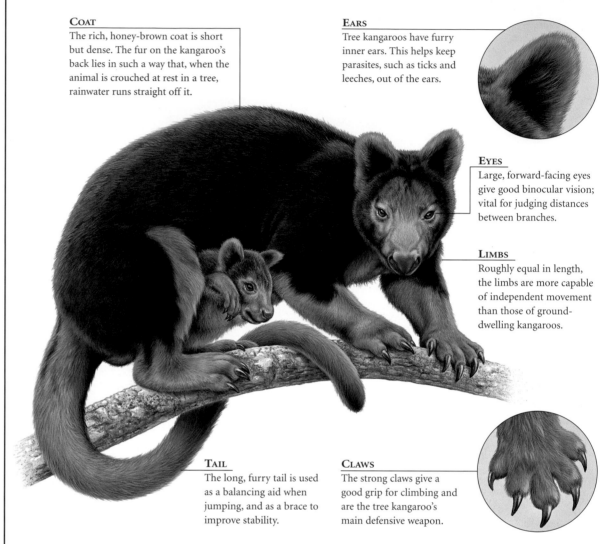

COAT
The rich, honey-brown coat is short but dense. The fur on the kangaroo's back lies in such a way that, when the animal is crouched at rest in a tree, rainwater runs straight off it.

EARS
Tree kangaroos have furry inner ears. This helps keep parasites, such as ticks and leeches, out of the ears.

EYES
Large, forward-facing eyes give good binocular vision; vital for judging distances between branches.

LIMBS
Roughly equal in length, the limbs are more capable of independent movement than those of ground-dwelling kangaroos.

TAIL
The long, furry tail is used as a balancing aid when jumping, and as a brace to improve stability.

CLAWS
The strong claws give a good grip for climbing and are the tree kangaroo's main defensive weapon.

CREATURE COMPARISONS

A tree kangaroo has a crown, or whorl, in the fur on its back, rather like the crown on our head. The whorl allows rain to run straight off the fur, and its position on the back relates to the amount of time the animal spends in the trees. In Doria's tree kangaroo — a good climber — the whorl is low on the back; this is the highest point of the animal as it crouches at rest. The Huon tree kangaroo's whorl is about halfway down the back. The grizzled tree kangaroo, which sleeps on the ground, has a whorl near the nape of its neck.

Grizzled tree kangaroo

Huon tree kangaroo

Doria's tree kangaroo

WHERE IN THE WORLD?

Found only on the Huon Peninsula of Papua New Guinea and on nearby Umboi Island, north of Australia. Lives in mountainous rainforests at altitudes ranging from 900–3000m (2953–9843m) above sea level.

RELATED SPECIES

There are probably seven species of tree kangaroo, including Goodfellow's tree kangaroo, which is also native to New Guinea.

· **ORDER** · *Diprotodonta* · **FAMILY** · *Phascolarctidae* · **GENUS & SPECIES** · *Phascolarctos cinereus*

KEY FEATURES

· Has evolved a unique digestive system for processing its diet of eucalyptus leaves.

· Spends its entire life in trees, descending only to move between them.

· At birth it is no bigger than a small coin.

· A newborn koala immediately makes its way to the mother's pouch, remaining there for six months.

VITAL STATISTICS

WEIGHT	Male 12kg (26.5lb); female 8kg (17.6lb)
LENGTH	63–80cm (24.8–31in)
SEXUAL MATURITY	1 year
MATING SEASON	December to February
GESTATION PERIOD	34–36 days
NUMBER OF YOUNG	1 (very rarely 2)
WEIGHT AT BIRTH	0.5g
LENGTH AT BIRTH	19mm
BIRTH INTERVAL	1 year
TYPICAL DIET	Almost exclusively eucalyptus leaves
LIFESPAN	13–18 years.

A compact, pear-shaped body and special claws enable the koala to climb and balance in the upper limbs of eucalyptus trees.

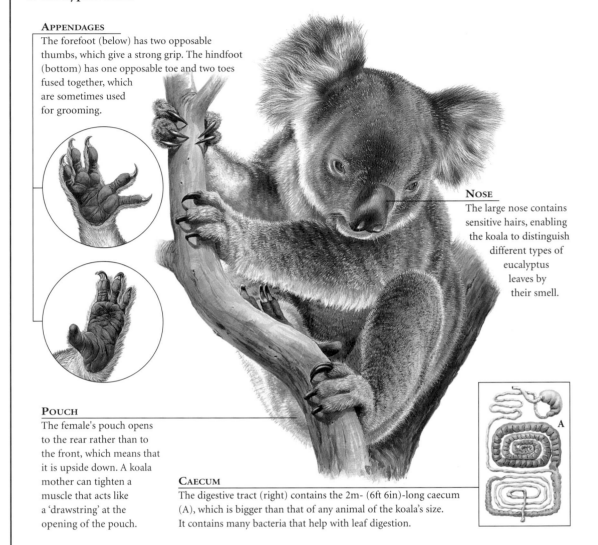

APPENDAGES
The forefoot (below) has two opposable thumbs, which give a strong grip. The hindfoot (bottom) has one opposable toe and two toes fused together, which are sometimes used for grooming.

NOSE
The large nose contains sensitive hairs, enabling the koala to distinguish different types of eucalyptus leaves by their smell.

POUCH
The female's pouch opens to the rear rather than to the front, which means that it is upside down. A koala mother can tighten a muscle that acts like a 'drawstring' at the opening of the pouch.

CAECUM
The digestive tract (right) contains the 2m- (6ft 6in)-long caecum (A), which is bigger than that of any animal of the koala's size. It contains many bacteria that help with leaf digestion.

CREATURE COMPARISONS

The wombat, another member of the Diprotodonta order of marsupials, is a forest dweller found in much of the koala's natural range. It is the koala's closest relative, sharing its stocky build, cheek pouches and tiny tail. The strongest evidence for their relationship is that both have a backward-pointing pouch. The wombat is slightly larger than the koala and lives on or below the forest floor, digging burrows that stretch for up to 13m (511.8ft).

Fossil evidence indicates that there was once a much wider variety within the Diprotodonta order. One Diprotodon living between 2 million to 100,000 years ago was as large as a rhinoceros.

Wombat

Koala

WHERE IN THE WORLD?

A native of eastern Australia's dry eucalyptus forests, east of the Great Dividing Range from mid Queensland in the north, south to New South Wales.

RELATED SPECIES

The koala has sometimes been placed in the family Phalangeridae, alongside the 20 species of possums and cuscuses that inhabit Australia, New Guinea and other islands of the southeast Pacific. However, it is now placed as the sole member of a single genus in a family of its own. Although it has no close relations, the koala probably has most in common with the wombats — marsupials classed in the family Vombatidae.

• **ORDER** • *Edentata* • **FAMILY** • *Bradypodidae* • **GENUS & SPECIES** • *Bradypus*

THREE-TOED SLOTH

With their grappling-hook claws, long arms and specialized coat, three-toed sloths are well equipped for a life spent high in the trees.

KEY FEATURES

- Feeds and sleeps while hanging upside down from tree branches.
- Slow-moving lifestyle and a variable body temperature enable it to survive on a low-energy vegetarian diet.
- So well adapted to a life in the trees that it is helplessly awkward on the ground.
- Relies on excellent camouflage for protection.

CLAWS
The three toes on each foot are fused together and move as a single unit. Each toe is tipped with a long, hooked claw. The sloth can hang by the claws alone, but can also grip branches and food between the claws and the single pad on the foot.

LIPS
Lacking sharp incisor teeth in its jaws, the sloth uses its horny lips to bite off mouthfuls of tough leaves.

SPINE
Three-toed sloths have eight to nine neck vertebrae, the highest number in any mammal. The extra vertebrae enable the sloth to look forward while hanging upside down.

COAT
The coarse hairs of the coat grow 'upwards' from a central parting on the stomach towards the ridge of the spine. This allows rain to run off when the sloth is upside-down.

ALGAE
Blue-green algae cover the surface of the hairs in the sloth's thick coat, providing camouflage when the sloth hangs among tree foliage.

VITAL STATISTICS

WEIGHT	3.5–4.5kg (7.7–9.9lb)
LENGTH	Head & Body: 56–60cm (22–23.6in) Tail; 6–7cm (2.4–2.7in)
SEXUAL MATURITY	3–4 years
MATING SEASON	All year, but predominantly March and April
GESTATION PERIOD	6 months
NUMBER OF YOUNG	1
BIRTH INTERVAL	1–2 years
TYPICAL DIET	Leaves, shoots and flowers of trees
LIFESPAN	12–20 years

CREATURE COMPARISONS

The two-toed sloth occupies roughly the same range as its three-toed relation. Two-toed sloths have two toes on the forelimbs and three toes on the hindlimbs, while the three-toed sloth has three toes all round. Two-toed sloths are about 25 per cent heavier, with shorter forelegs and a less mobile neck containing fewer vertebrae. Unlike three-toed sloths, two-toed sloths are active only at night: consequently, their eyes are larger. Two-toed sloths also eat a wider range of food, including small animals.

Three-toed sloth

Two-toed sloth

WHERE IN THE WORLD?

The three species of three-toed sloth are found in parts of South and Central America's tropical rainforests, from Honduras in the far north of the range, south through much of Brazil.

RELATED SPECIES

There are three species of three-toed sloth in the genus Bradypus: the brown-throated sloth, B. variegatus, the pale-throated sloth, B. tridactylus, and the maned sloth, B. torquatus. In addition, there are two species of two-toed sloth in the single genus Choleopus: Hoffman's sloth, C. hoffmanni and Linne's sloth, C. didactylus. Edentata, the order to which all sloths belong, contains two other major related groups — the armadillos and the anteaters.

NINE-BANDED ARMADILLO

•ORDER • *Edentata* • **FAMILY** • *Dasypodidae* • **GENUS & SPECIES** • *Dasypus novemcinctus*

KEY FEATURES

- Bears a protective armour of strong, bony plates and scales across its upperparts.
- Terrestrial mammal that digs its own burrows and snuffles frenetically through ground debris in search of food.
- Flexible diet and breeding habits enable it to survive in a wide range of habitats from dry grassland and open prairie to tropical forest.

Bands of hard plates on the back, head, limbs and tail of this armadillo protect it from the claws and teeth of predators and from thorny vegetation.

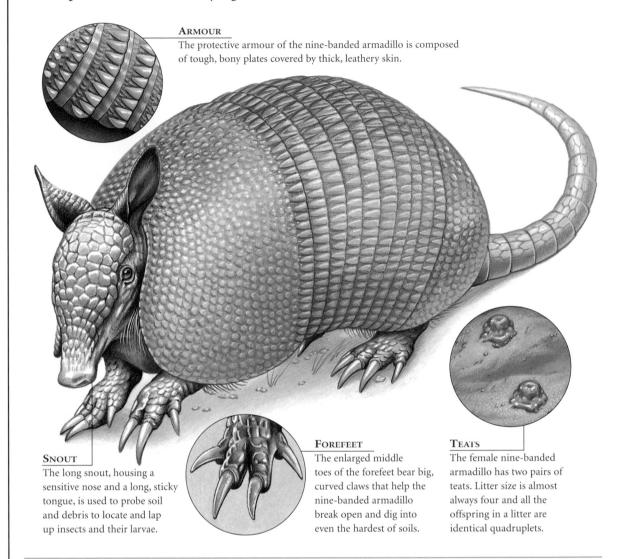

ARMOUR
The protective armour of the nine-banded armadillo is composed of tough, bony plates covered by thick, leathery skin.

SNOUT
The long snout, housing a sensitive nose and a long, sticky tongue, is used to probe soil and debris to locate and lap up insects and their larvae.

FOREFEET
The enlarged middle toes of the forefeet bear big, curved claws that help the nine-banded armadillo break open and dig into even the hardest of soils.

TEATS
The female nine-banded armadillo has two pairs of teats. Litter size is almost always four and all the offspring in a litter are identical quadruplets.

VITAL STATISTICS

WEIGHT	1–10kg (2.2–22lb)
LENGTH	Head & Body: 37–57cm (14.6–22.4in) Tail; 12–48cm (4.7–18.9in)
HEIGHT	15–25cm (5.9–9.8in)
SEXUAL MATURITY	1 year
MATING SEASON	July to August in north; November to January in south
GESTATION PERIOD	4 months, plus 3–4 months delayed implantation
NUMBER OF YOUNG	Usually 4
BIRTH INTERVAL	1 year
TYPICAL DIET	Arthropods, amphibians, reptiles, fungi, tubers, carrion
LIFESPAN	12–15 years

CREATURE COMPARISONS

The three-banded armadillo of southern South America is smaller than the nine-banded armadillo and, despite having just three bands, it is able to curl itself completely into a tight ball — unlike its nine-banded cousin. This ability is largely due to the sides of the front and rear shield plates hanging loosely from the skin, creating enough freedom of movement for the animal to roll up.

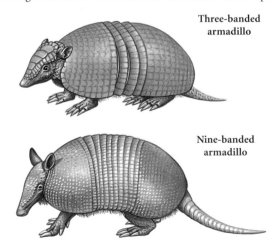

Three-banded armadillo

Nine-banded armadillo

WHERE IN THE WORLD?

Ranges from the southern United States through Central America and Amazonia to northern Argentina and Uruguay. Recently, it has expanded the northern and southern fringes of its range.

RELATED SPECIES

There are 20 species of armadillo in eight different genera, ranging throughout Central and South America. Only the nine-banded armadillo ranges as far north as Mexico and the United States. The biggest member of the family Dasypodidae, the giant armadillo (Priodontes maximus), can grow to 1.5m (4ft 9in) from head to tail. Yet even this species is only one third of the size of some prehistoric armadillos that once roamed South America.

251

• **ORDER** • *Edentata* • **FAMILY** • *Myrmecophagidae* • **GENUS & SPECIES** • *Myrmecophaga tridactyla*

GIANT ANTEATER

KEY FEATURES

- Has an elongated cylindrical snout housing a nose of exceptional sensitivity.
- Breaks open hard-baked termite mounds and ant nests with hook-like claws, which are also capable of inflicting deep wounds on enemies.
- Flicks its long, sticky tongue in and out more than twice a second while feeding to lap up 30,000 insects daily.

VITAL STATISTICS

WEIGHT	20–39kg (44–86lb)
LENGTH	Head & Body: 1–2m (3ft 3in–6ft 6in) Tail; 70–90cm (27.6–35.4in)
SHOULDER HEIGHT	60cm (23.6in)
SEXUAL MATURITY	2–3 years
MATING SEASON	All year, but March to May in southern parts of range
GESTATION PERIOD	190 days
NUMBER OF YOUNG	1
BIRTH INTERVAL	At least 9 months; sometimes 2 years
TYPICAL DIET	Ants and termites
LIFESPAN	26 years in captivity

The giant anteater is built for a singular purpose — to track down insects, break into their fortified colonies and lap them up with its long, sticky tongue.

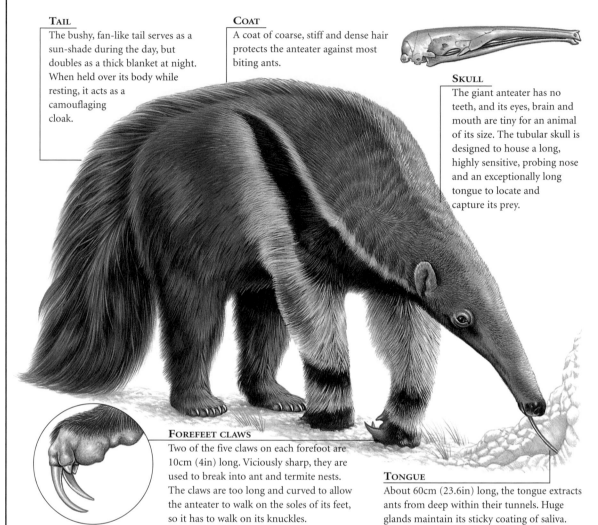

TAIL
The bushy, fan-like tail serves as a sun-shade during the day, but doubles as a thick blanket at night. When held over its body while resting, it acts as a camouflaging cloak.

COAT
A coat of coarse, stiff and dense hair protects the anteater against most biting ants.

SKULL
The giant anteater has no teeth, and its eyes, brain and mouth are tiny for an animal of its size. The tubular skull is designed to house a long, highly sensitive, probing nose and an exceptionally long tongue to locate and capture its prey.

FOREFEET CLAWS
Two of the five claws on each forefoot are 10cm (4in) long. Viciously sharp, they are used to break into ant and termite nests. The claws are too long and curved to allow the anteater to walk on the soles of its feet, so it has to walk on its knuckles.

TONGUE
About 60cm (23.6in) long, the tongue extracts ants from deep within their tunnels. Huge glands maintain its sticky coating of saliva.

CREATURE COMPARISONS

Less than half the giant anteater's size, with a much smaller snout and tail, the southern tamandua (Tamandua tetradactyla) feeds on tree-nesting ants and termites. It spends about 60 per cent of its time aloft, where its naked and prehensile, or grasping, tail helps it to climb through the branches. The tail firmly anchors the tamandua while it digs into insects' nests.

Whereas the giant anteater feeds by day or night, the tamandua is nocturnal and sleeps in tree hollows during the daylight hours. Both species have anal glands that produce a pungent scent, but the tamandua's nickname, 'stinker of the forest', refers to its particularly strong odour.

Giant anteater

Southern tamandua

WHERE IN THE WORLD?

Occurs in small, localized populations in savannah, swamps and open forests, from southern Mexico to South America, east of the Andes, south to northwest Argentina.

RELATED SPECIES
There are four species of anteater in three genera and all are confined to South and Central America. The giant anteater is the only ground-living species. The northern and the southern tamandua and the silky anteater, Cyclopes didactylus, are tree-living and nocturnal.

GOLDEN EAGLE

• ORDER • *Falconiformes* • FAMILY • *Accipitridae* • GENUS & SPECIES • *Aquila chrysaetos*

KEY FEATURES

- Able to soar effortlessly for long periods on its broad, 2m (7ft)-long wings.

- Ranges across home territories as large as 200 sq km (77 sq miles) — an area similar to that of a medium-sized city.

- Traditional nests, or eyries, may be used by generation after generation of golden eagles.

VITAL STATISTICS

WEIGHT	Male 3–5kg (6.6–7.7lb); female 4–7kg (8.8–15.4lb)
LENGTH	Head & Body: 75–90cm (29.5–35.4in) Tail; 25–35cm (9.8–13.8in)
WINGSPAN	2–2.2m (6ft 6in–7ft 2in) (females are larger than males)
SEXUAL MATURITY	4–5 years
BREEDING SEASON	February to July
NUMBER OF EGGS	Usually 2, but rarely 1 or 3
INCUBATION PERIOD	42–45 days
FLEDGING PERIOD	65–70 days
BREEDING INTERVAL	1 year
TYPICAL DIET	Mammals, birds, lizards, carrion
LIFESPAN	Up to 25 years

Flying high over great tracts of wilderness, the golden eagle uses its super-keen eyesight to scan the ground below for signs of potential prey.

EYE
Large, forward-pointing eyes give the golden eagle a wide field of binocular vision. Its eyesight is said to be about eight times sharper than that of a human.

WINGTIP
The finger-like wingtip feathers adust the airflow over the wing, allowing the eagle to fly slowly without 'stalling'.

BILL
Prey is torn up with the powerful, hooked bill. However, the female can use it with the delicacy of tweezers when feeding her young.

TALONS
Prey is grasped with the powerful talons (claws). The curved, viciously sharp hindclaw is its main killing tool.

INNER EYE
Cone cells that detect colour and movement are highly concentrated in a zone at the back of the eye called the fovea (A). This helps produce especially keen sight.

CREATURE COMPARISONS

All eagles have broad wings with 'fingered' tips, although there are many variations on wingshape. The crowned eagle (Spizaetus coronatus), for example, which flies over the dense forests of central Africa, has relatively short, rounded wings to help it manoeuvre in tight spaces between the trees.

The long and wide wings of the martial eagle (Polemaetus bellicosus) — the largest African eagle — are designed for very long periods on the wing. When hunting, martial eagles glide high over open grasslands and deserts in search of large birds, hares and even antelopes.

Crowned eagle

Martial eagle

WHERE IN THE WORLD?

Inhabits the west and north USA and eastern Canada, the mountainous parts of Europe, east through much of central and northern Asia. Also parts of Africa.

RELATED SPECIES

There are eight species of eagle in the genus Aquila, including the lesser spotted eagle (Aquila pomarina) of central Europe and Asia, which has a relatively small wingspan of about 1.4m (4ft 6in). Verreaux's eagle (Aquila verreauxii) of central and southern Africa has an impressive 2.3m (7ft 3in) wingspan. The Spanish race of the imperial eagle (Aquila heliaca) is one of the rarest of all eagles, with only about 60 pairs remaining in the wild.

• ORDER • *Falconiformes* • FAMILY • *Accipitridae* • GENUS & SPECIES • *Buteo buteo*

EURASIAN BUZZARD

The buzzard is a remarkably unspecialized bird of prey, which means that it is an extremely versatile hunter than can exploit a wide range of food.

KEY FEATURES

- A versatile hunter found in many types of habitat, the Eurasian buzzard is the most numerous large bird of prey over most of its wide range.
- Frequently hovers while scanning the ground below.
- Courtship involves a dramatic aerial display called 'skydancing', in which birds soar, dive and swoop.

PLUMAGE
The Eurasian buzzard shows more variation in its plumage than almost any other bird of prey. Its colour ranges from an overall reddish hue to nearly black, but typical birds are brown above with cream mottling on the underparts.

FEET
The feet are equipped with sharp talons for killing prey; the yellow lower legs are bare of feathers.

DARK PHASE
The Eurasian buzzard commonly occurs in a 'dark phase', appearing chocolate brown with just a few pale feathers on the breast. This phase is most common in the European part of its range.

WINGS
The wings are broad and generate large amounts of lift, allowing the buzzard to soar effortlessly for long periods. They are not especially long for a bird of its size but this gives the buzzard the advantage of manoeuvrability.

TAIL
The short tail is fanned when the buzzard soars and the outer feathers almost touch the trailing edges of the broad wings. Tail-fanning increases the surface area of the tail and gives fine steering control at slow soaring speeds.

VITAL STATISTICS

WEIGHT	Male 500–1200g (17.6–42.3oz); female 600–1300g (21.2–45.9oz)
LENGTH	50–57cm (19.7–22.4in)
WINGSPAN	1–1.3m (3ft 3in–4ft 3in)
SEXUAL MATURITY	2 or 3 years
BREEDING SEASON	Late March to August
NUMBER OF EGGS	1 to 5, usually 2 or 3
INCUBATION PERIOD	33–38 days
FLEDGING PERIOD	50–60 days
TYPICAL DIET	Small to medium-sized mammals, birds and reptiles; large insects, earthworms and carrion
LIFESPAN	25–30 years

CREATURE COMPARISONS

The Eurasian buzzard and Harris' hawk (Parabuteo unicinctus), one of its relations, share the compact build typical of most species of buzzard. A thickset neck, together with broad wings and a short tail, produce a stocky, 'all-rounder' physique.

Harris' hawk, like the Eurasian buzzard, uses a variety of hunting techniques to catch a wide range of prey. It is is found in dry, open habitats in southwest USA, and Central and South America. Unlike the Eurasian buzzard (and most birds of prey in general), it sometimes hunts cooperatively.

Eurasian buzzard

Harris' hawk

WHERE IN THE WORLD?

Widely distributed, breeding across much of Europe and parts of Asia to Japan and eastern Russia. Eastern populations winter in Africa, India and Southeast Asia.

RELATED SPECIES
Members of the buzzard subfamily Buteoninae are among the most widespread of all birds of prey. The 28 species in the genus Buteo are found throughout the world, except Antarctica and Australia. The red-tailed hawk (Buteo jamaicensis), of North and Central America and the Caribbean, and the jackal buzzard (Buteo rufofuscus), of East and South Africa, are abundant. However, the Galapagos hawk (Buteo solitarius) is now endangered.

HEN HARRIER

• ORDER • *Falconiformes* • FAMILY • *Accipitridae* • GENUS & SPECIES • *Circus cyaneus*

KEY FEATURES

- An elegant bird of prey that hunts at a leisurely pace, flying low over open country in search of small birds and mammals.
- In dramatic courtship aerobatics, the male tumbles in display or drops food to the female in a mid-air pass.
- Once severely persecuted in Britain, the hen harrier's communal winter roosts are again widespread.

VITAL STATISTICS

WEIGHT	Male 350g (12.3oz); female 530g (18.7oz)
LENGTH	44–52cm (17.3–20.5in)
WINGSPAN	1–1.2m (3ft 3in–3ft 9in)
SEXUAL MATURITY	2–3 years
BREEDING SEASON	April–June
NUMBER OF EGGS	3 to 6
INCUBATION PERIOD	29–31 days
FLEDGING PERIOD	32–42 days
BREEDING INTERVAL	1 year
TYPICAL DIET	Mainly small birds and rodents; also insects, frogs, reptiles, fish and carrion
LIFESPAN	Up to 16 years, but usually less than 12 years

The hen harrier's light build and long wings give it buoyant, energy-efficient flight, enabling it to stay airborne for long periods as it scans for prey.

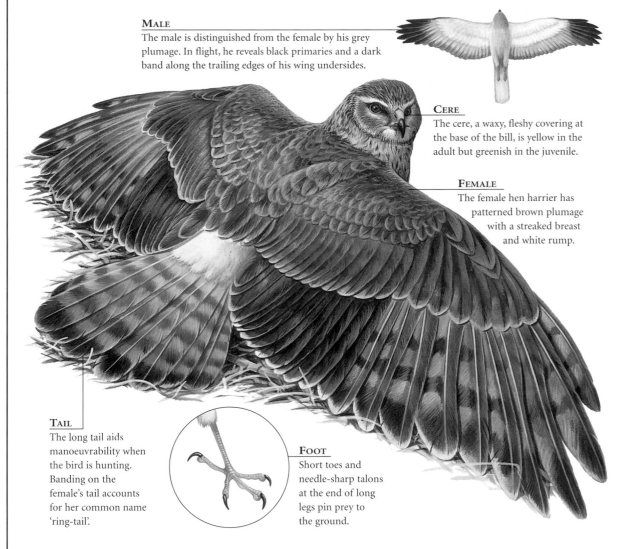

MALE
The male is distinguished from the female by his grey plumage. In flight, he reveals black primaries and a dark band along the trailing edges of his wing undersides.

CERE
The cere, a waxy, fleshy covering at the base of the bill, is yellow in the adult but greenish in the juvenile.

FEMALE
The female hen harrier has patterned brown plumage with a streaked breast and white rump.

TAIL
The long tail aids manoeuvrability when the bird is hunting. Banding on the female's tail accounts for her common name 'ring-tail'.

FOOT
Short toes and needle-sharp talons at the end of long legs pin prey to the ground.

CREATURE COMPARISONS

The hen harrier is the most common of the three harrier species that nest in Britain. The largest is the marsh harrier (Circus aeruginosus), which inhabits reedbeds and is widely distributed in Europe, Africa and Asia. The male marsh harrier is mainly dark chestnut-brown with grey wings and tail, while the female is chocolate-brown with a yellowish-cream head, throat and forewing.

Like the hen harrier, the marsh harrier hunts by flying low over the ground, but it does so at a slightly greater speed and its wingbeats are heavier.

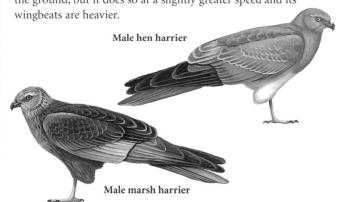

Male hen harrier

Male marsh harrier

WHERE IN THE WORLD?

Breeds in Britain, mainly in Scotland and Ireland, and throughout Europe, Siberia and North America. Winters

in Britain, southern Europe, North Africa, southern Asia and Central and South America.

RELATED SPECIES

Harriers, as a group, are found virtually throughout the world, but expert opinion on the number of species ranges from 9 to 13. Montagu's harrier, Circus pygargus, is the smallest and rarest harrier to breed in Britain. It looks similar to the hen harrier.

• **ORDER** • *Falconiformes* • **FAMILY** • *Accipitridae* • **GENUS & SPECIES** • *Gypaetus barbatus*

LAMMERGEIER

Massively built and distinctive in form, the lammergeier has the long and slender wings of a glider and the strength to lift heavy bones into the sky.

KEY FEATURES

- One of the world's largest birds of prey, this vulture has bold plumage and an impressive 'moustache'.
- Magnificent in the air, with a striking flight silhouette and the ability to soar for hours on end with minimal effort.
- Obtains most of its food by scavenging for carrion and breaking bones to expose the nutritious marrow.

BILL
Long, dark bristles obscure the true size of the lammergeier's hooked bill, which at nearly 8cm (3.1in) from flattened tip to wide base is the same length as the rest of the head.

FEET
The large feet, strong toes and sharp, curved claws are ideal for lifting and carrying food items. Other vultures can only carry food in the bill.

NECK
While most vultures have a bare head and neck for probing inside bloody, fresh carcasses, the lammergeier's rich orange feathers extend over its throat and nape.

VITAL STATISTICS

WEIGHT	4.5–7kg (9.9–15.4lb)
LENGTH	1–1.15m (3ft 3in–3ft 8in)
WINGSPAN	2.65–2.82m (8ft 7in–9ft 2in)
SEXUAL MATURITY	5 years
BREEDING SEASON	Varies according to region; January to July in southern Europe
NUMBER OF EGGS	Usually 1 or 2, occasionally 3
INCUBATION PERIOD	55–60 days
FLEDGING PERIOD	100–110 days
BREEDING INTERVAL	1 year
TYPICAL DIET	Hunts small mammals and birds; carrion
LIFESPAN	Unknown

CREATURE COMPARISONS

In general shape, the bird most resembling the lammergeier is the smaller Egyptian vulture (Neophron percnopterus), which has a similarly broad range. Confusion between the birds is unlikely, though, as the Egyptian vulture is only two-thirds the size of the lammergeier, with a striking white plumage and a much more delicate bill free of bristles. In both species the juvenile has dark plumage, but the larger size and narrower wing point of the lammergeier distinguishes it from the Egyptian vulture.

Both are principally carrion feeders and have been known to use rocks to break open food items. Using its bill, the Egyptian vulture hurls stones against ostrich eggs to feed on the contents.

Egyptian vulture

Lammergeier

WHERE IN THE WORLD?

Ranges across central and southwest Asia, from Turkey east to China and Mongolia. Also found in East and South Africa, the Atlas Mountains of North Africa, Corsica, Greece, the Pyrenees and the Arabian Peninsula.

RELATED SPECIES

Birds of prey form a large order, Falconiformes, made up of 5 families. The biggest family, Accipitridae, includes hawks, kites, buzzards, harriers, eagles and Old World vultures. The lammergeier is the sole member of its genus, but the family contains 13 other species of vulture spanning 8 genera. The 7 species of New World vulture form a separate family, Cathartidae, and are not closely related to their Old World counterparts.

AMERICAN HARPY EAGLE

• **ORDER** • *Falconiformes* • **FAMILY** • *Accipitridae* • **GENUS & SPECIES** • *Harpia harpyja*

The harpy eagle's armoury of split-second reflexes, needle-sharp talons and a massive, hooked bill leaves unwary animals with little chance of escape.

KEY FEATURES

- The heaviest bird of prey, with the largest feet and talons of any eagle.
- Strong enough to snatch adult monkeys and sloths from the treetops in mid flight.
- Pairs mate for life and raise a single chick once every three years.
- Its blend of brute force and ultra-sharp reflexes makes it one of the top rainforest predators.

VITAL STATISTICS

WEIGHT	Average 5kg (11lb) ; female heavier than male
LENGTH	90–130cm (35.4–51.2in)
WINGSPAN	2.3m (7ft 5in)
SEXUAL MATURITY	4–6 years
BREEDING SEASON	Varies according to habitat
NUMBER OF EGGS	1 to 2
INCUBATION PERIOD	About 55 days
BREEDING INTERVAL	3 years (rarely 2 years)
TYPICAL DIET	Tree-dwelling mammals, birds and reptiles; occasionally hunts rodents, peccaries and reptiles on the ground
LIFESPAN	Probably up to 30 years

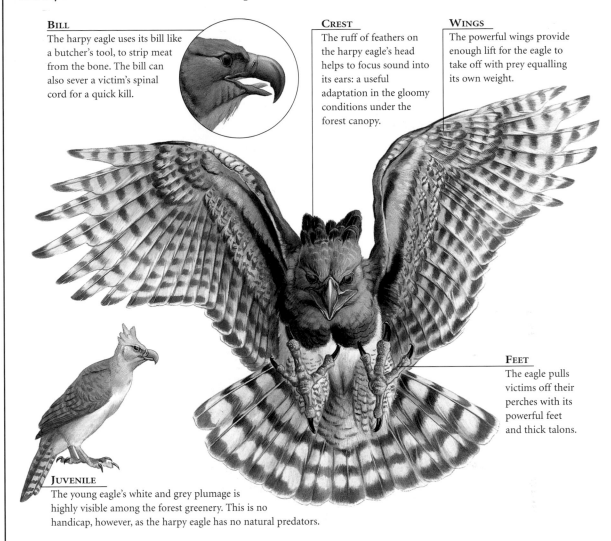

BILL
The harpy eagle uses its bill like a butcher's tool, to strip meat from the bone. The bill can also sever a victim's spinal cord for a quick kill.

CREST
The ruff of feathers on the harpy eagle's head helps to focus sound into its ears: a useful adaptation in the gloomy conditions under the forest canopy.

WINGS
The powerful wings provide enough lift for the eagle to take off with prey equalling its own weight.

FEET
The eagle pulls victims off their perches with its powerful feet and thick talons.

JUVENILE
The young eagle's white and grey plumage is highly visible among the forest greenery. This is no handicap, however, as the harpy eagle has no natural predators.

CREATURE COMPARISONS

The harpy eagle shares its name with another spectacular bird of prey that lives on the other side of the Pacific Ocean, in New Guinea. Like its American counterpart, the New Guinea harpy eagle (Harpyopsis novaeguinae) scans the canopy of tropical rainforests for medium-sized prey, such as tree kangaroos, but it also hunts in clearings and even visits gardens. However, the New Guinean species has a slimmer build, smaller bill and shorter wingspan, and never exceeds 90cm (35.4in) in length.

With its plumage of browns and greys, the New Guinea harpy eagle is much less conspicuous than the American harpy eagle. It is more often heard than seen, having a distinctive, far-carrying cry.

New Guinea harpy eagle   American harpy eagle

WHERE IN THE WORLD?

Thinly distributed over a wide range in the Americas, from Mexico south through the Amazon Basin to northern Argentina. It has vanished from many former haunts and is now classed as endangered.

RELATED SPECIES

There are 3 other harpy eagles: the New Guinea harpy eagle, Harpyopsis novaeguinae, the Philippine eagle, Pithecophaga jefferyi, and the Guiana crested eagle, Morphnus guianensis. As with the American harpy eagle, each of these is the only species in its genus. Harpy eagles belong to the large family Accipitridae, which also includes the 53 other species of eagle, as well as buzzards, kites, harriers and hawks. All accipitrids hunt live prey.

• ORDER • *Falconiformes* • FAMILY • *Accipitridae* • GENUS & SPECIES • *Milvus milvus*

RED KITE

KEY FEATURES

- Graceful aerobatics and a buoyant flight are the red kite's trademark.
- Constantly adjusts the angle of its long wings and deeply forked tail when airborne.
- Consumes carrion in large quantities, often feeding at refuse dumps.
- An opportunist, which frequently steals food from other large birds, or takes over their old nests.

VITAL STATISTICS

WEIGHT	Male 700–1000g (24.7–35.3oz); female 900–1200g (31.7–42.3oz)
LENGTH	61–66cm (24–26in)
WINGSPAN	1.6–1.9m (5ft 2in–6ft 2in)
SEXUAL MATURITY	2–4 years
BREEDING SEASON	Late March to July
NUMBER OF EGGS	2 to 4
INCUBATION PERIOD	31–32 days
FLEGLING PERIOD	50–60 days
BREEDING INTERVAL	1 year
TYPICAL DIET	Mainly carrion and small to medium-sized mammals and birds; reptiles, invertebrates
LIFESPAN	Up to 26 years

The red kite is a multipurpose bird of prey, adapted to catch live prey as well as to make a living scavenging on scraps and carrion.

JUVENILE PLUMAGE
The juvenile has a darker head and paler, duller body plumage than the adult, and its tail is less deeply forked, with a pale patch at the base.

PLUMAGE
The red kite has a warm, chestnut-coloured plumage mottled covered with dark markings, and a pale grey or whitish head. The tail is bright orange-brown above and pale grey with faint markings below: when viewed from this angle it can appear almost translucent.

TAIL
The kite frequently twists and fans its long and deeply forked tail, moving it from side to side like a rudder.

WINGS
Long wings are adapted to lengthy periods in the air and provide a high degree of manoeuvrability.

FEET & LEGS
The red kite's feet are spindly for a bird of prey of its size. Its talons are only slightly curved, while its legs are feathered only about halfway down — it has no need for protective leg feathers or powerful feet, since it feeds on small mammals and carrion.

CREATURE COMPARISONS

The red kite's closest relative, the black kite (Milvus migrans), is a much more abundant and widespread bird, found throughout the Old World. It has adapted well to life alongside humans, and is a common scavenger on the streets of cities from Africa to eastern Asia. The black kite is capable of snatching any food dropped or left unattended by humans with great agility and speed. As well as human refuse and carrion, it takes large amounts of fish when they are available — unlike its red relative — and is often found near freshwater. The ranges of both birds overlap in parts of Europe, but the red kite is easily distinguished from the black kite by its more deeply forked tail and the light patches near the wingtips.

Red kite

Black kite

WHERE IN THE WORLD?

Scarce, with a scattered range across Europe. About 90 per cent of the birds breed in Germany, France and Spain. There is a small but growing number in Britain, with a few in Morocco and on the Cape Verde Islands.

RELATED SPECIES

The 237 species in the large family Accipitridae include almost all birds of prey. Of these, 33 species are members of the kite subgroup. They include the American swallow-tailed kite (Elanoides forficatus), which has the most graceful flight of any bird of prey, the snail kite, (Rostrhamus sociabilis), which feeds on aquatic snails, and the brahminy kite (Haliastur indus), a common scavenger near to human habitation in India and Southeast Asia.

• ORDER • *Falconiformes* • FAMILY • *Accipitridae* • GENUS & SPECIES • *Necrosyrtes monachus*

HOODED VULTURE

KEY FEATURES

- Widespread across sub-Saharan Africa, scavenging carrion and a wide variety of organic matter.
- Attracted to farmland where livestock carcasses provide rich pickings.
- Flocks around food, but unable to compete with larger vultures.
- Fine bill can strip shreds of meat that are inaccessible to big birds.

VITAL STATISTICS

WEIGHT	1.6–2.6kg (3.5–5.7lb)
LENGTH	66–70cm (26–27.6in)
WINGSPAN	1.67–1.75m (5ft 5in– 5ft 7in)
SEXUAL MATURITY	1 year
BREEDING SEASON	All year round, but with regional variations
NUMBER OF EGGS	Usually 1
INCUBATION PERIOD	46–54 days
FLEDGING PERIOD	89–130 days
TYPICAL DIET	Carrion, waste and dung; also insects and their larvae
LIFESPAN	Not known

The hooded vulture's lean frame enables it to soar away on the mild, early morning air currents, giving it an advantage over heavier vultures.

FLIGHT
The wings are long and broad, and show six, deeply slotted primary (wingtip) feathers in flight.

BILL
The bill is too small to tear open large carcasses, but is suited to teasing out tiny morsels of flesh. It is also used like a pair of tweezers to pick insects and larvae from soil and dung.

HEAD
Beige down covers the crown. Thin, grey down covers the pink face and neck, which become flushed when the vulture is agitated.

PLUMAGE
The upperparts appear dark brown, and the flight feathers become paler towards the base. The upper chest and thighs are covered with downy white feathers.

FEET
The feet have short, thick toes and sharply hooked talons, helping the vulture perch securely while using its bill to strip carrion.

CREATURE COMPARISONS

The hooded vulture is dwarfed by many vulture species, such as the African white-backed vulture (Gyps africanus), with a wing span of 2.13m (7ft), and the lappet-faced vulture (Torgos tracheliotus), which has a wingspan of up to 2.75m (9ft). Both species share much of the hooded vulture's range and feeding habits, but are likely to drive their smaller cousin from a carcass while they take their fill.

All vultures have long, broad wings that enable them to soar for many hours, saving energy as they search for elusive food. A large vulture is slow and ungainly when on the ground and struggles to take off quickly if threatened. It often circles a carcass for long periods, checking for danger, before landing to eat.

African white-backed vulture

Hooded vulture

Lappet-faced vulture

WHERE IN THE WORLD?

Found in Africa, from Mauritania and Senegal in the west, east to Ethiopia, and south to South Africa. Absent from the dense forests of western-central Africa and Madagascar.

RELATED SPECIES

The hooded vulture is the only species in its genus, although it is related to the Egyptian vulture, Neophron percnopterus. Both species are members of the family Accipitridae, which also contains hawks and eagles.

• **ORDER** • *Falconiformes* • **FAMILY** • *Accipitridae* • **GENUS & SPECIES** • *Neophron percnopterus*

EGYPTIAN VULTURE

KEY FEATURES

- Uses a stone as a tool to crack open ostrich eggs, which are a favourite food item.
- Scavenges at rubbish tips and town markets, where it thrives on a diet of rotting rubbish.
- Performs a spectacular sky-dance as part of its courtship display, and nests in caves on cliff faces.

Agile and supremely efficient in flight, the Egyptian vulture is no beauty on the ground, where it walks with a typically hunched profile.

JUVENILE
First-year plumage is entirely dark brown. The bare, grey face soon turns yellow. More white feathers appear with each moult until adult plumage is acquired after five years.

BILL
The thin, hooked tip of the long bill is adapted for scavenging small food items and picking scraps off carcasses. It is not strong enough to tear through tough skin.

RUFF
Because it does not thrust its head deep into carcasses, the Egyptian vulture avoids the need for a bare neck, and instead has a shaggy ruff of pointed feathers.

FEET
With their sharp, curved claws, the feet are strong for a vulture, but they lack the gripping power of eagles and hawks. Only the lower leg is unfeathered.

FLIGHT
The wedge-shaped tail acts as a rudder in flight. The long wings are narrower than those of most other vultures.

VITAL STATISTICS

WEIGHT	1.6–2.2kg (3.5–4.8lb)
LENGTH	58–70cm (22.8–27.6in)
WINGSPAN	1.5–1.7m (4ft 9in–5ft 6in)
SEXUAL MATURITY	4–5 years
BREEDING SEASON	Mainly March–May
NUMBER OF EGGS	Usually 2
INCUBATION PERIOD	42 days
FLEDGING PERIOD	70–85 days
BREEDING INTERVAL	1 year
TYPICAL DIET	Carrion, organic waste, eggs, small mammals and insects
LIFESPAN	20 years in the wild; up to 37 years in captivity

CREATURE COMPARISONS

The black-breasted buzzard (Hamirostra melanosternon) is slightly smaller than its relative the Egyptian vulture, with a stockier build and a stouter bill. Found in Australia, the buzzard, like the vulture, prefers open, dry habitats and avoids forests. Its method of feeding is similar to that of the vulture, as it searches for carrion and small mammals while soaring on high, sweeping low over the ground or walking along. The black-breasted buzzard also eats large eggs, but in its case, they are usually emu eggs. It breaks the eggs with its bill or hurls large stones at them from a standing position.

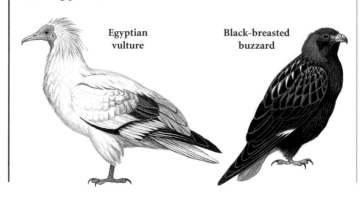

Egyptian vulture

Black-breasted buzzard

WHERE IN THE WORLD?

Found in much of Africa, southern Europe, Arabia and India. Birds in the north of the range spend the winter farther south.

RELATED SPECIES

The Egyptian vulture is among the smallest of the 15 species of Old World vulture, which are unrelated to their American counterparts — New World vultures. Its closest relations are the slightly larger hooded vulture, Necrosyrtes monachus, found in Africa, and the huge lammergeier, Gypaetus barbatus, which has a wingspan of almost 3m (9ft 8in) — double that of the Egyptian vulture — but otherwise resembles it in shape.

• **ORDER** • *Falconiformes* • **FAMILY** • *Accipitridae* • **GENUS & SPECIES** • *Polemaetus bellicosus*

MARTIAL EAGLE

KEY FEATURES

- Largest of all the African eagles.
- Extremely powerful, with the strength to kill a small antelope.
- Eyesight so sharp it can spot large prey from about 5km (3.1 miles) away.
- Hunts over an area in excess of 200 sq km (77.2 sq miles).

VITAL STATISTICS

WEIGHT	5–5.9kg (11–13lb)
LENGTH	79–84cm (31–33.1in)
WINGSPAN	2.1–2.6m (6ft 9in–8ft 5in). Female larger than male
SEXUAL MATURITY	5–6 years
BREEDING SEASON	Varies according to location
NUMBER OF EGGS	Rarely more than 1
INCUBATION PERIOD	55 days
BREEDING INTERVAL	1–3 years
TYPICAL DIET	Young antelope, ground squirrels, hares, guinea fowl, snakes and lizards
LIFESPAN	About 16 years

With its rapier-sharp talons, the martial eagle makes a fearsome aerial predator, swooping down to strike its prey with terrible force.

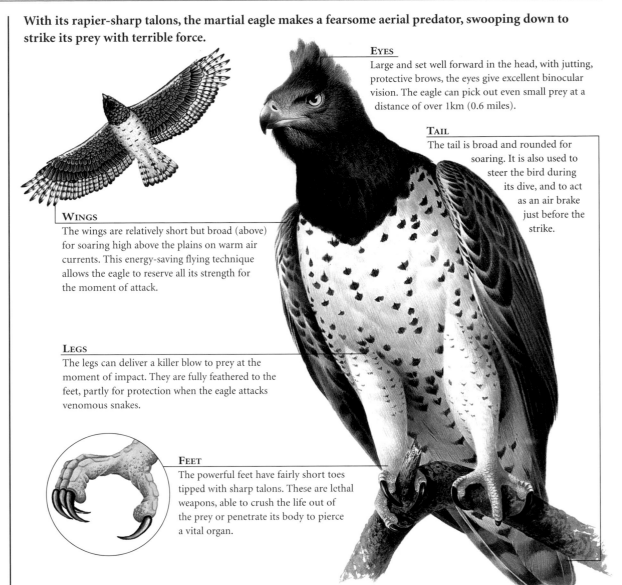

EYES
Large and set well forward in the head, with jutting, protective brows, the eyes give excellent binocular vision. The eagle can pick out even small prey at a distance of over 1km (0.6 miles).

TAIL
The tail is broad and rounded for soaring. It is also used to steer the bird during its dive, and to act as an air brake just before the strike.

WINGS
The wings are relatively short but broad (above) for soaring high above the plains on warm air currents. This energy-saving flying technique allows the eagle to reserve all its strength for the moment of attack.

LEGS
The legs can deliver a killer blow to prey at the moment of impact. They are fully feathered to the feet, partly for protection when the eagle attacks venomous snakes.

FEET
The powerful feet have fairly short toes tipped with sharp talons. These are lethal weapons, able to crush the life out of the prey or penetrate its body to pierce a vital organ.

CREATURE COMPARISONS

All eagles have a sharp, hooked bill to tear up their prey but the precise shape of the bill varies according to each eagle's diet. For example, the bald eagle of North America has a very sharply hooked bill for ripping through the scales and skin of slippery fish. The golden eagle's bill is a little less hooked, like that of the martial eagle, as it is suited to tearing the tough skin of the rabbits and birds that form the bulk of its prey.

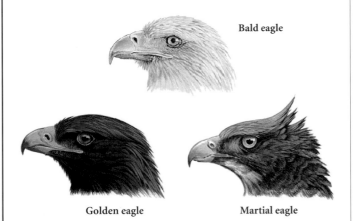

Bald eagle

Golden eagle

Martial eagle

WHERE IN THE WORLD?

Found throughout much of Africa south of the Sahara Desert. Avoids heavily forested areas, and most common (but nowhere numerous) over open savannah grasslands.

RELATED SPECIES

The martial eagle is a member of the family Accipitridae, which also includes hawks, Old World vultures, harriers and kites. Close relations in the family are the bald eagle and Bonelli's eagle, *Hieraaetus fasciatus*, of Europe, Africa and Asia.

• **ORDER** • *Falconiformes* • **FAMILY** • *Cathartidae* • **GENUS & SPECIES** • *Sarcoramphus papa*

KING VULTURE

KEY FEATURES

- A powerful scavenger that soars over the forests of Central and South America.
- One of the most strikingly coloured and odd-looking of all birds of prey.
- Often the first vulture to feed at a large carcass as its ultra-strong bill can rip through the toughest hide.

VITAL STATISTICS

WEIGHT	3–3.75kg (6.6–8.3lb)
LENGTH	71–81cm (27.9–31.9in)
WINGSPAN	1.8–1.98m (5ft 9in– 6ft 5in)
SEXUAL MATURITY	3–4 years
BREEDING SEASON	March to August
NUMBER OF EGGS	1
INCUBATION PERIOD	53–58 days
FLEDGING PERIOD	About 3 months
BREEDING INTERVAL	1 year
TYPICAL DIET	Carrion of a wide variety of species
LIFESPAN	Unknown

A powerful build and intimidating bill enable the colourful king vulture to dominate other South American vultures and rip into tough carcasses.

HEAD AND NECK
The head is adorned with brightly coloured, grooved wattles (loose folds of bare skin), while the neck has bright, bare skin.

BILL
The heavy bill is hooked for tearing through skin. Its fleshy base, the cere, is bright orange and bears an equally bright, multi-lobed wattle.

PLUMAGE
The king vulture has bold creamy white and black plumage and the male and female look alike. A bare patch of skin on the chest overlies the crop — a food storage sac in the gullet — which may bulge through the chest feathers when the bird has eaten a large meal.

FEET
The feet and talons are weak and are designed for walking. They are not adapted to tearing flesh or carrying food like those of most other birds of prey.

EYE
The eyes are colourful with a gleaming white iris surrounded by a bright red ring.

RUFF
A thick greyish ruff of short feathers surrounds the base of the neck.

JUVENILE
The young king vulture lacks the bold colours of the adult, being an overall greyish-black with similarly drab bare skin areas. It gains adult colouration gradually over about four years.

CREATURE COMPARISONS

The king vulture is a large vulture but two other species of vulture from the New World are larger still: the California condor, *Gymnogyps californianus*, and the huge Andean condor, *Vultur gryphus*. The latter bird is a member of the same family as the king vulture and is the world's largest bird of prey. The Andean condor can be over four times heavier than the king vulture, with large males weighing up to 12kg (26.5lb). It has an overall length of up to 1.3m (4ft 3in) and an impressive wingspan of up to 3.2m (10ft 5in). Like the king vulture, it has a bare neck to prevent soiling when feeding on carrion. The Andean condor has also been known to kill sickly or dying animals.

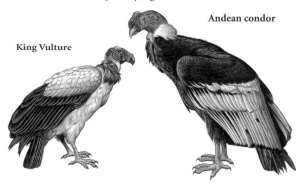

King Vulture

Andean condor

WHERE IN THE WORLD?

Ranges from central Mexico through Central America into South America, as far south as northern Argentina. Also found on the island of Trinidad in the Caribbean.

RELATED SPECIES

The king vulture is one of 7 species of New World vulture in the family Cathartidae, which also includes the American black vulture, the California and Andean condors, the lesser and greater yellow-headed vultures and the turkey vulture. New World vultures, though generally classified within the huge bird of prey order Falconiformes are now thought to be more closely related to storks, family Ciconiidae, in the order Ciconiiformes.

• **ORDER** • *Falconiformes* • **FAMILY** • *Cathartidae* • **GENUS & SPECIES** • *Vultur gryphus*

KEY FEATURES

- Soars at altitudes up to 5500m (18,040ft), and can spot an animal carcass from a distance of several kilometres.

- Has the largest wing area of any bird, allowing it to glide freely on rising air currents.

- Can devour nearly 8kg (17.6lb) of flesh at a single sitting, but may eat so much that it cannot take off again.

VITAL STATISTICS

WEIGHT	Male 11–15kg (24.2–33.1lb); female 8–11kg (17.6–24.2lb)
LENGTH	1–1.3m (3ft 3in–4ft 3in)
WINGSPAN	Up to 3m (9ft 8in)
SEXUAL MATURITY	6–8 years
BREEDING SEASON	Varies according to location
NUMBER OF EGGS	1
INCUBATION PERIOD	54–59 days
FLEDGING PERIOD	6 months
BREEDING INTERVAL	Every two years
TYPICAL DIET	Carrion of sheep, cattle, llamas and other mammals
LIFESPAN	Over 50 years

The Andean condor's huge wing area enables it to soar on air currents, and its dense plumage keeps it warm at high altitudes.

WINGS
Long and broad with an area of 6000 sq cm (930 sq in). Slotted tips give fine adjustment of 'trim,' like an aeroplane's flaps. After a full day in the air, the feathers become bent upward, but a night's rest and the morning sun help to straighten them.

FEMALE
Unlike other vultures, the female Andean condor differs from the male. She is smaller, and lacks his 'comb' and throat wattles.

BILL
The stout, hooked bill is used for tearing into tough hide and flesh.

TAIL
The broad, fan-shaped tail is spread out and used as a rudder when soaring.

HEAD
The head is bare, since feathers would be soiled by blood. Loose folds of skin aid heat loss at ground level, while a ruff of downy feathers acts like a snug scarf in the cold air at high altitudes.

CREATURE COMPARISONS

The Andean condor is not related to Old World (African and Eurasian) vultures, but shows closer affinities to storks. The African marabou stork, for example, has striking similarities to the condor. Like the condor, this stork is a bald-headed carrion eater, and locates its prey by soaring at great altitude on huge, deeply slotted wings.

Marabou stork

Andean condor

WHERE IN THE WORLD?

Found high in the Andes mountains of western South America, over the grasslands of Argentina south of the Rio Negro, and on the coasts of Peru and Chile.

RELATED SPECIES

The Andean condor is one of seven species of New World vulture in the family Cathartidae. Five are small vultures and include the king vulture. The only other condor species is the rare California condor.

• **ORDER** • *Falconiformes* • **FAMILY** • *Falconidae* • **GENUS & SPECIES** • *Falco peregrinus*

PEREGRINE FALCON

The peregrine is a formidable predator of the skies, superbly equipped to seek and intercept other birds in flight, like a living air-to-air missile.

KEY FEATURES

- Hunts other birds in the air; possesses the agility and flying skills to catch even the most aerobatic of species.
- Specializes in spectacular diving attacks on its prey at speeds of more than 180 km/h (111.8 mph).
- Kills victims by the devastating impact of its strike, or dispatches its quarry on the ground with a bite to the back of the neck.

VITAL STATISTICS

WEIGHT	540–1500g (19–52.9lb). Female larger than male
LENGTH	34–51cm (13.4–20.1in)
WINGSPAN	80–119cm (31–46.8in)
SEXUAL MATURITY	Usually 2–3 years
BREEDING SEASON	February to August in northern parts of range
NUMBER OF EGGS	3 to 4
INCUBATION PERIOD	29–32 days
FLEDGING PERIOD	About 6 weeks
BREEDING INTERVAL	1 year
TYPICAL DIET	Birds up to the size of a duck; small mammals
LIFESPAN	About 18 years

BILL
The hooked bill is used for tearing flesh. A notch helps deliver a clean bite to the back of a victim's neck, severing the spinal cord.

FEMALE
The female is 15–20 per cent larger than the male. She is more heavily spotted on the breast, and her flanks and tail bear heavier barring.

WINGS
The long, pointed wings beat deeply in level flight. In a dive, they are angled back, close to the body.

FEET
The talons are sharp and curved. They are used in an aerial attack to deliver a glancing blow to prey, with the hindclaw possibly raking the flesh in passing.

MALE PLUMAGE
Males in North America and Europe are a dark slate-grey above with a barred back and tail. The underparts are a pale pink-buff, with black spots on the breast. In other areas, males are a paler blue-grey or almost black above and white to reddish below.

CREATURE COMPARISONS

The peregrine falcon is one of many swift and deadly birds of prey in the family Falconidae. The merlin is a small falcon that often charges at its prey in a low-level attack. The common kestrel, smaller than the peregrine, is probably the world's most numerous falcon. The gyr falcon, largest of all the falcons, is more heavily built than other species, and has broader wings.

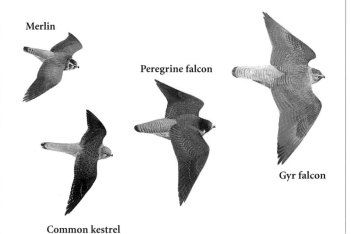

Merlin

Peregrine falcon

Gyr falcon

Common kestrel

WHERE IN THE WORLD?

Breeds in northern North America and northern Eurasia. Overwinters farther south in the Americas, Africa south of the Sahara, parts of Europe, Southeast Asia and Australia. Some populations are resident all year round.

RELATED SPECIES

The family Falconidae is generally held to contain about 40 species of falcon. These include the peregrine falcon's close relative, the Barbary falcon, or black shaheen, *Falco pelegrinoides*, and the endangered Mauritius kestrel, *Falco punctatus*.

GYRFALCON

• ORDER • *Falconiformes* • FAMILY • *Falconidae* • GENUS & SPECIES • *Falco rusticolus*

KEY FEATURES

- By far the largest and most powerful falcon.
- Its plumage ranges from almost pure white through shades of brown and grey to nearly black.
- Breeds farther north than any other bird of prey, nesting on coasts and tundra in the High Arctic and sub-Arctic.
- A superb hunter, it snatches prey in mid-air or from the ground.

VITAL STATISTICS

WEIGHT	Male 961–1321g (33.9–46.6lb); female 1.26–2.1kg (2.8–4.6lb)
LENGTH	48–60cm (18.9–23.6in)
WINGSPAN	1.2–1.35m (3ft 9in–4.4ft)
SEXUAL MATURITY	2–3 years
BREEDING SEASON	April–July
NUMBER OF EGGS	Up to 7; usually 3 or 4
INCUBATION PERIOD	34–36 days
FLEDGING PERIOD	46–53 days
TYPICAL DIET	Mainly small to medium-sized birds, especially grouse and seabirds, with a few lemmings and other mammals
LIFESPAN	Up to 13 years

The gyrfalcon is nearly twice as heavy as the peregrine falcon, which enables it to kill much bigger prey and helps it survive the bitter Arctic cold.

HEAD
The strong notch on the hooked bill's cutting edge is used to break the necks of prey.

DARK MORPH
Birds belonging to the dark morph, or colour variety (left), are slate-grey above and heavily spotted with dark grey below.

WINGS
The long wings are broader and less pointed than those of smaller falcons, giving the gyrfalcon greater acceleration and speed in the air.

WHITE MORPH
Birds belonging to the white morph have dark flecks on an otherwise white plumage. They are most common in northernmost regions, such as Greenland.

FEET
Each foot has four large, strong toes that can withstand massive impact as the falcon strikes prey. The sharp talons sink into the flesh of victims to hold them fast.

TAIL
In rapid flight the gyrfalcon keeps its long tail closed and tilts it from side to side as a rudder. The bird fans its tail feathers when soaring or landing.

CREATURE COMPARISONS

No bigger than a sparrow, the black-thighed falconet (Microhierax fringillarius) is the world's smallest bird of prey. It weighs a mere 28g (1oz) — a little over 1 per cent of a female gyrfalcon's weight. But, size apart, the two species of falcon have much in common. The falconet has sharply clawed feet for catching its prey of insects, lizards and small birds, and a hooked bill for pulling its food to pieces. Its eyesight is keen, and its wings are proportionately long.

A common resident of tropical forests in Thailand, Malaysia and Indonesia, the black-thighed falconet spots prey by perching on an exposed branch, often at the edge of a clearing or beside a river. It sometimes hunts in groups of up to ten birds, with the team members working together to outmanoeuvre the largest victims.

Black-thighed falconet

Gyrfalcon

WHERE IN THE WORLD?

Found in a broad band across northern Eurasia and North America, including coastal regions of Greenland and Iceland. Moves south in winter, sometimes reaching northwestern and central Europe.

RELATED SPECIES

The gyrfalcon is 1 of 37 species in the genus Falco, or falcons. Its closest relatives are the peregrine falcon, F. peregrinus, which occurs on every continent, and the saker, F. cherrug, which breeds mainly in the open steppes of central Asia. The falcons are members of the family Falconidae, together with the 9 species of falconet and pygmy-falcon, the 5 species of forest falcon, the 9 species of caracara, and the laughing falcon.

• ORDER • *Falconiformes* • FAMILY • *Falconidae* • GENUS & SPECIES • *Falco tinnunculus*

COMMON KESTREL

KEY FEATURES

- One of the most abundant and adaptable of all the world's falcons.
- A superb flier that can swoop, soar, dash and glide with equal and effortless grace.
- Hovers in the air while scanning the ground for prey, then drops like a stone for the kill.
- Takes advantage of human alterations to its natural habitat.

With its strong wings, lightweight body and fanned tail, the common kestrel hovers in the air, pinpointing prey with its super-keen eyesight.

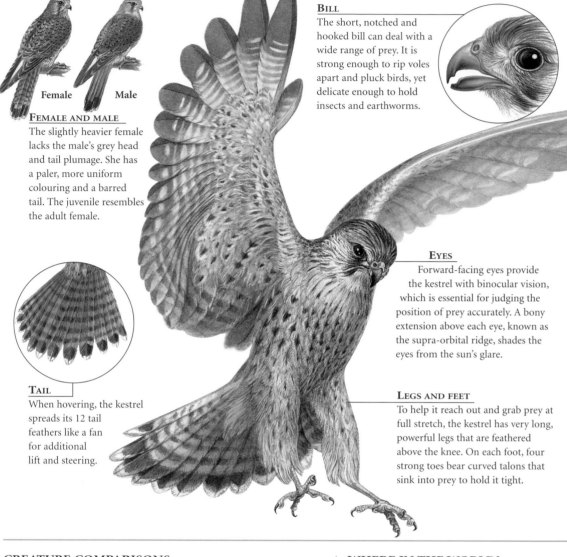

Female   Male

FEMALE AND MALE
The slightly heavier female lacks the male's grey head and tail plumage. She has a paler, more uniform colouring and a barred tail. The juvenile resembles the adult female.

BILL
The short, notched and hooked bill can deal with a wide range of prey. It is strong enough to rip voles apart and pluck birds, yet delicate enough to hold insects and earthworms.

EYES
Forward-facing eyes provide the kestrel with binocular vision, which is essential for judging the position of prey accurately. A bony extension above each eye, known as the supra-orbital ridge, shades the eyes from the sun's glare.

TAIL
When hovering, the kestrel spreads its 12 tail feathers like a fan for additional lift and steering.

LEGS AND FEET
To help it reach out and grab prey at full stretch, the kestrel has very long, powerful legs that are feathered above the knee. On each foot, four strong toes bear curved talons that sink into prey to hold it tight.

VITAL STATISTICS

WEIGHT	Male 150–215g (5.3–7.6lb); female 190–250g (6.7–8.8lb)
LENGTH	32–35cm (12.6–13.8in)
WINGSPAN	70–80cm (27.6–31in)
SEXUAL MATURITY	1–2 years
BREEDING SEASON	Depends on region
NUMBER OF EGGS	3 to 6
INCUBATION PERIOD	27–34 days
FLEDGING PERIOD	27–32 days
BREEDING INTERVAL	1 year
TYPICAL DIET	Small mammals, earthworms, small birds, lizards
LIFESPAN	Up to 16 years

CREATURE COMPARISONS

Weighing 350–450g (12.3–15.9oz) and measuring about 38cm (15in) from bill to tail, Eleonora's falcon (Falco eleonorae) is distinctly larger than the kestrel and has more pointed wings. It preys almost exclusively on small birds and dragonflies, which it catches in mid-air after a dramatic chase. Unlike the kestrel, Eleonora's falcon exists in two colour forms. Some 75 per cent of birds are dark grey above and creamy-orange with dark streaks below. The remaining 25 per cent are grey overall.

Eleonora's falcon is rarer than the kestrel: its population totals no more than 4000 breeding pairs distributed among 100 or so colonies; these are scattered among rocky islands in the Mediterranean and sea-cliffs on the North African coast.

Common kestrel

Eleonora's falcon

WHERE IN THE WORLD?

Found in a huge range that includes most of Europe and Asia (apart from the far north and east), parts of the Middle East

and Southeast Asia, and much of Africa excluding the Sahara and the equatorial forests.

RELATED SPECIES

The common kestrel is 1 of 13 species of kestrel in the genus Falco, which has a total of 38 members. The genus includes the American kestrel, F. sparverius: North America's smallest bird of prey.

CRESTED CARACARA

• **ORDER** • *Falconiformes* • **FAMILY** • *Falconidae* • **GENUS & SPECIES** • *Polyborus plancus*

The crested caracara shares many of the vultures' adaptations for a life spent scavenging carrion, but is fast and graceful when airborne, like a falcon.

KEY FEATURES

- An adaptable bird of prey that looks and behaves like a vulture.
- Eats virtually anything it finds, including carrion, a wide range of small animals and even insects.
- Frequently seen along roadsides, searching for animals killed by traffic.
- Usually silent, but has a distinctive cackling call, which gives the bird its name.

EYES
The caracara's superb eyesight is capable of detecting carrion and prey from afar.

FACE
In common with the vultures, the crested caracara has an area of naked skin around its bill. This prevents the caracara from fouling its feathers when it tears strips of flesh from bloody carcasses.

WINGS
The caracara flies swiftly on long, narrow wings with deeply 'fingered' tips, created by the long flight feathers.

FEET
Strong toes equipped with long, curving talons enable the caracara to keep hold of struggling prey and maintain its grip on carcasses while ripping into them.

LEGS
Long legs enable the caracara to make sudden dashes along the ground after reptiles, amphibians and insects.

VITAL STATISTICS

WEIGHT	850–1600g (30–56.4lb); male heavier than female
LENGTH	49–59cm (19.3–23.2in)
WINGSPAN	1.2–1.3m (3ft 9in–4ft 3in)
SEXUAL MATURITY	2 to 3 years
BREEDING SEASON	January to June in USA; almost year-round in South America
NUMBER OF EGGS	1 to 3; rarely 4
INCUBATION PERIOD	28 to 32 days
FLEDGING PERIOD	About 90 days
BREEDING INTERVAL	1 year
TYPICAL DIET	Carrion, scraps, reptiles, small mammals, invertebrates, birds' eggs
LIFESPAN	Up to 20 years

CREATURE COMPARISONS

Since its range is restricted to a handful of islands off the southeastern tip of South America, the striated caracara (Phalcoboenus australis) is rare compared to the crested caracara. It also has a more carrion-based diet, feeding mainly on dead seabirds, such as penguins and albatrosses. When the seabirds are not breeding, and their vast colonies are empty, the striated caracara hunts insects and scavenges sheep carcasses.

The two species of caracara occur side-by-side on the Falkland Islands, but are unlikely to be confused. The striated caracara is a rather drab, all-dark bird: fine streaking on the neck and breast is its only plumage feature.

Striated caracara

Crested caracara

WHERE IN THE WORLD?

Found from Florida and the USA's southwestern states (including Arizona and Texas) south as far the southernmost tip of Argentina. Also occurs in the Caribbean and on the Falkland Islands.

RELATED SPECIES

The 9 species of caracara resemble the New World vultures of the family Cathartidae, such as the turkey vulture, Cathartes aura, but are not closely related to them. The caracaras actually belong to the subfamily Polyborinae of the Falconidae, or falcons.

• ORDER • *Falconiformes* • FAMILY • *Sagittaridae* • GENUS & SPECIES • *Sagittarius serpentarius*

SECRETARY BIRD

KEY FEATURES

- The only bird of prey that hunts on foot, stalking through the long grass of the African savannah.
- Has spindly, stork-like legs that it uses for stamping on victims too big to be seized in the bill.
- Adorned with an untidy but distinctive crest of head feathers, which it raises when excited.

VITAL STATISTICS

WEIGHT	Up to 4kg (8.8lb); males are slightly heavier than females
LENGTH	1.25–1.5m (4ft 1in– 4ft 9in)
WINGSPAN	1.2m (3ft 9in)
SEXUAL MATURITY	2 years
BREEDING SEASON	All year (mainly spring and summer)
NUMBER OF EGGS	2 or 3
INCUBATION PERIOD	43–46 days
FLEDGING PERIOD	About 80 days
BREEDING INTERVAL	1 year
TYPICAL DIET	Rodents, reptiles, large insects
LIFESPAN	10–12 years

The secretary bird's long, scaly legs provide protection against venomous reptiles on the ground as it strides over Africa's grasslands in search of prey.

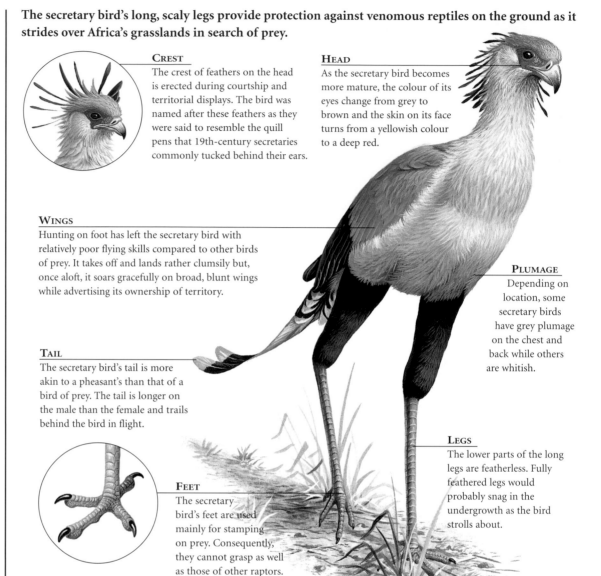

CREST
The crest of feathers on the head is erected during courtship and territorial displays. The bird was named after these feathers as they were said to resemble the quill pens that 19th-century secretaries commonly tucked behind their ears.

HEAD
As the secretary bird becomes more mature, the colour of its eyes change from grey to brown and the skin on its face turns from a yellowish colour to a deep red.

WINGS
Hunting on foot has left the secretary bird with relatively poor flying skills compared to other birds of prey. It takes off and lands rather clumsily but, once aloft, it soars gracefully on broad, blunt wings while advertising its ownership of territory.

PLUMAGE
Depending on location, some secretary birds have grey plumage on the chest and back while others are whitish.

TAIL
The secretary bird's tail is more akin to a pheasant's than that of a bird of prey. The tail is longer on the male than the female and trails behind the bird in flight.

FEET
The secretary bird's feet are used mainly for stamping on prey. Consequently, they cannot grasp as well as those of other raptors.

LEGS
The lower parts of the long legs are featherless. Fully feathered legs would probably snag in the undergrowth as the bird strolls about.

CREATURE COMPARISONS

Another large, long-legged bird of the African tropical savannah is the marabou stork. Growing to about 1.5m (4ft 9in) tall, the adult marabou stork is generally taller than the secretary bird. The stork's neck is bare since the bird regularly feeds on carrion, and feathers would become soiled. The bill is powerful enough to crack bones, and the marabou stork may wield it against vultures to force its way to the front of the queue when these birds gather at a carcass. The stork's diet also includes rodents, reptiles and insects. Both the secretary bird and the stork are generally silent, but during courtship displays make deep croaking grunts.

Secretary bird

Marabou stork

WHERE IN THE WORLD?

Found on open savannah and plains over much of sub-Saharan Africa, southwards to the Cape of South Africa. Absent only from forested and mountainous areas of western central Africa.

RELATED SPECIES

The secretary bird is the only representative of the family Sagittaridae. The family name derives from the Latin word sagittarius, meaning archer, and refers to the way the secretary bird, like an archer, stalks its prey stealthily on foot. This is the main feature that distinguishes it from the other 279 species of the order Falconiformes, whose members, such as hawks and eagles, either hunt on the wing or swoop down from a perch.

WILD TURKEY

• ORDER • *Galliformes* • FAMILY • *Meleagrididae* • GENUS & SPECIES • *Meleagris gallopavo*

KEY FEATURES

- Heavy bird that spends most of its time on the ground, but is a surprisingly powerful flier.
- Roosts in the trees at night, but the female nests among undergrowth during the breeeding season.
- Courting male displays iridescent plumage and bold skin colours to make himself irresistible to females.

VITAL STATISTICS

WEIGHT	Male 8–10kg (17.6–22lb); female 4kg (8.8lb)
LENGTH	Male 122cm (48in); female 91cm (35.8in)
WINGSPAN	Up to 110cm (43.3in)
SEXUAL MATURITY	Male 12 months; female 10 months
BREEDING SEASON	February to August
NUMBER OF EGGS	8 to 15
INCUBATION PERIOD	28 days
FLEDGING PERIOD	2–3 weeks
BREEDING INTERVAL	1 year
TYPICAL DIET	Fruits, seeds, vegetation, grain and maize, acorns, nuts and insects
LIFESPAN	5–7 years

The courting male ruffles his splendid body feathers, fans his luxuriant tail and gobbles loudly in an attempt to dazzle his female audience.

SNOOD
The turkey's featherless head is decorated with bright red and blue warty skin. A fleshy protuberance called a snood hangs from the forehead.

FEMALE
Smaller than the male, the female turkey has more feathers around her neck, and duller plumage.

PLUMAGE
The metallic dark brown plumage of the male is iridescent: in certain light it seems to contain the colours of the rainbow.

BEARD
The beard is a tuft of long, bristle-like feathers that grow from the male's breast. Unlike the rest of the plumage, the beard is not shed annually.

TAIL
The male usually holds his black-tipped tail feathers neatly behind; they are displayed only during courtship.

CREATURE COMPARISONS

The brush-turkey (Alectura lathami) belongs to the family Megapodiidae. It is a ground-feeder, like the wild turkey, using its powerful feet for raking up seeds and insects and to give it a sure grip when roosting in the trees. It is found in the rainforest, thick scrub and cultivated areas of eastern Australia.

The brush-turkey is smaller than the wild turkey, measuring around 70cm (27.6in) from head to tail. Its plumage takes on various shades of black and is less striking than that of its American counterpart.

The red-headed brush-turkey lacks the wild turkey's snood, but both birds have wattles (folds of skin around the throat). The brush-turkey's wattle is bright yellow.

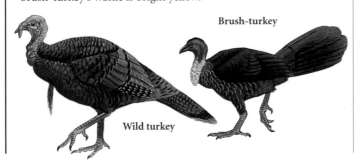

Brush-turkey

Wild turkey

WHERE IN THE WORLD?

Formerly widespread across North America, but now restricted to scattered areas of the USA and parts of northern Mexico.

RELATED SPECIES

Chickens, turkeys and gamebirds are classed in the order Galliformes. The wild or common turkey and the ocellated turkey, Meleagris ocellata, of South America are the only two members of the family Meleagrididae. The ocellated turkey lives in the semi-forested lowlands of the Yucatan Peninsula in Mexico, Guatemala and Honduras. Like its relative, the ocellated turkey has brilliant metallic plumage patterned in rich colours.

• **ORDER** • *Galliformes* • **FAMILY** • *Phasianidae* • **GENUS & SPECIES** • *Gallus gallus*

RED JUNGLEFOWL

Adorned with rich colours and fanciful feathers, the male red junglefowl uses his magnificent plumage to entice females during the breeding season.

KEY FEATURES

- The ancestor of domestic chickens, this colourful pheasant is a wild, yet wary bird.
- Lives under the rules of a group hierarchy established by ritual challenges and fighting.
- Cross-breeding with domestic poultry is causing concern for the genetic purity of the species.

PLUMAGE
The male erects the long feathers, or hackles, on his neck in courtship displays to attract potential mates. In summer, after the breeding season, the male moults his breeding plumage. The golden hackles are replaced by short, black feathers, and the impressive tail plumes fall off.

HEN
The hen's plumage is duller and more speckled than that of the male to help camouflage her while she is incubating eggs or brooding chicks.

HEAD
The male has fleshy wattles on the sides of his bill and a prominent comb on his crown. Females are attracted to the males with the biggest combs. A male's comb shrinks in size after the breeding season.

LEGS
The red junglefowl scratches the ground with its long, clawed toes when searching for food. The male has a sharp spur on the back of each leg for use in fights.

VITAL STATISTICS

WEIGHT	Male 673–1450g (23.7–51.1lb); female 485–1050g (17.1–37lb)
LENGTH	Male 65–75cm (25.6–29.5in); female 42–46cm (16.5–18.1in)
WINGSPAN	Male 65–80cm (25.6–31in); female 55–63cm (21.6–24.8in)
SEXUAL MATURITY	1 year
BREEDING SEASON	Dry season
NUMBER OF EGGS	4 to 9, but usually 5 or 6
INCUBATION PERIOD	18–20 days
FLEDGING PERIOD	Independent at 45–60 days
TYPICAL DIET	Seeds, grain, shoots, roots, fruit, insects
LIFESPAN	3 years

CREATURE COMPARISONS

Some 150 breeds of poultry — from 20cm- (7.9in)-long bantams to giant Brahma cockerels weighing 7kg (15.4lb)— have been developed since the red junglefowl was domesticated back in 3200 BC. Various types have been used for religious purposes, cock-fighting, meat, eggs and exhibition. Breed names include Scots dumpy, Sicilian buttercup and Transylvanian naked neck. A popular show variety is the black-red modern game bantam, which — despite its name — has existed for more than 100 years. Originally bred in Britain, it is smaller than the red junglefowl, with long legs, a slender body and no comb or throat wattles.

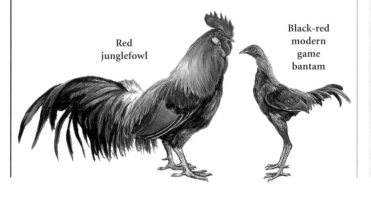

Red junglefowl

Black-red modern game bantam

WHERE IN THE WORLD?

Found from northeastern Pakistan and India east to southeastern China, and south through the Malay Peninsula to the islands of Sumatra, Java and Bali.

RELATED SPECIES

The red junglefowl is 1 of 48 species of pheasant in the family Phasianidae. These include 3 other species of junglefowl: the Ceylon junglefowl, Gallus lafayetii, from Sri Lanka, the grey junglefowl, G. sonneratii, from India and the green junglefowl, G. varius, from Java.

• ORDER • *Galliformes* • FAMILY • *Tetraonidae* • GENUS & SPECIES • *Lagopus mutus*

KEY FEATURES

- One of the few birds able to live throughout the year in the barren, windswept landscapes of the far north.

- Superbly camouflaged, with a plumage that changes from grey-brown in summer to pure white in winter.

- Avoids predators by lying flat against the ground and 'vanishing' from sight, fleeing only if danger persists.

VITAL STATISTICS

WEIGHT	370–600g (13–21.2lb)
LENGTH	34–36cm (13.4–14.2in)
WINGSPAN	54–60cm (21.2–23.6in)
SEXUAL MATURITY	1 year
BREEDING SEASON	May to September
NUMBER OF EGGS	5 to 8
INCUBATION PERIOD	21–23 days
FLEDGING PERIOD	10–15 days
TYPICAL DIET	Buds, shoots, flowers, leaves, seeds and berries
LIFESPAN	Unknown

A luxurious, insulating plumage that moults to match the changing seasons stops the ptarmigan from falling victim to predators and the bitter cold.

COMB
A fleshy lobe of red skin, known as a comb, rests just above each eye. The combs are much bigger and brighter in the male.

WINGS
The broad wings are attached to powerful chest muscles, allowing the ptarmigan to 'explode' into the air when spotted.

BILL
The ptarmigan's short bill is strong enough to split open seeds and snip leaves, flowers and shoots off bushes.

PLUMAGE
With the approach of winter, more and more white feathers appear among the ptarmigan's plumage, until black feathers near the eyes and tail (below) are the only dark areas left.

FEET
Feathers on the ptarmigan's feet grow longer and denser in winter to provide insulation from the frozen ground.

CREATURE COMPARISONS

Part of the ptarmigan's wide range overlaps with that of the capercaillie (Tetrao urogallus), one of the world's largest gamebirds. The two species are almost never seen side by side, however, since the capercaillie is restricted to coniferous forests, where it feeds on pine needles and berries. The male capercaillie weighs up to 9kg (19.8lb) and measures 85cm (33.5in) from bill to tail, whereas the female is only 60cm (23.6in) long — but this is still large enough to dwarf the ptarmigan.

In spring, male capercaillies assemble at traditional sites, known as leks, to attract females. They perform a highly ritualized breeding display, with their stiff tail-feathers splayed outwards like giant fans, and utter a loud, clicking call.

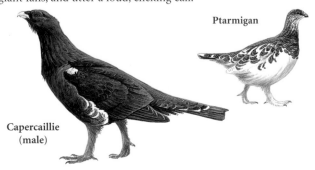

Capercaillie (male)

Ptarmigan

WHERE IN THE WORLD?

Found in a circumpolar band from northern North America east to Siberia, with outlying populations in Scotland and the Alps and Pyrenees mountain ranges.

RELATED SPECIES

The ptarmigan shares its genus with the white-tailed ptarmigan and the red grouse (known as the willow ptarmigan outside Britain and Ireland). There are 14 other species in 6 genera in the grouse family, Tetraonidae, including the spruce grouse, Dendragapus canadensis.

• **ORDER** • *Gasterosteiformes* • **FAMILY** • *Gasterosteidae* • **SPECIES** • *Gasterosteus aculeatus* THREE-SPINED STICKLEBACK

With sharp spines on its back and bony plates on its sides, the three-spined stickleback is effectively armoured against attack.

KEY FEATURES

- One of the few species of fish that can live in salt-water and freshwater environments.
- In the mating season, the male develops bright breeding colours and becomes highly aggressive.
- The male performs an elaborate courtship dance to entice egg-laying females into his nest.

VITAL STATISTICS

WEIGHT	Up to 10g (0.3oz), usually less
LENGTH	4–10cm (1.6–3.9in)
SEXUAL MATURITY	1–2 years
SPAWNING SEASON	Spring and summer
NUMBER OF EGGS	Usually 50 to 100 per brood
HATCHING PERIOD	7 to 20 days
BREEDING INTERVAL	1 to 12 broods a year
TYPICAL DIET	Insects and their larvae, worms, snails, zooplankton, crustaceans, and small fish
LIFESPAN	Up to 3 years in the wild; up to 4 years in an aquarium

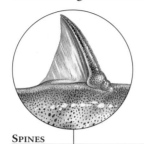

LATERAL LINE
Beneath the row of bony plates (or along the skin if there are no plates), there is a line of receptors. These connect to the lateral line canal beneath the skin, which detects vibrations in the water.

EYES
The retina has three sets of light receptors: two for underwater vision and one that senses light from above.

SPINES
Two long spines on the back and a third, smaller spine (sometimes absent) can be locked upright as a defence against predators.

BONY PLATES
The stickleback lacks scales; instead, it has a row of bony plates that function as body armour. The number of plates varies widely, and in some individuals they are absent.

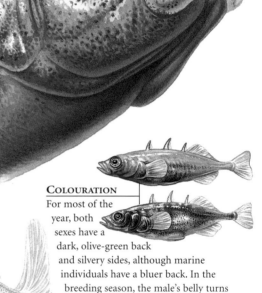

COLOURATION
For most of the year, both sexes have a dark, olive-green back and silvery sides, although marine individuals have a bluer back. In the breeding season, the male's belly turns orange or red and his eyes turn silver-blue or green.

CREATURE COMPARISONS

Like the three-spined stickleback, the nine-spined stickleback (*Pungitius pungitius*) is found around the northern hemisphere, in shallow ponds or sluggish rivers choked with vegetation. It occurs in fresh and brackish water, but rarely frequents seawater.

Varying in colour according to the time of year, the nine-spined stickleback is often greeny-gold, and smaller than the three-spined stickleback, but otherwise similar in appearance. Its spines are much shorter than those of its relative, and it often lacks the bony plates along its sides.

Three-spined stickleback

Nine-spined stickleback

WHERE IN THE WORLD?

Found throughout the northern hemisphere in freshwater lakes, ponds, streams and ditches, and in sea water around the Pacific and Atlantic coasts.

RELATED SPECIES

There are 5 genera in the stickleback family, Gasterosteidae, almost every one of which contains a single species. 2 genera are found in both freshwater and sea water. Sticklebacks are at present placed in the order Gasterosteiformes, along with shrimp fish, snipe fish, tube snouts, the seahorse and the pipefish. However, members of this order display only superficial similarities to each other, so a reclassification is imminent.

SEAHORSE

A seahorse is a fish — yet with its horse-like head, prehensile tail and upright swimming posture it hardly resembles a fish at all.

KEY FEATURES

- Male carries and nurtures the female's eggs in a brood pouch while they develop into young seahorses.

- When the young are fully developed in the brood pouch, the male seahorse 'goes into labour' to give birth.

- Adults pair for each breeding season, with each pair strengthening its bond every morning with a 'dance' duet.

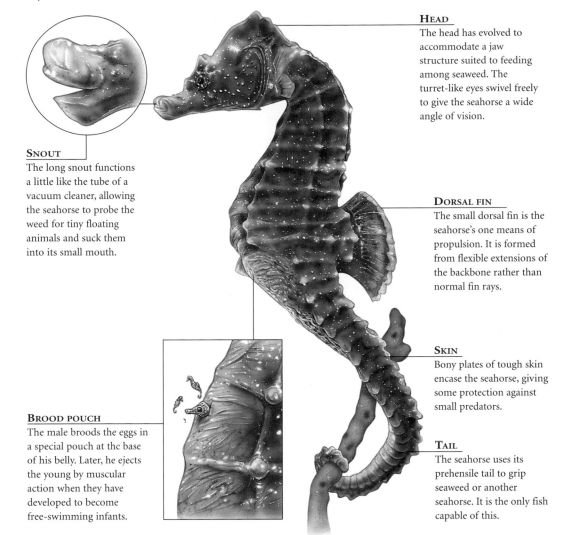

SNOUT
The long snout functions a little like the tube of a vacuum cleaner, allowing the seahorse to probe the weed for tiny floating animals and suck them into its small mouth.

BROOD POUCH
The male broods the eggs in a special pouch at the base of his belly. Later, he ejects the young by muscular action when they have developed to become free-swimming infants.

HEAD
The head has evolved to accommodate a jaw structure suited to feeding among seaweed. The turret-like eyes swivel freely to give the seahorse a wide angle of vision.

DORSAL FIN
The small dorsal fin is the seahorse's one means of propulsion. It is formed from flexible extensions of the backbone rather than normal fin rays.

SKIN
Bony plates of tough skin encase the seahorse, giving some protection against small predators.

TAIL
The seahorse uses its prehensile tail to grip seaweed or another seahorse. It is the only fish capable of this.

VITAL STATISTICS

WEIGHT	Up to 226g (8oz)
LENGTH	5–30.5cm (2–12in), depending on species
SEXUAL MATURITY	Varies according to species and local conditions
BREEDING SEASON	Summer
NUMBER OF YOUNG	Up to 1500 produced by female, depending on species
INCUBATION PERIOD	4–6 weeks
BIRTH INTERVAL	Several times each year
TYPICAL DIET	Small planktonic animals, such as crustaceans and fish fry
LIFESPAN	Up to 4 years

CREATURE COMPARISONS

Various body shapes and colours are displayed by different members of the seahorse family. The maned seahorse possesses a crest or 'mane' of dark spines; the golden seahorse displays the typical body shape but its skin is a rich golden colour. The bizarre outgrowths of the leafy sea-dragon provide camouflage among seaweeds.

Common seahorse, Hippocampus Hippocampus

Maned seahorse, H. ramulosus

Golden seahorse, H. kuda

Leafy sea-dragon, Phycodorus eques

WHERE IN THE WORLD?

Widespread in coastal waters in all the warmer oceans and seas of the world, including the Atlantic, Indian and Pacific Oceans, as well as the Mediterranean and Aegean Seas.

RELATED SPECIES

The family Sygnathidae includes about 25 species of seahorse and more than 100 species of pipefish, including the barred pipefish, Sygnathus auliscus. The widespread order Gasterosteiformes also includes the flute mouths, sticklebacks and shrimp fish.

• **ORDER** • *Gaviiformes* • **FAMILY** • *Gaviidae* • **GENUS & SPECIES** • *Gavia immer*

GREAT NORTHERN DIVER

KEY FEATURES

• Has an evocative, haunting call — among the loudest of any bird — that can carry for long distances across water.

• Able to fish underwater for several minutes, propelled by strong legs and webbed feet.

• Model parent that tends to its young closely. Chicks are carried on a parent's back or kept under a wing for warmth and protection.

VITAL STATISTICS

WEIGHT	2.8–4.5kg (6.2–9.9lb)
LENGTH	68–90cm (26.8–35.4in)
WINGSPAN	1.3–1.5m (4ft 3in–4ft 9in)
SEXUAL MATURITY	2 years
BREEDING SEASON	May to July
NUMBER OF EGGS	1 to 3, usually 2
INCUBATION PERIOD	25–30 days
FLEDGING PERIOD	12 weeks
BREEDING INTERVAL	1 year
TYPICAL DIET	Fish, molluscs, crustaceans, aquatic insects and vegetation
LIFESPAN	8 years in wild, but possibly up to 20 years in captivity

The great northern diver's streamlined body is enhanced by legs set far back, providing great manoeuvrability as well as power both on and under water.

BILL
The long, sharp, dagger-like bill is adapted to catching fish. The great northern diver strikes its prey with the bill partly open. It also uses its bill to stab at birds that come too close to its nest.

WINGS
The wings are relatively small and pointed. They carry a high wing loading (the ratio of a bird's bodyweight to its wing area), making it necessary for the great northern diver to patter over the surface of the water for some distance before the wings create enough lift to get the bird airborne.

WINTER PLUMAGE
In both sexes the boldly patterned black-and-white breeding plumage is replaced during winter by a much drabber version. The white-spotted back becomes uniformly dark, and the black throat becomes white.

LEGS & FEET
The short, powerful legs are set far back on the body. In this position the legs are able to move through a long backstroke to gain maximum thrust from the webbed feet. They also extend beyond the body to act as rudders for steering.

CREATURE COMPARISONS

Almost identical to the great northern diver, the white-billed diver is the largest of all the divers at up to 6.4kg (14.1lb) in weight. It differs chiefly in its slightly upturned, ivory-coloured bill, which gives rise to its nickname of 'banana-bill'. At the smallest end of the scale is the red-throated diver. It weighs only about 1kg (2.2lb). Being lighter than other divers, the red-throated diver is able to take off directly from dry land. In breeding plumage it is brownish with a scarlet throat-patch.

White-billed diver

Red-throated diver

Great northern diver

WHERE IN THE WORLD?

Breeds across northern North America, Iceland and Greenland. Winters as far south as California

and Florida. Wintering birds also occur in western and northern Europe. Has occasionally nested in Scotland.

RELATED SPECIES

The great northern diver is one of five birds in the genus Gavia. The others are the Pacific, the red-throated, the white-billed and the black-throated divers. The great northern diver has two subspecies: G. immer immer and G. i. elasson. The black-throated diver has three subspecies: G. arctica arctica, in northern Europe and Russia; G. a. suschkini, in western Siberia and eastern Asia; and G. a. viridigularis, in northeast Siberia and western Alaska.

• ORDER • *Gruiformes* • FAMILY • *Eurypygidae* • GENUS & SPECIES • *Eurypyga helias*

With its soft-feathered wings folded, the sun bittern looks a little like a heron, but its defensive display reveals a blaze of rich colour and pattern.

KEY FEATURES

- A heron-like wading bird that lives and feeds along tropical forest watercourses.
- Camouflaged by its plumage until it reveals brilliant wing 'eye-spots' in a spectacular defensive display.
- A specialist predator of fish and other aquatic life, it also hunts among the leaf litter.

VITAL STATISTICS

WEIGHT	180–250g (6.3–8.8lb)
LENGTH	44–48cm (17.3–18.9in)
WINGSPAN	60–70cm (23.6–27.6in)
SEXUAL MATURITY	1–2 years
BREEDING SEASON	Start of the rainy season
NUMBER OF EGGS	2
INCUBATION PERIOD	29–30 days
FLEDGING PERIOD	21 days
BREEDING INTERVAL	1 year
TYPICAL DIET	Small fish, frogs, insects and spiders
LIFESPAN	Unknown

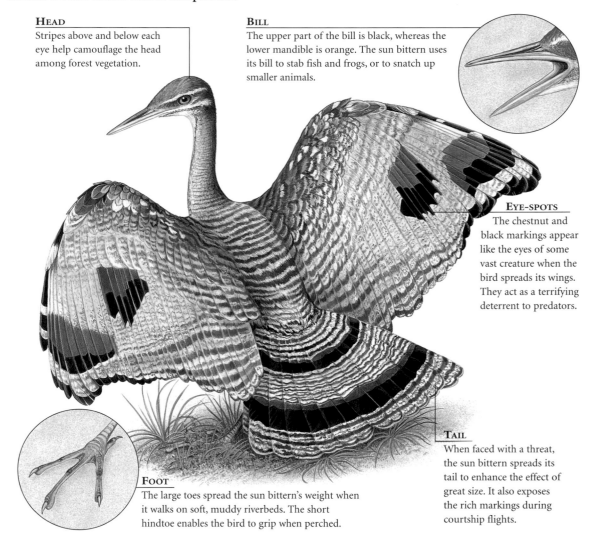

HEAD
Stripes above and below each eye help camouflage the head among forest vegetation.

BILL
The upper part of the bill is black, whereas the lower mandible is orange. The sun bittern uses its bill to stab fish and frogs, or to snatch up smaller animals.

EYE-SPOTS
The chestnut and black markings appear like the eyes of some vast creature when the bird spreads its wings. They act as a terrifying deterrent to predators.

TAIL
When faced with a threat, the sun bittern spreads its tail to enhance the effect of great size. It also exposes the rich markings during courtship flights.

FOOT
The large toes spread the sun bittern's weight when it walks on soft, muddy riverbeds. The short hindtoe enables the bird to grip when perched.

CREATURE COMPARISONS

The name bittern is generally used for birds of the heron family that live in dense waterside vegetation. Like the sun bittern, these true bitterns use a combination of stealth and camouflage to catch their prey.

The Old World bittern (Botaurus stellaris), one of the largest species, spends most of its life hidden in reedbeds, where it hunts fish and frogs. In contrast to the sun bittern's loud, staccato call, the Old World bittern utters a powerful boom that can be heard at a distance of almost 2km (1.2 miles).

Sun bittern

Old World bittern

WHERE IN THE WORLD?

Found in lowland tropical forests in Central and South America, from southern Mexico to Bolivia and the Amazon Basin.

RELATED SPECIES

The sun bittern is the sole species in its family. 3 races are distinguished by subtle plumage differences. Despite its name, the sun bittern is not related to the Old World bittern or the little bittern, Ixobrychus minutus, both of which are members of the heron family, Ardeidae.

• ORDER • *Gruiformes* • FAMILY • *Gruidae* • GENUS & SPECIES • *Grus japonensis*

JAPANESE CRANE

The crane's long legs and neck are not only useful for feeding; they also enhance the statuesque elegance of its dance rituals.

KEY FEATURES

- Dances exuberantly with its partner and other cranes, in rituals that extend beyond courtship into everyday life.
- Graceful but raucous ballet seems sometimes to be performed out of sheer joy.
- Japan's revered tancho, or 'bird of happiness,' this affectionate crane forms a lifelong pair bond and is upheld as a symbol of fidelity in marriage.

VITAL STATISTICS

WEIGHT	5.9–9kg (13–19.8lb)
HEIGHT	1.2m (3ft 9in)
WINGSPAN	2.13m (7ft)
SEXUAL MATURITY	3–4 years
MATING SEASON	March to May
NUMBER OF EGGS	2
INCUBATION PERIOD	4–5 weeks
FLEDGING PERIOD	11–13 weeks
BREEDING INTERVAL	1 year
TYPICAL DIET	Plants, grain, roots, insects, reptiles and small mammals
LIFESPAN	Up to 25 years

CROWN
The naked patch of red skin on the crown becomes enlarged and more intensely coloured in threat or courtship display.

BILL
Long, strong and pointed, the bill is both a dagger and a digger, used for stabbing at fish and animal prey, as well as rooting out food from the soil.

JUVENILE
The immature crane differs from the adult bird in having a brown neck and black tips to the primary (wingtip) feathers.

WINGS AND TAIL
When the crane's wings are folded, the short, white tail is hidden beneath a black bustle, formed by elongated and pointed inner wing feathers, known as tertials.

LEGS AND FEET
Long legs are typical of large birds that frequently wade in water. Adult cranes do not swim but chicks can do so remarkably well.

CREATURE COMPARISONS

All tall and elegant, cranes nevertheless vary greatly in size. Smallest is the delicate demoiselle crane of Asia and Africa, which stands little more than half the height of the Japanese crane. With its golden topknot, the 1m-tall crowned crane is a striking inhabitant of the African savannah. Up to 1.2m (3ft 9in) tall, the sandhill crane lives in Siberia and North America. Like the Japanese crane, it has a red crown.

Demoiselle crane

Japanese crane

Crowned crane

Sandhill crane

WHERE IN THE WORLD?

Breeds as a resident species in the northeast of Hokkaido island, northern Japan. Populations that breed in eastern Siberia and northern China migrate to winter farther south in eastern China and Korea.

RELATED SPECIES

The Japanese, or Manchurian, crane is one of 14 crane species, seven of which are threatened. The rarest, and the most closely related to the Japanese, is North America's whooping crane, with a total population of about 300.

• ORDER • *Gruiformes* • FAMILY • *Otididae* • GENUS & SPECIES • *Otis tarda*

GREAT BUSTARD

KEY FEATURES

- One of the world's heaviest flying birds; roams sparsely populated plains and farmland searching for food.
- Groups of turkey-sized males perform spectacular courtship displays in spring.
- Declining fast due to habitat destruction and disturbance, now classed as vulnerable by the IUCN (World Conservation Union).

VITAL STATISTICS

WEIGHT	Male 6–18kg (13.2–39.7lb); female 3.5–5.5kg (7.7–12.1lb)
LENGTH	75–100cm (29.5–39.4in)
WINGSPAN	1.9–2.6m (6ft 2in–8ft 5in)
SEXUAL MATURITY	Male 5–6 years; female 2–3 years
BREEDING SEASON	April–August
NUMBER OF EGGS	1 to 4
INCUBATION PERIOD	21–28 days
FLEDGING PERIOD	30–35 days; independent at 80–120 days
BREEDING PERIOD	1 year
TYPICAL DIET	Wide range of plant matter, insects and small vertebrates
LIFESPAN	Unknown

Shaped rather like a small ostrich, the great bustard strides along slowly on powerful legs, but its massive wings also enable it to fly.

BILL
The stubby, slightly down-curved bill suits the great bustard's varied diet. It is stout for cracking seeds and shearing plants, yet also dagger-like for stabbing prey.

NECK
The long, thick neck acts like a periscope, providing the bustard with the best possible view of its surroundings. In long grass and crops, the bird can look around while keeping the rest of its body hidden.

FLIGHT
To take off and stay aloft, the bustard needs huge wings that are broad along their whole length. Large white panels on both surfaces of the wings may help bustards spot one another at long range.

PLUMAGE
Dark brown wings camouflage the bustard when it is feeding on the ground. The feathers are loosely packed, allowing air to circulate so that the bustard can withstand the high temperatures of its dry inland environment.

TAIL
The short, broad tail is the same colour as the upperparts, and gives the bustard balance as it forages for food.

FOOT
The three forward-pointing toes are both thick and broad to support the bustard's great bulk. It has no need of a hindtoe, which smaller birds use when gripping perches.

CREATURE COMPARISONS

Like the great bustard, the red-crested bustard (Lophotis ruficrista) has a dramatic courtship display. The male rises vertically for 20m (65ft 6in) before performing a back-flip, folding his wings and plummeting to the ground as a fluffy ball. The red-crested bustard shares the strong legs and upright posture of its huge relative, but is a fraction of its size, weighing just 700g (24.7oz) on average.

Both species have delicately barred upperparts for camouflage, but whereas the great bustard has dark-brown, wave-like markings, the red-crested bustard's are cream and arrow-shaped, and instead of throat whiskers, the male is adorned with a long crest. The species is common in arid savannah and light woodland.

Great bustard

Red-crested bustard

WHERE IN THE WORLD?

Once found throughout much of the Eurasian lowlands, but now confined to isolated populations in Spain, eastern Europe, Ukraine and neighbouring regions, and northeastern China.

RELATED SPECIES
The great bustard is the sole member of the genus Otis. There are 10 other genera of bustards, totalling 24 species, in the family Otididae. These include the threatened houbara bustard, Chlamydotis undulata, of North Africa and the Middle East.

• **ORDER** • *Gruiformes* • **FAMILY** • *Rallidae* • **GENUS & SPECIES** • *Crex crex*

CORNCRAKE

KEY FEATURES

- Shy, skulking ground bird of rough grassland with a characteristic rasping, two-syllable call.
- Undertakes long, twice-yearly migrations.
- Threatened by loss of habitat and changing agricultural methods and classed as rare by the IUCN (World Conservation Union).

VITAL STATISTICS

WEIGHT	Male 130–210g (4.6–7.4lb); female 140–160g (4.9–5.6lb)
LENGTH	27–30cm (10.6–11.8in)
WINGSPAN	46–53cm (18.1–20.9in)
SEXUAL MATURITY	1 year
BREEDING SEASON	April–August
NUMBER OF EGGS	8 to 12
INCUBATION PERIOD	16–19 days
FLEDGING PERIOD	34–38 days
BREEDING INTERVAL	1 or 2 broods a year (2 in western Europe)
TYPICAL DIET	Insects and other invertebrates; green shoots, seeds
LIFESPAN	Not known

Bedecked in cryptic camouflage, the corncrake only forsakes ground cover if a close encounter with a predator forces it into flight.

WINGS AND TAIL
Folded for most of the year, in autumn the corncrake puts its rounded, rufous wings to good use by flying to Africa for the winter. The short tail helps the bird change direction in flight.

BILL
The corncrake uses its sharp-tipped bill for jabbing and snatching invertebrate prey from the ground and for pecking at seeds.

PLUMAGE
Little difference in plumage is apparent between the sexes, though the female has noticeably less bluish-grey colour on the head and neck than has the male.

CHICK
The chick emerges with a ready-grown coat of long, sooty down feathers ending in silky tips. Soon able to walk about, it vacates the nest within days of hatching.

FEET
The muscular legs and feet are adapted for a life of standing and foraging on the ground. The single hindtoe acts as a brace while the bird is walking on its three foretoes.

CREATURE COMPARISONS

The corncrake shares much of its breeding range with the water rail (*Rallus aquaticus*), though the two species select different living quarters. As its name suggests, the water rail is closely associated with marshes, swamps and ponds surrounded by emergent vegetation. Though slightly smaller in build than the corncrake, it has a much longer bill designed for probing in water and soft mud. Many of its populations are migratory, but, unlike those of the corncrake, they limit their travels to the Mediterranean region and southern Asia.

Corncrake

Water rail

WHERE IN THE WORLD?

Breeding range stretches from western Europe east through central Asia to central Siberia. Main winter range is in eastern and southern Africa.

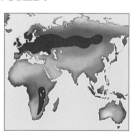

RELATED SPECIES

The sole member of its genus, the corncrake is 1 of 124 species in 41 genera in the family Rallidae. Family relatives include rails, coots, gallinules and crakes, such as the black crake, *Amaurornis flavirostris*, of southern Africa. The closest British relative is the spotted crake.

• **ORDER** • *Hydrozoa* • **FAMILY** • *Siphonophora* • **GENUS & SPECIES** • *Physalia physalis*

PORTUGUESE MAN-OF-WAR

KEY FEATURES

- Trails long tentacles, some of which are armed with powerful stinging cells to stun or kill fish and other prey.

- Sting is not powerful enough to kill a human, although it can cause severe pain that persists for several days.

- Relies on its gas-filled float to catch the winds and water currents, and carry it far across the open oceans.

VITAL STATISTICS

WEIGHT	Variable; mass made up mainly of water
FLOAT LENGTH	Up to 30cm (11.8in)
TENTACLE LENGTH	Usually up to 10m (3.9in) but may reach 60m (23.6in)
SEXUAL MATURITY	Unknown
BREEDING SEASON	Year-round
NUMBER OF YOUNG	Possibly millions in a single lifetime
BIRTH INTERVAL	Releases medusae (sexually active stages) almost continuously
TYPICAL DIET	Small fish and fish larvae, crustaceans, plankton
LIFESPAN	Unknown

The Portuguese man-of-war is not one organism, but a colony made up of many individual polyps, each performing a different function.

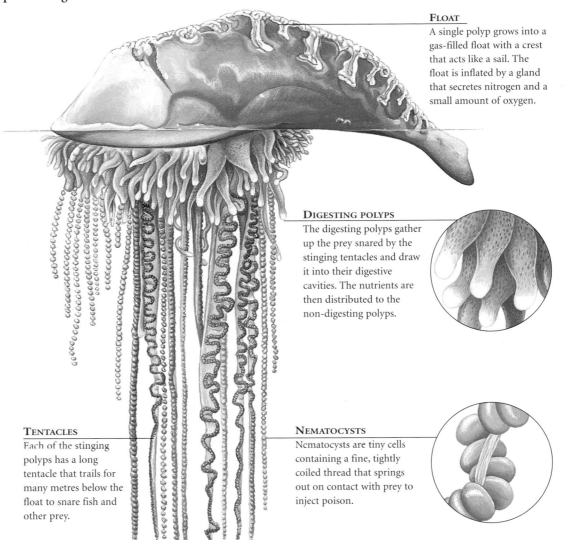

FLOAT
A single polyp grows into a gas-filled float with a crest that acts like a sail. The float is inflated by a gland that secretes nitrogen and a small amount of oxygen.

DIGESTING POLYPS
The digesting polyps gather up the prey snared by the stinging tentacles and draw it into their digestive cavities. The nutrients are then distributed to the non-digesting polyps.

TENTACLES
Each of the stinging polyps has a long tentacle that trails for many metres below the float to snare fish and other prey.

NEMATOCYSTS
Nematocysts are tiny cells containing a fine, tightly coiled thread that springs out on contact with prey to inject poison.

CREATURE COMPARISONS

Although the Portuguese man-of-war is often described as a jellyfish, it is actually a very different creature. A typical jellyfish, such as the compass jellyfish that is often found on the coast, is an individual animal capable of swimming actively, while the Portuguese man-of-war is a colony of many individuals that drifts passively with the wind and currents. The individuals that make up the man-of-war are polyps, while a true jellyfish is a medusa: an enlarged version of the sexually active stage in the man-of-war's complex lifecycle.

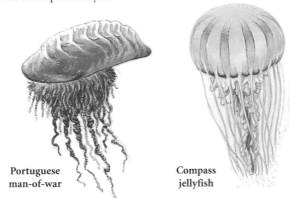

Portuguese
man-of-war

Compass
jellyfish

WHERE IN THE WORLD?

Normally found in warmer waters of the open Atlantic. However, strong winds often drive it inshore, so it frequently appears along the North Atlantic coasts of the Americas, Europe and Africa. Also found in the Mediterranean Sea.

RELATED SPECIES

The man-of-war is one of several oceanic animals in the order Hydrozoa, which contains about 2700 species, including freshwater hydras. Hydrozoans are distantly related to jellyfishes, class Scyphozoa, and to sea anemones and corals, class Anthozoa.

• **ORDER** • *Hymenoptera* • **FAMILY** • *Apidae* • **GENUS & SPECIES** • *Apis mellifera*

HONEYBEE

The honeybee's tiny, lightweight body contains many complex structures that include tongue, honey stomach, pollen baskets, wings and sting.

KEY FEATURES

- A social bee that lives in colonies of thousands, all controlled by a single fertile female: the queen.
- Communicates with scent and a dance 'language'.
- All the workers are female — drones (males) are produced only to mate with a new queen.
- One of the few truly domesticated insects.

VITAL STATISTICS

WEIGHT	Queen 0.23g (0.008oz) Worker 0.11g (0.003oz) Drone 0.2g (0.007oz)
LENGTH	Queen 16–20mm (0.62–0.78in) Worker 12–15mm (0.47–0.59in) Drone 14–18mm (0.55–0.70in)
NUMBER OF EGGS	Queen may lay 1.5 million eggs in total
LARVAL PERIOD	Queen 17 days, Worker 17–22 days, Drone 22–24 days
COLONY SIZE	40,000–80,000
TYPICAL DIET	Nectar and pollen turned into honey
LIFESPAN	Queen 3, but up to 6 years Worker 5–8 weeks Drone 2–3 weeks

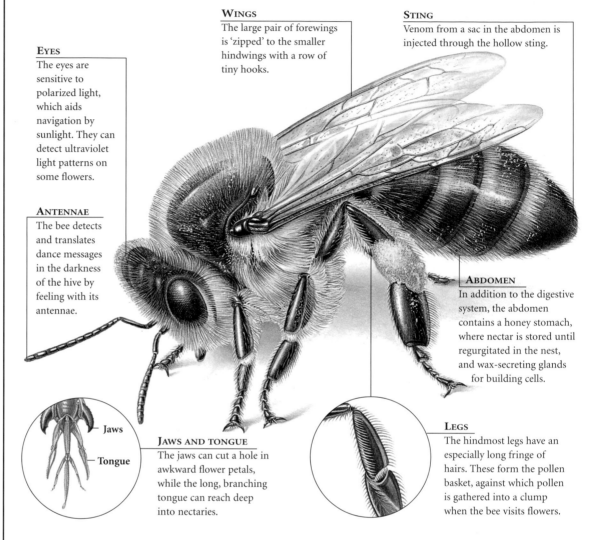

EYES
The eyes are sensitive to polarized light, which aids navigation by sunlight. They can detect ultraviolet light patterns on some flowers.

ANTENNAE
The bee detects and translates dance messages in the darkness of the hive by feeling with its antennae.

WINGS
The large pair of forewings is 'zipped' to the smaller hindwings with a row of tiny hooks.

STING
Venom from a sac in the abdomen is injected through the hollow sting.

ABDOMEN
In addition to the digestive system, the abdomen contains a honey stomach, where nectar is stored until regurgitated in the nest, and wax-secreting glands for building cells.

Jaws

Tongue

JAWS AND TONGUE
The jaws can cut a hole in awkward flower petals, while the long, branching tongue can reach deep into nectaries.

LEGS
The hindmost legs have an especially long fringe of hairs. These form the pollen basket, against which pollen is gathered into a clump when the bee visits flowers.

CREATURE COMPARISONS

With its organized army of workers, the honeybee has a much more structured society than many of the other species of bee that share its vast range. The larger, squatter leafcutter bee (Megachile species) cuts leaf sections to line a small, tubular nest in the soil. The social structure is much simpler, and there are no infertile workers. Bumble-bees (Bombus species) are covered in thick hair and are larger than honeybees. They make small nests of large wax cells, which contain no more than 100 to 400 workers. The colony is started anew every spring by the queen when she emerges from hibernation.

Honeybee

Leafcutter bee

Bumble-bee

WHERE IN THE WORLD?

Originally native to Africa, the Middle East and Europe, it has been domesticated and today thrives in

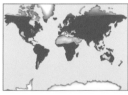

most temperate and tropical areas of the world.

RELATED SPECIES

There are at least 25,000 known species of bee, seven of them in the honeybee's genus, Apis. Apart from the western honeybee, A. mellifera, most are eastern, including the giant Oriental honeybee, A. dorsata, which makes a single exposed comb hanging from a tree or rock-face. A. mellifera itself takes many forms throughout the world. Most widespread is the 'Italian' honeybee, with orange bands on the abdomen.

• ORDER • *Hymenoptera* • FAMILY • *Formicidae* • GENUS & SPECIES • *Atta spp.*

LEAFCUTTER ANT

Long legs, powerful jaws and a flexible waist give the leafcutter ant the perfect bodyplan for its harvesting and farming activities.

KEY FEATURES

- Cuts leaf segments from plants, carrying them to a huge nest and 'farming' fungus on them for food.
- Different classes, or castes, of ants vary greatly in size and shape to suit specific tasks within the colony.
- Workers carrying sections of leaf are protected by tiny workmates that 'ride shotgun' on the leaf.

VITAL STATISTICS

LENGTH	Queen Up to 38mm (1.5in) Worker 1.2–7.5mm (0.05–0.29in) Soldier Up to 14mm (0.55in) Male Up to 16mm (0.62in)
SEXUAL MATURE	Adult is Maturity shortly after emerging
BREEDING SEASON	Mating flight December to April; queen lays eggs throughout year
TYPICAL DIET	Specially farmed fungus
LIFESPAN	Queen Up to 20 years Worker and soldier 6 months to 1 year Male Days or weeks

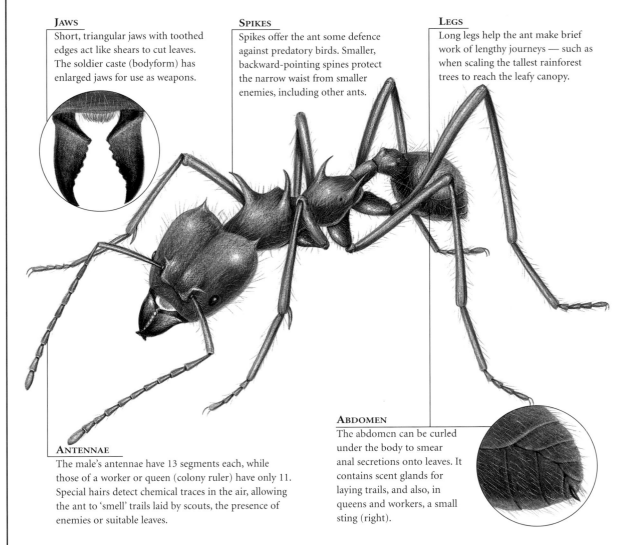

JAWS
Short, triangular jaws with toothed edges act like shears to cut leaves. The soldier caste (bodyform) has enlarged jaws for use as weapons.

SPIKES
Spikes offer the ant some defence against predatory birds. Smaller, backward-pointing spines protect the narrow waist from smaller enemies, including other ants.

LEGS
Long legs help the ant make brief work of lengthy journeys — such as when scaling the tallest rainforest trees to reach the leafy canopy.

ANTENNAE
The male's antennae have 13 segments each, while those of a worker or queen (colony ruler) have only 11. Special hairs detect chemical traces in the air, allowing the ant to 'smell' trails laid by scouts, the presence of enemies or suitable leaves.

ABDOMEN
The abdomen can be curled under the body to smear anal secretions onto leaves. It contains scent glands for laying trails, and also, in queens and workers, a small sting (right).

CREATURE COMPARISONS

Although they share a common habit of harvesting leaf segments, the different genera of leafcutter ants show subtle variations in form, food production and the structure of their societies — as shown below.

Atta: large and spiny leafcutters and the only genus to comprise a soldier caste, these ants form the largest colonies.

Acromyrmex: these leafcutters lack soldiers and build smaller nests, but are otherwise similar to Atta.

Trachymyrmex: smaller, less bristly ants, they grow edible fungus on plant material and insect faeces.

Cyphomyrmex: the smallest, and least bristly-coated leafcutters, they 'farm' their food on pieces of rotten fruit and insect faeces.

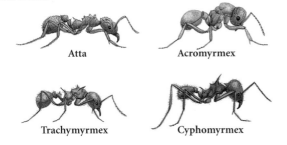

Atta Acromyrmex

Trachymyrmex Cyphomyrmex

WHERE IN THE WORLD?

Found in tropical forests of Central and South America, from Mexico south to Argentina. Also occurs in the West Indies, in the Lesser Antilles and on Barbados.

RELATED SPECIES

Leafcutter ants are also known as fungus ants, or fungus-growing ants. About 200 species occur in 12 genera. There are 15 species in the genus Atta. All leafcutters are found in the Americas, mainly Central and South America, but 1 species, Trachymyrmex septentionalis, is found as far north as New Jersey, USA. Atta cephalotes is the most widespread of the leafcutter ants, and lives in clearings in tropical rainforests.

• ORDER • *Hymenoptera* • FAMILY • *Formicidae* • GENUS & SPECIES • *Myrmecia spp.*

BULLDOG ANT

The bulldog ant's long legs equip it to hunt far and wide for prey, and its slender, flexible body allows it to bite and sting at the same time.

KEY FEATURES

- A group of primitive, medium-to-large ant species with long, powerful jaws, and a venomous sting for killing prey.
- Large and prominent sting delivers a painful wound in humans.
- Some species leap several centimetres or an inch to catch prey.

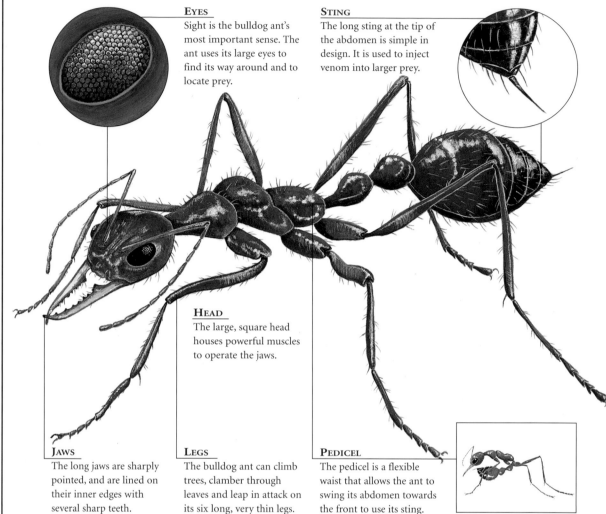

EYES
Sight is the bulldog ant's most important sense. The ant uses its large eyes to find its way around and to locate prey.

STING
The long sting at the tip of the abdomen is simple in design. It is used to inject venom into larger prey.

HEAD
The large, square head houses powerful muscles to operate the jaws.

JAWS
The long jaws are sharply pointed, and are lined on their inner edges with several sharp teeth.

LEGS
The bulldog ant can climb trees, clamber through leaves and leap in attack on its six long, very thin legs.

PEDICEL
The pedicel is a flexible waist that allows the ant to swing its abdomen towards the front to use its sting.

VITAL STATISTICS

LENGTH	8–38mm (0.3–1.5in)
SEXUAL MATURITY	A few days after emerging from pupa, about 100 days after hatching
MATING SEASON	Throughout the year
NUMBER OF EGGS	Thousands, although the majority are fed to larvae
INCUBATION PERIOD	2–3 weeks
BIRTH INTERVAL	Reproduction almost continual from spring to autumn
TYPICAL DIET	Insects and other small invertebrates; adults also feed on nectar from plants in winter
LIFESPAN	2–3 years

CREATURE COMPARISONS

Ants are among the world's most aggressive animals. Tenacious in attacking prey, the more social species sometimes fight to the death to destroy neighbouring ant colonies, and they possess fearsome weapons for the purpose. For instance, the army ant's box-like head is packed with muscles to operate its long, incurving jaws. The red ant squirts poisonous formic acid over its foes. The bulldog ant does not unite with others to defend its colony, but, armed at both ends to sting and bite, it nevertheless puts up a fight.

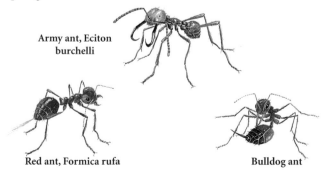

Army ant, Eciton burchelli

Red ant, Formica rufa

Bulldog ant

WHERE IN THE WORLD?

Most species are confined to mainland Australia and Tasmania and other, smaller offshore islands.

One species is found on the Pacific island of New Caledonia.

RELATED SPECIES

There are about 90 species in the bulldog ant genus, Myrmecia. They are all similar in shape, but are sometimes further classified in 2 subgenera, Myrmecia and Promyrmecia, according to the length of their antennae. The ant family, Formicidae, contains an estimated 9500–13,000 species numbering several trillion individuals. The family as a whole is found more or less worldwide in an almost infinite variety of habitats.

HORNET

• ORDER • *Hymenoptera* • FAMILY • *Vespidae* • GENUS & SPECIES • *Vespa crabro*

Flying around trees and bushes on its amber-coloured wings, this voracious predator spells danger for any insect too slow to escape its deadly attack.

KEY FEATURES

- One of the world's largest social insects, it lives in a highly organized colony ruled by a queen.
- Adults hunt for insects, carrying food back to the colony to feed the developing larvae.
- Usually nests in hollow trees, but sometimes sets up home in attics and outbuildings.

WINGS
The hornet has four wings. A row of tiny hooks locks the larger forewings to the smaller hindwings so that the two pairs beat powerfully together.

LEGS AND FEET
The six jointed legs end in clawed feet. The hornet usually attacks prey from behind, using its legs and feet to pin it down.

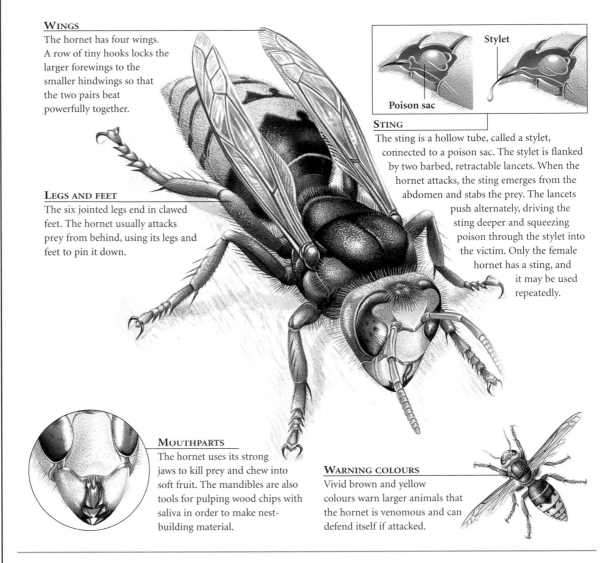

STING
The sting is a hollow tube, called a stylet, connected to a poison sac. The stylet is flanked by two barbed, retractable lancets. When the hornet attacks, the sting emerges from the abdomen and stabs the prey. The lancets push alternately, driving the sting deeper and squeezing poison through the stylet into the victim. Only the female hornet has a sting, and it may be used repeatedly.

Stylet

Poison sac

MOUTHPARTS
The hornet uses its strong jaws to kill prey and chew into soft fruit. The mandibles are also tools for pulping wood chips with saliva in order to make nest-building material.

WARNING COLOURS
Vivid brown and yellow colours warn larger animals that the hornet is venomous and can defend itself if attacked.

VITAL STATISTICS

WEIGHT	5–6g (0.17–0.21oz)
LENGTH	Female 23–35mm (0.9–1.4in); worker and male smaller
BREEDING SEASON	Spring to early autumn
NUMBER OF EGGS	Up to 400; all are laid by a single queen
BREEDING INTERVAL	1 year
TYPICAL DIET	Adult eats insects, nectar and other sugar-rich food from plants; larvae fed on insect pulp
LIFESPAN	Worker and male live for less than 1 year; queen may survive for over 5 years

CREATURE COMPARISONS

The hornet is similar to other social wasps, although its impressive size sets it apart. Most of its relatives, such as the common wasp (Vespula vulgaris) and the common yellow jacket (V. maculifrons), share a similar body shape, and also raise their young in elaborate nests. However, the potter wasp (Eumenes pomiformis), although a member of the same family as the hornet, leads a solitary life. Female potter wasps construct clay pots using earth and their own saliva, laying a single egg in each pot. They then stock each pot with caterpillars that they have paralyzed, to provide food for the developing grub.

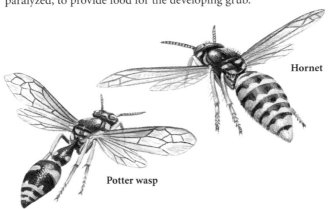

Hornet

Potter wasp

WHERE IN THE WORLD?

Found throughout Europe as far north as Lapland, and also in temperate parts of Asia. Introduced into the USA; now established from the east coast to Indiana.

RELATED SPECIES

The hornet belongs to the family Vespidae, which contains wasps that often live in large social groups or colonies. The German wasp, Vespula germanica, is another typical member of this family. Like the hornet, it has bold brown and yellow warning colours, and eyes with a characteristic deep notch near the antennae (feelers). The Vespidae are classed in the order Hymenoptera, which includes all wasps, bees and ants.

• ORDER • *Hyracoidea* • FAMILY • *Procaviidae* • GENUS & SPECIES • *Procavia*

ROCK HYRAX

KEY FEATURES

- A sociable creature that often huddles for warmth among rock crevices with other hyraxes.
- Distantly related to the elephant, sea-cow and aardvark, despite being the size of a rabbit.
- Depends on rocks for providing look-out points, shelter and protection from predators.

The rock hyrax has few defences against predators and lacks an in-built mechanism to regulate its temperature, yet it thrives in exposed, hot habitats.

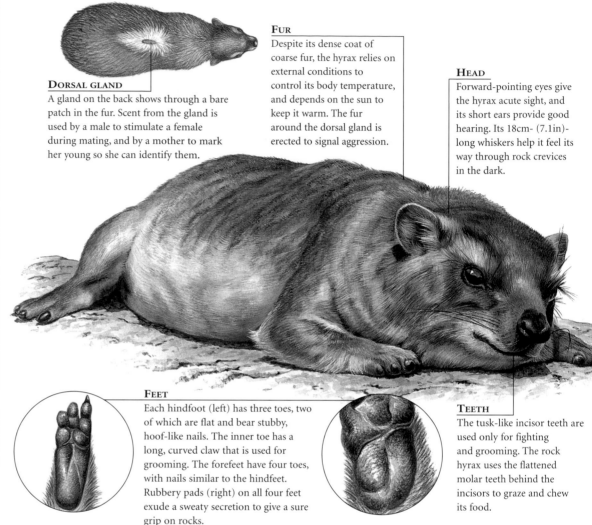

DORSAL GLAND
A gland on the back shows through a bare patch in the fur. Scent from the gland is used by a male to stimulate a female during mating, and by a mother to mark her young so she can identify them.

FUR
Despite its dense coat of coarse fur, the hyrax relies on external conditions to control its body temperature, and depends on the sun to keep it warm. The fur around the dorsal gland is erected to signal aggression.

HEAD
Forward-pointing eyes give the hyrax acute sight, and its short ears provide good hearing. Its 18cm- (7.1in)-long whiskers help it feel its way through rock crevices in the dark.

FEET
Each hindfoot (left) has three toes, two of which are flat and bear stubby, hoof-like nails. The inner toe has a long, curved claw that is used for grooming. The forefeet have four toes, with nails similar to the hindfeet. Rubbery pads (right) on all four feet exude a sweaty secretion to give a sure grip on rocks.

TEETH
The tusk-like incisor teeth are used only for fighting and grooming. The rock hyrax uses the flattened molar teeth behind the incisors to graze and chew its food.

VITAL STATISTICS

WEIGHT	2–5kg (4.4–11lb); male slightly heavier than female
LENGTH	55cm (21.6in), including stump-like tail
SHOULDER HEIGHT	20–30cm (7.9–11.8in)
SEXUAL MATURITY	16–17 months
MATING SEASON	Varies according to location, but usually during or after the rainy season
GESTATION PERIOD	202–245 days
NUMBER OF YOUNG	1 to 6
BIRTH INTERVAL	1 year
TYPICAL DIET	Coarse grass, leaves
LIFESPAN	9–12 years

CREATURE COMPARISONS

The hyrax family contains three genera and includes five species of rock hyrax (Procavia spp.), three species of bush hyrax and three species of tree hyrax, all of which are confined to Africa. The bush hyrax (Heterohyrax spp.) is smaller than the rock hyrax, with a whitish underside and narrower snout. Despite its name, the bush hyrax usually inhabits the same rocky outcrops as the rock hyrax. It feeds among bushes, eating leaves and twigs. The tree hyrax (Dendrohyrax spp.) is more agile, with elongated hands and feet for tree climbing. It has dense fur, but retains the naked patch, characteristic of all hyraxes, around the dorsal gland on its back.

Rock hyrax

Bush hyrax

WHERE IN THE WORLD?

Found in rocky areas ranging from West to East Africa and south to South Africa, north to Egypt and Lebanon, and east to parts of the Arabian peninsula.

RELATED SPECIES

The rock hyrax is a puzzle to zoologists. Although it looks like a large vole, its skeleton shows similarities to that of a rhinoceros. Its lower cheek teeth resemble those of a hippopotamus, and its hoof-like feet and reproductive system suggest it is related to the horse. Recent genetic research confirms that its closest relatives are the elephant, sea-cow and aardvark, with which it may have shared an ancient fossil ancestor.

EUROPEAN HEDGEHOG

• ORDER • *Insectivora* • FAMILY • *Erinaceidae* • GENUS & SPECIES • *Erinaceus europaeus*

Cloaked from head to tail in a protective coat made up of thousands of sharp spines, the European hedgehog has little to fear from predators.

KEY FEATURES

- Protects itself from danger by rolling up into a tight ball and presenting an all-over front of bristling spines.
- A nocturnal creature, which emerges from its nest at twilight to hunt for food.
- In the cooler regions of its range, it hibernates during the winter months when food is scarce.

VITAL STATISTICS

WEIGHT	400–1100g (14–38.3oz)
LENGTH	Head & Body: 13–30cm (5.1–11.8in) Tail; 1–5cm (0.4–2in)
SEXUAL MATURITY	1 year
MATING SEASON	May to September
GESTATION PERIOD	31–35 days
NUMBER OF YOUNG	2 to 7, usually 4 or 5
BIRTH INTERVAL	Normally 1 litter per year, occasionally 2
TYPICAL DIET	Mainly insects and worms, but also frogs, lizards, snakes, mice, young birds, plant matter and carrion
LIFESPAN	Up to 7 years

SPINES
The sharp spines are 2–3cm (0.8–1.2in) long. They contain air-filled chambers for lightness and strength. The hedgehog raises its spines in self defence, but they are also used to cushion falls.

SPINE ATTACHMENT
Each spine has a mobile attachment in the skin, which allows it to lie in different directions. A small muscle at the base of each spine pulls the spine erect.

FEET
Each five-toed foot has sharp, strong claws for digging. The hedgehog walks on the padded soles of its feet with a slow, rolling gait, although it can run quite quickly when necessary.

SNOUT
The long snout is tipped with a sensitive nose, which is always moist, enhancing the hedgehog's sense of smell.

CREATURE COMPARISONS

A family relation of the European hedgehog, the long-eared desert hedgehog (Hemiechinus auritus) is a little shorter from nose to tail but much lighter in weight, averaging about 250g (8.8oz). The long-eared desert hedgehog has whitish underparts and its spines are paler than its European counterpart.

The long ears that give the long-eared species its name may help to radiate excess body heat in its hot homelands — the dry and grassy steppe zones of Asia, from eastern Ukraine to Mongolia in the north, and from Libya to western Pakistan in the south. It also occurs in Cyprus. This hedgehog lives in burrows, up to 1.5m deep, unlike the European hedgehog, which makes leafy nests.

Long-eared desert hedgehog

European hedgehog

WHERE IN THE WORLD?

Occurs in a wide range of habitats over much of Europe, excepting northern Scandinavia, from Britain and Ireland in the west, east through parts of Russia.

RELATED SPECIES

The European hedgehog is one of 20 species in the family Erinaceidae. This family is divided into two subfamilies: the Galericinae, which contains the hairy, long-tailed gymnures, and the Erinaceinae, which includes 'true' hedgehogs, such as the Algerian hedgehog, Atelerix algirus.

• **ORDER** • *Insectivora* • **FAMILY** • *Erinaceidae* • **GENUS & SPECIES** • *Paraechinus aethiopicus*

DESERT HEDGEHOG

Adapted for life in a hostile climate, the desert hedgehog can also rely on the defensive curling behaviour typical of more familiar hedgehogs.

KEY FEATURES

- One of the smallest hedgehogs, but well equipped to survive in the inhospitable desert fringes.
- Preys on venomous creatures such as scorpions and snakes, using its spines to devastating effect.
- Avoids the worst of the desert heat by burrowing deep beneath the sandy surface during the day.

EARS
Large ears provide the desert hedgehog with an acute sense of hearing, which it uses to locate prey and predators at night.

COLOURATION
Most individuals are brown, but albino (all-white) and melanistic (black) individuals also occur.

SPINES
The spines, which are modified hairs, are strong but lightweight and flexible. They are the hedgehog's first line of defence against predators.

CURLED UP
By contracting the 'drawstring' muscle around the edge of its spiny overcoat, the hedgehog seals itself into a prickly ball.

FOOT
The hedgehog's underfur conceals surprisingly long legs, with long, sharp claws for burrowing and for subduing prey.

VITAL STATISTICS

WEIGHT	Up to 700g (24.7oz)
LENGTH	Head & Body: 14–27cm (5.5–10.6in) Tail; 1–4cm (0.4–1.6in)
SEXUAL MATURITY	9–11 months
MATING SEASON	July to August
GESTATION PERIOD	35–42 days
NUMBER OF YOUNG	2 to 6
BIRTH INTERVAL	1 year
TYPICAL DIET	Insects, spiders, scorpions, snakes, birds' eggs, carrion
LIFESPAN	Up to 8 years in the wild

CREATURE COMPARISONS

Although it looks quite different, the desert hedgehog is a near relative of the Malayan gymnure (Echinosorex gymnurus), also known as the moonrat. The moonrat is covered in long, coarse hair rather than spines, with a long, naked tail. It is larger than the hedgehog, with a longer, more flexible snout and a narrow body that allows it to investigate tight crevices for food. The moonrat lives in the remote forests and mangrove swamps of southeastern Asia, always near water. It is thought to be partly aquatic, and probably feeds on fish and frogs as well as insects and earthworms.

Malayan gymnure

Desert hedgehog

WHERE IN THE WORLD?

Lives on the semi-desert borders of the Sahara in Africa and the Arabian Desert, from Morocco east to Iraq in the north, and from Mauritania and Sudan east to the Arabian Peninsula in the south.

RELATED SPECIES

The desert hedgehog is 1 of 3 hedgehogs in the genus Paraechinus, which belongs to the family Erinaceidae and includes at least 9 other hedgehog species. It also contains 5 species of gymnure, which lack spines. The gymnures are so diverse in appearance and habit that each is classified within its own genus. The family Erinaceidae is 1 of 6 in the order Insectivora, which also includes shrews and moles.

• ORDER • *Insectivora* • FAMILY • *Soricidae* • SPECIES • *Blarina brevicauda*

NORTHERN SHORT-TAILED SHREW

KEY FEATURES

- A small and highly active predator that consumes its own weight in prey daily.
- Poisonous saliva flows through its grooved teeth to paralyze struggling victims.
- Has poor hearing and eyesight, detecting its quarry instead with its sensitive whiskers.

This tiny insectivore has a sharp bite, with which it injects poison produced in modified saliva glands to immobilize or kill its prey.

TEETH
The northern short-tailed shrew has 32 teeth. Grooves on the lower incisors channel poisonous saliva into wounds. Small points on the cheek teeth help to crush insects.

BODY
The cylindrical body is ideally shaped for tunnelling and for foraging in the undergrowth. However, its small volume in relation to surface area makes it highly vulnerable to the cold.

MUZZLE
The slightly conical muzzle bears several touch-sensitive whiskers for detecting prey. The keen sense of smell plays a vital part in the shrew's ability to find its way around.

FEET
Each foot has five toes tipped with sharp claws, used by the shrew to dig burrows or enlarge those of other animals for its use.

VITAL STATISTICS

WEIGHT	14–28g (0.5–1oz)
LENGTH	Head & Body: 7.5–10cm (2.9–3.9in) Tail; 2–3cm (0.8–1.2in)
SEXUAL MATURITY	2–3 months
MATING SEASON	March to May and August to September
GESTATION PERIOD	21 days or more
NUMBER OF YOUNG	5 to 7
BIRTH INTERVAL	2 to 4 litters each year
TYPICAL DIET	Earthworms, field voles, snails, insects and other invertebrates; occasionally lizards and mice
LIFESPAN	1–2 years

CREATURE COMPARISONS

Most shrews live in moist habitats, and some are highly aquatic. The Eurasian water shrew tunnels in riverbanks and ditches, preying on fish, frogs and invertebrates. The giant otter shrew lives in rivers and pools in central African rainforests. It swims with speed and agility, using its muscular, flattened tail for propulsion as it hunts for crabs and fish.

Northern short-tailed shrew

Eurasian water shrew

Giant otter shrew

WHERE IN THE WORLD?

Found in the USA and Canada, from Saskatchewan east to Nova Scotia in the north and from Kentucky east to Alabama and Florida in the south.

RELATED SPECIES

There are 289 species of shrew, including the Scilly shrew, *Crocidura suaveolens*. Other members of the order Insectivora include the solenodons of the West Indies, the tenrecs and golden moles of Africa, the hedgehogs and moles of Africa and Europe, and the moonrats of Southeast Asia

• **ORDER** • *Insectivora* • **FAMILY** • *Soricidae* • **GENUS & SPECIES** • *Neomys fodiens*

EURASIAN WATER SHREW

KEY FEATURES

- Tiny, hyperactive predator that hunts on the banks and in the water of freshwater streams and rivers.
- Builds a network of tunnels from its underground chambers to the water's edge.
- Contains toxins in its saliva that are useful for subduing the larger animals in its diet.

A few subtle adaptations to the basic shrew bodyplan enable this hunter to exploit prey bases that are denied to its exclusively land-based relatives.

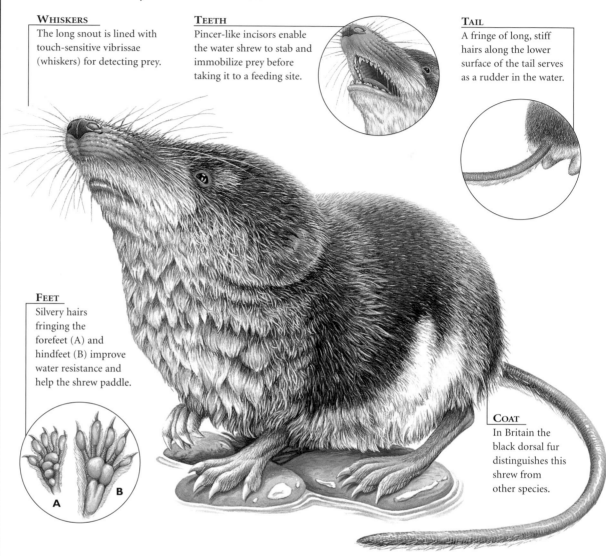

WHISKERS
The long snout is lined with touch-sensitive vibrissae (whiskers) for detecting prey.

TEETH
Pincer-like incisors enable the water shrew to stab and immobilize prey before taking it to a feeding site.

TAIL
A fringe of long, stiff hairs along the lower surface of the tail serves as a rudder in the water.

FEET
Silvery hairs fringing the forefeet (A) and hindfeet (B) improve water resistance and help the shrew paddle.

COAT
In Britain the black dorsal fur distinguishes this shrew from other species.

VITAL STATISTICS

WEIGHT	10–22g (0.3–0.8oz)
LENGTH	Head & Body: 7–9cm (2.7–3.5in) Tail; 7cm (2.7in)
SEXUAL MATURITY	6–8 months
MATING SEASON	April to October
GESTATION PERIOD	19–24 days
NUMBER OF YOUNG	3 to 12
BIRTH INTERVAL	2 to 3 litters a year
TYPICAL DIET	Land and water invertebrates including insects and their larvae, earthworms, molluscs, small fish and frogs, plant material
LIFESPAN	About 18 months

CREATURE COMPARISONS

The Asiatic water shrews of the genus Chimarrogale are slightly larger than their Eurasian counterpart, reaching a head-and-body length of 13.5cm (5.3in). They range from northern India to Japan and south to Southeast Asia. Despite their different habitats — the Eurasian water shrew has to contend with frozen rivers, while its Asiatic kin are found in tropical rainforests — these shrews have similar physical adaptations. Both genera have dense, water-repellent fur that aids buoyancy and stiff hairs fringing the feet to aid swimming. However, Asiatic water shrews have a more sparsely haired tail.

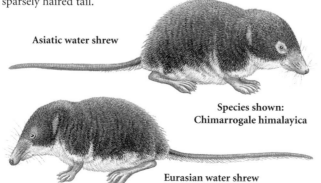

Asiatic water shrew

Species shown:
Chimarrogale himalayica

Eurasian water shrew

WHERE IN THE WORLD?

Found in many parts of northern Europe except Ireland and Iceland, extending through Asia to the Pacific coasts of Siberia, China and North Korea.

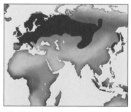

RELATED SPECIES

The genus Neomys also includes the Mediterranean or Miller's water shrew, N. anomalus, which lives on mainland southeastern and western Europe, sometimes in mountainous regions; and the Transcaucasian water shrew, N. schelkovnikovi, of Armenia, Georgia and Azerbaijan. Neomys belongs to the family Soricidae, which contains 289 shrew species. Shrews are classed in the order Insectivora, which also includes moles, hedgehogs and solenodons.

EURASIAN SHREW

• ORDER • *Insectivora* **• FAMILY •** *Soricidae* **• GENUS & SPECIES •** *Sorex araneus*

KEY FEATURES

*   Solitary and aggressive, this tiny hunter attacks any other shrew trespassing on its territory.
*   Leads a brief life, alternating short periods of rest with hectic bursts of activity along well worn runs.
*   Loses bodyheat rapidly, so must feed continually on the invertebrates living in its vegetated habitat.

VITAL STATISTICS

WEIGHT	5–15g (0.2–0.5oz)
LENGTH	Head & Body: 50–90mm (2–3.5in) Tail; 20–45mm (0.8–1.8in)
SEXUAL MATURITY	6–10 months
MATING SEASON	April to September
GESTATION PERIOD	25 days
NUMBER OF YOUNG	5 to 7 per litter
BIRTH INTERVAL	2 to 4 litters per season
TYPICAL DIET	Earthworms, insects, spiders and other invertebrates
LIFESPAN	15–18 months

Relying on its senses of touch and smell, the Eurasian shrew uses its long snout for probing among the leaf litter in search of invertebrates.

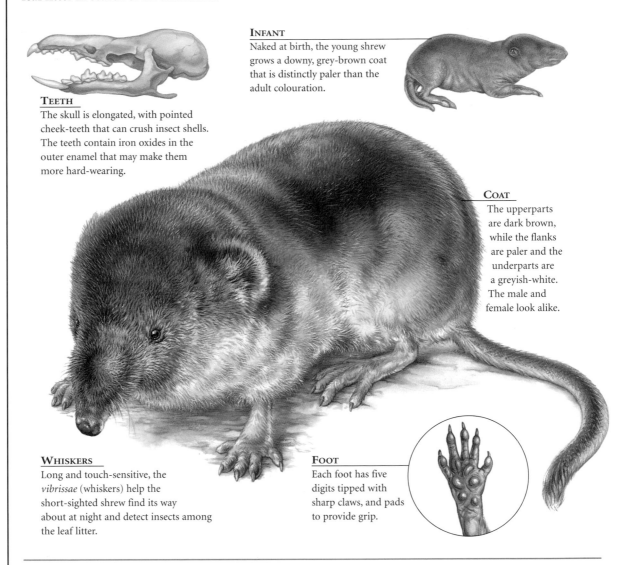

TEETH
The skull is elongated, with pointed cheek-teeth that can crush insect shells. The teeth contain iron oxides in the outer enamel that may make them more hard-wearing.

INFANT
Naked at birth, the young shrew grows a downy, grey-brown coat that is distinctly paler than the adult colouration.

COAT
The upperparts are dark brown, while the flanks are paler and the underparts are a greyish-white. The male and female look alike.

WHISKERS
Long and touch-sensitive, the *vibrissae* (whiskers) help the short-sighted shrew find its way about at night and detect insects among the leaf litter.

FOOT
Each foot has five digits tipped with sharp claws, and pads to provide grip.

CREATURE COMPARISONS

The piebald shrew, or Turkmenistan desert shrew (Diplomesodon pulchellum), leads a solitary life in the dry steppe and semi-desert of central Asia. Slightly smaller than the Eurasian shrew, the piebald shrew is named after its eye-catching coat colouration. It has greyish upperparts with a patch of white on its back. Its tail, feet and underparts are white.

Active mainly at night, the piebald shrew hunts insects and lizards. On catching a lizard, the piebald shrew bites off its head and consumes only the body, leaving the limbs and tail.

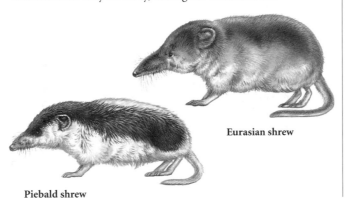

Eurasian shrew

Piebald shrew

WHERE IN THE WORLD?

Found in mainland Britain, Scandinavia, northern and eastern Europe, and into Siberia as far east as Lake Baikal. Absent from Ireland, Spain and most of France.

RELATED SPECIES

The Eurasian shrew is 1 of 58 species in Sorex, the genus of long-tailed shrews. Sorex is 1 of 22 genera in the family Soricidae, whose 289 species include the greater white-toothed shrew, Crocidura russula. Shrews are placed in the order Insectivora.

• ORDER • *Insectivora* • FAMILY • *Talpidae* • GENUS & SPECIES • *Talpa europaea*

EUROPEAN MOLE

Specialized for a subterranean way of life, the mole has a cylindrical body, reduced limbs and broad, flattened forefeet for digging.

KEY FEATURES

- Solitary mammal that spends most of its life underground, feeding almost solely on earthworms.
- Uses its spade-like, clawed forefeet to dig complex systems of permanent and semi-permanent tunnels.
- Remains active all year round, alternating short periods of rest with sudden bursts of work.

SKULL
The skull features a rounded back. The slender jaws contain 44 teeth, the greatest number found in placental mammals.

COAT
The short, velvety fur ranges in colour from near-black to golden, cream or white. The fur lies in any direction, helping the mole move backwards and forwards through its tunnels.

FORELIMBS
Short, stout bones give immense digging power. The coat extends fully to the wrists, reinforcing the impression of shortened limbs. The forefeet are permanently turned outwards; each has five digits tipped with long, stout claws for excavating soil.

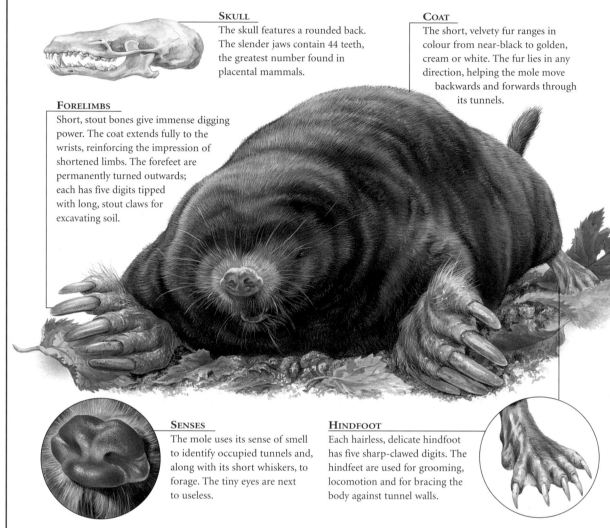

SENSES
The mole uses its sense of smell to identify occupied tunnels and, along with its short whiskers, to forage. The tiny eyes are next to useless.

HINDFOOT
Each hairless, delicate hindfoot has five sharp-clawed digits. The hindfeet are used for grooming, locomotion and for bracing the body against tunnel walls.

VITAL STATISTICS

WEIGHT	65–130g (2.3–4.6oz)
LENGTH	Head & Body: 9.5–18cm (3.7–7.1in) Tail; 1.5–4cm (0.6–1.6in)
SEXUAL MATURITY	6–12 months
MATING SEASON	Spring to early summer, sometimes late summer to early autumn depending on location
GESTATION PERIOD	4 weeks
NUMBER OF YOUNG	2 to 7
BIRTH INTERVAL	1 year
TYPICAL DIET	Earthworms, insect larvae and molluscs
LIFESPAN	3 years

CREATURE COMPARISONS

The star-nosed mole (Condylura cristata) is found in Canada and the United States. It is smaller than the European mole, reaching 10–12cm (3.9–4.7in) in bodylength but having a longer tail at about 8cm (3.1in). Its most distinctive characteristic is the ring of 22 fleshy rays, or tentacles, around its snout. As the mole forages, these bizarre extensions wriggle about to help it detect crustaceans, insects and earthworms. The star-nosed mole depends on damp or muddy soil, and some of its tunnels lead directly into water. It can obtain food from the bottom of ponds and streams, and, unlike the European mole, spends a lot of time foraging at night on the ground's surface.

European mole

Star-nosed mole

WHERE IN THE WORLD?

Found from Spain and mainland Britain east across Europe and Asia. Range extends to the north of the Urals and east into Siberia.

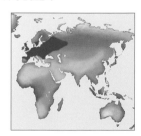

RELATED SPECIES

The European mole is 1 of 11 species of northern mole in the genus Talpa. The most widespread species is T. europaea, which is found across Europe, except in Ireland, and throughout Russia. Talpa is represented in central Siberia by T. altaica, and in the Far East by T. mizura on Honshu, Japan. The family Talpidae contains 8 other mole genera and also includes shrew moles and desmans. All belong to the order Insectivora.

COMMON TENREC

• ORDER • *Insectivora* • FAMILY • *Tenrecidae* • GENUS & SPECIES • *Tenrec ecaudatus*

KEY FEATURES

- World's largest insectivore, and one of several hedgehog-like species found on Madagascar.

- Forages at night for invertebrates, rootling through leaf litter with the aid of its long, whiskered snout.

- Highly prolific, the female can produce huge litters — but then has a hard time trying to feed them all.

VITAL STATISTICS

WEIGHT	1.5–2.5kg (3.3–5.5lb)
LENGTH	Head & Body: 25–40cm (9.8–15.7in) Tail; 10–15mm (3.9–5.9in)
SEXUAL MATURITY	35 days
MATING SEASON	October to November
GESTATION PERIOD	55–65 days
NUMBER OF YOUNG	Up to 32
BIRTH INTERVAL	1 year
TYPICAL DIET	Insects, worms, small vertebrates and fruit
LIFESPAN	Unknown in the wild; 6.5 years in captivity

The tenrec has a compact body for pushing through leaf litter, and scampers nimbly on its slender limbs. Though primitive, its teeth pack a powerful bite.

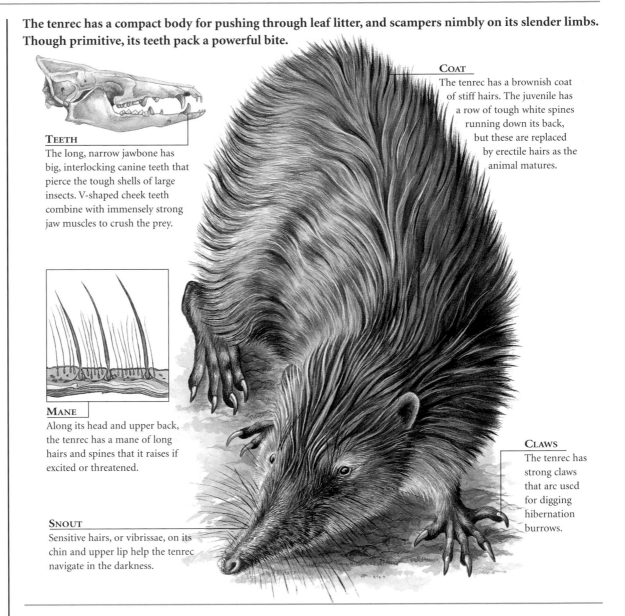

TEETH
The long, narrow jawbone has big, interlocking canine teeth that pierce the tough shells of large insects. V-shaped cheek teeth combine with immensely strong jaw muscles to crush the prey.

MANE
Along its head and upper back, the tenrec has a mane of long hairs and spines that it raises if excited or threatened.

SNOUT
Sensitive hairs, or vibrissae, on its chin and upper lip help the tenrec navigate in the darkness.

COAT
The tenrec has a brownish coat of stiff hairs. The juvenile has a row of tough white spines running down its back, but these are replaced by erectile hairs as the animal matures.

CLAWS
The tenrec has strong claws that are used for digging hibernation burrows.

CREATURE COMPARISONS

A smaller relative of the common tenrec is the streaked tenrec (*Hemicentetes semispinosus*), which is also found on Madagascar. Both have well hidden tails that seem to have no particular function and a stiff mane that is raised to scare off breeding rivals and predators. The streaked tenrec has a coat of sharp spines and white stripes that provide camouflage while it forages on the ground for insects. Unlike the common tenrec, the streaked tenrec protects itself by curling up into a ball, rather like a hedgehog, and relies on its spines for protection. The streaked tenrec is also more social than the common tenrec, often living in long communal burrow systems.

Tenrec

Streaked tenrec

WHERE IN THE WORLD?

Inhabits the inland plateaus and coastal regions of Madagascar. Introduced by humans to the Comoros Islands and to the small islands of Reunion and Mauritius in the Indian Ocean.

RELATED SPECIES

The family Tenrecidae contains another 22 species in 9 genera: the giant otter shrew, genus Potamogale; 2 dwarf otter shrews, genus Micropotamogale; the large-eared tenrec, genus Geogale; 3 rice tenrecs, genus Oryzorictes; the web-footed tenrec, genus Limnogale; 11 long-tailed tenrecs, genus Microgale; the large and small Madagascar hedgehogs, genera Setifer and Echinops; and the streaked tenrec, genus Hemicentetes.

• **ORDER** • *Isoptera* • **FAMILY** • *Termitidae* • **GENUS & SPECIES** • *Various*

TERMITE

KEY FEATURES

• Huge numbers of termites live together in complex and often vast, towering nests.

• A queen and her attendant king control the colony with chemical scents, while she is fed and her eggs are taken off to be brooded.

• Work is divided between the workers that forage and build and the soldiers that defend the colony.

VITAL STATISTICS

LENGTH	Workers and soldiers 1.5–15mm (0.06–0.6in); king 6–18mm (0.2–0.7in); queen up to 75mm (2.9in)
SEXUAL MATURITY	3 months from egg to mature winged adult
BREEDING SEASON	Varies, usually coincides with rain after long dry period
NUMBER OF EGGS	Up to 80,000 per day, but usually fewer
TYPICAL DIET	Fungi of the genus Termitomyces
LIFESPAN	Queen up to 17 years; colonies over 100 years old are known

The soldier termite uses its powerful jaws to protect the nest and the other members of its huge colony from marauders, such as armies of ants.

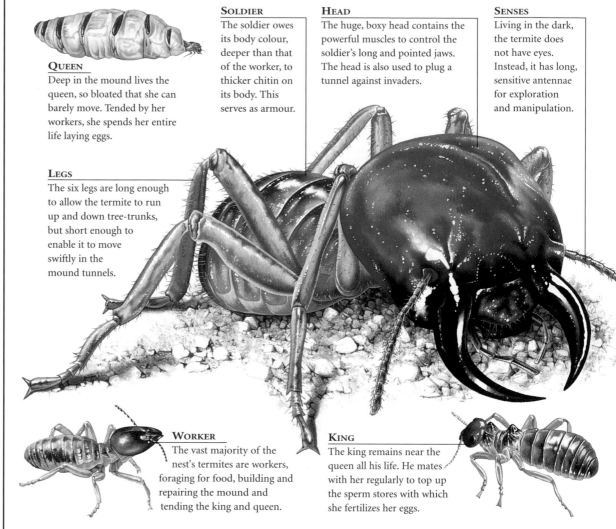

QUEEN
Deep in the mound lives the queen, so bloated that she can barely move. Tended by her workers, she spends her entire life laying eggs.

LEGS
The six legs are long enough to allow the termite to run up and down tree-trunks, but short enough to enable it to move swiftly in the mound tunnels.

SOLDIER
The soldier owes its body colour, deeper than that of the worker, to thicker chitin on its body. This serves as armour.

HEAD
The huge, boxy head contains the powerful muscles to control the soldier's long and pointed jaws. The head is also used to plug a tunnel against invaders.

SENSES
Living in the dark, the termite does not have eyes. Instead, it has long, sensitive antennae for exploration and manipulation.

WORKER
The vast majority of the nest's termites are workers, foraging for food, building and repairing the mound and tending the king and queen.

KING
The king remains near the queen all his life. He mates with her regularly to top up the sperm stores with which she fertilizes her eggs.

CREATURE COMPARISONS

Some of the variation among termites can be seen in these soldiers, which represent two subfamilies. Trinervitermes rettonianus (subfamily Nasutitermitinae) is much smaller than Macrotermes subhyalinus (Macrotermitinae), but just as significant is the difference in head shapes. M. subhyalinus has enlarged mandibles (jaws), powered by huge muscles in the head, that can literally snip the limbs off attacking ants.

The little T. rettonianus has virtually absent mandibles. Instead it possesses a pointed, snout-like projection on the front of its head. When disturbed, it squirts a sticky secretion from its snout. The liquid immobilizes attackers such as ants by entangling their legs and antennae.

Trinervitermes rettonianus

Macrotermes subhyalinus

WHERE IN THE WORLD?

Termites of the subfamily Macrotermitinae occur across Africa, and are widespread in

India, China and south and southeastern Asia, including the Malay Peninsula. Termites are also found in Australia.

RELATED SPECIES

There are 13 genera, or more than 300 species, of termite that grow fungus combs in their nests. All belong to the subfamily Macrotermitinae. There are more than 2300 species in the order Isoptera. The family Termitidae, the largest in the order, contains the higher, or mound-building, termites. These are typified by a rigid caste system, huge nest and complex social structure.

SNOWSHOE HARE

• ORDER • *Lagomorpha* • FAMILY • *Leporidae* • GENUS & SPECIES • *Lepus americanus*

The shy snowshoe hare is the staple prey of a number of predators, and depends for its survival on alertness, speed and seasonal camouflage.

KEY FEATURES

- Very broad hindfeet covered with thick fur enable this hare to move over deep snow.
- Its fur undergoes seasonal colour changes between reddish-brown in summer and white in winter.
- Maintains an intricate network of tracks that provide essential escape routes from predators.

EARS
The huge, mobile ears provide excellent hearing for pinpointing approaching predators.

JAWS
A toothless gap separates the incisors from the molars and premolars. The hare draws its lips into this gap when gnawing in order not to swallow any inedible fragments.

INCISORS
The snowshoe hare has two pairs of long, chisel-like incisors. These rootless teeth grow constantly, replacing the wear caused by abrasive food.

HINDFEET
The thick hairs on the soles of the broad hindfeet distribute weight over a large surface area, enabling the hare to move over crusted snow to escape heavier enemies.

COAT
The coat is made up of three layers: a short, dense underfur, a thin layer of longer hairs, and an outer layer of long, coarse hairs that change colour through the passing year.

VITAL STATISTICS

WEIGHT	1.4–1.8kg (3.1–4lb)
LENGTH	37.5–55cm (14.8–21.6in)
SEXUAL MATURITY	1 year
MATING SEASON	March to September
GESTATION PERIOD	30–38 days
NUMBER OF YOUNG	2 to 6
BIRTH INTERVAL	Up to 4 litters per year
TYPICAL DIET	Fresh grasses, shoots, leaves, berries, twigs, bark; some carrion
LIFESPAN	Up to 5 years in the wild; up to 7 years in captivity

CREATURE COMPARISONS

Like the snowshoe hare, the endangered hispid hare (Caprolagus hispidus), otherwise known as the bristly rabbit or Assam rabbit, is shy and reluctant to leave the shelter of the thatch grasslands or forests where it lives. Found in the foothills of the Himalayas, the hispid hare has a coarse coat with black-brown upperparts and paler underparts. Its short tail is dark brown.

At about 2.5kg (5.5lb), the hispid hare is heavier than the snowshoe hare, although it is shorter in body length, at 38–50cm (15–19.7in). It has a sturdier body and a more compact shape, with shorter, stouter hindlegs and smaller ears.

Hispid hare

WHERE IN THE WORLD?

Range extends from the northern treelines of Alaska and Canada, south through Newfoundland and Hudson Bay to northern New Mexico and California.

RELATED SPECIES

The snowshoe hare belongs to the genus Lepus, which contains 23 species of hare. Hares and rabbits belong to the family Leporidae, which contains 11 genera and 47 species. Rabbits are generally smaller than hares, and are adapted for burrowing, while hares are adapted for running fast. However, the black-tailed jackrabbit, L. californicus, and the Arctic hare, L. arcticus, dig burrows to avoid temperature extremes. The Arctic hare (Lepus arcticus) sometimes digs burrows as refuges for its young.

• ORDER • *Lagomorpha* • FAMILY • *Leporidae* • GENUS & SPECIES • *Lepus californicus*

BLACK-TAILED JACKRABBIT

Almost comical with its oversized ears, the black-tailed jackrabbit quickly turns into a streamlined streak as it bolts over open country.

KEY FEATURES

- Despite its name it is a hare, not a rabbit.
- Enormous ears function mainly as heat regulators, absorbing and losing heat by the flow of blood through them.
- Runs almost as fast as a racehorse, sustaining speeds of 60 km/h (37.3 mph).
- Frantic 'boxing matches' between the sexes are a regular part of complex courting rituals.

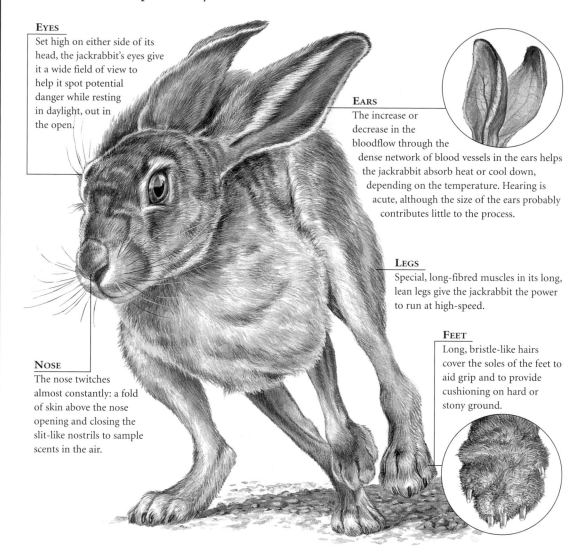

EYES
Set high on either side of its head, the jackrabbit's eyes give it a wide field of view to help it spot potential danger while resting in daylight, out in the open.

EARS
The increase or decrease in the bloodflow through the dense network of blood vessels in the ears helps the jackrabbit absorb heat or cool down, depending on the temperature. Hearing is acute, although the size of the ears probably contributes little to the process.

LEGS
Special, long-fibred muscles in its long, lean legs give the jackrabbit the power to run at high-speed.

FEET
Long, bristle-like hairs cover the soles of the feet to aid grip and to provide cushioning on hard or stony ground.

NOSE
The nose twitches almost constantly: a fold of skin above the nose opening and closing the slit-like nostrils to sample scents in the air.

VITAL STATISTICS

WEIGHT	Male 4–5kg (8.8–11lb); female 5–6kg (11–13.2lb)
LENGTH	Head & Body: 40–70cm (15.7–27.6in) Tail; 4–12cm (1.6–4.7in)
SEXUAL MATURITY	1 year
MATING SEASON	December to September
GESTATION PERIOD	41–47 days
NUMBER OF YOUNG	1 to 6
BIRTH INTERVAL	3–4 months
TYPICAL DIET	Succulent plants, grasses, twigs, bark
LIFESPAN	Up to 5 years in the wild; more than 6 years in captivity

CREATURE COMPARISONS

The familiar European, or domestic, rabbit (Oryctolagus cuniculus) is native to Europe and North Africa, but has been introduced widely across the world. It is considerably smaller than the jackrabbit, with much shorter legs and ears in relation to the size of its body. Its short, relatively chunky leg muscles favour brief bursts of acceleration, allowing it to bolt to the safety of its burrow. The jackrabbit, though, lives in the open and has long, lean muscles, suited to sustained speed over longer distances, to help it escape from predators.

European rabbit

Black-tailed jackrabbit

WHERE IN THE WORLD?

A native of the semi-arid lands of southwestern North America, it now ranges across much of the USA south to northern Mexico. Introduced to eastern parts of the USA.

RELATED SPECIES
Rabbits and hares belong to the family Leporidae, in the order Lagomorpha. The only other family in Lagomorpha is the Ochotonidae, comprising 21 species of pika, such as Ochotona princeps. Small and shy, it lives in the mountains of Asia and North America.

ARCTIC HARE

• **ORDER** • *Lagomorpha* • **FAMILY** • *Leporidae* • **GENUS & SPECIES** • *Lepus timidus*

KEY FEATURES

- Equipped with a coat that can change colour with the seasons to provide highly effective camouflage all through the year.
- Able to survive low temperatures that would kill many other animals of a similar size.
- Well developed at birth, the young Arctic hare is ready to fend for itself only a few days after being born.

VITAL STATISTICS

WEIGHT	2.5–5.8kg (5.5–12.8lb)
LENGTH	52–60cm (20.5–23.6in)
SEXUAL MATURITY	8 months
MATING SEASON	From January in Europe; from May in the High Arctic
GESTATION PERIOD	50 days
NUMBER OF YOUNG	3 to 6
BIRTH INTERVAL	Up to 4 litters per year
TYPICAL DIET	Almost any type of vegetation, but mainly grasses, heather, willow and birch shoots
LIFESPAN	Up to 12 years but usually much less

In the far north the Arctic hare shares its snowy habitat with eagles, falcons and wolves, so it has to be quick on its feet to stay out of trouble.

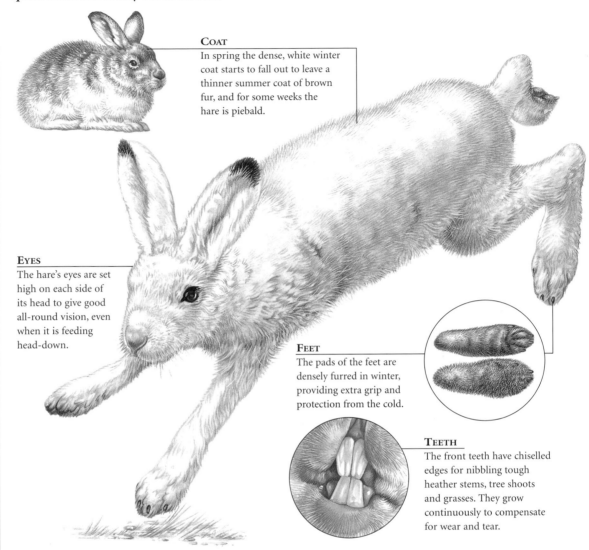

COAT
In spring the dense, white winter coat starts to fall out to leave a thinner summer coat of brown fur, and for some weeks the hare is piebald.

EYES
The hare's eyes are set high on each side of its head to give good all-round vision, even when it is feeding head-down.

FEET
The pads of the feet are densely furred in winter, providing extra grip and protection from the cold.

TEETH
The front teeth have chiselled edges for nibbling tough heather stems, tree shoots and grasses. They grow continuously to compensate for wear and tear.

CREATURE COMPARISONS

The Arctic hare is bigger than a rabbit, with longer legs and ears. The main reason for this is that rabbits are adapted for burrowing and, as a result, have evolved a more compact body shape for greater manoeuvrability in their tunnels.

The Arctic hare is adapted to life in the open, but its body shape is a compromise between the lean, athletic build of most other hares and the dumpy, rounded shape that helps retain heat in cold northern climates. Both the rabbit and hare have sensitive ears and prominent eyes to help alert them to danger from predators at all times.

Rabbit

Arctic hare

WHERE IN THE WORLD?

Lives throughout the Arctic on the tundra, the forests and mountains of Scandinavia, Russia, Siberia and Canada. Also found in Ireland, Scotland and the Alps.

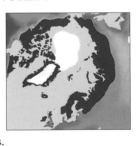

RELATED SPECIES

The Arctic hare is one of 21 species of hare found worldwide. A close relation is Lepus americanus, the snowshoe hare. Common over most of Canada and in parts of the western USA, including Alaska, south through the Rocky Mountains, this hare also has a pure white coat in winter. Like the Arctic hare, the white coat is replaced in summer by a brownish coat, although the underside of its body remains white year round.

• **ORDER** • *Lagomorpha* • **FAMILY** • *Leporidae* • **GENUS & SPECIES** • *Oryctolagus cuniculus*

EUROPEAN RABBIT

The European rabbit relies on its keen senses, communication skills and, ultimately, speed to evade its many predators.

KEY FEATURES

- A prolific breeder, a single female can produce more than 30 young in each breeding season.
- Digs complex burrow systems in soft soil that consist of numerous tunnels and nesting chambers.
- Eats its own droppings to retrieve important nutrients that passed through its system the first time around.

DIGESTIVE SYSTEM

The rabbit's digestive system is designed to cope with large quantities of vegetation. The appendix is enlarged into a stomach-like chamber called the caecum (A), which contains bacteria that aid the digestion of plant fibre. By the time the bacteria have done their work, the rabbit's food is rich in nutrients. Some of the nutrients are absorbed immediately, but most pass out in the rabbit's soft droppings. The rabbit eats these droppings to extract the remaining nutrients. The resulting waste from the soft droppings are excreted as hard pellets. This process is called coprophagy.

EARS

Long and mobile, the rabbit's ears are very sensitive and can pick up the faintest sound and pinpoint its direction.

HINDLEGS

The hindlegs are driven by large muscles that enable the rabbit to sprint at 40 km/h (24.8 mph). The elongated hindfeet are hairy below and have four, clawed toes for grip when running. The hindfeet are drummed on the ground to warn other rabbits of danger.

TAIL

If an individual senses danger and bolts, the tail cocks to reveal the white underside, which flashes a warning signal to other rabbits.

COAT

The fine-haired, soft coat varies in colour from black to pure white. However, most rabbits are grey-brown.

VITAL STATISTICS

WEIGHT	1.4–2.3kg (3.1–5.1lb)
LENGTH	Head & Body: 35–45cm (13.8–17.7in) Tail; 4–7cm (1.6–2.7in)
SHOULDER HEIGHT	15–20cm (5.9–7.9in)
SEXUAL MATURITY	3–24 months
MATING SEASON	Feb to July in Europe; Aug to Feb in the southern hemisphere; all year in Australia
GESTATION PERIOD	28–33 days
NUMBER OF YOUNG	1 to 9, but usually 5 to 6
BIRTH INTERVAL	2 litters per year, but up to 6 in Australia
TYPICAL DIET	Grasses, herbage, bark and twigs
LIFESPAN	Up to 9 years

CREATURE COMPARISONS

The European rabbit is larger than the Sumatra short-eared rabbit, *Nesolagus netscheri*, but less striking in appearance. Sporting grey stripes on a brown background, the Sumatra short-eared rabbit has a more defined coat pattern than any other wild rabbit or hare. The Sumatra short-eared rabbit can be found at high altitudes, usually occurring in forests 600–1400m (1969–4593ft) above sea level in the highlands of the Barisan Range, southwestern Sumatra. The Sumatra short-eared rabbit's future is threatened by loss of habitat to farmland.

Both rabbits are active mainly at night and rest underground during the day, although the Sumatra short-eared rabbit is not thought to dig its own burrows.

Sumatra short-eared rabbit

European rabbit

WHERE IN THE WORLD?

A native of France, Spain, Portugal and northwestern Africa, it has been introduced to much of Europe, Australia, New Zealand, Chile and Argentina.

RELATED SPECIES

The European rabbit is the only species in the genus Oryctolagus. It is a member of the family Leporidae, which consists of 47 species in 11 genera. This family can be roughly divided into two groups. One group contains the 23 species of hare, or jackrabbit, of the genus Lepus, while the other contains 24 species of rabbit in 10 genera, including 13 species of cottontail. All domestic rabbits are derived from the European rabbit.

• ORDER • *Lamniformes* • FAMILY • *Lamnidae* • GENUS & SPECIES • *Carcharodon carcharias*

GREAT WHITE SHARK

The spindle-shaped, streamlined body of the great white shark makes it one of the fastest—and most dangerous—fish in the sea.

KEY FEATURES

- The largest predatory shark, reaching a length of more than 6.1m (20ft) and a weight of up to 3175kg (7000lbs).
- The only shark that regularly attacks and eats warm-blooded animals, such as seals and dolphins.
- Adults have broad, serrated teeth up to 7.6cm (3in) long for slicing chunks out of large-bodied, thick-skinned prey.

SENSORY DEVICES
Small pores in the snout lead to receptors that pick up electrical nerve signals in the bodies of potential victims. Other sensors can detect blood in the water.

A BIGGER BITE
As the shark attacks, its snout lifts out of the way and the jaws protrude to align the teeth in the upper and lower jaws and to increase its biting capacity.

PECTORAL FINS
The winglike pectoral fins provide lift, holding the shark's body up in the water as it moves forward. If it stops swimming, it starts to sink.

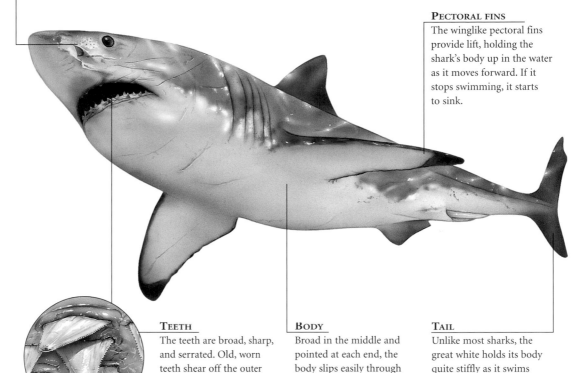

TEETH
The teeth are broad, sharp, and serrated. Old, worn teeth shear off the outer face of each jaw, and new, sharp teeth move up from behind to replace them.

BODY
Broad in the middle and pointed at each end, the body slips easily through the water. Rich oil in the shark's large liver improves its buoyancy.

TAIL
Unlike most sharks, the great white holds its body quite stiffly as it swims and drives itself along with its highly efficient tail, as a tuna does.

VITAL STATISTICS

WEIGHT	2722–3175kg (6000–7000lb)
LENGTH	3.6–7.6m (12–25ft). Female is usually larger than the male
SEXUAL MATURITY	About 7 years
MATING SEASON	Varies with habitat
GESTATION PERIOD	Probably about 12 months
NUMBER OF YOUNG	1 or 2
BIRTH INTERVAL	Unknown
TYPICAL DIET	Fish, squid, seals, dolphins, sea turtles, seabirds, and whale carcasses
LIFE SPAN	30–50 years

CREATURE COMPARISONS

Although the great white is the world's largest predatory shark, it is dwarfed by the whale shark, which reaches 12.2m (40ft). but may grow to 18.3m (60ft). Like the true whales, this immense fish feeds on the tiny, floating animals of the plankton by straining them out of the seawater, and is quite harmless to large animals.

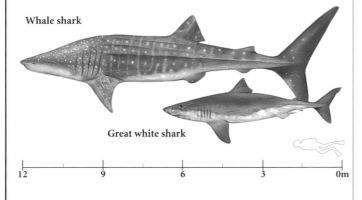

Whale shark

Great white shark

12   9   6   3   0m

WHERE IN THE WORLD?

Temperate oceans of the world, mainly off the coasts of North America, southern Africa, Australia, New Zealand, Japan, and parts of the Mediterranean.

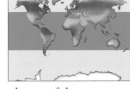

RELATED SPECIES

The great white shark belongs to the group known as the mackerel sharks. Four other species in this group include: the salmon shark, the shortfin mako, the longfin mako, and the porbeagle. They are all fast-swimming, highly streamlined hunters which are considered to be dangerous to man.

• **ORDER** • *Lepidoptera* • **FAMILY** • *Nymphalidae* • **GENUS & SPECIES** • *Various*

OWL BUTTERFLY

A giant among butterflies, the owl butterfly's kaleidoscopic colours are designed not to attract attention but to help conceal it in dappled forest light.

KEY FEATURES

- One of the world's largest butterflies, which in flight, is easily mistaken for a bird or bat.

- Unlike most butterflies, it is active mainly at dusk after spending the day resting and feeding under the dense forest canopy.

- The caterpillar, which sports an impressive crown of thorns on its head, is a non-stop eating machine with an enormous appetite.

VITAL STATISTICS

WINGSPAN	4.5–20cm (1.8–7.9in)
CATERPILLAR LENGTH	8–14cm (3.1–5.5in)
BREEDING SEASON	Varies according to location; usually during the wet season
NUMBER OF EGGS	Up to 150
HATCHING PERIOD	9–14 days
CHRYSALIS STAGE	18 days
BREEDING INTERVAL	Breeds only once; the female dies after laying her eggs
TYPICAL DIET	Caterpillar feeds on leaves; adult feeds on tree sap and rotting fruit
LIFESPAN	Adults live for an average of 40 days

COLOURING
The blue, yellow and orange patches on an owl butterfly's wings are not derived from pigments. They are interference colours produced by diffraction of the light falling on to a series of ridges on each scale.

PROBOSCIS
The mouthparts are formed into a proboscis (A) that lies coiled up beneath the head when not in use. The proboscis consists of a double tube held together with hooks and spines. It also contains a valve to prevent food from flowing back down the wrong way.

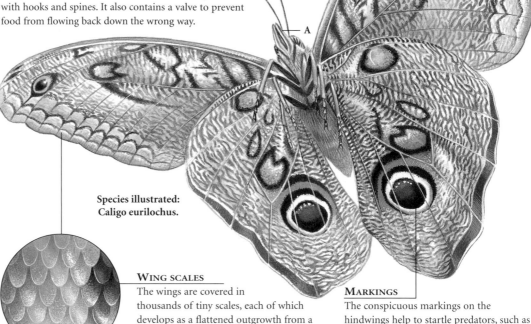

Species illustrated: Caligo eurilochus.

WING SCALES
The wings are covered in thousands of tiny scales, each of which develops as a flattened outgrowth from a single cell. The density of scales is 200–600 per sq mm.

MARKINGS
The conspicuous markings on the hindwings help to startle predators, such as birds: in low light the large spots look like an owl's eyes.

CREATURE COMPARISONS

With a wingspan of up to 10cm (3.9in), the European swallowtail, Papilio machaon, is significantly smaller than the owl butterfly. It is, however, more vibrantly coloured and the conspicuous 'tails' on each hindwing give it a far more distinctive shape.

Found on different continents, the owl butterfly and common European swallowtail both feed on high-energy food, but find it from quite different sources. Whereas the owl butterfly sucks sugary, fermenting fruit and sap, the swallowtail takes the nectar from flowers.

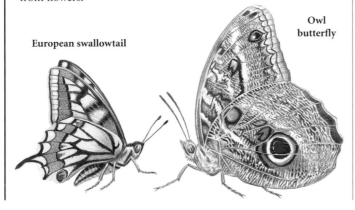

European swallowtail

Owl butterfly

WHERE IN THE WORLD?

Restricted to tropical areas of Central and South America, from central Mexico south to northern Argentina. Primarily a resident of cloud- and rainforests.

RELATED SPECIES
There are 80 species of owl butterfly in 12 genera in the order Lepidoptera. They form the subfamily Brassolinae within the very diverse family Nymphalidae. Another subfamily, the Morphinae, contains the big, metallic blue morpho butterflies, which inhabit the same forests as owl butterflies. In Asian forests, many members of the subfamily Amathusiinae are also very large. Like owl butterflies, they have eyespots on their wings.

• ORDER • *Lepidoptera* • FAMILY • *Papilionidae* • GENUS & SPECIES • *Various*

SWALLOWTAIL BUTTERFLY

Boldly patterned with dark lace-work, the swallowtail's striking wings are designed to confuse predators as well as to attract a mate.

KEY FEATURES

- Takes its name from the short 'tails' on its hindwings.
- The caterpillar protects itself from predators by waving a forked gland that exudes unpleasant chemicals.
- Males and females often have completely different wing colours and patterns.
- More than 500 species found worldwide.

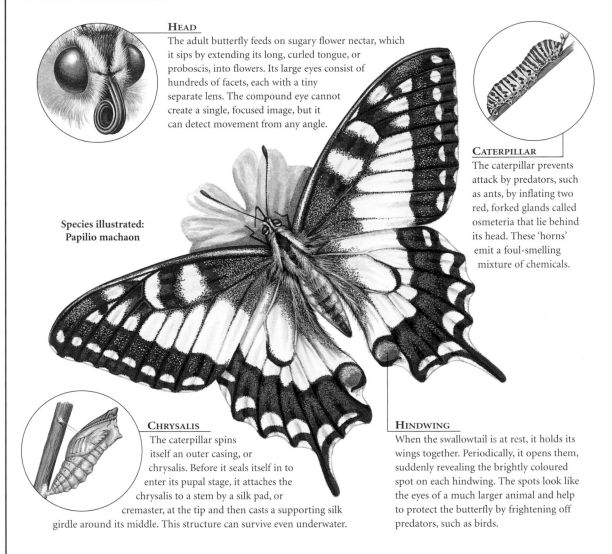

HEAD
The adult butterfly feeds on sugary flower nectar, which it sips by extending its long, curled tongue, or proboscis, into flowers. Its large eyes consist of hundreds of facets, each with a tiny separate lens. The compound eye cannot create a single, focused image, but it can detect movement from any angle.

Species illustrated:
Papilio machaon

CATERPILLAR
The caterpillar prevents attack by predators, such as ants, by inflating two red, forked glands called osmeteria that lie behind its head. These 'horns' emit a foul-smelling mixture of chemicals.

CHRYSALIS
The caterpillar spins itself an outer casing, or chrysalis. Before it seals itself in to enter its pupal stage, it attaches the chrysalis to a stem by a silk pad, or cremaster, at the tip and then casts a supporting silk girdle around its middle. This structure can survive even underwater.

HINDWING
When the swallowtail is at rest, it holds its wings together. Periodically, it opens them, suddenly revealing the brightly coloured spot on each hindwing. The spots look like the eyes of a much larger animal and help to protect the butterfly by frightening off predators, such as birds.

VITAL STATISTICS

WINGSPAN	4.4–20cm (1.7–7.9in)
CATERPILLAR LENGTH	6–7cm (2.4–2.7in)
BREEDING SEASON	Varies according to species and location
NUMBER OF EGGS	100 to 200
HATCHING PERIOD	8–12 days
CATERPILLAR STAGE	About 30 days
BREEDING INTERVAL	Tropical species breed almost continually; other species vary according to location
TYPICAL DIET	Caterpillar feeds on specific foodplants; adult feeds on flower nectar
LIFESPAN	A few weeks as an adult

CREATURE COMPARISONS

Most species of swallowtail are dwarfed by one of their relatives — the Asian birdwing (Troides superbus). With a wingspan that can measure up to 28cm (11in), this birdwing is one of the largest butterflies in the world. Its basic wing shape is similar to that of the swallowtail in that both have long, pointed forewings and rounded hindwings, but the birdwing lacks its relative's hindwing tails. Adults of both species feed on nectar, and are often found flying high above the tree canopy.

Swallowtail   Asian birdwing

WHERE IN THE WORLD?

Found mainly in tropical regions, but species also occur throughout all continents with the exception of the Arctic and Antarctica.

RELATED SPECIES
The order Lepidoptera is made up of 14,500 known species of butterfly together with more than 135,000 moths. It contains many families including the Papilionidae, to which the swallowtails belong, and the Nymphalidae, of which the Indian leaf butterfly, Kallima inachus is a member.

• ORDER • *Lepidoptera* • FAMILY • *Saturniidae* • GENUS & SPECIES • *Actias selene*

INDIAN MOON MOTH

KEY FEATURES

- Males and females spend almost all of their very brief adult lives attempting to meet up and mate.
- Male tracks down a female by following the trail of her special scent through the forest.
- Young caterpillars live together in a protective group, probably locating each other by chemical scents.

VITAL STATISTICS

LENGTH	Caterpillar: 10cm (3.9in) Moth: 13–14cm (5.1–5.5in)
WINGSPAN	15–16.5cm (5.9–6.5in)
SEXUAL MATURITY	Adult is mature upon emerging
MATING SEASON	All year
NUMBER OF EGGS	120 to 150
HATCHING PERIOD	10–30 days
LARVAL PERIOD	30–40 days
CHRYSALIS PERIOD	3–5 weeks
TYPICAL DIET	Caterpillar eats leaves of many plants; adult does not feed
LIFESPAN	Up to 20 days as an adult

The male Indian moon moth possesses acutely sensitive antennae for detecting the enticing scent that the female releases onto the breeze.

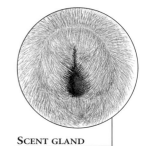

ANTENNAE
The male uses his feathery antennae to track the female's distinctive scent.

WINGS
The pale yellow colours blend in with the green and brown shades of the forest vegetation, helping to conceal the moon moth from predators.

CATERPILLAR
The caterpillar is coloured to match the foliage on which it lives. Spines on its body cause irritation and pain to any predator that tries to eat it, although yellow and black tufts help to warn predators that the caterpillar will taste foul.

EYESPOTS
Together with the shape of the wings, the eyespots give the appearance of a mammal's head, and may help to startle a predator.

WING TAILS
The long, showy tails on the wings help to draw a predator's attention away from the vulnerable head.

SCENT GLAND
A gland toward the rear of the female's abdomen releases the pheromone, or chemical scent.

CREATURE COMPARISONS

The Indian moon moth is one of many moon moths found worldwide. Actias luna of North America has shorter 'tails' than the Indian moth, and spans about 13cm (5.1in) between its rounded wingtips. Both species possess an eyespot on each wing, although in the American moth this mark connects with the crimson strip on each forewing edge. Argena mimosae, one of several African species, occurs from Congo to South Africa. This spectacular species is about 18cm (7.1in) long from forewing-tip to tail.

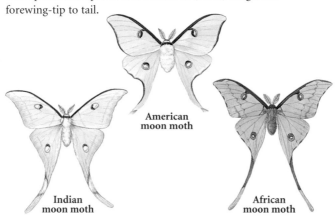

Indian moon moth

American moon moth

African moon moth

WHERE IN THE WORLD?

Found in forest and woodland in India, from Punjab, Uttar Pradesh and Bharat to Bihar. Also found in Bangladesh, Assam, Burma (Myanmar), Malaysia, Laos and parts of China.

RELATED SPECIES

The family Saturniidae contains about 1300 species, including the silkworm, Bombyx mori, which is farmed for the commercial production of silk. Many saturniid species, like the Indian moon moth, have developed a defence against predators in the form of eyespots.

• ORDER • *Lepidoptera* • FAMILY • *Sphingidae* • GENUS & SPECIES • *Acherontia atropos* DEATH'S HEAD HAWK-MOTH

Resting on a tree-trunk, the death's head hawk-moth is well camouflaged by its marbled brown wings. It flashes its yellow underwings if it is disturbed.

KEY FEATURES

- One of the largest insects found in Europe, it is named after the skull-like markings on its thorax.
- Long, slim upperwings enable it to fly swiftly and powerfully as it migrates from Africa to Europe.
- Caterpillar feeds voraciously on potato plants, while the adult raids the nests of bees for honey.

VITAL STATISTICS

WEIGHT	Adult 7g (0.25oz)
LENGTH	Adult; 4–5cm (1.6–2in) Caterpillar; 12.5cm (4.9in)
WINGSPAN	10–13cm (3.9–5.1in)
SEXUAL MATURITY	1–2 months
MATING SEASON	May–October
NUMBER OF EGGS	Up to 150
EGG TO ADULT	4–6 months
BREEDING INTERVAL	Adults usually die after breeding
TYPICAL DIET	Caterpillar eats nightshade plants; adult eats honey, tree sap and nectar
LIFESPAN	2–3 months as an adult

DEATH'S HEAD
The markings on the thorax (middle body section) vary between individuals. They may resemble the markings of queen bees, helping the moth to pacify worker bees as it raids their nests.

CATERPILLAR
The hairless caterpillar is yellow or brown with diagonal blue or purple stripes along its body and a horn at its rear. It has six legs near its head, plus four pairs of foot-like suckers on its abdomen and a pair on the hind end.

ANTENNAE
The spindle-shaped antennae are highly sensitive and can detect the tiniest amount of scent. They enable the moth to find a mate or locate honeybees' nests over great distances.

PROBOSCIS
Unlike most hawk-moths, the death's head has a short, stubby proboscis that it uses for drinking honey from hives and tree sap. The moth can also produce a sharp squeak by sucking air into its hollow organ.

WINGS
The narrow upperwings are much longer than the underwings and enable the moth to fly strongly. In flight they make a faint buzzing sound. Both sets of wings are covered with fine powdery scales that overlap like roofing tiles.

PUPA
The large pupa is shiny blackish-red with distinct body segments and wingcase grooves. The hard casing protects the insect as it undergoes metamorphosis from caterpillar into adult.

CREATURE COMPARISONS

Although it is a close relative of the death's head hawk-moth, the hummingbird hawk-moth (Macroglossum stellatarum) shows remarkably different feeding behaviour. As its name suggests, it is a versatile flier and can hover at flowerheads while probing deeply for nectar with its long proboscis. Many moths may feed on a single bush.

The hummingbird hawk-moth breeds in Europe, North Africa and the Middle East, and migrates more widely than the death's head hawk-moth. It reaches polar regions and even North America. Smaller than the death's head, the hummingbird hawk-moth is less colourful than many of its larger relatives.

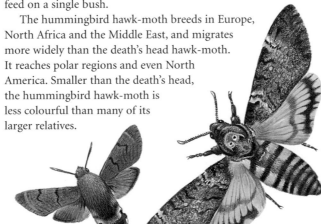

Hummingbird hawk-moth

Death's head hawk-moth

WHERE IN THE WORLD?

Found throughout Africa and parts of southwestern Asia, but avoids the driest regions. Migrates northwards into much of southern Europe, and some venture as far as Britain.

RELATED SPECIES

The death's head is 1 of 800 species of hawk-moth in the family Sphingidae. Most hawk-moths are big, powerful fliers, and many of them, such as the elephant hawk-moth, Deilephila elpenor, have markings and colouration to rival those of butterflies.

• **ORDER** • *Lithobiida* • **FAMILY** • *Lithobiidae* • **GENUS & SPECIES** • *Various*

CENTIPEDE

Scuttling across the ground in a blur of fluid movement, the common centipede attacks any small animal it locates with its antennae.

KEY FEATURES

- Long-bodied, multi-legged invertebrates capable of brisk and agile movements.
- Use antennae to locate small animals, which they kill with powerful claws laden with venom.
- Shun sunlight and spend the daytime hiding under stones or loose tree bark.

TAIL END
The last pair of legs trails backwards beyond the centipede's tail end and are not used for walking. Instead, they may have a sensory function, like a pair of hind antennae.

LEGS
Each body segment has a pair of long, multi-jointed legs. Members of the family Lithobiidae have 15 pairs of legs in total.

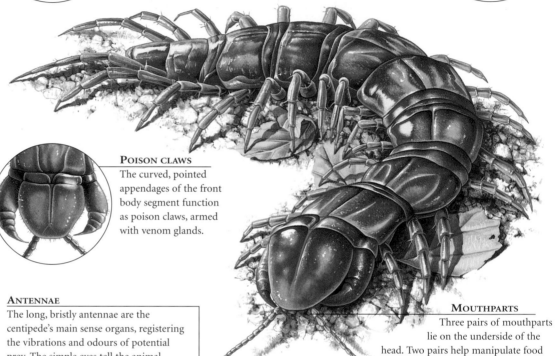

POISON CLAWS
The curved, pointed appendages of the front body segment function as poison claws, armed with venom glands.

ANTENNAE
The long, bristly antennae are the centipede's main sense organs, registering the vibrations and odours of potential prey. The simple eyes tell the animal only if it is in light or darkness. Some cave-dwelling species are totaly blind.

**Species illustrated:
Common centipede,
Lithobius forficatus**

MOUTHPARTS
Three pairs of mouthparts lie on the underside of the head. Two pairs help manipulate food into the mouth while the other pair functions as jaws for cutting.

VITAL STATISTICS

LENGTH	5–40mm (0.2–1.6in) depending on species
NUMBER OF LEGS	15 pairs
SEXUAL MATURITY	Varies according to species; several months or even years
BREEDING SEASON	Spring to autumn in temperate climates
EGGS	Laid singly or in small batches
HATCHING PERIOD	6–15 weeks, depending on species
TYPICAL DIET	Small insects, spiders, woodlice, snails, worms and other invertebrates
LIFESPAN	Up to 6 years

CREATURE COMPARISONS

The common or dark-brown centipede and the black millipede (Tachypodius niger) are both familiar invertebrates in Britain. At first glimpse the two animals seem similar, but closer examination reveals that the millipede has a cylindrical shape and many more body segments — up to 56. The millipede also has a far greater number of legs, with two pairs to each segment. The two species are in fact only distantly related, belonging to separate taxonomic classes. Both animals lurk by day in crevices and forage at night, yet their habits are very different: the millipede is a slow-moving plant eater whereas the centipede is a swift hunter.

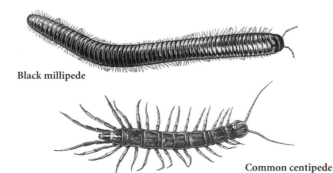

Black millipede

Common centipede

WHERE IN THE WORLD?

Found in temperate and tropical Eurasia and North and Central America. This family is absent from Australia, much of South America and most of Africa.

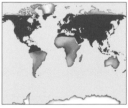

RELATED SPECIES

The Lithobiidae is one of the most familiar and widespread families of centipedes. It forms part of the order Lithobiida: centipedes that are flattened in shape. There are 3 other orders of centipedes, some members of which have especially long legs and very rapid movement, while others are thread-like burrowers with short but numerous legs. Altogether they form the class Chilopoda, with a total of some 3000 species.

ANGLERFISH

• **ORDER** • *Lophiiformes* • **FAMILY** • *Lophiidae* • **GENUS & SPECIES** • *Lophius piscatorius*

The anglerfish is little more than a vast mouth and a stretchy stomach: a living trap for unwary fish attracted by its tantalizing lure.

KEY FEATURES

- Voracious predator that attacks any prey within striking distance of its cavernous mouth.
- Attracts prey with a lure on the end of a spine resembling a fishing rod.
- Excellent skin camouflage allows it to lie in wait, undetected, on the seabed.

VITAL STATISTICS

WEIGHT	Up to 40kg (88.2lb)
LENGTH	Up to 1.8m (5ft 9in)
BREEDING SEASON	Spring to early summer
NUMBER OF EGGS	Thousands, laid in long ribbons of mucus
LARVAL STAGE	Larvae swim among plankton until about 7cm (2.3 in) long, before descending to the seabed
BREEDING INTERVAL	1 year
TYPICAL DIET	Small fish that feed on or near the seabed
LIFESPAN	Unknown

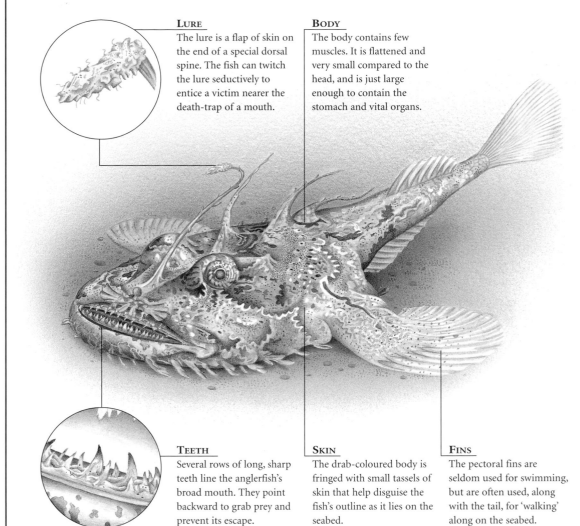

LURE
The lure is a flap of skin on the end of a special dorsal spine. The fish can twitch the lure seductively to entice a victim nearer the death-trap of a mouth.

BODY
The body contains few muscles. It is flattened and very small compared to the head, and is just large enough to contain the stomach and vital organs.

TEETH
Several rows of long, sharp teeth line the anglerfish's broad mouth. They point backward to grab prey and prevent its escape.

SKIN
The drab-coloured body is fringed with small tassels of skin that help disguise the fish's outline as it lies on the seabed.

FINS
The pectoral fins are seldom used for swimming, but are often used, along with the tail, for 'walking' along on the seabed.

CREATURE COMPARISONS

As a largely sedentary bottom-dweller, the anglerfish has a wholly different body form from a powerful, free-swimming species of a similar length, such as the Atlantic cod. The anglerfish does not need the blocks of powerful muscles and streamlined body that make the cod an efficient swimmer. The anglerfish's puny, vertically flattened body looks like an afterthought tacked onto its enormous head.

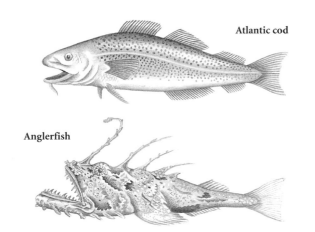

Atlantic cod

Anglerfish

WHERE IN THE WORLD?

Found on the continental shelves of coastal Europe and North Africa, in the eastern Atlantic Ocean and Mediterranean Sea.

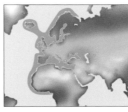

Usually stays on the seabed, but moves into deeper water during the breeding season.

RELATED SPECIES

The anglerfish belongs to the order Lophiiformes: all these fish have lures and other adaptations for trapping prey. Some of the strangest are the deep-sea anglerfish, which hunt in the dark ocean depths. These species have refined their lures to an incredible degree: the frontal spine is long and whip-like, and in some species the lure is luminous. Another relative is the sargassum fish, which looks very like the floating seaweed in which it skulks.

• **ORDER** • *Macroscelidea* • **FAMILY** • *Macroscelididae* • **GENUS & SPECIES** • *Various*

ELEPHANT SHREW

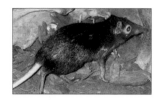

Using its sensitive snout to sniff out a meal, the compact and speedy elephant shrew employs its powerful hindlegs to outrun its prey before pouncing.

KEY FEATURES

- Takes its name from its long, mobile, trunk-like snout, which it uses to sniff out prey hiding underground.
- When escaping predators, runs at speeds of over 25km/h (15.3mph) through a network of self-made trails.
- Fights fiercely with other elephant shrews that trespass on its territory.

SKULL
The upper jaw is elongated to support the even longer, fleshy snout. The fang-like upper canines pierce and grip prey, while the closely set molars at the rear of the jaw are used to grind up food.

TONGUE
The long, tapered tongue can be pushed out to the tip of the snout, and is used to draw small prey, such as ants, into the mouth. The tongue darts in and out continuously as the shrew hunts.

TAIL
A gland on the undersurface of the tail exudes beads of moisture that have a musky smell. These excretions are used to scent mark territory.

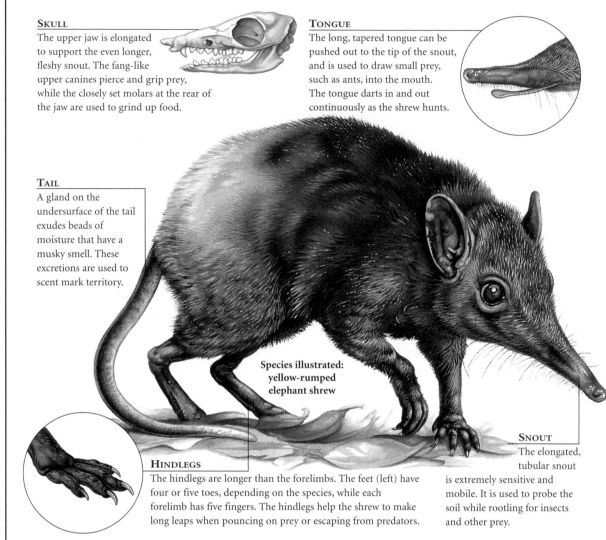

Species illustrated:
yellow-rumped
elephant shrew

HINDLEGS
The hindlegs are longer than the forelimbs. The feet (left) have four or five toes, depending on the species, while each forelimb has five fingers. The hindlegs help the shrew to make long leaps when pouncing on prey or escaping from predators.

SNOUT
The elongated, tubular snout is extremely sensitive and mobile. It is used to probe the soil while rootling for insects and other prey.

VITAL STATISTICS

WEIGHT	25–540g (0.9–19oz)
LENGTH	Head & Body: 9–32cm (3.5–12.2in) Tail; 8–27cm (3.1–10.6in)
SHOULDER HEIGHT	4–15cm (1.6–5.9in)
SEXUAL MATURITY	5–7 weeks
MATING SEASON	All year
GESTATION PERIOD	42–65 days
NUMBER OF YOUNG	1 to 3
BIRTH INTERVAL	Up to 4 litters per year
TYPICAL DIET	Mainly insects, but also small mammals, birds and vegetation
LIFESPAN	2–5 years

CREATURE COMPARISONS

The musk shrew (Suncus murinus), a 'true' shrew of the order Insectivora, is found in Africa and Asia. In Africa its range overlaps with several species of elephant shrew, including one of the largest — the yellow-rumped elephant shrew, Rhynchocyon chrysopygus.

Both the musk shrew and the elephant shrew have elongated snouts with long whiskers to help them find their insect food, but there the resemblance ends. Whereas elephant shrews are mainly diurnal, the musk shrew is nocturnal, sleeping by day in burrows or even in buildings. In fact, this species now commonly lives alongside humans and is a nuisance in homes, where it damages food stores.

Yellow-rumped
elephant shrew

Musk shrew

WHERE IN THE WORLD?

Elephant shrews are widespread across sub-Saharan Africa, although some species have a very limited and localized range. A single species occurs along the coast of North Africa.

RELATED SPECIES

The 15 species of elephant shrew belong to an order of their own — Macroscelidea — and are divided into 2 subfamilies. The 3 large species of the genus Rhynchocyon belong to the subfamily Rhynchocyoninae, while the 12 smaller species are placed in 3 genera in the subfamily Macroscelidinae. The smaller species include the forest elephant shrew, the short-eared elephant shrew and 10 species of long-eared elephant shrew.

• **ORDER** • *Mantodea* • **FAMILY** • *Mantidae* • **GENUS & SPECIES** • *Various*

With its triangular head, huge eyes and peculiar 'praying' stance, the predatory mantis looks like a creature from an alien world.

KEY FEATURES

- Ferocious predator that catches prey in a deadly spiked trap formed by its specially adapted forelegs.

- An expert in the art of concealment, it hunts by remaining stock-still, and striking at lighting speed.

- Lays eggs in batches in a spongy mass to protect them from predators.

- Large species can catch frogs and small birds.

VITAL STATISTICS

LENGTH	1–15cm (0.4–5.9in)
WINGSPAN	1.5–20cm (0.6–7.9in)
SEXUAL MATURITY	1–2 months
BREEDING SEASON	Summer in temperate areas, all year in the tropics, wet season in dry areas
NUMBER OF EGGS	Batches of 10–400 eggs; females lay up to 10 batches depending on the species
BREEDING INTERVAL	Ranges from a few weeks to 9 months
TYPICAL DIET	Mainly insects; large species also take frogs and young birds
LIFESPAN	From a few weeks to several months

FORELEGS
The forelegs are adapted for snatching and grasping. Two enlarged segments bristling with sharp spines clamp and pierce prey when they are snapped shut like a trap. The extensions at the tips act as grappling hooks to pull prey in towards the jaws.

HEAD
Enormous, high-set compound eyes give all-round vision for spotting predators and prey. The jaws are small but very powerful and capable of tearing prey apart. The head is very mobile and can be turned slightly backwards. Hairs on the neck register the head's position and relay the information to the brain to help the mantis strike accurately.

EYE SPOTS
Many species of mantis have eye spots near the base of the forelegs, which are flashed to startle enemies. As well as this visual display, mantids rub their wings against the abdomen to produce a distinct hissing sound.

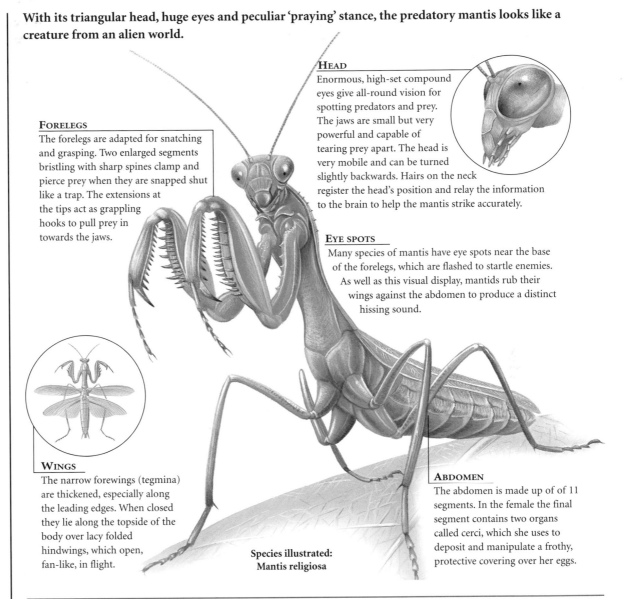

WINGS
The narrow forewings (tegmina) are thickened, especially along the leading edges. When closed they lie along the topside of the body over lacy folded hindwings, which open, fan-like, in flight.

Species illustrated:
Mantis religiosa

ABDOMEN
The abdomen is made up of of 11 segments. In the female the final segment contains two organs called cerci, which she uses to deposit and manipulate a frothy, protective covering over her eggs.

CREATURE COMPARISONS

All mantids have snap-trap forelegs, but the many species vary greatly in shape and colour. The praying mantis, Mantis religiosa, of the family Mantidae is found in Eurasia, North Africa and the USA. Its green colouring helps it to hide in vegetation. The more colourful species of mantis belong to the family Hymenopodidae. These include the flower mantis, Harpugomantis discolor, of southern Africa's savannahs, and the orchid mantis, Hympenopus coronatus, found in the rainforests of Southeast Asia. Both species live among flowers of a similar colour to their body.

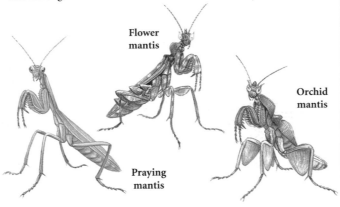

Flower mantis

Orchid mantis

Praying mantis

WHERE IN THE WORLD?

The many species of mantids are found in a wide variety of habitats throughout the world, including rainforests, savannahs, semi-deserts and gardens. Mantids are absent from deserts and polar regions.

RELATED SPECIES

There are about 2000 known species of mantis. They are divided into 8 families, which contain over 400 genera. The majority are the 'ordinary' slender mantids that belong to the family Mantidae, but some mantids, such as the members of the family Eremiaphilidae, are short, squat and wingless. Mantids, are now placed in their own order, but were once placed in the order Orthoptera, which contains crickets, locusts and grasshoppers.

• **ORDER** • *Marsupialia* • **FAMILY** • *Dasyuridae* • **GENUS & SPECIES** • *Dasyurus spp.*

QUOLL

This compact flesh-eater, with its lithe limbs and sharp claws, can make an assault on prey anywhere from ground level up to the high branches.

KEY FEATURES

• Carnivorous marsupial that lives in a variety of habitats, including the suburbs of Australian cities.

• Female produces more than 20 young, but is only capable of suckling less than half that number.

• Emerges from a daytime shelter to ambush or stalk prey either on the ground or in the trees.

EARS
Acute hearing helps the quoll track the rustle of its prey in the undergrowth.

TEETH
The long canines can dispatch prey in a single bite. Quolls are polyprotodont marsupials, having more than four incisors in the lower jaw (the eastern quoll has six).

Species illustrated:
eastern quoll,
Dasyurus viverrinus

COAT
The short, thick fur is greyish-brown with large white spots and blotches except on the unmarked tail. Some eastern quolls have black fur with white spots.

SNOUT
The quoll's keen sense of smell is a useful hunting aid, as are the quivering whiskers lining its tapering muzzle.

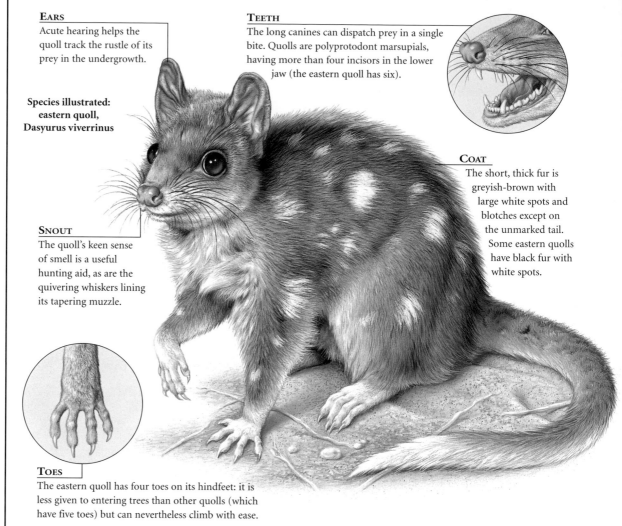

TOES
The eastern quoll has four toes on its hindfeet: it is less given to entering trees than other quolls (which have five toes) but can nevertheless climb with ease.

VITAL STATISTICS

WEIGHT	0.3–7kg (0.7–15.4lb)
LENGTH	Head & Body: 12–75cm (4.7–29.5in) Tail; 12–55cm (4.7–21.6in)
SEXUAL MATURITY	1 year
MATING SEASON	April to August, depending on species
GESTATION PERIOD	12–21 days
NUMBER OF YOUNG	1–8 (up to 30 in the eastern quoll, but only 6–8 survive)
TYPICAL DIET	Birds, small mammals, reptiles, insects, amphibians, earthworms, spiders, fruit, carrion, refuse in urban areas
LIFESPAN	Eastern quoll 3–4 years; other species unknown

CREATURE COMPARISONS

The kowari (*Dasyuroides byrnei*) lives in the arid regions of southwestern Queensland in Australia. Its larger relative the eastern quoll avoids these dry conditions and lacks the kowari's ability to enter a torpor (short-term hibernation) if food is scarce.

Despite rarely exceeding 140g (4.9oz) in weight, the kowari is a ferocious nocturnal predator that kills animals as big as itself, such as marsupial mice. Like the eastern quoll, the kowari has strong forelimbs for burrowing and four toes on each hindfoot.

Kowari

Eastern quoll

WHERE IN THE WORLD?

Once widespread across Australia, the various species are now confined to northern, eastern and southwestern areas. Also found on Tasmania and Papua New Guinea.

RELATED SPECIES

Of the 6 species of quoll, the tiger quoll, **Dasyurus maculatus**, is not only the largest but also the only quoll to have spots on its tail. Quolls belong to the Dasyuridae, a family of marsupial carnivores whose largest member is the Tasmanian devil, **Sarcophilus harrisii**.

TASMANIAN DEVIL

• ORDER • *Marsupialia* • FAMILY • *Dasyuridae* • GENUS & SPECIES • *Sarcophilus harrisii*

The Tasmanian devil may look like a ferocious hunter, but its bone-crushing teeth and muscle-packed body are adaptations for ripping into carrion.

KEY FEATURES

- Massively strong for its size, yet preys only on small or weakened animals.
- Feeds mainly by scavenging on carrion, using its armoury of crushing teeth to devour even the bones.
- Rivals fight fiercely and utter blood-curdling screams and growls while they gorge on the same carcass.

HEAD
The unusually broad, thick skull anchors huge muscles that provide the jaws with immense power.

TEETH
Heavy-duty molars line the sides of the jaws. These teeth resemble those of hyenas, which also specialize in cracking the bones of scavenged carrion.

FOREFOOT
Each forefoot has five toes, but unlike other marsupials, the hindfeet have just four. Every toe is tipped with a short but thick claw.

POUCH
The female's rear-opening pouch (not shown) is under her belly, between the hindlegs. Outside the breeding season the pouch closes up completely.

LIMBS
The Tasmanian devil's legs are stocky and muscular, giving it a rather clumsy gait. It rarely runs faster than 10km/h (6.2mph).

VITAL STATISTICS

WEIGHT	5–10kg (11–22lb)
LENGTH	Head & Body: 52–80cm (20.5–31in) Tail; 23–30cm (9–11.8in)
SEXUAL MATURITY	2 years
MATING SEASON	March to April
GESTATION PERIOD	31 days
NUMBER OF YOUNG	2 to 4
BIRTH INTERVAL	1 year
TYPICAL DIET	Mainly carrion; also live prey ranging from insects to other marsupials
LIFESPAN	Up to 8 years

CREATURE COMPARISONS

The Tasmanian devil shares much of its range with another large, carnivorous marsupial, the eastern quoll (Dasyurus viverrinus), which is also found in southeastern Australia, although it has been extremely rare there since the 1930s. Sometimes known as the 'native cat', the eastern quoll wears a tremendously variable coat of grey, brown, buff or black fur, and is liberally spotted with irregular-shaped white markings.

More slender and agile than its burly relative, the eastern quoll usually hunts rather than scavenges, killing small prey such as rats, mice and insects in its long, pointed jaws.

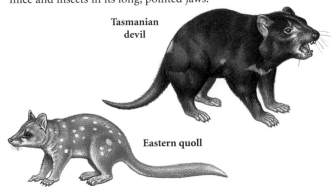

Tasmanian devil

Eastern quoll

WHERE IN THE WORLD?

Occurs in almost every type of habitat on the island of Tasmania. Once widespread on the Australian mainland, but has been extinct there for several hundred years.

RELATED SPECIES

The Tasmanian devil is the sole member of its genus but is closely related to the 3 species of quolls of the genus Dasyurus. Together, these are the largest species in the diverse family Dasyuridae. The 50 or so species in this family, often known as the marsupial carnivores, are grouped into 18 genera and occur across Australia and New Guinea. Many are mouse-sized, but all hunt a wide range of invertebrates and small mammals.

• ORDER • *Marsupialia* • FAMILY • *Didelphidae* • GENUS & SPECIES • *Didelphis virginiana*

VIRGINIA OPOSSUM

KEY FEATURES

- A resourceful marsupial that has adapted to live in a variety of habitats and eat almost anything.
- Capable of rearing three litters — totalling 20 or more young — in a single summer.
- Discourages predators by 'playing possum': pretending to be dead.

VITAL STATISTICS

WEIGHT	3–6kg (6.6–13.2lb)
LENGTH	Head & Body: 33–55cm (13–21.6in) Tail: 25–54cm (9.8–21.2in)
SEXUAL MATURITY	10 months
MATING SEASON	Winter
GESTATION PERIOD	12–13 days
NUMBER OF YOUNG	Usually up to 21 per litter
TIME IN POUCH	70 days
BIRTH INTERVAL	Up to 3 litters each season
TYPICAL DIET	Insects, small animals, fruit, carrion and scraps
LIFESPAN	About 2 years

Although it is well adapted for tree life, the Virginia opossum is just as ready to forage on the forest floor, or even in a suburban garden.

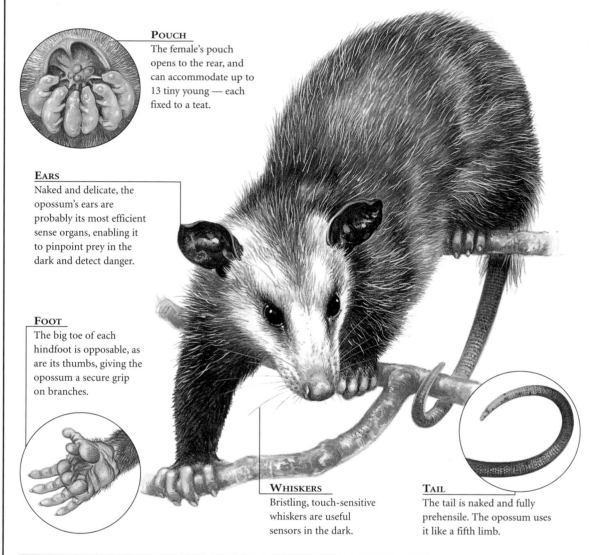

POUCH
The female's pouch opens to the rear, and can accommodate up to 13 tiny young — each fixed to a teat.

EARS
Naked and delicate, the opossum's ears are probably its most efficient sense organs, enabling it to pinpoint prey in the dark and detect danger.

FOOT
The big toe of each hindfoot is opposable, as are its thumbs, giving the opossum a secure grip on branches.

WHISKERS
Bristling, touch-sensitive whiskers are useful sensors in the dark.

TAIL
The tail is naked and fully prehensile. The opossum uses it like a fifth limb.

CREATURE COMPARISONS

The marsupials are often considered evolutionary 'losers' in comparison with placental mammals, which have tended to replace them when introduced to their habitats, but the Virginia opossum is a clear exception to this rule. The common brushtail possum (Trichosurus vulpecula) of Australia is a similar success story, ranging into the cities and suburbs as well as the remote woodlands of the interior. It feeds mainly on leaves and other plant material, often inflicting such damage that it is regarded as a pest — particularly in New Zealand, where it was introduced in about 1840.

Common brushtail possum

Virginia opossum

WHERE IN THE WORLD?

Range extends from Panama in the south, through eastern North America to the Great Lakes. It has also been introduced to the Pacific coast.

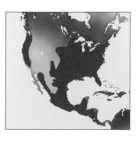

RELATED SPECIES

The genus Didelphis also includes the southern opossum and the white-eared opossum. There are 77 American opossum species in the family Didelphidae, which also contains the mouse opossums, genus Marmosa and is 1 of 18 marsupial families.

TREE KANGAROO

• **ORDER** • *Marsupialia* • **FAMILY** • *Macropodidae* • **GENUS & SPECIES** • *Dendrolagus spp.*

All kangaroos descended from a tree-dwelling ancestor; in reverting to an arboreal lifestyle, tree kangaroos have reversed millions of years of evolution.

KEY FEATURES

- A quarter of all species were unknown to science until the 1990s; seven are now listed as either vulnerable or endangered by the IUCN (World Conservation Union).
- Share a common ancestor with kangaroos, but are uniquely adapted to life in the trees.
- Remarkable mobility in their limbs equip tree kangaroos for acrobatic moves in the branches.

VITAL STATISTICS

WEIGHT	Up to 17kg (37.5in)
LENGTH	Head & Body: 52–81cm (20.5–31.9in) Tail; 42–93.5cm (16.5–36.8in)
SEXUAL MATURITY	2–3 years
MATING SEASON	Year round, but Australian species favour the rainy season
GESTATION PERIOD	Up to 45 days, average 32 days
NUMBER OF YOUNG	1, rarely twins
BIRTH INTERVAL	12–18 months
TYPICAL DIET	Leaves; some species also eat roots and fruit
LIFESPAN	Up to 20 years in captivity

HAIR WHORL
Tree kangaroos have a hair whorl to assist in shedding rainwater. The position of the whorl on the shoulders or back varies according to species.

HINDLIMBS
Unlike other kangaroos, a tree kangaroo can move its hindlimbs independently in order to walk as well as hop. This crucial adaptation enables the animal to manoeuvre on thin branches.

TAIL
The tree kangaroo uses its long tail as a balance and as a brace when climbing or leaping.

Species shown:
Grizzled tree kangaroo,
Dendrolagus inustus

HINDFOOT
With regard to feet, tree kangaroos divide into two groups. Bennett's and Lumholtz's tree kangaroos of Australia, and the grizzled tree kangaroo of New Guinea, are long-footed. Other New Guinea species are short-footed. Uniquely among marsupials, the hindfeet can rotate to face each other to grasp branches. Long, curved claws and thick, rough soles also help with gripping.

CREATURE COMPARISONS

A little smaller and daintier than tree kangaroos, forest wallabies (genus Dorcopsis) are also on the list of New Guinea's endangered marsupials. The three blackish-brown species are ground-dwellers and feed largely on grass. Like many kangaroos, they use the tail-tip as a fifth limb when bounding; this may account for the curious, roughened tip of their comparatively short tail.

The forest wallabies and tree kangaroos share a tooth structure unique among marsupials, with long, shearing premolars and a sharp shearing blade on the first molar, for chopping up plant matter.

Forest wallaby

Tree kangaroo

WHERE IN THE WORLD?

Australian populations are confined to tropical rainforests of the Cape York peninsula of northern Queensland. Those on the island of New Guinea occupy remote areas at varying altitudes.

RELATED SPECIES

New tree kangaroos of the genus Dendrolagus have only recently become known to science; there are now thought to be at least 10 separate species and 7 further subspecies. Tree kangaroos belong to the family Macropodidae, which contains all species of wallaby, and all kangaroos other than rat kangaroos; these are classified as Potoroidae. Kangaroos and wallabies are members of the order Marsupialia.

• **ORDER** • *Marsupialia* • **FAMILY** • *Macropodidae* • **GENUS & SPECIES** • *Macropus parryi*

WHIPTAIL WALLABY

KEY FEATURES

• The most social of all wallabies and kangaroos; lives in groups, called mobs, that can number up to 50 individuals.

• Active most of the day, only taking shelter to escape the midday heat and to sleep at night.

• Its muscular but slender tail, the longest of any wallaby species, acts as a prop when feeding and fighting and a balance when leaping.

VITAL STATISTICS

WEIGHT	Male 14–26kg (30.9–57.3in); female 7–15kg (15.4–33.1in)
LENGTH	Head & Body: Male 70–93cm (27.6–36.6in); female 65–75cm (25.6–29.5in) Tail; 73–104cm (28.7–40.9in)
SHOULDER HEIGHT	90–100cm (35.4–39.4in)
SEXUAL MATURITY	Female 18–30 months; male 24–36 months
MATING SEASON	Year round
GESTATION PERIOD	34–38 days
NUMBER OF YOUNG	1
BIRTH INTERVAL	9 months
TYPICAL DIET	Grasses and ferns
LIFESPAN	Up to 10 years in captivity

One of the largest wallabies, the slender and graceful whiptail wallaby moves extremely fast over short distances if alarmed.

EYES
Like all wallabies, the whiptail wallaby has good nocturnal vision. Light entering each eye hits the retina, and is reflected back onto it by the tapetum (a membrane composed of proteins and zinc).

retina

lens

tapetum

EARS
The large, erect ears can be rotated independently to detect sounds coming from any direction.

SKULL
The skull features an elongated snout. The cheek teeth erupt in slow succession over a long period, enabling the wallaby to survive on a diet of tough, abrasive food.

FORELEGS
The wallaby licks its forelegs in hot weather to increase cooling by evaporation. The paws, used for feeding, fighting and grooming, have a claw on each of the five digits.

COAT
The coat is soft, with grey-brown upperparts and a paler underside. The cheeks and ears are marked with bold white flashes.

POUCH
The female's forward-opening pouch contains four teats. It has a muscular top-band which prevents the offspring from falling out as its mother moves around.

TAIL
The long, slender tail acts as a prop when the wallaby sits down, and helps it balance while on the move.

TOES
The wallaby hops on its long fourth and shorter fifth toes. The first toe is absent, and the small, fused second and third toes are used for grooming.

CREATURE COMPARISONS

The tammar wallaby (Macropus eugenii) is much smaller than the whiptail wallaby, being about the same size as a rabbit. It lives on the opposite side of Australia from its relative, along the southwestern coast of the country and on several offshore islands. Its preferred habitat is made up of woody thickets and low shrub cover rather than eucalyptus forests. This ground cover prevents the tammar wallaby from forming mobs, so it is not as social as the whiptail. In some parts of its range, there is little freshwater available for drinking; like the whiptail, the tammar wallaby derives moisture from the plants it eats, but it can also survive by drinking sea water. After mating, the tammar wallaby can delay embryo development for as long as 11 months, in contrast to the 9 months managed by the whiptail.

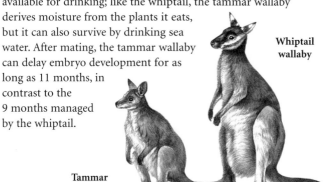

Whiptail wallaby

Tammar wallaby

WHERE IN THE WORLD?

Found in open eucalyptus forest and woodland of eastern Australia. Ranges from most of eastern Queensland south to the northeastern tip of New South Wales.

RELATED SPECIES
The whiptail wallaby is 1 of 14 species, divided into 3 subgenera, in the genus Macropus. The genus contains 3 species of wallaroo plus kangaroos and wallabies, including the red-necked wallaby, M. rufogriseus, which is mainly nocturnal.

RED-NECKED WALLABY

The red-necked wallaby relies on its senses to alert it to danger and on its large, well developed hindlimbs to power it away to safety.

KEY FEATURES

- Highly agile, it escapes predators by bounding along at speed on its long and powerful, spring-loaded hindlimbs.
- One of the most abundant and widespread of all wallaby species.
- A shy and retiring creature that spends the day resting in cover.
- Female is pregnant almost continually throughout her adult life.

VITAL STATISTICS

WEIGHT	Male 15–27kg; (33.1–59.5lb) female 11–16kg (24.2–35.3lb)
LENGTH	Head & Body: 66–92cm (26–36.2in); male larger than female Tail; 62–87cm (24.4–34.2in)
SHOULDER HEIGHT	About 80cm (31in)
SEXUAL MATURITY	Male 21–22 months; female 23–24 months
MATING SEASON	All year
GESTATION PERIOD	About 30 days
NUMBER OF YOUNG	1, sometimes twins
BIRTH INTERVAL	About 274 days
TYPICAL DIET	Grass and leaves; roots sometimes
LIFESPAN	Up to 15 years

EARS
Mobile and sensitive, the wallaby's ears are its first line of defence. At the first rustle of an approaching predator, the wallaby bounds away into cover.

FOREPAWS
Each forepaw has five claw-tipped fingers, which are used for plucking grass and grooming the fur.

HINDLIMBS
Each massive hindlimb is equipped with an elastic tendon that acts like a spring, catapulting the wallaby back into the air when it lands after each bounding stride.

FUR
This wallaby takes its name from the thick, reddish fur that covers its neck and shoulders. Very dense, the fur keeps the wallaby warm in the cooler parts of its range.

DIGESTIVE SYSTEM
The red-necked wallaby has a long and intricately folded stomach harbouring special bacteria that help break down the tough, fibrous plant matter of its diet.

TAIL
The long, muscular tail acts as a rudder, enabling the wallaby to change course when escaping predators. It also serves as a 'third leg' to support the animal.

CREATURE COMPARISONS

The red-necked wallaby is a medium-sized wallaby. Its relative the parma wallaby (Macropus parma) is one of the smallest species, with a head and body length of 42–53cm (16.5–20.9in).

Roughly the size of a chicken, the parma wallaby leads a highly secretive lifestyle in the rainforests of eastern New South Wales. It makes its grassy nest deep in the undergrowth, emerging at night to browse on low-growing vegetation. Like the red-neck, it uses a 'five-legged shuffle' when browsing — putting its forefeet down and bringing up its hindlegs, then perching on hindfeet and robust tail to feed. The thick forest vegetation is no obstacle to this fleet-footed marsupial, which bolts into the nearest cover when threatened.

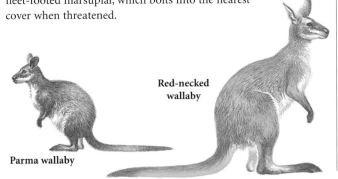

Red-necked wallaby

Parma wallaby

WHERE IN THE WORLD?

Occurs throughout Tasmania and along the southeastern coastal strip of Australia. Also found on islands in the Bass Strait (between Australia and Tasmania). Introduced to parts of New Zealand.

RELATED SPECIES

The red-necked wallaby and the whiptail wallaby, Macropus parryi, are just 2 of 8 wallabies in the genus Macropus. There are also 3 species of wallaroo and 3 species of kangaroo in the same genus. Overall, there are 29 species of wallaby in the family Macropodidae.

• **ORDER** • *Marsupialia* • **FAMILY** • *Macropodidae* • **GENUS & SPECIES** • *Macropus rufus*

RED KANGAROO

The red kangaroo's energy-efficient bounding gait allows it to range far and wide in search of food — even with a joey tucked snugly in the pouch.

KEY FEATURES

- Female nurtures her offspring, or joey, in a pouch on her belly, where it suckles and is protected for more than 21 weeks before first emerging.

- Female is almost continually pregnant with a tiny embryo. Further growth of the embryo is delayed until feeding conditions are suitable.

- Joey forms a close bond with its mother, remaining with her until it is sexually mature.

VITAL STATISTICS

WEIGHT	20–90kg (44–198.4lb)
LENGTH	Head & Body: 84–160cm (33.1–62.3in) Tail: 65–119cm (25.6–46.8in)
HEIGHT	Up to 1.78m (5ft 8in)
SEXUAL MATURITY	Female 15–20 months; male 20–24 months
BREEDING SEASON	All year round
GESTATION PERIOD	33 days
NUMBER OF YOUNG	1
TIME IN POUCH	First emerges after 190 days; leaves for good after 235 days
BIRTH INTERVAL	240 days
TYPICAL DIET	Grasses, herbs, flowering plants
LIFESPAN	Up to 25 years

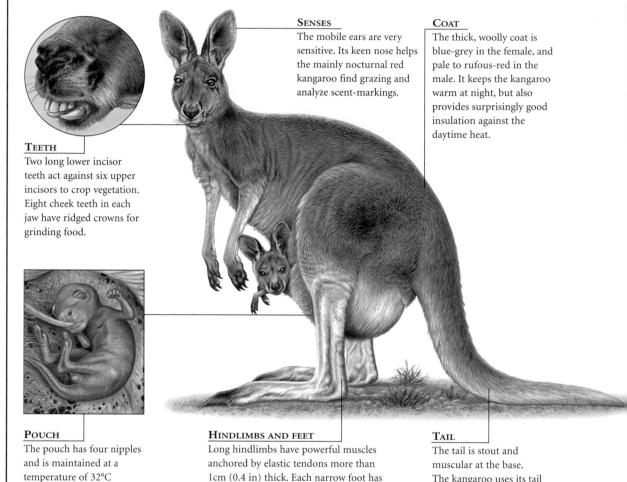

SENSES
The mobile ears are very sensitive. Its keen nose helps the mainly nocturnal red kangaroo find grazing and analyze scent-markings.

COAT
The thick, woolly coat is blue-grey in the female, and pale to rufous-red in the male. It keeps the kangaroo warm at night, but also provides surprisingly good insulation against the daytime heat.

TEETH
Two long lower incisor teeth act against six upper incisors to crop vegetation. Eight cheek teeth in each jaw have ridged crowns for grinding food.

POUCH
The pouch has four nipples and is maintained at a temperature of 32°C (89.6°F). Its muscular top-band stops the joey from falling out.

HINDLIMBS AND FEET
Long hindlimbs have powerful muscles anchored by elastic tendons more than 1cm (0.4 in) thick. Each narrow foot has two clawed toes. The feet give balance, and are used as weapons: against predators, and by males during fights with rivals.

TAIL
The tail is stout and muscular at the base. The kangaroo uses its tail as a prop when standing upright, and as a balance aid when moving at speed.

CREATURE COMPARISONS

Kangaroos and their smaller marsupial relatives have adapted to many different habitats in Australia and nearby New Guinea. The larger members of the family Macropodidae, such as the red kangaroo, graze on open, often rocky woodland or on plains. Medium-sized species, such as the red-leggedpademelon, live in wet forests and browse on leaves or graze on grasses. The smallest macropods are the short-nosed, rat-sized kangaroos, such as the boodie, which eats worms, invertebrates and eggs. Most of these small kangaroos live in dense cover, but the boodie is unique in that it regularly digs dens.

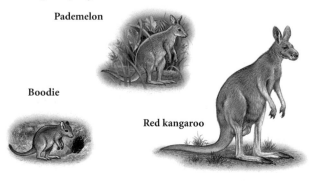

Pademelon

Boodie

Red kangaroo

WHERE IN THE WORLD?

Found across mainland Australia, where it inhabits an area of over 5,000,000 sq km (1,931,000 sq miles). Absent only from extreme northern, eastern, southwestern and southeastern parts of the continent.

RELATED SPECIES

In addition to the red kangaroo, the genus Macropus contains the eastern and the western grey kangaroo, eight species of wallaby and three species of wallaroo — including the common wallaroo, M. robustus, found throughout Australia.

ROCK WALLABY

• **ORDER** • *Marsupialia* • **FAMILY** • *Macropodidae* • **GENUS & SPECIES** • *Petrogale spp.*

Long feet with rough, gripping soles enable the rock wallaby to jump and climb rapidly across the smooth, hard surfaces of its rocky home.

Species illustrated:
Yellow-footed rock wallaby,
Petrogale xanthopus

KEY FEATURES

- Small to medium-sized cousins of the kangaroos adapted to living in rocky habitats.
- Several species are adorned with bright colours and markings that make them among the most distinctive of pouched mammals.
- A sociable animal living in colonies that, on large rocky plateaus, may contain several hundred animals.

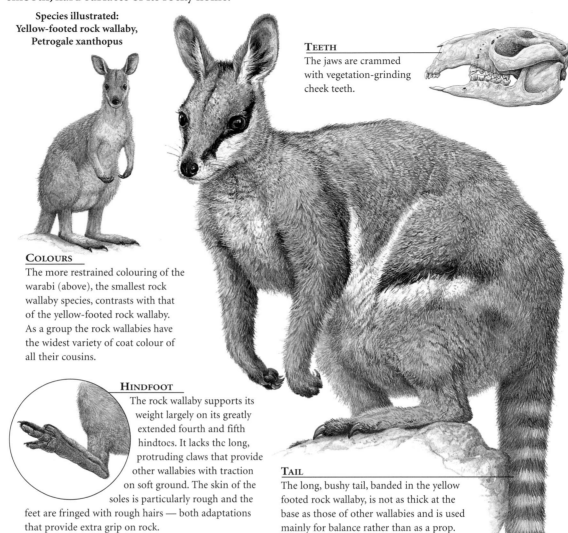

TEETH
The jaws are crammed with vegetation-grinding cheek teeth.

COLOURS
The more restrained colouring of the warabi (above), the smallest rock wallaby species, contrasts with that of the yellow-footed rock wallaby. As a group the rock wallabies have the widest variety of coat colour of all their cousins.

HINDFOOT
The rock wallaby supports its weight largely on its greatly extended fourth and fifth hindtoes. It lacks the long, protruding claws that provide other wallabies with traction on soft ground. The skin of the soles is particularly rough and the feet are fringed with rough hairs — both adaptations that provide extra grip on rock.

TAIL
The long, bushy tail, banded in the yellow footed rock wallaby, is not as thick at the base as those of other wallabies and is used mainly for balance rather than as a prop.

VITAL STATISTICS

WEIGHT	1–8kg (2.2–17.6lb)
LENGTH	Head & Body: 30–80cm (11.8–31in) Tail; 25–70cm (9.8–27.6in)
SEXUAL MATURITY	1–2 years
MATING SEASON	Varies according to species and climatic conditions
GESTATION PERIOD	28–30 days
POUCH LIFE	6–7 months
NUMBER OF YOUNG	1, rarely 2
TYPICAL DIET	Grasses, herbs, leaves, fruit, roots, bark
LIFESPAN	Up to 14 years in captivity

CREATURE COMPARISONS

The three species of nail-tailed wallaby (genus Onychogalea) are similar in size and appearance to the rock wallabies. Living in open woodland, the nail-tailed wallaby is active at night and spends its days under shelter — a shallow burrow dug under a grass tussock, rather than the rock crevices preferred by the rock wallaby. More solitary than the rock wallaby, it also has more typically kangaroo-like features, such as the thickened base of the tail and long claws on the hindfeet. The nail-tailed wallaby is named for the small, horny spur at the tip of its tail, the purpose of which is unknown.

WHERE IN THE WORLD?

Native only to the Australian continent and a few offshore islands that were connected to the mainland during the last ice age.

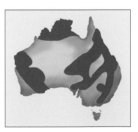

RELATED SPECIES

All 11 species of rock wallaby are part of the family Macropodidae, which contains all wallabies and kangaroos. Wallabies are generally distinguished from kangaroos according to the average adult weight of their species: those over 20kg (44lb) are kangaroos and the rest are wallabies. A third group, the rat-kangaroos, which consists of more than 25 species of tiny, rat-like marsupials, is classified under a separate family: the Potoroidae.

Nail-tailed wallaby

Rock wallaby

• **ORDER** • *Marsupialia* • **FAMILY** • *Macropodidae* • **GENUS & SPECIES** • *Setonix brachyurus*

QUOKKA

KEY FEATURES

- A tough and nimble marsupial, it is a hairy, miniature form of wallaby.
- Lives in a punishing environment, where shelter from the midday sun is essential to its survival.
- Females mate the day after giving birth, to ensure that at least one offspring survives each year.

VITAL STATISTICS

WEIGHT	Male 2.7–4.2kg (5.9–9.2lb); female 2.7–3.5kg (5.9–7.7lb)
LENGTH	Head & Body: 40–54cm (15.7–21.2in) Tail; 25–30cm
SHOULDER HEIGHT	28–35cm (11–13.8in)
SEXUAL MATURITY	1–2 years
MATING SEASON	January to February
GESTATION PERIOD	24–27 days
NUMBER OF YOUNG	1
BIRTH INTERVAL	1 year
TYPICAL DIET	Grasses, herbs, shoots and twigs
LIFESPAN	Up to 10 years

The quokka can bound rapidly on its muscular hindlegs, just like a small kangaroo, and its short but dextrous forelegs help it to gather food.

COAT
The quokka's brown-grey coat, tinged with red, blends well into the dry vegetation of its semi-arid habitat: especially important when it is sheltering during the heat of the day.

POUCH
The female's pouch is forward-facing and provides a secure retreat for the growing joey, which can suckle at any one of four mammae (teats).

TEETH
The teeth are suited to both browsing and grazing. Stout incisors and blade-like premolars shear vegetation, which is then ground up by broad molars.

FORELEGS
Each short foreleg has five clawed digits. The quokka uses its forelegs to pull twigs towards its mouth while feeding and to help it clamber into low bushes.

HINDLEGS
Strong and stocky hindlegs allow the quokka to accelerate rapidly and bound along with easy strides. Spring-like tendons help the muscles expand and contract with little effort and so conserve the quokka's energy.

CREATURE COMPARISONS

The common wallaroo (Macropus robustus) is one of 14 species in the genus Macropus, which contains all of the kangaroo and most of the wallaby species. Weighing in at around 50kg (110.2lb), the wallaroo can be ten times heavier than the quokka, and the male can be over 2m (6ft 6in) from nose to tail. Its robust build and powerful legs, which help it to make 9m (29ft 5in) bounds, means that the wallaroo can roam over much wider areas than the hare-sized quokka. Like the quokka, the wallaroo is able to survive on low-grade vegetation. It can also resist dehydration for even longer than the larger kangaroos and wallabies. Such qualities allow the wallaroo to exploit sparsely vegetated habitats.

Common wallaroo

Quokka

WHERE IN THE WORLD?

Now confined to swampy valleys near the city of Perth on the Australian mainland. Populations also occur on islands just off the southwestern coast.

RELATED SPECIES

The quokka is the only species within the genus Setonix, which is part of the large marsupial family Macropodidae (meaning 'large-footed'). All 50 species in this family have short forelegs and relatively large, elongated hindlegs adapted for hopping. They range from the minuscule musky rat kangaroo, which is a mere 42cm (16.5in) from head to tail, to the red kangaroo, which measures 3.4m (11ft 1in) and weighs about 90kg (198.4lb) — more than most adult humans.

PADEMELON

Resembling a tiny kangaroo, the dusky pademelon speeds through the undergrowth of New Guinea's forests, powered by its massive hindlegs.

KEY FEATURES

- Small relatives of kangaroos that live in the forests of eastern Australia and New Guinea.
- Graze on succulent grasses within clearings and at the forest fringe.
- Threatened in some areas by forest clearance, and hunted as pests on farmland and pasture.

VITAL STATISTICS

WEIGHT	Up to 10kg (22lb)
LENGTH	Head & Body: Up to 60cm (23.6in) Tail; 50cm (19.7in)
SEXUAL MATURITY	18 months
MATING SEASON	Throughout the year
GESTATION PERIOD	30 days, plus 200 days in pouch
NUMBER OF YOUNG	1
BIRTH INTERVAL	7 months
TYPICAL DIET	Leaves, herbs, grasses, seeds and fruit
LIFESPAN	5 years

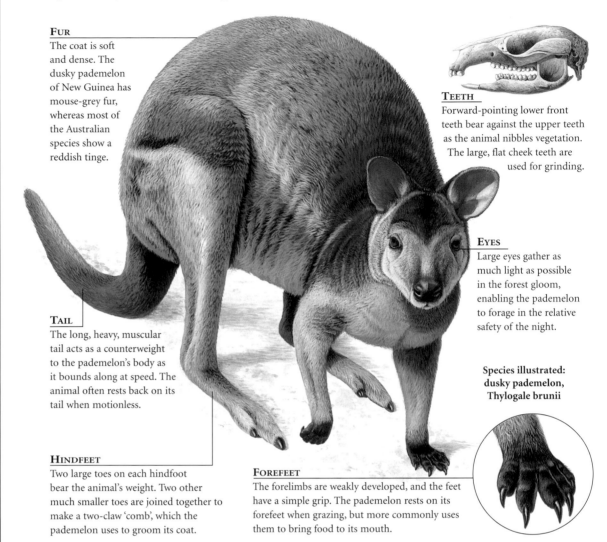

FUR
The coat is soft and dense. The dusky pademelon of New Guinea has mouse-grey fur, whereas most of the Australian species show a reddish tinge.

TAIL
The long, heavy, muscular tail acts as a counterweight to the pademelon's body as it bounds along at speed. The animal often rests back on its tail when motionless.

HINDFEET
Two large toes on each hindfoot bear the animal's weight. Two other much smaller toes are joined together to make a two-claw 'comb', which the pademelon uses to groom its coat.

FOREFEET
The forelimbs are weakly developed, and the feet have a simple grip. The pademelon rests on its forefeet when grazing, but more commonly uses them to bring food to its mouth.

TEETH
Forward-pointing lower front teeth bear against the upper teeth as the animal nibbles vegetation. The large, flat cheek teeth are used for grinding.

EYES
Large eyes gather as much light as possible in the forest gloom, enabling the pademelon to forage in the relative safety of the night.

Species illustrated: dusky pademelon, Thylogale brunii

CREATURE COMPARISONS

In Queensland, Australia, the red-legged pademelon shares parts of its forest habitat with its cousin the agile wallaby (Macropus agilis), which also occurs along Australia's northern coast. More closely related to the larger kangaroos, the agile wallaby is a more gregarious animal and is regularly found in groups of up to ten individuals. It favours river country where it feeds on grassy plains or in clearings. Like the pademelon it retreats to woodland or forest for shelter when not feeding, and this habit makes it vulnerable to forest clearance. It remains common however, and its fondness for crops such as sugar cane has made it the enemy of many farmers.

Agile wallaby

Red-legged pademelon

WHERE IN THE WORLD?

Restricted to New Guinea and nearby islands, the eastern coast of mainland Australia and Tasmania.

RELATED SPECIES

There are 4 species of pademelon in the genus Thylogale: the Tasmanian, red-legged, red-necked and dusky pademelons. Also known as scrub wallabies, they are smaller relatives of kangaroos, with similar physical features and habits. They are all members of the kangaroo family Macropodidae, which contains 56 species. The family is classed among the so-called diprotodont marsupials, which have two front teeth in the lower jaw.

• **ORDER** • *Marsupialia* • **FAMILY** • *Myrmecobiidae* • **GENUS & SPECIES** • *Myrmecobius fasciatus*

NUMBAT

A specialized termite-eater, the numbat has long claws to break open these insects' galleries and a long, probing, sticky tongue to lap them up quickly.

KEY FEATURES

- The only termite-eating marsupial, it sniffs out and unearths termites from the forest floor, and consumes as many as 20,000 in a single day.

- Whips its long, sticky tongue in and out of termites' winding tunnels to extract the insects in seconds.

- Unlike most marsupials it is active during the day.

COAT
The numbat is greyish-brown to reddish-brown with a horizontal black eyestripe. Six to ten white bars cross the back and rump — the exact spacing is unique to each individual numbat.

TAIL
Long, bushy and made up of stiff hairs. The tail is normally held in line with the body, but when the numbat is alarmed it holds it erect with the hairs fluffed out.

SNOUT
The snout is long and tapered for rootling on the forest floor. The numbat also uses its snout as a lever to turn over logs and stones while searching for food.

MAMMAE
The female is unusual among marsupials in that she lacks a pouch, and her four mammae (teats) are exposed on her underside. Long hair around the mammae protect the young while their mother roams the forest.

FOREFEET
Each forefoot (above) has five toes; each hindfoot has four. Long, sturdy claws on each toe enable the numbat to scratch into the earth to find food.

VITAL STATISTICS

WEIGHT	Male 350–700g (12.3–24.7oz); female 275–550g (9.7–19.4oz)
LENGTH	Head & Body: 23–27cm (9–10.6in) Tail; 17–21cm (6.7–8.3in)
SHOULDER HEIGHT	12–15cm (4.7–5.9in)
SEXUAL MATURITY	Male 2 years; female 1 year
MATING SEASON	January
GESTATION PERIOD	14 days
NUMBER OF YOUNG	Unknown, but only up to four can survive as the female has only four mammae
BIRTH INTERVAL	1 year
TYPICAL DIET	Termites
LIFESPAN	3 to 5 years

CREATURE COMPARISONS

A relative of the numbat, the quoll (Dasyurus hallucatus), also known as the native 'cat' or the tiger 'cat', inhabits woodland and rocky areas of northern Australia in a range extending from northern Western Australia east to northern and eastern Queensland.

With a head and body length of 24–35cm (9.4in– 13.8in), the quoll is one of the smallest of the marsupial 'cats'. Its upperparts are greyish-brown, with a distinctive pattern of white spots on the back and sides. These contrast with the numbat's pronounced stripes. Unlike the numbat, the female has a pouch, but it consists simply of lateral folds of skin over her eight teats. The quoll's diet is more varied than the numbat's — it eats vegetation as well as insects .

Numbat

Quoll

WHERE IN THE WORLD?

Formerly ranged in a broad arc across southern Western Australia east to New South Wales. Now confined to a corner of Western Australia.

RELATED SPECIES

The numbat is the only species within the family Myrmecobiidae. It was once grouped with the family Dasyuridae, which contains over 50 species and includes marsupial 'mice', 'cats' and the Tasmanian devil. The numbat was linked to this group because, like some species of Dasyurid, it lacks a pouch, and shelters in a hollow log, like many of the marsupial 'mice'. Later, though, it was judged to be sufficiently different to need separate classification.

• ORDER • *Marsupialia* **• FAMILY •** *Peramelidae* **• GENUS & SPECIES •** *Perameles nasuta*

LONG-NOSED BANDICOOT

The long-nosed bandicoot is a highly active opportunist feeder that uses its long, sensitive nose, strong limbs and sharp claws to find its food.

KEY FEATURES

- A forest-dwelling marsupial with a long sensitive snout to sniff out a very varied range of food.
- Has one of the shortest gestation periods of all mammals, and one of the highest reproduction rates.
- The female's pouch, or marsupium, opens to the rear and can hold five youngsters at a time.

VITAL STATISTICS

WEIGHT	850–1100g (30–38.8oz)
LENGTH	Head & Body: 31–43cm (12.2–16.9in) Tail; 7.5–17cm (2.9–6.7in)
SEXUAL MATURITY	Male 5 months; female 4 months
MATING SEASON	All year
GESTATION PERIOD	12.5 days
NUMBER OF YOUNG	1 to 5, but usually 2 to 4
BIRTH INTERVAL	62–63 days
TYPICAL DIET	Insects and other invertebrates; lizards and mice; fruit, seeds and other plant matter
LIFESPAN	2–3 years

SNOUT
The bandicoot's slender, sensitive nose is adapted for sniffing out food from the forest floor.

EMBRYONIC INFANT
Two days into the pregnancy, an embryo is the size of a full stop. By the time of its birth, about 10 days later, the infant is around 1cm (0.4in) in length (shown about twice life-size, above). Fur appears after 40 days, and the eyes open five to ten days later.

HINDFEET
The small second and third digits (the first is absent) on the long hindfeet are syndactylous (partially fused together), forming a grooming comb for the stiff fur. The sharp claws are also used for digging.

POUCH
The pouch opens to the rear and extends along the female's belly. Inside there are eight teats arranged in two rows of four. After birth, each infant climbs into the pouch, still attached to an umbilical cord, and suckles.

CREATURE COMPARISONS

The numbat, Myrmecobius fasciatus, is an Australian marsupial that inhabits open scrub woodland and desert areas. Like the long-nosed bandicoot, the numbat has a long, tapering jaw containing at least 48 teeth (the bandicoot has 46 or 48). Unlike the bandicoot, the female numbat does not have a pouch, instead her young cling to her long belly fur. The numbat is also active by day, rather than at night. The clearest difference between the species lies in the dramatic, striped pattern of the numbat's coat.

Numbat

Long-nosed bandicoot

WHERE IN THE WORLD?

Found mainly in foreststo the east of the Great Dividing Range in Australia, from Cooktown in northern Queensland south to Geelong in Victoria.

RELATED SPECIES

There are 21 species of bandicoot in the family Peramelidae and two closely related species of rabbit-eared bandicoot, or bilbies, that are now placed in a family of their own—Thylacomidae. These are the greater bilby, Macrotis lagotis and the lesser bilby, M. leucura.

• **ORDER** • *Marsupialia* • **FAMILY** • *Petauridae* • **GENUS & SPECIES** • *Dactylopsila trivergata*

STRIPED POSSUM

The striped possum moves through its forest home with speed and agility, leaping between trees to investigate beneath the bark for tasty grubs.

KEY FEATURES

- A small rainforest marsupial with black-and-white patterning all over its head and body.
- Superb climber that walks along branches with a strange rowing action, and rarely touches the ground.
- Uses its long fourth finger to winkle wood-boring insect larvae out of tree cavities.

VITAL STATISTICS

WEIGHT	280–440g (10–15.5oz)
LENGTH	Head & Body: 24–28cm (9.4–11in) Tail; 31–39cm (12.2–15.3in)
SEXUAL MATURITY	9–10 months
MATING SEASON	February to August in Queensland; year round in New Guinea
GESTATION PERIOD	17–18 days; young leave the pouch after 60 days
NUMBER OF YOUNG	1, rarely 2
BIRTH INTERVAL	1 year
TYPICAL DIET	Insects and their larvae; leaves, fruit and honey
LIFESPAN	Unknown in the wild; 5 years in captivity

TEETH
The long lower incisors project forwards and are useful for gouging timber.

FUR
The striped fur helps camouflage the possum in its rainforest home.

SENSES
Large, forward-facing eyes provide good binocular vision, even at night: essential for judging distances. Sensitive whiskers also aid navigation.

FEET
Long, lightly furred toes have sharp, hooked claws for a secure hold on tree bark.

HANDS
The fourth finger, with its hooked claw, is twice the length of the others. This special adaptation helps the possum extract insects from cracks and holes in branches.

TAIL
The prehensile tail has a naked underside at its tip to provide extra grip when wrapped around a branch. It also serves as a rudder and air-brake during leaps.

CREATURE COMPARISONS

Leadbeater's possum (Gymnobelideus leadbeateri) is a close relative of the striped possum. Living in eucalyptus forests in the misty highlands of eastern Victoria, Australia, Leadbeater's possum is greyish with a pale underbelly.

It is smaller than the striped possum, reaching a head-and-body length of 17cm (6.7in). Its tail, up to 20cm (7.9in) long, is incapable of grasping. Leadbeater's possum also lacks the elongated fourth finger of the striped possum. This reflects its different diet, of which plant sap and gum make up 80 per cent and invertebrates just 20 per cent.

Striped possum

Leadbeater's possum

WHERE IN THE WORLD?

Found throughout the lowland rainforests of New Guinea, and distributed over a restricted range in the rainforests

and adjacent woodlands of northern Queensland in northeast Australia.

RELATED SPECIES

The striped possum shares its genus with 3 other species, including the long-fingered triok of New Guinea. Like the striped possum, the triok feeds on wood-boring grubs, but is more terrestrial than its almost exclusively tree-dwelling relative. Members of the genus Dactylopsila are characterized by a long fourth finger and 3 dark stripes on the head. The family Petauridae contains 6 genera and 23 species, including various gliders.

SUGAR GLIDER

• ORDER • *Marsupialia* • FAMILY • *Petauridae* • GENUS & SPECIES • *Petaurus breviceps*

Supple membranes linking its limbs allow the sugar glider to travel safely from tree to tree as it searches for nectar and sap.

KEY FEATURES

- Glides on flight membranes from tree to tree to feed on nectar-rich flowers.
- Steers to left or right by adjusting the tension in each patagium — the thin, furred gliding membrane.
- Uses its long, furry tail like a rudder to change direction and balance itself when flying and climbing.

VITAL STATISTICS

WEIGHT	Male 113–150g; (4–5.3oz) female 100–135g (3.5–4.8oz)
LENGTH	Head & Body: 15–20cm (5.9–7.9in) Tail; 15–20cm (5.9–7.9in)
SEXUAL MATURITY	Female 1 year; male 1.5 years
MATING SEASON	August in southeastern Australia; probably all year in New Guinea
GESTATION PERIOD	16 days, but offspring later spend 70 days developing in pouch
NO. OF YOUNG	1 to 3
TYPICAL DIET	Nectar, pollen, sap, fruit, gum; insects, larvae
LIFESPAN	Up to 7 years

MOUTH
The sugar glider uses its sharp incisor teeth to gouge holes in trees to expose the sugary sap, and uses its tongue to lap nectar from blossoms.

FEET
Small, but long-clawed feet provide the sugar glider with an excellent grip when climbing.

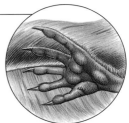

PATAGIUM
The patagium (gliding membrane) stretches from wrist to ankle on each side. It is folded close to the body when not in use.

SCENT GLANDS
Special glands on the chest, pouch, flanks, feet and at the base of the tail produce scent. The odours help the sugar glider to recognize other members of its group.

POUCH
Like all marsupials, the female sugar glider gives birth to tiny, embryonic offspring, which then crawl into her pouch to continue their early development.

TAIL
The furry tail helps the glider balance when flying and climbing. It is prehensile — capable of grasping branches and carrying nesting material.

CREATURE COMPARISONS

Other gliding mammals include the seven species of scaly-tailed flying squirrel of western and central Africa, and the 38 species of flying squirrel of North America, Europe and Southeast Asia. Although they look like the sugar glider and have similar lifestyles, these species are placental mammals and not marsupials: their young develop in the womb, rather than in an external pouch.

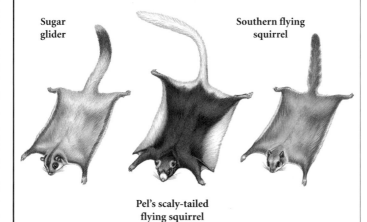

Sugar glider

Southern flying squirrel

Pel's scaly-tailed flying squirrel

WHERE IN THE WORLD?

Found in coastal northern and eastern Australia, New Guinea and surrounding islands. European settlers introduced the sugar glider to Tasmania in the early part of the 19th century.

RELATED SPECIES

The sugar glider is one of four species in the genus Petaurus. These natives of New Guinea and Australia include the yellow-bellied, or fluffy, glider, Petaurus australis, and the squirrel glider, P. norfolcensis. The Petaurus species' closest relatives are the striped possums, genus Dactylopsila, which are non-gliding insect-eaters. The greater glider, Petauroides volans, is the largest gliding marsupial, weighing up to 1.8kg (4lb).

• **ORDER** • *Marsupialia* • **FAMILY** • *Petauridae* • **GENUS & SPECIES** • *Pseudocheirus peregrinus*

RING-TAILED POSSUM

With sharp eyesight, flexible digits and a muscular tail, the ring-tailed possum is well equipped for nightly feeding expeditions in the forests of Australia.

KEY FEATURES

- Curls its long, muscular tail around branches of trees as an anchor while searching for food.
- Digestive system is able to break down the toxins contained in eucalyptus leaves, its principal food.
- Uses twigs, grass and bark to build football-sized nests, called dreys, sometimes high in the forest canopy.

SKULL
The narrow skull is almost pointed at the snout; large molars (cheek teeth) grind the leafy diet.

FUR
The coat is usually grey-brown, with cream colouring on the underbelly. The white tail tip distinguishes this species from other possums.

FOREFOOT
The first two digits of each forefoot are opposable, acting like thumbs to the other three digits, giving the possum a firm grasp when it climbs. Sharp claws may be used to defend a territory from intruders.

TAIL
The tail tapers to a point; the underside near the tip is naked in order to grip branches tightly.

VITAL STATISTICS

WEIGHT	700–1000g (24.7–35.3oz)
LENGTH	Head & Body: 16–50cm (6.3–19.7in) Tail: 17–40cm (6.7–15.7in)
SHOULDER HEIGHT	15cm (5.9in)
SEXUAL MATURITY	Female 1 year; male 1–2 years
MATING SEASON	April–October, some regional variation
GESTATION PERIOD	Thought to be 2–3 weeks. Young leave pouch at 16–18 weeks
NUMBER OF YOUNG	1 to 3, usually 2
BIRTH INTERVAL	1 year, rarely 6 months
TYPICAL DIET	Eucalyptus leaves, fruit, flowers, bark
LIFESPAN	4–5 years

CREATURE COMPARISONS

The striped possum (Dactylopsia trivigata), a native of New Guinea and northern Queensland, is another member of the family Petauridae. It is remarkable for the unpleasant, penetrating odour originating from its scent glands. Like the ring-tailed possum, it is a nocturnal forest-dweller. As an insect-eater, the striped possum moves more rapidly and nimbly than its plant-eating cousin. Its lean body is a little shorter than that of the ring-tailed possum, and is easily distinguished by the three dark stripes running parallel down its back. Its tail is half as long again as its body.

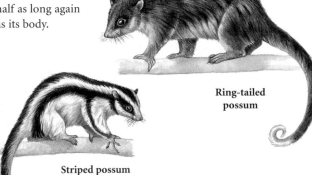

Ring-tailed possum

Striped possum

WHERE IN THE WORLD?

A native of the forests and more open woodlands of northern, eastern, and extreme southwestern Australia; also widespread in Tasmania.

RELATED SPECIES

The ring-tailed possum is 1 of 12 species in the genus Pseudocheirus. There are 6 genera of tree-dwelling possums in the family Petauridae, including the sugar glider possum, Petaurus breviceps. Possums, like most native Australian mammals, belong to the order Marsupialia.

CUSCUS

• ORDER • *Marsupialia* • FAMILY • *Phalangeridae* • GENUS & SPECIES • *Phalanger spp.*

KEY FEATURES

• Able to find food, shelter and defence in the tree canopy, from which they seldom descend.

• Equipped with excellent vision, enabling them to forage for plant material and seek out invertebrates at night.

• A long tail capable of gripping, and specially linked toes on the hindfeet, provide stability and purchase on high branches.

VITAL STATISTICS

WEIGHT	1–2.5kg (2.2–5.5lb)
LENGTH	Head & Body: 32–60cm (12.6–23.6in) Tail: 24–61cm (9.4–24in)
SHOULDER HEIGHT	15–20cm (5.9–7.9in)
SEXUAL MATURITY	1 year
MATING SEASON	Year-round
GESTATION PERIOD	15–18 days
NUMBER OF YOUNG	Up to 3, but only 1 or 2 are reared
TIME IN POUCH	4–5 months
BIRTH INTERVAL	2 years
TYPICAL DIET	Fruit, leaves and flowers; small vertebrates and insects; birds' eggs
LIFESPAN	Up to 11 years

Sharp, curved claws and a long tail with a prehensile tip help the cuscus clamber with a sure grip among the forest branches.

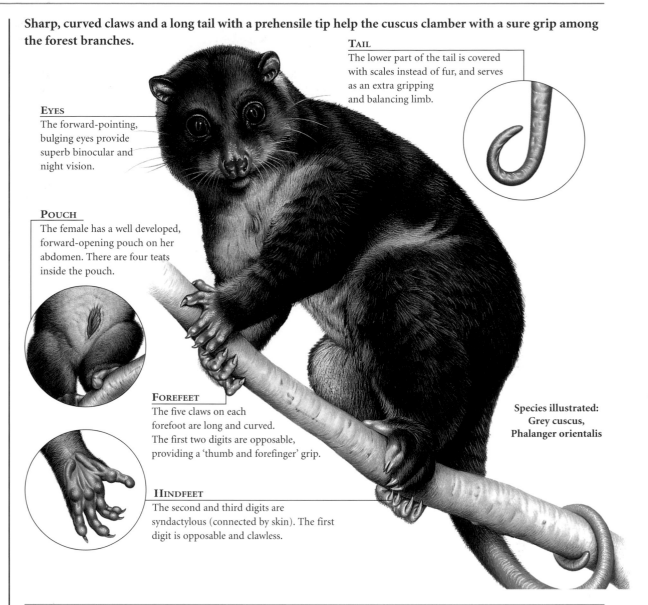

TAIL
The lower part of the tail is covered with scales instead of fur, and serves as an extra gripping and balancing limb.

EYES
The forward-pointing, bulging eyes provide superb binocular and night vision.

POUCH
The female has a well developed, forward-opening pouch on her abdomen. There are four teats inside the pouch.

FOREFEET
The five claws on each forefoot are long and curved. The first two digits are opposable, providing a 'thumb and forefinger' grip.

HINDFEET
The second and third digits are syndactylous (connected by skin). The first digit is opposable and clawless.

Species illustrated:
Grey cuscus,
Phalanger orientalis

CREATURE COMPARISONS

The spotted cuscus (Spilocuscus maculatus) and its relative the black-spotted cuscus (S. rufoniger) are neighbours of the grey cuscus and other members of the genus Phalanger, but are confined to altitudes below 820m (2690ft). As their names suggest, they are often richly coloured: the coat of the male spotted cuscus may sport soft grey or red-brown splashes.

The spotted cuscus is larger than its Phalanger cousins, weighing up to 6kg (16lb). Its ears, however, are comparatively small. Like its relatives, the spotted cuscus is almost completely arboreal. Moving through the trees at night with the aid of its prehensile tail, it feeds on the leaves and fruits of vegetation, having a particular fondness for fig trees.

Grey cuscus

Spotted cuscus

WHERE IN THE WORLD?

Native to the tropical rainforests and thick woodlands of New Guinea and surrounding islands, with one species also occurring in northern Queensland in Australia.

RELATED SPECIES

There are 8 species of cuscus in the genus Phalanger, and 2 species in the genus Spilocuscus. Both genera belong to the Phalangeridae, 1 of 16 families in the order Marsupialia. Other members of this family include the scaly-tailed possum, Wyulda squamicaudata, and 3 species of brushtail possum (genus Trichosurus). The common brushtail possum, widespread in Australia, has been introduced to New Zealand, where it thrives.

• ORDER • *Marsupialia* • FAMILY • *Phalangeridae* • SPECIES • *Trichosurus vulpecula*

COMMON BRUSHTAIL POSSUM

The brushtail possum relies on its good eyesight, strong feet and gripping tail to help it scramble safely among the branches in its nightly search for food.

KEY FEATURES

- Lives in trees, and uses its long, powerful tail as a fifth limb to manoeuvre along the branches.
- Adaptable feeder that can broaden its normal vegetarian diet to include insects, small birds, lizards and human refuse.
- Despite recent changes throughout its habitat it thrives as a species, and in some areas, notably New Zealand, it has become rather a pest.

VITAL STATISTICS

WEIGHT	1.3–5kg (2.9–11lb)
LENGTH	Head & Body: 30–55cm (11.8–21.6in) Tail: 25–35cm (9.8–13.8in)
SHOULDER HEIGHT	9–12cm (3.5–4.7in)
SEXUAL MATURITY	1 year; female sometimes 9 months
MATING SEASON	March to May, lesser peak September to November
GESTATION PERIOD	17–18 days
NUMBER OF YOUNG	1
BIRTH INTERVAL	1 year; rarely 6 months
TYPICAL DIET	Shoots, flowers, leaves, fruit, insects, urban refuse
LIFESPAN	13 years, but usually less than 11 years

SKULL
The eye sockets are large, accounting for the possum's excellent night vision. The unspecialized teeth reflect the wide diet.

COAT
The thick, woolly coat needs regular grooming. It is usually grey-brown, often paler underneath. Individuals in parts of Queensland are reddish.

GLAND
A gland on the chest produces a substance that the possum uses, along with a secretion from the anal gland, to mark its territory.

HINDFEET
Four of the digits are equipped with a needle-sharp claw. There is no claw on the first digit, which works like a thumb to provide a firm grip. The second and third digits are partially webbed.

TAIL
The long, bushy tail gives its name to the species. It is muscular with a naked undersurface, and can grip branches.

CREATURE COMPARISONS

The scaly-tailed possum (*Wyulda squamicaudata*) is restricted to the Kimberley Plateau just north of the Great Sandy Desert in Western Australia. Smaller than the brushtail possum, it has a bodylength of up to 40cm (15.7in) and weighs 1–2kg (2.2–4.4lb). Like its more widespread cousin, it has a prehensile tail. But unlike any other member of the family Phalangeridae, its tail is covered in scaly skin and has a densely furred base.

The scaly-tailed possum feeds at night among the few trees in its habitat, climbing down at sunrise to shelter among the rocks from the relentless daytime heat.

Brushtail possum

Scaly-tailed possum

WHERE IN THE WORLD?

Native to forests and woodlands around Australia, especially in the east and southwest; present also in the arid interior. Widespread in Tasmania, and introduced to New Zealand.

RELATED SPECIES
Trichosurus vulpecula comprises 4 subspecies. The genus includes the mountain brushtail possum, T. caninus, of Australia. Relatives in the family Phalangeridae include the spotted cuscus, Phalanger maculatus, of Australia and New Guinea.

• **ORDER** • *Marsupialia* • **FAMILY** • *Thylacomyidae* • **GENUS & SPECIES** • *Macrotis lagotis*

Despite its fragile appearance, the bilby is a tough survivor adapted to the rigours of life in Australia's arid outback.

KEY FEATURES

- A desert forager able to survive in one of the world's harshest landscapes.
- Has one of the shortest gestation periods, relative to adult body size, of any mammal.
- Under serious threat and classed as vulnerable by the IUCN (World Conservation Union).

VITAL STATISTICS

WEIGHT	0.3–1.6kg (0.7–3.5lb)
LENGTH	Head & Body: Male 30–55cm (11.8–21.6in), female 29–39cm (11.4–15.3in) Tail: 20–29cm (7.9–11.4in)
SEXUAL MATURITY	13 weeks
MATING SEASON	Variable
GESTATION	13 days
TIME IN POUCH	75 days
NUMBER OF YOUNG	1 to 3
BIRTH INTERVAL	9 weeks
TYPICAL DIET	Insects, worms, seeds, fruit, roots, fungi
LIFESPAN	3–5 years

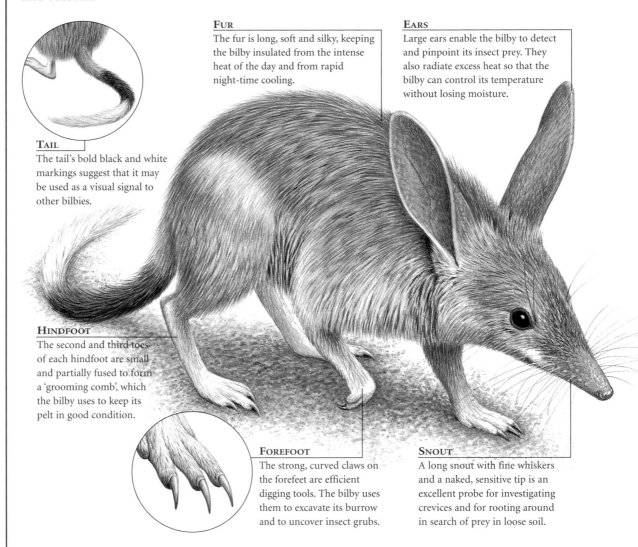

TAIL
The tail's bold black and white markings suggest that it may be used as a visual signal to other bilbies.

FUR
The fur is long, soft and silky, keeping the bilby insulated from the intense heat of the day and from rapid night-time cooling.

EARS
Large ears enable the bilby to detect and pinpoint its insect prey. They also radiate excess heat so that the bilby can control its temperature without losing moisture.

HINDFOOT
The second and third toes of each hindfoot are small and partially fused to form a 'grooming comb', which the bilby uses to keep its pelt in good condition.

FOREFOOT
The strong, curved claws on the forefeet are efficient digging tools. The bilby uses them to excavate its burrow and to uncover insect grubs.

SNOUT
A long snout with fine whiskers and a naked, sensitive tip is an excellent probe for investigating crevices and for rooting around in search of prey in loose soil.

CREATURE COMPARISONS

The bilby is closely related to the seven species of short-nosed bandicoot (genus Isodon). These marsupials are very similar in size and form but lack the bilby's arid habitat adaptations — the long probing snout, large, heat-radiating ears and silky pelt.

Short-nosed bandicoots live in much more fertile regions of Australia and New Guinea. In their moist, forested habitat, the bandicoots have no need to dig burrows for shelter, and instead nest among leaf litter on the forest floor. Like the bilby, bandicoots feed mainly on insects and worms which they dig up with their sharp claws.

Species illustrated: **Isodon macrourus**

Bilby

Short-nosed bandicoot

WHERE IN THE WORLD?

Once widespread throughout Australia's interior, but now restricted mainly to a few isolated regions in the northwest quarter of the continent.

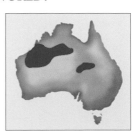

RELATED SPECIES

The bilby is 1 of 2 species in its genus, although the lesser bilby, Macrotis leucura, may now be extinct. The bilbies' closest relatives are the 21 species of bandicoot in 7 genera in the family Peramelidae. All are members of the order Marsupialia, which is represented in Australasia and the Americas and includes kangaroos and wallabies, the koala, possums and opossums among its 280 species.

• ORDER • *Marsupialia* • FAMILY • *Vombatidae* • GENUS & SPECIES • *Vombatus ursinus*

COMMON WOMBAT

A compact, muscular body and long, strong claws enable this dedicated digger to excavate a complex system of underground burrows.

POUCH
The pouch opens to the rear to prevent soil or sand thrown up during burrowing from entering. The young suckles from one of two nipples within.

TEETH
None of the teeth are rooted, having instead a pulpy base. They grow constantly throughout the wombat's life. The incisors at the front of the jaw have hard enamel on only the front and sides so that they wear to sharp, chisel edges for slicing tough vegetation.

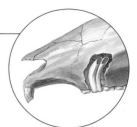

KEY FEATURES

- A powerfully built bear-like marsupial with a stumpy body designed for digging and living in a network of underground burrows.
- Its teeth grow constantly, like those of rodents, to cope with a diet of tough grass and roots.
- Nurses its offspring in a rear-opening pouch.

COAT
The coat is coarse and varies in colour from buff or grey to dark brown or black.

BODY
Compact with short, thick legs and a broad tapering skull. This body plan helps the wombat force its way through rooty ground when burrowing.

FEET
Each foot has five toes. All toes have claws except for the stunted inner toe on each hindfoot (far left). The claws are stout and long for digging.

VITAL STATISTICS

WEIGHT	22–39kg (48.5–86lb)
LENGTH	Head & Body: 90–115cm (35.4–45.3in) Tail: 2.5cm (1in)
SEXUAL MATURITY	2 years
MATING SEASON	Year round
GESTATION PERIOD	Not known
TIME IN POUCH	Up to 180 days
NUMBER OF YOUNG	Usually 1, rarely 2
BIRTH INTERVAL	2 years
TYPICAL DIET	Grasses, leaves, roots, fungi, inner bark from trees
LIFESPAN	5 years in wild; up to 20 years in captivity

CREATURE COMPARISONS

The southern hairy-nosed wombat, Lasiorhinus latifrons, lives across southern Australia in semi-arid grassland and dry forest. It is easily distinguished from the common wombat by its smaller size, longer ears, broad snout and silky coat. Its snout is also mostly covered by hair, unlike the common wombat's, which is bald.

At especially favourable sites the southern hairy-nosed wombat sometimes lives alongside others of its kind in large burrow complexes, known as warrens. Although these may hold a dozen or so animals, the wombats largely lead separate lives.

WHERE IN THE WORLD?

Found mainly in forests and uplands in eastern Australia, along the Great Dividing Range. Also occurs in Tasmania, and Flinders Island in the Bass Strait.

RELATED SPECIES

As well as the common wombat, the family Vombatidae also contains the southern and northern hairy-nosed wombats: Lasiorhinus latifrons and L. krefftii respectively. Wombats belong to the order Marsupialia, which includes kangaroos, wallabies and the koala.

Southern hairy-nosed wombat

Common wombat

• ORDER • *Monotremata* • FAMILY • *Ornithorhyncidae* • GENUS & SPECIES • *Ornithorhynchus anatinus* DUCKBILL PLATYPUS

The duckbill platypus's webbed and clawed feet, sensitive bill and paddle-like tail equip it for a highly aquatic lifestyle.

KEY FEATURES

- Has the beak of a duck and the body of a mammal — it even lays eggs.
- Hunts with its eyes and ears closed, using its highly sensitive bill to detect the minute electrical fields given out by its prey.
- Male produces enough venom to kill a dog.

POISON SPURS
A gland in each hindleg produces venom and is connected by a duct to a hollow spur at the ankle. This spur is erected to inject the venom. The male alone possesses the spurs.

BILL
Millions of tiny, jelly-filled pits line the pliable bill. When swimming, the platypus closes its nostrils and uses the pits to sense minute changes in electric fields. The bill does not contain teeth.

TAIL
The tail is used as a rudder when swimming, and also acts as a major fat-storage organ.

FOREFEET
The webbed forefeet are used for swimming. When the platypus needs to walk or dig, the webs are turned back to reveal broad nails.

EYES AND EARS
The ear slits lie behind the eyes. The platypus swims with its eyes and ears closed, using its electrical senses to find its way.

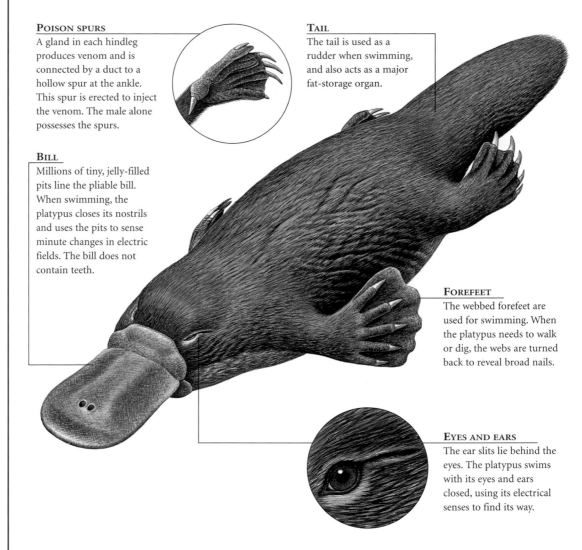

VITAL STATISTICS

WEIGHT	Male 0.9–2.5kg (2–5.5lb); female 0.7–1.6kg (1.5–3.5lb)
LENGTH	Head & Body: 38–59cm (15–23.2in) Tail: 27–38cm (10.6–15in)
SEXUAL MATURITY	2 years
MATING SEASON	August to October
GESTATION PERIOD	2 weeks
INCUBATION PERIOD	10–14 days
NUMBER OF YOUNG	1 to 3, usually 2
TYPICAL DIET	Mostly insect larvae. Also fish, freshwater crayfish, worms, tadpoles and frogs.
LIFESPAN	Up to 15 years in the wild

CREATURE COMPARISONS

Monotremes all lay eggs, but otherwise their reproduction is just like other mammals. A female echidna lays a single egg, which she carries in a pouch until it hatches. Because the female platypus spends most of her time in the water, she incubates her eggs in the safety of a burrow. Both echidnas and platypuses feed their hatchling young with milk.

Long-nosed echidna

Short-nosed echidna

Platypus

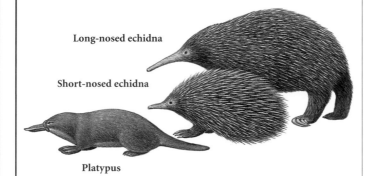

WHERE IN THE WORLD?

Freshwater habitats in eastern Australia, from Cooktown in Queensland south to Tasmania. Also introduced to Kangaroo Island, South Australia.

RELATED SPECIES

There are only three living species in three genera in the order Monotremata — the egg-laying mammals. These are the duckbill platypus and two echidnas, or spiny anteaters: the short-nosed echidna, Tachyglossus aculeatus, and the long-nosed echidna, Zaglossus bruijni. Today, monotremes are found only in Australia and New Guinea, but the fossil record suggests they may once have been more widespread.

• **ORDER** • *Monotremata* • **FAMILY** • *Tachyglossidae* • **GENUS & SPECIES** • *Tachyglossus aculeatus* SHORT-BEAKED ECHIDNA

The echidna is a living fossil — it has remained largely unchanged since its ancestors walked the Earth along with the dinosaurs 110 million years ago.

KEY FEATURES

- One of the world's most extraordinary mammals: the female lays eggs and produces milk to feed its young.

- Eggs are incubated in a temporary pouch on the female's abdomen.

- Has a covering of fur yet bristles all over with long sharp spines for defence.

SKULL
The echidna's skull resembles that of a bird, with its long beak-like jaws. The rostrum (upper jaw) is almost tubular while the lower jaw is more slender. Teeth are absent.

SNOUT
The echidna has a small head with a long snout, which it uses to sniff out ants and termites and then probe deeply into their nests.

LIMBS
The male has a redundant spur (1) on both of its hindlimbs. Both sexes have long, flattened claws, which are used for digging (2).

MOUTH AND TONGUE
Insect prey is drawn into the echidna's mouth on its sticky tongue. Inside the mouth two sets of plates — one at the base of the tongue, another on the roof of the mouth — crush the food. The tongue is 15–18cm (5.9–7.1in) long and very mobile.

VITAL STATISTICS

WEIGHT	Male 4–6kg (8.8–13.2lb); female 2–5kg (4.4–11lb)
LENGTH	35–53cm (13.8–20.9in)
SEXUAL MATURITY	Not known
MATING SEASON	May to September
GESTATION PERIOD	21–28 days
INCUBATION PERIOD	10–11 days
NUMBER OF YOUNG	1
BREEDING INTERVAL	1 year
TYPICAL DIET	Mainly ants and termites, but also worms and small beetles
LIFESPAN	30–40 years

CREATURE COMPARISONS

The short-beaked echidna is one of several mammals that have evolved specialized hairs that form protective spines. In the northern hemisphere, the echidna's counterparts are the three species of hedgehog (Erinaceus europaeus, E. concolor and E. amurensis). Like the echidna, hedgehogs have a coat of spines that covers their body except for the face, legs and underparts. Hedgehogs curl up into a tight ball for protection, unlike the echidna, which uses a different protective strategy. If attacked, the echidna rapidly digs itself into the ground, leaving only its sharp spines exposed.

Short-beaked echidna

Hedgehog

WHERE IN THE WORLD?

Occurs in a variety of habitats, from semi-arid lands to alpine areas, throughout mainland Australia, New Guinea, and Tasmania.

RELATED SPECIES
The only other echidna is the long-beaked echidna (Zaglossus bruijni), which is restricted to New Guinea. Echidnas belongs to the order Monotremata, which means 'one opening' and refers to the cloaca: the common opening through which bodily waste is passed and via which reproduction takes place. Monotremata has one other member — the platypus, Ornithorhynchus anatinus, which is sometimes called the duck-billed platypus.

• ORDER • *Neuroptera* • FAMILY • *Myrmeleonidae* • GENUS & SPECIES • *Myrmeleon formicarius*

ANTLION

KEY FEATURES

- The robust antlion larva may spend over three years as a fierce predator before it turns into a delicate, winged adult that lives for just a few weeks.

- Larva excavates a cunning trap for passing insects and then 'sandblasts' its victims to prevent their escape.

- Huge, pincer jaws enable the larva to seize and devour prey.

VITAL STATISTICS

LENGTH	Adult 45mm (1.8in); larva 6–8mm (0.2–0.3in)
WINGSPAN	65mm (2.5mm)
BREEDING SEASON	May–August (northern hemisphere); October–January (southern hemisphere)
SEXUAL MATURITY	As soon as adult leaves pupa, about 3 years after hatching
NUMBER OF EGGS	Not known
BREEDING INTERVAL	Adult dies after breeding
TYPICAL DIET	Aphids, small insects, pollen, nectar Ants, small spiders, woodlice
LIFESPAN	About 3 years

The antlion larva digs a precision sand trap and waits at the bottom of it ready to bombard prey with sand grains so that it slips into its waiting jaws.

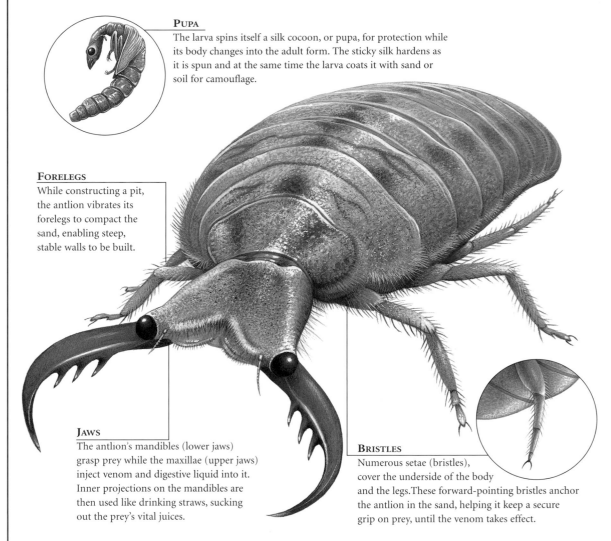

PUPA
The larva spins itself a silk cocoon, or pupa, for protection while its body changes into the adult form. The sticky silk hardens as it is spun and at the same time the larva coats it with sand or soil for camouflage.

FORELEGS
While constructing a pit, the antlion vibrates its forelegs to compact the sand, enabling steep, stable walls to be built.

JAWS
The antlion's mandibles (lower jaws) grasp prey while the maxillae (upper jaws) inject venom and digestive liquid into it. Inner projections on the mandibles are then used like drinking straws, sucking out the prey's vital juices.

BRISTLES
Numerous setae (bristles), cover the underside of the body and the legs. These forward-pointing bristles anchor the antlion in the sand, helping it keep a secure grip on prey, until the venom takes effect.

CREATURE COMPARISONS

The adult antlion has a long, slender body and long, narrow wings heavily laced with a network of veins. Its weak, fluttery flight action is often mistaken for that of a small dragonfly, or damselfly, such as the banded blackwing (Calopteryx splendens), which has a similarly shaped body to an antlion, together with translucent, veined wings, which it holds upright over its body when perched at rest on waterside vegetation. Viewed more closely, however, the antlion has much longer antennae while the banded blackwing has brighter body colouring.

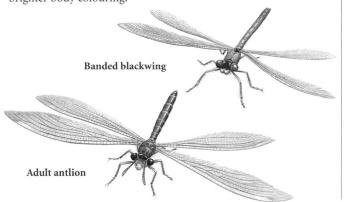

Banded blackwing

Adult antlion

WHERE IN THE WORLD?

The antlion occurs across the dry, tropical and subtropical regions of Asia, the Americas, Australia and New Zealand. It is also found in Central and Northern Europe, as far north as Scandinavia.

RELATED SPECIES

There are about 2000 species of antlion in the family Myrmeleonidae. Its closest relatives live mainly in tropical and subtropical climates, and include lacewings and mantispids. These are predators with similar mouthparts to the antlion. Hemerobius stigmaterus is a common species of brown lacewing in North America. The small, very lively, predatory larvae are diligent hunters of aphids, earning the species the name of 'aphid lion'.

• **ORDER** • *Octopoda* • **FAMILY** • *Octopodidae* • **GENUS & SPECIES** • *Hapalochlaena maculosa*

BLUE-RINGED OCTOPUS

KEY FEATURES

- Bright blue circles warn other animals that it is one of the oceans' most venomous creatures.
- Traps prey species with powerful, suckered arms and paralyzes them with venom.
- Able to subdue its colour pattern when relaxed, and to intensify it when disturbed.

VITAL STATISTICS

WEIGHT	90g (3.2oz)
LENGTH	Body: 7.5cm (2.9in) Tentacles; 11.5cm (4.5in)
SEXUAL MATURITY	2 years
MATING SEASON	Usually spring
NUMBER OF EGGS	Variable: usually a few dozen
INCUBATION PERIOD	90 days
BREEDING INTERVAL	Male dies soon after mating; female dies about a month after producing her eggs.
TYPICAL DIET	Crabs and other crustaceans; some fish
LIFESPAN	Probably 2 years

The octopus's supple body allows it to squeeze through tiny gaps to chase prey, and its tentacles can be extended rapidly to grab its victim.

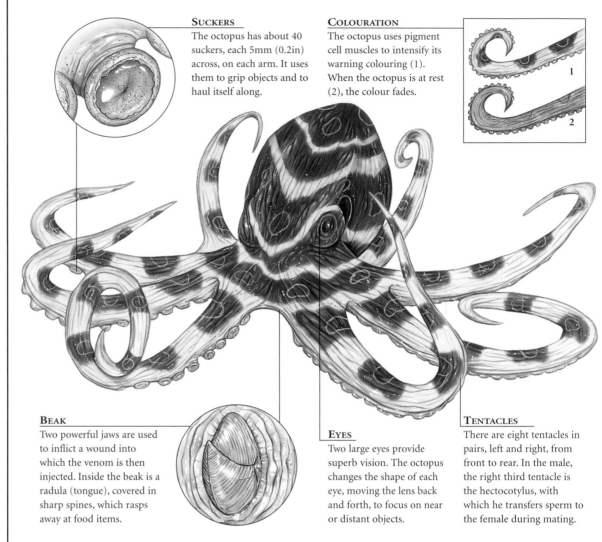

SUCKERS
The octopus has about 40 suckers, each 5mm (0.2in) across, on each arm. It uses them to grip objects and to haul itself along.

COLOURATION
The octopus uses pigment cell muscles to intensify its warning colouring (1). When the octopus is at rest (2), the colour fades.

BEAK
Two powerful jaws are used to inflict a wound into which the venom is then injected. Inside the beak is a radula (tongue), covered in sharp spines, which rasps away at food items.

EYES
Two large eyes provide superb vision. The octopus changes the shape of each eye, moving the lens back and forth, to focus on near or distant objects.

TENTACLES
There are eight tentacles in pairs, left and right, from front to rear. In the male, the right third tentacle is the hectocotylus, with which he transfers sperm to the female during mating.

CREATURE COMPARISONS

The octopus is one of many tentacled creatures in the class Cephalopoda. Squid have eight tentacles of equal length, as well as two longer tentacles that shoot out to capture prey. They have a long, thin internal shell known as a quill. Cuttlefish resemble squid in their tentacle plan but have a flattened internal shell. Nautiluses have up to 90, non-suckered tentacles; membranes between the tentacles secrete the material for the shell.

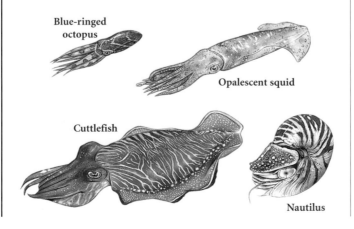

Blue-ringed octopus

Opalescent squid

Cuttlefish

Nautilus

WHERE IN THE WORLD?

Found in the shallow waters of the Indian and western Pacific Oceans, from Sri Lanka to Indonesia, Japan and Australia.
Especially common on coral reefs.

RELATED SPECIES

The closest relative of the blue-ringed octopus is *Hapalochlaena lunulata*, which also has blue ring markings, as well as wavy blue stripes on its head, mantle and tentacles. There are about 150 known species of octopus in the world, including the common octopus, *Octopus vulgaris*. This intelligent and adaptable species reaches 3m (9ft 8in) from head to tentacle-tip, and is found throughout the world's tropical and temperate oceans.

COMMON OCTOPUS

• ORDER • *Octopoda* • FAMILY • *Octopodidae* • GENUS & SPECIES • *Octopus vulgaris*

The soft-bodied octopus represents a nutritious meal for predators, but its remarkable physical adaptations ensure that few are spotted.

KEY FEATURES

- Bottom-dwelling master of camouflage that waits for unsuspecting victims to venture within its grasp.
- One of the most advanced invertebrates, equipped with superb vision and an armoury of weapons.
- Can change its colour, pattern and texture at will, and disorientate its enemies with ink.

MANTLE
The mantle is a muscular sac containing the vital organs. The octopus can fill it with water, and rapidly change skin colour and pattern using chromatophores (special pigment cells).

INK SAC AND GILLS
The octopus extracts oxygen from sea water by sucking water over its gills. The ink sac is attached to the gut.

Ink sac   Gill

FUNNEL
Water in the mantle is forced out of a mobile funnel, enabling the octopus to propel itself in any direction, expel ink and excreta and oxygenate its eggs.

SUCKERS
Each of the eight arms carries twin rows of powerful suckers; these are also highly sensitive, enabling the octopus to explore surface textures and potential prey items.

MOUTH
Located at the hub of the tentacles, the mouth comprises a tough keratin beak and a radula (toothed, rasp-like tongue) for boring into and dismembering armoured prey.

VITAL STATISTICS

WEIGHT	Up to 25kg (55.1lb)
LENGTH	Body: Up to 25cm (9.8in) Tentacles: Up to 1.3m (4ft 3in)
SEXUAL MATURITY	2 years
BREEDING SEASON	Spring
NUMBER OF EGGS	150,000
BREEDING INTERVAL	Once in a lifetime
TYPICAL DIET	Crustaceans, other molluscs; carrion including octopus
LIFESPAN	Male 2–8 years; female 2 years. Individuals in captivity rarely live longer than a few weeks

CREATURE COMPARISONS

The lesser octopus (Eledone cirrhosa) is smaller than the common octopus, reaching a tentacle length of 1m (3ft 3in). It occurs in the North Atlantic at greater depths and in colder water than the common octopus.

There are other distinct differences between the two species. The lesser octopus has smoother skin and a fin ridge around its body. It has only one row of suckers on its tentacles, whereas the common octopus has two rows. Unlike the common octopus, the lesser octopus does not guard its eggs.

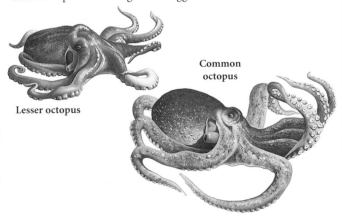

Lesser octopus

Common octopus

WHERE IN THE WORLD?

Found near the coast in tropical, subtropical and temperate seas around the world, from California south to Brazil and from Japan south to Australia.

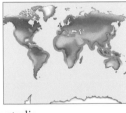

RELATED SPECIES

As a cephalopod mollusc, the common octopus is related to squid, cuttlefish and, more distantly, shellfish and snails. It is a member of the Octopodidae family, which contains 24 genera and includes a huge range of octopuses — large, small, venomous, edible — found in the world's seas. The giant Pacific octopus may reach an armspan of 9.6m (31ft 5in), while the tiny Octopus arborescens of Sri Lanka spans just 5cm (2in) on average.

• **ORDER** • *Odonata* • **FAMILY** • *Aeshnidae* • **GENUS & SPECIES** • *Aeshna cyanea* SOUTHERN HAWKER DRAGONFLY

So successful is the dragonfly's basic bodyplan that it has remained virtually unchanged for hundreds of millions of years.

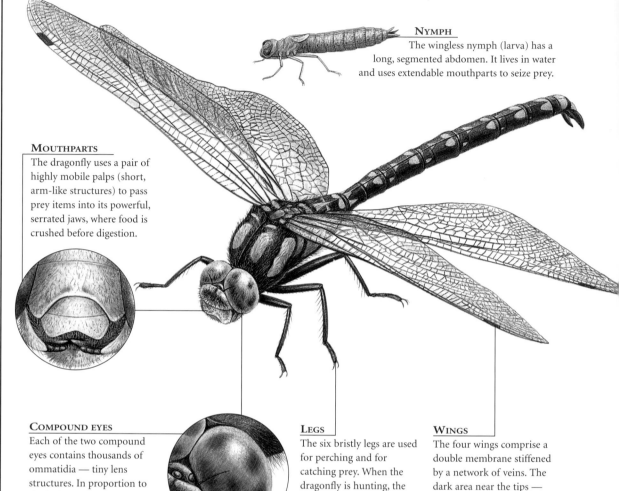

NYMPH
The wingless nymph (larva) has a long, segmented abdomen. It lives in water and uses extendable mouthparts to seize prey.

KEY FEATURES

- One of the fastest of all flying insects, capable of reaching over 40 km/h (24.8 mph) in short bursts.
- An aerial acrobat: can hover, loop-the-loop and fly backwards to capture prey and avoid predators.
- Possesses huge compound eyes, each with nearly 30,000 facets, giving sharp, all-round colour vision.

MOUTHPARTS
The dragonfly uses a pair of highly mobile palps (short, arm-like structures) to pass prey items into its powerful, serrated jaws, where food is crushed before digestion.

COMPOUND EYES
Each of the two compound eyes contains thousands of ommatidia — tiny lens structures. In proportion to the body size, the eyes are larger than those of any other animal.

LEGS
The six bristly legs are used for perching and for catching prey. When the dragonfly is hunting, the legs are held in a cup shape and are used to scoop up small flying insects.

WINGS
The four wings comprise a double membrane stiffened by a network of veins. The dark area near the tips — the pterostigma — controls the degree to which the wings flex during flight.

VITAL STATISTICS

LENGTH	Nymph: 3.8–5cm (1.5–2in) Adult: 6.4–7.6cm (2.5–3in)
WINGSPAN	9–10cm (3.5–3.9in)
SEXUAL MATURITY	2–3 years
MATING SEASON	July to October
NUMBER OF EGGS	Up to about 1000
HATCHING TIME	In northern areas, the eggs overwinter and hatch in spring
NYMPH TO ADULT	Up to 2 years
TYPICAL DIET	Nymph eats fish fry, worms, insect larvae; adult eats gnats and mosquitoes
LIFESPAN	Nymph up to 2 years; adult up to 4 weeks

CREATURE COMPARISONS

The order Odonata, to which the southern hawker dragonfly belongs, includes two suborders: the true dragonflies (Anisoptera) and the damselflies (Zygoptera). Damselflies are usually smaller than dragonflies, with a more delicate body and a less powerful flight. Unlike a dragonfly, a damselfly folds it wings together over its back when resting. The eyes of a damselfly are widely spaced and simpler than those of a dragonfly, whose eyes are so large that they usually touch one another.

Adult dragonflies and damselflies both hunt in a similar fashion, scooping insect prey out of the air. In both suborders, too, the nymphs are aquatic, and ensnare their prey with deadly jaws on an extendable facial 'mask'.

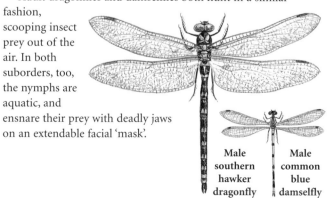

Male southern hawker dragonfly

Male common blue damselfly

WHERE IN THE WORLD?

Ranges across the lowlands of Europe from Spain to southern Scandinavia and as far east as Russia. Also found in parts of Turkey and in North Africa.

RELATED SPECIES
Close relatives of the southern hawker include the similarly sized common hawker, *Aeshna juncea*, of Europe, Asia and North America, and the green darner, *Anax junius*, which ranges from Costa Rica north through the USA and Canada to Alaska.

DESERT LOCUST

• ORDER • *Orthoptera* • FAMILY • *Acrididae* • GENUS & SPECIES • *Schistocerca gregaria*

Its lightweight body, tenacious jaws and powerful legs enable the desert locust to strip vegetation and leave a trail of destruction.

KEY FEATURES

- One of the world's most notorious insects, capable of stripping crops on a biblical scale and ruining local economies.
- Leads an inoffensive solitary life or swarms in vast numbers, depending upon the weather and availability of food.
- A complex lifecycle includes eggs that can survive several years in the desert sands and then hatch after brief rainfall.

VITAL STATISTICS

LENGTH	Up to 90mm (35.4in); male tends to be smaller than female
SEXUAL MATURITY	After the fourth moult; the time this takes varies
BREEDING SEASON	Usually after rain
BREEDING INTERVAL	Eggs can remain dormant in the ground for years
NUMBER OF EGGS	5 or 6 pods of about 100 eggs each
TYPICAL DIET	Leaves, stems, flowers and fruits of wild plants and cultivated crops
LIFESPAN	30–50 days as a hopper; 4–5 months as an adult

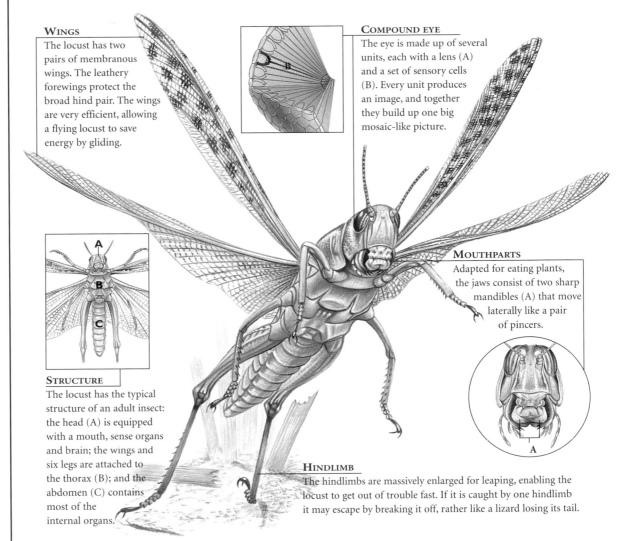

WINGS
The locust has two pairs of membranous wings. The leathery forewings protect the broad hind pair. The wings are very efficient, allowing a flying locust to save energy by gliding.

COMPOUND EYE
The eye is made up of several units, each with a lens (A) and a set of sensory cells (B). Every unit produces an image, and together they build up one big mosaic-like picture.

MOUTHPARTS
Adapted for eating plants, the jaws consist of two sharp mandibles (A) that move laterally like a pair of pincers.

STRUCTURE
The locust has the typical structure of an adult insect: the head (A) is equipped with a mouth, sense organs and brain; the wings and six legs are attached to the thorax (B); and the abdomen (C) contains most of the internal organs.

HINDLIMB
The hindlimbs are massively enlarged for leaping, enabling the locust to get out of trouble fast. If it is caught by one hindlimb it may escape by breaking it off, rather like a lizard losing its tail.

CREATURE COMPARISONS

Although the desert locust is probably the most destructive species of locust, it is closely followed by the migratory locust (*Locusta migratoria*), which occurs across much of Africa, southern Asia and the Malay Peninsula. It also strays into Europe, sometimes as far north as Britain. It is smaller than the desert locust, growing to about 60mm long. Like the desert locust it has a sedentary phase, when it is usually solitary, and a swarming migratory phase.

In both species, adults may change colours. The migratory locust has a brown body that appears green when sedentary or yellow when swarming. When the desert locust swarms, it turns from a sandy hue to a vibrant orange or yellow.

Desert locust

Migratory locust

WHERE IN THE WORLD?

Found throughout northern Africa, often crossing the most barren parts of the Sahara during migrations. Also occurs in East Africa, and from the Arabian Peninsula east to Bangladesh.

RELATED SPECIES
The desert locust is classified in the family Acrididae along with the short-horned grasshoppers. This large family, with about 10,000 species, is grouped together with 5 much smaller families in the suborder Caelifera. This is 1 of 2 suborders in the order Orthoptera, which contains all grasshopper-like insects; the other suborder is the Ensifera, which contains crickets and long-horned grasshoppers, also known as katydids.

• **ORDER** • *Passeriformes* • **FAMILY** • *Bombycillidae* • **GENUS & SPECIES** • *Bombycilla garrulus*

WAXWING

KEY FEATURES

- Has wax-like ornaments on its wings, and thick, silky feathers to insulate it from sub-Arctic temperatures.
- Sporadically leaves its home to roam randomly when its food supply cannot support the population.
- Indulges in an unusual courtship display, where a gift is passed back and forth between a mating pair.

VITAL STATISTICS

WEIGHT	50–80g (1.8–2.8oz)
LENGTH	20cm (7.9in)
WINGSPAN	32–35cm (12.6–13.8in)
SEXUAL MATURITY	1–2 years
BREEDING SEASON	Late May to June
NUMBER OF EGGS	4 to 7
INCUBATION PERIOD	12–15 days
FLEDGING PERIOD	14–16 days
BREEDING INTERVAL	1 year
TYPICAL DIET	Birch, spruce and alder seeds; fruits and buds; mosquitoes and midges
LIFESPAN	Up to 12 years

The elegantly crested waxwing is easy to identify by the loud, rattling noise made by its wing appendages when it is taking off and landing.

CREST
The adult male's head plumes normally sweep upwards and reach a length of 5–7cm (2–2.7in). The female's head plumes are a little shorter and sweep backwards.

BILL
The waxwing has a short, stubby bill and a wide mouth, enabling it to swallow most berries whole.

WINGS
The species gets its name from the red, wax-like appendages that extend from the tips of the inner wing feathers.

JUVENILE
The young waxwing has a shorter crest and is drabber than its parents. It lacks the black bib, and the few red tips on its wings are very small.

TAIL
The short, black tail has a bold yellow tip. Some birds have waxy red tips on their tail as well as on their wings.

CREATURE COMPARISONS

The waxwing family includes four species of silky flycatcher; one of these is known only by its scientific generic name: the phainopepla (Phainopepla nitens). It occurs from Mexico into southwestern USA.

The male phainopepla is glossy black with white flashes on his primary wing feathers, while the female is olive-grey. The species is much slighter in build than the waxwing but roughly the same length, although its tail accounts for about half of its overall 20cm (7.9in). The phainopepla shares the waxwing's swept-back crest and soft plumage. It is very fond of mistletoe berries, and catches flying insects in spectacular swoops.

Phainopepla

Waxwing

WHERE IN THE WORLD?

Breeds in sub-Arctic regions of northern Europe, Siberia, Alaska and western Canada. Usually migrates in the autumn to the south of its breeding range.

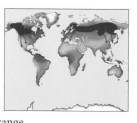

RELATED SPECIES

The waxwing shares its name with only 2 other species, both of which are very similar to the bird found in Europe. The cedar waxwing, Bombycilla cedrorum, breeds in the United States and eastern Canada, while the Japanese waxwing, B. japonica, occurs in Japan and northern Manchuria, China. The cedar waxwing is smaller with no yellow on its wings, while the Japanese species has a red-tipped tail but lacks the waxy tips.

• ORDER • *Passeriformes* • FAMILY • *Sturnidae* • GENUS & SPECIES • *Buphagus erythrorhynchus, B. africanus*

OXPECKER

Sharing the powerful feet and stiff, prop-like tail of woodpeckers, the oxpecker can keep a secure grip on animals as they walk along.

KEY FEATURES

- Makes a living by feeding on the parasitic insects that infest big game and cattle.

- Hitches a lift on its hosts, snapping up prey with its scissor-like bill.

- Tolerated by its hosts because it performs a valuable service.

- Nests communally, with each breeding pair being supported by up to three or four individuals.

BILL
The stout bill is flattened on both sides. The oxpecker uses its bill to work its way through the fur of its host. The yellow-billed oxpecker is distinguished by the yellow base to its bill.

JUVENILE
A young oxpecker is darker brown than its parents. Its bill is dark olive at first, but gradually takes on adult colouration after four months.

WINGS
Held half-open, the oxpecker's wings help it balance on its mobile perch.

Species illustrated:
Red-billed oxpecker,
Buphagus erythrorhynchus

FEET
The short, strong feet have three toes facing forwards and one to the rear, each armed with a long, sharp claw.

TAIL
Long, stiffened tail feathers brace the oxpecker against animals' bodies in much the same way as woodpeckers' tails brace them against tree-trunks.

VITAL STATISTICS

WEIGHT	50g (1.8oz)
LENGTH	20–22cm (7.9–8.7in)
WINGSPAN	30cm (11.8in)
SEXUAL MATURITY	1 year
BREEDING SEASON	Wet season: September to February
NUMBER OF EGGS	1 to 5, usually 2 or 3
INCUBATION PERIOD	12–14 days
FLEDGING PERIOD	26–30 days
TYPICAL DIET	Mainly ticks, bloodsucking flies and lice; some loose skin and blood from open wounds
LIFESPAN	Unknown

CREATURE COMPARISONS

The cattle egret (Bubulcus ibis), a member of the heron family, is not a relative of the oxpecker but shares its savannah habitat, and the two birds are often found alongside each other, associating with large grazing animals. However, the egret does not get its food directly off the animals' bodies. Instead, it walks alongside them snapping up grasshoppers, locusts and beetles flushed from the vegetation as the heavy grazers wander over the grassland. Unlike the oxpecker, the egret is an uninvited dinner guest and gives nothing back to the grazers in return for its own meals.

Standing about 50cm (19.7in) tall, the egret is much bigger than the oxpecker. Long legs enable it to walk quickly while following feeding herds, and large feet provide it with a stable, secure platform on rough ground.

Red-billed
oxpecker

Cattle
egret

WHERE IN THE WORLD?

Found from Sudan and Ethiopia in East Africa, across to the western coast of the continent, and south through Kenya, Uganda and Tanzania to South Africa.

RELATED SPECIES

There are 2 species of oxpecker in the genus Buphagus: the red-billed oxpecker, B. erythrorhynchus, and the yellow-billed oxpecker, B. africanus. They are both confined to sub-Saharan Africa, but the red-billed species is less common. Oxpeckers belong to the large starling family, Sturnidae, which contains about 105 other species, including the mynahs of southeastern Asia and the Eurasian starling.

• **ORDER** • *Passeriformes* • **FAMILY** • *Certhiidae* • **GENUS & SPECIES** • *Certhia familiaris*

EURASIAN TREECREEPER

Using its strong claws as climbing hooks, the Eurasian treecreeper walks up tree-trunks to extract prey from the bark with its fine, tweezer-like bill.

KEY FEATURES

- A sparrow-sized bird of woodland and forests.
- Creeps up tree-trunks and along branches to probe the bark for hidden insects and spiders.
- Climbs each tree in the same way, by starting near its base and moving up the trunk in spirals.
- Small groups survive winter nights by huddling together for warmth in spaces behind loose bark.

VITAL STATISTICS

WEIGHT	8–12g (0.3–0.4oz)
LENGTH	12.5cm (4.9in)
WINGSPAN	17.5–21cm (6.9–8.3in)
SEXUAL MATURITY	1 year
BREEDING SEASON	April to August
NUMBER OF EGGS	3 to 9; usually 5 to 6
INCUBATION PERIOD	14–15 days
FLEDGING PERIOD	14–16 days
BREEDING INTERVAL	1 year
TYPICAL DIET	Invertebrates, such as insects (as well as their eggs), spiders and woodlice; some seeds in winter
LIFESPAN	Up to 9 years

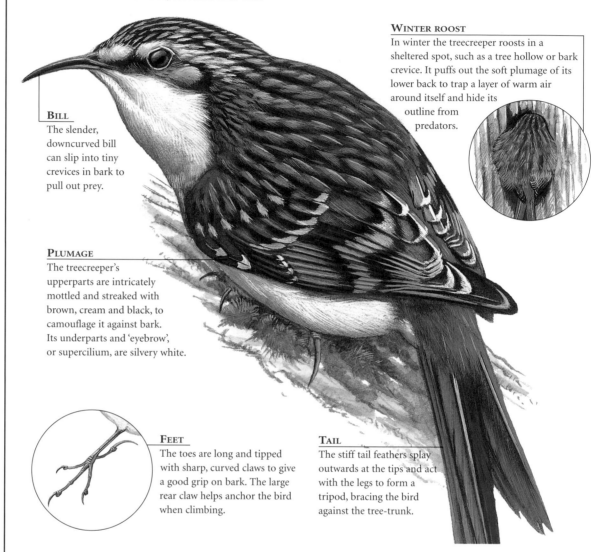

BILL
The slender, downcurved bill can slip into tiny crevices in bark to pull out prey.

PLUMAGE
The treecreeper's upperparts are intricately mottled and streaked with brown, cream and black, to camouflage it against bark. Its underparts and 'eyebrow', or supercilium, are silvery white.

FEET
The toes are long and tipped with sharp, curved claws to give a good grip on bark. The large rear claw helps anchor the bird when climbing.

TAIL
The stiff tail feathers splay outwards at the tips and act with the legs to form a tripod, bracing the bird against the tree-trunk.

WINTER ROOST
In winter the treecreeper roosts in a sheltered spot, such as a tree hollow or bark crevice. It puffs out the soft plumage of its lower back to trap a layer of warm air around itself and hide its outline from predators.

CREATURE COMPARISONS

Many birds can climb up vertical surfaces, but few are as skilled as the wallcreeper (Tichodroma muraria), which is found in rocky gorges and on high crags in many mountain ranges in Europe and Asia. It climbs rock faces in search of insects, and can even cling underneath overhangs of rock.

The wallcreeper has a similar bodyplan to the treecreeper, but it is larger and lacks the long, stiffened tail that its relative uses as a brace. Instead, it flicks open its colourful, scarlet-and-black wings for balance and support. The female wallcreeper's plumage is greyer than the male's, with less red on the wings.

Wallcreeper (male)

Eurasian treecreeper

WHERE IN THE WORLD?

Found in most of Europe and in a broad band east across temperate Asia to eastern China and Japan. Separate populations occur in the Caucasus Mountains (between the Black and Caspian Seas) and the Himalayas.

RELATED SPECIES

There are 7 species of small, tree-climbing bird in the treecreeper family, Certhiidae, including 5 species of treecreeper and the brown and spotted-grey creepers. The Certhiidae are very similar in appearance and habits to the Sittidae: a family of agile, tree- and rock-climbing birds that includes the wallcreeper and 21 species of nuthatch. The Certhiidae and Sittidae belong to the Passeriformes, an order that contains more than 5700 species.

DIPPER

• ORDER • *Passeriformes* • FAMILY • *Cinclidae* • GENUS & SPECIES • *Cinclus cinclus*

To cope with the ravages of rough water and spray, the dipper has to waterproof its feathers, while its eyes and nostrils are protected by special membranes.

KEY FEATURES

- Perches on rocks in foaming mountain torrents while constantly bobbing — or dipping — up and down, waiting to launch into the water to catch aquatic prey.
- Equally skilled at wading in the shallows, plunging into whitewater, or walking along stony streambeds.
- Builds its nest only a few metres from running water.

NICTITATING MEMBRANE
The surface of each eyeball is cleaned by a transparent membrane, called a nictitating membrane, which is flicked across the eye. The dipper blinks these membranes in time with each 'bob' of its body.

NOSTRILS
A broad membrane just above the nostrils closes off the nasal passages when the dipper dives under water.

PLUMAGE
To prevent its plumage from becoming waterlogged, the dipper spends long periods preening and applying waterproof oil from a large preen gland above its tail.

JUVENILE
The juvenile is an overall dull grey. Its underparts have white feathers with black tips, which creates a 'scaly' appearance.

FEET
Long claws enable the dipper to clamber over rocks. The feet are not webbed as the bird uses its wings to 'fly' when under water.

VITAL STATISTICS

WEIGHT	50–70g (1.8–2.5oz)
LENGTH	17–19cm (6.7–7.5in)
WINGSPAN	24cm (9.4in)
SEXUAL MATURITY	1 year
BREEDING SEASON	February to June
NUMBER OF EGGS	1 to 8, usually 4 to 5
INCUBATION PERIOD	12–18 days, usually 16 days
FLEDGING PERIOD	22 days
TYPICAL DIET	Large aquatic invertebrates (mainly caddis fly larvae); some fish, snails, worms, leeches and crustaceans
LIFESPAN	5 years

CREATURE COMPARISONS

Across its wide range in Europe and Asia, the dipper has evolved into several distinct subspecies, each with a slightly different plumage. The northern European subspecies (Cinclus cinclus cinclus) lacks the rich chestnut band just below the white breast, that is a distinctive feature of the subspecies found in Britain and Ireland (C. c. gularis). In central Asia, the subspecies C. c. leucogaster has almost all-white underparts.

All subspecies of the dipper are characterized by a plump body and squarish tail, which is cocked upwards. Their lifestyles, too, are similar, and all share the characteristic habit of bobbing, or dipping, up and down.

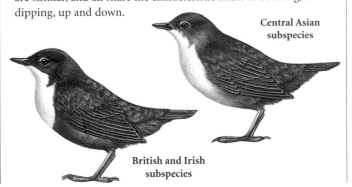

Central Asian subspecies

British and Irish subspecies

WHERE IN THE WORLD?

Lives on and beside rapidly flowing streams in upland Europe and in mountainous regions of northwest Africa, the northern Middle East, Russia and central Asia.

RELATED SPECIES

The dipper belongs to the family Cinclidae, which contains four other species. Three species occur in the Americas: the American dipper of North and Central America, the white-capped dipper of South America, and the rufous-throated dipper of Argentina. The brown dipper is found in Asia. All are inhabitants of swift-flowing rivers and streams. Dippers are closely related to thrushes, in the large family Turdidae, which has 310 members.

• **ORDER** • *Passeriformes* • **FAMILY** • *Corvidae* • **GENUS & SPECIES** • *Corvus corax*

RAVEN

As large and powerful as a buzzard-sized bird of prey, the raven turns into a ruthlessly efficient hunter if its usual diet of carrion is in short supply.

KEY FEATURES

- The world's largest perching bird.
- Eats any animal, dead or alive, that it is able to kill or tear into with its massive bill.
- Superbly skilled in the air, performing dramatic aerobatic displays.
- Adapts to a vast range of climates and habitats, from ice-cold Arctic lands and Himalayan peaks to searingly hot deserts.

BILL
The heavy-duty bill, with sharp-cutting edges, is used to strike lethal hammer blows at live prey and tear strips of flesh from carcasses.

SKULL
Although the raven has relatively small eyes for a bird of its size, they are set in large eye-sockets. The bill is longer than the skull itself.

PLUMAGE
The all-black, glossy plumage shows a shimmering iridescence in strong sunlight, rather like the effect created when oil is spilled onto water. The highlights are mainly purple, with hints of blue, bronze, red and green.

JUVENILE
Less of a glossy black than the adult and has an iris that is bluish-grey (below) rather than dark brown.

VITAL STATISTICS

WEIGHT	410–1350g (14.5–47.6oz)
LENGTH	60–67cm (23.6–26.4in)
WINGSPAN	1.2–1.5m (3ft 9in–4ft 9in)
SEXUAL MATURITY	2–6 years
BREEDING SEASON	February to June
NUMBER OF EGGS	2 to 7 (usually 4 to 6)
INCUBATION PERIOD	20–21 days
FLEDGING PERIOD	35–49 days
BREEDING INTERVAL	1 year
TYPICAL DIET	Mainly carrion and scraps; also a huge range of live prey, bird eggs and seeds
LIFESPAN	Up to 13 years in wild; 30 or more years in captivity

CREATURE COMPARISONS

At first sight, the raven, carrion crow (Corvus corone corone) and rook (C. frugilegus) appear to be very similar: all are large, glossy-black birds, with long, broad wings and fairly long tails. The latter pair, however, are only two thirds of the raven's size, and a closer look reveals that the raven's head, wings and tail project further out from its body, giving it a more elongated, cross-shaped silhouette.

The carrion crow has a scaled-down version of the raven's bill, with which it kills insects and other small prey, or tears at carrion. Unlike both the carrion crow and the raven, which have sturdy black bills, the rook has a relatively slender, grey bill, for digging invertebrates out of earth.

Carrion crow

Raven

Rook

WHERE IN THE WORLD?

Found across much of the northern hemisphere, from the Arctic (in Alaska and northern Canada, coastal Greenland, the far north of Scandinavia and eastern Siberia), south to the tropics (in Honduras, Guatemala and Mexico).

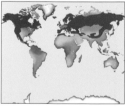

RELATED SPECIES

Of the 115 species of crow in the family Corvidae, 42 are known as 'typical crows'. Grouped together in the genus Corvus, these include the rook, jackdaw and carrion crow, as well as the 9 species of ravens. The remaining 73 species, split into 25 genera, include the black-billed magpie.

CHAFFINCH

• ORDER • *Passeriformes* • FAMILY • *Fringillidae* • GENUS & SPECIES • *Fringilla coelebs*

The chaffinch has bolder white wing patches than any other Eurasian finch, and is one of the best adapted to feeding from the ground.

KEY FEATURES

- One of Europe's most abundant songbirds and most colourful finches.
- Sings in 'dialects' that vary from place to place.
- Gathers during the winter in single-sex flocks, migrating as far south as the Nile Delta in Africa.
- Builds a beautifully delicate nest.

WINGS
Long wings help the chaffinch when migrating. The double white wing-bar is one of the easiest ways of identifying the species.

FEMALE
The subtle colours of the female help to camouflage her on the nest. Although her colours are paler than the male's plumage, they form a similar pattern.

BILL
The bill is heavy enough to crack open tough seeds, and its long, pointed profile helps the bird peck insects from leaves.

FOOT
The hind toe is long to enable the chaffinch to walk on the ground, but is also strong enough to help it perch.

VITAL STATISTICS

WEIGHT	20–28g (0.7–1oz)
LENGTH	14.5cm (5.7in)
WINGSPAN	24.5–28.5cm (9.6–11.2in)
SEXUAL MATURITY	1 year
BREEDING SEASON	April to July
NUMBER OF EGGS	4 or 5
INCUBATION PERIOD	11–13 days
FLEDGING PERIOD	12–15 days
BREEDING INTERVAL	1 or 2 broods per year
TYPICAL DIET	Seeds, beechmast, insects
LIFESPAN	Up to 14 years

CREATURE COMPARISONS

In contrast to the prolific chaffinch, the blue chaffinch (Fringilla teydea) is the rarest finch in Europe, with about 2500 pairs confined to pinewoods on the mountainsides of Tenerife and Gran Canaria in the Canary Islands. The blue chaffinch has a larger body and bill than the chaffinch. As a non-migrant, however, it has comparatively shorter wings. It feeds mainly on pine seeds, and so its future depends on the survival of the forests. When foraging in the trees, it starts at the top and works its way down searching for insects, especially moths. It also spends a lot of time foraging among fallen pine needles on the forest floor.

Chaffinch (male)

Blue chaffinch (male)

WHERE IN THE WORLD?

Found in Western Europe, central Russia and the Middle East. Northern European and Russian breeding birds migrate southwestwards in winter.

RELATED SPECIES

The chaffinch belongs to the large order of Passeriformes, or perching birds, which contains about 5300 species. It is a member of the finch family, Fringillidae, which is represented worldwide by 148 species. The other 2 species in the genus Fringilla are the brambling, F. montifringilla, which breeds in sub-Arctic birchwoods and flies south in winter, and the blue chaffinch, F. teydea, of the Canary Islands.

• ORDER • *Passeriformes* **• FAMILY •** *Hirundinidae* **• GENUS & SPECIES •** *Riparia riparia*

SAND MARTIN

Long, streamlined wings and a forked tail give the sand martin a fast, buoyant flight and the manouvrability to catch flying insects.

BILL
The bill is short but has a wide gape to help scoop up insects.

TAIL
The forked tail is used as a rudder for executing tight turns at speed. The feathers are spread out when landing, acting as an airbrake to reduce speed.

WINGS
Swept-back, long and streamlined, the wings give the sand martin superb aerobatic skills. In flight, the martin swoops and dips less frequently than a swallow.

FEET
The long, narrow toes acts as hooks to grip the vertical banks where the martin nests. They are also used as digging tools for tunnelling into soft, sandy soil.

KEY FEATURES

- Spends most of its life in the air, darting in light, aerobatic flight.
- Feeds mainly on flying insects, which it catches while on the wing.
- Nests in steep sandy, banks excavating a breeding tunnel that may be up to 90cm (35.4in) deep.
- Migrates thousands of kilometres between the southern and northern hemispheres each year.

VITAL STATISTICS

WEIGHT	11.4–14.5g (0.4–0.5oz)
LENGTH	11–12cm (4.3–4.7in)
WINGSPAN	21cm (8.3in)
SEXUAL MATURITY	1 year
BREEDING SEASON	May to July
NUMBER OF EGGS	4 to 6
INCUBATION PERIOD	14–15 days
FLEDGING PERIOD	22 days
BREEDING INTERVAL	2 clutches a year on average
TYPICAL DIET	Small flying insects
LIFESPAN	Up to 9 years

CREATURE COMPARISONS

Two relatives that are often seen flying alongside the sand martin are the Eurasian swallow and the house martin. It can be difficult to distinguish one from the other, although the swallow is the largest of the three. It also has the longest tail feathers and the most pointed wings. The house martin has less curved wings and a striking white rump, while the sand martin is distinguished by a breast band.

All these birds feed on flying insects; the house martin tending to fly the highest, while the swallow hunts near to the ground or over water.

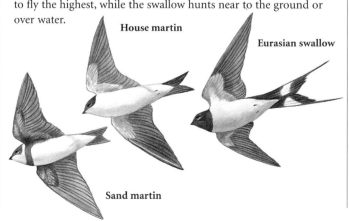

House martin

Eurasian swallow

Sand martin

WHERE IN THE WORLD?

Found during the summer throughout temperate regions of North America, Europe and Asia, including parts of

China. Spends the winter months in South America, Africa and parts of central Asia.

RELATED SPECIES
The sand martin, sometimes called the bank swallow, belongs to the family Hirundinidae, which contains about 80 species. This family is part of the largest order of birds, Passeriformes, which contains nearly 6000 species — about 60 per cent of all the world's known bird species. Within this order the sand martin belongs to the suborder Oscines, which includes relatives such as larks, thrushes, sparrows flycatchers and tits.

• ORDER • *Passeriformes* • FAMILY • *Laniidae* • GENUS & SPECIES • *Lanius excubitor*

GREAT GREY SHRIKE

The great grey shrike has keen eyesight and a pointed, hooked bill, enabling it to catch and kill insects, small mammals and birds.

KEY FEATURES

- Can take birds and insects on the wing, like some falcons, but is more closely related to crows than to birds of prey.
- Stores food by impaling carcasses of insects, small mammals, reptiles and birds on thorns or barbed wire.
- Survives in colder climates than other shrikes, making small migrations southwards when food is scarce.

BILL
The great grey shrike has a hooked and notched upper mandible, which is adapted for killing and tearing prey.

PLUMAGE
Both sexes share identical grey, white and black plumage, with the distinctive black 'mask'.

JUVENILE
The juvenile's grey plumage is tinged with brown. The black on its face is narrower and less bold than that of the adult, giving the younger bird a softer appearance.

TAIL
The long, stiff tail is used as a rudder in flight and also to provide balance when the bird perches.

FOOT
The shrike has three toes pointing forwards and a strong hindtoe — characteristic of perching birds. Its feet may be used to strike flying prey out of the air.

VITAL STATISTICS

WEIGHT	48–81g (1.7–2.8oz)
LENGTH	24–25cm (9.4–9.8in)
WINGSPAN	30–34cm (11.8–13.4in)
SEXUAL MATURITY	1 year
BREEDING SEASON	March to May, depending on region
NUMBER OF EGGS	4 to 7
INCUBATION PERIOD	14–19 days
FLEDGING PERIOD	15–18 days
BREEDING INTERVAL	1 to 3 broods a year
TYPICAL DIET	Large insects, small mammals, birds, reptiles
LIFESPAN	Oldest ringed bird 5 years 9 months

CREATURE COMPARISONS

The great grey shrike and the fiery-breasted bush-shrike (*Malaconotus cruentus*), a bird resident to West Africa, are about the same size but their colours differ enormously. The great grey shrike is a predominantly black-and-white bird, while its African relative has olive-and-yellow upperparts and an orange-red breast. With its black stripe through its eye and heavier, shiny black bill, the great grey shrike has a much more aggressive appearance than the bush-shrike. Although the two species share similar diets, the bush-shrike hunts in the canopies of dense forest, in contrast to the great grey shrike, which prefers more open country.

Fiery-breasted bush-shrike

Great grey shrike

WHERE IN THE WORLD?

Found in a wide band around the northern hemisphere. Common across Canada and the northern USA, Europe and Asia. Some northerly breeders winter farther south, into the Middle East and Africa.

RELATED SPECIES

The great grey shrike belongs to the genus Lanius, which holds 25 species of shrike. The genus is part of the family Laniidae, which contains 70 species of songbird with a hooked and slightly flattened bill, including the four-coloured bush-shrike, Telephorus quadricolor.

• **ORDER** • *Passeriformes* • **FAMILY** • *Menuridae* • **GENUS & SPECIES** • *Menura novaehollandiae*

SUPERB LYREBIRD

KEY FEATURES

- Pheasant-sized, it is one of the largest and most remarkable of all perching birds.
- The male is one of the most outstanding singers of all birds, and also has an unrivalled capacity for mimicking the sounds of other birds and animals.
- The male's long, lacy, ornamental tail feathers form a spectacular veil that covers its body during courtship displays.

VITAL STATISTICS

WEIGHT	Male 525–1183g (18.5–41.7oz); female 625–1364g (22–48.1oz)
LENGTH	Male 80–100cm (31–39.4in); female 74–86cm (29.1–33.9in)
WINGSPAN	Unknown
SEXUAL MATURITY	Male 3–8 years; female about 2 year
BREEDING SEASON	May to October
NUMBER OF EGGS	1
INCUBATION PERIOD	About 6 weeks
FLEDGING PERIOD	About 6 weeks
TYPICAL DIET	Insects and their larvae, worms and other invertebrates
LIFESPAN	Up to 20 years

The male superb lyrebird flaunts his beautiful train of filmy, shimmering tail feathers and pours out his elaborate song to advertise for prospective mates.

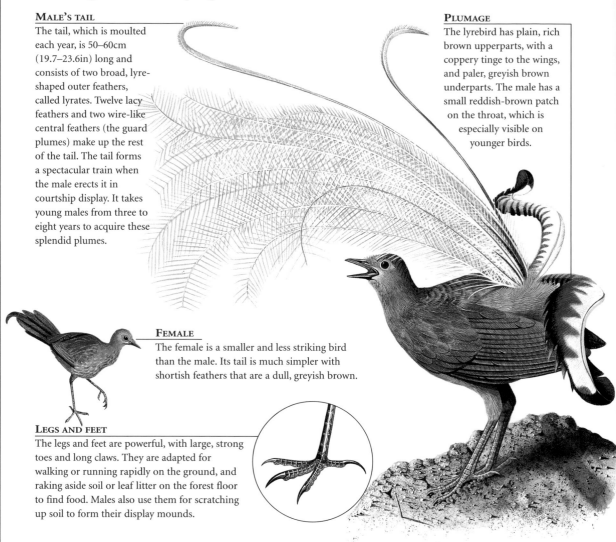

MALE'S TAIL
The tail, which is moulted each year, is 50–60cm (19.7–23.6in) long and consists of two broad, lyre-shaped outer feathers, called lyrates. Twelve lacy feathers and two wire-like central feathers (the guard plumes) make up the rest of the tail. The tail forms a spectacular train when the male erects it in courtship display. It takes young males from three to eight years to acquire these splendid plumes.

FEMALE
The female is a smaller and less striking bird than the male. Its tail is much simpler with shortish feathers that are a dull, greyish brown.

LEGS AND FEET
The legs and feet are powerful, with large, strong toes and long claws. They are adapted for walking or running rapidly on the ground, and raking aside soil or leaf litter on the forest floor to find food. Males also use them for scratching up soil to form their display mounds.

PLUMAGE
The lyrebird has plain, rich brown upperparts, with a coppery tinge to the wings, and paler, greyish brown underparts. The male has a small reddish-brown patch on the throat, which is especially visible on younger birds.

CREATURE COMPARISONS

Although no relation of the superb lyrebird, the Western capercaillie (Tetrao urogallus), a member of the grouse family found in coniferous forests of northern Eurasia, also has a remarkable courtship display involving spreading of the tail feathers accompanied by an extraordinary song. In the case of the Western capercaillie, though, the song is hardly melodious, often being described as a succession of accelerating 'plops', like water dripping into a bucket, followed by a loud pop, like a cork being pulled out of a bottle, and ending with a wheezing gurgle.

The turkey-like Western capercaillie is stockier than the superb lyrebird, but like the lyrebird has short, rounded and weak wings.

Western capercaillie

Superb lyrebird

WHERE IN THE WORLD?

Found in southeastern Australia, ranging from southeastern Queensland to southern Victoria. In 1934 the species was introduced to central and southeast Tasmania, where its numbers have increased significantly.

RELATED SPECIES

There are two subspecies of superb lyrebird: the southeastern superb lyrebird, Menura n. novaehollandiae, and the northern superb lyrebird, M. n. edwardi, which occurs along the northern margins of the species' range. Albert's lyrebird, M. alberti, is also found in this area.

· ORDER · *Passeriformes* **· FAMILY ·** *Muscicapidae* **· GENUS & SPECIES ·** *Ficedula hypoleuca*

PIED FLYCATCHER

KEY FEATURES

- A small songbird of open woodland.
- Catches insects in mid-air during brief sallies from its perch.
- Male often mates with two or even three females, but usually helps to raise only the first family.
- Spends three months a year migrating between its summer and winter homes.

VITAL STATISTICS

WEIGHT	11–15g (0.4–0.5oz)
LENGTH	12.5–13cm (4.9–5.1in)
WINGSPAN	21–24cm (8.3–9.4in)
SEXUAL MATURITY	1–2 years
BREEDING SEASON	Late April–August
NUMBER OF EGGS	5 to 8
INCUBATION PERIOD	13–15 days
FLEDGING PERIOD	14–17 days
TYPICAL DIET	Insects, especially flies, butterflies, moths, caterpillars and beetles; some fruit in autumn
LIFESPAN	Up to 15 years

Constantly flitting around woodland clearings, the energetic and speedy pied flycatcher is highly effective at catching insects in mid-air.

FEMALE
The female has brown upperparts and slightly smaller white wing patches than the male. She lacks the white patch or spots on her forehead.

WINGS
The broad, relatively short wings provide the bird with good manoeuvrability when flying.

MARKINGS
The male's prominent white forehead patch is often divided into two spots.

BILL
The bill is short and stubby with a broad gape — the ideal shape for catching insects on the wing. Stiff hairs around the bill, known as rictal bristles, help to sweep flying insects towards the flycatcher's mouth. They also protect its eyes and nostrils from damage by collisions with large insects.

FOOT
The pied flycatcher has three forward-facing toes and a single, longer and stronger rear-facing toe for grasping perches.

TAIL
The long, broad tail enables the bird to turn sharply in flight.

CREATURE COMPARISONS

Even experienced observers can have difficulty in distinguishing the pied flycatcher and its closest relative, the collared flycatcher (Ficedula albicollis). The male collared flycatcher has a thick white band right around his neck, and has larger white patches on his forehead and wings. The collared flycatcher also has slightly longer wings than the pied flycatcher, but this difference is hard to see from a distance.

The collared flycatcher's breeding range lies farther south than that of its relative, stretching from easternmost France east to European Russia and north only as far as the Baltic Sea. But the surest way to tell the pair apart is by how they sound. The collared flycatcher's song is noticeably longer, slower and quieter: its commonest call is tsrr.

Pied flycatcher

Collared flycatcher

WHERE IN THE WORLD?

Breeds from Britain and western Europe east through Scandinavia and central Europe to central Russia and Siberia, and in

northwestern Africa. Winters in sub-Saharan West Africa.

RELATED SPECIES

The pied flycatcher is 1 of nearly 30 species in the genus Ficedula, which also includes the semi-collared or half-collared flycatcher, F. semitorquata. Ficedula is the largest of 9 genera in the family Muscicapidae, or Old World flycatchers. Most of the family's 110 members are found in Africa, Australasia and southeastern Asia. Close relatives of the Old World flycatchers include the whistlers, fantails, monarchs and chats.

• **ORDER** • *Passeriformes* • **FAMILY** • *Paradisaeidae* • **GENUS & SPECIES** • *Paradisaea raggiana* RAGGIANA BIRD OF PARADISE

A bird built for display, the male spends up to five months of every year in moult — shedding his old feathers and growing a fresh set of plumes.

KEY FEATURES

- Bold plumage and a dazzling courtship display make this bird one of the wonders of the natural world.
- Males dance in treetops, showing off their bright red, lacy plumes in cascades of shimmering colour.
- Female chooses the most impressive dancer for a mate, then raises her brood alone.

FEMALE
The female is smaller than, and very different from, the fully plumed male. Her male chicks resemble her until they begin to acquire adult plumage.

BILL
Resembling that of its crow-like ancestors, the powerful bill is typical of many fruit-eating birds. In the male it is powder-blue inside and out.

WINGS
The short, rounded wings are used for display, and are also strong enough to carry a plumed male through the air, although his undulating flight appears laboured.

LEGS AND FEET
Stout and strong, the legs give the displaying male a firm grip of his perch as he arches forward, seemingly beyond the point of balance. As with the bill, the legs and feet are very like those of a crow.

PLUMES
Lacy feathers up to 50cm (19.7in) long grow from each side of the breast; their bases are usually hidden by the wings when the bird is not displaying.

VITAL STATISTICS

WEIGHT	Male 311–340g (11–12oz); female 170–200g (6–7oz)
LENGTH	Male 71cm (27.9in) including plumes; female 28cm (11in)
WINGSPAN	48–63.5cm (18.9–25in)
SEXUAL MATURITY	Male 4–6 years; female 2 years
BREEDING SEASON	September to November
NUMBER OF EGGS	1 or 2
INCUBATION PERIOD	About 20 days
FLEDGING PERIOD	19–20 days
TYPICAL DIET	Mainly fruit; some insects
LIFESPAN	Probably up to 16 years

CREATURE COMPARISONS

The finery of the Raggiana bird of paradise is equalled by the blue bird of paradise, which displays upside-down, flaring its wings and calling raucously. Wallace's standardwing, with 15cm (5.9in) plumes sprouting from its wing joints, is one of the few birds of paradise that live outside New Guinea — on the Moluccan islands.

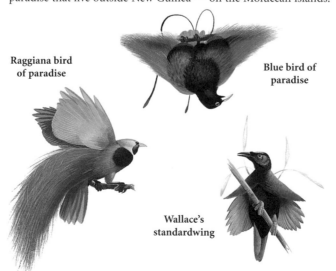

Raggiana bird of paradise

Blue bird of paradise

Wallace's standardwing

WHERE IN THE WORLD?

Found in southern and eastern Papua New Guinea, from Milne Bay in the east, north to the Huon Peninsula, and west almost to the border of Irian Jaya.

RELATED SPECIES

Most of the 43 bird of paradise species live in Papua New Guinea, including the red bird of paradise, but a few species are found in the Moluccan islands and Australia.

GOLDCREST

• ORDER • *Passeriformes* • FAMILY • *Sylviidae* • GENUS & SPECIES • *Regulus regulus*

KEY FEATURES

- Europe's smallest bird, dwarfed even by a sparrow and, on average, weighing no more than a medium-sized coin.
- Hunts tiny insects and spiders in the treetops, where it flutters, hovers and climbs to track down its prey.
- Always on the move, it must feed for at least 90 per cent of the time each day in winter just to stay alive.

VITAL STATISTICS

WEIGHT	4–8g (0.1–0.3oz)
LENGTH	9cm (3.5in)
WINGSPAN	13.5–15.5cm (5.3–6.1in)
SEXUAL MATURITY	1 year
BREEDING SEASON	April to August
NUMBER OF EGGS	7 to 10 in each clutch
INCUBATION PERIOD	15–17 days
FLEDGING PERIOD	17–22 days
NUMBER OF BROODS	Up to 2 each year
TYPICAL DIET	Tiny spiders and insects (mainly flies, caterpillars and aphids)
LIFESPAN	Up to 7 years, but usually less than 1 year

Beautifully camouflaged in its lofty treetop home, the minuscule goldcrest is almost invisible to humans as it moves acrobatically in search of prey.

CREST
Although the male goldcrest usually hides his crest, flattening it along the top of his head, he raises and spreads it like a glowing flame when excited or courting a female. Black borders make the crest's brilliant colours seem even brighter.

PLUMAGE
To help it blend in with its surroundings, the goldcrest has plain, greyish-green upperparts and pale buff underparts. The male has an orange flush to the centre of his crest, but the female's crest is all-yellow.

BILL
The tiny spike of a bill is adapted to picking prey off leaves or from narrow crevices in bark.

FEET
The goldcrest's short-toed feet have long, fine claws for grasping small twigs at the ends of branches and hanging upside-down from them.

CREATURE COMPARISONS

Competing with the goldcrest for the title of smallest European bird is the fractionally heavier firecrest (*Regulus ignicapillus*), which is named after the vibrant, orange-red streak that runs along the centre of its crest. The firecrest is usually more easily distinguished from its relative by the bolder patterning of its head plumage: a black stripe passes across the eye and a thick white one lies above it. Whereas the firecrest looks rather fierce, the goldcrest seems to have a surprised expression — an effect created by the pale feathers that surround its pure black eye.

Both species are very active in their behaviour, and both inhabit woodlands, although the firecrest does not share the goldcrest's preference for coniferous trees.

Firecrest

Goldcrest

WHERE IN THE WORLD?

Breeds from Britain and Ireland east across Europe, southern Siberia and parts of central Asia to Japan. Northern populations move southwards for the winter.

RELATED SPECIES

The goldcrest belongs to a group of 6 tiny birds, known as the kinglets, which includes the firecrest, Canary Islands goldcrest, Taiwan firecrest and the ruby- and golden-crowned kinglets. The kinglets are often classed as a subfamily (Regulinae) in the warbler family, Sylviidae, whose 400 or so members include the whitethroats, gnatcatchers, tailorbirds, cisticolas, reed warblers, leaf warblers and prinias. All are restlessly active, insect-hunting birds.

• **ORDER** • *Pelecaniformes* • **FAMILY** • *Fregatidae* • **GENUS & SPECIES** • *Fregata magnificens* MAGNIFICENT FRIGATEBIRD

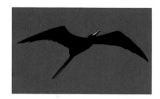

KEY FEATURES

- An aggressive pirate of the skies, it forces other seabirds to give up their catch of fish.
- Long wings, a streamlined shape and low bodyweight give it great manoeuvrability in the air.
- Snatches fish from the sea's surface and steals eggs and chicks from other birds' nests.

VITAL STATISTICS

WEIGHT	1–1.5kg (2.2–3.3lb)
LENGTH	90–115cm (35.4–45.3in)
WINGSPAN	2–2.5m (6ft 6in–8ft 2in)
BREEDING SEASON	Throughout the year, but in some locations favours the dry season
NUMBER OF EGGS	1
INCUBATION PERIOD	40–50 days
FLEDGLING PERIOD	20–24 weeks
BREEDING INTERVAL	2 years
TYPICAL DIET	Flying-fish, squid, offal, scraps, seabird eggs and chicks

Well adapted to an aerial existence, the magnificent frigatebird is a maurauder of the tropical coasts of North and South America.

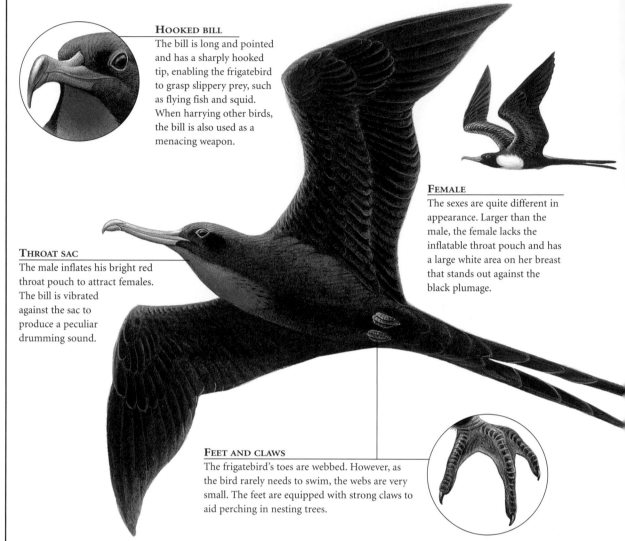

HOOKED BILL
The bill is long and pointed and has a sharply hooked tip, enabling the frigatebird to grasp slippery prey, such as flying fish and squid. When harrying other birds, the bill is also used as a menacing weapon.

FEMALE
The sexes are quite different in appearance. Larger than the male, the female lacks the inflatable throat pouch and has a large white area on her breast that stands out against the black plumage.

THROAT SAC
The male inflates his bright red throat pouch to attract females. The bill is vibrated against the sac to produce a peculiar drumming sound.

FEET AND CLAWS
The frigatebird's toes are webbed. However, as the bird rarely needs to swim, the webs are very small. The feet are equipped with strong claws to aid perching in nesting trees.

CREATURE COMPARISONS

The red-footed booby (Sula sula) occupies the same range as the magnificent frigatebird, and often nests in the same colony. It also frequently falls victim to the frigatebird's harrying tactics. Whereas the frigatebird is supremely buoyant in the air, the red-footed booby appears cumbersome, with its heavy body and laboured flight. When feeding, the booby dives vertically from 10–30m (32ft 8in–98ft 4in) into the sea, fully submerging itself in pursuit of fish, and propelling itself during the chase by its webbed feet. Unlike the frigatebird, which rarely gets its plumage wet, the booby has well developed oil glands above the tail that provide waterproofing.

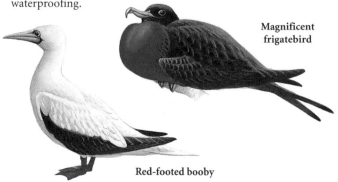

Magnificent frigatebird

Red-footed booby

WHERE IN THE WORLD?

Found along coasts from Florida to Brazil, and Baja California to Ecuador. Lives on the Galapagos Islands and off the West African coast on the Cape Verde Islands.

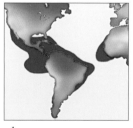

RELATED SPECIES

There are five species of frigatebird in the single genus Fregata, of which the great frigatebird (Fregata minor) has the widest distribution. Two species have restricted ranges: F. aquila is confined to breeding on Ascension Island and F. andrewsi to Christmas Island. The smallest species is the lesser frigatebird, F. ariel. Frigatebirds belong to the order Pelecaniformes, which also includes pelicans, gannets, boobies and cormorants.

• ORDER • *Pelecaniformes* • FAMILY • *Pelecanidae* • GENUS & SPECIES • *Pelecanus onocrotalus*

GREAT WHITE PELICAN

KEY FEATURES

- An extremely gregarious species that nests in colonies numbering thousands of birds.
- Assembles on the water into flotillas that work together to herd and capture fish.
- Extends its huge pouch beneath the surface like a net to scoop up its prey.

VITAL STATISTICS

WEIGHT	9–15kg (19.8–33.1lb)
LENGTH	1.5–1.75m (4ft 9in– 5ft 7in)
WINGSPAN	2.3–3.6m (7ft 5in–11ft 8in)
SEXUAL MATURITY	Probably 3–4 years
BREEDING SEASON	Varies with location
NUMBER OF EGGS	1 to 3; usually 2
INCUBATION PERIOD	29–36 days
FLEDGING PERIOD	About 10 weeks
BREEDING INTERVAL	1 year
TYPICAL DIET	Fish, mostly freshwater species
LIFESPAN	Up to 25 years in the wild

The great white pelican swims strongly and with precise control, dipping its head to scoop up slippery prey in its bizarre, pouched bill.

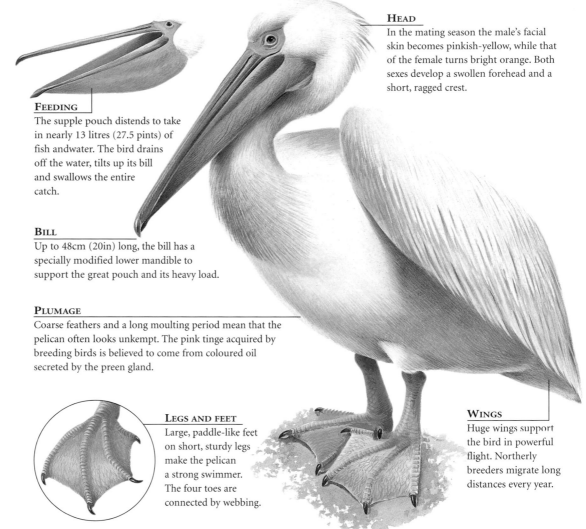

FEEDING
The supple pouch distends to take in nearly 13 litres (27.5 pints) of fish and water. The bird drains off the water, tilts up its bill and swallows the entire catch.

BILL
Up to 48cm (20in) long, the bill has a specially modified lower mandible to support the great pouch and its heavy load.

PLUMAGE
Coarse feathers and a long moulting period mean that the pelican often looks unkempt. The pink tinge acquired by breeding birds is believed to come from coloured oil secreted by the preen gland.

HEAD
In the mating season the male's facial skin becomes pinkish-yellow, while that of the female turns bright orange. Both sexes develop a swollen forehead and a short, ragged crest.

LEGS AND FEET
Large, paddle-like feet on short, sturdy legs make the pelican a strong swimmer. The four toes are connected by webbing.

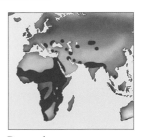

WINGS
Huge wings support the bird in powerful flight. Northerly breeders migrate long distances every year.

CREATURE COMPARISONS

The American white pelican (Pelecanus erythrorhynchos) looks much like the great white pelican, but has a more orange bill on which it grows a flattened plate as an adornment in the breeding season. Like its cousin it often hunts cooperatively and is mainly a freshwater species. The brown pelican (P. occidentalis) is a strictly marine bird and occurs along the North and South American Pacific coasts and throughout the Gulf of Mexico and the Caribbean Sea. Uniquely among pelicans, it hunts by plunge-diving.

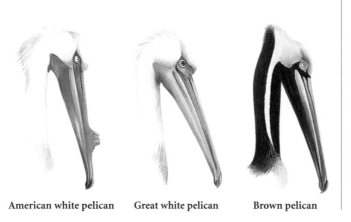

American white pelican   Great white pelican   Brown pelican

WHERE IN THE WORLD?

Widespread through Africa with major strongholds in the Rift Valley. Also found in India, Pakistan, Iraq, Russia and the Danube River delta in Romania.

RELATED SPECIES

The pelican family contains 7 species in 1 genus. The largest species is the 1.8m- (5ft 9in)-long Dalmatian pelican, Pelecanus crispus, an endangered bird that overlaps the great white pelican in parts of Europe and Asia. 3 of the other 5 species are confined to Africa, Asia and Australia.

• ORDER • *Pelecaniformes* • FAMILY • *Phalacrocoracidae* • GENUS & SPECIES • *Phalacrocorax carbo*

GREAT CORMORANT

After out-manoeuvring fish during brief but frenetic underwater chases, the great cormorant must stretch out in the sun to dry its bedraggled wings.

KEY FEATURES

- Pursues fish underwater at high speed, following their every twist and turn with its sinuous body.
- Lacks naturally water-repellent plumage and so must spend hours sunbathing to dry its soaked feathers.
- Rarely seen alone, this sociable species fishes, roosts and breeds in groups — often with other waterbirds.

BILL
Long, and tipped with a formidable hook, the bill's mandibles deliver a crushing bite. In addition, the cormorant's tongue has a very rough surface. These adaptations equip it for seizing fast-moving, slippery and often heavy fish.

BREEDING PLUMAGE
When breeding, a subtle crest develops and slender white feathers, filoplumes, appear on the head and neck.

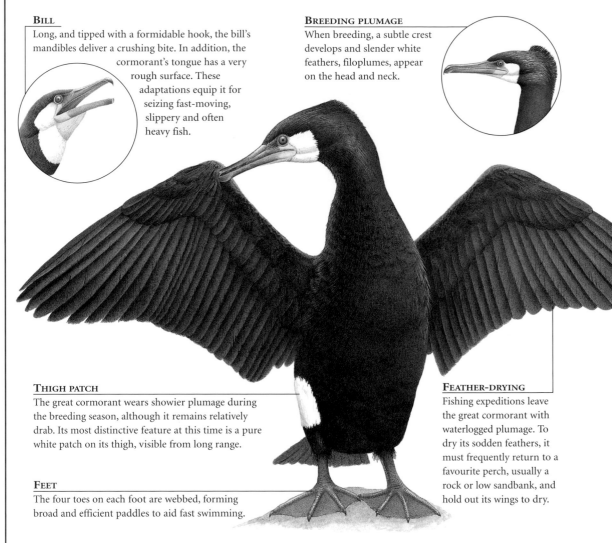

THIGH PATCH
The great cormorant wears showier plumage during the breeding season, although it remains relatively drab. Its most distinctive feature at this time is a pure white patch on its thigh, visible from long range.

FEATHER-DRYING
Fishing expeditions leave the great cormorant with waterlogged plumage. To dry its sodden feathers, it must frequently return to a favourite perch, usually a rock or low sandbank, and hold out its wings to dry.

FEET
The four toes on each foot are webbed, forming broad and efficient paddles to aid fast swimming.

VITAL STATISTICS

WEIGHT	1.8–2.8kg (4–6.2lb)
LENGTH	80–100cm (31–39.4in)
WINGSPAN	1.3–1.6m (4ft 3in–5ft 3in)
SEXUAL MATURITY	3–5 years
BREEDING SEASON	April to June in northern hemisphere; all year in tropics
NUMBER OF EGGS	2 to 6, normally 3 or 4
INCUBATION PERIOD	27–31 days
FLEDGING PERIOD	50 days
TYPICAL DIET	Fish, with some crustaceans and amphibians
LIFESPAN	10–12 years

CREATURE COMPARISONS

Over a large part of its European range, the great cormorant shares its marine habitat with the similar-looking, but smaller and slimmer, European shag (Phalacrocorax aristotelis). The shag is an almost exclusively fish-eating, saltwater species of cormorant that inhabits rocky coasts and islands. It rarely moves inland.

When breeding, the shag's plumage acquires a green gloss, which matches its unusual emerald-green eyes. Its breeding dress is completed by a small crest that protrudes from its forehead like a quiff when erect. Both birds have a rather reptilian appearance as a result of their serpentine necks and scaly-looking plumage, which is due to pale feather-tips on their back and wings.

European shag

Great cormorant

WHERE IN THE WORLD?

Scattered populations occur on coasts, rivers and lakes in Greenland, eastern North America, Europe, Africa, central and Southeast Asia, India, Japan and Australia.

RELATED SPECIES

There are 29–33 species of cormorant (the precise number is disputed) in the family Phalacrocoracidae. All are aquatic, and completely black or blackish with white patches. Ten species are endemic to islands — they are each confined to just a few remote islands in the southern oceans. One such species, the Galapagos cormorant (Phalacrocorax harrisi), has lost the ability to fly. Close relatives of the cormorants include pelicans, gannets and boobies.

• ORDER • *Pelecaniformes* • FAMILY • *Sulidae* • GENUS & SPECIES • *Sula bassana*

The northern gannet is equipped for life as a specialized fish-eater and flies great distances on its long wings to track down prey.

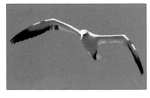

KEY FEATURES

- Glides over the ocean for hours on end, 'riding' the rising currents of air deflected by the waves.
- Hits the sea at a speed of 100 km/h (62.1 mph) when diving after shoals of fish.
- Stores its catch in a throat pouch until it is ready to be swallowed.
- Before it can fly, the single young leaves its nest and starts to swim southwards for the winter.

VITAL STATISTICS

WEIGHT	2.4–3.6kg (5.3–7.9lb)
LENGTH	87–100cm (34.2–39.4in)
WINGSPAN	1.65–1.8m (5ft 4in– 5ft 9in)
SEXUAL MATURITY	4–5 years
BREEDING SEASON	April to September
NUMBER OF EGGS	1
INCUBATION PERIOD	43 days
FLEDGING PERIOD	91 days
BREEDING INTERVAL	1 year
TYPICAL DIET	Fish: mainly shoaling species, such as herring and mackerel
LIFESPAN	15 years

JUVENILE
The juvenile's plumage is dark brown, probably to signal to aggressive adult males that it is not a rival. During noisy disputes, adults often attack each other — even their own mates on occasion.

THROAT POUCH
Large fish are held in an expandable throat pouch until they are ready to be fully swallowed. As many as ten fish have been found in the throat pouches of some gannets.

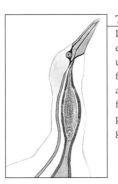

FEET
All four toes of each foot are webbed, providing the power to drive the bird through the water in pursuit of fish. During incubation the gannet wraps its feet around its egg, like a blanket, helping to keep it warm.

BILL
Tiny serrations along the cutting edges of the gannet's mandibles act rather like the teeth of a fine saw, slicing into the skin of squirming fish to hold them securely.

CREATURE COMPARISONS

Slightly smaller than its relative the northern gannet, the masked booby (Sula dactylatra), sometimes called the blue-faced booby, ranges over all areas of tropical oceans and nests on the flat, open ground of tropical islands. The booby is much lighter than the northern gannet, which allows this long-winged bird to take off from islands where there is often very little wind to provide lift.

Both species have a mainly brilliant white plumage, but the northern gannet is characterized by creamy-yellow feathers on its head. The masked booby also has black trailing edges on its wings and tail, whereas the gannet is black on its wingtips alone.

Northern gannet   Masked booby

WHERE IN THE WORLD?

Confined to the northern Atlantic Ocean, breeding on the coasts of Iceland, Norway, France, Britain, Ireland and

northeastern Canada. Winters out at sea, south as far as the coasts of northern Africa and southeastern USA.

RELATED SPECIES

There are 2 other species of gannet in the genus Sula: the Australian gannet S. serrator and the Cape, or African, gannet S. capensis. Both species fish in the same dramatic way as the northern gannet, but inhabit temperate oceans in the southern hemisphere. Sula also contains 6 species of booby: the blue-footed, red-footed, brown, masked, Peruvian and Abbott's boobies. These birds take the place of gannets in tropical seas.

• **ORDER** • *Perciformes* • **FAMILY** • *Belontiidae* • **GENUS & SPECIES** • *Betta splendens*

SIAMESE FIGHTING FISH

The small, but pugnacious Siamese fighting fish haunts murky ditches, swamps and rice paddies hunting for insects and other small prey.

KEY FEATURES

- Territorial males are highly aggressive towards each other and frequently engage in spectacular fights.
- Unlike most fish, it can breathe air at the surface, enabling it to live in stagnant, murky waters.
- Domesticated centuries ago, it is now one of the world's most popular aquarium fish.

VITAL STATISTICS

WEIGHT	Under 10g (0.3oz)
LENGTH	Male up to 6.5cm (2.5in); female up to 5cm (2in)
SEXUAL MATURITY	4 months
SPAWNING SEASON	Unknown
NUMBER OF EGGS	Up to 500
BREEDING INTERVAL	Unknown
TYPICAL DIET	Insects, larvae, crustaceans, aquatic worms, fish fry
LIFESPAN	About 2 years

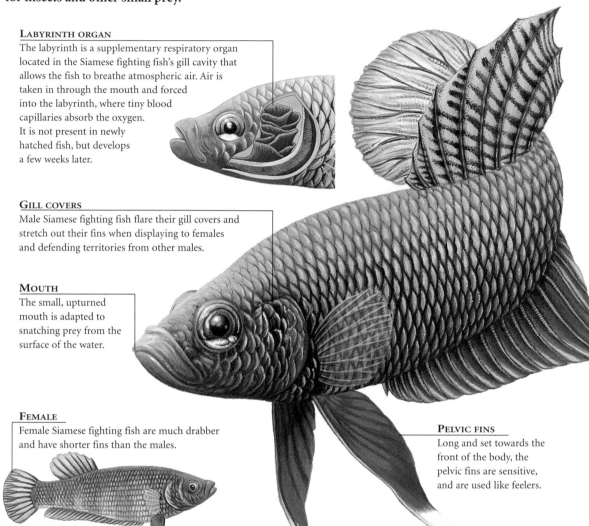

LABYRINTH ORGAN
The labyrinth is a supplementary respiratory organ located in the Siamese fighting fish's gill cavity that allows the fish to breathe atmospheric air. Air is taken in through the mouth and forced into the labyrinth, where tiny blood capillaries absorb the oxygen. It is not present in newly hatched fish, but develops a few weeks later.

GILL COVERS
Male Siamese fighting fish flare their gill covers and stretch out their fins when displaying to females and defending territories from other males.

MOUTH
The small, upturned mouth is adapted to snatching prey from the surface of the water.

FEMALE
Female Siamese fighting fish are much drabber and have shorter fins than the males.

PELVIC FINS
Long and set towards the front of the body, the pelvic fins are sensitive, and are used like feelers.

CREATURE COMPARISONS

Domestic selective breeding of the wild Siamese fighting fish over many decades has resulted in many different forms — most of which look quite different to the original wild form. The most common aquarium-bred form, and perhaps the most spectacular, is the veiltail fighting fish.

The veiltail fighting fish differs from the wild fighting fish in several ways, most notably in its exaggerated fin size. It is also bred in a wide range of colours, with single colours predominating rather than the sparkling, multi-hued iridescence that characterizes the wild fish. Domestic veiltail fighting fish also tend to be larger than their wild counterparts.

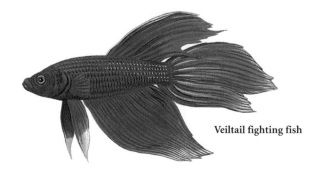

Veiltail fighting fish

WHERE IN THE WORLD?

Originally native to freshwaters of parts of Southeast Asia, particularly Thailand (formerly Siam) and the Malaysian Peninsula. Introduced elsewhere in the tropics, and bred in aquariums worldwide.

RELATED SPECIES

The Siamese fighting fish is one of seven species of fighting fish in the genus Betta, which includes the Java fighting fish (B. picta) and the Borneo fighting fish (B. taeniata). Fighting fish belong to the vast order of perch-like fish, Perciformes, which has some 8000 species, and includes mackerel and gobies. The fighting fish's family, Belontiidae, contains the first tropical fish to be brought to Europe — the paradise fish.

BLENNY

• ORDER • *Perciformes* • FAMILY • *Blenniidae* • GENUS & SPECIES • *Lipophrys spp.*

Most blennies rely on dull markings for concealment, but in the breeding season the males of some species blaze with colour.

KEY FEATURES

- Small, bottom-dwelling fish of rocky coasts and shorelines, particularly common in rockpools.
- Regularly spends long periods out of water at low tide, holed up in damp crevices.
- Male's elaborate courtship display encourages females to lay their eggs within his territory.

BLENNY YOUNG
While still in the egg (left), the embryonic larvae resemble tadpoles, with large eyes and no fins. By the time they are 2cm long they resemble miniature versions of their parents.

FEMALE
Like the male, a female peacock blenny has a bold spot behind the eye. Being free-roaming, she is otherwise more drab, to protect her from predators.

MOUTH
Large, toughened lips and strong, sharp teeth enable the blenny to prise open barnacles and small mussels.

GLANDS
Glands on the anal fins secrete slime to protect the scaleless body. The slime coating helps the blenny to escape from a predator's grasp and to slip into tiny crevices.

STRIPES
Like some other species, the peacock blenny has stripes to break up the outline of its body and so make it less visible to predators against a rocky or weedy background. Some species have blotches for the same reason.

PECTORAL FINS
Bony rods strengthen the pectoral fins, enabling the blenny to clamber into crevices when out of the water at low tide.

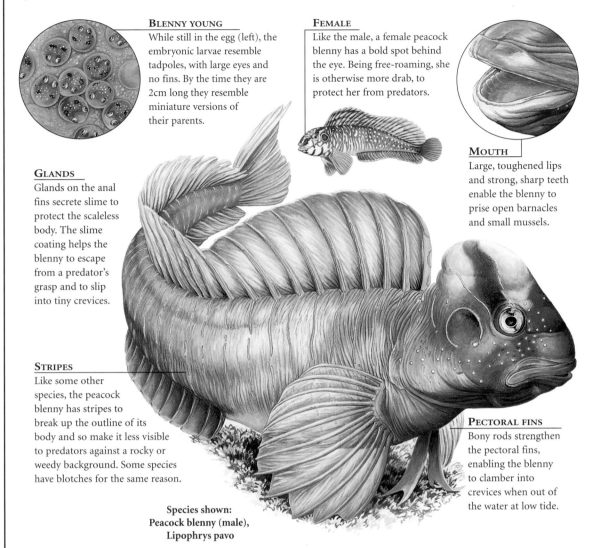

**Species shown:
Peacock blenny (male),
Lipophrys pavo**

VITAL STATISTICS

WEIGHT	Up to 100g (3.5oz), depending on species
LENGTH	4–30cm (1.6–11.8in); most species less than 10cm (3.9in)
SEXUAL MATURITY	2–3 years
BREEDING SEASON	February to August, depending on species
NUMBER OF EGGS	Up to 200, depending on species
HATCHING PERIOD	40–60 days, depending on temperature
BREEDING INTERVAL	1 to 3 times a year
TYPICAL DIET	Small molluscs, crustaceans, fish and algae
LIFESPAN	Unknown

CREATURE COMPARISONS

Like many blennies of the Lipophrys genus, the 18cm (7 in)-long butterfly blenny (Blennius ocellaris) is found on the seabed of the eastern Atlantic and Mediterranean. It is found at all depths up to 100m (328.1ft), as well as the intertidal coastal zone. Well camouflaged, it is active mainly at night and hides from predators in crevices during the day. The much smaller, 4.5cm- (1.8in)-long black-headed blenny (L. nigriceps, not shown to scale) has a bright red body. It is far less abundant and widespread than the butterfly blenny, being found only on a few Mediterranean coastlines, in rocky intertidal crevices.

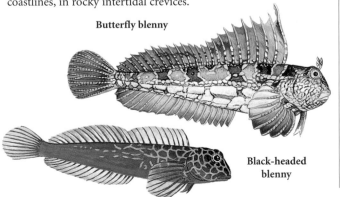

Butterfly blenny

Black-headed blenny

WHERE IN THE WORLD?

Found in rocky coastal waters in the North Sea, Irish Sea and English Channel, and in the eastern North Atlantic as far south as Senegal in western Africa. Also occurs in the Mediterranean Sea and Black Sea.

RELATED SPECIES

There are 11 species in the genus Lipophrys, which is just a small part of the family Blenniidae. In total the suborder Blennioidei comprises 6 families, 138 genera and approximately 800 species, including the black-faced blenny, Tripterygion delaisi.

• **ORDER** • *Perciformes* • **FAMILY** • *Cichlidae* • **GENUS & SPECIES** • *Cichlasoma spp.*

SOUTH AMERICAN CICHLIDS

Found farther north than any other cichlid, the Rio Grande perch inhabits the rivers and lakes of northern Mexico and Texas.

KEY FEATURES

- A freshwater genus characterized by its parental care, which is untypical of fish behaviour.
- Aggressively territorial during the breeding season, males often attack rivals to drive them away.
- Some members exploit food sources that become available when rainfall floods their forest habitat.

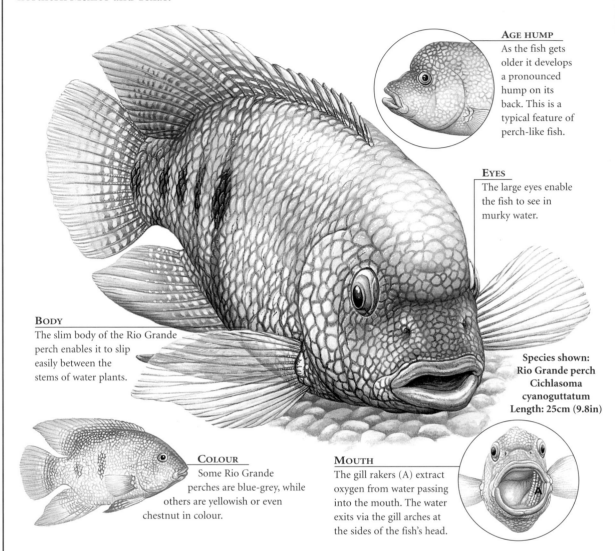

AGE HUMP
As the fish gets older it develops a pronounced hump on its back. This is a typical feature of perch-like fish.

EYES
The large eyes enable the fish to see in murky water.

BODY
The slim body of the Rio Grande perch enables it to slip easily between the stems of water plants.

Species shown:
**Rio Grande perch
Cichlasoma
cyanoguttatum**
Length: 25cm (9.8in)

COLOUR
Some Rio Grande perches are blue-grey, while others are yellowish or even chestnut in colour.

MOUTH
The gill rakers (A) extract oxygen from water passing into the mouth. The water exits via the gill arches at the sides of the fish's head.

VITAL STATISTICS

LENGTH	Up to 30cm (11.8in)
SEXUAL MATURITY	Within a year
SPAWNING SEASON	Wet season, which occurs between May and September depending on region
NUMBER OF EGGS	Up to 500
INCUBATION PERIOD	3–7 days
BREEDING INTERVAL	1 year
TYPICAL DIET	Worms, shrimps, adult insects and their larvae
LIFESPAN	Unknown

CREATURE COMPARISONS

The zebra cichlid (Cichlasoma nigrofasciatum) frequents waters in Guatemala. Growing to little more than 10cm (3.9in), it is about one-third of the size of the acara bandeira (C. festivum), a denizen of the Amazon Basin and waterways of northern Guiana.

These species illustrate the rich diversity of cichlid colouration. The black stripes of the zebra cichlid lie on a blue background and stop short of its snout, which is less pointed than that of its relative. The yellowish-green acara bandeira has a black eye spot on its tail fin and a pair of long pelvic fins. Like most members of their genus, both species are fiercely protective of their young.

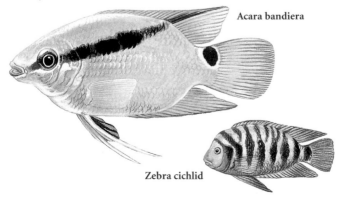

Acara bandeira

Zebra cichlid

WHERE IN THE WORLD?

Found in the lakes and rivers of southern North America and throughout Central and South America, from Mexico, through the Amazon and Orinoco basins, to the southern borders of Brazil.

RELATED SPECIES

The genus Cichlasoma belongs to the Cichlidae family, which has more than 1000 species in South America and Africa. Many cichlids live in Amazonia, but more than half are found in the lakes of East Africa, such as the Malawi zebra cichlid, Pseudotrophes zebra.

• ORDER • *Perciformes* • FAMILY • *Cichlidae* • GENUS & SPECIES • *Pterophyllum scalare*

KEY FEATURES

- Native to the Amazon River system, but more familiar as a specimen in tropical fish tanks.
- Deep body is flattened sideways like a dish, with fins elongated into long, wing-like rays, and stripes that serve as camouflage.
- Lays its eggs on a plant leaf or stem and carefully protects its young, moving them to a 'nursery' site by sucking them into its mouth.

VITAL STATISTICS

LENGTH	Up to 15cm (5.9in)
SEXUAL MATURITY	8–12 months
SPAWNING SEASON	During seasonal floods
NUMBER OF EGGS	Usually 100 to 200
HATCHING TIME	1–3 days
BREEDING INTERVAL	10–15 days
TYPICAL DIET	Insect larvae and water-fleas
LIFESPAN	10–18 years in aquaria; unknown in wild

Its slim shape, vertical stripes and elongated fins have evolved to disguise the angelfish as it hovers almost motionless among water-weeds or roots.

GILL
The gill flaps are situated behind the eyes. Behind the flap, the gills are a mass of feathery projections, swollen red with blood. Water is taken through the mouth and passed over the gills, where oxygen is absorbed.

FINS
The angelfish has a tall dorsal fin (1); a wedge-shaped caudal fin (2); two pectoral fins (3), which are flaps behind the gills; a prominent anal fin with a long point (4); and two thin, trailing ventral fins (5).

HEAD
Like other cichlids, the angelfish has a single nostril on each side of its head, compared to two in most fish.

FRY
Baby angelfish (fry) are tadpole-like in shape. They are only 4mm (0.2in) long at hatching, with the yolk sac still attached. They lose the yolk sac within a week and grow to 1cm long in two weeks (below).

STRIPES
A typical angelfish has four stripes: one through the base of its tail, two down its body, and one passing through its eye. The stripes function as camouflage. Through selective breeding, many aquarium fish lack these stripes.

CREATURE COMPARISONS

Like the angelfish, the discus fish (Symphysodon aequifasciatus) lives in slow moving stretches of the Amazon and other rivers in South America. The discus fish is slightly larger than its relative, and its fins are more rounded. It too has vertical stripes, but they are usually more difficult to see.

The two species differ in the care of their young. As the young discus fish are developing, the adults grow a layer of protein on their skin. Once the young fish can swim freely they attach themselves to one or other of their parents and feed on this proteinous secretion.

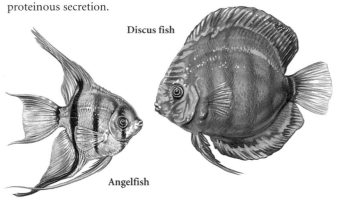

Discus fish

Angelfish

WHERE IN THE WORLD?

Found in the Amazon and its tributaries, such as the Rio Negro and Rio Tapajós. Angelfish, possibly of different species, are also found in the Guyana and Orinoco rivers farther north.

RELATED SPECIES

The genus Pterophyllum was once divided into three species in different South American rivers, but these may instead be varieties of a single species. The family Cichlidae contains more than 1000 species of cichlid, with 500 species identified in Lake Malawi, Africa alone. There are at least 8000 species in the order Perciformes, ranging from anglerfish and perch in freshwater habitats to swordfish, tuna and mackerel in the seas.

• ORDER • *Perciformes* • FAMILY • *Gobiidae* • GENUS & SPECIES • *Periophthalmus spp.*

MUDSKIPPER

The mudskipper possesses a range of unusual adaptations that make it possible for this remarkable fish to live part of its life out of the water.

KEY FEATURES

- Amphibious fish that spend a large part of their lives out of water, feeding and breeding on mudflats.
- Some individuals use their pectoral fins to move on dry land in a way that resembles 'skipping'.
- Certain species have specially adapted fins that enable them to climb the shoots of mangrove trees.

TAIL FIN
The tail, or caudal, fin has short, strong rays on its lower part, while the upper rays are long and slender. The lower rays prop up the mudskipper while on land. In the water, the tail fin is whipped from side to side to propel the fish forward.

SKIN
The mudskipper can absorb oxygen through its skin, as long as it remains moist, when out of the water. In the male, the skin takes on brighter hues in the spawning season to attract a mate.

MOUTH POUCHES
The mouth contains feathery gill chambers. When on land, the mudskipper must regularly refill these chambers with water so that it can continue to extract oxygen via its gills.

EYES
The eyes are mounted in turret-like pods on top of the head. They enable the mudskipper to see, frog-style, even when its body is submerged.

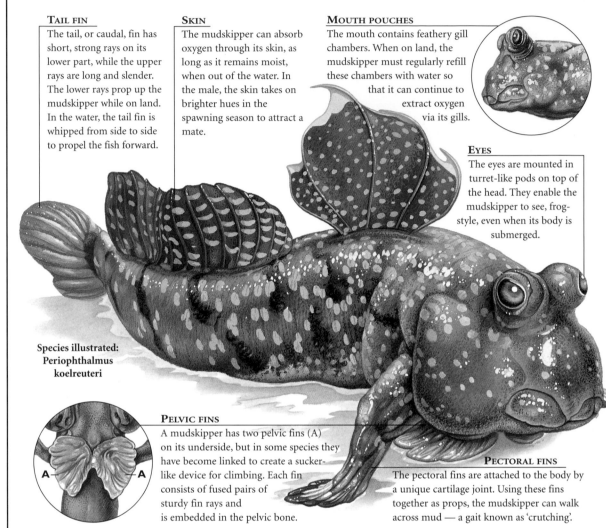

Species illustrated:
Periophthalmus koelreuteri

PELVIC FINS
A mudskipper has two pelvic fins (A) on its underside, but in some species they have become linked to create a sucker-like device for climbing. Each fin consists of fused pairs of sturdy fin rays and is embedded in the pelvic bone.

PECTORAL FINS
The pectoral fins are attached to the body by a unique cartilage joint. Using these fins together as props, the mudskipper can walk across mud — a gait known as 'crutching'.

VITAL STATISTICS

WEIGHT	Average 10g (0.3oz)
LENGTH	15–30cm (5.9–11.8in)
SEXUAL MATURITY	Unknown
SPAWNING SEASON	Peaks during rainy seasons; can be twice a year in some regions
NUMBER OF EGGS	Several hundred
HATCHING TIME	14–21 days
BREEDING INTERVAL	1 year (depends on region)
TYPICAL DIET	Smaller species tend to eat algae and minute aquatic life forms; larger species eat small crabs, insects, worms and small fish
LIFESPAN	Up to 5 years

CREATURE COMPARISONS

The various species of mudskipper can often be distinguished by their colouration and by their fin profiles. The dorsal fin of Periophthalmus barbarus, an Asian mudskipper, stretches along much of the fish's back and has a long pointed ray at the front. In P. chrysospilos, the front ray is even more elongated, to the extent that the ray may stand twice the height of the body. The dorsal fin of P. koelreuteri is curled and leaf-like, sometimes with a shortened first ray. Depending on the species of mudskipper, the dorsal fin has from 8 to 17 rays.

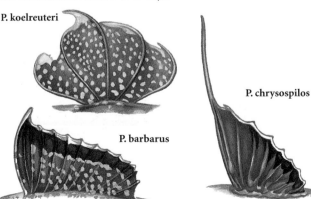

P. koelreuteri

P. barbarus

P. chrysospilos

WHERE IN THE WORLD?

Found in mangrove swamps along parts of the coastlines of Africa, India, Southeast Asia, northern Australia and islands in the southwest Pacific Ocean.

RELATED SPECIES
The mudskipper genus, Periophthalmus, is one of the 3 goby genera in the family Gobiidae. The other 2 genera, Scartelaos and Boleophthalmus, also contain species that inhabit mudflats, such as the goggle-eyed mudskipper, Boleophthalmus

CLEANER WRASSE

• ORDER • *Perciformes* • FAMILY • *Labridae* • GENUS & SPECIES • *Labroides spp.*

The sleek, brightly coloured cleaner wrasse is ideally shaped for slipping between the teeth and gills of its reef-dwelling customers.

KEY FEATURES

- A group of colourful coral reef fish that feed on the parasites and fungal infections that plague other fish.
- Usually very small, enabling them to fit into the mouth and gills of larger fish.
- Vital to the health of other reef fish, who start to lose condition if the cleaning service is suspended.

MOUTH
The cleaner wrasse has a small mouth packed with teeth. The jaws can be extended, enabling the fish to grip parasites and pull them free.

STRIPES
Bright colouration enables other fish to identify the cleaner wrasse easily in the dappled light of the reef waters and approach it for a grooming session.

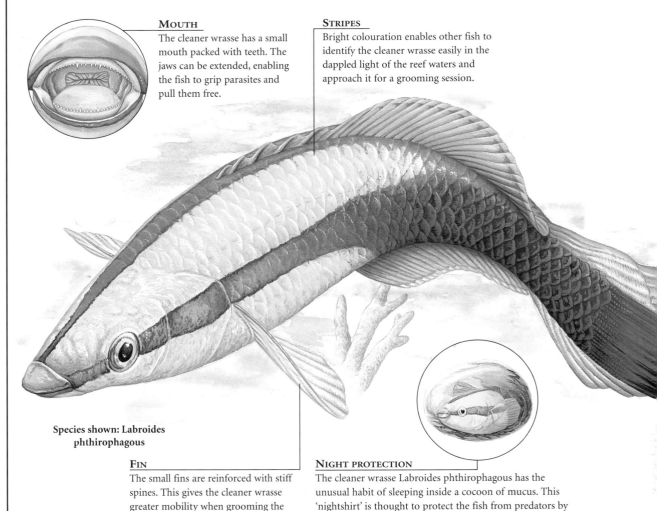

Species shown: Labroides phthirophagous

FIN
The small fins are reinforced with stiff spines. This gives the cleaner wrasse greater mobility when grooming the crevices of a fish's mouth and gills.

NIGHT PROTECTION
The cleaner wrasse Labroides phthirophagous has the unusual habit of sleeping inside a cocoon of mucus. This 'nightshirt' is thought to protect the fish from predators by preventing its scent from spreading through the water.

VITAL STATISTICS

WEIGHT	Under 5g (0.2oz)
LENGTH	5–10cm (2–3.9in)
SEXUAL MATURITY	Unknown
SPAWNING SEASON	November to December in Australia
NUMBER OF EGGS	Probably thousands
BREEDING INTERVAL	Annual
TYPICAL DIET	External parasites of other fish, plus worms and shrimps
LIFESPAN	Unknown

CREATURE COMPARISONS

There are several species of cleaner wrasse in the genus Labroides. They come in a variety of body colours but share the same basic pattern of blue or black stripes. Although they vary in appearance, cleaner wrasses are recognized by the other reef fish. This familiarity prevents the cleaner wrasses being eaten by their potential customers. The cleaner wrasses have lines of 35–50 small scales along the body. The dorsal fin contains 9–11 rays and 9 spines. The spines are stiffer than the rays; they provide extra support for the fin and a measure of defence.

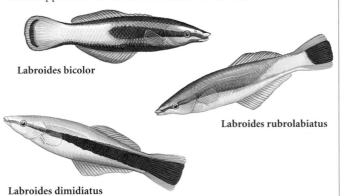

Labroides bicolor

Labroides rubrolabiatus

Labroides dimidiatus

WHERE IN THE WORLD?

Cleaner wrasses are found in the Pacific and Indian oceans, on the coral reefs that grow in the warm, shallow waters surrounding tropical coasts and islands.

RELATED SPECIES

There are about 600 species of wrasse in more than 60 genera in the family Labridae. Precise figures are unknown since many wrasses change their colour as they grow, and as a result some species have acquired two different names. The cleaner wrasses tend to be small, but some members of the family grow to around 3m (9ft 8in). The wrasses belong to the Perciformes, a large order of perch-like fish characterized by their spiny fins.

• **ORDER** • *Perciformes* • **FAMILY** • *Percidae* • **GENUS & SPECIES** • *Perca fluviatilis*

PERCH

KEY FEATURES

- One of the most common freshwater fish, widespread in lowland rivers, canals and still waters.

- An active predator that both ambushes small fish from cover and chases them in open water.

- Lurks in reeds and weeds, where it is camouflaged by the bold black bars on its olive-green flanks.

VITAL STATISTICS

WEIGHT	Up to 4.75kg (10.5lb), but usually about 1.2kg (2.6lb)
LENGTH	18–51cm (7.1–20.1in), but usually about 35cm (13.8in)
SEXUAL MATURITY	3–4 years
BREEDING SEASON	April–May
NUMBER OF EGGS	About 45,000 per kg of bodyweight
BREEDING INTERVAL	1 year
TYPICAL DIET	Animal plankton, insects and small fish
LIFESPAN	10–13 years

Dramatic dark stripes and brick-red pelvic, anal and tail fins make the perch among the most strikingly beautiful and distinctive of all freshwater fish.

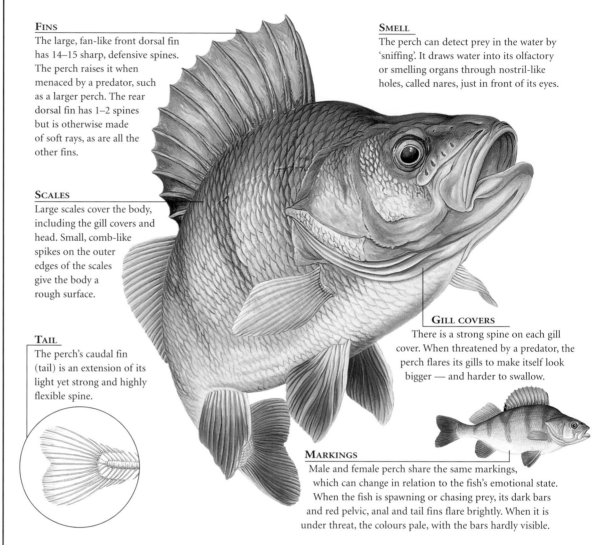

FINS
The large, fan-like front dorsal fin has 14–15 sharp, defensive spines. The perch raises it when menaced by a predator, such as a larger perch. The rear dorsal fin has 1–2 spines but is otherwise made of soft rays, as are all the other fins.

SCALES
Large scales cover the body, including the gill covers and head. Small, comb-like spikes on the outer edges of the scales give the body a rough surface.

TAIL
The perch's caudal fin (tail) is an extension of its light yet strong and highly flexible spine.

SMELL
The perch can detect prey in the water by 'sniffing'. It draws water into its olfactory or smelling organs through nostril-like holes, called nares, just in front of its eyes.

GILL COVERS
There is a strong spine on each gill cover. When threatened by a predator, the perch flares its gills to make itself look bigger — and harder to swallow.

MARKINGS
Male and female perch share the same markings, which can change in relation to the fish's emotional state. When the fish is spawning or chasing prey, its dark bars and red pelvic, anal and tail fins flare brightly. When it is under threat, the colours pale, with the bars hardly visible.

CREATURE COMPARISONS

The zander, or pike-perch (Stizostedion lucioperca), like the perch, is a member of the family Percidae, and lives in much the same waters. Both fish share a similar body plan but the perch is shorter and more thickset while the zander, at up to 1.2m (3ft 9in) in length and 18kg (39.7lb) in weight, is very much larger. The perch's mouth contains lots of small, sharp teeth; the exclusively fish-eating zander has a much a larger mouth and longer, more prominent teeth. The zander is darkish-green on its back with grey-green sides and grey fins. The perch varies in colour, but generally its back is greenish brown-grey, with yellowish sides broken up by 5–9 dark stripes.

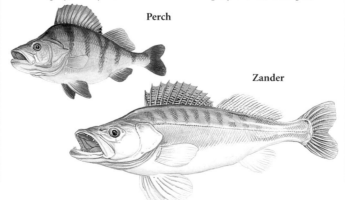

Perch

Zander

WHERE IN THE WORLD?

Common across Europe, except northernmost and southernmost parts, and across northern Asia as far east as Siberia.

RELATED SPECIES

Perciformes is the largest order of fish, with about 8000 species, 1400 genera and 150 families. The Percidae family contains 15 genera and 96 species. The North American yellow perch, Perca flavescens, looks almost identical to P. fluviatilis, and was once thought to be the same species. In Europe the pope or ruffe, Gymnocephalus cernua, looks like a much smaller, drabber version of P. fluviatilis. It lives mainly in canals and slow rivers.

• ORDER • *Perciformes* • FAMILY • *Pomacentridae* • GENUS & SPECIES • *Amphiprion percula*

COMMON CLOWNFISH

The clownfish is never found far from a host anemone on a reef; to stray into the open waters would expose this slow swimmer to many predators.

KEY FEATURES

- Protects itself from the many predators of the coral reef by living among the stinging tentacles of a large sea anemone.

- Secretes an especially thick, protective layer of mucus over its body to avoid being stung by its host sea anemone.

VITAL STATISTICS

LENGTH	Up to 9cm (3.5in); male smaller than female
SEXUAL MATURITY	1–2 years
MATING SEASON	Throughout the year in warmer regions; during the warmest months in cooler regions
NUMBER OF EGGS	200 to 400
HATCHING TIME	7–8 days
PLANKTONIC PHASE	7–10 days
TYPICAL DIET	Planktonic animals; some algae
LIFESPAN	5–10 years

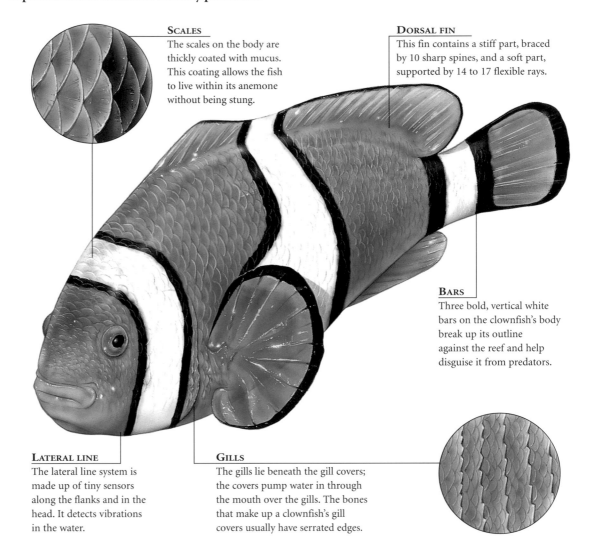

SCALES
The scales on the body are thickly coated with mucus. This coating allows the fish to live within its anemone without being stung.

DORSAL FIN
This fin contains a stiff part, braced by 10 sharp spines, and a soft part, supported by 14 to 17 flexible rays.

BARS
Three bold, vertical white bars on the clownfish's body break up its outline against the reef and help disguise it from predators.

LATERAL LINE
The lateral line system is made up of tiny sensors along the flanks and in the head. It detects vibrations in the water.

GILLS
The gills lie beneath the gill covers; the covers pump water in through the mouth over the gills. The bones that make up a clownfish's gill covers usually have serrated edges.

CREATURE COMPARISONS

Clownfish species differ most obviously from each other in their colour patterns. For example, in contrast to the tear-shaped middle bar of the common clownfish (Amphiprion percula), the Barrier Reef clownfish (A. akindynos) has a relatively straight bar on the midside. It also has an all-white tail, rather than an orange tail. The spine-cheeked clownfish (A. biaculeatus), however, differs from all other clownfish in having a pair of large spines beneath each eye. For this reason, some scientists place this species in a separate genus, Premnas.

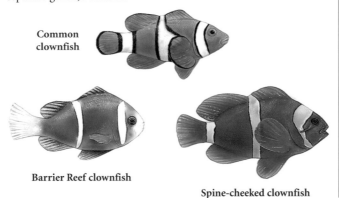

Common clownfish

Barrier Reef clownfish

Spine-cheeked clownfish

WHERE IN THE WORLD?

Lives in the tropical eastern Indian Ocean, South China Sea and Western Pacific, east as far as the Solomon Islands and Vanuatu.

RELATED SPECIES

The common clownfish is one of 28 species of the genus Amphiprion, which includes the Red Sea clownfish, A. bicinctus. Clownfish are all members of the damselfish family Pomacentridae, a group of small, reef-dwelling fish that live in tropical or warm temperate waters.

• ORDER • *Perciformes* • FAMILY • *Scaridae* • GENUS & SPECIES • *Scarus species*

PARROTFISH

The brilliant colours and dazzling patterns for which the parrotfish is known are displayed only by the large, dominant males.

KEY FEATURES

- Uses a beak, formed from fused teeth, to graze on tiny plants that grow on the limestone of coral reefs.
- Territorial males are spectacularly colourful.
- Female can change her appearance, and even her sex, taking on glowing colours and dazzling patterns to increase her breeding potential.

SMALL MATURE FORM
Females and subordinate males do not have the dominant male's spectacular colouration. Their skins are mainly dull brown, red, green and grey in colour, and the patterns are much less dazzling. Both sexes can, however, change into dominant males when the opportunity arises.

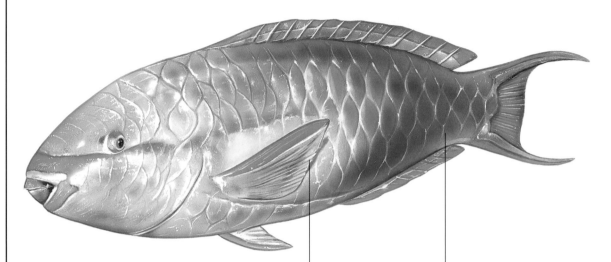

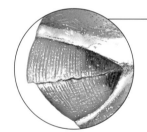

TEETH
The teeth are fused into a beak for rasping algae from the surface of boulders and coral reefs. The scrapings are ground up by the throat teeth. The front teeth grow back as soon they become worn.

PECTORAL FINS
The flexible fins permit delicate movements, and usually the fish just sculls using only these fins, moving from one grazing patch to the next. The tail and body muscles are used only in emergencies.

SKIN
The skin is covered with smooth scales, although part of the head and the fins are naked. The skin and scales are richly coloured in the dominant male, and during sexual displays these colours intensify further.

VITAL STATISTICS

WEIGHT	From tiny to more than 54kg (119lb)
LENGTH	From very small to over 1.22m (4ft)
SEXUAL MATURITY	2–3 years
BREEDING SEASON	Some species breed all year round; others breed during fortnightly high spring tides, or at particular times of day
NUMBER OF EGGS	Hundreds to thousands released at any one spawning
BREEDING INTERVAL	Not known
TYPICAL DIET	Algae and other plants on reefs
LIFESPAN	5 years

CREATURE COMPARISONS

Among all species of parrotfish, the dominant breeding males are brightly coloured, and between them they sport all the colours of the rainbow. The fins, scales and skin are elaborately patterned.

The large dominant males of the Scarus gibbus, S. schlegeli and S. tricolor species demonstrate some of the huge variety of colour, pattern and fin shape that exists among parrotfish.

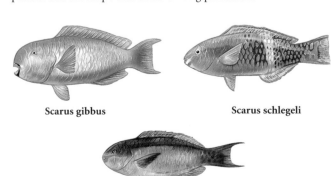

Scarus gibbus

Scarus schlegeli

Scarus tricolor

WHERE IN THE WORLD?

Found in tropical coastal waters, associated with coral reefs. Most species live in the eastern Indian and western Pacific Oceans — the world's richest marine habitats.

RELATED SPECIES

There are nine genera of parrotfish, of which the largest is the genus Scarus, containing about 50 species. The other genera include some forms that live in seagrass beds in shallow, warm water and lack the fused, beak-like teeth of Scarus species. All the parrotfish species are members of the order Perciformes, a group of about 8000 species that includes highly colourful species of butterfly fish, clownfish and angelfish.

AFRICAN WILD ASS

• **ORDER** • *Perissodactyla* • **FAMILY** • *Equidae* • **GENUS & SPECIES** • *Equus asinus*

KEY FEATURES

- A small, rare member of the horse family that has a familiar domestic form — the donkey.
- Tough enough to survive on a diet of nutrient-poor plants in searingly hot, stony deserts.
- Climbs rock outcrops and cliffs with ease, to shelter from the midday sun and hide from predators.

VITAL STATISTICS

WEIGHT	275kg (606.3lb)
LENGTH	Head & Body: 2.1m (6ft 9in) Tail: 45cm (17.7in)
SHOULDER HEIGHT	1.25m (4ft 1in)
SEXUAL MATURITY	2 years, but rarely breeds before 4–5 years
MATING SEASON	Peaks during wet season (July to August)
GESTATION PERIOD	About 360 days
NUMBER OF YOUNG	1
BIRTH INTERVAL	1 year
TYPICAL DIET	Grazes grasses, sedges and forbs; browses shrubs and bushes
LIFESPAN	25–45 years

The sturdily built African wild ass has a pale coat that blends in with its desert home and narrow hoofs for climbing among rocky terrain.

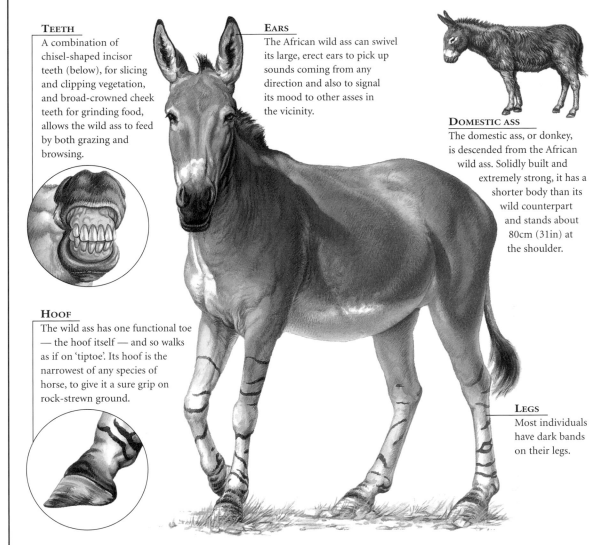

TEETH
A combination of chisel-shaped incisor teeth (below), for slicing and clipping vegetation, and broad-crowned cheek teeth for grinding food, allows the wild ass to feed by both grazing and browsing.

EARS
The African wild ass can swivel its large, erect ears to pick up sounds coming from any direction and also to signal its mood to other asses in the vicinity.

DOMESTIC ASS
The domestic ass, or donkey, is descended from the African wild ass. Solidly built and extremely strong, it has a shorter body than its wild counterpart and stands about 80cm (31in) at the shoulder.

HOOF
The wild ass has one functional toe — the hoof itself — and so walks as if on 'tiptoe'. Its hoof is the narrowest of any species of horse, to give it a sure grip on rock-strewn ground.

LEGS
Most individuals have dark bands on their legs.

CREATURE COMPARISONS

The Asiatic wild ass (Equus hemionus) looks very similar to the African wild ass, but its coat tends to be a warm shade of fawn or tan, rather than sandy-grey, and it lacks the dark leg-markings of its African relative. Less obvious differences are its shorter ears, mane and tail, and broader hoofs, suited to the prevailing terrain of its habitats: salt flats, sandy deserts and arid steppes.

The Asiatic wild ass has four subspecies, the onager, khur, kulan and dziggetai, which live in isolated parts of northern Iran, India, Turkmenistan and China. Like the African wild ass, the khur and onager are very rare.

African wild ass

Asiatic wild ass

WHERE IN THE WORLD?

Once ranged from southern Ethiopia north to Iraq and west as far as eastern Morocco, but now reduced to four small populations along the Red Sea's African coastline, in Sudan, Eritrea, Ethiopia and Somalia.

RELATED SPECIES

The family Equidae comprises a single genus, Equus, containing the African and Asiatic wild asses and 5 other species: Przewalski's horse, the domestic horse and the 3 species of zebra — the plains and mountain zebras and Grevy's zebra, Equus grevyi.

• **ORDER** • *Perissodactyla* **FAMILY** • *Equidae* **GENUS & SPECIES** • *Equus zebra*

MOUNTAIN ZEBRA

Despite its stocky, donkey-like appearance, the mountain zebra is nimble and agile, and hardy enough to survive in bleak, rocky uplands.

KEY FEATURES

- Distinctively marked with bold stripes — but exactly why remains something of a mystery.
- Grazes sparse grasses that it seeks out at altitudes of up to 2000m (6562ft) in semi-arid mountains.
- Lives in small breeding herds protected by a dominant stallion, who has to regularly fight off rivals.

NECK
The zebra's neck, like its head, is elongated as an adaptation to grazing. Unlike other zebras, it has a small but distinct dewlap: a pendulous fold of skin, hanging down from the neck.

STRIPES
Black stripes cover every part of the body except the stomach and inner thigh area. The stripes are horizontal on the legs and rump.

LEGS
Short and thick compared to the legs of many other members of the horse family. This arrangement gives the zebra a low centre of gravity, aiding balance on the steep slopes of its hilly home.

TEETH
Chisel-like incisors at the front of the mouth are used to crop grass, while hard-crowned molars to the rear grind up the food.

FOOT
The mountain zebra's foot consists of a greatly enlarged single digit, the terminal bone of which bears a broad, spade-shaped hoof made of keratin — the same material as human fingernails.

VITAL STATISTICS

WEIGHT	250–370kg (551.2–815.7lb)
LENGTH	Head & Body: 2.1–2.6m (6ft 9in–8ft 5in) Tail: 40–55cm (15.7–21.6in)
SHOULDER HEIGHT	1.15–1.5m (3ft 8in–4ft 9in)
SEXUAL MATURITY	Male 3.5 years; female 2 years
MATING SEASON	Throughout the year
GESTATION PERIOD	1 year
NUMBER OF YOUNG	1
BIRTH INTERVAL	1–3 years
TYPICAL DIET	Predominantly grasses, occasional twigs and leaves
LIFESPAN	20–25 years

CREATURE COMPARISONS

The African wild ass, a native of northeastern Africa (and formerly of the Middle East), is the ancestor of the domestic ass and was one of the first animals to be domesticated as a beast of burden. Like the mountain zebra, it is a member of the genus Equus and the two species share many similarities in overall shape. The ass, however, is lighter in colour than the zebra, and has a slighter build. The greyish-brown coat of the African wild ass provides some camouflage against the dry stony landscape in which it is found. Its long hoofs — the narrowest of any Equus species — help it to keep a good footing on the loose rocky ground.

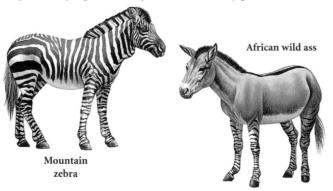

Mountain zebra

African wild ass

WHERE IN THE WORLD?

Once widespread over the mountainous areas of southwest Africa, from Angola and Namibia to Transvaal, but now much reduced. Also found in Cape Province.

RELATED SPECIES

There are 2 subspecies of mountain zebra, **Equus zebra zebra**, or the Cape mountain zebra, and **E. z. hartmannae**, or Hartmann's zebra. Equidae, the horse family, consists of a single genus, Equus. This has 7 species, including the very rare Przewalski's horse, **Equus przewalskii**.

WHITE RHINOCEROS

• ORDER • *Perissodactyla* • FAMILY • *Rhinocerotidae* • GENUS & SPECIES • *Ceratotherium simum*

Low-slung, armoured with thick skin and sporting formidable horns, the massive white rhino need fear no predator on the grassy African plains.

KEY FEATURES

- Fearsome horns and a thick hide mean that the white rhino has no natural predators, but human desire for rhino horn is endangering the species.

- Wallows in water and mud to cool off, rid itself of parasites and keep its skin supple.

- Wide and flexible lips shear short grasses with ease.

VITAL STATISTICS

WEIGHT	Male 2000–3600kg (4409–7937lb) female 1400–1700kg (3086–3748lb)
LENGTH	Head & Body: 3.3–4.2m (10ft 8in–13ft 8in) Tail: 50–70cm (19.7–27.6in)
SHOULDER HEIGHT	1.5–1.8m (4ft 9in–5ft 9in)
SEXUAL MATURITY	Male 10–12 years; female 6–7 years
MATING SEASON	All year, peaks Oct–Dec in southern, Feb–June Central Africa
GESTATION PERIOD	16 months
NUMBER OF YOUNG	1
BIRTH INTERVAL	2–3 years
TYPICAL DIET	Grass
LIFESPAN	40–50 years

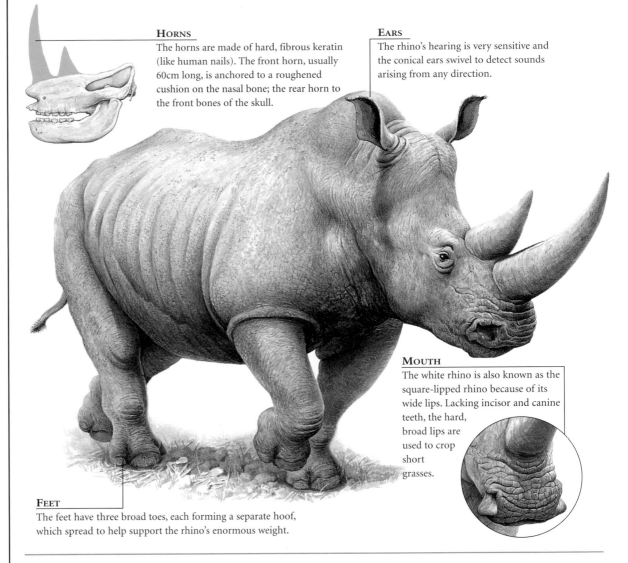

HORNS
The horns are made of hard, fibrous keratin (like human nails). The front horn, usually 60cm long, is anchored to a roughened cushion on the nasal bone; the rear horn to the front bones of the skull.

EARS
The rhino's hearing is very sensitive and the conical ears swivel to detect sounds arising from any direction.

MOUTH
The white rhino is also known as the square-lipped rhino because of its wide lips. Lacking incisor and canine teeth, the hard, broad lips are used to crop short grasses.

FEET
The feet have three broad toes, each forming a separate hoof, which spread to help support the rhino's enormous weight.

CREATURE COMPARISONS

The white rhino and the hippo are almost evenly matched for the title of the second largest land animal. Hippos are heavier, and the largest are a little longer than the largest white rhinos. However, the white rhino stands taller at the shoulder. Although the shoulder height of both species is about eye level to an average human male, a white rhino weighs about 45 times as much as a man, while a hippo weighs nearly 60 times as much.

Hippo

White rhino

WHERE IN THE WORLD?

The southern subspecies lives on scattered parks and reserves in southern Africa, while the northern subspecies is confined to Garamba National Park in the Democratic Republic of Congo (Zaire).

RELATED SPECIES

The are 2 subspecies of white rhino, the southern, C. simum simum, and the northern, C. simum cottoni, and 4 other rhino species in all: the Asian one-horned rhinos, Rhinoceros unicornis and R. sondaicus, the Sumatran, Dicerorhinus sumatrensis and the black, (Diceros bicornis).

• **ORDER** • *Perissodactyla* • **FAMILY** • *Rhinocerotidae* • **GENUS & SPECIES** • *Diceros bicornis*

BLACK RHINOCEROS

KEY FEATURES

- Fearsome horn acts as a deterrent and also as a weapon that can toss a lion bodily into the air.
- Surprisingly agile and capable of charging at speeds reaching 50 km/h (31 mph).
- Protected by its bulk and thick hide from predators, although calves can fall victim to hyenas and lions.

VITAL STATISTICS

WEIGHT	1360–1815kg (2998–4001lb)
LENGTH	Head & Body: 3–3.8m (9ft 8in–12ft 5in) Tail: 68cm (26.8in) Front horn; 45–127cm (17.7–50in)
SHOULDER HEIGHT	1.4–1.6m (4ft 6in–5ft 2in)
SEXUAL MATURITY	Female 4–6 years; male 7–9 years
MATING SEASON	Throughout the year
GESTATION PERIOD	419–478 days
NUMBER OF YOUNG	1
BIRTH INTERVAL	2–5 years
TYPICAL DIET	Leaves, buds and shoots of small trees and bushes; herbs, clover and fruit
LIFESPAN	30–40 years

The black rhino is an animal heavyweight, equipped with a huge head, massive body and thick, sturdy limbs — yet it is surprisingly nimble.

HORNS
The two horns are used mainly for defence and for display. They are composed of keratin, a complex protein.

EARS
The rhino's large ears are highly mobile, helping it to locate the source of sounds that it finds suspicious.

SHOULDERS
The neck and shoulder bones have large, spiny attachments to hold the muscles that support the huge, heavy head.

SKIN
The thick, armour-like skin protects the rhino against predators, but the lack of sweat glands means that the rhino must bathe often to cool off.

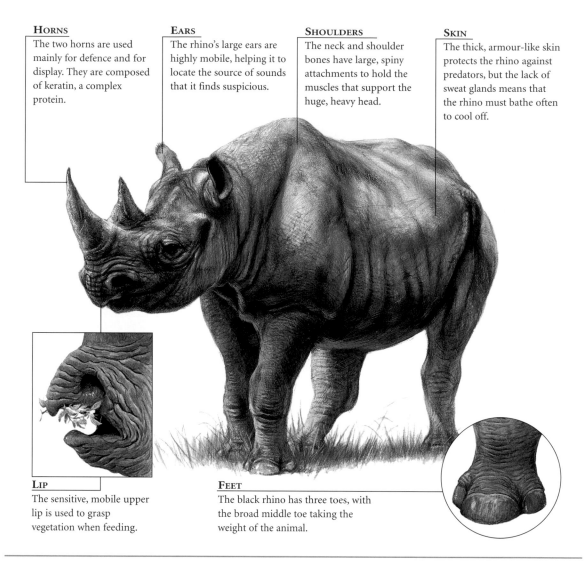

LIP
The sensitive, mobile upper lip is used to grasp vegetation when feeding.

FEET
The black rhino has three toes, with the broad middle toe taking the weight of the animal.

CREATURE COMPARISONS

The white rhino is up to 50 per cent larger than the black rhino. The word 'white' comes from an Afrikaans word meaning 'wide.' This refers to the white rhino's broad mouth, which is used to crop grasses. Because it is a grazer, the white rhino keeps mainly to the plains, seldom sharing the black rhino's range.

Black rhino   White rhino

WHERE IN THE WORLD?

Now reduced to pockets within its former range throughout Africa south of the Sahara. Prefers scrub or wooded terrain to open grassland or humid forest.

RELATED SPECIES

There are five species in the rhinoceros family, Rhinocerotidae. The black rhino and white rhino are native to Africa; the Indian, Javan and the very rare Sumatran rhino, *Dicerorhinus sumatrensis*, range from India through Southeast Asia as far as Indonesia.

INDIAN RHINO

• **ORDER** • *Perissodactyla* • **FAMILY** • *Rhinocerotidae* • **GENUS & SPECIES** • *Rhinoceros unicornis*

The Indian rhino's tough, almost prehistoric-looking hide, impressive horn and enormous bulk provide comprehensive protection against predators.

KEY FEATURES

- Thick, deeply folded hide has rivet-like lumps: it looks, and acts, rather like armour-plating.
- Single, stout horn is a powerful weapon against predators, but the sharp teeth are used in fights with rival males.
- Wallows in mud and water to keep cool and ward off biting parasites.
- Despite its bulk, often lives in dense vegetation.

VITAL STATISTICS

WEIGHT	Male 2200kg (4850lb); female 1600kg (3527lb)
LENGTH	Head & Body: 3.1–3.8m (10ft 2in–12ft 5in) Tail: 70–80cm (27.6–31in)
SHOULDER HEIGHT	1.6–1.8m (5ft 2in–5ft 9in)
SEXUAL MATURITY	Male 7 years; female 5 years
MATING SEASON	All year
GESTATION PERIOD	460–490 days
NUMBER OF YOUNG	1
BIRTH INTERVAL	Up to 3 years
TYPICAL DIET	Grasses and aquatic plants; shoots, stems and foliage of woody shrubs; fruit and crops
LIFESPAN	Up to 45 years

SKELETON
To support its bulk, the rhino has short, pillar-like legs. Broad toes stop it sinking into soft ground.

SKIN & TAIL
Although the 'warty', loose-fitting skin is very thick, it has blood-vessels close to the surface that attract horseflies and other blood-sucking insects, so the tail is used as a fly-swat to help drive them away.

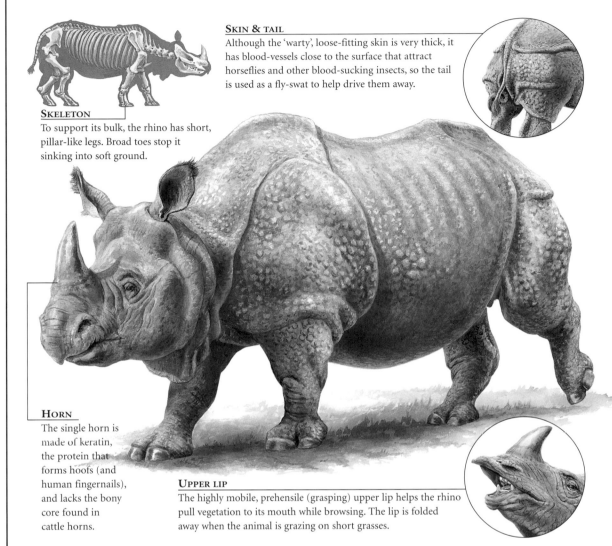

HORN
The single horn is made of keratin, the protein that forms hoofs (and human fingernails), and lacks the bony core found in cattle horns.

UPPER LIP
The highly mobile, prehensile (grasping) upper lip helps the rhino pull vegetation to its mouth while browsing. The lip is folded away when the animal is grazing on short grasses.

CREATURE COMPARISONS

The Sumatran rhino (Dicerorhinus sumatrensis) is a more primitive species than the Indian rhino and has hardly changed over the last 40 million years: it is closely related to the woolly rhinoceros that became extinct 15,000 years ago. Also known as the hairy, or Asian two-horned, rhino, it sports a pair of short, rounded horns and is covered by a thin coat of long, rather coarse hairs.

One of the smallest rhinos, the Sumatran rhino weighs 1000–2000kg (2205–4409lb) and stands just 1.1–1.5m (3ft 6in–4ft 9in) at the shoulder. It is now endangered, surviving in small and scattered populations in Sumatra, Borneo, Malaysia and Thailand.

Indian rhinoceros

Sumatran rhinoceros

WHERE IN THE WORLD?

Once found on floodplains throughout the north of the Indian subcontinent, but the population of just 1500 animals is now confined to Kazingira and Royal Chitwan national parks in India and Nepal, and a few other reserves.

RELATED SPECIES

The rhinoceros family, Rhinocerotidae, contains 5 species in 4 genera: the Indian and Javan rhinos, or Asian one-horned rhinos, in the genus Rhinoceros; the Sumatran rhino in Dicerorhinus; the white rhino in Ceratotherium; and the black rhino in Diceros. Rhinos belong to the order Perissodactyla, or odd-toed ungulates, which also includes the tapirs in the family Tapiridae and the horses, asses and zebras in the family Equidae.

• **ORDER** • *Perissodactyla* • **FAMILY** • *Tapiridae* • **GENUS & SPECIES** • *Tapirus indicus*

MALAYAN TAPIR

KEY FEATURES

• An Asian counterpart to the three tapir species found in the forests of South America.

• An excellent swimmer; always feeds close to well worn escape paths that lead to water.

• Increasingly rare. Listed as vulnerable by the IUCN (World Conservation Union).

This heavyweight uses its bulk to crash through dense undergrowth, its specially adapted feet helping it tread safely over treacherous marshland.

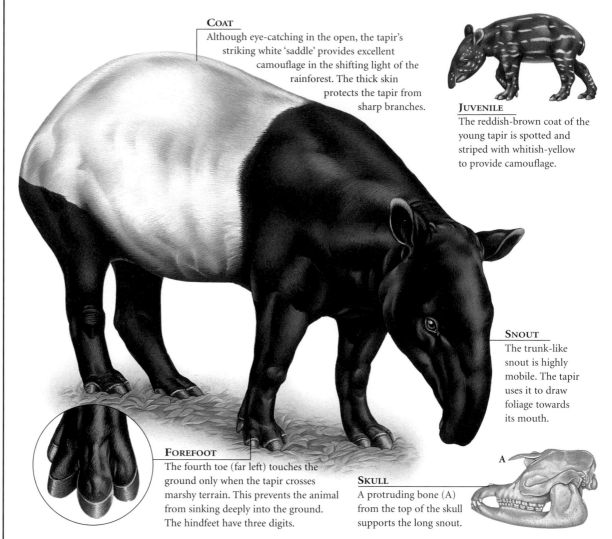

COAT
Although eye-catching in the open, the tapir's striking white 'saddle' provides excellent camouflage in the shifting light of the rainforest. The thick skin protects the tapir from sharp branches.

JUVENILE
The reddish-brown coat of the young tapir is spotted and striped with whitish-yellow to provide camouflage.

SNOUT
The trunk-like snout is highly mobile. The tapir uses it to draw foliage towards its mouth.

FOREFOOT
The fourth toe (far left) touches the ground only when the tapir crosses marshy terrain. This prevents the animal from sinking deeply into the ground. The hindfeet have three digits.

SKULL
A protruding bone (A) from the top of the skull supports the long snout.

VITAL STATISTICS

WEIGHT	260–375kg (573.2–826.7lb)
LENGTH	250cm (98.4in)
SHOULDER HEIGHT	100cm (39.4in)
SEXUAL MATURITY	3 years
MATING SEASON	All year
GESTATION PERIOD	390–400 days
NUMBER OF YOUNG	Usually 1
BIRTH INTERVAL	2 years
TYPICAL DIET	Leaves, grasses, aquatic plants and young twigs
LIFESPAN	Up to 30 years in captivity

CREATURE COMPARISONS

The mountain tapir lives in the Andes of South America, from northwestern Venezuela to northwestern Peru. Unlike its lowland Asian relative, this tapir can be found at elevations of 4500m (14760ft). Weighing up to 175kg (385.8lb), the mountain tapir is smaller, but has a similar body shape. The woolly brown coat keeps the mountain tapir warm, and unlike the Malayan tapir, it has white markings around its lips. Both species forage for tender vegetation at dusk and dawn. The mountain tapir is listed as vulnerable by the IUCN (World Conservation Union).

Malayan tapir

Mountain tapir

WHERE IN THE WORLD?

Found from southern Burma (Myanmar), through Thailand and the Malay Peninsula to Sumatra. A small number may be present on Borneo.

RELATED SPECIES

The Malayan tapir is the heaviest of the 4 species in the genus Tapirus. The other 3 species are found in South America, and are the Brazilian tapir, T. terrestris, the mountain tapir, T. pinchaque, and Baird's tapir, T. bairdii.

• ORDER • *Perissodactyla* • FAMILY • *Tapiridae* • GENUS & SPECIES • *Tapirus terrestris*

A flexible proboscis and acute senses, combined with a bullet-shaped head and agile legs, make the Brazilian tapir an expert forager and escape artist.

KEY FEATURES

- Its stocky, yet streamlined, body with short, slender legs is ideal for pushing through dense undergrowth.
- Roots around for tender plant food using its mobile, sensitive proboscis (extended snout).
- Never straying far from water, it is able to make an amphibious escape at a moment's notice.

VITAL STATISTICS

WEIGHT	180–320kg (396.8–705.5lb)
LENGTH	Head & Body: 1.8–2.5m (5ft 9in–8ft 2in) Tail: 5–13cm (2–5.1in)
SHOULDER HEIGHT	73–120cm (28.7–47.2in)
SEXUAL MATURITY	3–4 years
MATING SEASON	Prior to the rainy season in the wild; captive female in oestrus every 50–80 days
GESTATION PERIOD	385–412 days
NUMBER OF YOUNG	1, rarely 2
BIRTH INTERVAL	18 months
TYPICAL DIET	Vegetation, fruit
LIFESPAN	35 years in captivity, unknown in wild

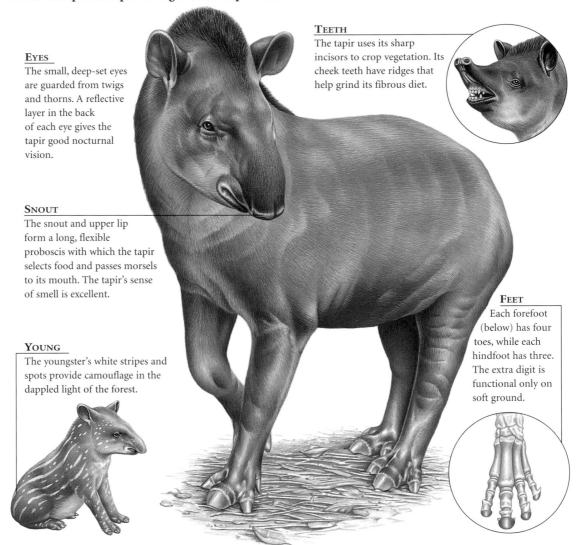

EYES
The small, deep-set eyes are guarded from twigs and thorns. A reflective layer in the back of each eye gives the tapir good nocturnal vision.

TEETH
The tapir uses its sharp incisors to crop vegetation. Its cheek teeth have ridges that help grind its fibrous diet.

SNOUT
The snout and upper lip form a long, flexible proboscis with which the tapir selects food and passes morsels to its mouth. The tapir's sense of smell is excellent.

YOUNG
The youngster's white stripes and spots provide camouflage in the dappled light of the forest.

FEET
Each forefoot (below) has four toes, while each hindfoot has three. The extra digit is functional only on soft ground.

CREATURE COMPARISONS

Apart from its unusual colouring, the Malayan tapir (*Tapirus indicus*) is almost identical in size and form to its South American cousin. The distinctive black-and-white patterning of this nocturnal animal is a highly effective camouflage in the moonlit jungle.

The remarkable similarity between these two species, separated today by vast oceans, is evidence of the land bridges, created by reduced sea levels during glacial periods, that enabled ancestral tapirs to disperse widely.

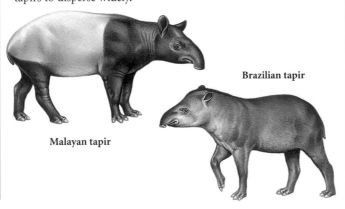

Brazilian tapir

Malayan tapir

WHERE IN THE WORLD?

Found in tropical and deciduous forests to the east of the Andes Mountains in South America. Ranges from Venezuela south to the forests' fringes on the Grand Chaco plains of northern Argentina.

RELATED SPECIES

Tapirus, the sole genus within the family Tapiridae, also includes the mountain tapir, T. pinchaque, and Baird's tapir, T. bairdii, of South America. The Malayan tapir, T. indicus, of Southeast Asia is sometimes placed in the subgenus Acrocodia. The family Tapiridae is classed in the order Perissodactyla, or odd-toed ungulates (hoofed mammals), which also includes the horses, family Equidae, and the rhinos, family Rhinocerotidae.

• **ORDER** • *Phoenicopteriformes* • **FAMILY** • *Phoenicopteridae* • **GENUS & SPECIES** • *Phoenicopterus ruber* GREATER FLAMINGO

The greater flamingo has legs that resist the burning chemicals in some of its feeding waters and a special bill to trap tiny organisms.

KEY FEATURES

- Inhabits tropical salt-pans, lagoons and alkaline lakes.
- Skin on the feet and legs is able to withstand the burning effects of caustic soda, which is found in alkaline lakes.
- Breeds in huge colonies that may contain over a million individuals.
- Uses its extraordinary specialized bill to filter food from shallow water.

BILL
The bill's edges and inner surfaces are lined with rows of lamellae (1) — layers of bone covered in fine hairs — which can be raised and lowered. These trap tiny organisms when the tongue is pushed forward and squeezes water through the lamellae.

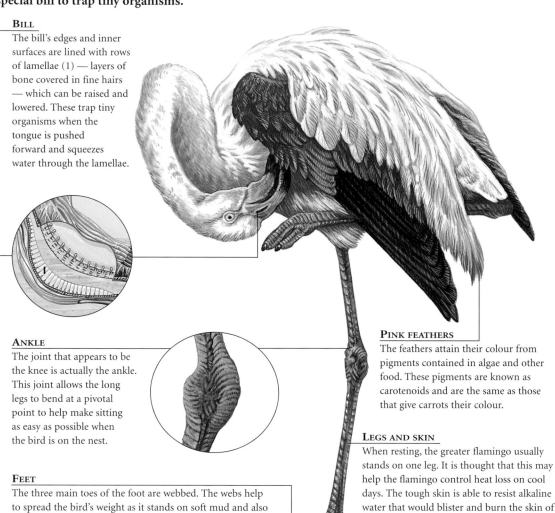

ANKLE
The joint that appears to be the knee is actually the ankle. This joint allows the long legs to bend at a pivotal point to help make sitting as easy as possible when the bird is on the nest.

FEET
The three main toes of the foot are webbed. The webs help to spread the bird's weight as it stands on soft mud and also act as paddles when the flamingo swims.

PINK FEATHERS
The feathers attain their colour from pigments contained in algae and other food. These pigments are known as carotenoids and are the same as those that give carrots their colour.

LEGS AND SKIN
When resting, the greater flamingo usually stands on one leg. It is thought that this may help the flamingo control heat loss on cool days. The tough skin is able to resist alkaline water that would blister and burn the skin of other animals.

VITAL STATISTICS

WEIGHT	2.1–4.1kg (4.6–9lb)
LENGTH	1.2–1.45m (3ft 9in– 4ft 8in)
WINGSPAN	1.4–1.65m (4ft 6in– 5ft 4in)
SEXUAL MATURITY	5–6 years
BREEDING SEASON	Variable; throughout the year according to locality
NUMBER OF EGGS	1, rarely 2
INCUBATION PERIOD	27–31 days
FLEDGING PERIOD	65–90 days
BREEDING INTERVAL	One year
TYPICAL DIET	Aquatic invertebrates, algae, seeds of marsh plants
LIFESPAN	Up to 33 years in the wild, over 45 years in captivity

CREATURE COMPARISONS

The greater flamingo's unusually shaped bill is matched by another pink-plumed bird that is found alongside the flamingo in the Caribbean: the roseate spoonbill (Ajaia ajaja). Holding its mandibles slightly open, the spoonbill feeds by sweeping its bill vertically from side to side through shallow water. The spoon-shaped bill is equipped with numerous vibration-sensitive receptors. When aquatic organisms touch the receptors the bill rapidly snaps shut. Both species rely on their bill structure to feed without seeing their food.

Greater flamingo   Roseate spoonbill

WHERE IN THE WORLD?

Found mainly on lagoons and large inland lakes in Africa, the Middle East, India and Sri Lanka. Extends
into subtropical southern Europe. A deep pink variety occurs in the Caribbean and on the Galapagos Islands.

RELATED SPECIES

The Puna and Andean flamingo, (Phoenicoparrus jamesi and P. andinus), have restricted ranges in South America, occurring at high altitude on the salt lakes of southern Peru and western Bolivia, northwest Argentina and southern Chile. Both are characterized by having yellow, not pink, on the bill, and no hindtoe. Known for its huge gatherings in East Africa, the lesser flamingo (Phoeniconaias minor) also occurs in northwest India, and Pakistan.

• ORDER • *Pholidota* • FAMILY • *Manidae* • GENUS & SPECIES • *Manis temmincki*

CAPE PANGOLIN

The Cape pangolin may look like a giant, animated artichoke, but its overlapping scales provide a tough defence against its enemies.

KEY FEATURES

- Covered with sharp-edged, overlapping scales for protection against predators, and rolls itself into a ball when threatened.
- Eats ants, which it catches with a long, sticky tongue.
- Threatened by habitat loss and hunting, it is listed as endangered by the IUCN (World Conservation Union).

VITAL STATISTICS

WEIGHT	7–18kg (15.4–39.7lb); male up to 50 per cent heavier than female
LENGTH	Head & Body: 34–61cm (13.4–24in) Tail: 31–50cm (12.2–19.7in)
SEXUAL MATURITY	2 years
MATING SEASON	All year
GESTATION PERIOD	130–150 days
NUMBER OF YOUNG	1
BIRTH INTERVAL	About 6 months
TYPICAL DIET	Ants, termites and beetle larvae
LIFESPAN	Unknown

SKULL
The tapering skull is made of dense bone. Teeth are absent, as food is ground up in the stomach.

INFANT
The newborn's scales are soft and flexible, but harden after two days.

HEAD
The facial skin lacks scales but is thick and tough. Heavy lids protect the eyes from ant stings and bites, and muscles seal the nostrils and the ear openings.

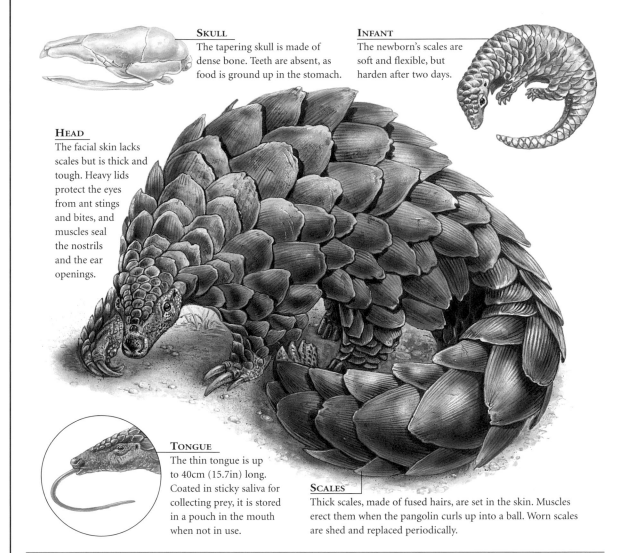

TONGUE
The thin tongue is up to 40cm (15.7in) long. Coated in sticky saliva for collecting prey, it is stored in a pouch in the mouth when not in use.

SCALES
Thick scales, made of fused hairs, are set in the skin. Muscles erect them when the pangolin curls up into a ball. Worn scales are shed and replaced periodically.

CREATURE COMPARISONS

Pangolins look rather like armadillos, a family of 20 species found in the Americas. Although unrelated, the two animal families have evolved similar features as a result of adapting to a similar lifestyle. Scientists refer to this as convergent evolution. Both animals have a very long, sticky tongue for eating insects. They have thick hide and body armour, for protection from biting, stinging prey and as a defence against larger predators. But while pangolins have separate scales, armadillos have flexible bands of bony plates overlaid by horn. And unlike pangolins, armadillos have teeth for crushing their prey.

Long-nosed armadillo

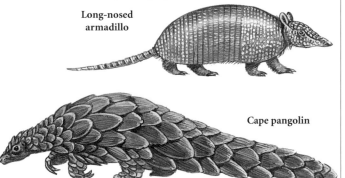

Cape pangolin

WHERE IN THE WORLD?

Found only in Africa: from Chad and Sudan, south through eastern Africa, to Namibia and much of South Africa.

RELATED SPECIES

The order Pholidota contains just 1 family, Manidae, with only 1 genus, Manis. Of the 7 species of pangolin, 3 live in Asia: the Chinese pangolin, M. pentadactyla; the Indian pangolin, M. crassicaudata; and the Malayan pangolin, M. javanica. The other 4 are African. They comprise the Cape pangolin; the giant pangolin, M. gigantea; the small-scaled tree pangolin, M. tricuspis; and the long-tailed pangolin, M. tetradactyla.

• **ORDER** • *Piciformes* • **FAMILY** • *Picidae* • **GENUS & SPECIES** • *Dendrocopos major* GREAT SPOTTED WOODPECKER

Solid and strong, the great spotted woodpecker is perfectly adapted to life as a living percussion drill for nest building and searching tree-trunks for food.

KEY FEATURES

- Male makes a loud drumming noise to attract a mate and proclaim his territory.
- Beak is used like a combined hammer and chisel to drill into trees and branches and carve out deep nest holes.
- Skull has strengthened bone structure and shock-absorbing cartilage around the bill to protect the brain and other organs when hammering.

VITAL STATISTICS

WEIGHT	70–100g (27.6–39.4in)
LENGTH	22–23cm (8.7–9in
WINGSPAN	34–39cm (13.4–15.3in)
BREEDING SEASON	April to July
NUMBER OF EGGS	4 to 7
INCUBATION PERIOD	10–13 days
FLEDGING PERIOD	20–24 days
BREEDING INTERVAL	1 year
TYPICAL DIET	Insects and wood-boring larvae; spiders, worms, molluscs; seeds, fruits, nuts, sap; nestlings and eggs of other birds
LIFESPAN	Up to 11 years in the wild

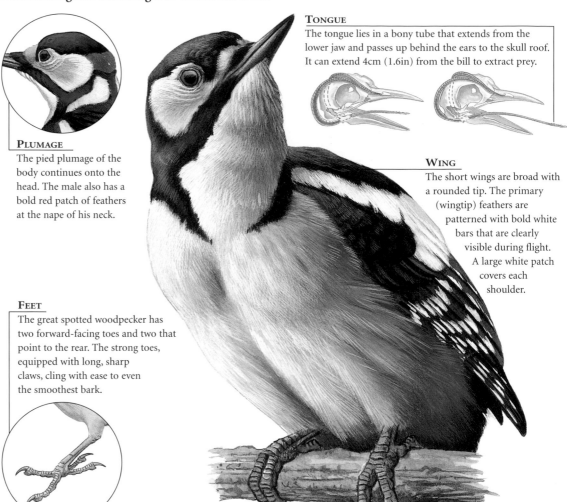

PLUMAGE
The pied plumage of the body continues onto the head. The male also has a bold red patch of feathers at the nape of his neck.

FEET
The great spotted woodpecker has two forward-facing toes and two that point to the rear. The strong toes, equipped with long, sharp claws, cling with ease to even the smoothest bark.

TONGUE
The tongue lies in a bony tube that extends from the lower jaw and passes up behind the ears to the skull roof. It can extend 4cm (1.6in) from the bill to extract prey.

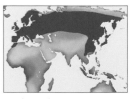

WING
The short wings are broad with a rounded tip. The primary (wingtip) feathers are patterned with bold white bars that are clearly visible during flight. A large white patch covers each shoulder.

CREATURE COMPARISONS

The Nubian woodpecker (Campethera nubica) has olive-grey upperparts patterned with small, yellowish spots. Its underparts are white with black spots, and the nape of the neck is bright red. The male also has red feathers extending over his crown and a red stripe under each eye. At 18cm (7.1in), this bird is a little smaller than the great spotted woodpecker.

The Nubian woodpecker is widespread in Sudan, Uganda, Kenya and Tanzania, where it lives in open bush country and woodlands of acacia thorn trees. Like the great spotted woodpecker, it is a cunning feeder. It taps the fruits of the baobab tree in order to induce ants to emerge, which it then scoops up with its long, sticky tongue.

Nubian woodpecker

Great spotted woodpecker

WHERE IN THE WORLD?

Widespread through much of Europe and Asia. Absent from Ireland and the northernmost reaches of Scandinavia and Scotland. Present wherever there are trees with sufficient growth to accommodate nest-holes.

RELATED SPECIES

The Picidae family is divided into 3 subfamilies. Woodpeckers belong to the subfamily Picinae, which contains 169 species and is represented throughout Europe, USA, Africa and Asia. There are 2 species of wryneck in the subfamily Jynginae. Wrynecks are small, brown, ground-feeding birds found in Europe, Africa and Asia. In the subfamily Picumninae there are 29 species of piculet, which inhabit tropical America, Africa and Asia.

• **ORDER** • *Pinnipedia* • **FAMILY** • *Odobenidae* • **GENUS & SPECIES** • *Odobenus rosmarus*

The enormous bulk of a walrus and its thick layer of oily blubber beneath the skin are essential adaptations to a life spent in ice-cold waters.

KEY FEATURES

- Keeps warm by living mainly in water and having a bulky body — adult males can weigh over 1500kg (3307lb).
- When on land, defends itself against predators, such as polar bears, by living in herds of several thousand.
- Distinctive tusks help it to climb onto ice floes, and are used in battles with other walruses.

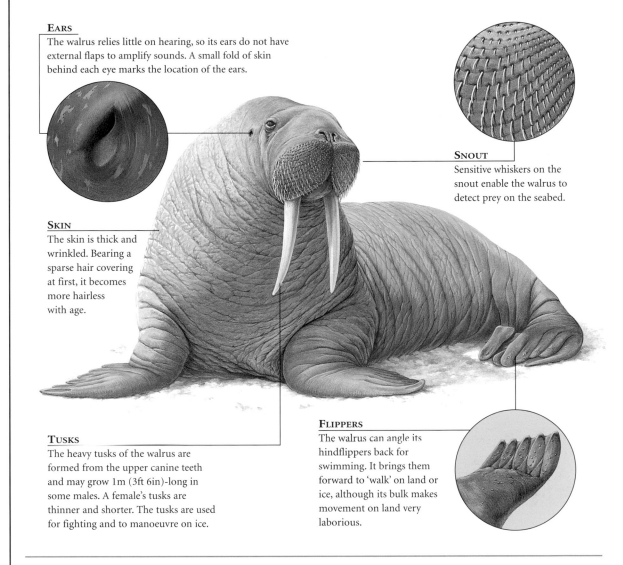

EARS
The walrus relies little on hearing, so its ears do not have external flaps to amplify sounds. A small fold of skin behind each eye marks the location of the ears.

SNOUT
Sensitive whiskers on the snout enable the walrus to detect prey on the seabed.

SKIN
The skin is thick and wrinkled. Bearing a sparse hair covering at first, it becomes more hairless with age.

TUSKS
The heavy tusks of the walrus are formed from the upper canine teeth and may grow 1m (3ft 6in)-long in some males. A female's tusks are thinner and shorter. The tusks are used for fighting and to manoeuvre on ice.

FLIPPERS
The walrus can angle its hindflippers back for swimming. It brings them forward to 'walk' on land or ice, although its bulk makes movement on land very laborious.

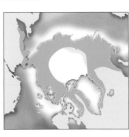

VITAL STATISTICS

WEIGHT	815–1680kg (1797–3704lb)
LENGTH	2.75–3.65m (9–12ft)
SHOULDER HEIGHT	1m (3ft 3in); male is slightly larger than female
SEXUAL MATURITY	5–8 years
MATING SEASON	February to April
GESTATION PERIOD	11 months
NUMBER OF YOUNG	1
BIRTH INTERVAL	2 years
TYPICAL DIET	Molluscs and shellfish
LIFESPAN	Up to 40 years

CREATURE COMPARISONS

Up to 3.2m (10ft 5in) long and weighing up to 1270kg (2800lb) the Steller sea lion is almost as large as the walrus. It shares part of the walrus's Pacific range, and is also found farther south. The Steller sea lion, like all other pinnipeds, lacks the long tusks of the walrus. Sea lions and walruses can both turn their hindflippers forward to move around on land, unlike the related true seals.

Steller sea lion

Walrus

WHERE IN THE WORLD?

Found around the edges of the Arctic, on the coasts of northern North America, Greenland, northern Norway, Siberia and the Kamchatka peninsula.

RELATED SPECIES

The walrus, which is the only member of its family, is the largest member of the order Pinnipedia. The name of the order comes from the Latin words meaning 'feather feet' because all of its members have all four feet modified into flippers. All pinnipeds also have streamlined bodies. The order includes two other families: one is composed of the sea lions and the fur seals, and the other is made up of earless, or true, seals, such as the grey seal.

• **ORDER** • *Pinnipedia* • **FAMILY** • *Otariidae* • **GENUS & SPECIES** • *Arctocephalus spp.*

SOUTHERN FUR SEAL

KEY FEATURES

- A group of eared seals, related to sea lions, that rely on fat and thick fur to keep warm.
- Spend most of the year at sea, but come ashore to breed on remote beaches.
- Long foreflippers give them both speed and mobility on land.
- Hunted to the brink of extinction in the 19th century, they are now flourishing again.

VITAL STATISTICS

WEIGHT	Male 165kg (363.8lb); female 55kg (121.3lb)
LENGTH	Male 180cm (70.9in); female 145cm (57in)
SEXUAL MATURITY	Male 7–10 years; female 4–5 years
MATING SEASON	October to December, which is the southern spring
GESTATION PERIOD	12 months, including 4-month delayed implantation period
NUMBER OF YOUNG	1
BIRTH INTERVAL	1–2 years
TYPICAL DIET	Fish, squid and krill
LIFESPAN	Up to 25 years

Powered by its large, muscular foreflippers, the southern fur seal twists and turns in the water, using its sharp teeth to grip slippery prey.

MALE AND FEMALE
A male can be more than three times heavier than a female. A thick mane of fur on his neck protects him from injury during rivalry fights.

TEETH
Most of the seal's teeth are sharp pegs, adapted for catching slippery fish, but the males use their long canines for fighting.

FUR
A layer of coarse, waterproof guard hairs covers a dense, insulating underfur.

Male

Female

Species illustrated: Sub-Antarctic fur seal, *Arctocephalus tropicalis*

EYES
The eyes are adapted for seeing underwater. On the surface they work well enough in bright light, but when the pupils enlarge in dim light the resulting image is blurred.

MUZZLE
Water pressure helps keep the nostrils closed while the seal stays underwater. The sensitive whiskers help it find food in the gloomy water.

FOREFLIPPERS
The foreflippers propel the seal in the water and are strong enough to support it on land.

CREATURE COMPARISONS

Hooker's sea lion (Phocarctos hookeri), like other sea lions, is closely related to fur seals. Sea lions are similar in both looks and habits to fur seals, but have blunter muzzles and do not have a thick, woolly undercoat. Sea lions also tend to be darker and larger — the male Hooker's sea lion can weigh 400kg (881.8lb). This species shares its sub-Antarctic habitat with the southern fur seals, but other sea lions breed in warmer regions, including the Pacific coasts of North America. Hooker's sea lion is also unusual in that it often shelters up to 2km(1.2 miles) inland, in the forests of several tiny islands south of New Zealand.

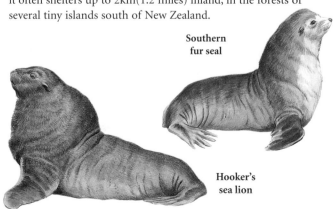

Southern fur seal

Hooker's sea lion

WHERE IN THE WORLD?

Found in the southern Atlantic, Pacific and Indian oceans, occurring as far north as the west coast of the

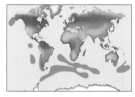

USA. Breeds on southern continental coasts and sub-Antarctic islands, except for the Galapagos fur seal.

RELATED SPECIES

There are 8 species of southern fur seal, all of which are classified in the genus Arctocephalus. Fur seals, together with the sea lions and the northern fur seal, Callorhinus ursinus, make up the family Otariidae.

NORTHERN FUR SEAL

• ORDER • *Pinnipedia* • FAMILY • *Otariidae* • GENUS & SPECIES • *Callorhinus ursinus*

KEY FEATURES

- Seasonal traveller that swims north to breed on one of five island groups in the North Pacific.
- Sleeps during the middle of the day, spending the night-time making a series of dives for food.
- Not a particularly sociable animal, with both sexes displaying aggression in the large breeding colonies.

VITAL STATISTICS

WEIGHT	Male 175–275kg (385.8–606.3lb); female 30–50kg (66.1–110.2lb)
LENGTH	Male about 2.1m (6ft 9in); female about 1.4m (4ft 6in)
SEXUAL MATURITY	Male 10–12 years; female 3–7 years
MATING SEASON	June to August
GESTATION PERIOD	Almost 1 year with 4 months delayed implantation
NUMBER OF YOUNG	1 (twins occur very rarely)
BIRTH INTERVAL	1 year
TYPICAL DIET	Squid, capelin, octopus, hake, herring, anchovy
LIFESPAN	Up to 30 years

The large flippers of the northern fur seal are strong and mobile, propelling it rapidly through icy waters and helping it to move about on land.

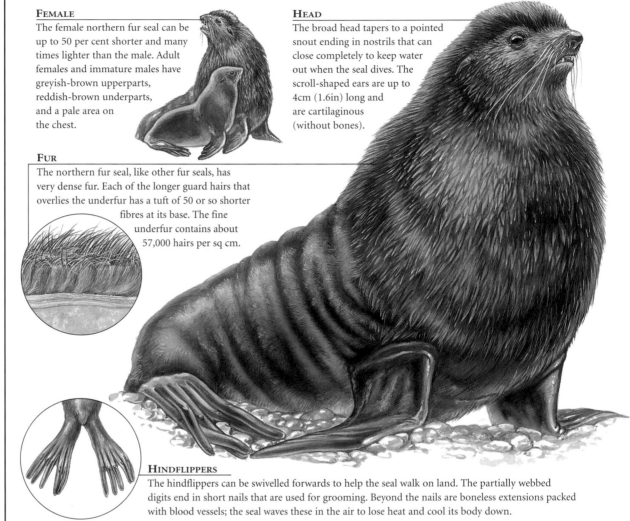

FEMALE
The female northern fur seal can be up to 50 per cent shorter and many times lighter than the male. Adult females and immature males have greyish-brown upperparts, reddish-brown underparts, and a pale area on the chest.

HEAD
The broad head tapers to a pointed snout ending in nostrils that can close completely to keep water out when the seal dives. The scroll-shaped ears are up to 4cm (1.6in) long and are cartilaginous (without bones).

FUR
The northern fur seal, like other fur seals, has very dense fur. Each of the longer guard hairs that overlies the underfur has a tuft of 50 or so shorter fibres at its base. The fine underfur contains about 57,000 hairs per sq cm.

HINDFLIPPERS
The hindflippers can be swivelled forwards to help the seal walk on land. The partially webbed digits end in short nails that are used for grooming. Beyond the nails are boneless extensions packed with blood vessels; the seal waves these in the air to lose heat and cool its body down.

CREATURE COMPARISONS

The Cape fur seal (Arctocephalus pusillus), one of 8 species of southern fur seal, is found in waters off southern Africa and Australia. It is slightly larger than the northern fur seal, with some males reaching 2.3m (7ft 5in) long and weighing up to 360kg (793.7lb). Like other southern fur seals, the Cape fur seal has furred foreflippers; the fur ending in a gentle curve near the middle of its 'fingers'. The foreflipper of the northern fur seal, however, is naked below the wrist, and its ears and hindlimbs are longer than those of its southern counterpart. Both seals breed on rocky shorelines; but the Cape fur seal sometimes hauls out on sandy beaches.

Cape fur seal

Northern fur seal

WHERE IN THE WORLD?

Distributed over a broad arc of the northern Pacific Ocean from the Sea of Japan in the west, east to the west coast of North America as far south as California.

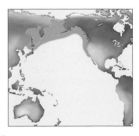

RELATED SPECIES

The northern fur seal is the sole member of its genus Callorhinus and is one of the 14 species of 'eared' seals in the family Otariidae, which also includes sea lions. The other members of the order Pinnipedia are the walrus (the only species in the family Odobenidae) and the 19 true, or 'earless', seals from the family Phocidae. True seals move awkwardly on land because they cannot support themselves on their foreflippers.

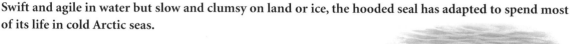

• **ORDER** • *Pinnipedia* • **FAMILY** • *Phocidae* • **GENUS & SPECIES** • *Cystophora cristata*

HOODED SEAL

KEY FEATURES

- Has the shortest weaning period of any mammal: pups are abandoned when only days old.
- Male inflates startling black and red nasal sacs during his breeding display.
- Able to dive to depths of 300m (984ft) in search of food and stay underwater for up to 20 minutes.

VITAL STATISTICS

WEIGHT	Male 200–400kg (440.9–881.8lb); female 145–300kg (319.7–661.4lb)
LENGTH	Male 2.5–2.7m (8ft 2in–8ft 8in); female 2–2.2m (6ft 6in–7ft 2in)
SEXUAL MATURITY	Female 3 years; male 4–6 years
MATING SEASON	Early spring
GESTATION PERIOD	About 250 days; up to 360 or so with delayed implantation
NUMBER OF YOUNG	1
BIRTH INTERVAL	1 year
TYPICAL DIET	Fish, molluscs, shrimps
LIFESPAN	35 years

Swift and agile in water but slow and clumsy on land or ice, the hooded seal has adapted to spend most of its life in cold Arctic seas.

HOOD
The male's enlarged nasal cavity forms a black hood which begins behind the eyes and hangs down in front of the mouth. In aggressive displays an adult male inflates this sac to twice the size of a football. The male can also blow a bubble-gum-like red balloon out of his nose by closing one nostril and blowing through the other.

HINDFLIPPERS
Acting almost as one limb, the thick and muscular hindflippers move from side to side to power the hooded seal through the water.

TEETH
The hooded seal is distinguished from other true seals by having only two upper and one lower pair of incisor teeth. The cheek teeth are widely spaced and peg-like.

PUP
The pup sheds lanugo (its first coat) while in the womb, emerging onto the ice covered in short, slate-blue fur with a creamy underside.

FOREFLIPPER
A versatile paddle, the foreflipper also swivels dexterously, enabling the seal to groom most parts of its body.

CREATURE COMPARISONS

Like the hooded seal, the Ross seal (Ommatophoca rossii) is the only member of its genus. It lives at the other end of the world, among the heavy pack ice of the Antarctic. Undiscovered until the 1840s because of its remote habitat, the Ross seal, with its strange trilling call, remains the least known of all seal species. Similar in size to a female hooded seal, the Ross seal grows to about 2m (6ft 6in) in length, with little difference in size between the sexes. It has a distinctive profile with a short snout and broad head, and faint streaking on the throat and cheeks. Whereas the hooded seal feeds mainly on fish, the Ross seal's diet is dominated by deep-water squid.

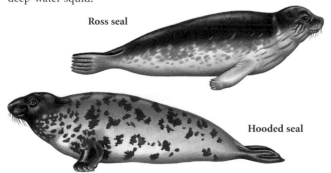

Ross seal

Hooded seal

WHERE IN THE WORLD?

Found in the deep waters of the North Atlantic, from Greenland south as far as Newfoundland, and east to the Svalbard islands north of Scandinavia.

RELATED SPECIES

The hooded seal is 1 of 19 species in the true seal family Phocidae, which includes the bearded seal, Erignathus barbatus. There are 2 other families in the order Pinnipedia: the Odobenidae with 1 species, the walrus, and the Otariidae, the eared seals, with 14 species.

• **ORDER** • *Pinnipedia* • **FAMILY** • *Phocidae* • **GENUS & SPECIES** • *Erignathus barbatus*

BEARDED SEAL

The luxuriant whiskers on the bearded seal's face help it locate food amid the swirling sediment stirred up as it forages on the seabed.

KEY FEATURES

- A heavily whiskered seal that lives on the floating pack ice of the Arctic seas.
- Feeds on shellfish and other creatures of the seabed, which it locates by touch in the submarine gloom.
- A favourite prey of polar bears, and of the traditional Inuit (Eskimo) hunters of the Arctic.

SKULL
Deep jaws give the seal a large mouth cavity. This may help it generate the suction it needs to rip molluscs from their shells. The cusped cheek teeth become worn down by the seal's gritty diet.

HINDFLIPPERS
The hindlimbs are enclosed by the body as far as the ankles. The 'feet' are modified into flippers, which, as in all true seals, give propulsion in the water.

HEAD
The small head, along with the foreflippers, is sometimes a rusty reddish-brown. The seal makes breathing holes by ramming thin ice with its head.

BODY
A thick insulating layer of fat, or blubber, helps the seal retain bodyheat in the cold Arctic.

WHISKERS
The long, thick whiskers, which form a bushy moustache, sprout from thick fleshy pads on the seal's muzzle. Sensory cells at the base of each whisker carry detailed tactile information to the brain.

FOREFLIPPERS
The square-ended foreflippers are modified forelegs or arms, with a full set of finger bones. The stout claws make effective ice-picks when the seal has to haul out on sea ice or dig breathing holes.

VITAL STATISTICS

WEIGHT	200–360kg (440.9–793.7lb)
LENGTH	2–2.7m (6ft 6in–8ft 8in) Sexes similar in size; smallest individuals found in the Sea of Okhotsk
SEXUAL MATURITY	Male 6–7 years; female 5–6 years
MATING SEASON	April–May
GESTATION PERIOD	9 months, plus 2-month delayed-implantation
NUMBER OF YOUNG	1
BIRTH INTERVAL	1 year
TYPICAL DIET	Bottom-living shellfish and fish
LIFESPAN	Male 25 years; female 30 years

CREATURE COMPARISONS

The Arctic pack ice is the home of several different species of seal, including the spotted seal (Phoca largha) of the North Pacific and adjacent seas. Much smaller than the bearded seal, the spotted seal weighs no more than 90kg (198.4lb) or so. Like the bearded seal, it is a true seal: its small foreflippers are not used in swimming and make it clumsy on land. (Eared seals use their strong foreflippers for propulsion, and are much more agile on land.)

The spotted seal feeds mainly on fish in coastal waters, as well as the odd octopus or crab. In summer, it often moves into the estuaries of Arctic rivers to prey on salmon returning to spawn.

Spotted seal

Bearded seal

WHERE IN THE WORLD?

Lives in shallow seas all around the Arctic, including the Bering Sea and the Sea of Okhotsk.

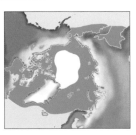

RELATED SPECIES

The bearded seal is the only member of the genus **Erignathus**. It is grouped with the hooded seal, harp seal, grey seal and others in the subfamily Phocinae: the true or earless seals of the northern seas. Together with southern true seals, such as the elephant seal, they form the family Phocidae. There are 2 other families in the order Pinnipedia: the eared seals, Otariidae, which includes sea lions and fur seals, and Odobenidae, containing only the walrus.

• **ORDER** • *Pinnipedia* • **FAMILY** • *Phocidae* • **GENUS & SPECIES** • *Halichoerus grypus*

GREY SEAL

Steered by small foreflippers and powered by immensely strong back muscles, the grey seal uses its sharp teeth to grab its slippery prey.

KEY FEATURES

- Female comes ashore to give birth, suckle her pup and mate with several males, all within a month.
- Spends much of the year feeding at sea to sustain it through periods on land when it cannot eat at all.
- Superb swimmer whose lack of agility on land is compensated by its ability to dive for long periods.

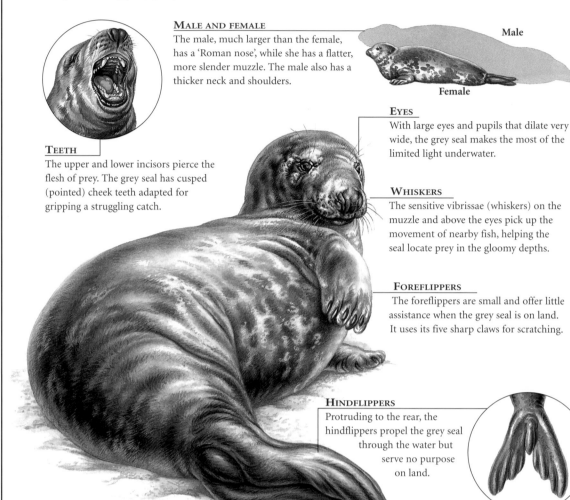

MALE AND FEMALE
The male, much larger than the female, has a 'Roman nose', while she has a flatter, more slender muzzle. The male also has a thicker neck and shoulders.

Male

Female

TEETH
The upper and lower incisors pierce the flesh of prey. The grey seal has cusped (pointed) cheek teeth adapted for gripping a struggling catch.

EYES
With large eyes and pupils that dilate very wide, the grey seal makes the most of the limited light underwater.

WHISKERS
The sensitive vibrissae (whiskers) on the muzzle and above the eyes pick up the movement of nearby fish, helping the seal locate prey in the gloomy depths.

FOREFLIPPERS
The foreflippers are small and offer little assistance when the grey seal is on land. It uses its five sharp claws for scratching.

HINDFLIPPERS
Protruding to the rear, the hindflippers propel the grey seal through the water but serve no purpose on land.

VITAL STATISTICS

WEIGHT	Male 170–310kg (374.8–683.4lb) female 105–185kg (231.5–407.9lb)
LENGTH	1.65–2.45m (5ft 4in–8ft)
SEXUAL MATURITY	Male 6, female 3–5 years
MATING SEASON	January to February in west Atlantic; September to December in east Atlantic; March to April in Baltic
GESTATION PERIOD	214–240 days plus 125 days delayed-implantation
NUMBER OF YOUNG	Usually 1
BIRTH INTERVAL	1 year
TYPICAL DIET	Fish and crustaceans
LIFESPAN	35 years

CREATURE COMPARISONS

A related neighbour of the grey seal is the ringed seal (Phoca hispida), which occurs in the North Pacific and North Atlantic. The ringed seal is the smaller of the two, with males rarely exceeding 1.5m (4ft 9in) in length. Adults usually have a silvery-grey coat marked with black, pale-ringed spots.

The ringed seal differs from the grey seal in its choice of breeding sites, usually hauling out on stable ice sheets. As winter draws on, it maintains openings in the ice, which it uses as breathing holes. It can keep them open in ice sheets up to 2m (6ft 6in) thick.

Ringed seal

Grey seal

WHERE IN THE WORLD?

Found in the North Atlantic off the coast of Canada and Norway, around the Faeroe Islands, and off Britain. Smaller populations occur in the Baltic Sea.

RELATED SPECIES

The grey seal is 1 of 19 species in the true seal family, Phocidae, including the hooded seal, Cystophora cristata. True seals use their hindflippers to swim, while the eared seals (family Otariidae) use their foreflippers. Along with the walrus (Odobenidae), seals form the order Pinnipedia.

LEOPARD SEAL

• ORDER • *Pinnipedia* • FAMILY • *Phocidae* • GENUS & SPECIES • *Hydrurga leptonyx*

A superb swimmer and hunter, the leopard seal has a sinuous, muscular body and is armed with savage teeth and powerful jaws.

KEY FEATURES

- Only seal that regularly preys on warm-blooded creatures, including penguins and other seals.
- A powerful swimmer in the cold seas off Antarctica, but moves awkwardly on land or ice floes.
- Far-ranging in its pursuit of food, it sometimes occurs as far north as the coast of South Africa.

VITAL STATISTICS

WEIGHT	Male 325kg (716.5lb); female 370kg (815.7lb)
LENGTH	Male 2.8m (9ft 2in); female 3m (9ft 8in)
SEXUAL MATURITY	Male 4 years; female 3 years
MATING SEASON	November to February
GESTATION PERIOD	9 months, plus 3 months delayed implantation
NUMBER OF YOUNG	1
BIRTH INTERVAL	1–2 years
TYPICAL DIET	Krill, fish, squid, penguins and other seabirds, young seals
LIFESPAN	About 25 years

MALE & FEMALE
Like many seals, the female leopard seal (top) is bigger than the male (bottom). Adult females are about 5 per cent longer than males, and 13 per cent heavier.

MOUTH
The leopard seal's wide gape is emphasized by a long, flattened head, giving it a reptilian look. Apart from its large canine teeth, the leopard seal has curving cheek teeth, each with three pointed lobes. These are used to strain krill out of seawater.

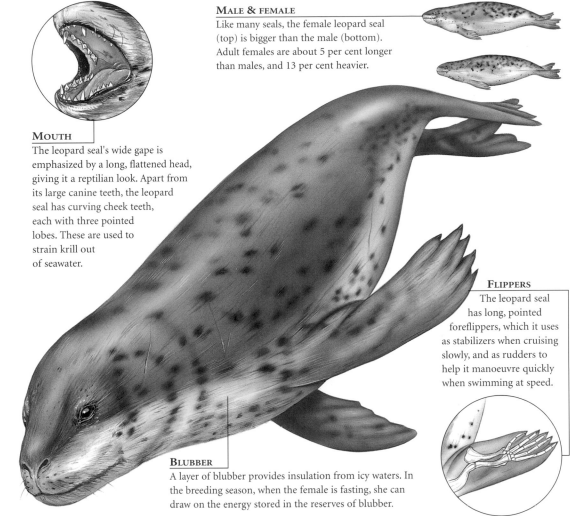

FLIPPERS
The leopard seal has long, pointed foreflippers, which it uses as stabilizers when cruising slowly, and as rudders to help it manoeuvre quickly when swimming at speed.

BLUBBER
A layer of blubber provides insulation from icy waters. In the breeding season, when the female is fasting, she can draw on the energy stored in the reserves of blubber.

CREATURE COMPARISONS

The Antarctic fur seal, which occupies part of the same sub-Antarctic range as the leopard seal, is an eared seal belonging to the family Otariidae. It has small external ears and a distinct, dog-like nose. In contrast, the leopard seal is a true seal of the family Phocidae, and lacks ear flaps and has nostrils that merge into its muzzle. The structure of the hindflippers of the Antarctic fur seal means that it can stand and move on all fours, but the leopard seal, like other true seals, lies flat on the ice and moves by undulating its body aided by the foreflippers.

Antarctic fur seal

Leopard seal

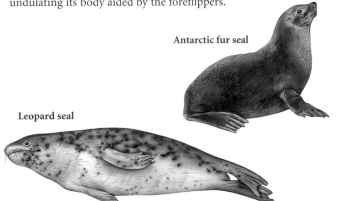

WHERE IN THE WORLD?

Ranges from the fringes of Antarctica's pack ice in the summer, north towards the coasts of South America, South Africa and Australia in the winter.

RELATED SPECIES

The leopard seal is related to monk seals in the subfamily Monachinae. The Mediterranean monk seal, Monachus monachus, has been reduced to a few hundred animals scattered thinly along the Adriatic, Aegean and North African coasts. It is classified as endangered by the IUCN (World Conservation Union) and, due to hunting, is listed on Appendix 1 of CITES, the Convention on International Trade in Endangered Species.

• **ORDER** • *Pinnipedia* • **FAMILY** • *Phocidae* • **GENUS & SPECIES** • *Leptonychotes weddelli*

WEDDELL SEAL

The Weddell seal's sleek body is covered with blubber to keep it warm while it dives and twists through near-freezing waters after its fish prey.

KEY FEATURES

- Protected by a thick layer of blubber, it thrives in the icy waters surrounding Antarctica.
- Dives to depths greater than 500m (1640ft), aided by muscles that carry their own oxygen supply.
- Bites breathing holes in the sheet ice that forms on the sea surface, and keeps these open all year round.

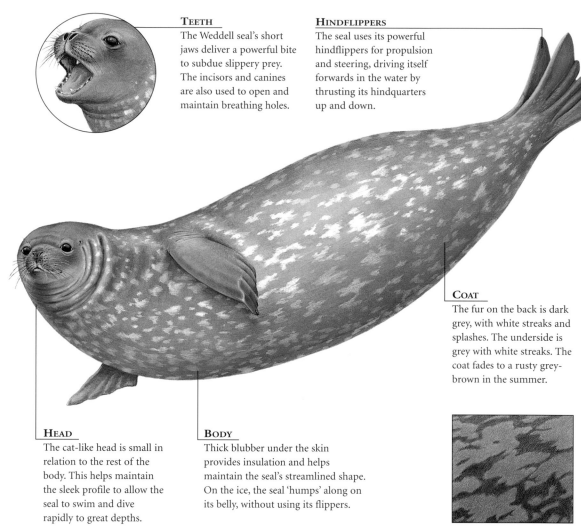

TEETH
The Weddell seal's short jaws deliver a powerful bite to subdue slippery prey. The incisors and canines are also used to open and maintain breathing holes.

HINDFLIPPERS
The seal uses its powerful hindflippers for propulsion and steering, driving itself forwards in the water by thrusting its hindquarters up and down.

COAT
The fur on the back is dark grey, with white streaks and splashes. The underside is grey with white streaks. The coat fades to a rusty grey-brown in the summer.

HEAD
The cat-like head is small in relation to the rest of the body. This helps maintain the sleek profile to allow the seal to swim and dive rapidly to great depths.

BODY
Thick blubber under the skin provides insulation and helps maintain the seal's streamlined shape. On the ice, the seal 'humps' along on its belly, without using its flippers.

VITAL STATISTICS

WEIGHT	385–450kg (848.8–992.1lb)
LENGTH	2.4–2.9m (7ft 9in–9ft 5in)
SEXUAL MATURITY	3–6 years
MATING SEASON	Usually December
GESTATION PERIOD	11 months, including 2-month delayed implantation
NUMBER OF YOUNG	1
BIRTH INTERVAL	1 year
TYPICAL DIET	Mostly Antarctic cod and other fish, but also a variety of crustaceans
LIFESPAN	25 years or more

CREATURE COMPARISONS

There are many seal species found on or around Antarctica, and each has its own specialized diet. Despite its name, the crabeater seal feeds mainly on the tiny, shrimp-like krill, which it strains from the water using its unusual lobed teeth. The crabeater seal does not compete with the Weddell seal for food, remaining, instead, in shallower waters and on pack ice. The leopard seal is a large and powerful hunter that preys heavily on other seal species — including the Weddell seal — as well as penguins and fish.

Crabeater seal

Weddell seal

Leopard seal

3   1.5   0 m

WHERE IN THE WORLD?

Around Antarctica, usually within sight of land. Avoids mobile pack ice, but will emerge onto ice shelves and land. Occasionally seen as far north as New Zealand.

RELATED SPECIES
The Weddell seal is one of the 19 species of true seals making up the family Phocidae. Relatives include the grey seal, common in temperate waters, and the northern elephant seal, a giant species that lives along the Pacific coast of North America.

CRABEATER SEAL

•ORDER• *Pinnipedia* •FAMILY• *Phocidae* •GENUS & SPECIES• *Lobodon carcinophagus*

KEY FEATURES

- The most abundant by far of the seals, and one of the most numerous of all large mammals.

- Rests, mates and gives birth on the floating pack ice that rings the continent of Antarctica.

- Does not hunt crabs as its name suggests, but feeds exclusively on swarms of crustaceans known as krill.

VITAL STATISTICS

WEIGHT	200–300kg (440.9–661.4lb); female slightly bigger than male
LENGTH	2.35–2.6m (7ft 7in–8ft 5in)
SEXUAL MATURITY	2–4 years
MATING SEASON	October to December
GESTATION PERIOD	11 months
NUMBER OF YOUNG	1
BREEDING INTERVAL	1 year
TYPICAL DIET	Krill
LIFESPAN	Over 30 years

In icy Antarctic waters, the crabeater seal relies on its supreme agility to grab mouthfuls of prey, which are then strained through its specialized teeth.

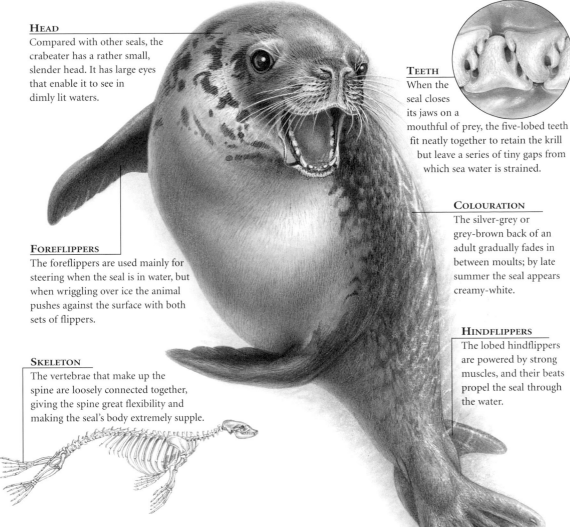

HEAD
Compared with other seals, the crabeater has a rather small, slender head. It has large eyes that enable it to see in dimly lit waters.

TEETH
When the seal closes its jaws on a mouthful of prey, the five-lobed teeth fit neatly together to retain the krill but leave a series of tiny gaps from which sea water is strained.

COLOURATION
The silver-grey or grey-brown back of an adult gradually fades in between moults; by late summer the seal appears creamy-white.

FOREFLIPPERS
The foreflippers are used mainly for steering when the seal is in water, but when wriggling over ice the animal pushes against the surface with both sets of flippers.

HINDFLIPPERS
The lobed hindflippers are powered by strong muscles, and their beats propel the seal through the water.

SKELETON
The vertebrae that make up the spine are loosely connected together, giving the spine great flexibility and making the seal's body extremely supple.

CREATURE COMPARISONS

The bearded seal (Erignathus barbatus) is found at the opposite pole to the crabeater. Similar in length, the Arctic-dwelling bearded seal is more robust and rounded in shape, weighing up to 360kg (793.7lb). Its silver-grey fur is more uniform in colour, lacking flecks, but its head and foreflippers are often a rusty or reddish-brown. The bearded seal's foreflippers are squarer in shape than those of the crabeater, and the bushy vibrissae (whiskers) on its face give rise to its common name.

Bearded seal

Crabeater seal

WHERE IN THE WORLD?

Seldom strays far beyond the limit of winter pack ice surrounding Antarctica, and moves nearer shore in summer following the retreating ice.

RELATED SPECIES

The crabeater is the sole species in Lobodon, 1 of 10 genera in the family of true seals, Phocidae. The 19 species in this family are distinguished by their lack of external ear flaps, and by their method of swimming by a combination of body movements and strokes of the hindflippers. In contrast, eared seals, comprising the sea lions and fur seals in the family Otariidae, swim only with their foreflippers. Along with the walrus, seals form the order Pinnipedia.

• ORDER • *Pinnipedia* • FAMILY • *Phocidae* • GENUS & SPECIES • *Mirounga spp.*

ELEPHANT SEAL

The blubbery bulk and huge nasal bulb of a mature bull elephant seal might seem grotesque and ungainly, but they represent much-coveted sexual status.

KEY FEATURES

- Marine mammals that feed in the deep sea but mass together on shore to breed.
- True giants among seals, the huge males have about three times the bulk of the females.
- Males possess a curious, inflatable extension to the snout and engage in fearsome battles for mates.

VITAL STATISTICS

WEIGHT	Male 3200kg (7055lb); female 900kg (1984lb). Southern species larger than northern
LENGTH	Male up to 4.9m (16ft); female up to 3m (9ft 8in)
SEXUAL MATURITY	Male at 4–6 years; female at 2–3 years
MATING SEASON	September to October in south; January to February in north
GESTATION PERIOD	11 months
NUMBER OF YOUNG	1
BIRTH INTERVAL	1 year
TYPICAL DIET	Squid and fish
LIFESPAN	Up to 20 years

PROBOSCIS
It takes up to 8 years before a male's fleshy proboscis is fully developed; a pendulous enlargement of the nasal cavity, it swells with blood during the breeding season and amplifies the bull's aggressive roars.

TEETH
The male uses his enlarged canines for biting and slashing his adversary when threat turns to combat.

FEMALE
Reproductive rivalry favours the evolution of ever larger bulls, and the size difference between the sexes is among the greatest of any mammal: cows are less than two-thirds the length of bulls.

Male

Female

NECK SHIELD
Sparring fights during youth create extensive scarring on the throat and neck. This massed scar tissue thickens and toughens the skin: a useful defence against attacks in adult battles for dominance.

FLIPPERS
Elephant seals may be clumsy on land but they move through the sea with great power, propelled mainly by alternating beats of their trailing hindflippers.

Species shown: northern elephant seal, Mirounga angustirostris

CREATURE COMPARISONS

One other seal species has a nasal projection similar to that of the male elephant seal. Males of the hooded seal, which lives in Arctic waters, develop an inflatable proboscis that is almost as impressive as that of the elephant seal. This species is, however, much smaller. A male hooded seal seldom matches the body length of a mature female elephant seal, let alone a bull, and his snout appears all the more prominent when inflated.

The hooded seal also has much less variable skin colouration. Elephant seals can range from yellowish to dark brown, while the hooded seal is grey with black blotching.

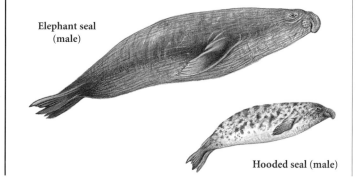

Elephant seal (male)

Hooded seal (male)

WHERE IN THE WORLD?

The northern elephant seal ranges along the Pacific coast of North America; the southern elephant seal is found throughout the Antarctic Ocean.

RELATED SPECIES

Most seals and sea lions in the order Pinnipedia are true seals, family Phocidae; there are 10 genera, with a total of 19 species. The southern and northern elephant seals, Mirounga angustirostris and M. leonina respectively, are sometimes grouped with 2 species of monk seal and 4 species of Antarctic seal in a subfamily, Monachinae. Other pinnipeds include the walrus, family Odobenidae, as well as 14 species of eared seal, family Otariidae.

MONK SEAL

· ORDER · *Pinnipedia* · FAMILY · *Phocidae* · GENUS & SPECIES · *Monachus*

A swift and graceful swimmer, the monk seal dives to the ocean floor where its speed and agility enable it to catch a variety of elusive prey.

KEY FEATURES

· The only seals that inhabit tropical seas.

· Specially adapted hindflippers and a streamlined body allow for fast, powerful swimming.

· Hunting and persecution have led to a sharp decline. Two species classified as endangered and one as extinct by the IUCN (World Conservation Union).

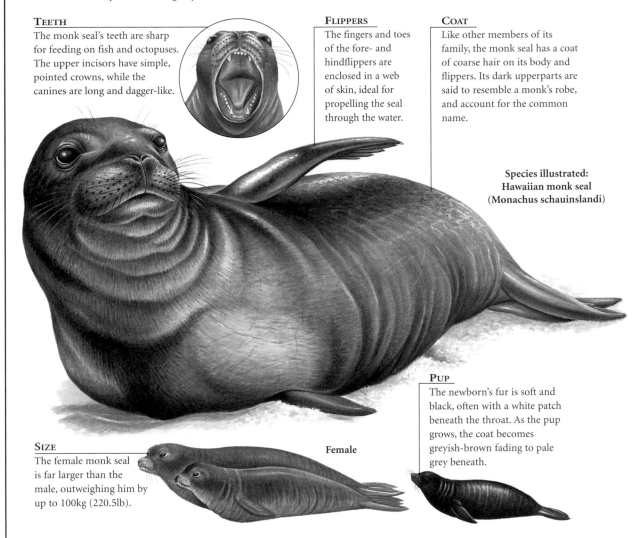

TEETH
The monk seal's teeth are sharp for feeding on fish and octopuses. The upper incisors have simple, pointed crowns, while the canines are long and dagger-like.

FLIPPERS
The fingers and toes of the fore- and hindflippers are enclosed in a web of skin, ideal for propelling the seal through the water.

COAT
Like other members of its family, the monk seal has a coat of coarse hair on its body and flippers. Its dark upperparts are said to resemble a monk's robe, and account for the common name.

Species illustrated:
Hawaiian monk seal
(*Monachus schauinslandi*)

PUP
The newborn's fur is soft and black, often with a white patch beneath the throat. As the pup grows, the coat becomes greyish-brown fading to pale grey beneath.

SIZE
The female monk seal is far larger than the male, outweighing him by up to 100kg (220.5lb).

Female

VITAL STATISTICS

WEIGHT	Male 170–260kg (374.8–573.2lb); female 220–300kg (485–661.4lb)
LENGTH	Male 2.1–2.6m (6ft 9in–8ft 5in); female 2.3–2.7m (7ft 5in–8ft 8in)
SEXUAL MATURITY	5 years
MATING SEASON	Hawaiian monk seal December to August; Mediterranean monk seal April to December
GESTATION PERIOD	300–330 days
NUMBER OF YOUNG	1
BIRTH INTERVAL	2 years
TYPICAL DIET	Fish, cephalopods, crustaceans
LIFESPAN	Up to 30 years

CREATURE COMPARISONS

The Baikal seal (*Phoca sibirica*), like the monk seal, is a true or earless seal. At only 1.2–1.4m (3ft 9in–4ft 6in) long and about 62–70kg (136.7–154.3lb) in weight, it is one of the smallest of seals. Its coat is steel-grey, sometimes with dark spots on the upperparts.

Unlike the monk seal, which inhabits warm tropical seas, the Baikal seal lives in Lake Baikal, Siberia. In this vast, chilly body of freshwater, the seal eats fish and invertebrates. The lake freezes over in winter, so the female gives birth in a snow lair over a breathing hole in the ice. Sharp claws help her move on the slippery surface.

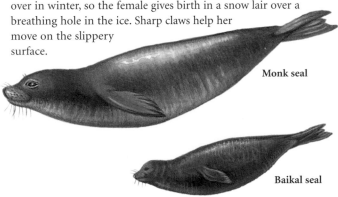

Monk seal

Baikal seal

WHERE IN THE WORLD?

Scattered populations occur in the Mediterranean and around the Hawaiian islands. Caribbean species and Black Sea population now thought to be extinct.

RELATED SPECIES

There are three species of monk seal in the genus Monachus: the Hawaiian monk seal, M. schauinslandi; the Caribbean monk seal, M. tropicalis, now thought to be extinct; and the Mediterranean monk seal, M. monachus. Monk seals belong to the family Phocidae. This family also contains the crabeater seal, which, with an Antarctic population of perhaps 30 million individuals, presents a stark contrast to the monk seals' situation.

· ORDER · *Pinnipedia* · FAMILY · *Phocidae* · GENUS & SPECIES · *Phoca vitulina*

COMMON SEAL

The common seal is purpose-built for life in the water, with powerful hindflippers, a sleek, streamlined body and all-over insulation.

KEY FEATURES

- Mammal that lives mainly in the sea but has to come ashore to give birth and raise its pups.
- Spends most of its life in coastal waters, occasionally swimming a long way up rivers.
- Lithe and agile swimmer that uses a battery of senses to catch primarily shoaling fish.

BLUBBER
A thick layer of blubber under the skin keeps the seal warm in cold water. It also acts as an energy reserve — especially useful for breeding females, which must fast while rearing young.

SKULL
The head is small. The large eyes face forwards, for seeing well in poor underwater light; they enable the seal to judge the distance of prey and predators, such as killer whales and polar bears. The seal's hearing is acute for pinpointing prey.

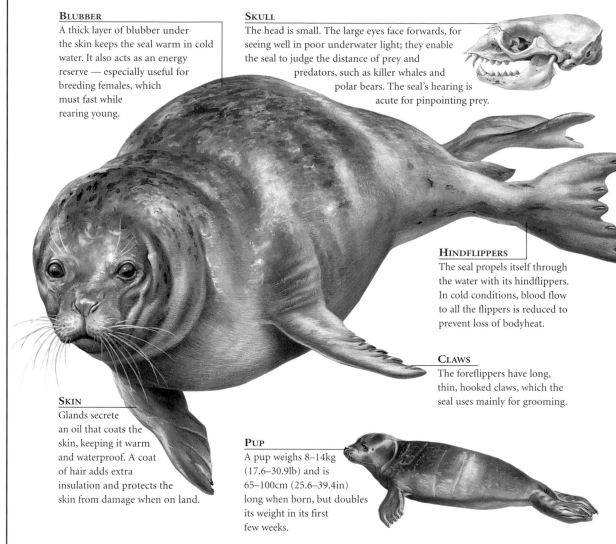

HINDFLIPPERS
The seal propels itself through the water with its hindflippers. In cold conditions, blood flow to all the flippers is reduced to prevent loss of bodyheat.

CLAWS
The foreflippers have long, thin, hooked claws, which the seal uses mainly for grooming.

SKIN
Glands secrete an oil that coats the skin, keeping it warm and waterproof. A coat of hair adds extra insulation and protects the skin from damage when on land.

PUP
A pup weighs 8–14kg (17.6–30.9lb) and is 65–100cm (25.6–39.4in) long when born, but doubles its weight in its first few weeks.

VITAL STATISTICS

WEIGHT	Male 70–150kg (154.3–330.7lb); female 60–110kg (132.3–242.5lb)
LENGTH	Male up to 1.9m (6ft 2in); female up to 1.7m (5ft 6in)
SEXUAL MATURITY	Male 3–6 years; female 2–5 years
MATING SEASON	February to October
GESTATION PERIOD	About 330 days
NUMBER OF YOUNG	1, sometimes 2
BIRTH INTERVAL	1 year
TYPICAL DIET	Fish, squid, shellfish and crabs
LIFESPAN	Male up to 26 years; female up to 32 years

CREATURE COMPARISONS

The ribbon seal (Phoca fasciata) of the North Pacific shares part of the common seal's range. It is easy to distinguish, being slightly smaller, with a more slender body and more vivid markings. Male ribbon seals are black, females brownish-red. Both sexes have four white bands: one around the neck, one around each foreflipper, and one around the hindquarters. The common seal, by contrast, varies in colour from dark grey to dull yellow, with black or brown patches. The tones are usually paler on its underside, for countershading camouflage to hide it from underwater predators. Females are generally smaller and lighter, but the same colour as males.

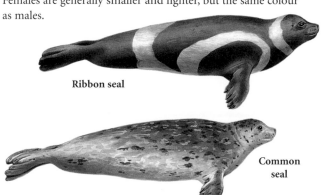

Ribbon seal

Common seal

WHERE IN THE WORLD?

Confined to the northern hemisphere off Atlantic and Pacific coasts, mainly within 40–70°N. Small populations inhabit lakes in northern Quebec, Canada.

RELATED SPECIES

There are 3 families of pinnipeds: the Phocidae, or true or hair seals; the Otariidae, or eared seals, which includes sea lions; and the Odobenidae, whose sole member is the walrus. The common seal is 1 of 19 seals in 10 genera in the Phocidae family, which includes the ribbon seal and the crabeater seal, Lobodon carcinophagus. True or hair seals lack external ears and have well developed claws and relatively small flippers.

• ORDER • *Pleuronectiformes* • FAMILY • *Pleuronectidae* • GENUS & SPECIES • *Platichthys flesus*

FLOUNDER

With its bizarre eye arrangement and amazing ability to change colour, the flounder is tailored like few other fish to a life spent skulking on the seabed.

KEY FEATURES

- Flat-bodied, bottom-dwelling fish with both eyes on the upper side of its face.
- Changes its skin colour and pattern like a chameleon to match its background and hide from enemies.
- Feeds mainly at night, drifting inshore with the tide to snap up burrow-dwelling shellfish and worms.

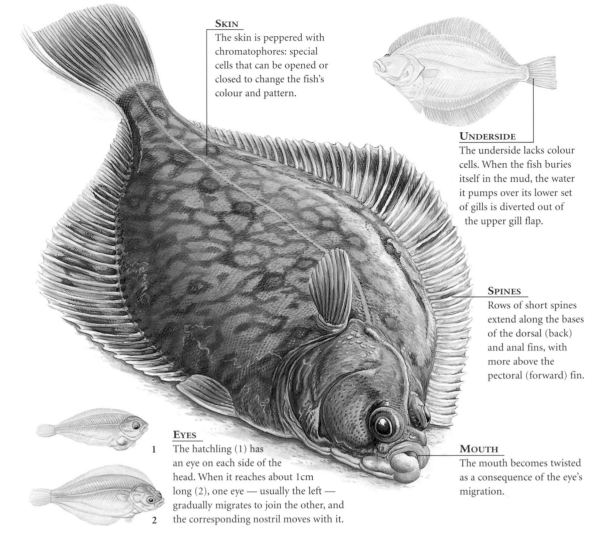

SKIN
The skin is peppered with chromatophores: special cells that can be opened or closed to change the fish's colour and pattern.

UNDERSIDE
The underside lacks colour cells. When the fish buries itself in the mud, the water it pumps over its lower set of gills is diverted out of the upper gill flap.

SPINES
Rows of short spines extend along the bases of the dorsal (back) and anal fins, with more above the pectoral (forward) fin.

EYES
The hatchling (1) has an eye on each side of the head. When it reaches about 1cm long (2), one eye — usually the left — gradually migrates to join the other, and the corresponding nostril moves with it.

MOUTH
The mouth becomes twisted as a consequence of the eye's migration.

VITAL STATISTICS

WEIGHT	Up to 3kg (6.6lb)
LENGTH	Up to 51cm (20.1in); average 30cm (11.8in)
SEXUAL MATURITY	1–3 years
SPAWNING SEASON	February to May, depending on temperature
NUMBER OF EGGS	Up to a million per spawning
HATCHING TIME	1 week
BREEDING INTERVAL	Annual
TYPICAL DIET	Crustaceans, marine worms, molluscs and small fish
LIFESPAN	Up to 20 years

CREATURE COMPARISONS

The flounder is dwarfed by the turbot (Scophthalmus maximus), an active hunter of other fish which grows to about a metre long and almost as broad. The turbot has both eyes on its left side, while most flounders are 'right-eyed'. The flounder has more in common with its close relative the plaice (Pleuronectes platessa). This flatfish, identifiable by its overall patterning of orange spots, lives on seabeds at depths of 200m (656ft), in contrast to the flounder's limit of 55m (180.4ft). Unlike the flounder, the turbot and plaice are prized food-fishes.

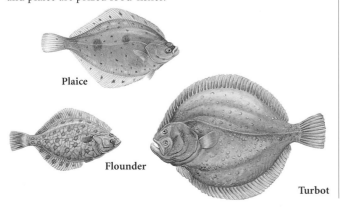

Plaice

Flounder

Turbot

WHERE IN THE WORLD?

Coastal waters, as well as the lower reaches of rivers, from Arctic Scandinavia south through Europe to North Africa. Also occurs in the Baltic and Black seas.

RELATED SPECIES

The flounder is a typical member of the Pleuronectidae, 1 of 7 families in the flatfish order Pleuronectiformes. Its 8 near relatives in northern European seas include the halibut, Hippoglossus hippoglossus. The family is widespread in the world's temperate waters.

• ORDER • *Podicipediformes* **• FAMILY •** *Podicipedidae* **• GENUS & SPECIES •** *Podiceps cristatus*

GREAT CRESTED GREBE

A fast and agile swimmer both on the water surface and beneath it, the great crested grebe is designed for high-speed pursuit of aquatic prey.

KEY FEATURES

- Pursues prey underwater, propelled by rear-set legs with lobed feet, which give maximum driving power.
- In the breeding season, both sexes grow elegant crest feathers for their elaborate, ritualized displays.
- Constructs a floating nesting platform out of aquatic vegetation on clean lakes, rivers and reservoirs.

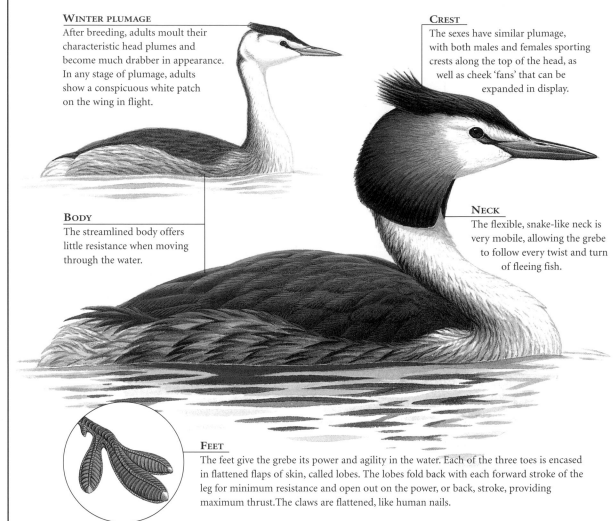

WINTER PLUMAGE
After breeding, adults moult their characteristic head plumes and become much drabber in appearance. In any stage of plumage, adults show a conspicuous white patch on the wing in flight.

CREST
The sexes have similar plumage, with both males and females sporting crests along the top of the head, as well as cheek 'fans' that can be expanded in display.

BODY
The streamlined body offers little resistance when moving through the water.

NECK
The flexible, snake-like neck is very mobile, allowing the grebe to follow every twist and turn of fleeing fish.

FEET
The feet give the grebe its power and agility in the water. Each of the three toes is encased in flattened flaps of skin, called lobes. The lobes fold back with each forward stroke of the leg for minimum resistance and open out on the power, or back, stroke, providing maximum thrust. The claws are flattened, like human nails.

VITAL STATISTICS

WEIGHT	600–1500g (21.2–52.9oz)
LENGTH	46–61cm (18.1–24in)
SEXUAL MATURITY	2 years
BREEDING SEASON	Varies according to locality: April to July in Europe; all year round in Africa; November to March in Australia
NUMBER OF EGGS	1 to 7, but usually 3 to 5
INCUBATION PERIOD	25–31 days
FLEDGING PERIOD	71–79 days
BREEDING INTERVAL	1 year
TYPICAL DIET	Small fish, frogs, tadpoles, aquatic insects, crayfish and molluscs

CREATURE COMPARISONS

The great crested grebe, like many grebes, has head feathers in the form of crests, ruffs or tufts, which are used in breeding displays. Several species also have brightly coloured decorative plumes just behind the eye, which contrast with the colour of the rest of the head, as in the black-necked grebe, Podiceps nigricollis, of North America and Europe. The horned grebe, P auritus, which occurs across the north of the same two continents, has elongated golden tufts lying along each side of a black head.

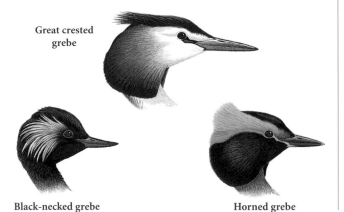

Great crested grebe

Black-necked grebe

Horned grebe

WHERE IN THE WORLD?

Found on freshwaters and coasts across parts of Europe and central Asia as far east as China. Also found in southern and eastern Africa, New Zealand and Australia.

RELATED SPECIES

There are 21 species of grebe in five genera. The little grebe, Tachybaptus ruficollis, sometimes called the dabchick, mainly eats invertebrates and has a short and sturdy bill. Fish-eating grebes, such as Clark's grebe, Aechmophorus clarkii, tend to have long, pointed bills.

• ORDER • *Primates* • FAMILY • *Callitrichidae* • GENUS & SPECIES • *Callimico goeldii*

GOELDI'S MONKEY

Equipped for a fast-track life on the branches and vines of the rainforest, Goeldi's monkey uses its keen senses to monitor its dense, leafy home.

KEY FEATURES

- A small, rare primate that lives in tight-knit family groups in dense, undisturbed tropical rainforest.
- Family members communicate using an expressive repertoire of whistles and trills.
- Produces a single offspring in each litter, unlike other species of marmoset and tamarin, which normally give birth to twins.

VITAL STATISTICS

WEIGHT	390–860g (13.8–30.3oz)
LENGTH	Head & Body: 21–24cm (8.3–9.4in) Tail: 25–32cm (9.8–12.6in)
SEXUAL MATURITY	18–24 months
MATING SEASON	Local dry season
GESTATION PERIOD	139–180 days
NUMBER OF YOUNG	Usually 1, rarely twins
BIRTH INTERVAL	6–12 months
TYPICAL DIET	Fruit, insects, amphibians, reptiles and small mammals
LIFESPAN	Up to 18 years in captivity; unknown in the wild

TAIL
The long tail provides balance as the monkey scampers about in the trees in its fast, jerky fashion.

TEETH
Goeldi's monkey uses its long canines for piercing flesh and tearing skin from firm fruit. It uses its molars to crush insect bodies.

HANDS
The hands are primitive compared with those of most primates, which have opposable thumbs for grasping. Goeldi's monkey grips by hooking its long fingers around a branch or food item, such as a piece of fruit, and pressing it against the pad on the heel of its palm.

CREATURE COMPARISONS

Although Goeldi's monkey and the slender loris (Loris tardigradus) are both modest-sized, tree-dwelling primates that feed on small animals and plant material, that is where their similarities end. The slender loris, which is found in the tropical forests of southern India and Sri Lanka, is active by night, has no tail and moves very slowly in the trees. This contrasts greatly with the rapid daytime movements of Goeldi's monkey. The slender loris's hands and feet are also very different from those of Goeldi's monkey — it has no claws, but its thumbs and big toes are opposable, enabling it to grasp slim branches.

Slender loris

Goeldi's monkey

WHERE IN THE WORLD?

Found in the upper Amazon Basin region of South America. Has a patchy distribution that includes southern Colombia, eastern Ecuador and Peru, and northern Bolivia.

RELATED SPECIES

Goeldi's monkey is the only species in the genus Callimico. It is 1 of 21 species of marmoset, tamarin and lion tamarin in the New World family Callitrichidae, which includes the common marmoset, Callithrix jacchus of eastern Brazil.

• ORDER • *Primates* **• FAMILY •** *Callitrichidae* **• GENUS & SPECIES •** *Callithrix jacchus*

COMMON MARMOSET

KEY FEATURES

- Small, highly active, tree-living primate that spends its life in close-knit groups.
- Gouges out small holes in the bark of trees to release sticky, edible gum.
- Has a high breeding rate, commonly rearing four young per year.

VITAL STATISTICS

WEIGHT	230–260g (8.1–9.2oz)
LENGTH	Head & Body: 17–20cm (6.7–7.9in) Tail: 25–30cm (9.8–11.8in)
SEXUAL MATURITY	Female 12 months; male 16 months
MATING SEASON	All year round
GESTATION PERIOD	148 days
NUMBER OF YOUNG	1 to 4, usually 2 or 3
BIRTH INTERVAL	About 160 days
TYPICAL DIET	Fruit, tree sap and gum, insects and small vertebrates
LIFESPAN	Up to 16 years in captivity

Compact and nimble, the common marmoset could almost be mistaken for a squirrel were it not for its striped tail and tiny but unmistakable primate face.

SKULL
Armed with long canines for killing insects and well developed incisors for gnawing at bark, the marmoset's skull is dominated by large, forward-facing eye sockets, emphasizing the importance of vision in its lifestyle.

TUFTS
The large, white ear tufts accentuate the size of the common marmoset's head and differentiate it from other marmoset species, many of which have spectacular facial adornments such as crests and moustaches.

HANDS
A long palm and fingers ending in sharp claws give excellent grip. But unlike most monkeys, the common marmoset does not have opposable thumbs, so it is less adept at manipulating objects.

TAIL
The marmoset's long, ringed tail serves as a counterbalance to keep it stable as it runs and jumps through the trees.

FUR
Although it lives in the tropics, the common marmoset has thick fur to keep it warm at night. Like many small animals, it loses heat quickly, and with its highly active lifestyle it cannot afford to waste any more energy than necessary by shivering.

CREATURE COMPARISONS

The black tufted-eared marmoset is very closely related to the common marmoset and until 1988 was considered to be a subspecies of its cousin. Today regarded as a species in its own right, the black tufted-eared marmoset lives in family groups, typically of three to nine individuals. These groups have smaller home ranges than most other marmosets. Occasionally, they associate with rare golden-headed lion tamarins. The black tufted-eared marmoset relies heavily on sticky tree sap as a source of food and, like the common marmoset, daubs scent near the sap holes where it regularly feeds.

Black tufted-eared marmoset

Common marmoset

WHERE IN THE WORLD?

Occurs across northeastern Brazil almost wherever there are trees, from the coast of Ceará south to Alagoas and more than 1000km (621.4 miles) inland into the states of Bahia, Piaui and Goias.

RELATED SPECIES

The common marmoset is 1 of 11 species in the genus Callithrix, including the pygmy marmoset. The marmosets and 3 other South American genera, comprising the tamarins and Goeldi's monkey, make up the family Callitrichidae.

• ORDER • *Primates* • FAMILY • *Callitrichidae* • GENUS & SPECIES • *Cebuella pygmaea*

PYGMY MARMOSET

The pygmy marmoset is a tiny primate that has carved itself a niche in the Amazonian ecosystem by adapting to a highly specialized diet.

KEY FEATURES

- The smallest living monkey in the world.
- A specialized feeder that uses long incisors to gouge holes in trees and tap the nutritious gum and sap within.
- Has an unusual breeding system in which only the dominant pair of a troop breeds, while their offspring from previous years remain 'single' to help out with their new brothers and sisters.

VITAL STATISTICS

WEIGHT	107–141g (3.8–5oz)
LENGTH	Head & Body: 11–15cm (4.3–5.9in) Tail: 17–23cm (6.7–9in)
SEXUAL MATURITY	18–24 months
MATING SEASON	All year
GESTATION PERIOD	About 140 days
NUMBER OF YOUNG	1 to 3, but usually non-identical twins
BIRTH INTERVAL	5–7 months
TYPICAL DIET	Tree exudates (gum and sap), invertebrates, occasionally fruits and buds
LIFESPAN	5–8 years

CLAWS
Equipped with sharp, sickle-shaped claws, the pygmy marmoset can cling to tree-trunks at any angle. Long fingers on the hands (above) also help the marmoset probe for invertebrates in holes and crevices.

TEETH
To get at tree sap and gum, the pygmy marmoset anchors its upper incisors into the bark and gouges upwards with its long lower incisors. The lower incisors lack hard enamel on the inner surface, so they are self-sharpening and remain chisel-tipped with use.

EYES
Excellent eyesight with binocular vision helps the pygmy marmoset judge distances as it leaps between the branches.

TAIL
The marmoset uses its long tail for balance when scampering among the trees. However, despite its great length, the tail is not capable of gripping.

CREATURE COMPARISONS

The pied tamarin (Saguinus bicolor) of Brazil is about twice the size of the pygmy marmoset, which is so small it would fit into a baked bean can. The pied tamarin differs from its tiny relative in other ways, too. Unlike the pygmy marmoset, which feeds mainly on tree sap and gum, the pied tamarin concentrates on fruits, buds and invertebrates. Fruit trees are widely scattered and do not ripen at the same time, so the pied tamarin must travel over a home range of 20ha (49.4 acres) or more to obtain food. This is in great contrast to the pygmy marmoset, which is sometimes able to obtain all the food it needs from a single tree.

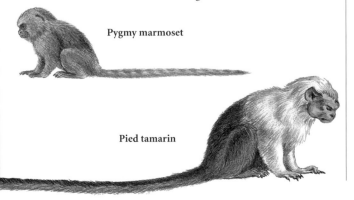

Pygmy marmoset

Pied tamarin

WHERE IN THE WORLD?

The pygmy marmoset occurs in lowland forest in the upper Amazon Basin region. It spans a range that includes western Brazil, northern Bolivia, eastern Peru and Ecuador, and a patch of southeastern Colombia.

RELATED SPECIES

The pygmy marmoset is the only species in the genus Cebuella. However, it is one of 21 species of New World monkey in the family Callitrichidae. The other species are the 3 short-tusked marmosets of the genus Callithrix, the Goeldi's monkey of the genus Callimico, the 12 tamarins of the genus Saguinus, and the 4 lion tamarins of the genus Leontopithecus. As primates, the family Callitrichidae is related to apes and humans.

• **ORDER** • *Primates* • **FAMILY** • *Callitrichidae* • **GENUS & SPECIES** • *Leontopithecus rosalia*

GOLDEN LION TAMARIN

KEY FEATURES

- The most colourful monkey in the world.
- 'Helpers' in the family group assist in rearing their younger siblings.
- South America's most threatened primate and the subject of a worldwide conservation plan.
- Adults of the same sex are extremely aggressive toward one another and, if confronted, they may fight to the death.

VITAL STATISTICS

WEIGHT	600–800g (–28.2oz)
LENGTH	Head & Body: 20–34cm (7.9–13.4in) Tail: 32–40cm (12.6–15.7in)
SEXUAL MATURITY	Male 2 years; female 18 months
MATING SEASON	Spring to autumn
GESTATION PERIOD	125–132 days
NUMBER OF YOUNG	Almost always gives birth to twins
BIRTH INTERVAL	One litter per year; two if the first litter dies
TYPICAL DIET	Fruit, insects, spiders, small vertebrates, gum, sap and resin
LIFESPAN	15 years in captivity; 5–8 years in wild

The golden lion tamarin's fiery coat is not its only distinguishing feature. Its claws are highly unusual and are the secret of its agility among trees.

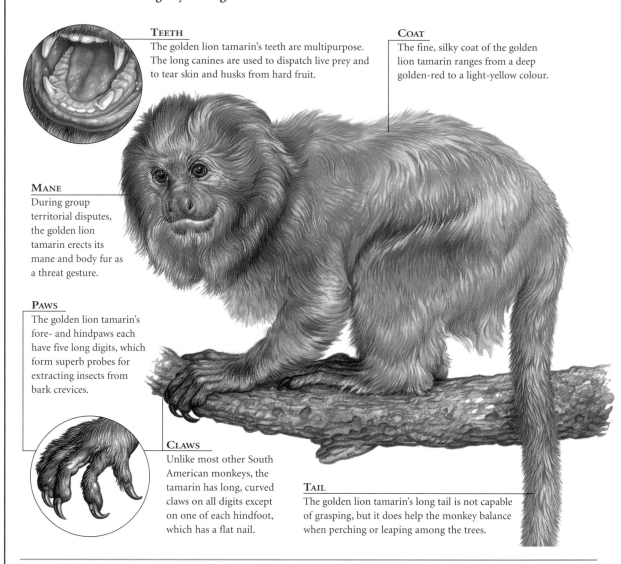

TEETH
The golden lion tamarin's teeth are multipurpose. The long canines are used to dispatch live prey and to tear skin and husks from hard fruit.

COAT
The fine, silky coat of the golden lion tamarin ranges from a deep golden-red to a light-yellow colour.

MANE
During group territorial disputes, the golden lion tamarin erects its mane and body fur as a threat gesture.

PAWS
The golden lion tamarin's fore- and hindpaws each have five long digits, which form superb probes for extracting insects from bark crevices.

CLAWS
Unlike most other South American monkeys, the tamarin has long, curved claws on all digits except on one of each hindfoot, which has a flat nail.

TAIL
The golden lion tamarin's long tail is not capable of grasping, but it does help the monkey balance when perching or leaping among the trees.

CREATURE COMPARISONS

The pygmy marmoset is a close relative of the golden lion tamarin, but feeds in a different way: it is a specialized gum-feeder. The pygmy marmoset uses the long incisors that project beyond its short incisors to gouge tiny holes in tree-trunks. Gum oozes from the holes and the marmoset laps it up. The lion tamarin has projecting incisors, too, but these are much shorter than its canines and are not used for gouging — the tamarin simply uses them to scrape up leaked sap.

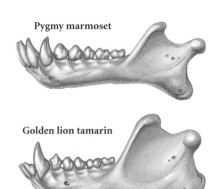

Pygmy marmoset

Golden lion tamarin

WHERE IN THE WORLD?

Native of the Atlantic coastal rainforest of southeastern Brazil. Most wild individuals are found in reserves among this rainforest, while nearly half the total population exists in zoos.

RELATED SPECIES

The golden lion tamarin is one of four lion tamarins in the genus Leontopithecus. The others are the black lion tamarin, the golden-headed lion tamarin and the black-faced lion tamarin. All four species live in the lowland rainforests of southeastern Brazil.

EMPEROR TAMARIN

• ORDER • *Primates* • FAMILY • *Callitrichidae* • GENUS & SPECIES • *Saguinus imperator*

The flamboyant-looking emperor tamarin is no larger than a tree squirrel, but its small stature has many benefits in the tightrope world of the forest.

KEY FEATURES

- Small, lightweight and agile monkey, able to scamper along the slenderest branches of the rainforest canopy.
- The luxuriant moustache is used in displays and helps the tamarin to identify others of its species.
- Lives in an extended family group that fiercely defends a territory and drives away intruders.

VITAL STATISTICS

WEIGHT	About 400g (14oz)
LENGTH	Head & Body: 16–30cm (6.3–11.8in) Tail: 20–38cm (7.9–15in)
SEXUAL MATURITY	16–20 months
MATING SEASON	All year
GESTATION PERIOD	140–145 days
NUMBER OF YOUNG	Almost always gives birth to twins
BIRTH INTERVAL	1 year
TYPICAL DIET	Fruit, nectar, insects, spiders, small vertebrates and tree sap
LIFESPAN	Up to 17 years in captivity; about 12 years in the wild

EYES
Sharp eyes with excellent binocular vision allow the tamarin to judge distances when leaping through the forest canopy.

TEETH
The long canines are used to scrape up tree sap, impale insects and other animal matter, and pierce fruit skin.

MOUSTACHE
The white moustache trails from the muzzle to the chest, and is thought to serve a purpose in display. It also helps individuals to identify each other in dim forest light.

TAIL
The exceptionally long tail is not prehensile (grasping), but serves as an important balancing aid while the tamarin scampers along branches.

FOREPAWS
The forepaws have five long fingers, each with a sharp claw to help the tamarin grip branches.

FEET
There are five digits on each foot, four of which are long and clawed. The short fifth digit has a flat nail for grooming.

CREATURE COMPARISONS

With their wide array of tufts, manes and moustaches the tamarins are some of the most extravagantly adorned species of New World primates. The emperor tamarin is distinguished by its white moustache, while Geoffroy's tamarin (Saguinus geoffroyi), found from Costa Rica to northwestern Colombia, sports a bold, white crest running along its crown. However, one of the most striking of all the tamarin species is the aptly named cotton-top tamarin (Saguinus oedipus) of Colombia. This species has a tousled shock of long, white hair.

Geoffroy's tamarin

Emperor tamarin

Cotton-top tamarin

WHERE IN THE WORLD?

Sparsely distributed within forested areas of the upper reaches of the River Amazon, including parts of southeastern Peru, northwestern Bolivia and northwestern Brazil.

RELATED SPECIES

The emperor tamarin is one of 21 species in the family Callitrichidae. This includes the 12 tamarins of the genus Saguinus, the 4 lion tamarins of the genus Leontopithecus, the 3 short-tusked marmosets of the genus Callithrix, Goeldi's monkey of the genus Callimico and the pygmy marmoset of the genus Cebuella. The family Callitrichidae belongs to the order Primates, which also includes apes, lemurs, tree shrews and humans.

• **ORDER** • *Primates* • **FAMILY** • *Callitrichidae* • **GENUS & SPECIES** • *Saguinus oedipus*

COTTON-TOP TAMARIN

Thanks to its diminutive size, strong limbs and curved claws, the cotton-top tamarin can grip the widest tree-trunk and the thinnest leaf stalk with ease.

KEY FEATURES

- Small, highly active tree-dwelling primate that forages at most levels of the forest.
- Distinguished by a brilliant white shock of long hair on its head.
- Highly vocal, with several different sounds used for communication.
- Becoming rare; classified as endangered by the IUCN (World Conservation Union).

VITAL STATISTICS

WEIGHT	350–510g (12.3–18oz)
LENGTH	Head & Body: 20.5–25.5cm (8–10in) Tail: 30.7–41.1cm (12–16.2in)
SEXUAL MATURITY	Male 24 months; female 18 months
MATING SEASON	January to February
GESTATION PERIOD	140 days
NUMBER OF YOUNG	1 to 3, usually non-identical twins
BIRTH INTERVAL	8 months
TYPICAL DIET	Fruit, seeds and animal matter, including insects, mice and birds
LIFESPAN	About 13 years

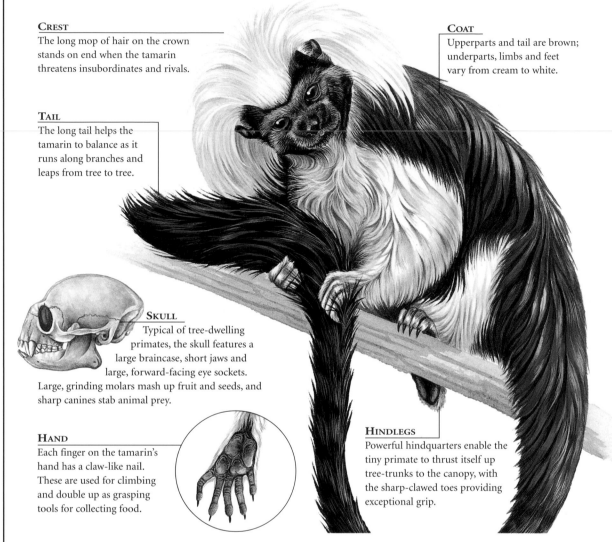

CREST
The long mop of hair on the crown stands on end when the tamarin threatens insubordinates and rivals.

TAIL
The long tail helps the tamarin to balance as it runs along branches and leaps from tree to tree.

COAT
Upperparts and tail are brown; underparts, limbs and feet vary from cream to white.

SKULL
Typical of tree-dwelling primates, the skull features a large braincase, short jaws and large, forward-facing eye sockets. Large, grinding molars mash up fruit and seeds, and sharp canines stab animal prey.

HAND
Each finger on the tamarin's hand has a claw-like nail. These are used for climbing and double up as grasping tools for collecting food.

HINDLEGS
Powerful hindquarters enable the tiny primate to thrust itself up tree-trunks to the canopy, with the sharp-clawed toes providing exceptional grip.

CREATURE COMPARISONS

The golden-handed tamarin (Saguinus midas) is slightly larger than the cotton-top tamarin. It lacks its relative's distinctive head hair but has unmistakable bright golden hands and feet. It is found farther south than the cotton-top, in the rainforests of northern Brazil, Guyana, French Guiana and Surinam.

Both species eat mainly fruit and insects, but the golden-handed tamarin spends most of its time foraging near the top of the canopy. A typical golden-handed tamarin group has about six members; it defends its territory from others of the same species, but sometimes associates with bare-ear marmosets.

Golden-handed tamarin

Cotton-top tamarin

WHERE IN THE WORLD?

Found only in secondary wet and dry forest and low vine tangles in northwestern Colombia between the Atrato, Cauca and Magdalena rivers, from sea level to altitudes of 1500m (4921ft).

RELATED SPECIES

The cotton-top tamarin belongs to the family Callitrichidae, which contains 21 species of tamarin and marmoset in 5 genera. The cotton-top shares its genus with 11 other tamarins, including the emperor tamarin, Saguinus imperator.

• ORDER • *Primates* • FAMILY • *Cebidae* • GENUS & SPECIES • *Alouatta seniculus*

RED HOWLER MONKEY

The red howler monkey spends most of its life high in the rainforest, and has a range of special adaptations to meet its daily needs in the treetops.

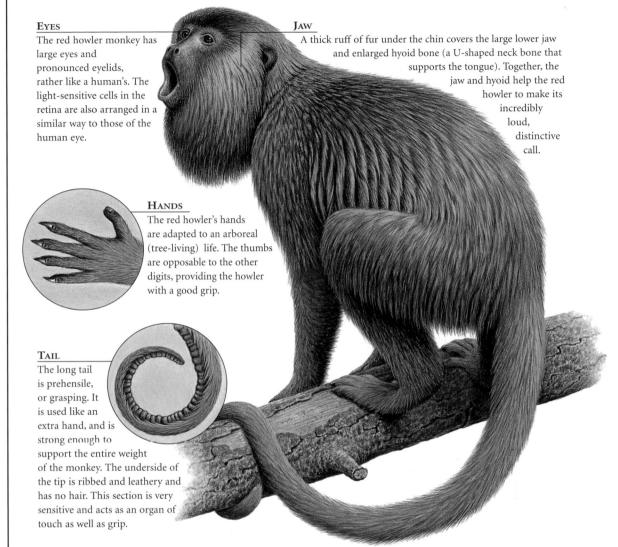

EYES
The red howler monkey has large eyes and pronounced eyelids, rather like a human's. The light-sensitive cells in the retina are also arranged in a similar way to those of the human eye.

JAW
A thick ruff of fur under the chin covers the large lower jaw and enlarged hyoid bone (a U-shaped neck bone that supports the tongue). Together, the jaw and hyoid help the red howler to make its incredibly loud, distinctive call.

HANDS
The red howler's hands are adapted to an arboreal (tree-living) life. The thumbs are opposable to the other digits, providing the howler with a good grip.

TAIL
The long tail is prehensile, or grasping. It is used like an extra hand, and is strong enough to support the entire weight of the monkey. The underside of the tip is ribbed and leathery and has no hair. This section is very sensitive and acts as an organ of touch as well as grip.

KEY FEATURES

- Has one of the loudest calls in the world — a penetrating howling that can be heard through 3km (2 miles) of forest.
- Lives mainly among the trees — especially in the upper canopy — only occasionally coming to the ground to feed.
- Breeding males are very competitive, and a male that wins control of a group usually kills the former leader's offspring.

VITAL STATISTICS

WEIGHT	Male 6.5–9kg (14.3–19.8lb); female 4–6.5kg (8.8–14.3lb)
LENGTH	Head & Body: Male 49–72cm (19.3–28.3in); female 46–57cm (18.1–22.4in) Tail: 49–75cm (19.3–29.5in)
SEXUAL MATURITY	Male about 5 years; female about 4 years
MATING SEASON	Throughout the year
GESTATION PERIOD	184–194 days
NUMBER OF YOUNG	Usually 1
BIRTH INTERVAL	About 17 months
TYPICAL DIET	Mainly leaves; some fruit and flowers
LIFESPAN	16–20 years

CREATURE COMPARISONS

Like the red howler, the white-faced saki monkey (Pithecia pithecia) is found across a broad band of northern South America and inhabits the upper parts of the forest canopy. However, the white-faced saki is much smaller in size and very different facially from the red howler.

The white-faced saki monkey has a small, delicate face, framed by a cowl of longish, pale hair. The male's facial hair (right) is whitish or reddish, while the female has a white to pale red-brown stripe extending from the eyes to the corners of the mouth.

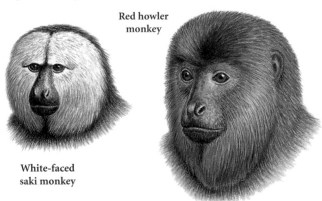

Red howler monkey

White-faced saki monkey

WHERE IN THE WORLD?

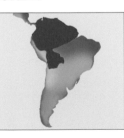

Found across South America from Venezuela and Colombia in the north through eastern Ecuador, northeastern Peru and Amazonian Brazil south to Bolivia.

RELATED SPECIES

The red howler monkey is one of 6 species of howler monkey in the genus Alouatta. The other 5 are: the Mexican black, or Guatemalan, howler, A. villosa; the mantled howler, A. palliata; the red-handed howler, A. belzebul; the brown howler, A. fusca; and the black howler, A. caraya. The howlers are among the largest of the 44 members in the family Cebidae — the New World monkeys, which are found over the Americas from Mexico to Argentina.

• ORDER • *Primates* • FAMILY • *Cebidae* • GENUS & SPECIES • *Cacajao calvus*

BALD UAKARI

KEY FEATURES

• Virtually hairless, bright red face and short, wispy hair on the back of its head give this tree-dwelling primate a disconcertingly human appearance.

• Restricted to the wettest forest regions, where the ground is seasonally flooded and permanently waterlogged.

• Listed as endangered by the IUCN (World Conservation Union).

VITAL STATISTICS

WEIGHT	3.5–4kg (7.7–8.8lb)
LENGTH	Head & Body: 51–70cm (20.1–27.6in) Tail: 14–19cm (5.5–7.5in)
SEXUAL MATURITY	3–4 years
MATING SEASON	October to May
GESTATION PERIOD	180–190 days
NUMBER OF YOUNG	1
BIRTH INTERVAL	2 years
TYPICAL DIET	Fruit, seeds, flowers and leaves; insects
LIFESPAN	Up to 20 years in captivity

There are two subspecies of the bald uakari: one has a red coat, the other white. But both have an almost naked head and shockingly red facial skin.

EAR
The uakari's ears are startlingly human in appearance, but its hearing is more acute than ours.

WHITE UAKARI
The white uakari (Cacajao calvus calvus) has a greyish-white coat.

COAT
The long, shaggy coat of the red uakari varies from dull brown to rich chestnut.

FACE
When the uakari is upset or excited, its face flushes an even deeper red.

EYES
Large, forward-facing eyes give excellent binocular vision, essential for accurately judging distances.

HAND
The uakari has a strong grip thanks to a long, powerful thumb and four fingers. In contrast to humans, the inner fingers are the shortest.

TAIL
The tail is relatively short. As the bald uakari travels quite slowly through the canopy, it does not need a long tail to enhance its balance.

CREATURE COMPARISONS

The red-backed saki (Chiropotes satanas), also known as the bearded saki, is another large, tree-dwelling monkey of South America. It has a much larger range than the bald uakari, occurring in Brazil, Surinam, French Guiana, Guyana and Venezuela.

The red-backed saki has a completely black face, a thick black beard and a long, bushy tail. As well as swamp forest, it lives in rainforest and mountain savannah forest, where it moves more rapidly and acrobatically than the bald uakari. It also eats more fruit than the uakari, and less animal prey.

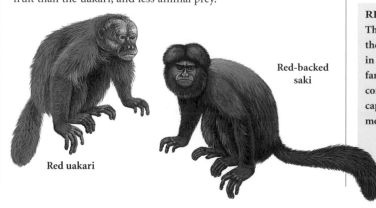

Red uakari

Red-backed saki

WHERE IN THE WORLD?

Found in the rainforests of the upper Amazon in South America. Its range covers western Brazil, southern Colombia and northern Peru, extending to the foothills of the Andes.

RELATED SPECIES

The bald uakari shares the genus Cacajao with the black uakari, C. melanocephalus, which lives in Venezuela and Brazil. Uakaris are part of the family Cebidae, or New World monkeys, which contains 44 species in 12 genera. These include capuchin monkeys, howler monkeys, spider monkeys, sakis, titi monkeys and squirrel monkeys.

BROWN CAPUCHIN MONKEY

• **ORDER** • *Primates* • **FAMILY** • *Cebidae* • **GENUS & SPECIES** • *Cebus apella*

KEY FEATURES

- Vocal resident of rainforests in South America, frequently found in marauding troops.
- Each group is led by a dominant male, with its members foraging in a set formation.
- Usually the female courts the male, attracting his attention with gestures and seductive calls.

VITAL STATISTICS

WEIGHT	1.7–4.5kg (3.7–9.9lb)
LENGTH	Head & Body: 30–55cm (11.8–21.6in) Tail: 30–56cm (11.8–22in)
SEXUAL MATURITY	Male 8 years; female 3–4 years
MATING SEASON	Throughout the year
GESTATION PERIOD	160 days
NUMBER OF YOUNG	1
BIRTH INTERVAL	1 year, sometimes 2
TYPICAL DIET	Fruit, seeds, insects and small vertebrates
LIFESPAN	35–45 years

The capuchin's long limbs, prehensile tail and well developed hands and feet make it one of the Amazon's natural acrobats.

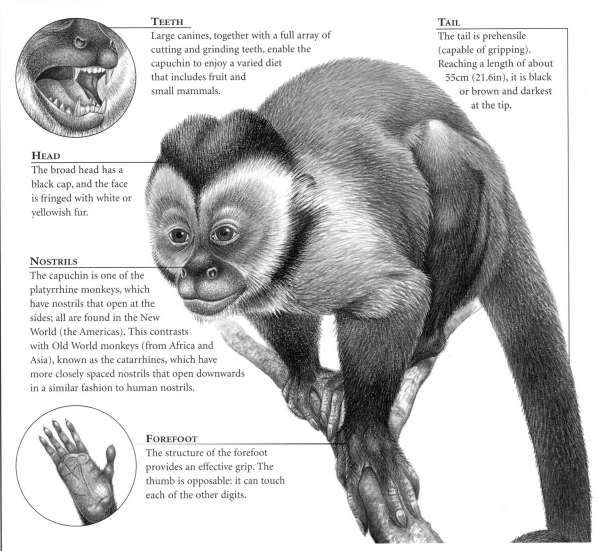

TEETH
Large canines, together with a full array of cutting and grinding teeth, enable the capuchin to enjoy a varied diet that includes fruit and small mammals.

TAIL
The tail is prehensile (capable of gripping). Reaching a length of about 55cm (21.6in), it is black or brown and darkest at the tip.

HEAD
The broad head has a black cap, and the face is fringed with white or yellowish fur.

NOSTRILS
The capuchin is one of the platyrrhine monkeys, which have nostrils that open at the sides; all are found in the New World (the Americas). This contrasts with Old World monkeys (from Africa and Asia), known as the catarrhines, which have more closely spaced nostrils that open downwards in a similar fashion to human nostrils.

FOREFOOT
The structure of the forefoot provides an effective grip. The thumb is opposable: it can touch each of the other digits.

CREATURE COMPARISONS

Occurring in Venezuela, the Guianas and northeastern Brazil, the Guianan saki monkey (Pithecia pithecia) is a neighbour of the capuchin. It is a little longer, reaching 70cm (27.6in) from head to rump, but is usually lighter, rarely topping 1.7kg (4.5lb). Whereas the male and female capuchin are similar in colour, the shaggy coat of the saki is black in males and greyish-brown in females. The saki lives in small, quiet groups and eats fruit and leaves. Although it lacks the prehensile tail of the capuchin, it is highly acrobatic — accounting for its local name of 'flying monkey'.

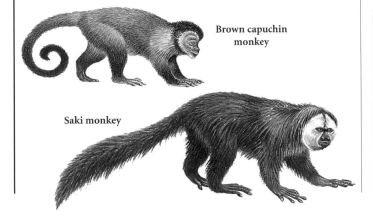

Brown capuchin monkey

Saki monkey

WHERE IN THE WORLD?

Found east of the Andes in South America, from Colombia and Venezuela through the Amazon Basin and south to Paraguay and northern Argentina.

RELATED SPECIES
The brown capuchin monkey is 1 of 4 species in its genus, which belongs to the family of New World monkeys, the Cebidae. Found in Central and South America, the family includes the red uakari, Cacajao calvus, which lives close to water.

• **ORDER** • *Primates* • **FAMILY** • *Cebidae* • **GENUS & SPECIES** • *Lagothrix lagotricha*

WOOLLY MONKEY

Although larger and heavier set than many tree-dwelling monkeys, the woolly monkey's long, strong, prehensile tail gives it great agility among the branches.

KEY FEATURES

- One of the largest of all New World monkeys, yet it is a tremendously agile tree dweller, swinging from branch to branch with fluid ease.
- Uses its long tail as a balancing aid and as a fifth limb to secure itself on a high perch.
- Moves between every level of thick forests, from the ground cover of the forest floor to the upper canopy some 60m (197ft) high.

VITAL STATISTICS

WEIGHT	5.5–10.8kg (12.1–23.8lb)
LENGTH	Head & Body: 50–68cm (19.7–26.8in) Tail: 60–72cm (23.6–28.3in)
SEXUAL MATURITY	Male 5 or more years; female 4 years
MATING SEASON	All year round
GESTATION PERIOD	225 days
NUMBER OF YOUNG	1
BIRTH INTERVAL	Estimated at 3 years
TYPICAL DIET	Mainly fruits, supplemented with nuts seeds, leaves and some insects
LIFESPAN	Up to 25 years

LIMBS
Long and powerful, the limbs are designed to allow the monkey to move easily and with agility through the trees.

EYES
The monkey's eyes are large and forward-facing. The arrangement of light-sensitive cells in the retina is similar to that of a human eye.

TAIL
The tail is prehensile (grasping) and is naked, ribbed and leathery on the underside at the tip. The woolly monkey uses its tail as an additional limb, and it can hang by it comfortably with no support from its other limbs.

COAT
The hair is short, and woolly with a thick underfur. Colouration ranges from blue-grey and greyish-brown to blackish-brown.

FINGERS
The fingers are thick and muscular. The thumb is well developed compared to other Cebid monkeys, and helps in grasping branches.

CREATURE COMPARISONS

Members of the same family, the capuchin and woolly monkeys are very different in appearance. The capuchin monkey, Cebus capucinus, of Central and South America, is smaller and more slightly built, with a head and body length of 30–57cm (11.8–22.4in) and weighing only 1–3.3kg (2.2–7.3lb). Unlike the short-haired woolly monkey, long hairs cover the body and tail of the capuchin. The long, white hair on the head resembles the cowl of a Capuchin friar and gives this monkey its common name. The capuchin is also known as the ring-tail monkey because it often curls its prehensile tail when it is resting.

Capuchin monkey

Woolly monkey

WHERE IN THE WORLD?

Found in South America, east of the Andes, in Colombia, Ecuador and Peru to the Tapajós River and the Mato Grosso of central Brazil.

RELATED SPECIES

There are two species of woolly monkey in the genus Lagothrix: the variably coloured L. lagotricha and the red-brown L. flavicauda of Peru. Both species belong to the family Cebidae, or New World monkeys, which also includes the spider monkeys, such as Ateles paniscus.

SQUIRREL MONKEY

• **ORDER** • *Primates* • **FAMILY** • *Cebidae* • **GENUS & SPECIES** • *Saimiri sciureus*

KEY FEATURES

- A nimble creature that is at home at all levels in the rainforest, moving freely between the ground and the highest branches with ease.
- Lives in large 'troops', cooperating on feeding expeditions and when threatened by predators.
- The least threatened and most numerous of all South American primates, despite ongoing hunting and habitat loss.

VITAL STATISTICS

WEIGHT	750–1100g (26.4–38.8oz)
LENGTH	Head & Body: 26–36cm (10.2–14.2in) Tail: 35–43cm (13.8–16.9in)
SEXUAL MATURITY	Male 5 years; female 3 years
MATING SEASON	September to November
GESTATION PERIOD	152–168 days
NUMBER OF YOUNG	1
BIRTH INTERVAL	1 year
TYPICAL DIET	Fruits, berries, nuts, seeds, insects, flowers, buds, leaves, spiders and small vertebrates
LIFESPAN	7–10 years

With its keen eyesight and excellent coordination, the squirrel monkey is well equipped to leap effortlessly among the trees and vines of the rainforest.

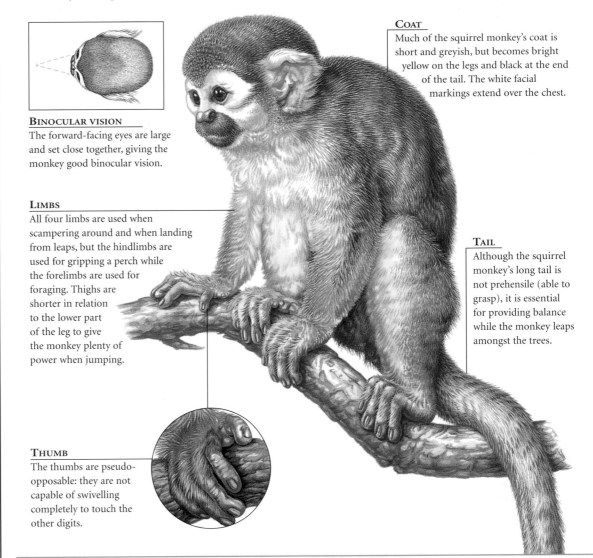

BINOCULAR VISION
The forward-facing eyes are large and set close together, giving the monkey good binocular vision.

LIMBS
All four limbs are used when scampering around and when landing from leaps, but the hindlimbs are used for gripping a perch while the forelimbs are used for foraging. Thighs are shorter in relation to the lower part of the leg to give the monkey plenty of power when jumping.

THUMB
The thumbs are pseudo-opposable: they are not capable of swivelling completely to touch the other digits.

COAT
Much of the squirrel monkey's coat is short and greyish, but becomes bright yellow on the legs and black at the end of the tail. The white facial markings extend over the chest.

TAIL
Although the squirrel monkey's long tail is not prehensile (able to grasp), it is essential for providing balance while the monkey leaps amongst the trees.

CREATURE COMPARISONS

Unlike the squirrel monkey or, indeed, any other monkey species, the Douroucoulis, or night monkeys, of the genus Aotus are, as their name implies, nocturnal. Their eyes are very large and the retinas contain only rods (light-sensitive cells). This adaptation gives night monkeys exceptional night vision, enabling them to pursue a nocturnal pattern of activity when other monkey species must rest.

A laryngeal pouch, an inflatable sac under the chin, amplifies night monkeys' calls, which include up to 50 different sounds. Squirrel monkeys do not have this pouch, but they are also very vocal.

Squirrel monkey

Night monkey

WHERE IN THE WORLD?

Lives in the tropical rainforests of South America, from the eastern edges of the Andes in Colombia and northern Peru to northeastern Brazil.

RELATED SPECIES

There are four other species within the genus Saimiri, which all go by the name of squirrel monkey. One of these species, the endangered Saimiri oerstedii, is found in a small area along the Pacific coast of Costa Rica and Panama; the other species live in South America. They are all diurnal (day-active) and form larger groups than any other New World monkeys, sometimes congregating in groups as large as 300 individuals.

DIANA MONKEY

The Diana monkey's striking coat pattern is designed to emphasize its body language at long range, sending signals to other members of its troop.

KEY FEATURES

- A colourful monkey with a distinctive creamy, or white, ruff and beard.
- Nimble and agile, it spends most of its life on high forest branches.
- Communicates with other members of its troop by calls, facial expressions and its conspicuous markings.
- Listed as vulnerable by the IUCN (World Conservation Union).

TEETH
Long, wide incisors are used to slice through tough fruit skin. Food is then pulped with the flat molars. The large canines also help pierce fruit but are used mainly in threat displays.

FACE
The Diana monkey employs a wide range of facial expressions, such as grins, grimaces and yawns, backed up with a variety of calls. Together, these are used to communicate its moods, such as anger, appeasement, sexual arousal and fear. The long beard (pointed in males) and pale ruff contrast with the dark face, further emphasizing its expressions.

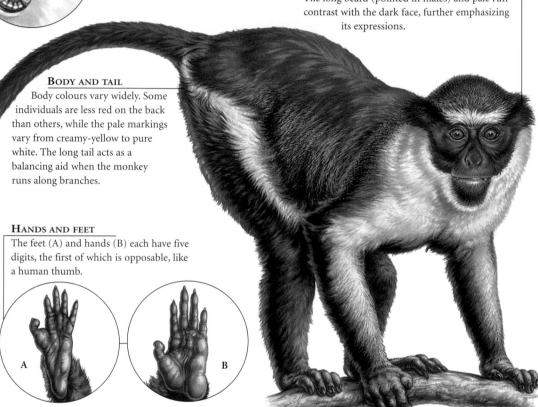

BODY AND TAIL
Body colours vary widely. Some individuals are less red on the back than others, while the pale markings vary from creamy-yellow to pure white. The long tail acts as a balancing aid when the monkey runs along branches.

HANDS AND FEET
The feet (A) and hands (B) each have five digits, the first of which is opposable, like a human thumb.

VITAL STATISTICS

WEIGHT	Male 4–7kg (8.8–15.4lb); female 2.5–3.5kg (5.5–7.7lb)
LENGTH	Head & Body: 40–55cm (15.7–21.6in) Tail: 50–80cm (19.7–31in)
SEXUAL MATURITY	3–5 years
MATING SEASON	All year
GESTATION PERIOD	150–180 days
NUMBER OF YOUNG	1; rarely 2
BIRTH INTERVAL	12 months
TYPICAL DIET	Mainly fruit and seeds; also flowers, buds, leaves and insects
LIFESPAN	Up to 30 years

CREATURE COMPARISONS

Slightly smaller than the Diana monkey, the red-tailed guenon (Cercopithecus ascanius) differs mainly in colour. It has a distinctive, reddish-chestnut tail and long, creamy-white cheek whiskers that draw attention to the area of naked blue skin around its eyes. Although both monkeys are mainly fruit-eaters, the red-tailed guenon eats more insects, which make up about a quarter of its diet.

The Diana monkey prefers primary rainforest, whereas the red-tailed guenon thrives in secondary and regenerating forest. During territorial disputes, female red-tailed guenons defend troop boundaries, whereas among Diana monkeys it is the males that perform this role.

Diana monkey

Red-tailed guenon

WHERE IN THE WORLD?

Found in scattered strongholds among the primary tropical rainforests of West Africa, from Sierra Leone east through Liberia and the Ivory Coast to Ghana.

RELATED SPECIES

There are 26 species, all known as guenons, in the genus Cercopithecus, including the blue monkey, C. mitis. There are 2 subspecies of Diana monkey, C. d. diana and C. d. roloway, although some sources classify the latter as a species in its own right.

• ORDER • *Primates* • FAMILY • *Cercopithecidae* • GENUS & SPECIES • *Colobus guereza*

The contrasting coat of the guereza and its extravagant tail tuft serve to enhance the impact of its loud territorial claims in the forest canopy.

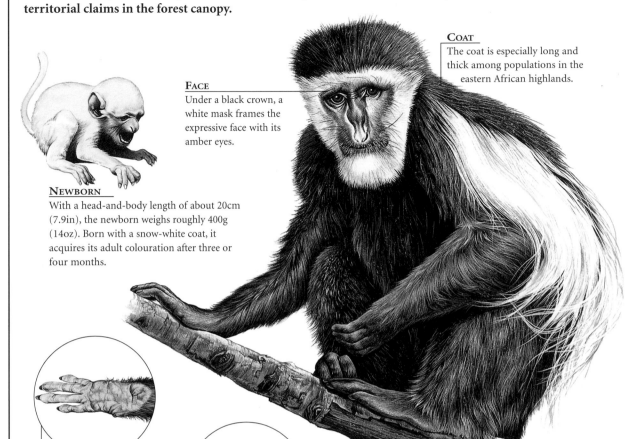

KEY FEATURES

- Strikingly coloured primate with a white mask around its face, white flanks and a fluffy white tail tuft.
- Reduced thumbs on its forelimbs enhance its movement through trees.
- Specialized stomach for digesting mature leaves and neutralizing plant toxins allows it to live and feed in areas unsuitable for many other primates.

FACE
Under a black crown, a white mask frames the expressive face with its amber eyes.

COAT
The coat is especially long and thick among populations in the eastern African highlands.

NEWBORN
With a head-and-body length of about 20cm (7.9in), the newborn weighs roughly 400g (14oz). Born with a snow-white coat, it acquires its adult colouration after three or four months.

HAND
Each hand has four fingers. The thumb is effectively absent; although dexterity is impaired, swinging through trees is made much easier.

FOOT
Five digits on each foot and naked soles provide superb grip on branches.

VITAL STATISTICS

WEIGHT	5.4–23kg (11.9–50.7lb); male usually a third heavier than female
LENGTH	Head & Body: 45–70cm (17.7–27.6in) Tail: 52–90cm (20.5–35.4in)
SEXUAL MATURITY	Male 5–6 years; female 3–4 years
MATING SEASON	Year round
GESTATION PERIOD	Average 180 days
NUMBER OF YOUNG	1, rarely 2
BIRTH INTERVAL	20 months
TYPICAL DIET	Leaves, fruit, flowers and twigs; soil and clay from termite mounds
LIFESPAN	Up to 20 years

CREATURE COMPARISONS

The western red colobus monkey (Piliocolobus badius) occurs in the forests of Sierra Leone, Liberia, Guinea and the Ivory Coast. A little smaller than the guereza, it too has a two-tone coat, but its upperparts are black or slate and its belly, flanks and limbs sport varying reddish hues.

The red colobus is not strongly territorial. Its troops, each numbering up to 80 individuals including several adult males, occupy a large home range compared to that of the guereza, and readily share it with neighbours.

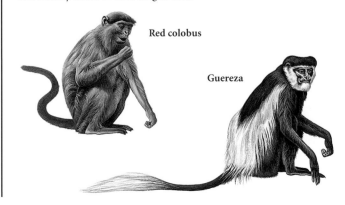

Red colobus

Guereza

WHERE IN THE WORLD?

Found in equatorial Africa, from Nigeria east through Cameroon, Gabon, northern Congo, the Central African Republic, northeastern Zaire and southern Sudan to northern Tanzania.

RELATED SPECIES

The guereza is 1 of 5 species of black-and-white colobus in the genus Colobus, 1 of 10 genera in the leaf monkey subfamily, Colobinae. Leaf monkeys, also comprising the langurs and snub-nosed monkeys, have large salivary glands and a complex stomach. Other monkeys of Africa and Asia, including the guenons, baboons and macaques among others, comprise the subfamily Cercopithecinae. They are heavier and less arboreal than colobines.

• **ORDER** • *Primates* • **FAMILY** • *Cercopithecidae* • **GENUS & SPECIES** • *Macaca fuscata*

JAPANESE MACAQUE

Long, dense fur and a sturdy, compact body help the Japanese macaque to cope with the cold winters of northern Japan.

KEY FEATURES

- A monkey that gathers in large troops based around a core of closely related females.
- Not shy of humans, and often takes advantage of the food left out by monks in remote temples.
- Since 1968, members of a particular troop have used hot springs to keep warm in the snowy mountains.

VITAL STATISTICS

WEIGHT	8.3–18kg (18.3–39.7lb)
LENGTH	Head & Body: 47–60cm (18.5–23.6in) Tail: 7–12cm (2.7–4.7in)
SEXUAL MATURITY	3–5 years
MATING SEASON	Autumn–spring, depending on location
GESTATION PERIOD	6 months
NUMBER OF YOUNG	1
BIRTH INTERVAL	Usually 2 years
TYPICAL DIET	Fruit, insects, young leaves
LIFESPAN	Up to 30 years (female lives longer than the male)

TEETH
The Japanese macaque has the same number and arrangement of teeth as a human, but the canine (biting) teeth of the male are much longer.

RUMP
When the female is in breeding condition in autumn her naked rump turns deep pink and swells slightly. This shows that she is ready to mate and helps her to attract a male.

FEET
Like other monkeys, the Japanese macaque walks on the flats of its feet, rather than on its toes. This gives it a rather plodding gait as it walks over the ground.

TAIL
Monkeys' tails provide balance but have poor blood circulation. In cold conditions, therefore, they quickly suffer from frost-bite. The macaque's tail, however, is short to help the animal cope with the winter cold.

HAND
The macaque has an opposable thumb, like humans, which allows it to grip branches, hold food and groom itself or other macaques.

CREATURE COMPARISONS

The rhesus monkey (Macaca mulatta) of Afghanistan, India, China and Vietnam, is about the same size as the Japanese macaque, but is less dumpy and usually weighs less than half as much. Its tail, at 19–30cm (7.5–11.8in), is much longer than that of the Japanese macaque, probably because its homelands are warmer and it does not risk heat loss through its extremities. Its fur is also shorter and a richer brown in colour, with a pale underside. The two species do, however, share similarly pink and hairless faces and rumps, and both are proficient swimmers.

Rhesus monkey

Japanese macaque

WHERE IN THE WORLD?

Found on three of the four main islands of Japan — Honshu, Shikoku and Kyushu — and some of the smaller, surrounding islands.

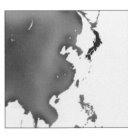

RELATED SPECIES

There are 16 species in the genus Macaca divided into four species groups. The Japanese macaque belongs to the same group as the rhesus monkey, whereas the liontail macaque, M. silenus, of southwest India is grouped with the Barbary ape and 5 other species.

RHESUS MACAQUE

• **ORDER** • *Primates* • **FAMILY** • *Cercopithecidae* • **GENUS & SPECIES** • *Macaca mulatta*

Alert and inquisitive, the rhesus macaque is built for a life spent largely on the ground, where it bounces nimbly along on all fours.

KEY FEATURES

- A ground-dwelling primate that forages on a wide range of food, from cultivated crops to scraps and waste matter discarded by humans.
- Highly sociable, living in sizeable groups that divide up when they become too large.
- Social structure is two-tiered, with females dominating the family groups but remaining subordinate to the males.

VITAL STATISTICS

WEIGHT	5.5–7.7kg (12.1–17lb)
LENGTH	Head & Body: 47–64cm (18.5–25.2in) Tail: 19–30cm (7.5–11.8in)
SEXUAL MATURITY	3–4 years
MATING SEASON	Autumn, but varies across range
GESTATION PERIOD	165 days
NUMBER OF YOUNG	Usually 1
BIRTH INTERVAL	1 year
TYPICAL DIET	Fruits, roots and herbs. Also occasional insects and small animals
LIFESPAN	Up to 29 years

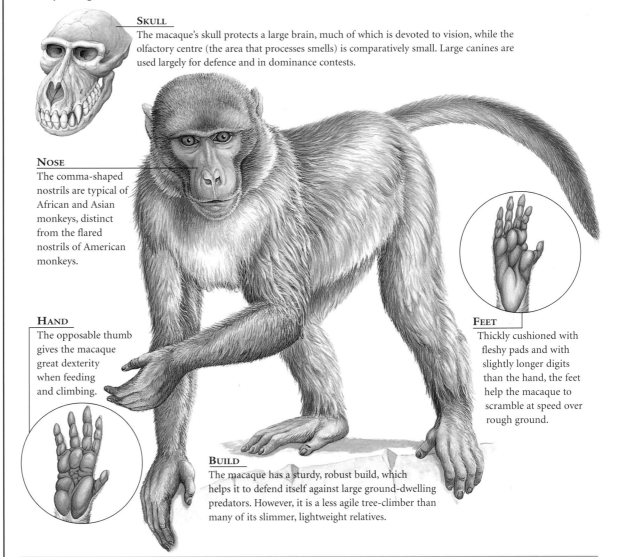

SKULL
The macaque's skull protects a large brain, much of which is devoted to vision, while the olfactory centre (the area that processes smells) is comparatively small. Large canines are used largely for defence and in dominance contests.

NOSE
The comma-shaped nostrils are typical of African and Asian monkeys, distinct from the flared nostrils of American monkeys.

HAND
The opposable thumb gives the macaque great dexterity when feeding and climbing.

FEET
Thickly cushioned with fleshy pads and with slightly longer digits than the hand, the feet help the macaque to scramble at speed over rough ground.

BUILD
The macaque has a sturdy, robust build, which helps it to defend itself against large ground-dwelling predators. However, it is a less agile tree-climber than many of its slimmer, lightweight relatives.

CREATURE COMPARISONS

The Moor macaque (*Macaca maura*), also known as the Sulawesi macaque, is less widespread than the rhesus macaque. Found in Southeast Asia on Sulawesi, Bacan and other nearby islands, the moor macaque is stockily built like the rhesus macaque, and this is further exaggerated by its very short tail. Unlike the rhesus, its naked face is dark, with a thick 'beard' of white fur under the chin. The moor macaque's coat, like that of other macaques of Sulawesi, is much darker than that of the rhesus, and the male sometimes sports a crest of hair on the crown of the head. Like the rhesus, it is active during the day but it spends more time in the trees since it lives in tropical primary rainforests.

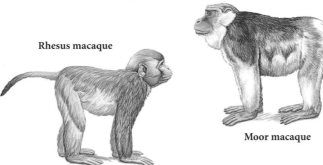

Rhesus macaque

Moor macaque

WHERE IN THE WORLD?

Found from eastern Afghanistan, eastwards across northern and central India, to Nepal, southern China and parts of Southeast Asia.

RELATED SPECIES

The rhesus macaque is 1 of 16 species in the genus Macaca. The genus belongs to the family Cercopithecidae, whose members are commonly referred to as the cheek-pouched monkeys because they store food in their cheeks. All members of the genus are found in Asia, apart from the barbary ape, M. sylvanus, which occurs in northern Africa and Gibraltar. Macaques live in a wider range of habitats than any other primate except for humans.

• ORDER • *Primates* • FAMILY • *Cercopithecidae* • GENUS & SPECIES • *Macaca silenus*

LION-TAILED MACAQUE

A muscular physique and tenacious hand grip help this impressively maned macaque clamber acrobatically through the tropical forest canopy.

KEY FEATURES

- The only species of macaque to sport a long mane around its face, as well as a tuft-tipped tail.
- So well adapted to its Indian rainforest home that it cannot adjust to new habitats created by human intrusion.
- Perilously close to extinction because of habitat destruction, it is classified by the IUCN (World Conservation Union) as endangered.

VITAL STATISTICS

WEIGHT	Male up to 10kg (22lb); female up to 6kg (13.2lb)
LENGTH	Head & Body: 46–61cm (18.1–24in) Tail: 25–38cm (9.8–15in)
SEXUAL MATURITY	Male 8 years; female 5 years
MATING SEASON	Year round, though births peak in the rainy seasons
GESTATION PERIOD	165 days
NUMBER OF YOUNG	1
BIRTH INTERVAL	At least 2 years
TYPICAL DIET	Fruit, leaves, seeds,grasses; invertebrates and small-reptiles
LIFESPAN	Female up to 9 years; male not known

TAIL
The characteristic tuft on the tail-tip gives this species its name.

TEETH
At the front of the jaws, long canines and sharp incisors are useful tools for opening timber to expose grubs. Ridged molars (cheek teeth) crush leaves and fruit.

COAT
The overall black coat is set off by a luxuriant, grey-brown facial mane that extends down the chest to the belly, distinguishing this species from others.

NEWBORN
The baby's face and digits are covered in short, pinkish hair. Its soft, distinctive coat is replaced after two months, and the face tufts develop with maturity.

HANDS
Thick pads and an opposable thumb enhance the macaque's grip on branches.

CREATURE COMPARISONS

Like the lion-tailed macaque, the pig-tailed macaque (Macata nemestrina) lives in wet evergreen forest. It has a far wider distribution, however, occurring from eastern India to Indonesia. Its coat features varying shades of brown, with a paler underbelly and dark brown facial patches. Although the adult pig-tailed macaque has impressively whiskered cheeks, it cannot compete with its cousin's magnificent mane. Weighing more than 15kg (33.1lb), the pig-tailed macaque is slightly heavier than the lion-tailed macaque and is slightly less arboreal in habit. When disturbed, it usually takes refuge on the forest floor instead of fleeing through the trees.

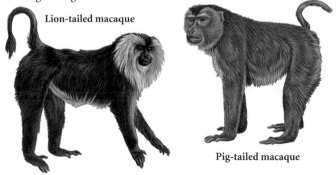

Lion-tailed macaque

Pig-tailed macaque

WHERE IN THE WORLD?

Confined to tiny, isolated pockets in upland evergreen tropical forests of the Western Ghats, the mountain range that borders the western coast of India.

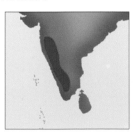

RELATED SPECIES

The lion-tailed macaque belongs to the genus Macaca, which contains 16 species including the Celebes ape, Macaca nigra, of northeastern Sulawesi in Indonesia.

• **ORDER** • *Primates* • **FAMILY** • *Cercopithecidae* • **GENUS & SPECIES** • *Macaca sylvanus*

BARBARY APE

Powerful limbs, gripping hands and naked palms and soles mean that the Barbary ape is just as comfortable in the trees as on the ground.

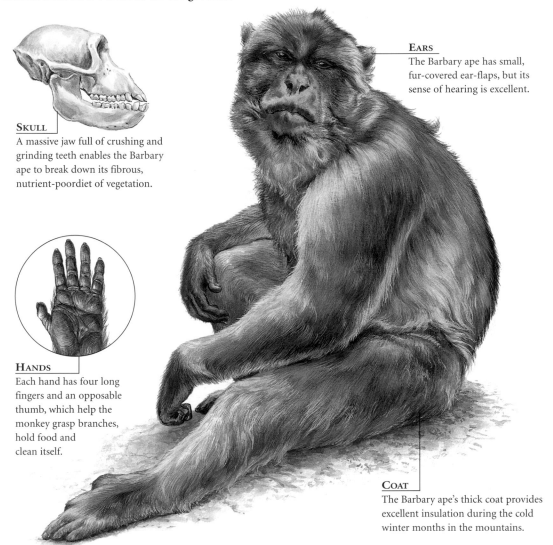

SKULL
A massive jaw full of crushing and grinding teeth enables the Barbary ape to break down its fibrous, nutrient-poordiet of vegetation.

HANDS
Each hand has four long fingers and an opposable thumb, which help the monkey grasp branches, hold food and clean itself.

EARS
The Barbary ape has small, fur-covered ear-flaps, but its sense of hearing is excellent.

COAT
The Barbary ape's thick coat provides excellent insulation during the cold winter months in the mountains.

KEY FEATURES

- The only African primate to occur north of the Sahara, and the only species of monkey whose home range includes part of Europe.
- A resourceful and robust creature able to eke out a living on snow-covered mountains.
- Lives in large, social 'troops' in which newborns are used by males as 'buffers' to keep the peace.

VITAL STATISTICS

WEIGHT	Male 7–15kg (15.4–33.1lb); female 4–7kg (8.8–15.4lb)
LENGTH	Male 65–75cm (25.6–29.5in); female 50–65cm (19.7–25.6in)
SHOULDER HEIGHT	Male 50cm (19.7in); female 45cm (17.7in)
SEXUAL MATURITY	3–4 years
MATING SEASON	Year-round, peaks November to March
GESTATION PERIOD	210 days
NUMBER OF YOUNG	1, rarely twins
BIRTH INTERVAL	1 year
TYPICAL DIET	Mainly fruit, leaves, seeds, roots, grasses; occasionally invertebrates
LIFESPAN	20 years

CREATURE COMPARISONS

Although members of the same genus, the Barbary ape and southern India's extremely rare liontail macaque (Macaca silenus) are very different in appearance. While the Barbary ape has a neutral yellowish-brown coat, the liontail stands out with its shiny, black-brown coat and large, lion-like 'mane' and tasselled tail.

Unlike the Barbary ape, which spends most of its time on the ground, the liontail macaque is almost entirely arboreal and rarely descends from the trees. Its diet is also more restricted than that of its African relative, as it feeds almost entirely on fruit.

Barbary ape

Liontail macaque

WHERE IN THE WORLD?

Found in northwest Africa across Morocco and Algeria. A small but famous population also lives on the Rock of Gibraltar — a tiny British colony in southern Spain.

RELATED SPECIES

The Barbary ape is 1 of 16 species of macaque in the genus Macaca. The other 15 live exclusively in Asia, and include the Celebes ape, M. nigra, found in the forests of northeastern Sulawesi. All macaques belong to the Old World monkey family, Cercopithecidae.

• ORDER • *Primates* • FAMILY • *Cercopithecidae* • GENUS & SPECIES • *Mandrillus sphinx*

MANDRILL

One of the most striking of all primates, the mandrill uses the vivid hues of its skin as an extra 'language' to express social status and emotions.

KEY FEATURES

- Receptive female develops large, red genital swellings to attract a mate.
- Male possesses bright blue and scarlet ridges on the nasal bones, mimicking the colours of his genitalia.
- When aroused, buttock skin becomes reddish-purple; this is believed to attract a mate.

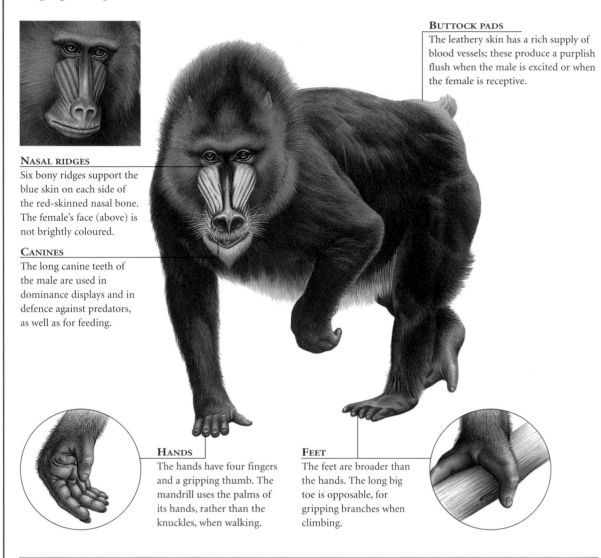

BUTTOCK PADS
The leathery skin has a rich supply of blood vessels; these produce a purplish flush when the male is excited or when the female is receptive.

NASAL RIDGES
Six bony ridges support the blue skin on each side of the red-skinned nasal bone. The female's face (above) is not brightly coloured.

CANINES
The long canine teeth of the male are used in dominance displays and in defence against predators, as well as for feeding.

HANDS
The hands have four fingers and a gripping thumb. The mandrill uses the palms of its hands, rather than the knuckles, when walking.

FEET
The feet are broader than the hands. The long big toe is opposable, for gripping branches when climbing.

VITAL STATISTICS

WEIGHT	Male 25–54kg (; female 8–11kg (17.6–24.2lb)
LENGTH	61–84cm (24–33.1in)
SHOULDER HEIGHT	51cm (20.1in)
SEXUAL MATURITY	Male 6–7 years; female 3.5 years
MATING SEASON	September to December
GESTATION PERIOD	168–176 days
NUMBER OF YOUNG	1
BIRTH INTERVAL	2–3 years
TYPICAL DIET	Fruit and other plant matter; invertebrates; small mammals, reptiles, birds and their eggs
LIFESPAN	Up to 40 years

CREATURE COMPARISONS

The mandrill's relatives include the olive and gelada baboons. Neither species possesses the bony ridges on the nasal bones, and although the gelada has a slight crest, this is less pronounced than that of the male mandrill. The gelada does, however, have a bare red patch on its chest, reminiscent of the mandrill's colourful buttocks. The olive and gelada baboons both live in ordered groups, but they inhabit open savannah, rather than the forest habitat of the mandrill. The gelada differs from all other baboons in having nostrils that open to the sides of the nose instead of to the front.

Mandrill

Olive baboon

Gelada baboon

WHERE IN THE WORLD?

Found only in tropical, closed-canopy rainforests in central Africa: from the banks of the Sanaga River in Cameroon, south to Equatorial Guinea, Gabon and Congo.

RELATED SPECIES

The mandrill's closest relative is the drill, *Mandrillus leucophaeus*, which is found in the forests north of the Sanaga River in Cameroon and south of the Cross River in Nigeria. The drill's range is much more restricted than that of the mandrill, and it is much rarer, with perhaps fewer than 5000 remaining in the wild. Also related to the mandrill are the five species of baboon, genus Papio, which are widespread throughout Africa.

PROBOSCIS MONKEY

• ORDER • *Primates* • FAMILY • *Cercopithecidae* • GENUS & SPECIES • *Nasalis larvatus*

The proboscis monkey exploits every level of the mangrove forest, making spectacular leaps high in the trees and descending to swim in the water below.

KEY FEATURES

- The adult male's extravagantly long, tongue-shaped nose attracts females during the breeding season.
- An outstanding swimmer, the proboscis monkey can also dive underwater with ease and even jump into the water from great heights.
- Spends much of the day feeding on abundant, but nutritionally poor, mangrove vegetation.

VITAL STATISTICS

WEIGHT	Male 16–23kg (35.3–lb); female 7–11kg (15.4–24.2lb)
LENGTH	Head & Body: Male 66–76cm (26–29.9in); female 53–61cm (20.9–24in) Tail: 62–75cm (24.4–29.5in)
SEXUAL MATURITY	4–5 years
MATING SEASON	All year
GESTATION PERIOD	166 days
NUMBER OF YOUNG	1
BIRTH INTERVAL	1 year
TYPICAL DIET	Leaves and shoots of mangrove and pedada trees; some other fruit and flowers
LIFESPAN	About 20 years

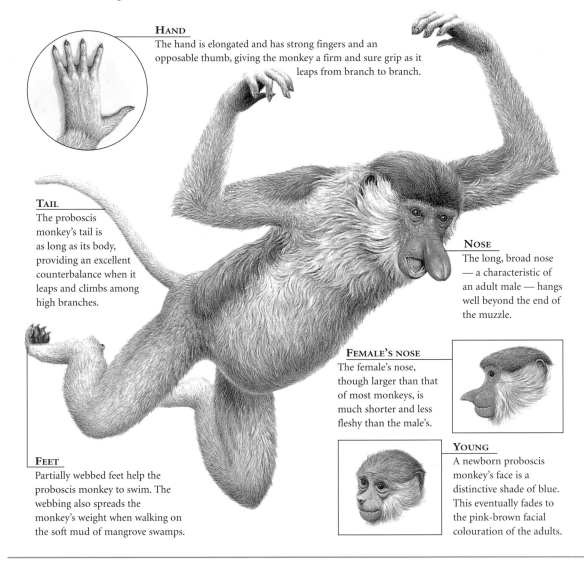

HAND
The hand is elongated and has strong fingers and an opposable thumb, giving the monkey a firm and sure grip as it leaps from branch to branch.

TAIL
The proboscis monkey's tail is as long as its body, providing an excellent counterbalance when it leaps and climbs among high branches.

FEET
Partially webbed feet help the proboscis monkey to swim. The webbing also spreads the monkey's weight when walking on the soft mud of mangrove swamps.

NOSE
The long, broad nose — a characteristic of an adult male — hangs well beyond the end of the muzzle.

FEMALE'S NOSE
The female's nose, though larger than that of most monkeys, is much shorter and less fleshy than the male's.

YOUNG
A newborn proboscis monkey's face is a distinctive shade of blue. This eventually fades to the pink-brown facial colouration of the adults.

CREATURE COMPARISONS

The golden snub-nosed monkey (Pygathrix roxellanae), like the proboscis monkey, is also named after its distinctive nose, which is small, flat and hardly protrudes from its rounded face. Its nostrils point straight forward rather than downwards as in the proboscis monkey.

There are five species of snub-nosed monkey but very little is known about them as they live in very remote habitats: the golden snub-nosed monkey is believed to inhabit the upper canopy of mountain forests in Tibet, northern India and southern China.

Golden snub-nosed monkey

Proboscis monkey

WHERE IN THE WORLD?

Confined to the mangrove swamps and rainforests in the coastal lowlands of Borneo, one of the largest Indonesian islands. It is now absent from many areas where it was once common, due to habitat destruction.

RELATED SPECIES

The proboscis monkey belongs to the family Cercopithecidae, which contains 19 genera and nearly 100 species, including baboons, the drill and mandrill, and langurs, or leaf monkeys. The leaf monkeys take their name from their diet, which consists almost exclusively of leaves and seeds. There are eight species of leaf monkey and four species are found in Borneo in the same habitat as the proboscis monkey.

• **ORDER** • *Primates* • **FAMILY** • *Cercopithecidae* • **GENUS & SPECIES** • *Papio hamadryas*

HAMADRYAS BABOON

Growing to twice the weight of the female, the male hamadryas baboon is an impressive creature adorned with a spectacular mane: his badge of authority.

KEY FEATURES

- A powerful monkey that lives on the ground in barren habitats.
- Its complex societies are based upon clans of related males, each of which has his own harem of females and young.
- The male's canines serve only to establish his dominance in the clan.
- At night, baboons join clans to sleep together in hundreds-strong troops.

VITAL STATISTICS

WEIGHT	Male 15–20kg (33.1–44lb); female 10–15kg (22–33.1lb)
LENGTH	Head & Body: Male 70–95cm (27.6–37.4in); female 50–65cm (19.7–25.6in) Tail: 37–60cm (14.6–23.6in)
SHOULDER HEIGHT	40–65cm (15.7–25.6in)
SEXUAL MATURITY	5–7 years
MATING SEASON	All year
GESTATION PERIOD	170–173 days
NUMBER OF YOUNG	1
BIRTH INTERVAL	About 2 years
TYPICAL DIET	Grass seeds, roots, bulbs, fruits and insects; rarely small animals
LIFESPAN	35 years

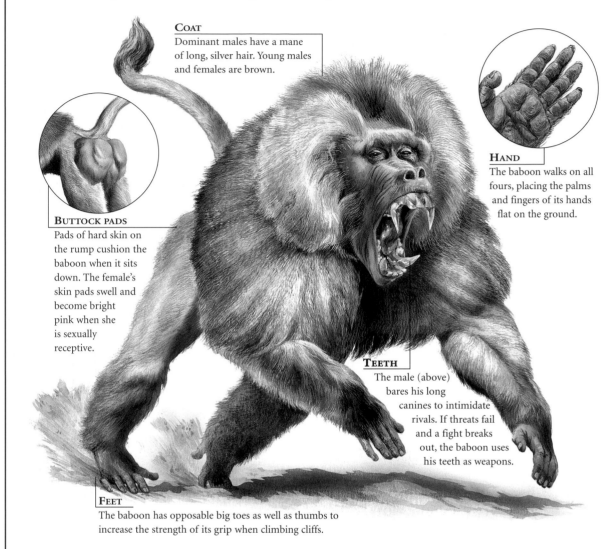

COAT
Dominant males have a mane of long, silver hair. Young males and females are brown.

HAND
The baboon walks on all fours, placing the palms and fingers of its hands flat on the ground.

BUTTOCK PADS
Pads of hard skin on the rump cushion the baboon when it sits down. The female's skin pads swell and become bright pink when she is sexually receptive.

TEETH
The male (above) bares his long canines to intimidate rivals. If threats fail and a fight breaks out, the baboon uses his teeth as weapons.

FEET
The baboon has opposable big toes as well as thumbs to increase the strength of its grip when climbing cliffs.

CREATURE COMPARISONS

The relationship between the various members of the baboon family is highly complex, and scientists disagree over how many species exist. The olive baboon (Papio cynocephalus) is found in much of East Africa, and its range overlaps with that of the hamadryas baboon in Ethiopia.

The two baboons are genetically similar, so it is not surprising that they interbreed, producing hybrid offspring with characteristics from both species.

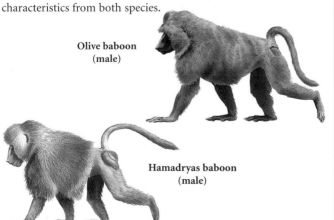

Olive baboon (male)

Hamadryas baboon (male)

WHERE IN THE WORLD?

Found in the arid lands of the Horn of Africa, in parts of Ethiopia, Eritrea, Sudan and Somalia, and across the Red Sea in the highlands of southwestern Saudi Arabia, Yemen and South Yemen.

RELATED SPECIES

Most biologists consider there to be 6 species of baboon: the hamadryas, olive, chacma and western baboons, the mandrill and the drill. The baboons are members of the subfamily Cercopithecinae, or 'typical monkeys', together with the mangabeys, macaques and guenons. The gelada baboon, another cercopithecine, is placed on its own in the genus Theropithecus; it is probably the ancestor of all modern baboons, but is not itself a true baboon.

DOUC LANGUR

• **ORDER** • *Primates* • **FAMILY** • *Cercopithecidae* • **GENUS & SPECIES** • *Pygathrix nemaeus & P. nigripes*

KEY FEATURES

- Among the most sumptuously coloured of all primate species, with almond-shaped eyes and powder-blue eyelids.
- The two species can be differentiated from each other by the colour of their lower limbs: one has chestnut-red fur, the other black fur.
- Both species are classified as endangered by the IUCN (World Conservation Union).

VITAL STATISTICS

WEIGHT	8–11kg (17.6–24.2lb)
LENGTH	Head & Body: 55–70cm (21.6–27.6in) Tail: 56–76cm (22–29.9in)
SEXUAL MATURITY	4–5 years
MATING SEASON	Year round
GESTATION PERIOD	165–190 days
NUMBER OF YOUNG	1
BIRTH INTERVAL	16 months
TYPICAL DIET	Leaves, fruit, buds, seeds and flowers
LIFESPAN	Up to 30 years

Unmistakable in its multicoloured livery, the douc langur swings deftly from branch to branch, aided by its long arms and counterbalancing tail.

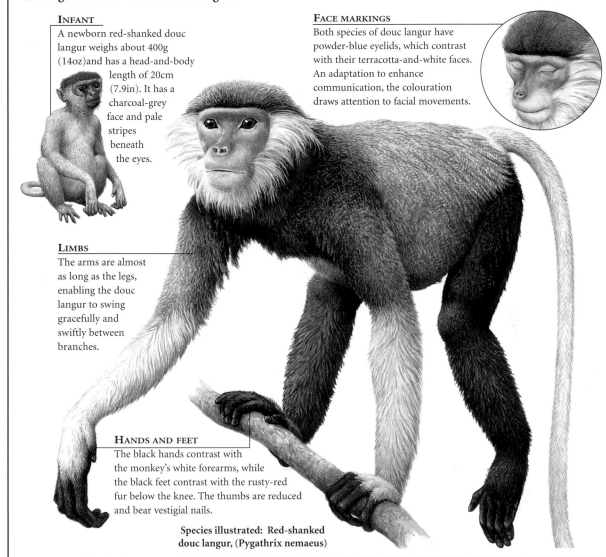

INFANT
A newborn red-shanked douc langur weighs about 400g (14oz) and has a head-and-body length of 20cm (7.9in). It has a charcoal-grey face and pale stripes beneath the eyes.

FACE MARKINGS
Both species of douc langur have powder-blue eyelids, which contrast with their terracotta-and-white faces. An adaptation to enhance communication, the colouration draws attention to facial movements.

LIMBS
The arms are almost as long as the legs, enabling the douc langur to swing gracefully and swiftly between branches.

HANDS AND FEET
The black hands contrast with the monkey's white forearms, while the black feet contrast with the rusty-red fur below the knee. The thumbs are reduced and bear vestigial nails.

Species illustrated: Red-shanked douc langur, (*Pygathrix nemaeus*)

CREATURE COMPARISONS

The golden snub-nosed monkey (Rhinopithecus roxellana) is a close relative of the douc langur, and has even been placed in the same genus, Pygathrix, by some experts. It lives in mountainous regions on the southeastern slopes of the Tibetian plateau. It favours mixed bamboo, conifer and deciduous forest at altitudes of 2000–3000m (6562–9843ft). It is bulkier than the douc langur, weighing up to 39kg (86lb). Consequently, the snub-nosed monkey is too heavy to travel along the thinnest branches, and spends more time in lower levels of the forest.

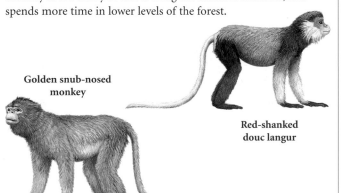

Golden snub-nosed monkey

Red-shanked douc langur

WHERE IN THE WORLD?

Found in Southeast Asia, in a handful of rainforest areas scattered across eastern Cambodia, Laos and Vietnam.

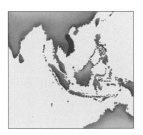

RELATED SPECIES

There are 2 species of douc langur: the black-shanked douc, Pygathrix nigripes, and the red-shanked, P. nemaeus. The silvered langur, Trachypithecus cristatus, is a close relative of the douc langurs.

• **ORDER** • *Primates* • **FAMILY** • *Cercopithecidae* • **GENUS & SPECIES** • *Semnopithecus entellus*

HANUMAN LANGUR

KEY FEATURES

- Lives in close-knit family groups; dominant male regularly replaced by challenger who then may kill some or all of his predecessor's young.
- Very widespread but threatened everywhere by habitat loss; listed as endangered by the IUCN (World Conservation Union).

VITAL STATISTICS

WEIGHT	5–24kg (11–52.9lb); male much heavier than female
LENGTH	Head & Body: 41–78cm (16.1–30.7in) Tail: 69–108cm (27.2–42.5in)
SEXUAL MATURITY	Male 5–7 years; female 3–4 years
MATING SEASON	Throughout the year
GESTATION PERIOD	200 days
NUMBER OF YOUNG	1, rarely 2
BIRTH INTERVAL	16 months
TYPICAL DIET	Leaves, buds, flowers, seeds, fungi, pith, roots, gum, sap; insects
LIFESPAN	Up to 20 years in the wild; 25 years in captivity

The Hanuman langur has the form and physique of an arboreal primate but spends most of its time on the ground, loping along in a stately manner.

YOUNG
The newborn has a dark coat, which soon pales to the silvery-brown adult colouration.

TAIL
The long tail has a tuft at the tip. The langur often curls its tail over its back when on the ground.

TEETH
The molars (cheek teeth) have pointed cusps. The langur has thick enamel on the inside of its lower incisors, and long canines that the male bares in rivalry fights.

FEET
Strong toes enable the langur to grasp trunks and spring between branches, but they are short enough to allow it to walk easily on flat ground.

HANDS
The black hands have naked palms, long fingers and short thumbs. The langur walks on all four limbs.

CREATURE COMPARISONS

The grizzled leaf monkey (Presbytis comata), or grizzled sureli, is one of the Hanuman langur's closer relatives. It lives in the mountain forests of Java in Indonesia. The grizzled sureli is smaller than the Hanuman langur, reaching a weight of 7kg (15.4lb), and has a shorter tail in proportion to its body. Its grey coat sports a handsome white underbelly.

Living in highly cohesive groups of up to 12 individuals, the grizzled sureli spends more time in the trees than does the Hanuman langur. It prefers the middle and upper layers of the canopy, and troops sleep at least 20m (66ftft) above the ground.

Hanuman langur

Grizzled sureli

WHERE IN THE WORLD?

Found throughout the Indian subcontinent and Sri Lanka, and north into the Himalayas of Pakistan, Bhutan, Burma (Myanmar) and Bangladesh.

RELATED SPECIES

The Hanuman langur is the sole member of its genus Semnopithecus, 1 of 19 in the family Cercopithecidae, or Old World monkeys. Some authorities have placed the Hanuman langur in the genus Presbytis, which includes 8 species of leaf monkey found in Indonesia. They are smaller than the Hanuman langur and lack prominent brow ridges. Old World monkeys occur in Africa, Asia, Japan and the Malay Archipelago.

• ORDER • *Primates* • FAMILY • *Cercopithecidae* • GENUS & SPECIES • *Theropithecus gelada*

GELADA BABOON

The gelada is unique among monkeys in having bright scarlet skin-patches on the throat and chest. However, their function is not properly understood.

KEY FEATURES

- Blood-red patches of naked skin on the throat and chest single out this baboon from its relatives.
- An excellent rock climber, the gelada baboon spends no time in trees.
- Uniquely for a primate, grasses make up around 95 per cent of its diet.
- Bands of geladas are often several hundred strong: among the largest formed by any primate.

VITAL STATISTICS

WEIGHT	Male 20kg (44lb); female 14kg (30.9lb)
LENGTH	Head & Body: 50–74cm (19.7–29.1in) Tail: 32–50cm (12.6–19.7in)
SEXUAL MATURITY	Male 8 years; female 3 years
MATING SEASON	February to April
GESTATION PERIOD	6 months
NUMBER OF YOUNG	1 or 2
BIRTH INTERVAL	1 year
TYPICAL DIET	Mainly grasses; some leaves, roots and seeds
LIFESPAN	20 years or more

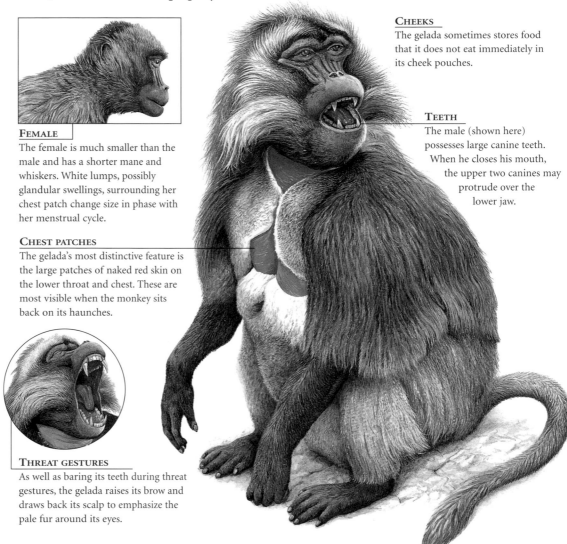

FEMALE
The female is much smaller than the male and has a shorter mane and whiskers. White lumps, possibly glandular swellings, surrounding her chest patch change size in phase with her menstrual cycle.

CHEST PATCHES
The gelada's most distinctive feature is the large patches of naked red skin on the lower throat and chest. These are most visible when the monkey sits back on its haunches.

THREAT GESTURES
As well as baring its teeth during threat gestures, the gelada raises its brow and draws back its scalp to emphasize the pale fur around its eyes.

CHEEKS
The gelada sometimes stores food that it does not eat immediately in its cheek pouches.

TEETH
The male (shown here) possesses large canine teeth. When he closes his mouth, the upper two canines may protrude over the lower jaw.

CREATURE COMPARISONS

In some central Ethiopian valleys the gelada feeds alongside a distant relative: the Hamadryas baboon (Papio hamadryas). Although they are similar in build, the two species are easily distinguished. Hamadryas baboons have paler, silvery hair and red faces, and their nostrils open much lower down on the snout. Both species have buttock pads, but those of the Hamadryas baboon are an eye-catching red, while those of the gelada baboon are a sombre black.

Hamadryas baboon

Gelada baboon

WHERE IN THE WORLD?

Occurs only in or near the deep, rocky gorges that cut through the central plateau of the Ethiopian highlands. Confined to the provinces of Shewa, Begemdir, Tigre and Wolo.

RELATED SPECIES

The gelada is the sole surviving representative of its genus — one of 14 within the Cercopithecidae family of Old World monkeys. Its closest living relatives are the several other species of baboon found across sub-Saharan Africa, of which the drill and mandrill are the largest.

• **ORDER** • *Primates* • **FAMILY** • *Daubentoniidae* • **GENUS & SPECIES** • *Daubentonia madagascariensis*

AYE-AYE

KEY FEATURES

- A bizarre relative of the lemurs; like them, it is found only on the island of Madagascar.
- Uses its extraordinary middle finger to winkle insect larvae from the bark of dead or decaying wood.
- Persecuted by local people, and listed as endangered by the IUCN (World Conservation Union).

VITAL STATISTICS

WEIGHT	About 2kg (4.4lb)
LENGTH	Head & Body: 36–44cm (14.2–17.3in) Tail: 50–60cm (19.7–23.6in)
SEXUAL MATURITY	2 years
MATING SEASON	Throughout the year
GESTATION PERIOD	160 days
NUMBER OF YOUNG	Usually 1
BIRTH INTERVAL	2–3 years
TYPICAL DIET	Insect larvae and fruit
LIFESPAN	Up to 26 years in captivity

Navigating the branches with the help of its excellent eyesight, the aye-aye forages at night, when its dark coat helps conceal it from predators.

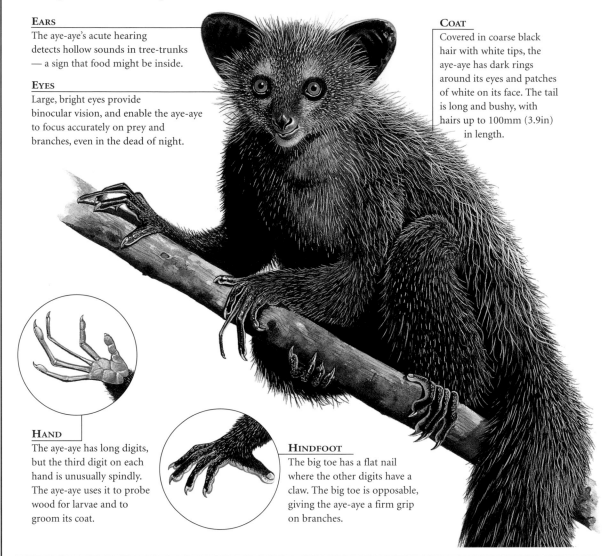

EARS
The aye-aye's acute hearing detects hollow sounds in tree-trunks — a sign that food might be inside.

EYES
Large, bright eyes provide binocular vision, and enable the aye-aye to focus accurately on prey and branches, even in the dead of night.

COAT
Covered in coarse black hair with white tips, the aye-aye has dark rings around its eyes and patches of white on its face. The tail is long and bushy, with hairs up to 100mm (3.9in) in length.

HAND
The aye-aye has long digits, but the third digit on each hand is unusually spindly. The aye-aye uses it to probe wood for larvae and to groom its coat.

HINDFOOT
The big toe has a flat nail where the other digits have a claw. The big toe is opposable, giving the aye-aye a firm grip on branches.

CREATURE COMPARISONS

The greater dwarf lemur (Cheirogaleus major) is found in the rainforests and dry forests of Madagascar. Smaller than the aye-aye, this lemur has a sand-coloured coat with dark rings around its eyes. Both primates have a fleshy nose, but the lemur has smaller ears and a less bushy tail. Like the aye-aye, the dwarf lemur eats insects and fruits, but it extends its diet to include young leaves and flowers. Although the dwarf lemur stores fat in its tail to help it through lean times, it must become dormant between the dry-season months of April to September, when fruit becomes scarce.

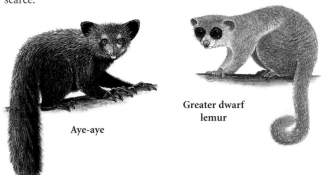

Greater dwarf lemur

Aye-aye

WHERE IN THE WORLD?

Found in the eastern forests of Madagascar, which is the world's fourth-largest island and is located off the East African coast in the Indian Ocean.

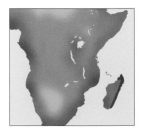

RELATED SPECIES

The aye-aye is the sole member of the family Daubentoniidae. It belongs to the order Primates, which includes 181 species, but more specifically it is a member of the suborder Prosimii. This means 'before apes': Prosimians are said to be less highly evolved than other primates. The suborder contains 35 species in 6 families, including the bushbabies, lemurs, tarsiers, dwarf and mouse lemurs, indris and sifakas, pottos and lorises.

• ORDER • *Primates* • FAMILY • *Hylobatidae* • GENUS & SPECIES • *Hylobates lar*

LAR GIBBON

KEY FEATURES

- One of the most acrobatic and fast-moving of all the primates — it virtually flies from tree to tree in its forest home.
- Feisty and fiercely territorial, family groups chase away rivals from feeding areas with much howling and screaming.
- Male and female couples perform duets each morning to advertise their territory and reinforce their pair-bond.

VITAL STATISTICS

WEIGHT	5–8kg (11–17.6lb)
LENGTH	45–63cm (17.7–24.8in)
SEXUAL MATURITY	8–9 years
MATING SEASON	All year
GESTATION PERIOD	210–230 days
NUMBER OF YOUNG	1, rarely twins
BIRTH INTERVAL	2–2.5 years
TYPICAL DIET	Mainly fruit; also other plant matter, insects and some small vertebrates
LIFESPAN	25 years or more

A master of its aerial world, the lar gibbon swings through the trees at great speed, covering up to 9m (29ft 5in) with each flying leap.

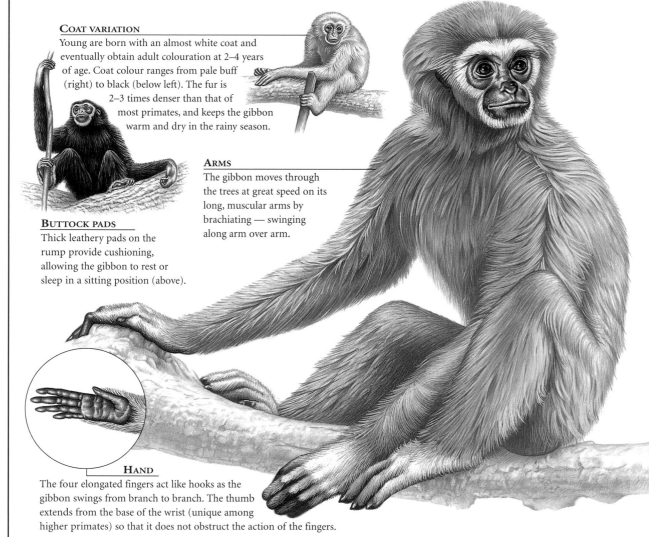

COAT VARIATION
Young are born with an almost white coat and eventually obtain adult colouration at 2–4 years of age. Coat colour ranges from pale buff (right) to black (below left). The fur is 2–3 times denser than that of most primates, and keeps the gibbon warm and dry in the rainy season.

ARMS
The gibbon moves through the trees at great speed on its long, muscular arms by brachiating — swinging along arm over arm.

BUTTOCK PADS
Thick leathery pads on the rump provide cushioning, allowing the gibbon to rest or sleep in a sitting position (above).

HAND
The four elongated fingers act like hooks as the gibbon swings from branch to branch. The thumb extends from the base of the wrist (unique among higher primates) so that it does not obstruct the action of the fingers.

CREATURE COMPARISONS

Species of gibbon are most easily told apart by their head shape. The lar gibbon, for example, has a very rounded head, while that of the crested gibbon, H. concolor, is more pointed. The silvery gibbon, H. moloch, has a distinctive, dark-brown cap. Male and female silvery gibbons are blue-grey, while male crested gibbons are black and the females are golden or grey-brown.

These three species are confined to Southeast Asia, but do not share the same range. The silvery gibbon is only found in Java, while the crested gibbon occurs in southeastern China, Laos, Vietnam and eastern Cambodia.

Lar gibbon

Crested gibbon

Silvery gibbon

WHERE IN THE WORLD?

Ranges from northern parts of the island of Sumatra, through the Malay Peninsula, Thailand and parts of Burma

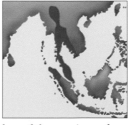

(Myanmar) to the borders of the province of Yunnan in southwestern China.

RELATED SPECIES
The lar gibbon is one of 9 species of gibbon, or 'lesser apes', in the genus Hylobates. All species, such as the grey gibbon, H. muelleri, are found in Southeast Asia. Their closest relatives are the 'great apes' of the family Pongidae, most of which are found in Africa.

• **ORDER** • *Primates* • **FAMILY** • *Hylobatidae* • **GENUS & SPECIES** • *Hylobates syndactylus*

SIAMANG GIBBON

KEY FEATURES

- Like other gibbons, swings its long arms rhythmically to move hand-over-hand through the forest canopy.

- Mates for life and both parents rear their offspring, who take up to three years to become fully independent.

- Male and female sing duets at the top of their voices to defend their territory and strengthen the pair-bond.

VITAL STATISTICS

WEIGHT	Male 12–14kg (26.5–30.9lb); female 10–11kg (22–24.2lb)
LENGTH	75–90cm (29.5–35.4in)
SEXUAL MATURITY	8–9 years
MATING SEASON	All year
NUMBER OF YOUNG	1
GESTATION PERIOD	190–240 days
BIRTH INTERVAL	2–3 years
TYPICAL DIET	Leaves, fruit, flowers and some insects
LIFESPAN	25–30 years

Tremendously strong arms and a lean, athletic torso help the siamang swing gracefully between the branches.

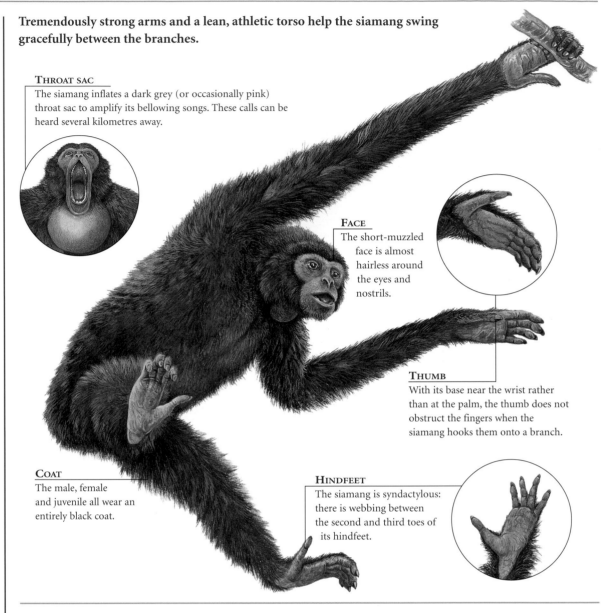

THROAT SAC
The siamang inflates a dark grey (or occasionally pink) throat sac to amplify its bellowing songs. These calls can be heard several kilometres away.

FACE
The short-muzzled face is almost hairless around the eyes and nostrils.

THUMB
With its base near the wrist rather than at the palm, the thumb does not obstruct the fingers when the siamang hooks them onto a branch.

COAT
The male, female and juvenile all wear an entirely black coat.

HINDFEET
The siamang is syndactylous: there is webbing between the second and third toes of its hindfeet.

CREATURE COMPARISONS

The siamang is the largest species of gibbon, weighing twice as much as one of the smallest and rarest species, the Kloss's gibbon (*Hylobates klossii*), which lives on the Mentawai Islands off western Sumatra. As in the siamang, the male and female Kloss's gibbon are black overall. The two species differ markedly in their vocal behaviour: Kloss's pairs do not sing duets. The male begins with a solo performance of pure notes and dramatic trills before dawn. Then, about an hour after sunrise, his mate sings her own rousing refrain.

In both species, the adults are caring and devoted parents: adult Kloss's gibbons even help their young secure a territory of their own.

Siamang gibbon

Kloss's gibbon

WHERE IN THE WORLD?

Found in lowland forests south of the Perak River on the Malay Peninsula, and across the Barisan Mountains on the Indonesian island of Sumatra.

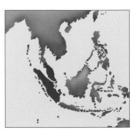

RELATED SPECIES

The siamang is 1 of 9 gibbon species in the family Hylobatidae, including the lar or white-handed gibbon, Hylobates lar. Gibbons are known as lesser apes, linking them with the other Old World tailless primates: the great apes (the chimpanzee, bonobo, orang-utan and gorillas).

INDRI

As big as a gibbon, and almost as agile, the powerful indri is well designed for a life spent jumping from tree to tree.

KEY FEATURES

- Largest of Madagascar's lemur species.
- Leaps through the rainforest, feeding on vegetation.
- Lives in a family unit that sings loudly and often to reinforce pair-bonds and defend its territory.
- Threatened by habitat loss; classified as endangered by the IUCN (World Conservation Union).

VITAL STATISTICS

WEIGHT	7–10kg (15.4–22lb)
LENGTH	Head & Body: 61–90cm (24–35.4in) Tail: 5–6.4cm (2–2.5in)
SEXUAL MATURITY	3 years, but first breeds at 7–9 years
MATING SEASON	January and February
GESTATION PERIOD	120–150 days
NUMBER OF YOUNG	1
BIRTH INTERVAL	2–3 years
TYPICAL DIET	Leaves, fruit and flowers; occasionally bark and soil
LIFESPAN	Unknown

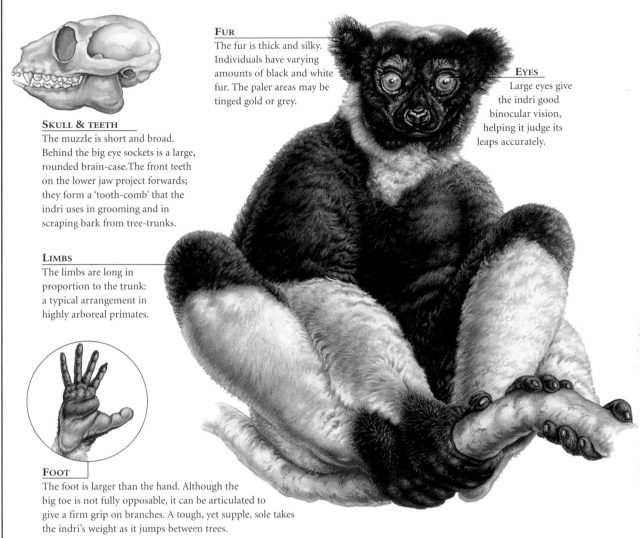

SKULL & TEETH
The muzzle is short and broad. Behind the big eye sockets is a large, rounded brain-case. The front teeth on the lower jaw project forwards; they form a 'tooth-comb' that the indri uses in grooming and in scraping bark from tree-trunks.

FUR
The fur is thick and silky. Individuals have varying amounts of black and white fur. The paler areas may be tinged gold or grey.

EYES
Large eyes give the indri good binocular vision, helping it judge its leaps accurately.

LIMBS
The limbs are long in proportion to the trunk: a typical arrangement in highly arboreal primates.

FOOT
The foot is larger than the hand. Although the big toe is not fully opposable, it can be articulated to give a firm grip on branches. A tough, yet supple, sole takes the indri's weight as it jumps between trees.

CREATURE COMPARISONS

The avahi, or woolly lemur (Avahi laniger), is a close relative of the indri and shares many of its characteristics. Like the indri, the avahi is confined to Madagascar's rainforests, although it has a wider range along the island's eastern coast and also occurs in the northwest. It, too, is endangered by habitat loss.

Both animals spend most of their time in the trees foraging for buds and leaves. The avahi lives in small groups of up to four individuals and uses various vocalizations to communicate, as does its relative. But unlike the indri, the avahi is nocturnal and spends the daylight hours asleep in hollow trees or among thick vegetation. By feeding at night, the avahi avoids direct competition with the larger indri.

Avahi

Indri

WHERE IN THE WORLD?

Found only in the coastal and montane rainforest of northeastern Madagascar from sea level to altitudes of about 1500m (4921ft). Now restricted to protected rainforest reserves and national parks.

RELATED SPECIES

The indri is a primate closely related to lorises, pottos and tarsiers. The family Indriidae, to which it belongs, contains 3 genera and 12 species of lemur, including Verreaux's sifaka, Propithecus verreauxi. The indri is the only member of its genus.

• **ORDER** • *Primates* • **FAMILY** • *Lemuridae* • **GENUS & SPECIES** • *Eulemur mongoz*

MONGOOSE LEMUR

The mongoose lemur's lightweight build, long tail and sure grip enable it to move freely in the forest canopy of Madagascar.

TAIL
Long and bushy, the tail acts as a balancing aid when the lemur is moving through the trees at speed.

TEETH
The lemur's molar (grinding) teeth are ideal for pulping soft fruit.

FACE
The male has a white snout and his face is framed by red fur; the female has a darker face framed by white fur.

COAT
Both sexes have a greyish-brown coat overall, but the male's is slightly darker and the female has a browner back. The underparts are pale brown to white.

HAND
Each hand has raised, fleshy pads to provide a firm grip on branches.

KEY FEATURES

- Moves nimbly through the forest canopy, eating leaves, flowers and fruit from the branches.
- Lives in a small family group that stays within its own patch of forest.
- Survival is threatened by forest clearance, which is occurring throughout its island home of Madagascar. Listed on CITES (Convention on International Trade in Endangered Species).

VITAL STATISTICS

WEIGHT	2–2.5kg (4.4–5.5lb)
LENGTH	Head & Body: 35–45cm (13.8–17.7in) Tail: 45–50cm (17.7–19.7in)
SEXUAL MATURITY	18 months
MATING SEASON	April to June
GESTATION PERIOD	114–128 days
NUMBER OF YOUNG	1 (sometimes twins)
BIRTH INTERVAL	1 year
TYPICAL DIET	Leaves, fruit and flowers
LIFESPAN	20 years or more

CREATURE COMPARISONS

The hairy-eared dwarf lemur (Allocebus trichotis) is extremely rare. One of the very few specimens ever to be captured came from the forests of eastern Madagascar and had a head-and-body length of just 13cm (5.1in) with a 17cm- (6.7in)-long tail. This diminutive lemur shares with its larger relative a similar greyish-brown coat colour but has distinctive tufts of long hair around its ears and a reddish-brown tail. Since both these lemurs are tree-dwellers, they have well developed hindlimbs and strong hands for climbing. Like the mongoose lemur, the hairy-eared dwarf lemur's dependence on trees means that its future is inextricably linked to the survival of its forest habitat.

Hairy-eared dwarf lemur

Mongoose lemur

WHERE IN THE WORLD?

Found in forested areas in the northwestern part of Madagascar. Populations also occur on two islands, Moheli and Anjouan, in the Comoros Islands group, which lies between Madagascar and the African mainland.

RELATED SPECIES

The lemur superfamily, Lemuroidea, has 5 families, including the Lemuridae, or true lemurs. This family contains 12 species in 5 genera and includes the mongoose lemur. Also within the superfamily of lemurs is the extremely rare aye-aye, Daubentonia madagascariensis.

• ORDER • *Primates* • FAMILY • *Lemuridae* • GENUS & SPECIES • *Lemur catta*

RING-TAILED LEMUR

The ring-tailed lemur has a complex social life, which is reflected in its physical adaptations, notably its nose, teeth and scent glands.

KEY FEATURES

- Unlike most lemurs, which live mainly in trees, it spends a great deal of time running around on the ground.
- Lives in mixed-sex social groups of up to 20 individuals, in which the females are dominant over the males.
- The long, barred tail serves as a warning 'flag' and as a scent dispenser in confrontations between territorial males.

VITAL STATISTICS

WEIGHT	2.3–3.5kg (5–7.7lb)
LENGTH	Head & Body: 39–46cm (15.3–18.1in) Tail: 56–62cm (22–24.4in)
SEXUAL MATURITY	Male 2.5 years; female 20 months
MATING SEASON	April to June
GESTATION PERIOD	120–136 days
NUMBER OF YOUNG	Normally 1, twins are rare
BIRTH INTERVAL	1 year
TYPICAL DIET	Mainly fruit, but also leaves and other plant parts
LIFESPAN	Unknown in the wild; 15–18 years in captivity

TEETH
The lower incisors and canines, which lie at an acute angle to the jaw, are used comb-like to groom the fur and to gouge tree bark to obtain the sap.

NOSE
The projecting, pointed muzzle is tipped with a moist, dog-like nose. The lemur uses its nose to detect the ripeness of fruits, as well as for reading the scent markings of other lemurs.

PADS
The leathery palms and soles enable the lemur to run and leap sure-footedly along the ground and in the trees, while the long digits help it to manipulate food, climb and groom itself and other lemurs.

SCENT GLANDS
Both sexes have a dark scent gland near each wrist. The male also has a horny projection near the gland (below), which he uses to rub branches and deposit his scent.

CREATURE COMPARISONS

The black lemur (Eulemar macaco), like the ring-tailed lemur, belongs to the family Lemuridae. The black lemur lives in small groups in the hot, damp forests of northwestern Madagascar. Whereas male and female ring-tailed lemurs are almost identical, apart from a slight size difference, the male black lemur is completely black, while the female is a ruddy brown and has startling, white ear tufts.

Although similar in size, the ring-tailed lemur lacks the black lemur's pronounced neck ruff and ear tufts. The black lemur spends most of its time in the forest canopy, and is active mainly during the day.

Black lemur

Ring-tailed lemur

WHERE IN THE WORLD?

Inhabits forest and dry scrub areas of the southwestern and southern regions of the island of Madagascar, from Taolanaro in the south, north to Morondava on the western coast.

RELATED SPECIES

The ring-tailed lemur is one of 10 species belonging to the family Lemuridae, or true lemurs. There are, however, 21 other species of lemur in four separate families. The Avahi or woolly lemur, Avahi laniger belongs to the family Indriidae. All lemur species are found in Madagascar.

• **ORDER** • *Primates* • **FAMILY** • *Lemuridae* • **GENUS & SPECIES** • *Varecia variegata*

RUFFED LEMUR

With its strong limbs, lightweight body and dexterous feet, the ruffed lemur has the physical adaptations to climb trees with masterful precision.

KEY FEATURES

- Forms stable social groups led by dominant females, who take control when choosing food and selecting mates.
- Equipped with a wide variety of far-carrying alarm calls to alert group members to specific dangers.
- Rarely descends to the forest floor, spending most of its life in the forest canopy feeding on fruits and flowers.

SKULL
The skull is elongated with a slender, fox-like muzzle. The cheek teeth have pointed crowns. The lower canines and incisors protrude forwards and are used in mutual grooming sessions.

TAIL
The long, bushy tail provides extra balance in the trees.

COAT
Both sexes share a similar two-tone coat colouration. A luxuriant ruff of bushy white fur frames the face and gives the species its common name.

SUBSPECIES
The red ruffed lemur, Varecia variegata rubra, has a rusty-red coat with a white nape and rump. The tail, face and inner surfaces of the limbs are black.

HINDFOOT
The hindfoot has a padded sole with distinct ridges. It provides a grip strong enough to support the lemur as it hangs upside-down.

VITAL STATISTICS

WEIGHT	3.5–4kg (7.7–8.8lb)
LENGTH	Head & Body: 50–60cm (19.7–23.6in) Tail: 60–65cm (23.6–25.6in)
SEXUAL MATURITY	2 years
MATING SEASON	May to July
GESTATION PERIOD	90–102 days
NUMBER OF YOUNG	Up to 6, usually 2 to 3
BIRTH INTERVAL	1 year
TYPICAL DIET	Fruit, leaves, nectar, seeds
LIFESPAN	15–20 years

CREATURE COMPARISONS

The crowned lemur (Eulemur coronatus) is found in dry tropical forest and humid forest margins in northern Madagascar. Smaller than its relative, it also displays different colouration in the sexes: the male is dark grey with a black-tipped tail, whereas the female is pale grey. A black cap, common to both sexes, accounts for the species' name.

The crowned lemur is active day and night, feeding mainly on leaves, fruit, and flowers. Like the ruffed lemur, the crowned lemur spends most of its time above ground, although it occasionally descends to eat fallen fruit.

Ruffed lemur

Crowned lemur

WHERE IN THE WORLD?

Native to the mainly lowland eastern forests of Madagascar, which lies off the east coast of Africa in the Indian Ocean.

RELATED SPECIES

There are 2 subspecies of ruffed lemur: the black-and-white race, Varecia variegata variegata, and the red race, V. v. rubra. They belong to the family Lemuridae, whose 12 species include the black lemur, Eulemur macaco, of northern Madagascar.

• ORDER • *Primates* • FAMILY • *Lorisidae* • GENUS & SPECIES • *Galago senegalensis*

LESSER BUSH BABY

The bush baby uses its excellent sense of hearing to navigate and hunt at night. The large eyes are specially adapted to work well in low light.

KEY FEATURES

- Huge eyes and large ears enable the bush baby to detect small prey animals in the treetops at night.

- Can track the flight path of a moth, and then grab the insect from mid-air, in near-total darkness.

- Uses scents and calls to mark its territory, since these signals can be detected in darkness.

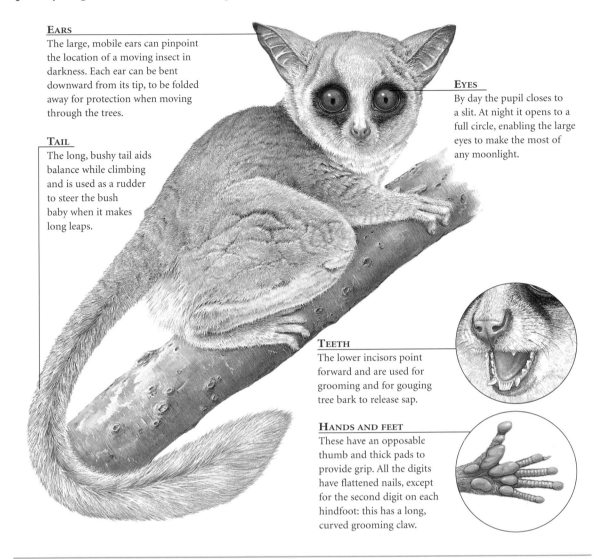

EARS
The large, mobile ears can pinpoint the location of a moving insect in darkness. Each ear can be bent downward from its tip, to be folded away for protection when moving through the trees.

TAIL
The long, bushy tail aids balance while climbing and is used as a rudder to steer the bush baby when it makes long leaps.

EYES
By day the pupil closes to a slit. At night it opens to a full circle, enabling the large eyes to make the most of any moonlight.

TEETH
The lower incisors point forward and are used for grooming and for gouging tree bark to release sap.

HANDS AND FEET
These have an opposable thumb and thick pads to provide grip. All the digits have flattened nails, except for the second digit on each hindfoot: this has a long, curved grooming claw.

VITAL STATISTICS

WEIGHT	128–300g (4.5–10.6oz)
LENGTH	Head & Body: 18–20cm (7.1–7.9in) Tail: 20–25cm (7.9–9.8in)
SEXUAL MATURITY	10 months
MATING SEASON	Follows rainy season, so varies with location
GESTATION PERIOD	123 days
NUMBER OF YOUNG	1 or 2, occasionally 3
BIRTH INTERVAL	Annual or twice every year, depending on location
TYPICAL DIET	Insects, fruit, small birds and their eggs, mice, lizards, tree sap
LIFESPAN	14 years in captivity; not known in wild

CREATURE COMPARISONS

As primates, bush babies share their ancestry with humans, monkeys and apes (higher primates), but their closest relatives are the other members of the family Lorisidae — the pottos and lorises of Africa and Asia — and other lower primates, such as lemurs and tarsiers. Unlike the higher primates, lorisids, lemurs and tarsiers all have a well-developed sense of smell, a moist snout and a fur-covered face.

Bush baby

Potto

Tarsier

Slow loris

WHERE IN THE WORLD?

Found across Africa south of the Sahara, in wooded areas bordering rainforest from Senegal east to northern Ethiopia, and from Somalia and Mozambique south to Angola and Tanzania.

RELATED SPECIES

Experts disagree on exact numbers, but most believe there to be nine species of bush baby in four genera. These are: three dwarf bush babies, Galago alleni, G. zanzibaricus and G. demidoff; two needle-clawed bush babies, Euoticus inustus and E. elegantulus; two species of greater bush baby, Otolemur garnettii and O. crassicaudatus, as well as two species of lesser bush baby, Galago moholi and G. senegalensis.

• **ORDER** • *Primates* • **FAMILY** • *Lorisidae* • **GENUS & SPECIES** • *Nycticebus coucang*

SLOW LORIS

Slow but sure, the loris grips the branches of its forest home with firm hands and feet that it can move with lightning speed when prey is in range.

KEY FEATURES

- A stealthy and slow moving primate, it sleeps unseen during the day and hunts under cover of darkness.
- An opportunistic feeder with an iron stomach, it eats insects that no other predator would touch.
- Legally protected as a result of increasing rarity — a consequence of widespread habitat destruction.

VITAL STATISTICS

WEIGHT	1.01–1.37kg (2.2–3lb)
LENGTH	23–38cm (9–15in)
SEXUAL MATURITY	8–12 months
MATING SEASON	All year round
GESTATION PERIOD	193 days
NUMBER OF YOUNG	1, rarely twins
BIRTH INTERVAL	Roughly 1 year
TYPICAL DIET	Insects, fruit, leaves, seeds, lizards, birds and their eggs
LIFESPAN	Up to 12 years 8 months in captivity; unknown in wild

SKULL
The slow loris's skull is typical of a prosimian: it has a relatively large brain-case but lacks the high brow and flat face of the higher primates.

EYES
Large, forward-facing eyes help the loris judge distances and see very well at low light levels.

HANDS
With a strong, opposable thumb and thickly padded fingers, the hands exert a vice-like grip around branches or unwary prey.

FEET
Even more powerful than its hands, the loris's feet anchor it to a branch as it lunges for prey. The reduced second digit on each foot has a special grooming claw.

CREATURE COMPARISONS

The angwantibo (Arctocebus calabarensis), or golden potto, of equatorial Africa has a lot in common with the slow loris despite the fact that these two representatives of the family Lorisidae have been geographically separated for millions of years. Like the loris, the angwantibo is a nocturnal tree-dweller living in an almost identical tropical rainforest habitat. It has very similar adaptations to this way of life, including strong, grasping hands and feet, large eyes for good night vision and a stealthy pursuit of prey. It also shares the loris's ability to eat unpalatable invertebrates.

Angwantibo

Slow loris

WHERE IN THE WORLD?

Found in wooded areas across southeastern Asia, from Assam in northeast India through southeast China and south to Indonesia.

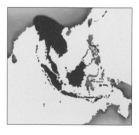

RELATED SPECIES

The slow loris shares its genus with just 1 other species: the lesser slow loris, Nycticebus pygmaeus. Other members of its family, Lorisidae, include the slender loris, Loris tardigradus, and the African pottos and bush babies. The slow loris is also related to the lemurs.

• ORDER • *Primates* • FAMILY • *Pongidae* • GENUS & SPECIES • *Gorilla gorilla*

LOWLAND GORILLA

KEY FEATURES

- Commonly believed to be fierce and aggressive but, in fact, is a peaceful, gentle creature that rarely resorts to fighting.
- As the largest living primate, it has no natural enemies or predators, but, sadly, is threatened by humans.
- Lives in close-knit groups — led by a dominant male — that travel, eat, sleep and raise young together.

VITAL STATISTICS

WEIGHT	Male 135–275kg (297.6–606.3lb); female 70–140kg (154.3–308.6lb)
STANDING HEIGHT	Male 1.6–1.8m (5ft 2in–5ft 9in); female 1.4–1.5m (4ft 6in–4ft 9in)
SEXUAL MATURITY	Male 10 years; female 8 years
MATING SEASON	All year round
GESTATION PERIOD	251–295 days
NUMBER OF YOUNG	1 (twins occur rarely)
BIRTH INTERVAL	3.5–4.5 years
TYPICAL DIET	Leaves, shoots, stems and fruits
LIFESPAN	Up to 50 years

The stocky and muscular lowland gorilla has long, powerful arms to strip vegetation and bark from trees, and strong jaws that mash fruit.

EARS
The gorilla has small, human-like ears that are almost completely hidden by fur. Hearing is very sharp.

JAWS
A ridge of bone on the cheek of the skull (above), forms an anchor for the powerful jaw muscles. The ridge is especially well developed in males; in females it is smaller, and in some cases may even be absent.

HAIR
At about ten years of age — when a male reaches sexual maturity — he develops a silvery-white 'saddle' on his back. Such males are known as 'silverbacks'.

HANDS
Each hand has four long fingers and an opposable 'thumb'. The gorilla is unable to spread its hands out flat, and must walk, with fingers curled, on its knuckles.

FEET
Each broad foot has four long outer toes and one shorter inner toe. The gorilla normally walks on all-fours, but sometimes stands and moves for short distances on two legs.

CREATURE COMPARISONS

The chimpanzee and the orang-utan are relatives of the gorilla, which, like the gorilla, are large, hairy tailless primates. All three of these apes share common features, such as a powerful barrel-chest, long arms and shorter legs and opposable thumbs and big toes. The orang's big toes, though, are much reduced compared to the chimpanzee and gorilla, probably because it spends more time in the trees than the other two species.

| Chimpanzee | Orang-utan | Lowland gorilla |

WHERE IN THE WORLD?

The western lowland gorilla occurs in areas of Cameroon, Central African Republic, Congo, Gabon and Equatorial Guinea, while the eastern lowland gorilla is found in the Democratic Republic of Congo (Zaire).

RELATED SPECIES

The genus Gorilla contains only one species, Gorilla gorilla, of which there are three subspecies: the western lowland gorilla, G. g. gorilla; the eastern lowland gorilla, G. g. graueri; and the mountain gorilla, G. g. beringei. Along with the chimpanzee, bonobo (pygmy chimpanzee) and orang-utan, the gorilla belongs to the family Pongidae: the 'great apes'. Nine species of gibbon in the family Hylobatidae make up the 'lesser apes'.

• **ORDER** • *Primates* • **FAMILY** • *Pongidae* • **GENUS & SPECIES** • *Pan paniscus*

BONOBO

Long arms, a narrow chest and strong hook-like hands perfectly equip this lightweight primate for a life spent mainly in the trees of its forest home.

KEY FEATURES

- First identified in 1929, when it was thought to be a subspecies of the chimpanzee; it is still one of the least-known apes.
- Much less aggressive than the chimpanzee, with longer limbs and a relatively slender body.
- Regular sexual activity maintains the strong bonds within each group.
- Probably the closest living relative of humans.

VITAL STATISTICS

WEIGHT	Male 40–50kg (88.2–110.2lb) female 30–35kg (66.1–77.2lb)
LENGTH	70–83cm (27.6–32.7in)
HEIGHT	1.05–1.3m (3ft 4in–4ft 3in) to top of head when standing
SEXUAL MATURITY	9–12 years
MATING SEASON	All year
NUMBER OF YOUNG	Usually 1
GESTATION PERIOD	230–240 days
BIRTH INTERVAL	5 years
TYPICAL DIET	Fruit, seeds and leaves, also eggs and honey. On rare occasions, invertebrates, fish, mammals and carrion
LIFESPAN	30–45 years

HEAD
The bonobo's head is smaller and more rounded in shape than that of the chimpanzee, it was the examination of bonobo skulls by museum curators that led to it being called the pygmy chimpanzee.

TEETH
Long, pointed canine teeth are used mainly for display (as here) but may also serve to tear the flesh of the bonobo's occasional animal prey. Broad, flat molars deal with the more usual diet of tough leaves and fruit.

ARMS
Long, strong arms allow the bonobo to swing through the trees with great agility. They reach to below the knee when it stands or walks erect, which it does more frequently than any other great ape.

HANDS
Elongated fingers and short thumbs enable the bonobo to form its hand into a hook when swinging through the trees.

CREATURE COMPARISONS

It is easy to mistake the bonobo for its more familiar relative, the chimpanzee. Due to its muscular limbs and broader chest, however, the chimpanzee can weigh half as much again as the bonobo. Its skull is also larger, and supports a more powerful jaw, which is most prominent in adult males (right). The chimpanzee's pinkish skin is usually lighter than the bonobo's, which tends to be greyish. Although the chimpanzee is an able climber and nests in trees each night, it is generally far more terrestrial than the bonobo, as befits its bulkier build.

Bonobo

Chimpanzee

WHERE IN THE WORLD?

Restricted to fragmented areas of lowland forest in the Democratic Republic of Congo (formerly Zaire), within a zone enclosed by the Congo, Lualaba and Kasai rivers. Also introduced to shores of Lake Tanganyika.

RELATED SPECIES

The bonobo is by far the smallest of the 4 species of great ape in the family Pongidae. The other species are: the chimpanzee (Pan troglodytes) of west and central Africa (its closest relative), the gorilla (Gorilla gorilla) of central Africa and the orang-utan (Pongo pygmaeus) of the islands of Borneo and Sumatra. Pongidae is one of 11 families of Primates — the order that includes the Hominidae, a family with a single species: human beings.

CHIMPANZEE

The chimpanzee's high intelligence and superb hand–eye coordination allows it to manipulate objects with almost human-like dexterity.

KEY FEATURES

- Individuals form close, lifelong bonds, which are reinforced during mutual grooming routines.
- Occasionally hunts prey in a coordinated attack.
- Closely related to humans; like us, it is highly social, but occasionally also reflects the darker, more war-like face of human nature.

VITAL STATISTICS

WEIGHT	27–68kg (59.5–150lb)
LENGTH	71–91cm (27.9–35.8in)
SEXUAL MATURITY	7 years, but does not breed until 12–15 years old
MATING SEASON	All year
GESTATION PERIOD	230 days
NUMBER OF YOUNG	1
BIRTH INTERVAL	3 years, often longer
TYPICAL DIET	Fruit, leaves, berries, nuts, insects and, occasionally, mammals and birds
LIFESPAN	Up to 60 years

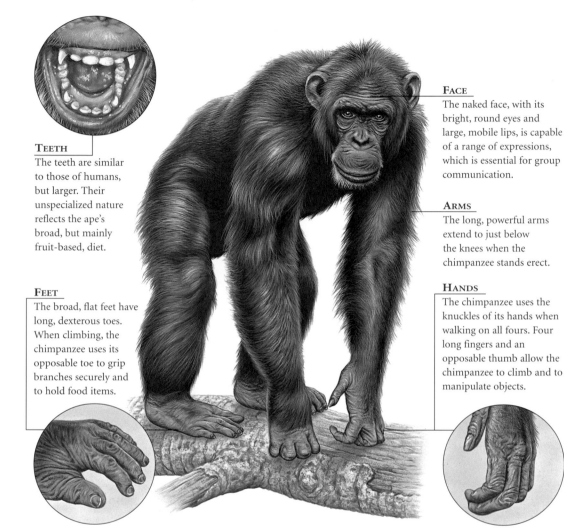

TEETH
The teeth are similar to those of humans, but larger. Their unspecialized nature reflects the ape's broad, but mainly fruit-based, diet.

FEET
The broad, flat feet have long, dexterous toes. When climbing, the chimpanzee uses its opposable toe to grip branches securely and to hold food items.

FACE
The naked face, with its bright, round eyes and large, mobile lips, is capable of a range of expressions, which is essential for group communication.

ARMS
The long, powerful arms extend to just below the knees when the chimpanzee stands erect.

HANDS
The chimpanzee uses the knuckles of its hands when walking on all fours. Four long fingers and an opposable thumb allow the chimpanzee to climb and to manipulate objects.

CREATURE COMPARISONS

The gorilla, a close relation of the chimpanzee, shares many of the chimp's physical features, including long, powerful arms, a short back and short legs. Both gorilla and chimpanzee males acquire a silver back as they mature. The gorilla is, however, much more massively built, weighing nearly four times as much as the chimpanzee. The gorilla also has a distinctive high domed crest on the head. This crest serves as an anchor for the powerful jaw muscles the gorilla needs to chew tough leaves. The gorilla's great bulk means that it climbs trees less frequently than any other ape.

Gorilla

Chimpanzee

WHERE IN THE WORLD?

Found in forests and woodland in West and Central Africa, from Guinea east to Uganda, and south as far as Lake Tanganyika and the Congo River.

RELATED SPECIES

The family Pongidae also includes the gorilla, Gorilla gorilla, of central Africa, the orang-utan, Pongo pygmaeus, of Borneo and Sumatra, and the bonobo, Pan paniscus, of the Congo.

• **ORDER** • *Primates* • **FAMILY** • *Pongidae* • **GENUS & SPECIES** • *Pongo pygmaeus*

ORANG-UTAN

Long, extremely strong arms and dextrous hands equip the large and weighty orang-utan for life in its high-rise rainforest home.

KEY FEATURES

- Female is one of the most caring and gentle mothers in the animal world; the male takes no part in rearing the young.
- Offspring may remain with the mother for up to eight years, during which time it is given lessons in survival and parenthood.
- Although solitary for most of its time, it forms lifelong bonds with others, which are renewed during occasional forest encounters.

VITAL STATISTICS

WEIGHT	Male 59–91kg (130.1–200.6lb); female 36–50kg (79.4–110.2lb)
LENGTH	Head & Body: 1.5m (4ft 9in)
SEXUAL MATURITY	Usually 7 years, but male does not breed until 13–15 years old
BREEDING SEASON	All year round
GESTATION PERIOD	233–265 days
NUMBER OF YOUNG	1
BIRTH INTERVAL	3–4 years; often much longer
TYPICAL DIET	Mainly fruit; also leaves, berries, nuts; occasionally small mammals, birds and eggs
LIFESPAN	35–40 years

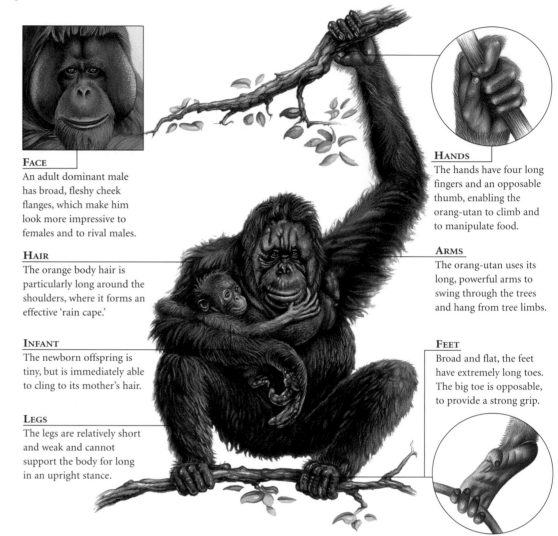

FACE
An adult dominant male has broad, fleshy cheek flanges, which make him look more impressive to females and to rival males.

HAIR
The orange body hair is particularly long around the shoulders, where it forms an effective 'rain cape.'

INFANT
The newborn offspring is tiny, but is immediately able to cling to its mother's hair.

LEGS
The legs are relatively short and weak and cannot support the body for long in an upright stance.

HANDS
The hands have four long fingers and an opposable thumb, enabling the orang-utan to climb and to manipulate food.

ARMS
The orang-utan uses its long, powerful arms to swing through the trees and hang from tree limbs.

FEET
Broad and flat, the feet have extremely long toes. The big toe is opposable, to provide a strong grip.

CREATURE COMPARISONS

The orang-utan shares part of its range with the lar gibbon, another tree dweller. Both move through the treetops by brachiating (swinging along arm over arm), but the gibbon leaps from branch to branch with great agility and speed, whereas the orang-utan moves slowly, reaching out with its strong arms to grab a branch before hauling its body along.

Orang-utan

Lar gibbon

WHERE IN THE WORLD?

The orang-utan is found in the lowland rainforests of the islands of Sumatra and Borneo in Southeast Asia. There are two subspecies: one that is exclusive to Sumatra, the other to Borneo.

RELATED SPECIES

The orang-utan has two subspecies, Pongo pongo pygmaeus from Borneo, and P. p. abelii from Sumatra. Family relations include the gorilla and chimp.

TARSIER

• ORDER • *Primates* • FAMILY • *Tarsiidae* • GENUS & SPECIES • *Tarsius spp.*

Small enough to fit in the palm of a human hand, this odd-looking primate has the huge eyes and swivelling head of an owl and springs about like a tree frog.

KEY FEATURES

- Tiny nocturnal predators that have enormous eyes and a head that can rotate almost full circle.
- Tree-living, they cling to branches and move about with agile leaps of up to 6m (19ft 7in) — 30 times their own body length.
- 'Living fossils', these primitive primates have barely changed since they first appeared about 45 million years ago.

VITAL STATISTICS

WEIGHT	80–165g (2.8–5.8oz)
LENGTH	Head & Body: 8.5–16cm (3.3–6.3in) Tail: 13.5–27.5cm (5.3–10.8in)
SEXUAL MATURITY	15–18 months
MATING SEASON	Throughout the year, with births peaking from February to April
GESTATION PERIOD	6 months
NUMBER OF YOUNG	1
BIRTH INTERVAL	Unknown
TYPICAL DIET	Insects, spiders, scorpions and small vertebrates including birds and bats
LIFESPAN	8–12 years

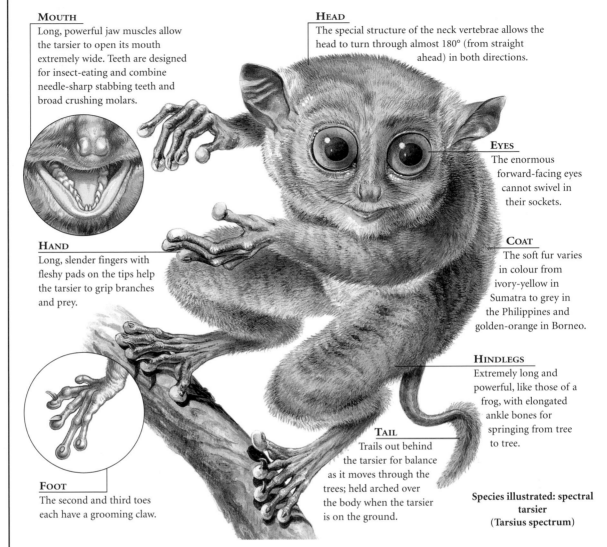

MOUTH
Long, powerful jaw muscles allow the tarsier to open its mouth extremely wide. Teeth are designed for insect-eating and combine needle-sharp stabbing teeth and broad crushing molars.

HAND
Long, slender fingers with fleshy pads on the tips help the tarsier to grip branches and prey.

FOOT
The second and third toes each have a grooming claw.

HEAD
The special structure of the neck vertebrae allows the head to turn through almost 180° (from straight ahead) in both directions.

EYES
The enormous forward-facing eyes cannot swivel in their sockets.

COAT
The soft fur varies in colour from ivory-yellow in Sumatra to grey in the Philippines and golden-orange in Borneo.

HINDLEGS
Extremely long and powerful, like those of a frog, with elongated ankle bones for springing from tree to tree.

TAIL
Trails out behind the tarsier for balance as it moves through the trees; held arched over the body when the tarsier is on the ground.

Species illustrated: spectral tarsier (Tarsius spectrum)

CREATURE COMPARISONS

The tarsier's African counterpart, the bush baby (Galago senegalensis), is similar in shape to the tarsier but has a bushier tail and a larger, heavier build — its head-and-body length is up to 20cm (7.9in) and it weighs up to 300g (10.6oz). Like the tarsier, the bush baby is active during the hours of twilight and darkness and moves through its treetop habitat by leaping. Unlike the tarsier, however, the bush baby lives in groups, constructs sleeping nests, and regularly supplements its diet of small invertebrates with plant material, such as the gum from acacia trees.

Tarsier

Bush baby

WHERE IN THE WORLD?

The 4 species of tarsier are found on many of the islands of Southeast Asia, including Borneo, southern Sumatra, parts of Java, the southeastern Philippines, Sulawesi and a number of small islands in between.

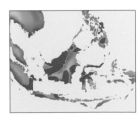

RELATED SPECIES

The 4 species of tarsier in the genus Tarsius all differ slightly in appearance: the spectral tarsier, Tarsius spectrum, has a scaly, slightly tufted tail and a white spot behind each ear; the Philippine-tarsier, T. syrichta, has a virtually naked tail; the western tarsier, T. bancanus, has a bushy tuft covering the last quarter of its tail; and the smallest species, the pygmy tarsier, T. pumilus, has a buff-coloured spot behind each ear.

• **ORDER** • *Proboscidea* • **FAMILY** • *Elephantidae* • **GENUS & SPECIES** • *Elephas maximus*

ASIAN ELEPHANT

This forest titan is well equipped to uproot and eat the densest foliage. Standing over 2m (6ft 6in) tall at the shoulders, an adult elephant fears few predators.

KEY FEATURES

- One of the world's largest living land animals, second in size only to its African cousin.
- Vast bulk and inefficient digestion mean that it must consume huge quantities of plant matter every day.
- Lives in extended, family-based herds led by the eldest female.

SKULL
The massive skull is necessary to support the muscles that power the trunk and the heavy, branch-crushing jaws. Its structure combines strength with relative lightness, although it still comprises up to 25 per cent of the bodyweight.

EARS
To prevent the body from overheating in the tropical climate, the undersides of the ears are richly supplied with blood vessels; by flapping its ears, the elephant can radiate heat.

TEETH
Most males, and a few females too, have tusks. The cheek teeth, 24 in total, are ridged for grinding tough plant food. As they wear out they are pushed forward, and eventually out, by new teeth growing behind.

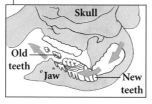

Skull

Old teeth

Jaw

New teeth

MUSTH GLAND
Behind the male's eye is a gland that secretes a black, sticky fluid during periods when he displays aggressive and sexual behaviour.

FOOT
Fatty pads embed the bones, spreading the animal's weight. Despite its size the elephant leaves light tracks and can move through the forest almost silently.

Toes Fatty pad

VITAL STATISTICS

WEIGHT	Male up to 6 tonnes (6.6 tons); female up to 3.5 tonnes (3.8 tons)
LENGTH	5.5–6.4m (18–21ft)
SHOULDER HEIGHT	Male 2.5–3m (8ft 2in–9ft 8in); female 2.4–2.6m (7ft 9in–8ft 5in)
SEXUAL MATURITY	About 10 years
MATING SEASON	End of rainy season to start of dry season
GESTATION PERIOD	19–22 months
NUMBER OF YOUNG	Usually 1
BIRTH INTERVAL	About 4 years
TYPICAL DIET	Grass, leaves, bamboo, bark, plantains,
LIFESPAN	Up to 60 years on average, rarely 70–80

CREATURE COMPARISONS

About 20 per cent larger than its Asian relative, the African elephant (*Loxodonta africana*) is the largest living land animal. Most African elephants live on the savannah, a more open and arid habitat than that of the Asian elephant, but large numbers of an African subspecies, the forest elephant (*L. a. cyclotis*), inhabit a rainforest habitat very similar to the jungles of India. The main differences between the two species are physical. The Asian elephant has smaller ears, a rounded back and a twin-domed forehead. Its tusks are smaller, and the tip of its trunk has just one flexible 'finger' while the African's trunk has two.

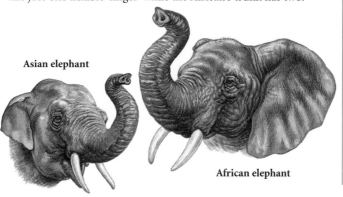

Asian elephant

African elephant

WHERE IN THE WORLD?

Once ranged from Iraq, through India to northern China. Today restricted to isolated regions in India, Sri Lanka, Malaysia, Indonesia and southern China.

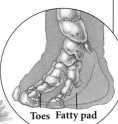

RELATED SPECIES

Experts recognize 4 subspecies of Asian elephant: the Indian, *Elephas maximus bengalensis*; the Sri Lankan, *E. m. maximus*; the Sumatran, *E. m. sumatrana*; and the Malaysian, *E. m. hirsutus*. The family Elephantidae consists of just 2 species in 2 genera: the Asian elephant and the African elephant, *Loxodonta africana*. Elephantidae is the sole family in the order Proboscidea.

• **ORDER** • *Proboscidea* • **FAMILY** • *Elephantidae* • **GENUS & SPECIES** • *Loxodonta africana*

AFRICAN ELEPHANT

The heavy elephant relies on its flexible trunk as a multi-purpose tool, using it for feeding, detecting scent, trumpeting and hosing itself down.

KEY FEATURES

- Long-lived, a female elephant invests most of her adult years rearing and caring for her young.

- Related females live together in tightly-knit groups, headed by a matriarch. Mature males live alone or in 'bachelor herds.'

- Reluctant to ignore abandoned or lost young of its own species, the female elephant sometimes adopts an orphan infant.

EARS
The vast ears are laced with blood vessels, and the elephant wafts them back and forth to lose heat.

TEMPORAL GLANDS
These glands open behind each eye. During breeding, or as a result of stress or pain, they swell and weep a strong-smelling secretion.

TRUNK
The trunk is highly flexible, and capable of both powerful and delicate movements. The nostrils at the tip are highly sensitive.

TUSKS
The tusks are elongated upper incisor teeth, formed from ivory, and grow continually. They are used for ripping tree bark and digging, and may be used in display and as weapons.

MAMMARIES
Unusually among four-footed mammals, the elephant's mammary glands are situated on the chest, rather than in the pelvic region.

FEET
The foot bones press downward under load, compressing a fatty cushion that expands and spreads the elephant's weight.

VITAL STATISTICS

WEIGHT	Male up to 6 tonnes (6.6 tons); female smaller
LENGTH	Male up to 4m (13ft 1in), head to rump; female up to 3.3m (10ft 8in).
SHOULDER HEIGHT	Male up to 3.27m (10ft 7in); female about 2.7m (8ft 8in)
SEXUAL MATURITY	About 10 years
BREEDING SEASON	All year
GESTATION PERIOD	22 months
NUMBER OF YOUNG	1
BIRTH INTERVAL	3–4 years
TYPICAL DIET	Grasses, foliage, shrubs, fruit, flowers, roots
LIFESPAN	50–60 years

CREATURE COMPARISONS

The African elephant differs markedly from the Asiatic elephant. The Asiatic elephant is generally smaller than the African elephant, and has a distinctly arched back. The Asiatic elephant's ears are very much smaller, as are the tusks — which, in the female, do not protrude from the mouth. The Asiatic elephant has only one 'lip' on the tip of its trunk, whereas the African elephant has two.

Asiatic elephant

African elephant

WHERE IN THE WORLD?

Once widespread in Africa, mainly south of the Sahara Desert, but now patchily distributed. Many live in national parks, although 70 per cent of the elephant's present range lies outside protected areas.

RELATED SPECIES

There are two subspecies of African elephant: the savannah, or bush, elephant, Loxodonta africana africana, and the forest elephant, L. a. cyclotis. Elephants have no close relatives, but may be distantly related to hyraxes, such as the rock hyrax or dassie.

• **ORDER** • *Procellariiformes* • **FAMILY** • *Procellariidae* • **GENUS & SPECIES** • *Puffinus puffinus*

MANX SHEARWATER

Gliding on its long, straight wings the Manx shearwater is completely at home above the vast open ocean, where it can smell prey from afar.

KEY FEATURES

- Spends eight months of the year out at sea, following currents and winds in its search for fish and squid.

- Glides effortlessly, skimming the ocean waves and only rarely flapping its long, slender wings.

- Nests on remote islands, but must travel to and from its burrow by night as it is totally defenceless on land.

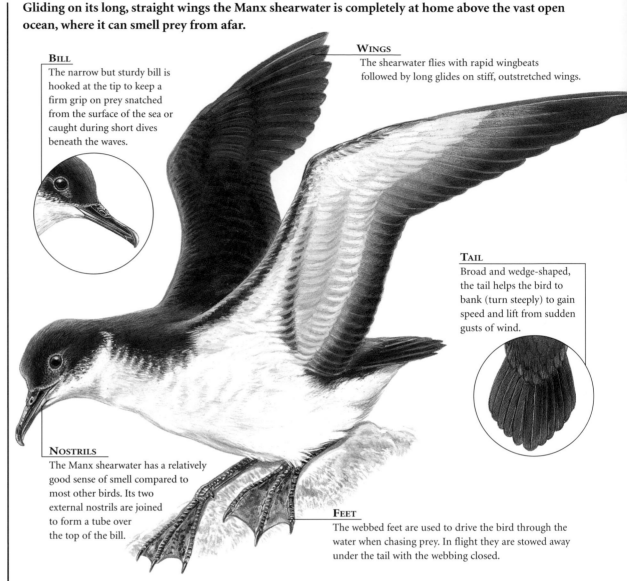

BILL
The narrow but sturdy bill is hooked at the tip to keep a firm grip on prey snatched from the surface of the sea or caught during short dives beneath the waves.

WINGS
The shearwater flies with rapid wingbeats followed by long glides on stiff, outstretched wings.

TAIL
Broad and wedge-shaped, the tail helps the bird to bank (turn steeply) to gain speed and lift from sudden gusts of wind.

NOSTRILS
The Manx shearwater has a relatively good sense of smell compared to most other birds. Its two external nostrils are joined to form a tube over the top of the bill.

FEET
The webbed feet are used to drive the bird through the water when chasing prey. In flight they are stowed away under the tail with the webbing closed.

VITAL STATISTICS

WEIGHT	340–455g (12–16oz)
LENGTH	35cm (13.8in)
WINGSPAN	85cm (33.5in)
SEXUAL MATURITY	5 years
BREEDING SEASON	April to August
NUMBER OF EGGS	1
INCUBATION PERIOD	51–54 days
FLEDGING PERIOD	70 days
BREEDING INTERVAL	1 year
TYPICAL DIET	Fish, small squid and crustaceans
LIFESPAN	Up to 20 years

CREATURE COMPARISONS

It is difficult to tell shearwaters apart, since they fly fast and low over the ocean — frequently disappearing from sight into the troughs between waves — and only come to land after sunset. The Manx and little shearwaters (*Puffinus assimilis*) are no exception, and from a distance look very similar indeed.

As its name suggests, however, the little shearwater is one of the smallest true shearwaters, with a wingspan of just 63cm (24.8in). In addition, although both species have dark, blackish upperparts that contrast with their pale undersides, the little shearwater has more white on its face, which gives it a quite different facial 'expression'. It is widespread, breeding in the North Atlantic and the oceans between South Africa and Australasia.

Manx shearwater

Little shearwater

WHERE IN THE WORLD?

Breeds on offshore islands in the northeastern Atlantic (from Iceland south to Madeira), along the east coast of North America and in the Mediterranean. Wanders the South Atlantic from August until April.

RELATED SPECIES

Nearly a third of all seabirds belong to the order Procellariiformes, including the 20 or so species of shearwaters, and the prions, fulmars, albatrosses and petrels. The tiny Wilson's storm-petrel, *Oceanites oceanicus*, is probably the most common of all seabirds.

• ORDER • *Psittaciformes* • FAMILY • *Psittacidae* • GENUS & SPECIES • *Ara ararauna*

BLUE AND YELLOW MACAW

KEY FEATURES

- One of the largest and gaudiest of all parrots, familiar worldwide as a showpiece cage-bird.
- Lives in tropical forests, where it flies just above the canopy in noisy chattering flocks.
- Uses its massive bill to crack open tough nuts and hard seed cases.
- Eats clay — possibly to gain important minerals and to aid digestion.

Despite its dandyish plumage, the blue and yellow macaw appears remarkably well camouflaged in its rainforest habitat.

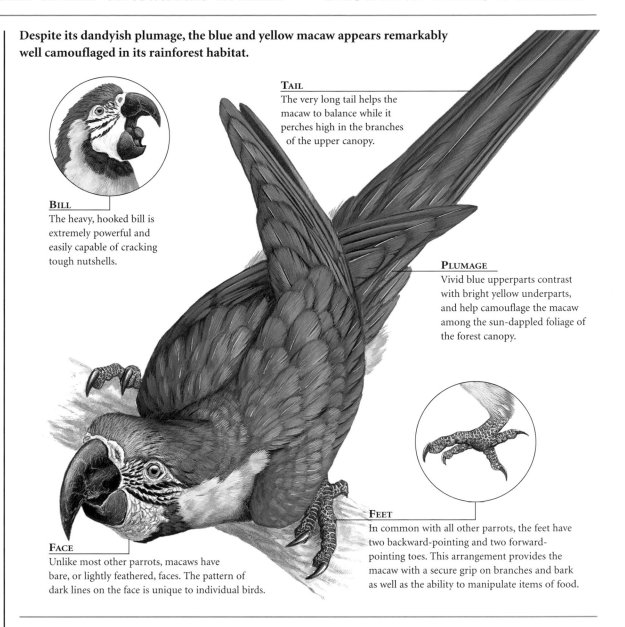

TAIL
The very long tail helps the macaw to balance while it perches high in the branches of the upper canopy.

BILL
The heavy, hooked bill is extremely powerful and easily capable of cracking tough nutshells.

PLUMAGE
Vivid blue upperparts contrast with bright yellow underparts, and help camouflage the macaw among the sun-dappled foliage of the forest canopy.

FEET
In common with all other parrots, the feet have two backward-pointing and two forward-pointing toes. This arrangement provides the macaw with a secure grip on branches and bark as well as the ability to manipulate items of food.

FACE
Unlike most other parrots, macaws have bare, or lightly feathered, faces. The pattern of dark lines on the face is unique to individual birds.

VITAL STATISTICS

WEIGHT	750–1000g (26.4–35.3oz)
LENGTH	Up to 90cm (35.4in) (nearly half of which is tail)
WINGSPAN	80–90cm (31–35.4in)
SEXUAL MATURITY	Probably 3–4 years
BREEDING SEASON	Varies according to region
NUMBER OF EGGS	2
INCUBATION PERIOD	24–26 days
FLEDGING PERIOD	3 months
BREEDING INTERVAL	Usually more than 1 year
TYPICAL DIET	Seeds, fruits and nuts
LIFESPAN	Up to 50 years in captivity

CREATURE COMPARISONS

The scarlet macaw has much in common with the blue and yellow macaw. Similar in size and build, it is also brightly coloured, is widely distributed and highly sought after as a cage-bird. Apart from the main colour differences, the scarlet macaw has plain whitish cheek patches, lacking the individualized patterns of the blue and yellow macaw. The range of the two species overlaps in parts and where they share the same areas, the blue and yellow macaw is often the more common bird in open habitats. The scarlet macaw is also found throughout Brazil and northern Bolivia but ranges farther north to southern Mexico, making it the most widely distributed macaw. Like the blue and yellow macaw, the scarlet macaw is under threat through deforestation and trapping.

Scarlet macaw

Blue and yellow macaw

WHERE IN THE WORLD?

Native to forested lowland areas of Central and South America, from eastern Panama south through the Amazon basin to northern Bolivia and southeastern Brazil. Also found on the island of Trinidad.

RELATED SPECIES

The parrot family, Psittacidae, to which the blue and yellow macaw belongs, contains 340 species. Among its members are lovebirds, parrotlets and the budgerigar, as well as other members of the genus Ara, such as the green-winged macaw, A. chloroptera.

• **ORDER** • *Psittaciformes* • **FAMILY** • *Psittacidae* • **GENUS & SPECIES** • *Eclectus roratus*

ECLECTUS PARROT

By pairing its strong grasping feet with its sturdy, hooked bill, the eclectus parrot can handle food and clamber among treetop foliage with great skill.

KEY FEATURES

- Eye-catching in a scarlet and violet-blue plumage, the female is strikingly different from the green male.
- Feasts on rainforest fruits and nuts, aided by its powerful yet sensitive bill.
- More often heard than seen, despite being abundant and brilliantly coloured, as it lives high in the canopy.

VITAL STATISTICS

WEIGHT	400–600g (14.1–21.2oz)
LENGTH	35cm (13.8in)
WINGSPAN	50cm (19.7in)
SEXUAL MATURITY	Probably 3 or 4 years
BREEDING SEASON	All year, with August to January peaks in Australia
NUMBER OF EGGS	2
INCUBATION PERIOD	26 days
FLEDGING PERIOD	72 days
BREEDING INTERVAL	1 year
TYPICAL DIET	Fruits, nuts, seeds, leaf buds and nectar
LIFESPAN	20–30 years

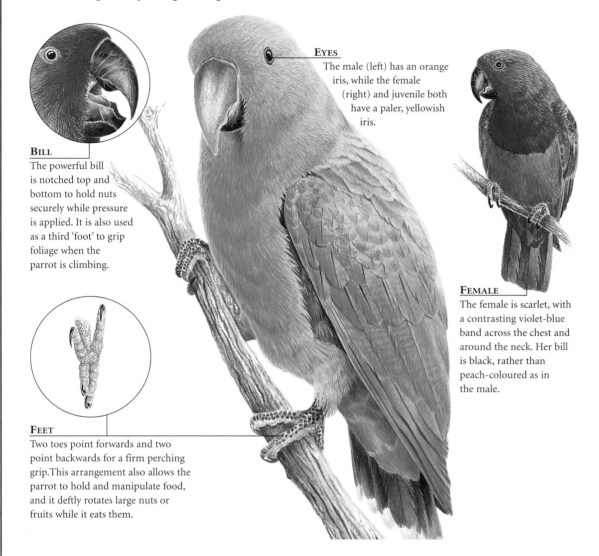

BILL
The powerful bill is notched top and bottom to hold nuts securely while pressure is applied. It is also used as a third 'foot' to grip foliage when the parrot is climbing.

EYES
The male (left) has an orange iris, while the female (right) and juvenile both have a paler, yellowish iris.

FEET
Two toes point forwards and two point backwards for a firm perching grip. This arrangement also allows the parrot to hold and manipulate food, and it deftly rotates large nuts or fruits while it eats them.

FEMALE
The female is scarlet, with a contrasting violet-blue band across the chest and around the neck. Her bill is black, rather than peach-coloured as in the male.

CREATURE COMPARISONS

The eclectus parrot is much stouter than its relation the Australian king parrot (Alisterus scapularis), and weighs on average twice as much. Like the eclectus parrot, however, the sexes look quite different from each other. The female is green, except for a crimson belly, whereas the male is also crimson on his breast, head and neck, with a blue rump and tail.

The Australian king parrot inhabits the Great Dividing Range, which runs from north to south parallel to Australia's eastern coast, as well as the coastal strip. It is absent from the only part of the continent where the eclectus parrot occurs: Cape York Peninsula at the northern tip of Queensland.

WHERE IN THE WORLD?

Found in parts of Southeast Asia, from the Sunda Strait in the west to the Solomon Islands in the east, including New Guinea. Also occurs in northeastern Australia.

RELATED SPECIES

There are 340 species of parrot within 3 families in the order Psittaciformes. The largest family, Psittacidae, includes the buff-faced pygmy parrot, Micropsitta pusio, which at 8.4cm (3.3in) long is the world's smallest parrot.

Eclectus parrot (male)

Australian king parrot (male)

KAKAPO

• ORDER • *Psittaciformes* • FAMILY • *Psittacidae* • GENUS & SPECIES • *Strigops habroptilus*

As large as a domestic cat and flightless, the kakapo is an owl-like parrot that is adapted to earn a living on the ground under cover of the night.

KEY FEATURES

- The world's only flightless parrot — and, at about 100 times the weight of a budgerigar, the heaviest.
- Almost wiped out in its natural habitat by predators introduced by humans, it now survives on only a few small islands under strict protection.
- Unusually for a parrot, it is almost always solitary.

WINGS
Although the kakapo cannot fly, it opens its broad wings to help it to balance when climbing or running. It can also make a controlled free-fall from up to 5m (16ft 4in) high on outstretched wings.

FACIAL DISC
The bowl-like facial disc is defined by small feathers. The disc, which is common to owls, may help to focus sound.

PLUMAGE
The kakapo's plumage is dull, moss-green above and green-yellow below, with fine brown and yellow bars. In the past, the plumage provided camouflage against the giant predatory birds that once lived in New Zealand.

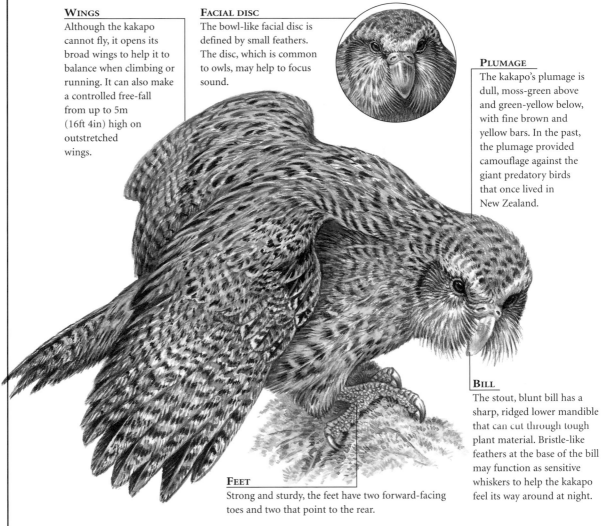

BILL
The stout, blunt bill has a sharp, ridged lower mandible that can cut through tough plant material. Bristle-like feathers at the base of the bill may function as sensitive whiskers to help the kakapo feel its way around at night.

FEET
Strong and sturdy, the feet have two forward-facing toes and two that point to the rear.

VITAL STATISTICS

WEIGHT	Male 2.5kg (5.5lb); female 2kg (4.4lb)
LENGTH	63cm (24.8in)
SEXUAL MATURITY	6–8 years
BREEDING SEASON	December to May
NUMBER OF EGGS	2 to 4
INCUBATION PERIOD	30 days
FLEDGING PERIOD	10–12 weeks
BREEDING INTERVAL	3–5 years; 'relocated' birds breed more frequently
TYPICAL DIET	Fruits, seeds, leaves, stems and roots
LIFESPAN	At least 20 years: some individuals probably reach 30–40 years

CREATURE COMPARISONS

The kakapo resembles another large parrot that is native to New Zealand: the kea (Nestor notabilis). The kea, however, is a powerful and agile flier. The bill of this closely related species is much larger than the kakapo's and is strongly hooked, with a long, sharply pointed upper mandible. Unlike the kakapo, the kea is not exclusively vegetarian; it uses its bill to grub up burrowing invertebrates from the ground, and as a meat-hook to tear into carrion — especially sheep carcasses.

Kakapo   Kea

WHERE IN THE WORLD?

Native to New Zealand, but extinct across its former natural range on the mainland. Introduced to three nearby islands: Little Barrier Island, Codfish Island and Maud Island.

RELATED SPECIES

The kakapo's closest relatives are probably the ground parrot and the little-known night parrot of Australia. There are six species of parrot native to New Zealand. Of these, the red-crowned parakeet is the only one to occur elsewhere: on Norfolk Island and New Caledonia.

• ORDER • *Rodentia* • FAMILY • *Bathyergidae* • GENUS & SPECIES • *Heterocephalus glaber*

NAKED MOLE RAT

The naked mole rat's bizarre appearance is part of a series of adaptations to life underneath the arid African grasslands.

KEY FEATURES

- Pink, wrinkled skin is almost entirely hairless.
- Spends its whole life below the scorching East African savannah in a complex of underground tunnels, where its near-blindness is not a disadvantage.
- Lives in colonies ruled by a single female — a similar social structure to that of ants and bees.

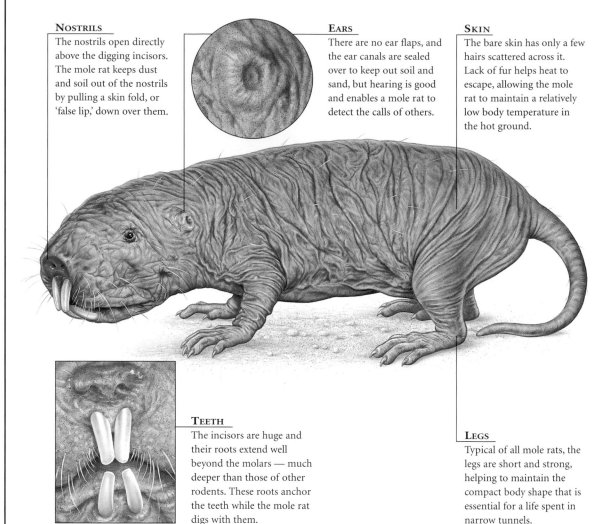

NOSTRILS
The nostrils open directly above the digging incisors. The mole rat keeps dust and soil out of the nostrils by pulling a skin fold, or 'false lip,' down over them.

EARS
There are no ear flaps, and the ear canals are sealed over to keep out soil and sand, but hearing is good and enables a mole rat to detect the calls of others.

SKIN
The bare skin has only a few hairs scattered across it. Lack of fur helps heat to escape, allowing the mole rat to maintain a relatively low body temperature in the hot ground.

TEETH
The incisors are huge and their roots extend well beyond the molars — much deeper than those of other rodents. These roots anchor the teeth while the mole rat digs with them.

LEGS
Typical of all mole rats, the legs are short and strong, helping to maintain the compact body shape that is essential for a life spent in narrow tunnels.

VITAL STATISTICS

WEIGHT	28–85g (1–3oz)
LENGTH	Head & Body: 7.5–9cm (2.9–3.5in) Tail: 2.5–3.8cm (1–1.5in)
SHOULDER HEIGHT	2.5–3.8cm (1–1.5in)
SEXUAL MATURITY	Unknown
MATING SEASON	Throughout the year
GESTATION PERIOD	70 days
NUMBER OF YOUNG	Usually 3 to 11, but up to 20 recorded
BIRTH INTERVAL	Unknown
TYPICAL DIET	Mostly roots of grasses; tubers and bulbs
LIFESPAN	5 years in the wild; 10 years in captivity

CREATURE COMPARISONS

The Cape dune mole rat, native to the dunes and plains of South Africa, is the largest member of the mole rat family, weighing 16 times more than the naked mole rat, with a body length of more than 30cm (11.8in). Despite the difference in size and coat, these two mole rat species have a remarkably similar body shape — a reflection of their burrowing lifestyles.

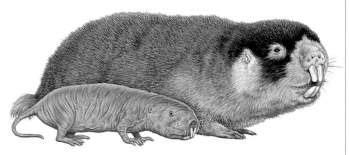

Naked mole rat   Cape dune mole rat

WHERE IN THE WORLD?

Found beneath the thorn tree savannah of East Africa, ranging from Ethiopia and Somalia to northern Kenya, where the light, sandy soil is suitable for digging extensive burrow systems.

RELATED SPECIES

The family Bathyergidae contains nine species in five genera. These species are native to Africa, south of the Sahara, although about 30 million years ago they ranged as far as Mongolia. Mole rats are related to the cane rat, which has a similar range, but lives above ground.

CUBAN HUTIA

• ORDER • *Rodentia* • FAMILY • *Capromyidae* • GENUS & SPECIES • *Capromys spp.*

KEY FEATURES

- Rat-like rodents that catch small animals to supplement their diet of plant matter.
- Confined to Cuba — although closely related species are found on Hispaniola, Jamaica and the Bahamas.
- Several species are listed as endangered or extinct by the IUCN (World Conservation Union).

VITAL STATISTICS

WEIGHT	0.5–7kg (1.1–15.4lb), depending on species
LENGTH	Head & Body: 22–50cm (8.7–19.7in) Tail: 15–30cm (5.9–11.8in)
SEXUAL MATURITY	10 months
BREEDING SEASON	All year round
GESTATION PERIOD	110–140 days
NUMBER OF YOUNG	1 to 6
BREEDING INTERVAL	1 or 2 litters a year
TYPICAL DIET	Leaves, bark, fruit; invertebrates, small mammals and reptiles
LIFESPAN	Up to 11 years in captivity

Moving agilely through the branches in search of food, the hutia clings on with its well developed feet while using its tail to provide balance.

HEAD AND BODY
The hutia's head is broad with a square muzzle. The body is robust and stocky, with relatively short legs.

FUR
Rough and untidy in appearance, the fur consists of an outer coat of long, coarse guard hairs with a softer undercoat.

TAIL
The tail is furred. Two species have a prehensile tail, and the others use their tail for balance as they forage in the trees.

COLOURATION
The fur varies from yellowish-brown to buff and even black. In some individuals, the guard hairs are white, giving the animal a silvery appearance.

TEETH
Sharp incisors enable the hutia to sever tough plant matter as well as deliver a killing blow to small creatures.

FEET
The hutia has broad feet with prominent claws, which enable it to climb easily and grip objects. The first digit is greatly reduced in some species.

Species illustrated: Desmarest's or Cuban hutia, Capromys pilorides

CREATURE COMPARISONS

Like most Cuban hutias, the bushy-tailed cloud rat (Crateromys schadenbergi) is an agile tree-living rodent. An island-dweller from the Philippines, it shares much of the hutia's diet of leaves, fruit and other plant matter. Making its nests high up in the trees, it too is seriously threatened by forest clearance. A close relative of mice and rats, the cloud rat is much furrier than the hutia and almost ferret-like in appearance. Its most striking feature is its thick bushy tail, which reaches 45cm (17.7in) in length — far longer than its body. Dark brown or black in colour, the cloud rat is sometimes adorned with a paler band round its upper body. Unlike the hutia, it has a full-length first digit on each foot.

Desmarest's hutia

Bushy-tailed cloud rat

WHERE IN THE WORLD?

Found throughout most of the Caribbean island of Cuba and some smaller islands nearby.

RELATED SPECIES

Of the 14 species in the genus Capromys, 4 are known only from skeletal remains. There are 2 other genera of hutias in the family Capromyidae. The genus Geocapromys, now confined to Jamaica and the Bahamas, contains 5 species. The genus Plagiodontia contains 2 species living on Haiti and the Dominican Republic, with another 5 species known only from bones. The other member of the Capromyidae is the coypu of South America.

• **ORDER** • *Rodentia* • **FAMILY** • *Capromyidae* • **GENUS & SPECIES** • *Myocastor coypus*

COYPU

Resembling a cross between a beaver and a rat, the coypu has evolved many features, such as webbed hindfeet, that enable it to exploit aquatic habitats.

KEY FEATURES

- Digs burrows and tunnels in the banks of lakes and rivers, from which it emerges at night to forage.
- Spends long periods underwater in search of aquatic plants and other food items.
- Feral populations exist in countries where the animal has been farmed for its fur and escaped into the wild.

VITAL STATISTICS

WEIGHT	7–10kg (15.4–22lb)
LENGTH	Head & Body: 45–62cm (17.7–24.4in) Tail: 25–42cm (9.8–16.5in)
SHOULDER HEIGHT	25–28cm (9.8–11in)
SEXUAL MATURITY	3–8 months
MATING SEASON	Non-seasonal but September to October in colder areas
GESTATION PERIOD	128–132 days
NUMBER OF YOUNG	Up to 12, usually 5 or 6
BIRTH INTERVAL	2 to 3 litters a year
TYPICAL DIET	Reeds and other aquatic plants; rarely molluscs
LIFESPAN	2–3 years in the wild; up to 6 years in captivity

FUR
When underwater, the coypu's long, coarse outer fur flattens down to streamline the body and keep water out of the nutria — the soft, velvety underfur.

SKULL
The eyes and nose are high on the skull to allow the coypu to breathe and see above the water while swimming. It has long, broad incisors and large molars for cutting and grinding.

TAIL
The cylindrical tail is long and hairless, like that of a rat. It is scaly and tapers to a point.

HINDFOOT
The hindfoot is made up of five long digits, four of which are connected by webbing to enable the coypu to swim strongly.

FOREFOOT
The forefoot is smaller than the hindfoot and has no webbing. The four long digits face a small thumb.

CREATURE COMPARISONS

Resembling a large cavy (guinea pig), the pacarana (Dinomys branickii) is a slow moving animal with a thickset body, powerful legs and a stout, hairy tail. Slightly larger than the coypu, this rare and distinctive creature is most easily identified by the rows of white spots that run down its back, which contrast strongly with its dark background fur. Unlike the coypu, the pacarana is not an aquatic animal and has a more upright stance for foraging in the upland forests of South America, where it eats a variety of plant matter. Both the pacarana and the coypu possess strong claws for digging and burrowing — the pacarana often removing soil alongside rock crevices to create a suitable shelter.

Coypu

Pacarana

WHERE IN THE WORLD?

Native to the streams, lakes and marshes of temperate South America. Feral populations exist in North America, Europe and Asia, where the coypu was introduced because of the value of its fur.

RELATED SPECIES

The coypu is a member of the family Capromyidae, which contains 4 genera and 33 species. All of these species, with the notable exception of the coypu, live on Caribbean islands and are known as hutias. Unlike the coypu, the 12 species of hutia live exclusively on land; several species, such as the Cuban hutias in the genus Capromys, are skilled climbers. The family Capromyidae is part of the order Rodentia, the largest order of mammals.

NORTH AMERICAN BEAVER

• ORDER • *Rodentia* • FAMILY • *Castoridae* • GENUS & SPECIES • *Castor canadensis*

KEY FEATURES

- The animal world's greatest builder, it fells trees up to 50cm (19.7in) in diameter to dam rivers and streams.

- Equipped for a semi-aquatic life with waterproof fur and webbed feet to drive it through the water.

- Constructs a dome-shaped wooden lodge with an underwater entrance hidden from predators.

VITAL STATISTICS

WEIGHT	12–25kg (26.5–55.1in)
LENGTH	Head & Body: 60–80cm (23.6–31in) Tail: 25–45cm (9.8–17.7in) long; 10–13cm (3.9–5.1in) wide
SEXUAL MATURITY	1–2 years
MATING SEASON	January to February
GESTATION PERIOD	100–110 days
NUMBER OF YOUNG	1 to 9
BIRTH INTERVAL	1 year
TYPICAL DIET	Leaves, ferns, herbs, grasses, algae, twigs and woody stems
LIFESPAN	15–24 years

Thickset in a waterproof overcoat and with teeth to match the power of a chainsaw, the beaver is purpose built for a life of labour in the water.

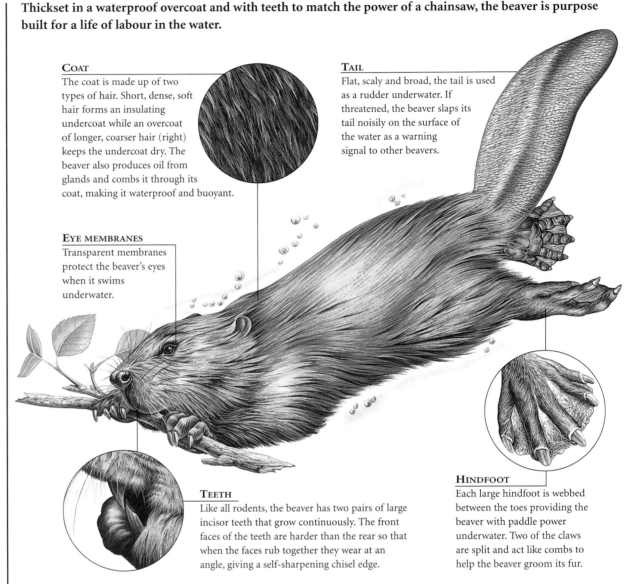

COAT
The coat is made up of two types of hair. Short, dense, soft hair forms an insulating undercoat while an overcoat of longer, coarser hair (right) keeps the undercoat dry. The beaver also produces oil from glands and combs it through its coat, making it waterproof and buoyant.

TAIL
Flat, scaly and broad, the tail is used as a rudder underwater. If threatened, the beaver slaps its tail noisily on the surface of the water as a warning signal to other beavers.

EYE MEMBRANES
Transparent membranes protect the beaver's eyes when it swims underwater.

TEETH
Like all rodents, the beaver has two pairs of large incisor teeth that grow continuously. The front faces of the teeth are harder than the rear so that when the faces rub together they wear at an angle, giving a self-sharpening chisel edge.

HINDFOOT
Each large hindfoot is webbed between the toes providing the beaver with paddle power underwater. Two of the claws are split and act like combs to help the beaver groom its fur.

CREATURE COMPARISONS

The sewellel (Aplodontia rufa) is sometimes called the mountain beaver and, like the beaver, is a rodent — although it belongs to a different family. Its range, in scattered sites from southwestern British Columbia to California, overlaps that of the beaver. The sewellel has a rather beaver-like body but it lives on land rather than in water. It is also a 'builder' and constructs a complex network of tunnels to live in. During the winter months, it may retire underground, living on food that it gathered and stored earlier in the year. When it leaves its burrow to forage, it seldom strays more than a few metres or feet.

Sewellel

North American beaver

WHERE IN THE WORLD?

Found throughout most of North America south from the Arctic Circle across Alaska and Canada to northern Mexico.

RELATED SPECIES
The Eurasian beaver, Castor fibe, found in forested parts of northern and central Europe and Asia, is a close relative of the North American beaver. Only isolated populations survive in western Europe, although the species has been reintroduced to some areas. The two species look very similar and share aquatic habits, although in many parts of its range the Eurasian beaver lives in holes dug into riverbanks rather than in a lodge.

• **ORDER** • *Rodentia* • **FAMILY** • *Castoridae* • **GENUS & SPECIES** • *Castor fiber*

EUROPEAN BEAVER

Bulky and powerful, with a pair of chisel teeth that can fell a small tree within minutes, the beaver is one of nature's finest engineers.

KEY FEATURES

- A heavyweight rodent that uses its gnawing front teeth to fell trees for dam-building material.
- Adults pair for life and live in close-knit family groups with young of varying ages.
- Almost exterminated by fur hunters, now increasing again in many areas.

VITAL STATISTICS

WEIGHT	20–35kg (44–77.2lb)
LENGTH	Head & Body: 70–100cm (27.6–39.4in) Tail: 30–40cm (11.8–15.7in)
SEXUAL MATURITY	2.5 years
BREEDING SEASON	January to February
GESTATION PERIOD	100 days
NUMBER OF YOUNG	2 to 5
BREEDING INTERVAL	1 year
TYPICAL DIET	Green plants, seeds and roots in summer, tree bark in winter
LIFESPAN	Up to 20 years

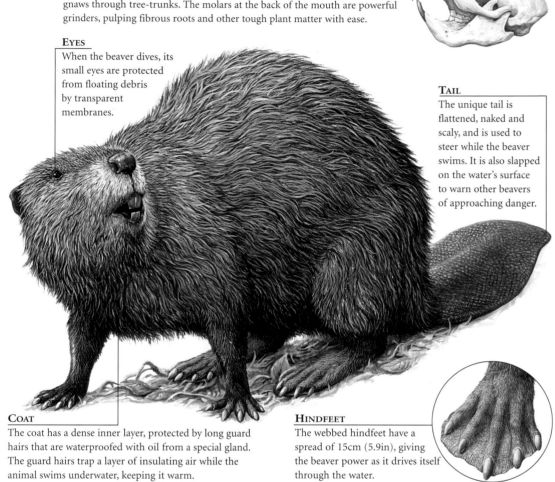

TEETH
The big incisors grow constantly to make up for wear and tear as the beaver gnaws through tree-trunks. The molars at the back of the mouth are powerful grinders, pulping fibrous roots and other tough plant matter with ease.

EYES
When the beaver dives, its small eyes are protected from floating debris by transparent membranes.

TAIL
The unique tail is flattened, naked and scaly, and is used to steer while the beaver swims. It is also slapped on the water's surface to warn other beavers of approaching danger.

COAT
The coat has a dense inner layer, protected by long guard hairs that are waterproofed with oil from a special gland. The guard hairs trap a layer of insulating air while the animal swims underwater, keeping it warm.

HINDFEET
The webbed hindfeet have a spread of 15cm (5.9in), giving the beaver power as it drives itself through the water.

CREATURE COMPARISONS

The coypu (Myocastor coypus), which is also known as the Chilean beaver, is one of the beaver's closest relatives. A native of South America, it has been introduced to many parts of Europe. Like the beaver, it spends most of its life in or near water, although it lacks some of the beaver's more refined adaptations for an aquatic existence, such as the flattened, oar-like tail. The coypu tends to dig its burrows in riverbanks — a habit shared by many European beavers, while the North American beaver more regularly constructs elaborate dams.

European beaver

Coypu

WHERE IN THE WORLD?

Found in the forests of Germany, Poland, Norway and Russia, as well as the Rhône Valley of France. Reintroduced to Finland, Sweden and Austria.

RELATED SPECIES

There are only 2 species of beaver: the European beaver, Castor fiber, and North American beaver, C. canadensis, although some zoologists claim that they are the same species. Beavers belong to the family Castoridae, which is 1 of 7 families of squirrel-like rodents in the suborder Sciuromorpha. There are 3 suborders in the vast order Rodentia, containing over 1700 species grouped into 30 families.

•ORDER • *Rodentia* •FAMILY • *Caviidae* •GENUS & SPECIES • *Dolichotis patagonum*

Looking like an unlikely cross between a hare and a small antelope, the mara is equipped for making a rapid escape from predators on the grasslands.

KEY FEATURES

- Also known as the Patagonian hare, the mara is a rodent, closely related to the cavy or guinea-pig.
- Similar in size and shape to a hare, with long ears but much longer, antelope-like legs.
- Pairs for life, and rears its young in 'crèches' along with the young of up to 15 other mara pairs.

VITAL STATISTICS

WEIGHT	9–16kg (19.8–35.5lb)
LENGTH	Head & Body: 69–75cm (27.2–29.5in) Tail:
SHOULDER HEIGHT	About 45cm (17.7in)
SEXUAL MATURITY	Male 6 months; female 3 months
MATING SEASON	June–July and September–October
GESTATION PERIOD	About 90 days
NUMBER OF YOUNG	1 to 3
BIRTH INTERVAL	3–4 months
TYPICAL DIET	Grass and herbs
LIFESPAN	About 10 years

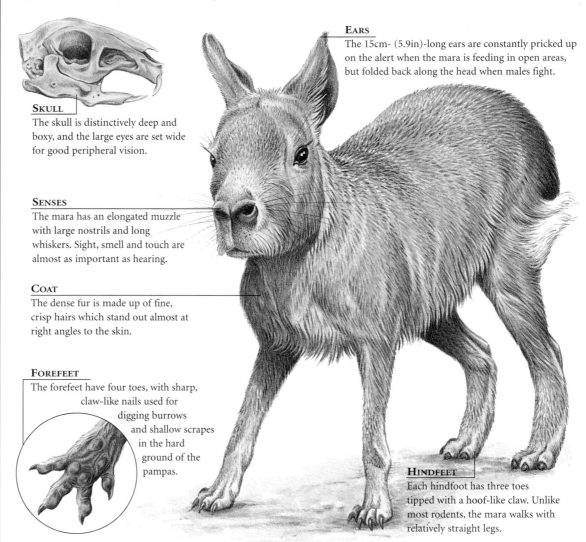

SKULL
The skull is distinctively deep and boxy, and the large eyes are set wide for good peripheral vision.

SENSES
The mara has an elongated muzzle with large nostrils and long whiskers. Sight, smell and touch are almost as important as hearing.

COAT
The dense fur is made up of fine, crisp hairs which stand out almost at right angles to the skin.

FOREFEET
The forefeet have four toes, with sharp, claw-like nails used for digging burrows and shallow scrapes in the hard ground of the pampas.

EARS
The 15cm- (5.9in)-long ears are constantly pricked up on the alert when the mara is feeding in open areas, but folded back along the head when males fight.

HINDFEET
Each hindfoot has three toes tipped with a hoof-like claw. Unlike most rodents, the mara walks with relatively straight legs.

CREATURE COMPARISONS

The rock cavy (Kerodon rupestris) is a much smaller South American relative of the mara. It lives in rocky outcrops and burrows under stones in the dry scrubland of northeastern Brazil. The male cavy defends a patch of rocks and has access to several females, so — unlike its relative — the rock cavy has a harem-based mating system. In addition to foraging on the ground, the rock cavy climbs trees to feed on leaves. This stocky, short-limbed rodent has strongly muscled hindlegs; like the mara, it makes powerful leaps to escape predators.

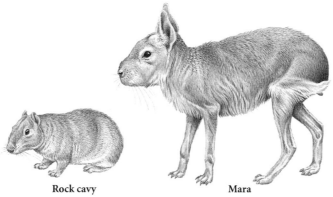

Rock cavy   Mara

WHERE IN THE WORLD?

Confined in the wild to the pampas grasslands of central and southern Argentina. Maras have also been introduced into Brittany, France, where there is a small feral colony.

RELATED SPECIES

The mara belongs to the genus Dolichotis, whose only other member is the rare and little known salt desert cavy, D. salinicola. About two-thirds the size of the mara, it lives in southern Bolivia, Paraguay and northern Argentina. The Caviidae family includes 17 species in 5 genera, all native to South America. The best known caviid is the guinea-pig, Cavia porcellus, first domesticated for its meat some 3000 years ago but today popular as a pet.

• ORDER • *Rodentia* • FAMILY • *Chinchillidae* • GENUS & SPECIES • *Chinchilla laniger, C. brevicaudata*

CHINCHILLA

The compact body of the chinchilla helps it retain heat on the Andean slopes, while its long whiskers aid navigation between the rocks at night.

KEY FEATURES

- The super-dense fur of this small rodent insulates it against the cold of night on its bare mountain home.
- Relies on acute hearing for defence against predators.
- Overhunted in the 19th century; today's wild populations are classified as endangered by the IUCN (World Conservation Union).

EARS
This night-time feeder relies on its acute hearing to detect the approach of predators.

EYES
In bright light, each pupil contracts to form a narrow slit, and opens into a disc in darker conditions.

HINDFOOT
Long, padded hindfeet help the chinchilla sit steadily on its haunches while it manipulates food with its forefeet.

SKULL
Like all rodents, the chinchilla has two pairs of continuously growing incisor teeth at the front of the jaws. A gap separates these gnawing teeth from the grinding cheek teeth.

WHISKERS
Touch-sensitive whiskers help the chinchilla feel its way in the dark.

FUR
Each follicle can produce more than 60 hairs, making the chinchilla's fur the most dense of any mammal.

Species illustrated:
Long-tailed chinchilla

VITAL STATISTICS

WEIGHT	Male up to 500g (17.6oz); female up to 800g (28.2oz)
LENGTH	Head & Body: 22.5–38cm (8.8–15in) Tail: 7.5–15cm (2.9–5.9in)
SEXUAL MATURITY	8 months
MATING SEASON	May to November
GESTATION PERIOD	110 days
NUMBER OF YOUNG	2 to 6
BIRTH INTERVAL	6 months
TYPICAL DIET	Grass and herbs
LIFESPAN	Up to 20 years in captivity; about 10 years in the wild

CREATURE COMPARISONS

The mountain viscacha (Lagidium viscacia) lives close by its relative, the chinchilla. It occurs in dry, rugged upland regions of the high Andes in Peru, Bolivia, Chile and Argentina. Like the chinchilla, the mountain viscacha lives at elevations up to 5000m (16400ft); it is equipped with a luxuriant coat and a long, furred tail to fight off the biting wind. It shares the chinchilla's habit of basking and grooming by day and seeking night-time refuge among rock crevices. The viscacha differs from the chinchilla in bearing only a single young after mating, and the juvenile takes a few months longer to reach maturity.

In common with the chinchilla, the viscacha has been heavily hunted for its fur, and its populations are declining.

Mountain viscacha

Chinchilla

WHERE IN THE WORLD?

Wild populations occur in the Andes Mountains in parts of Peru, Bolivia, Chile and northern Argentina. Bred commercially throughout the world.

RELATED SPECIES

Most mammal experts recognize 2 species in the genus Chinchilla. The long-tailed chinchilla, C. laniger, has a smaller range than its short-tailed relative, C. brevicaudata, which is found in the Andes of Peru, Bolivia, Chile and Argentina. The family Chinchillidae also includes the viscachas, which comprise 3 mountain species and 1 plains species. Chinchillas and viscachas are among 1814 members of the order Rodentia.

• ORDER • *Rodentia* • FAMILY • *Dasyproctidae* • GENUS & SPECIES • *Dasyprocta spp*

With its long, slender legs and acute senses, the agouti is well equipped to detect and escape the numerous predators that would make it a meal.

KEY FEATURES

- Long-legged, hare-sized rodents that forage on the ground in rainforest and other dense habitats.
- Avid harvesters of fallen fruit and seeds, some of which they store for times of future scarcity.
- Of nervous disposition owing to the constant threat of attack from forest carnivores.

VITAL STATISTICS

WEIGHT	1.3–4kg (2.9–8.8lb)
LENGTH	Head & Body: 41–62cm (16.1–24.4in) Tail: 1–3.5cm (0.4–1.4in)
SEXUAL MATURITY	Probably 8–12 months
MATING SEASON	Year-round in most species
NUMBER OF YOUNG	1 to 4 but usually 1 or 2
GESTATION PERIOD	104–120 days
BIRTH INTERVAL	Usually 1 year; some agoutis mate twice a year
TYPICAL DIET	Fruit, nuts, seeds, succulent plants; one species also eats insects and crabs
LIFESPAN	Up to 17 years in captivity

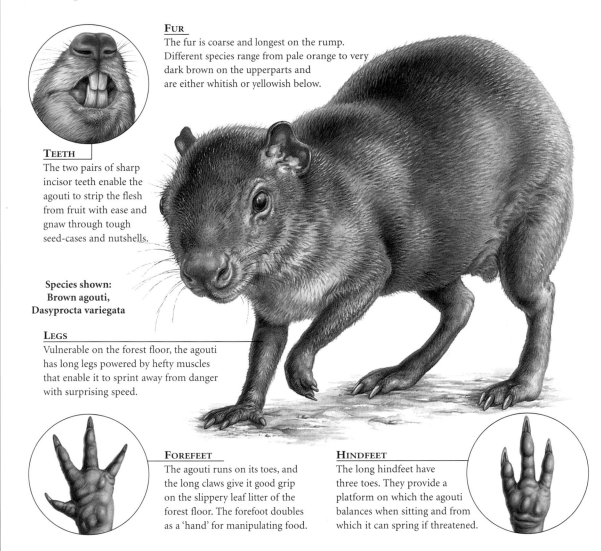

FUR
The fur is coarse and longest on the rump. Different species range from pale orange to very dark brown on the upperparts and are either whitish or yellowish below.

TEETH
The two pairs of sharp incisor teeth enable the agouti to strip the flesh from fruit with ease and gnaw through tough seed-cases and nutshells.

Species shown:
**Brown agouti,
Dasyprocta variegata**

LEGS
Vulnerable on the forest floor, the agouti has long legs powered by hefty muscles that enable it to sprint away from danger with surprising speed.

FOREFEET
The agouti runs on its toes, and the long claws give it good grip on the slippery leaf litter of the forest floor. The forefoot doubles as a 'hand' for manipulating food.

HINDFEET
The long hindfeet have three toes. They provide a platform on which the agouti balances when sitting and from which it can spring if threatened.

CREATURE COMPARISONS

The two species of acouchi are close relatives of the agoutis, and in some regions the ranges of the two animals overlap. North of the River Amazon in Brazil, for example, the red acouchi (*Myoprocta exilis*) occurs alongside the red-rumped agouti. Unlike agoutis, however, acouchis are restricted to undisturbed rainforest. Acouchis are about two-thirds the size of agoutis and have a more prominent tail. Like their more widespread cousins, they forage on the forest floor for fruit, nuts and seeds and utter a wide range of vocalizations. Both species are active by day and rest at night in leaf nests, which they build in disused armadillo burrows or hollow logs.

Agouti

Acouchi

WHERE IN THE WORLD?

Range across most of the American tropics, from southern Mexico through Central America and South America to the northern fringes of Argentina. Also occur on several offshore islands.

RELATED SPECIES

The genus Dasyprocta contains 11 species of agouti, the most widespread of which are the Central American agouti, Dasyprocta punctata, the red- or orange-rumped agouti, D. leporina, the black agouti, D. fuliginosa and Azara's agouti, D. azarae. Along with the acouchis of the genus Myoprocta, the agoutis make up the family Dasyproctidae, one of 13 families in the rodent suborder Hystricomorpha.

• ORDER • *Rodentia* • FAMILY • *Dasyproctidae* • GENUS & SPECIES • *Myoprocta acouchy*

GREEN ACOUCHI

KEY FEATURES

- Lives in small family units in the dense riverside undergrowth of tropical rainforests.
- Poorly equipped for defending itself in a fight, it relies on speed and agility to elude predators.
- Forages on the forest floor during the day, digging small holes and storing food for the dry season.

VITAL STATISTICS

WEIGHT	600–1300g (21.2–45.9oz)
LENGTH	Head & Body: 32–38cm Tail: 4.5–7cm
SEXUAL MATURITY	8 months
MATING SEASON	Throughout the year but peaks during the winter months (June–October)
GESTATION PERIOD	90–100 days
NUMBER OF YOUNG	Usually twins
BIRTH INTERVAL	112 days on average
TYPICAL DIET	Seeds, fruit, nuts and roots
LIFESPAN	4 years in wild; 7 years in captivity

With its sleek, compact profile and long hindlimbs, the acouchi has the ideal body shape for scampering through forest thickets.

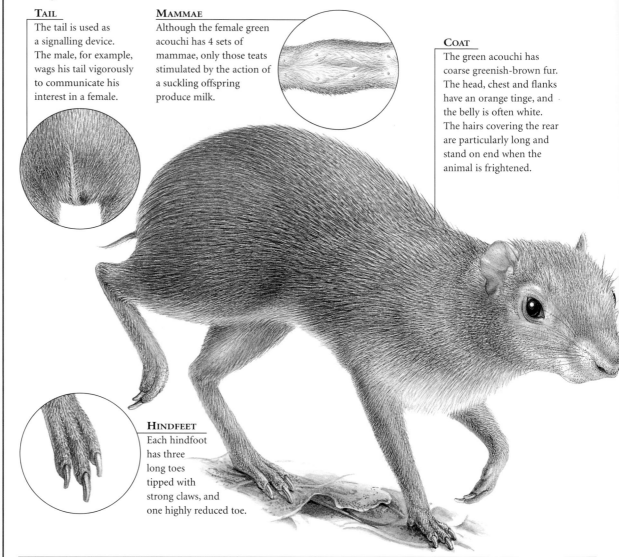

TAIL
The tail is used as a signalling device. The male, for example, wags his tail vigorously to communicate his interest in a female.

MAMMAE
Although the female green acouchi has 4 sets of mammae, only those teats stimulated by the action of a suckling offspring produce milk.

COAT
The green acouchi has coarse greenish-brown fur. The head, chest and flanks have an orange tinge, and the belly is often white. The hairs covering the rear are particularly long and stand on end when the animal is frightened.

HINDFEET
Each hindfoot has three long toes tipped with strong claws, and one highly reduced toe.

CREATURE COMPARISONS

Like the green acouchi, its close relative the paca (Agouti paca) lives in South American rainforests. The paca is much larger, measuring 60–80cm (23.6–31in) and weighing 6.3–12kg. (13.9–26.5lb). It also has long rump hairs, but has practically no tail. The paca's brown coat has a cryptic pattern of spots and lines on the flanks, helping it stay hidden from predators.

The two species differ in habit: the paca is nocturnal and digs its own burrows, while the green acouchi forages during the day and sleeps above ground in leaf nests.

Green acouchi

Paca

WHERE IN THE WORLD?

Found east of the Andes mountain range in the rainforests of southern Colombia, eastern Ecuador, northern Peru and the Amazon Basin of Brazil.

RELATED SPECIES

The green acouchi is one of 2 species in its genus. The red acouchi, Myoprocta exilis, has a similar distribution to the green acouchi, leading some authorities to think that they are colour variations of the same species. Both acouchis belong to the family Dasyproctidae, which comprises 13 species divided between 2 genera. Members share a number of physical features — for example, hindlimbs longer than forelimbs.

DESERT JERBOA

• ORDER • *Rodentia* • FAMILY • *Dipodidae* • GENUS & SPECIES • *Jaculus jaculus*

Looking rather like a minuscule kangaroo, the desert jerboa is adapted for tunnelling into the desert sand and running or leaping to outpace predators.

KEY FEATURES

- Hardy enough to live in barren lands and deserts, it has enormous hindlegs for fast hopping and snowshoe-like feet to stop it from sinking in sand.
- Shelters from the scorching midday sun in deep burrows, emerging to feed during the cool of night.
- Extracts all the water it needs from plants and seeds.

VITAL STATISTICS

WEIGHT	45–55g (1.6–1.9oz)
LENGTH	Head & Body: 11cm (4.3in) Tail: 15cm (5.9in)
SEXUAL MATURITY	Within first year
MATING SEASON	Varies across range: Feb to Sept in Egypt; Oct to Feb in Sudan
GESTATION PERIOD	25–30 days
NUMBER OF YOUNG	2 to 5
BIRTH INTERVAL	Three litters a year on average
TYPICAL DIET	Seeds, stems and roots of grasses and other plants; rarely insects
LIFESPAN	Probably less than 2 years

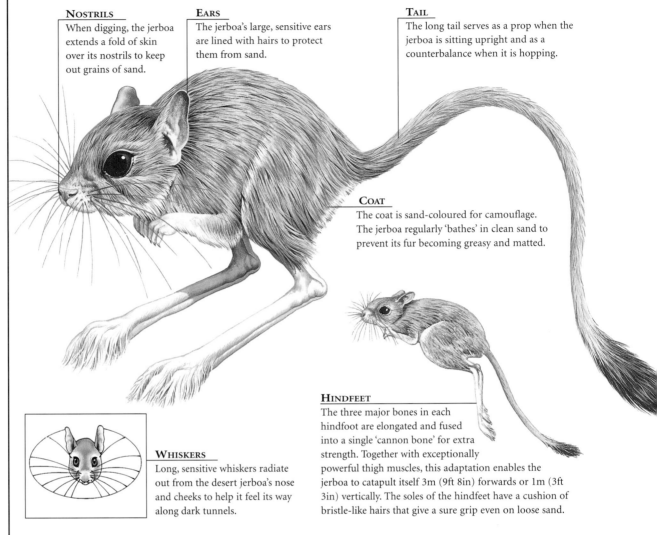

NOSTRILS
When digging, the jerboa extends a fold of skin over its nostrils to keep out grains of sand.

EARS
The jerboa's large, sensitive ears are lined with hairs to protect them from sand.

TAIL
The long tail serves as a prop when the jerboa is sitting upright and as a counterbalance when it is hopping.

COAT
The coat is sand-coloured for camouflage. The jerboa regularly 'bathes' in clean sand to prevent its fur becoming greasy and matted.

WHISKERS
Long, sensitive whiskers radiate out from the desert jerboa's nose and cheeks to help it feel its way along dark tunnels.

HINDFEET
The three major bones in each hindfoot are elongated and fused into a single 'cannon bone' for extra strength. Together with exceptionally powerful thigh muscles, this adaptation enables the jerboa to catapult itself 3m (9ft 8in) forwards or 1m (3ft 3in) vertically. The soles of the hindfeet have a cushion of bristle-like hairs that give a sure grip even on loose sand.

CREATURE COMPARISONS

Three species of jumping mouse, which are extremely difficult to tell apart, look similar to the desert jerboa and share its ability to leap a great distance relative to body size. Jumping mice can cover up to 1m in a single bound and spring several times in quick succession. Unlike the desert jerboa, however, they normally move on all fours or by short hops, and resort to longer hops only when fleeing predators.

Jumping mice live in meadows and woodland, especially by water, and have developed excellent swimming and bush-climbing skills. All three species are confined to North America.

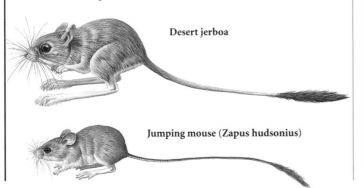

Desert jerboa

Jumping mouse (Zapus hudsonius)

WHERE IN THE WORLD?

Ranges across North Africa, the Sahara and the Middle East, from Morocco and Mauritania east as far as Iran, and from Turkey south to Sudan and Ethiopia.

RELATED SPECIES

There are 32 species of jerboa, divided into 11 genera in the family Dipodidae. All live in deserts, steppes and other dry areas, but only 5 almost identical species in the genus Jaculus are known as desert jerboas. The 2 species of fat-tailed jerboas in the genus Pygeretmus are named after their habit of storing fat in their tails. Many species have enlarged ears as well as hindlegs: the long-eared jerboa's ears are longer than its head.

• **ORDER** • *Rodentia* • **FAMILY** • *Erethizontidae* • **GENUS & SPECIES** • *Erethizon dorsatum* NORTH AMERICAN PORCUPINE

With impressive defensive adaptations and exceptional climbing skills, the North American porcupine is highly successful in its wooded habitat.

KEY FEATURES

- Robust rodent equipped with a coat of sharp, barbed quills, which are a highly effective defence.
- Prefers wooded habitats and is an excellent climber, clambering high into the crowns of trees.
- Has strong teeth for gnawing, and digests coarse food such as pine needles and tree bark.

VITAL STATISTICS

WEIGHT	Up to 18kg (39.7lb)
LENGTH	Head & Body: 65–86cm (25.6–33.9in) Tail: 15–30cm (4.3–11.8in)
SEXUAL MATURITY	Male 30 months; female 18 months
MATING SEASON	Late autumn to early winter
GESTATION PERIOD	205–217 days
NUMBER OF YOUNG	1, rarely 2
BIRTH INTERVAL	1 year
TYPICAL DIET	Varied, from berries to bark
LIFESPAN	Up to 18 years

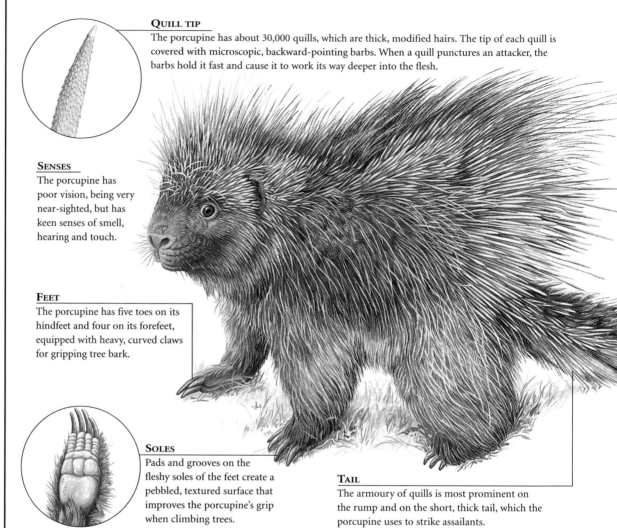

QUILL TIP
The porcupine has about 30,000 quills, which are thick, modified hairs. The tip of each quill is covered with microscopic, backward-pointing barbs. When a quill punctures an attacker, the barbs hold it fast and cause it to work its way deeper into the flesh.

SENSES
The porcupine has poor vision, being very near-sighted, but has keen senses of smell, hearing and touch.

FEET
The porcupine has five toes on its hindfeet and four on its forefeet, equipped with heavy, curved claws for gripping tree bark.

SOLES
Pads and grooves on the fleshy soles of the feet create a pebbled, textured surface that improves the porcupine's grip when climbing trees.

TAIL
The armoury of quills is most prominent on the rump and on the short, thick tail, which the porcupine uses to strike assailants.

CREATURE COMPARISONS

Old World (African and Eurasian) porcupines, such as the Malayan porcupine (Hystrix brachyura), live on the ground, whereas New World porcupines, like the North American species, are mostly arboreal in habit.

The Malayan porcupine has rattle quills at the end of its tail, which are slender for most of their length with a thicker section at the tip. The increased diameter section is thin-walled and hollow, so that several quills vibrating together produce a hiss-like rattle. This startling noise is used to deter potential predators.

Malayan porcupine

North American porcupine

WHERE IN THE WORLD?

Its range covers most of North America, from Alaska and Canada to northern Mexico, although it is absent from parts of central and southern USA.

RELATED SPECIES

New World porcupines, family Erethizontidae, comprise 10 species in 4 genera. These include the prehensile-tailed porcupines, such as Sphiggurus vestitus. Porcupines belong to the suborder of cavy-like rodents, Caviomorpha, within the order Rodentia.

• ORDER • *Rodentia* • FAMILY • *Geomyidae* • GENUS & SPECIES • *Various*

KEY FEATURES

- Small burrowing mammals found only in North and Central America.
- Chew through the toughest plant matter with large, sharp incisor teeth.
- Named after the voluminous cheek pouches in which food and bedding material are carried.

VITAL STATISTICS

WEIGHT	50–400g (1.8–14oz) depending on species
LENGTH	Head & Body: 8–30cm (3.1–11.8in) Tail: 5–12cm (2–4.7in)
SEXUAL MATURITY	3–12 months
MATING SEASON	All year in some species, seasonal in others
GESTATION PERIOD	17–20 days
NUMBER OF YOUNG	1 to 11
BIRTH INTERVAL	1 to 3 litters a year
TYPICAL DIET	Roots, tubers, leaves and seeds
LIFESPAN	4 years

A thickset animal with muscular forelimbs and long claws, the pocket gopher is perfectly adapted for life as a tunneller.

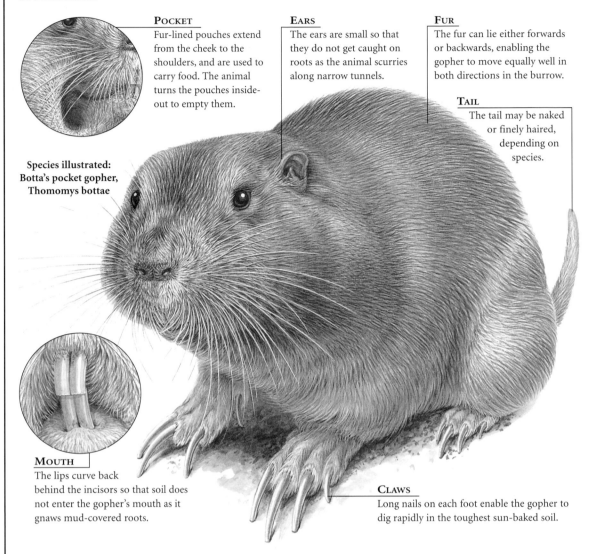

POCKET
Fur-lined pouches extend from the cheek to the shoulders, and are used to carry food. The animal turns the pouches inside-out to empty them.

EARS
The ears are small so that they do not get caught on roots as the animal scurries along narrow tunnels.

FUR
The fur can lie either forwards or backwards, enabling the gopher to move equally well in both directions in the burrow.

TAIL
The tail may be naked or finely haired, depending on species.

Species illustrated:
Botta's pocket gopher,
Thomomys bottae

MOUTH
The lips curve back behind the incisors so that soil does not enter the gopher's mouth as it gnaws mud-covered roots.

CLAWS
Long nails on each foot enable the gopher to dig rapidly in the toughest sun-baked soil.

CREATURE COMPARISONS

Botta's pocket gopher (Thomomys bottae) and the plains pocket gopher (Geomys bursarius) are representatives of the two largest genera of pocket gophers — the western and eastern respectively. Botta's pocket gopher tolerates a wide variety of mountain and lowland habitats by spending most of its time underground, hiding in its burrow to escape the harshest weather. The plains pocket gopher, however, forages more often above ground, and is found predominantly on lowland prairie and farmland. Common in central and southern USA, it is often regarded as a pest.

Botta's pocket gopher

Plains pocket gopher

WHERE IN THE WORLD?

Found throughout much of North and Central America, from southern Canada, the USA and Mexico south to Costa Rica and Panama; also northwest Colombia.

RELATED SPECIES

There are 6 genera of pocket gophers in the family Geomyidae. In the USA, Canada and Mexico Thomomys, the western pocket gophers, contains 9 species, while Geomys, the eastern pocket gophers, contains 8 species. The genera Orthogeomys, Zygogeomys, Pappageomys and Cratogeomys contain a total of 20 species found solely in Mexico and Central America. Pocket gophers belong to the large mammal order Rodentia.

• ORDER • *Rodentia* • FAMILY • *Gliridae* • GENUS & SPECIES • *Glis glis*

EDIBLE DORMOUSE

Sharp claws and a thick tail help the edible dormouse to keep its balance when climbing trees or leaping from branch to branch in its forest home.

KEY FEATURES

• Found in many parts of Europe from northern Spain east through Central Europe and into Russia. Also the islands of Sardinia, Corsica, Sicily, Crete and Corfu, and in Turkey and Iran. Introduced to Britain.

EARS
Large, rounded ears help gather sound and provide the dormouse with excellent hearing.

OFFSPRING
The naked newborn young (shown here actual size) are helpless and totally dependent on their mother. They open their eyes after four weeks.

FEET
All four feet are equipped with sharp, curved claws and rough pads on the toes that help tree-climbing.

TAIL
The long, bushy tail is used like a tightrope walker's pole, helping the dormouse to keep its balance when scampering along branches.

VIBRISSAE
Stiff, bristly hairs, known as vibrissae, extend up to 6cm (2.4in) from the muzzle. Highly touch-sensitive, these hairs help the dormouse find its way around at night.

VITAL STATISTICS

WEIGHT	70–180g (2.5–6.3oz)
LENGTH	Head & Body: 13–19cm (5.1–7.5in) Tail: 11–15cm (4.3–5.9in)
SEXUAL MATURITY	9–10 months
MATING SEASON	June to August
GESTATION PERIOD	20–30 days
NUMBER OF YOUNG	2 to 10 (usually 4 to 6)
BIRTH INTERVAL	1 year
TYPICAL DIET	Seeds, berries, nuts; insects; occasionally nestlings
LIFESPAN	Up to 5 years in the wild; more than 8 years in captivity

CREATURE COMPARISONS

The common dormouse (Muscardinus avellanarius) is the smallest species of dormouse and the only species that is native to Britain. It is about half the size of the edible dormouse, reaching about 16cm (6.3in) long from nose to tail tip. It is also less than a quarter of its relative's weight and has a much less bushy tail.

Both species typically prefer to live in wooded areas, although the common dormouse does not climb as high into trees as the edible dormouse. The common dormouse is often associated with hazel trees as it is very fond of the nuts, and this has given it the alternative name of 'hazel mouse'.

Edible dormouse

Common dormouse

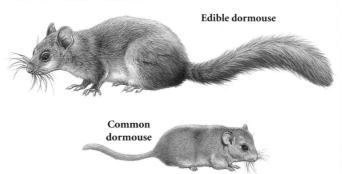

WHERE IN THE WORLD?

Found in many parts of Europe from northern Spain east through Central Europe and into Russia. Also the islands of Sardinia, Corsica, Sicily, Crete and Corfu, and in Turkey and Iran. Introduced to Britain.

RELATED SPECIES

The edible dormouse is the sole member of its genus, Glis, and belongs to the family Gliridae, which contains nine genera and 20 species of dormice in all. Dormice are very agile and most species are excellent tree climbers. Ten species of dormouse live in the forested and rocky areas of sub-Saharan Africa. The remainder are scattered across the world, ranging from Europe through central and southern Asia east to Mongolia and Japan.

CAPYBARA

• **ORDER** • *Rodentia* • **FAMILY** • *Hydrochaeridae* • **GENUS & SPECIES** • *Hydrochaeris hydrochaeris*

A highly unusual and strange-looking rodent, the capybara is equipped for a life spent grazing both in and out of the water.

KEY FEATURES

- The largest rodent in the world: at maturity it is, on average, about the size of a large dog.
- At the first sign of danger, it dives for cover in water — its only defence against predators.
- Very vocal, unlike most rodents, it purrs contentedly when feeding and barks loudly when in danger.

VITAL STATISTICS

WEIGHT	27–79kg (59.5–174lb)
LENGTH	1–1.3m (3ft 3in–4ft 3in)
SHOULDER HEIGHT	Up to 50cm (19.7in)
SEXUAL MATURITY	15 months
MATING SEASON	Year round, with peaks at the beginning of the rainy season
GESTATION PERIOD	4–5 months
NUMBER OF YOUNG	1 to 8, but usually 4 or 5
BIRTH INTERVAL	1 year, sometimes 2 litters in a year if conditions are favourable
TYPICAL DIET	Mainly grasses in or near water
LIFESPAN	8–10 years

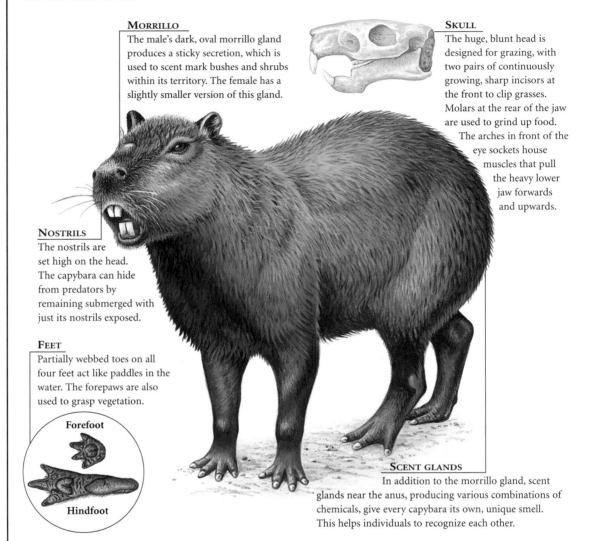

MORRILLO
The male's dark, oval morrillo gland produces a sticky secretion, which is used to scent mark bushes and shrubs within its territory. The female has a slightly smaller version of this gland.

SKULL
The huge, blunt head is designed for grazing, with two pairs of continuously growing, sharp incisors at the front to clip grasses. Molars at the rear of the jaw are used to grind up food. The arches in front of the eye sockets house muscles that pull the heavy lower jaw forwards and upwards.

NOSTRILS
The nostrils are set high on the head. The capybara can hide from predators by remaining submerged with just its nostrils exposed.

FEET
Partially webbed toes on all four feet act like paddles in the water. The forepaws are also used to grasp vegetation.

Forefoot

Hindfoot

SCENT GLANDS
In addition to the morrillo gland, scent glands near the anus, producing various combinations of chemicals, give every capybara its own, unique smell. This helps individuals to recognize each other.

CREATURE COMPARISONS

The coypu (Myocastor coypus) is another semi-aquatic, South American rodent that spends even more time in water than the capybara — most of its waking hours. Its fully webbed hindfeet also mean that it is a better swimmer. The coypu is a fraction of the weight of the capybara, weighing only 5–10kg (11–22lb), and about half the size with a head and body length of only 43–64cm (16.9–25.2in).

Both creatures have coarse hair, but the coypu's coat has an area of thick, velvety fur on its belly. This fur has been highly sought after since the early 19th century, and the coypu has been farmed for its fur throughout the world.

Coypu

Capybara

WHERE IN THE WORLD?

Found in Panama in Central America, and to the east of the Andes in South America from Colombia and the Guianas south to Uruguay and northeastern Argentina.

RELATED SPECIES

The capybara is the only member of the family Hydrochaeridae. It is, however, classified in the suborder Caviomorpha, which contains some 188 species of rodent. Most caviomorphs have big heads, plump bodies, slender legs and short tails, as in the case of the guinea pig (cavy) and the capybara. Others, however, such as some of the 55 species of spiny rats belonging to the family Echimyidae, look more like common rats and mice.

• **ORDER** • *Rodentia* • **FAMILY** • *Hystricidae* • **GENUS & SPECIES** • *Hystrix africaeaustralis*

CAPE PORCUPINE

The porcupine's excellent senses of hearing and smell, plus a menacing mass of quills, enable it to detect and repel even the fiercest of predators.

KEY FEATURES

- Spectacular array of quills can inflict a painful and potentially lethal septic wound on predators.
- Uses hollow tail rattles, like a rattlesnake, to signal warning or excitement.
- Inhabits elaborate burrows where both parents care for the young in a 'clan' system.

BACK BRISTLES
A mane of long, white bristles runs down the neck. These bristles, along with shorter ones on the nose, can be raised to act as a sensory aid.

QUILLS
Minutely barbed quills up to 40cm (15.7in) long cover both the hind part of the back and upper side of the tail, and are the porcupine's main defence.

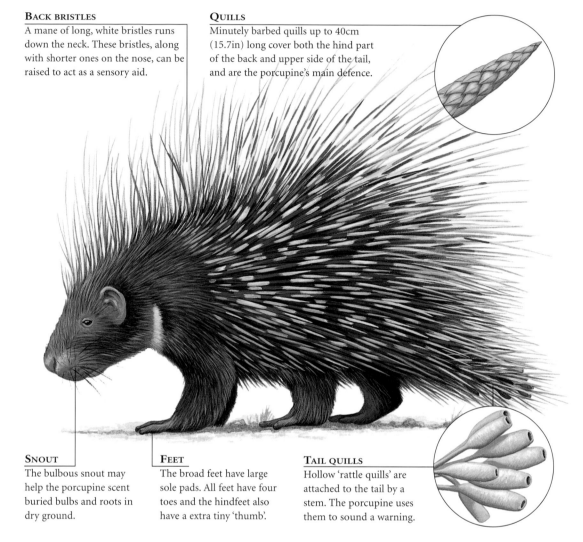

VITAL STATISTICS

WEIGHT	10–30kg (22–66.1lb)
LENGTH	Head & Body: 60–84cm (23.6–33.1in) Tail: 5–18cm (2–7.1in)
SHOULDER HEIGHT	38cm (15in)
SEXUAL MATURITY	2 years
MATING SEASON	December to March in south; July to December in mid Africa
GESTATION PERIOD	6–8 weeks
NUMBER OF YOUNG	2 to 4
BIRTH INTERVAL	1 year, though occasionally 2 litters per year
TYPICAL DIET	Plant parts and fruit
LIFESPAN	20–30 years

SNOUT
The bulbous snout may help the porcupine scent buried bulbs and roots in dry ground.

FEET
The broad feet have large sole pads. All feet have four toes and the hindfeet also have a extra tiny 'thumb'.

TAIL QUILLS
Hollow 'rattle quills' are attached to the tail by a stem. The porcupine uses them to sound a warning.

CREATURE COMPARISONS

The eight members of the Hystricidae family are known as Old World porcupines; their native range extends across Africa and Asia. The New World (American) porcupines form the family Erethizontidae, with ten species. New World porcupines live mainly in trees, and some have a prehensile (grasping) tail that can grip branches.

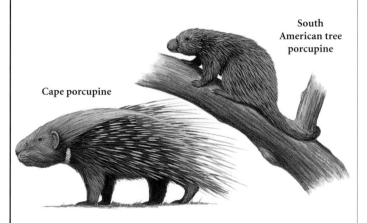

Cape porcupine

South American tree porcupine

WHERE IN THE WORLD?

A native of much of Africa south of the equator in a wide variety of habitats, excepting regions of moist, tropical rainforest and areas of desert extremes.

RELATED SPECIES

The genus Hystrix has three species, known as the 'large porcupines.' All are native to Africa and Asia, but one, H. cristata, the crested porcupine, has been introduced into parts of Europe. The three Hystrix species resemble each other closely and can be interbred in captivity.

• **ORDER** • *Rodentia* • **FAMILY** • *Muridae* • **GENUS & SPECIES** • *Clethrionomys glareolus*

BANK VOLE

Robust and rounded, the bank vole is ideally adapted to tunnelling through thick, matted vegetation, where it finds ample food and some protection.

KEY FEATURES

- Constructs an extensive network of tunnels just below the ground to avoid detection by predators.
- A prolific breeder whose population is subject to 3–4 year cycles of dramatic increase followed by a sudden crash in numbers.
- Forages in hedges and trees for a wide range of vegetable matter, and eats insects and carrion.

VITAL STATISTICS

WEIGHT	14–36g (0.5–1.3oz)
LENGTH	Head & Body: 8–11cm (3.1–4.3in) Tail: 3.5–7.2cm (1.4–2.8in)
SEXUAL MATURITY	4–5 weeks; can be inhibited by the presence of other adults
MATING SEASON	March to October
GESTATION PERIOD	18–20 days
NUMBER OF YOUNG	3 to 7; three or more litters per year
BREEDING INTERVAL	17–18 days
TYPICAL DIET	Grasses, leaves, fruit, nuts, other plant parts; fungi; insects
LIFESPAN	Up to 18 months

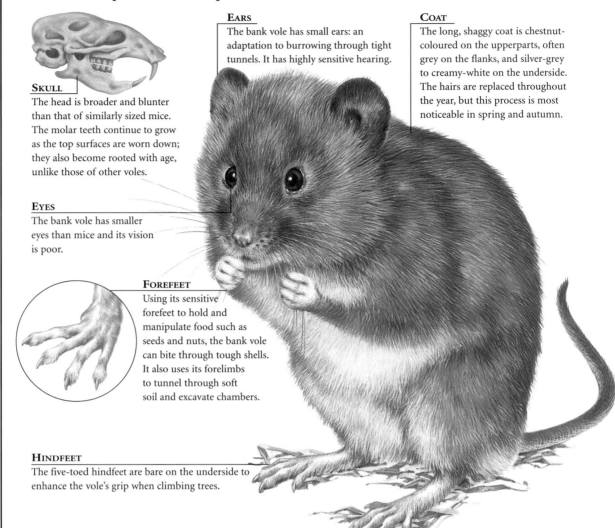

SKULL
The head is broader and blunter than that of similarly sized mice. The molar teeth continue to grow as the top surfaces are worn down; they also become rooted with age, unlike those of other voles.

EYES
The bank vole has smaller eyes than mice and its vision is poor.

FOREFEET
Using its sensitive forefeet to hold and manipulate food such as seeds and nuts, the bank vole can bite through tough shells. It also uses its forelimbs to tunnel through soft soil and excavate chambers.

HINDFEET
The five-toed hindfeet are bare on the underside to enhance the vole's grip when climbing trees.

EARS
The bank vole has small ears: an adaptation to burrowing through tight tunnels. It has highly sensitive hearing.

COAT
The long, shaggy coat is chestnut-coloured on the upperparts, often grey on the flanks, and silver-grey to creamy-white on the underside. The hairs are replaced throughout the year, but this process is most noticeable in spring and autumn.

CREATURE COMPARISONS

Like the bank vole, the common vole (Microtus arvalis) is widespread across much of Europe, but it is absent from Britain. It thrives on cultivated land, but whereas the bank vole prefers drier terrain, the common vole favours wet meadows, plantations, ditches and marshlands. Unlike bank voles, during the breeding season the territories of common voles do not overlap.

The common vole has a yellow-brown back and pale grey underparts, and is a little larger and heavier than the bank vole, reaching a total length of 17.5cm (6.9in) and an average weight of 50g (1.8oz).

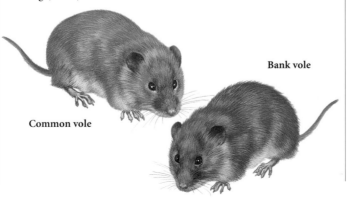

Common vole

Bank vole

WHERE IN THE WORLD?

Common over most of Europe from the Swedish tundra south to Italy, including mainland Britain and several small

neighbouring islands. There are two isolated populations in central Russia and Siberia.

RELATED SPECIES

The bank vole is 1 of 6 species of red-backed vole in the genus Clethrionomys. Voles and lemmings make up the subfamily Arvicolinae, which also includes the field vole, Microtus agrestis. All voles are placed in the family Muridae.

• ORDER • *Rodentia* • FAMILY • *Muridae* • GENUS & SPECIES • *Gerbillus spp.*

NORTHERN PYGMY GERBIL

Looking like a cross between a mouse and a miniature kangaroo, the pygmy gerbil has many adaptations for a life spent in a searingly hot, dry climate.

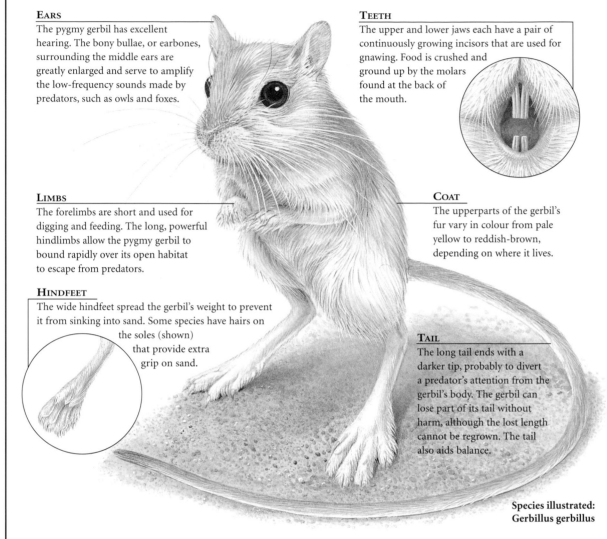

EARS
The pygmy gerbil has excellent hearing. The bony bullae, or earbones, surrounding the middle ears are greatly enlarged and serve to amplify the low-frequency sounds made by predators, such as owls and foxes.

TEETH
The upper and lower jaws each have a pair of continuously growing incisors that are used for gnawing. Food is crushed and ground up by the molars found at the back of the mouth.

LIMBS
The forelimbs are short and used for digging and feeding. The long, powerful hindlimbs allow the pygmy gerbil to bound rapidly over its open habitat to escape from predators.

COAT
The upperparts of the gerbil's fur vary in colour from pale yellow to reddish-brown, depending on where it lives.

HINDFEET
The wide hindfeet spread the gerbil's weight to prevent it from sinking into sand. Some species have hairs on the soles (shown) that provide extra grip on sand.

TAIL
The long tail ends with a darker tip, probably to divert a predator's attention from the gerbil's body. The gerbil can lose part of its tail without harm, although the lost length cannot be regrown. The tail also aids balance.

Species illustrated:
Gerbillus gerbillus

KEY FEATURES

- Tiny, but tough creature that is hardy enough to live in deserts and other inhospitable lands.
- Equipped with expandable cheek pouches to carry food back to its daytime burrow, which can be a simple hole or a complex system of tunnels.
- Can live without drinking throughout its entire life.

VITAL STATISTICS

WEIGHT	10–63g (0.3–1.4oz)
LENGTH	Head & Body: 5–13cm (2–5.1in) Tail: 6–18cm (2.4–7.1in)
SEXUAL MATURITY	About 6 months
MATING SEASON	All year
GESTATION PERIOD	20–22 days
NUMBER OF YOUNG	1 to 8, but usually 4 to 5
BIRTH INTERVAL	1 to 3 litters per year, depending on species
TYPICAL DIET	Mainly seeds, herbs, roots; occasionally insects
LIFESPAN	Up to 8 years in captivity; probably about 2 years in the wild

CREATURE COMPARISONS

The fat-tailed gerbil (Pachyuromys duprasi) of North Africa shares many features with the pygmy gerbil. It has the same large eyes, long whiskers and modified hearing apparatus, but here the likeness ends. The fat-tailed gerbil is larger at 10–13cm (3.9–5.1in) and has a stockier build. Its hindfeet are also shorter. But the most marked difference is in the length and shape of the tail. The fat-tailed gerbil's tail is short, reaching only about a third of the length of its head and body, and is shaped like a club. Fat is stored in the tail and can be converted to energy when food is in short supply. In parts of the Sahara both species share the same habitat, but they do not compete for food as the fat-tailed gerbil is insectivorous (insect-eating).

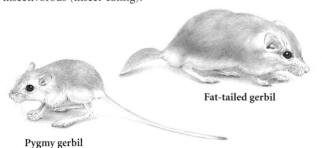

Fat-tailed gerbil

Pygmy gerbil

WHERE IN THE WORLD?

Found throughout northern Africa as far south as Kenya. Its range also extends east to the Arabian Peninsula and continues through Iran to western India.

RELATED SPECIES

There are 38 species of northern pygmy gerbil in the genus Gerbillus. They belong to the family Muridae in the order Rodentia along with rats, mice, hamsters, voles and lemmings. Muridae is by far the largest family of mammals with 1138 known species. The northern pygmy gerbils are closely related to the 4 species of southern pygmy gerbil of the genus Gerbillurus, which are found in Angola, Namibia, Botswana and South Africa.

NORWAY LEMMING

• **ORDER** • *Rodentia* • **FAMILY** • *Muridae* • **GENUS & SPECIES** • *Lemmus lemmus*

The Norway lemming is a sturdy and compact burrowing rodent that makes its home in the icy tundra of northern Europe.

KEY FEATURES

- Compact and thickly furred plant-eating rodent.
- Abounds on the Scandinavian tundra, where many predators depend on it as a source of food.
- Reproduces rapidly with periodic population explosions leading to swarming mass migrations during which many thousands die.

VITAL STATISTICS

WEIGHT	50–115g (1.8–4oz)
LENGTH	Head & Body: 13–15cm (5.1–5.9in) Tail: 1.5–2cm (5.9–0.8in)
SEXUAL MATURITY	Female 14 days; male 1 month
MATING SEASON	Spring to autumn
GESTATION PERIOD	Around 20 days
NUMBER OF YOUNG	1 to 13
BIRTH INTERVAL	Around 55 days
TYPICAL DIET	Grass and other ground plants
LIFESPAN	Up to 2 years

TAIL
Furred to reduce heat loss, the tail is short enough not to hinder the lemming in its snug burrows.

FUR
Both sexes sport a boldly coloured coat of dense, waterproof fur.

SKULL
The thickset skull has 12 molars and 4 permanently growing incisors. Powerful jaw muscles help the lemming grind tough plants.

EARS
The short, fur-covered ears are extremely sensitive and provide the lemming with advanced warning of approaching predators, such as Arctic foxes.

FOREFOOT
The small and thickly furred forefoot has four sharp claws and a fifth that is specially flattened and enlarged. This claw helps the lemming burrow under the snow.

WHISKERS
Touch-sensitive whiskers enable the lemming to navigate in its dark burrow.

CREATURE COMPARISONS

The wood lemming (Myopus schisticolor) inhabits upland, mossy bogs and coniferous forest from Norway all the way to Siberia and northern Mongolia. Weighing up to 30g (1.1oz), it is significantly lighter than the Norway lemming and, except for a reddish-brown area on the centre of its back, is uniform in colour. It feeds on mosses, the stems of red whortleberry and the bark of juniper bushes. Like its tundra-living relative, it breeds throughout the winter if conditions are favourable, producing a large number of smaller litters, and its population expands accordingly. It also undertakes migrations but not on the same spectacular and self-destructive scale as the Norway lemming.

Norwegian lemming

Wood lemming

WHERE IN THE WORLD?

Found in northern Europe from Norway, Sweden and Finland east into northwestern Russia.

RELATED SPECIES

The Norway lemming shares its genus with 2 other species: the Siberian lemming, Lemmus sibiricus, which is found in Arctic Russia as well as Alaska and parts of northeastern Canada; and the Amur lemming, L. amurensis, which is restricted to eastern Siberia. Lemmings belong to the family Muridae, which includes voles, rats and mice, and is the largest mammalian family containing over 1000 species.

• **ORDER** • *Rodentia* • **FAMILY** • *Muridae* • **GENUS & SPECIES** • *Micromys minutus*

HARVEST MOUSE

A tiny harvester of cereal seeds, the harvest mouse uses its tail as a grasping limb, nimbly scaling its high-rise world of the stems and stalks.

KEY FEATURES

- One of the world's smallest rodents, it weighs about the same as a medium-sized coin.
- Females build a neat, spherical nursery nest among tall, green stems when pregnant.
- Searches for food using the stalks of plants as aerial walkways, aided by its fifth limb — a grasping tail.

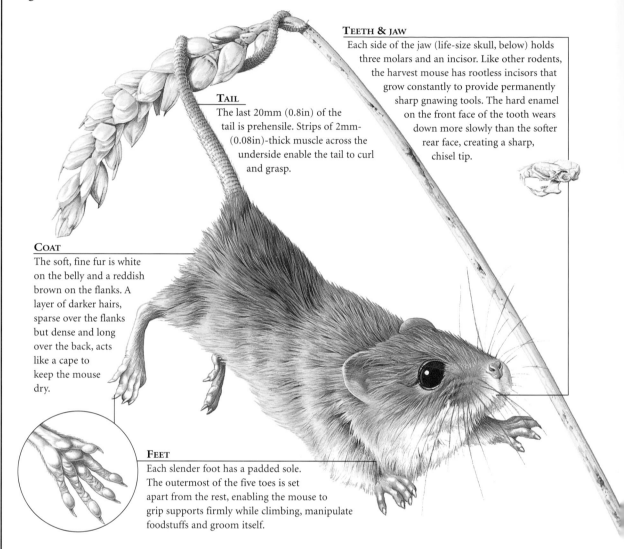

TAIL
The last 20mm (0.8in) of the tail is prehensile. Strips of 2mm- (0.08in)-thick muscle across the underside enable the tail to curl and grasp.

TEETH & JAW
Each side of the jaw (life-size skull, below) holds three molars and an incisor. Like other rodents, the harvest mouse has rootless incisors that grow constantly to provide permanently sharp gnawing tools. The hard enamel on the front face of the tooth wears down more slowly than the softer rear face, creating a sharp, chisel tip.

COAT
The soft, fine fur is white on the belly and a reddish brown on the flanks. A layer of darker hairs, sparse over the flanks but dense and long over the back, acts like a cape to keep the mouse dry.

FEET
Each slender foot has a padded sole. The outermost of the five toes is set apart from the rest, enabling the mouse to grip supports firmly while climbing, manipulate foodstuffs and groom itself.

VITAL STATISTICS

WEIGHT	5–7g (0.2–0.25oz)
LENGTH	Head & Body: 55–85mm (2.2–3.3in) Tail: 50–85mm (2–3.3in)
SEXUAL MATURITY	35–45 days
MATING SEASON	Late May to December in W. Europe; March to December in E. Europe and Asia
GESTATION PERIOD	17–19 days
NUMBER OF YOUNG	1 to 13, usually 5 or 6
BIRTH INTERVAL	17–18 days
TYPICAL DIET	Seeds, fruit; insects, carrion
LIFESPAN	less than 6 months in the wild; up to 5 years in captivity

CREATURE COMPARISONS

The harvest mouse is not alone in its diminutive dimensions, the Australian hopping mouse is another tiny species — although it is not quite as small as the harvest mouse. Both mice face the problem of keeping their bodies at the right temperature, but have different ways of achieving it. The harvest mouse, for example, converts most of its food intake into energy to keep warm. The Australian hopping mouse (*Notomys fuscus*) has a proportionally smaller surface area than the harvest mouse, which helps it to conserve heat. Consequently, it does not need to eat as often. It also adjusts its body temperature by tunnelling into the ground where it can keep cool or stay warm depending on conditions.

Australian hopping mouse

Harvest mouse

WHERE IN THE WORLD?

Found throughout much of western Europe east across central Asia as far as Siberia and Japan in the north, and south to Hong Kong and Taiwan.

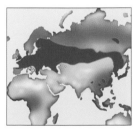

RELATED SPECIES

The harvest mouse is the only species in its genus. It belongs to the largest of all mammal families, Muridae, which contains 1138 rodent species, including lemmings, rats, voles, gerbils and mice, such as the striped grass mouse *Lemniscomys striatus*.

FIELD VOLE

• ORDER • *Rodentia* • FAMILY • *Muridae* • GENUS & SPECIES • *Microtus agrestis*

Scuttling along its vegetated tunnels, the field vole uses its sharp teeth for feeding and relies on its acute hearing for defence and communication.

KEY FEATURES

- A diminutive mammal that is highly aggressive, particularly towards members of its own species.

- Leads a short but hyperactive life, breeding very quickly to compensate for high mortality rates.

- Uses well worn runways between feeding sites, often forming a network that radiates from the nest.

TAIL
The tail is pinker and shorter than that of the otherwise similar bank vole and gives the field vole its alternative name of short-tailed vole.

COAT
The coarse fur is brown with whitish underparts. The sexes are similar in colour, but juveniles are generally darker.

EARS
Hearing is important, as each species of vole has its own range of calls for threatening rivals, signalling alarm or attracting mates. Unlike the very similar common vole, the field vole has hair inside its small ears and on the upper edge.

SKULL AND TEETH
The four chisel-shaped incisors have sharp edges for cropping grass and stripping bark, while the 12 flattened molars are used for grinding. The field vole has a small extra enamel lobe on the inside of its middle upper molar, distinguishing it from other similar species. Typical of rodents, the field vole has a gap, known as the diastema, between its incisors and molars.

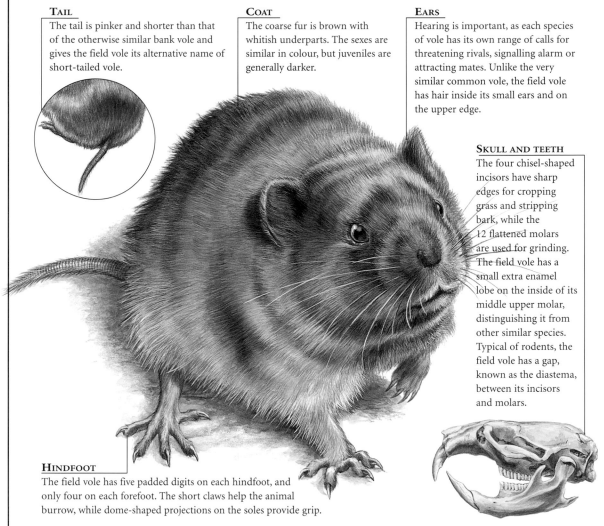

HINDFOOT
The field vole has five padded digits on each hindfoot, and only four on each forefoot. The short claws help the animal burrow, while dome-shaped projections on the soles provide grip.

VITAL STATISTICS

WEIGHT	14–50g (0.5–1.8oz)
LENGTH	Head & Body: 7.8–13.5cm (3.1–5.3in) Tail: 1.8–4.9cm (0.7–1.9in)
SEXUAL MATURITY	Male 40 days; female 28 days
MATING SEASON	Throughout the year, but mainly March to October
GESTATION PERIOD	18–20 days
NUMBER OF YOUNG	2 to 7
BIRTH INTERVAL	2 to 7 litters per year
TYPICAL DIET	Grass, roots, bulbs, tree bark, insect larvae
LIFESPAN	2 years

CREATURE COMPARISONS

A giant in comparison to its cousin the field vole, the muskrat (Ondatra zibethicus) grows up to 68cm (26.8in) from nose to tail. Unlike the field vole, the muskrat has five toes on each of its feet. The toes are fringed with stiff bristles to help propel the muskrat in the water, and its tail is laterally flattened to act as a rudder. A native of North America, the muskrat was introduced to Europe in 1905 for its fur, which is known as musquash. The animal escaped into the wild and established itself in the rivers, lakes and marshlands of central and northern Europe. Like the field vole, it is a prolific breeder, reproducing throughout the year in the southern part of its range, though only during summer in the north.

Field vole

Muskrat

WHERE IN THE WORLD?

Found throughout northern, western and central Europe, but absent from Ireland. Its range extends east to the Ural Mountains and south to Mongolia.

RELATED SPECIES
The field vole is 1 of 67 species in its genus Microtus, which is the largest in the family Muridae. This family contains a total of 110 species in 18 different genera, though even a careful examination of tooth structures (the usual method of classifying rodents) has not been sufficient to differentiate reliably between all species. The field vole is similar to the bank vole but lacks its chestnut-coloured back.

• ORDER • *Rodentia* • FAMILY • *Muridae* • GENUS & SPECIES • *Mus musculus*

HOUSE MOUSE

Agile, alert and with a keen sense of smell, the house mouse is neatly equipped to locate food and negotiate hidden passages within the confines of buildings.

KEY FEATURES

- Small, adaptable rodent with a wide-ranging diet and a capacity for rapid breeding.
- Thrives in and around human habitation, and has done so throughout recorded history.
- Adjusts its reproductive and territorial behaviour to match food supplies and living conditions.

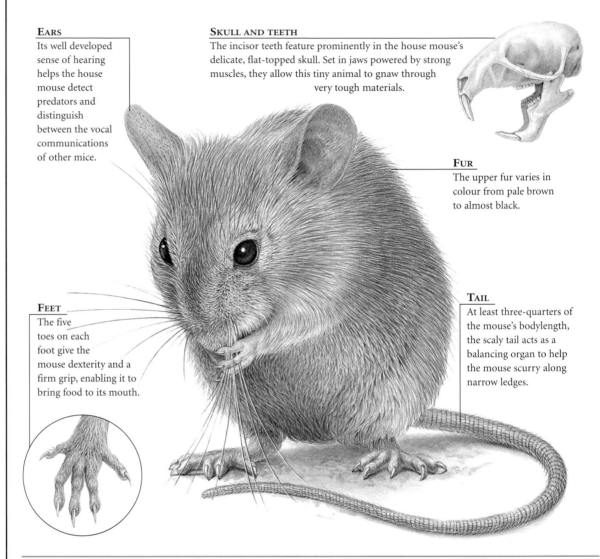

EARS
Its well developed sense of hearing helps the house mouse detect predators and distinguish between the vocal communications of other mice.

SKULL AND TEETH
The incisor teeth feature prominently in the house mouse's delicate, flat-topped skull. Set in jaws powered by strong muscles, they allow this tiny animal to gnaw through very tough materials.

FUR
The upper fur varies in colour from pale brown to almost black.

FEET
The five toes on each foot give the mouse dexterity and a firm grip, enabling it to bring food to its mouth.

TAIL
At least three-quarters of the mouse's bodylength, the scaly tail acts as a balancing organ to help the mouse scurry along narrow ledges.

VITAL STATISTICS

WEIGHT	12–30g (0.4–1.1oz)
LENGTH	Head & Body: 65–95mm (0.2–0.4in) Tail: 60–100mm (2.4–3.9in)
SEXUAL MATURITY	5–7 weeks
MATING SEASON	All year in buildings; usually seasonal in the wild
NUMBER OF YOUNG	3 to 12
BIRTH INTERVAL	5 to 10 litters per year
GESTATION PERIOD	19–21 days
TYPICAL DIET	Wide range of vegetable and animal matter, including household materials
LIFESPAN	1–2 years

CREATURE COMPARISONS

The spiny mice of Asia and Africa are one of many genera of rodents that bear a superficial resemblance to the house mouse and its close relatives. Like the house mouse, some species of spiny mice, such as the Egyptian spiny mouse (*Acomys cahirinus*), can be found living in and around human settlements. As its name suggests, the spiny mouse has a coat of especially stiff bristles, which some predators may find unpalatable. Another feature of this species is its brittle tail, which breaks off easily should an enemy grab it; this enables the mouse to escape. Many lizards display the same tactic; unlike them, the spiny mouse cannot grow a replacement.

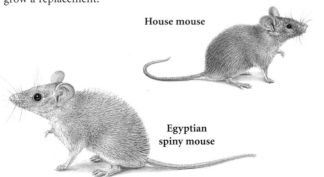

House mouse

Egyptian spiny mouse

WHERE IN THE WORLD?

Commonly found wherever there is human habitation, including remote oceanic islands and settlements within inhospitable regions such as deserts.

RELATED SPECIES

The house mouse belongs to the genus Mus, which is commonly divided into a further 4 subgenera and includes the African pygmy mice and the shrew mice of tropical Asia. The genus Mus is 1 of more than 260 genera of mice, rats and other closely related rodents such as voles, hamsters and gerbils in the family Muridae — the most species-rich family of all the world's mammals, containing 1100 species.

• **ORDER** • *Rodentia* • **FAMILY** • *Muridae* • **GENUS & SPECIES** • *Ondatra zibethicus*

This amphibious rodent relies on its webbed hindfeet for propulsion. A dense coat of guard hairs protects it from becoming waterlogged.

KEY FEATURES

- Lives rather like a beaver, occupying a burrow or a 'lodge' nest in watery habitats.

- A powerful, musky scent is secreted by the adult male during the mating season.

- A well adapted swimmer that forages on aquatic vegetation as well as small aquatic animals.

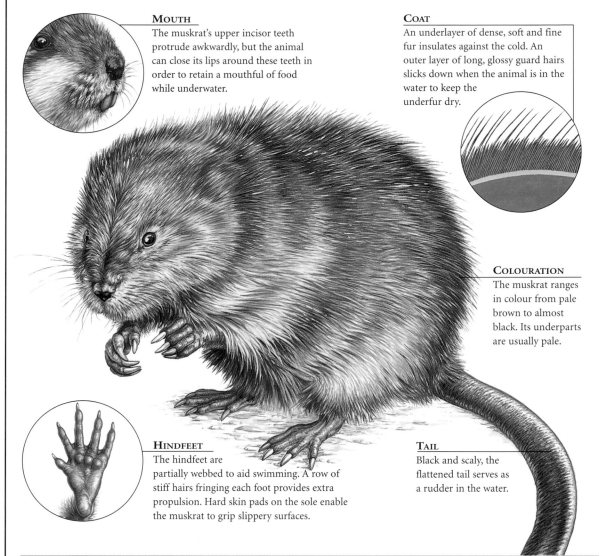

MOUTH
The muskrat's upper incisor teeth protrude awkwardly, but the animal can close its lips around these teeth in order to retain a mouthful of food while underwater.

COAT
An underlayer of dense, soft and fine fur insulates against the cold. An outer layer of long, glossy guard hairs slicks down when the animal is in the water to keep the underfur dry.

COLOURATION
The muskrat ranges in colour from pale brown to almost black. Its underparts are usually pale.

HINDFEET
The hindfeet are partially webbed to aid swimming. A row of stiff hairs fringing each foot provides extra propulsion. Hard skin pads on the sole enable the muskrat to grip slippery surfaces.

TAIL
Black and scaly, the flattened tail serves as a rudder in the water.

VITAL STATISTICS

WEIGHT	540–1800g (19–63.5oz)
LENGTH	Head & Body: 23–32cm (9–12.6in) Tail: 18–30cm (7.1–11.8in)
SEXUAL MATURITY	10–12 months
MATING SEASON	March to September in northern range; non-seasonal in south
GESTATION PERIOD	25–30 days
NUMBER OF YOUNG	1 to 11, average 6
BIRTH INTERVAL	10–12 weeks
TYPICAL DIET	Mainly aquatic vegetation such as cat-tails and rushes; also small fish and frogs
LIFESPAN	2–3 years

CREATURE COMPARISONS

The round-tailed muskrat (Neofiber alleni) is a native of Florida and the swampy areas along the border between the US states of Florida and Georgia — a range from which the muskrat is absent.

The round-tailed species is the smaller of the two, reaching about 22cm (8.7in) in length and weighing at most 350g (12.3oz). Although it is also a good swimmer, the round-tailed muskrat lacks the webbing on its cousin's hindfeet. This difference accounts for a slightly different preferred habitat: the round-tailed muskrat inhabits boggy, but not truly aquatic, areas.

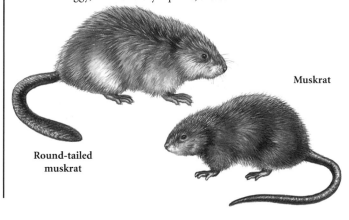

Round-tailed muskrat

Muskrat

WHERE IN THE WORLD?

Native to North America. Absent from tundra and from much of the south. Introduced to, and now numerous in, Europe and Asia, from Sweden to Japan.

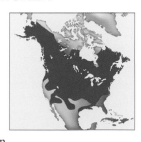

RELATED SPECIES

The muskrat is the sole member of the genus *Ondatra*. Scientists classify the muskrat, along with the voles and lemmings, in the subfamily Microtinae, which belongs to the largest of all mammalian families, the Muridae. This family also contains rats, mice and gerbils and belongs to the order Rodentia. Rodents are found worldwide except on Antarctica, some remote oceanic islands, and a few islands off New Zealand and the West Indies.

• **ORDER** • *Rodentia* • **FAMILY** • *Muridae* • **GENUS & SPECIES** • *Rattus norvegicus*

BROWN RAT

The sleek, compact brown rat scuttles nimbly on sharp-clawed toes, 'tasting' the air with finely tuned nostrils and navigating with its whiskers.

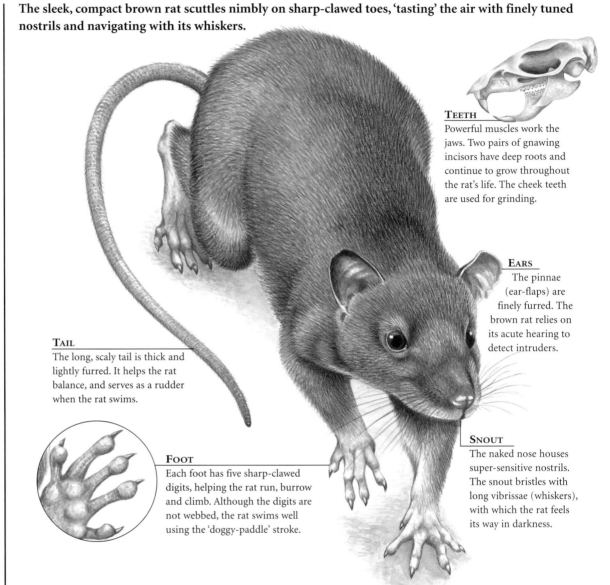

KEY FEATURES

- Notoriously successful rodent that breeds at a prolific rate and eats almost any organic matter.
- Thrives in rural and urban habitats, including sewers, spreading several potentially fatal diseases.
- An instinctive mistrust of unfamiliar objects and food sources makes this pest very difficult to eradicate.

TEETH
Powerful muscles work the jaws. Two pairs of gnawing incisors have deep roots and continue to grow throughout the rat's life. The cheek teeth are used for grinding.

EARS
The pinnae (ear-flaps) are finely furred. The brown rat relies on its acute hearing to detect intruders.

SNOUT
The naked nose houses super-sensitive nostrils. The snout bristles with long vibrissae (whiskers), with which the rat feels its way in darkness.

TAIL
The long, scaly tail is thick and lightly furred. It helps the rat balance, and serves as a rudder when the rat swims.

FOOT
Each foot has five sharp-clawed digits, helping the rat run, burrow and climb. Although the digits are not webbed, the rat swims well using the 'doggy-paddle' stroke.

VITAL STATISTICS

WEIGHT	250–500g (8.8–17.6in)
LENGTH	Head & Body: 18–25cm (7.1–9.8in) Tail: 15–20cm (5.9–7.9in)
SEXUAL MATURITY	2–3 months
MATING SEASON	Throughout the year
GESTATION PERIOD	23 days
NUMBER OF YOUNG	6 to 12
BIRTH INTERVAL	2–3 months
TYPICAL DIET	Cereals, root crops, and human refuse
LIFESPAN	1 year in the wild

CREATURE COMPARISONS

A similar-looking, though much smaller, member of the genus Rattus is the moss forest rat (R. niobe). Like its cousin, the forest rat has a scaly tail, sharp-clawed digits, delicate ears and a tapering snout. The forest rat is a tropical species, living in the mountains of New Guinea and spending the rainy season in dense cover. It digs more readily than the brown rat, and excavates a U-shaped burrow with an entrance at each end. Unlike the brown rat, the forest rat is not closely associated with human settlements. It differs also in the size of its litters: these usually contain no more than three offspring.

Moss forest rat

Brown rat

WHERE IN THE WORLD?

Originated around the Caspian Sea, and unknown in western Europe until about 1000AD. Now found worldwide apart from the polar extremes.

RELATED SPECIES

The brown rat is 1 of 51 species in the genus Rattus, most of which live in Asia and Australia. The brown rat's most familiar relative in Britain is the black or ship rat, R. rattus. Adapted to warm climates, in Britain this species is confined mainly to buildings; it lacks the brown rat's ability to range widely during cooler periods and is now common only in tropical regions. Rattus belongs to the family Muridae, the largest family in the order Rodentia.

• ORDER • *Rodentia* **• FAMILY •** *Muridae* **• GENUS & SPECIES •** *Rattus rattus*

BLACK RAT

Scent plays an important part in the nocturnal world of the black rat, and the senses of sight and hearing are also well developed.

KEY FEATURES

- Lives and feeds in warehouses and grain stores.
- Carries many diseases, including bubonic plague, the terrifying Black Death that killed 25 million people in Europe during the 14th century.
- Responsible, along with other rodents, for annual damage totalling about $1 billion in the USA alone.

NOSE AND WHISKERS
The black rat has a very keen sense of smell. Several touch-sensitive whiskers along the snout help it feel its way about in dim light.

COAT
Despite its name, the black rat is actually more often grey-brown above and pale grey, or even creamy white, beneath. Long guard hairs on the back and flanks help keep water off the skin.

TEETH
The incisors (front teeth) grow constantly, so the rat gnaws regularly to keep them to length. When gnawing, the lips fill the gap between the incisors and the molars, keeping debris from the mouth.

PAWS
There are four long, clawed toes on each forepaw, and five on each hindpaw. The rat uses its toes to grip and run along ropes or power lines, and its claws to cling and climb on rough surfaces.

TAIL
The hairless tail, longer than the head and body combined, provides balance when the rat is climbing.

VITAL STATISTICS

WEIGHT	140–200g (4.9–7oz)
LENGTH	Head & Body: Up to 23cm (9in) Tail: Up to 25cm (9.8in)
SEXUAL MATURITY	3–5 months
MATING SEASON	Year round, with peaks in spring and autumn in temperate regions
GESTATION PERIOD	21 days
NUMBER OF YOUNG	5 to 10
BIRTH INTERVAL	Up to 12 litters per year
TYPICAL DIET	Almost anything although fruits and cereals are favoured
LIFESPAN	Up to 4 years

CREATURE COMPARISONS

The black rat can be distinguished from its close relative the brown, or Norway, rat by a number of features other than colour — both species show much colour variation. In general, the black rat is the smaller of the two, with a proportionally longer tail and a sleeker, glossier coat. The ears of the brown rat are pale and covered with hairs, while the larger ears of the black rat are pink and hairless.

Black rat

Brown rat

WHERE IN THE WORLD?

Found alongside humans in many habitats across tropical and temperate regions of the world.

Absent from deserts and from far northern and polar regions.

RELATED SPECIES

Nearly 40 per cent of all mammal species belong to the order Rodentia, which, as well as rats and mice, includes beavers, squirrels, gophers and porcupines. Largest of all rodents is the South American capybara, which may grow to 132cm (52in) long and weigh a hefty 65kg (143.3lb).

• ORDER • *Rodentia* • FAMILY • *Muridae* • GENUS & SPECIES • *Arvicola terrestris*

WATER VOLE

KEY FEATURES

- Lives on the banks and in the water of streams and rivers.
- A prolific breeder, capable of producing five litters each year.
- Often wrongly referred to as the water rat, it is in fact only a distant relative of the true rats.
- Loses heat quickly from its small body and spends a lot of the time foraging for food.

VITAL STATISTICS

WEIGHT	150–350g (5.3–12.3oz)
LENGTH	Head & Body: 12–26cm (4.7–10.2in) Tail: 8–17.5cm (3.1–6.9in)
SEXUAL MATURITY	8 weeks
BREEDING SEASON	March to October
GESTATION PERIOD	3 weeks
NUMBER OF YOUNG	4 to 6 per litter
BIRTH INTERVAL	Up to 5 litters a year
TYPICAL DIET	Grasses, reeds, sedges, roots and bulbs; also hunts insects and shellfish
LIFESPAN	Up to 3 years

Although the water vole lacks webbed feet, its waterproof coat and buoyant body allow it to take advantage of a habitat denied to many rodents.

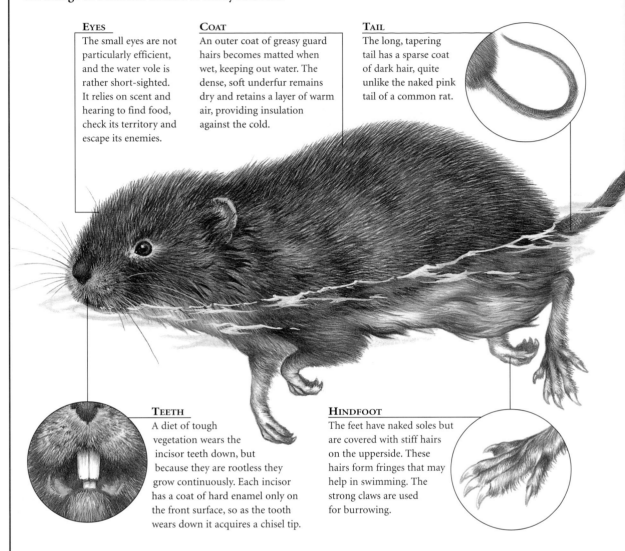

EYES
The small eyes are not particularly efficient, and the water vole is rather short-sighted. It relies on scent and hearing to find food, check its territory and escape its enemies.

COAT
An outer coat of greasy guard hairs becomes matted when wet, keeping out water. The dense, soft underfur remains dry and retains a layer of warm air, providing insulation against the cold.

TAIL
The long, tapering tail has a sparse coat of dark hair, quite unlike the naked pink tail of a common rat.

TEETH
A diet of tough vegetation wears the incisor teeth down, but because they are rootless they grow continuously. Each incisor has a coat of hard enamel only on the front surface, so as the tooth wears down it acquires a chisel tip.

HINDFOOT
The feet have naked soles but are covered with stiff hairs on the upperside. These hairs form fringes that may help in swimming. The strong claws are used for burrowing.

CREATURE COMPARISONS

The high mountain vole (Alticola roylei) lives on the bare summits of the western Himalayas and the high mountains of southern Siberia. It is much smaller than its aquatic relative, and is usually a shade of grey or brown with white underparts. Both voles have dense fur covering their ears, but the high mountain vole has a flattened skull that is thought to be an adaptation for living under rock crevices. While the water vole is active night and day, the high mountain vole tends to be nocturnal. Both voles store food for the winter.

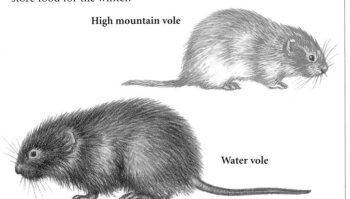

High mountain vole

Water vole

WHERE IN THE WORLD?

Found in a broad band across Europe and much of northern and central Asia, from Britain east to Siberia and Mongolia. Its European range does not include Ireland, Italy and most of France and the Iberian Peninsula.

RELATED SPECIES

There are 3 species of water vole found worldwide, and at least 110 species of vole and lemming. They are grouped in a subfamily, Microtinae, to distinguish them from the various rats and mice that make up the rest of the family Muridae, which with more than 1100 species is the biggest of all mammal families. Murids naturally occur worldwide, with the exception of New Zealand and a few islands in the polar regions and the West Indies.

COMMON DORMOUSE

• ORDER • *Rodentia* • FAMILY • *Myoxidae* • GENUS & SPECIES • *Muscardinus avellanarius*

KEY FEATURES

- Forages among the branches of its woodland habitat, sleeping in a high-rise nest during the day.
- Hibernates for half the year, living off reserves of body fat built up during the summer months.
- Relies on covered runways to travel between trees and escape the attention of predators.

VITAL STATISTICS

WEIGHT	20–35g (0.7–1.2oz) prior to hibernation; 12–16g (0.4–0.6oz) after hibernation
LENGTH	Head & Body: 60–90mm (23.6–35.4in) Tail: 55–75mm (21.6–29.5in)
SEXUAL MATURITY	Breeds in first year
MATING SEASON	May to September
GESTATION PERIOD	22–24 days
NUMBER OF YOUNG	2 to 7
BIRTH INTERVAL	2 litters per season
TYPICAL DIET	Fruit, seeds, flowers, pollen, insects, nuts
LIFESPAN	4–5 years

Equipped with specially adapted feet and a lightweight body, the common dormouse scrambles among the branches in search of food.

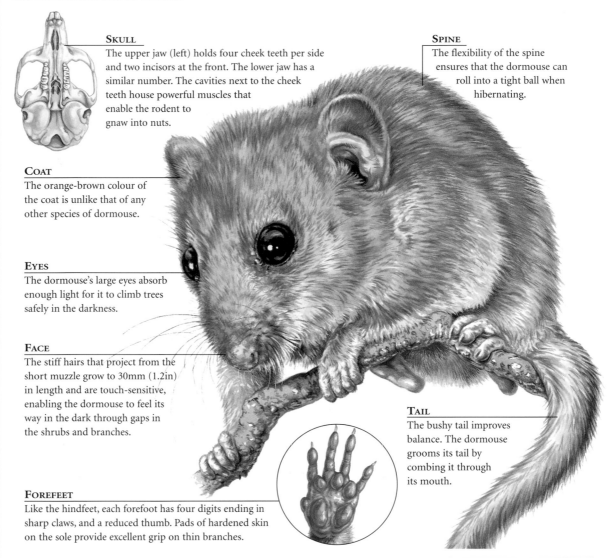

SKULL
The upper jaw (left) holds four cheek teeth per side and two incisors at the front. The lower jaw has a similar number. The cavities next to the cheek teeth house powerful muscles that enable the rodent to gnaw into nuts.

COAT
The orange-brown colour of the coat is unlike that of any other species of dormouse.

EYES
The dormouse's large eyes absorb enough light for it to climb trees safely in the darkness.

FACE
The stiff hairs that project from the short muzzle grow to 30mm (1.2in) in length and are touch-sensitive, enabling the dormouse to feel its way in the dark through gaps in the shrubs and branches.

FOREFEET
Like the hindfeet, each forefoot has four digits ending in sharp claws, and a reduced thumb. Pads of hardened skin on the sole provide excellent grip on thin branches.

SPINE
The flexibility of the spine ensures that the dormouse can roll into a tight ball when hibernating.

TAIL
The bushy tail improves balance. The dormouse grooms its tail by combing it through its mouth.

CREATURE COMPARISONS

Found in Europe, North Africa and on some Mediterranean islands, the garden dormouse (Eliomys quercinus) is larger than its common cousin. Its head-and-body length can reach 17cm (6.7in) and it can weigh as much as 120g (4.2oz) prior to winter hibernation. In contrast to the common dormouse's distinctive orange coat, the garden dormouse has less uniform colouring, sporting a creamy underside with grey-brown upperparts and black markings on the face. Its tail is often a colourful mixture of brown, black and white. The garden dormouse builds tree-nests up to 3m (9ft 8in) above the ground, but unlike its cousin it is also found in areas that lack trees.

Garden dormouse

Common dormouse

WHERE IN THE WORLD?

Found throughout Europe, except in northern parts; absent also from Spain and Ireland. Occurs as far south as Greece, and east to the Volga River in Russia.

RELATED SPECIES

The common dormouse is the sole species in its genus and 1 of 20 species in the dormouse family, once known as Gliridae but now called Myoxidae. The family includes the mouse-like dormouse, Myomimus personatus, and the edible dormouse, Myoxus glis.

• **ORDER** • *Rodentia* • **FAMILY** • *Pedetidae* • **GENUS & SPECIES** • *Pedetes capensis*

SPRINGHARE

KEY FEATURES

- A squirrel-like rodent that has evolved into the African equivalent of a small kangaroo.
- Adapted for survival on arid grasslands, where food is scarce and predators are plentiful.
- Built for speed on flat, open terrain, where it bounds along on spring-loaded legs.

VITAL STATISTICS

WEIGHT	3–4kg (6.6–8.8lb)
LENGTH	Head & Body: 35–43cm (13.8–16.9in) Tail: 37–47cm (14.6–18.5in)
SEXUAL MATURITY	1 year
MATING SEASON	All year
GESTATION PERIOD	78–82 days
NUMBER OF YOUNG	1
BIRTH INTERVAL	Average of 3 litters per year
TYPICAL DIET	Tender, wild grasses, bulbs and roots, plus cultivated crops; occasionally insects
LIFESPAN	Up to 15 years

Able to leap 3m (9ft 8in) in a single bound, the springhare is equipped to live on dry, open ground where danger can come from any direction.

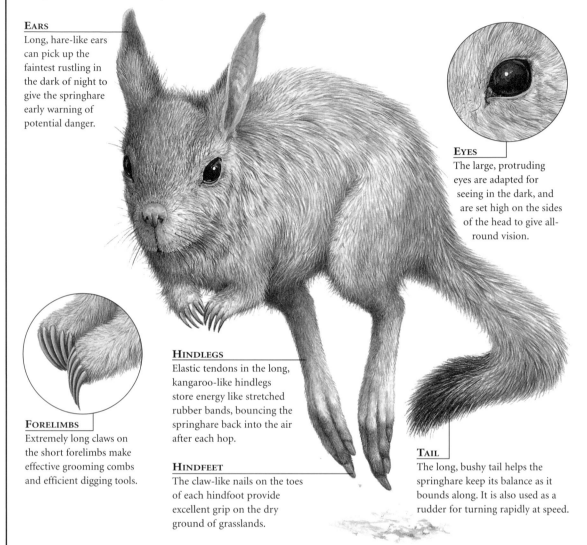

EARS
Long, hare-like ears can pick up the faintest rustling in the dark of night to give the springhare early warning of potential danger.

EYES
The large, protruding eyes are adapted for seeing in the dark, and are set high on the sides of the head to give all-round vision.

FORELIMBS
Extremely long claws on the short forelimbs make effective grooming combs and efficient digging tools.

HINDLEGS
Elastic tendons in the long, kangaroo-like hindlegs store energy like stretched rubber bands, bouncing the springhare back into the air after each hop.

HINDFEET
The claw-like nails on the toes of each hindfoot provide excellent grip on the dry ground of grasslands.

TAIL
The long, bushy tail helps the springhare keep its balance as it bounds along. It is also used as a rudder for turning rapidly at speed.

CREATURE COMPARISONS

A relation of the springhare, the desert jerboa, *Jaculus jaculus*, shares the same basic body plan and has evolved a similar way of life. Both live in Africa and spend the day underground in extensive burrows, emerging by night to feed. Their long, powerful hindlegs enable them to range widely over arid lands while foraging for food, and to make a quick getaway from desert foxes and other predators. At about the size of a rabbit, the springhare is nearly four times the size of its diminutive relative.

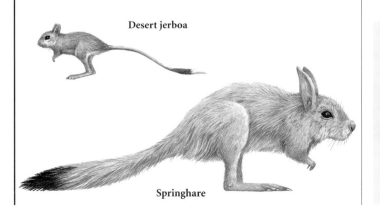

Desert jerboa

Springhare

WHERE IN THE WORLD?

Found in two separate regions of Africa: the savannahs of southwestern Somalia, Kenya and Tanzania; and from mid Angola south to eastern Cape Province in South Africa.

RELATED SPECIES

The springhare is the only species in the genus Pedetes and the only member of the family Pedetidae. However, it belongs to the largest of all mammalian orders, Rodentia, which contains over 1700 species of rodent. Typically, rodents are divided into 3 suborders, and the springhare belongs to the suborder Sciuromorpha, or squirrel-like rodents. Relations in this suborder include the scaly-tailed flying squirrels of Africa.

BLACK-TAILED PRAIRIE DOG

• **ORDER** • *Rodentia* • **FAMILY** • *Sciuridae* • **GENUS & SPECIES** • *Cynomys ludovicianus*

KEY FEATURES

- A sociable species of squirrel, living in colonies in vast, treeless plains.
- Digs complex burrow systems, with chambers, connecting passages and a choice of several exits.
- Named a 'dog' after its loud bark, which alerts others to danger.
- Once a common pest on cattle ranches, but now rare after decades of persecution by ranchers.

VITAL STATISTICS

WEIGHT	1.1–1.35kg (2.4–2.8lb)
LENGTH	Head & Body: 28–33cm (11–13in) Tail: 7.5–10cm (2.9–3.9in)
SEXUAL MATURITY	2 years
MATING SEASON	Late winter to early spring; varies with location
GESTATION PERIOD	30–35 days
NUMBER OF YOUNG	2 to 8
BIRTH INTERVAL	1 year
TYPICAL DIET	Grasses and low-growing plants; some invertebrates, especially grasshoppers and beetles
LIFESPAN	Male 5 years; female up to 8 years

The black-tailed prairie dog's muscular forelegs, compact body and thick fur coat enable it to burrow furiously and run down tunnels with ease.

EARS
Small ears lie flat against the prairie dog's head to maximize its freedom of movement underground.

SKULL
The enlarged skull houses strong muscles, enabling the animal to cut through underground roots.

WHISKERS
Stiff whiskers help the prairie dog feel its way along dark passages.

FORELEGS
The prairie dog uses its powerful forelegs to dig burrows. It kicks the loose soil away with its larger hindlegs.

FUR
A dense coat of coarse fur protects the prairie dog from flying stones and soil particles when tunnelling and keeps it warm during the cold winters of the prairies.

TAIL
The prairie dog flicks its tuft-like tail up and down when nervous.

HINDFEET
Long toes tipped with strong claws provide a secure footing when sitting upright to scan around.

CREATURE COMPARISONS

The South African ground squirrel (Xerus inauris) thrives in sandy, open grasslands and leads a similar life to the black-tailed prairie dog. It forms large colonies, taking turns to scan the territory for predators, and crops grasses right to the ground with its strong teeth.

The ground squirrel has a slimmer body, with a smaller, more rounded head. Longer hindlegs give it a more upright posture, and the squirrel's long, bushy tail acts like a flag when it is alarmed.

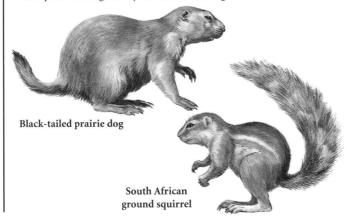

Black-tailed prairie dog

South African ground squirrel

WHERE IN THE WORLD?

Found in the prairies of central North America, from southern Canada to northernmost Mexico. Its range stretches west as far as the foothills of the Rocky Mountains.

RELATED SPECIES

The 5 species of prairie dog are divided into 2 groups: the black-tailed and Mexican prairie dogs, which do not hibernate, and the white-tailed, Gunnison's and Utah prairie dogs, which do. Prairie dogs belong to the genus Cynomys, 1 of 49 genera in the squirrel family, Sciuridae. Among the prairie dogs' closest relatives are the 11 species of marmot, in the genus Marmota, and the 38 species of ground squirrel, or suslik, in Spermophilus.

• ORDER • *Rodentia* • FAMILY • *Sciuridae* • GENUS & SPECIES • *Glaucomys volans*

SOUTHERN FLYING SQUIRREL

The flying squirrel glides gracefully through the trees by unfurling the fur-covered membranes that are attached to its hind- and forelegs.

KEY FEATURES

• Feeds at night, sailing through the air from treetop to treetop to nibble nuts and seeds.

• Glides up to 45m (148ft) between tree-trunks with the use of patagia — supple, stretchy sheets of skin and muscle that are attached to its legs on each side.

• Young flying squirrels stay with their mothers much longer than other rodents in order to master the ability to 'fly'.

VITAL STATISTICS

WEIGHT	170–225g (6–7.9oz)
LENGTH	Head & Body: 23–28cm (9–11in) Tail: 13–18cm (5.1–7.1in)
SEXUAL MATURITY	1–2 years
MATING SEASON	January to August
GESTATION PERIOD	40 days
NUMBER OF YOUNG	2 to 6
BIRTH INTERVAL	1 year
TYPICAL DIET	Acorns and other nuts; seeds, bark of twigs, lichen, buds, shoots and other plant matter; fungi spiders, insects, birds' eggs and nestlings
LIFESPAN	Up to 10 years

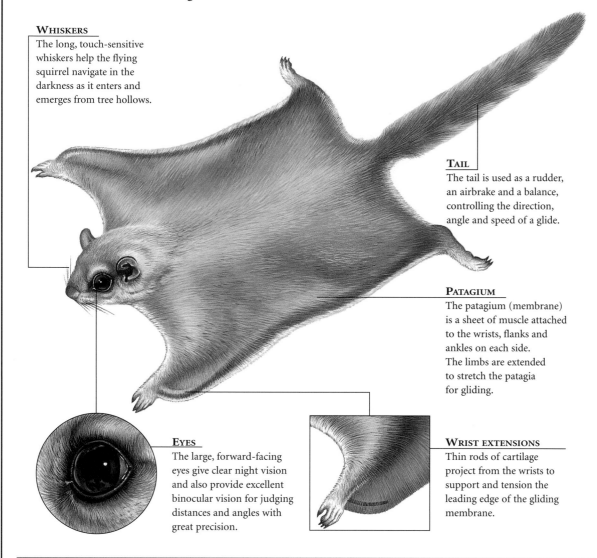

WHISKERS
The long, touch-sensitive whiskers help the flying squirrel navigate in the darkness as it enters and emerges from tree hollows.

TAIL
The tail is used as a rudder, an airbrake and a balance, controlling the direction, angle and speed of a glide.

PATAGIUM
The patagium (membrane) is a sheet of muscle attached to the wrists, flanks and ankles on each side. The limbs are extended to stretch the patagia for gliding.

EYES
The large, forward-facing eyes give clear night vision and also provide excellent binocular vision for judging distances and angles with great precision.

WRIST EXTENSIONS
Thin rods of cartilage project from the wrists to support and tension the leading edge of the gliding membrane.

CREATURE COMPARISONS

The southern flying squirrel is one of 14 squirrel species that can glide on special membranes. Other mammals share this ability, too, including the two species of flying lemur, or colugo, native to various parts of Southeast Asia. The colugos glide between trees on supple, wing-like membranes, but they have a much greater patagium area than the flying squirrels, with extra membranes extending between the hindlegs and tail tip on both sides. With all four limbs spreadeagled, a colugo assumes the shape of a kite and can glide distances of up to 70m (230ft), losing as little as 30cm (11.8in) in altitude for every 3.5m (11ft 5in) travelled. Like the southern flying squirrel, colugos inhabit tall woodland, using their gliding abilities to gain access to edible vegetation growing high in the leafy canopy.

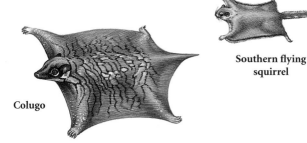

Southern flying squirrel

Colugo

WHERE IN THE WORLD?

Ranges from eastern Canada south across the deciduous, coniferous and subtropical forests of eastern North America. Also found throughout the Yucatan Peninsula in Mexico and south to Honduras in Central America.

RELATED SPECIES

The other member of the genus Glaucomys is the slightly larger northern flying squirrel, G. sabrinus, which is found in Canada and parts of the bordering USA, including Alaska, south through the Appalachians. American flying squirrels are among 260 species in the squirrel family, Sciuridae, which also includes the giant flying squirrels, genus Petaurista, of southeastern Asia, and the Russian flying squirrel, Pteromys volans, of Europe and Asia.

ALPINE MARMOT

•**ORDER** • *Rodentia* • **FAMILY** • *Sciuridae* • **GENUS & SPECIES** • *Marmota marmota*

KEY FEATURES

- Large colony-forming rodent that grazes in open meadows at high altitudes.
- Excavates burrows, which offer hibernation sites over winter and refuges from predators in summer.
- Shrill alarm call is a familiar sound to walkers and climbers in the high peaks and valleys.

VITAL STATISTICS

WEIGHT	5–7.5kg (11–16.5lb)
LENGTH	Head & Body: 50–60cm (19.7–23.6in) Tail: 13–19cm (5.1–7.5in)
SEXUAL MATURITY	2–3 years
MATING SEASON	April–May
GESTATION PERIOD	30–32 days
NUMBER OF YOUNG	2 to 6
BIRTH INTERVAL	1 year
TYPICAL DIET	Grasses, sedges, herbs, occasionally invertebrates
LIFESPAN	Up to 20 years in captivity

With its compact body and short, sturdy limbs, the alpine marmot is an expert burrower that can dig up to 10m (33ft) of tunnel in 24 hours.

SKULL
Short and compact, the skull is solidly built to support the powerful jaws. The long incisors are used to shear through fibrous vegetation.

FUR
The thick, coarse, greyish-brown fur keeps the animal warm at night. The marmot moults every year during early summer.

EARS
The ears are buried in the marmot's thick fur, which protects them from the cold of the animal's high-altitude habitat.

FOREFEET
The forefeet are adapted for delicately grasping and manipulating objects, as well as for excavating hard soil. Each digit has a sharp claw.

CREATURE COMPARISONS

The striped ground squirrel (Euxerus erythropus) is a burrowing relative of the alpine marmot, although it regularly uses termite mounds as a home instead of digging an extensive tunnel system. Whereas the marmot inhabits Europe's mountains, the squirrel thrives in the open woodlands and savannah of central and western Africa. Much shorter than the marmot, the ground squirrel has a lithe build and is a fraction of its cousin's weight. Its tail, however, is longer, allowing the ground squirrel to hold it over its back as a shade against the tropical sunshine. In some areas, poultry farmers regard the squirrel as a pest due to its egg-stealing habits.

Striped ground squirrel

Alpine marmot

WHERE IN THE WORLD?

Native to the high Alps, Carpathians and Tatra mountains of Europe. Introduced into the central Pyrenees and the Massif Central of France.

RELATED SPECIES

The alpine marmot is the largest of the 11 species in the genus Marmota. There are 50 genera, containing 260 species of squirrel-like animals, within the family Sciuridae, including both arboreal and ground-living forms, such as flying squirrels, chipmunks, and prairie dogs. The family Sciuridae is a major branch of the order Rodentia, and its members are found worldwide except in Australia, Madagascar and southern South America.

• **ORDER** • *Rodentia* • **FAMILY** • *Sciuridae* • **GENUS & SPECIES** • *Sciurus carolinensis*

GREY SQUIRREL

Its short, but powerful legs, sharp claws and long, bushy tail give the grey squirrel complete confidence as it runs and leaps among the trees.

KEY FEATURES

- An adaptable opportunist that has learned to live alongside humans in parks and gardens.
- Able to exploit a wide variety of food resources, from nuts and seeds to insects and even baby birds.
- Adapted for life in the treetops with sharp claws and good eyesight for gauging distances between trees.

TEETH
The front incisor teeth, in common with those of other rodents, grow continuously to compensate for wear as the squirrel gnaws through nuts and other tough plant foods.

TAIL
The big, bushy tail provides balance as the squirrel darts along slender branches, and can be used as a rudder to adjust the squirrel's direction as it leaps through the air.

TOES AND CLAWS
Each forefoot (1) and hindfoot (2) has five toes, but the forefoot's fifth toe (1A) is tiny and set like a fixed thumb. The needle-sharp claws pierce tree bark to give a secure grip on branches.

VITAL STATISTICS

WEIGHT	200–1000g (7–35.3oz)
LENGTH	Head & Body: 20–32cm (7.9–12.6in) Tail: 20–31cm (7.9–12.2in)
SEXUAL MATURITY	1 year
MATING SEASON	Winter and from late spring to early summer
GESTATION PERIOD	About 44 days
NUMBER OF YOUNG	1 to 9, but usually 3
BIRTH INTERVAL	Two litters per year
TYPICAL DIET	Nuts, fruits, buds, shoots, tree-sap, insects, seeds and fungi
LIFESPAN	10–12 years

CREATURE COMPARISONS

The chestnut-coloured red squirrel, Sciurus vulgaris, with its conspicuous ear tufts, is slightly smaller than its relative the grey squirrel. In autumn, when the grey squirrel lays down 20 per cent extra weight in fat, the red squirrel only lays down 10 per cent. Until the 1940s Britain's native squirrel, the red squirrel, was widespread, but it is now increasingly rare. One reason is loss of its natural habitat. But whereas the grey squirrel is adaptable enough to colonize the regenerating woodland, the native red only really thrives in mature forest. Unlike the grey squirrel, the red squirrel also needs to stay close to a source of water.

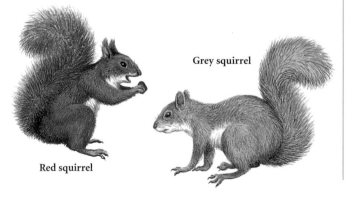

Grey squirrel

Red squirrel

WHERE IN THE WORLD?

A native of southeastern Canada and the eastern United States, from Ontario and New Brunswick south to Florida.

Introduced to Britain in the 19th-century.

RELATED SPECIES

The grey squirrel is one of 267 species of squirrel, distributed in 49 genera within the family Sciuridae. Other squirrels include ground squirrels, such as the prairie dog, and flying squirrels, such as the eastern flying squirrel. As members of the order Rodentia, which contains more than 1700 species in all, squirrels are related to other rodents, including rats, mice, coypus, beavers, jerboas, agoutis, gophers and porcupines.

• ORDER • *Rodentia* • FAMILY • *Sciuridae* • GENUS & SPECIES • *Spermophilus parryii*

ARCTIC GROUND SQUIRREL

The Arctic ground squirrel staves off the deadly effects of the brutal tundra winter with its thick fur coat and its ability to burrow underground.

SKULL
The skull is large and broad to hold powerful masseter muscles that raise the lower jaw and assist in chewing. Chisel-like incisors at the front of the jaws are used to gnaw through tough vegetation.

TAIL
The relatively long tail is well insulated with dense fur to prevent precious heat from escaping the squirrel's body.

FUR
Quite long, dense fur provides the Arctic ground squirrel with an insulating, all-round coat. The animal moults twice during its active summer months, gaining a greyer and thicker winter coat prior to hibernation.

PAWS
The four toes on each forepaw are armed with a set of claws capable of rapidly scraping away soil as the animal tunnels its way beneath the turf.

POUCHES
The cheeks are loose and stretchy, forming handy pouches in which the rodent can carry stores of food to its hibernation burrow.

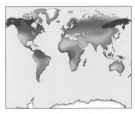

KEY FEATURES

- Burrowing rodent that dwells in the harsh and bleak environment of the Arctic tundra, where food and shelter are in limited supply.
- Hibernates during the bitter winter months, sealed safely within an underground chamber.
- Squeezes its breeding and feeding activities into the few warm months of summer, when the Arctic tundra comes to life.

VITAL STATISTICS

WEIGHT	650–790g (22.9–27.9oz)
LENGTH	Head & Body: 30–40cm (11.8–15.7in) Tail: 7–13cm (2.7–5.1in)
SEXUAL MATURITY	About 11 months
MATING SEASON	April to May
GESTATION PERIOD	23–31 days
NUMBER OF YOUNG	5 to 10
BIRTH INTERVAL	1 year
TYPICAL DIET	Mainly seeds, leaves, stems, roots, flowers and fruit, but occasionally insects, small vertebrates and carrion
LIFESPAN	Male up to 6 years; female up to 11 years

CREATURE COMPARISONS

One of the Arctic ground squirrel's North American relatives is the thirteen-lined ground squirrel, *Spermophilus tridecemlineatus*, which ranges from the Canadian prairies south to Texas. It is similar in size and appearance, and both species also share impressive burrowing skills. Nevertheless, the thirteen-lined ground squirrel is rather more brisk in its movements above ground. The most striking difference, however, between these two species is their fur. While the Arctic ground squirrel has a relatively plain, greyish-brown coat, the 13 lines of its cousin's coat are made up from bright spots and stripes.

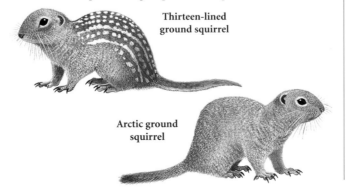

Thirteen-lined ground squirrel

Arctic ground squirrel

WHERE IN THE WORLD?

Occupies the northern portions of the continents that encircle the North Pole — from Mongolia and southern Siberia eastwards to the Kamchatka peninsula, and from Alaska to northern Canada.

RELATED SPECIES

The Arctic ground squirrel is one of 38 species of ground squirrel in the genus Spermophilus. These include 3 species of golden-mantled ground squirrel, 1 of which is S. lateralis. The genus Spermophilus is part of the great mammalian order of rodents, Rodentia.

• **ORDER** • *Rodentia* • **FAMILY** • *Sciuridae* • **GENUS & SPECIES** • *Sciurus vulgaris*

RED SQUIRREL

Acrobatic and nimble, the red squirrel scampers along flimsy branches like a high-speed tightrope-walker, often making bold leaps from tree to tree.

KEY FEATURES

- Survives the winter without hibernating by storing huge quantities of seeds and fungi in autumn.
- Leaps between trees to avoid time-wasting descents to the ground, and to escape from predators.
- Its populations fluctuate dramatically from year to year according to food supplies and the weather.

SKULL AND TEETH
Like others rodents', the squirrel's incisors grow constantly so that they never wear out. They are used to open pine cones and seeds.

TAIL
The long bushy tail is used as a balancing aid while climbing and as a rudder when leaping from tree to tree. When angry, the squirrel waves its tail like a flag.

EAR TUFTS
Conspicuous ear tufts start growing in late summer. At their thickest in winter, they gradually become thinner and virtually disappear for most of the summer months.

EYES
The eyes are positioned high on the sides of the skull, allowing the squirrel to see upwards without having to tilt its head. This helps it to spot predators, such as pine martens or birds of prey, approaching silently from above.

FOREFOOT
Each of the four toes on the forefeet is equipped with a sharp claw. These provide such a secure hold on tree bark that they can support the squirrel's entire weight with ease.

VITAL STATISTICS

WEIGHT	220–450g (7.8–15.9oz)
LENGTH	Head & Body: 18–24cm (7.1–9.4in) Tail: 14–19.5cm (5.5–7.7in)
SEXUAL MATURITY	9–10 months
MATING SEASON	December to February (first litter) and March to June (second or only litter)
GESTATION PERIOD	36–42 days
NUMBER OF YOUNG	Usually 3 or 4 per litter
BIRTH INTERVAL	3 months for a second litter
TYPICAL DIET	Tree seeds, fruits, shoots and bark; also fungi, insects, birds' eggs and nestlings
LIFESPAN	3 (sometimes up to 6) years

CREATURE COMPARISONS

Dwarfing its red northern relative, the Indian giant squirrel (Ratufa indica), from the tall forests of central and southern India, can reach a length of 1m (3ft 3in), half of which is its bushy tail. It weighs up to 3kg (6.6lb) — six times heavier than the largest recorded red squirrel. Nevertheless, it is a highly skilled climber that spends nearly all of its life in the forest canopy. The giant squirrel's size and strength enable it to leap 7m (23ft) between trees and, like the red squirrel, it uses its tail to steer in mid-air.

The Indian giant squirrel is just as variable in colour as the red squirrel and sometimes occurs in a garish coat of yellow, orange, red, grey and black fur. Like the red squirrel, however, it always has predominantly pale underparts.

Indian giant squirrel

Red squirrel

WHERE IN THE WORLD?

Found over much of Europe, east through northern Asia to northeastern China and northern Japan. Absent from Mediterranean islands and parts of England and Wales.

RELATED SPECIES

The squirrel family contains about 260 species in 50 genera and is one of the larger families in the order Rodentia. The majority of squirrels are tree-dwellers, but the black-tailed prairie dog, Cynomys ludovicianus, is one of about 90 species in the squirrel family that live on the ground.

PIKE

• ORDER • *Salmoniformes* • FAMILY • *Esocidae* • GENUS & SPECIES • *Esox lucius*

Excellent camouflage, savage teeth and a muscular body that can produce lightning bursts of acceleration make the pike a supreme freshwater hunter.

KEY FEATURES

- Menacing jaws, a streamlined body and voracious appetite have earned it the tag of 'freshwater shark'.

- Lies concealed in ambush among aquatic vegetation, darting out to seize prey — including other pike.

- Lives long and grows large and heavy in slow-moving rivers and lakes that contain plenty of fish prey.

VITAL STATISTICS

WEIGHT	Male 4–5kg (8.8–11lb); female up to 34kg (75lb)
LENGTH	Male 60–90cm (23.6–35.4); female up to 1.5m (4ft 9in)
SEXUAL MATURITY	3–4 years
BREEDING SEASON	February to May
NUMBER OF EGGS	16,000 to 70,000
BREEDING INTERVAL	1 year
TYPICAL DIET	Mainly fish; also water voles, rats, waterbirds
LIFESPAN	Male 7–10 years; female up to 25 years

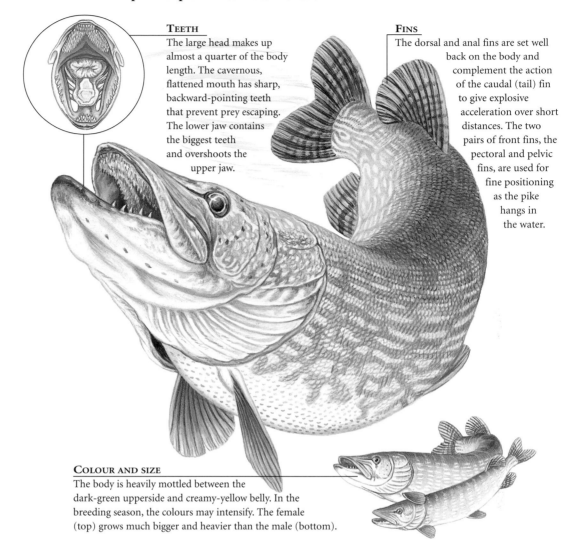

TEETH
The large head makes up almost a quarter of the body length. The cavernous, flattened mouth has sharp, backward-pointing teeth that prevent prey escaping. The lower jaw contains the biggest teeth and overshoots the upper jaw.

FINS
The dorsal and anal fins are set well back on the body and complement the action of the caudal (tail) fin to give explosive acceleration over short distances. The two pairs of front fins, the pectoral and pelvic fins, are used for fine positioning as the pike hangs in the water.

COLOUR AND SIZE
The body is heavily mottled between the dark-green upperside and creamy-yellow belly. In the breeding season, the colours may intensify. The female (top) grows much bigger and heavier than the male (bottom).

CREATURE COMPARISONS

Although not closely related, the pike and barracuda are both voracious predators and share similar features. Both have a long body with large jaws packed with sharp, backward-pointing teeth and a lower jaw that is longer than the upper. The dorsal and anal fins on both fish are near the tail, providing rapid acceleration. The pike is normally found in freshwater while the barracuda is a marine fish of open water, hunting near reefs and often following shoals of fish far out to sea. The pike is a solitary ambusher of prey, whereas the barracuda often forms a large 'hunting pack' that actively chases other fish.

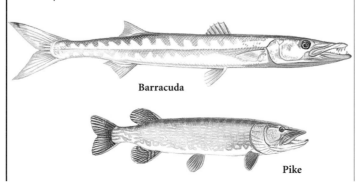

Barracuda

Pike

WHERE IN THE WORLD?

Common throughout most of Europe, except for Spain, Portugal, Greece and southern Italy. It is also found in northern USA and parts of Canada.

RELATED SPECIES

There are five species in the family Esocidae and all are found in the northern hemisphere. The others are the muskellunge, *Esox masquinongy*, which is larger than the pike; the chain pickerel, *E. niger*, and the grass pickerel, *E. americanus*, both of which are smaller; and the Siberian or Amur pike, *E. reicherti*, which is similar in size to the pike. All members of the family hunt by ambushing their prey from aquatic vegetation.

• **ORDER** • *Salmoniformes* • **FAMILY** • *Salmonidae* • **GENUS & SPECIES** • *Oncorhynchus mykiss*

RAINBOW TROUT

Named after the iridescent colours along its flanks, the streamlined and powerfully built rainbow trout is one of the most beautiful freshwater fish.

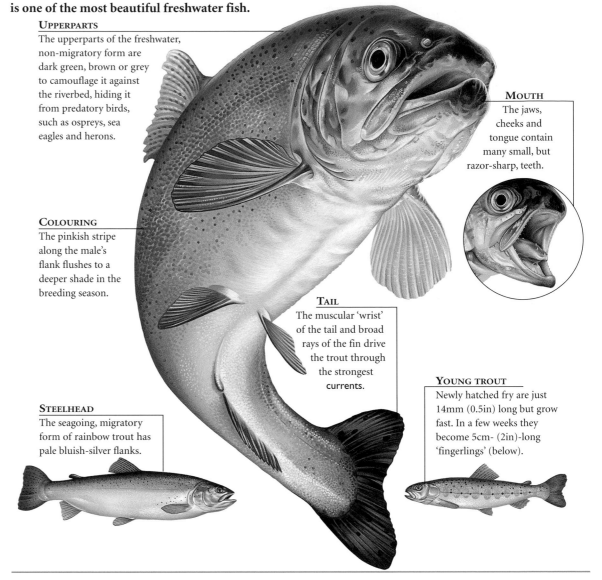

KEY FEATURES

• Speckled and often highly coloured, it is one of the world's most familiar fish.

• A voracious predator that forages both at the water's surface and on the riverbed.

• Migratory form only leaves the sea to spawn, while non-migratory form lives its entire life in freshwater.

UPPERPARTS
The upperparts of the freshwater, non-migratory form are dark green, brown or grey to camouflage it against the riverbed, hiding it from predatory birds, such as ospreys, sea eagles and herons.

COLOURING
The pinkish stripe along the male's flank flushes to a deeper shade in the breeding season.

MOUTH
The jaws, cheeks and tongue contain many small, but razor-sharp, teeth.

TAIL
The muscular 'wrist' of the tail and broad rays of the fin drive the trout through the strongest currents.

STEELHEAD
The seagoing, migratory form of rainbow trout has pale bluish-silver flanks.

YOUNG TROUT
Newly hatched fry are just 14mm (0.5in) long but grow fast. In a few weeks they become 5cm- (2in)-long 'fingerlings' (below).

VITAL STATISTICS

LENGTH	Up to 1m (3ft 3in)
WEIGHT	Up to 15kg (33.1lb)
SEXUAL MATURITY	1–4 years
SPAWNING SEASON	Spring
NUMBER OF EGGS	2000 per kilogram of female's weight
HATCHING PERIOD	4–7 weeks
BIRTH INTERVAL	1 year; migratory form often spawns only once during its life
TYPICAL DIET	Insects, especially flies; aquatic invertebrates, crustaceans, small fish
LIFESPAN	8–9 years; up to 20 years in captivity

CREATURE COMPARISONS

A relative of the rainbow trout, the brown trout (Salmo trutta) is native to many European, northern African and western Asian rivers and lakes, but has also been introduced to Canada and the USA. A familiar fish of the chalk rivers and upland streams of Britain, it is found in unpolluted and well oxygenated waterways. Like the rainbow trout, some brown trout migrate to the sea before returning to freshwater to breed. The sea's rich feeding grounds enable these sea trout to grow far larger than those living solely in freshwater. Both the brown trout and the rainbow trout have similar feeding habits although, where the two species inhabit the same river, it is usually the rainbow trout that dominates.

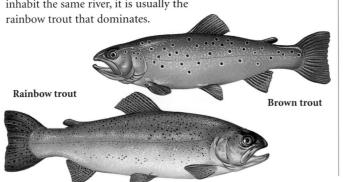

Rainbow trout

Brown trout

WHERE IN THE WORLD?

Native to the northern Pacific Ocean and its feeder rivers in the USA, Canada and Siberia. Introduced to many countries for sport fishing and food.

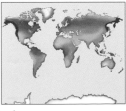

RELATED SPECIES

The rainbow trout, which in North America has at least 7 subspecies, is a member of the genus Oncorhynchus. This genus includes all Pacific trout and salmon species, such as the sockeye salmon. Atlantic species, including the brown trout and Atlantic salmon, belong to the genus Salmo. These genera are part of the family Salmonidae, which contains other streamlined predatory fish, such as the whitefish, grayling and charr.

SOCKEYE SALMON

• ORDER • *Salmoniformes* • FAMILY • *Salmonidae* • GENUS & SPECIES • *Oncorhynchus nerka*

KEY FEATURES

- Begins and ends its life in freshwater, but grows to maturity in the Pacific Ocean.

- Travels thousands of kilometres before returning to the very stream where it originally hatched.

- Navigates at sea by reference to the sun and moon, star patterns and the Earth's magnetic field.

VITAL STATISTICS

WEIGHT	Usually 1.8–2.7kg (4–5.9lb), but up to 6.8kg (15lb)
LENGTH	Up to 90cm (35.4in)
SEXUAL MATURITY	3–5 years
BREEDING SEASON	Autumn, when the temperature begins to drop
NUMBER OF EGGS	3000 to 4000
HATCHING PERIOD	About 3 months
TYPICAL DIET	Fry eat freshwater plankton and aquatic invertebrates; maturing fish eat crustaceans, small fish and squid
LIFESPAN	Up to 5 years

As a male sockeye salmon struggles upstream to spawn, he undergoes great bodily changes in preparation for breeding.

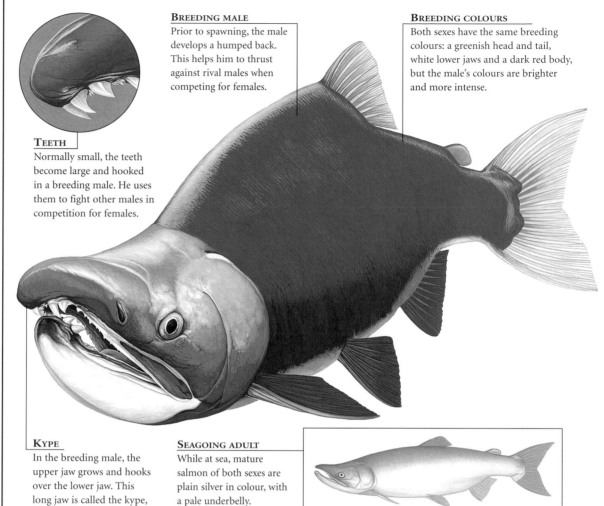

BREEDING MALE
Prior to spawning, the male develops a humped back. This helps him to thrust against rival males when competing for females.

BREEDING COLOURS
Both sexes have the same breeding colours: a greenish head and tail, white lower jaws and a dark red body, but the male's colours are brighter and more intense.

TEETH
Normally small, the teeth become large and hooked in a breeding male. He uses them to fight other males in competition for females.

KYPE
In the breeding male, the upper jaw grows and hooks over the lower jaw. This long jaw is called the kype, and is lacking in the female.

SEAGOING ADULT
While at sea, mature salmon of both sexes are plain silver in colour, with a pale underbelly.

CREATURE COMPARISONS

The male Atlantic salmon (Salmo salar), like the sockeye salmon, develops a kype before spawning. His breeding colours, however, are less bold, and his body is less humped. Unlike the sockeye salmon, the Atlantic salmon often survives spawning, returning to the sea to feed again, and then to repeat the entire cycle, perhaps several times during its life.

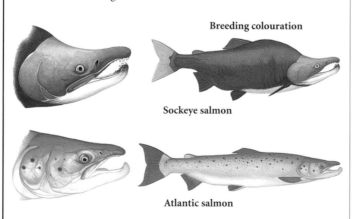

Breeding colouration

Sockeye salmon

Atlantic salmon

WHERE IN THE WORLD?

Found in rivers, lakes and streams around the North Pacific, from California to Alaska, west to the Aleutians and the Kamchatka Peninsula and south to Japan.

RELATED SPECIES

The sockeye salmon is 1 of several species of Pacific salmon whose generic name Oncorhynchus means 'hooked snout'. They include the coho salmon and rainbow trout. Pacific salmon are closely related to the Atlantic salmon, Eurasian salmon and brown trout.

• ORDER • *Scleractinia* • FAMILY • *Various* • GENUS & SPECIES • *Various*

HARD CORAL

The brain corals, named for their typical shape, are hard corals that form boulder-like colonies whose surfaces are covered with ridges and valleys.

KEY FEATURES

- Extraordinary and ancient creatures that combine elements of plant and animal physiology.
- Form clustering colonies made up of millions of genetically identical individuals known as polyps.
- Over generations of skeleton-building, these colonies form the rich, sheltering habitat of a coral reef.

VITAL STATISTICS

DIAMETER OF COLONY	Up to 2m (6ft 6in)
DIAMETER OF POLYP	Up to 3cm (1.2in)
RATE OF GROWTH	1–3cm (0.4–1.2in) a year
SPAWNING SEASON	Spring
NUMBER OF YOUNG	Countless millions of eggs and sperm are released by each colony, although very few survive
PERIOD AS LARVA	Several days to weeks
LIFESPAN	Unknown, but a colony may certainly survive many decades

COLONIAL BODY
The brain coral is not a single animal, but a mass of individual polyps that have been replicated from a single founder. They are genetically identical and share a rudim entary nervous system.

STINGERS
Polyps feed mainly on small crustaceans. They catch their prey with tentacles lined with stinging cells called nematocysts. These shoot out hollow threads that inject a paralyzing poison.

Stinger
Nematocyst
Tentacle

Species illustrated: **Symphyllia radians**

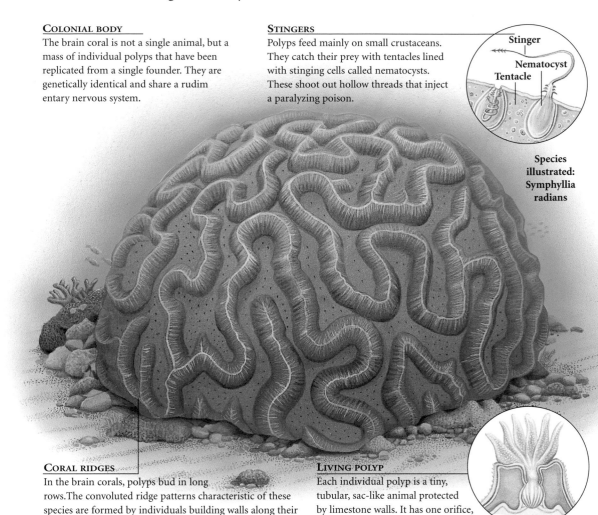

CORAL RIDGES
In the brain corals, polyps bud in long rows. The convoluted ridge patterns characteristic of these species are formed by individuals building walls along their sides but not between each other.

LIVING POLYP
Each individual polyp is a tiny, tubular, sac-like animal protected by limestone walls. It has one orifice, which is fringed by feeding tentacles.

CREATURE COMPARISONS

Reef corals, like all creatures, compete with each other for resources — in this case sunlight to sustain the single-celled plants that live within their bodies, and the shower of food that drifts in the water. They can be broadly divided into three kinds according to the competitive strategies they have adopted. Star corals (genus Astroides) rely on sheer mass, growing into huge sheet or boulder formations that tend to make up the bulk of a reef. Staghorn corals (genus Acropora) need only a small area to anchor themselves but branch out into vast, tree-like colonies. Plate corals (genus Turbinaria) form great flat expanses that overshadow other corals and monopolize the available light.

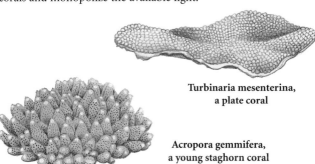

Turbinaria mesenterina,
a plate coral

Acropora gemmifera,
a young staghorn coral

WHERE IN THE WORLD?

Found off Indian, Pacific and western Atlantic Ocean coastlines at latitudes between 30° North and 30° South, at water depths to a maximum of 70m (229.7ft).

RELATED SPECIES

There are several coral orders. In addition to hard or 'true' corals, there are soft corals, order Alcynacea — including species of Sinularia — and fan corals, order Gorgonacea. All belong to the phylum Cnidaria, along with sea anemones, hydras, jellyfish and their relatives.

• ORDER • *Scorpaeniformes* • FAMILY • *Scorpaenidae* • GENUS & SPECIES • *Pterois volitans*

LIONFISH

The lionfish's flamboyant appearance, with its long spines and oversized fins, is designed to conceal it and to help it to ambush prey on coral reefs.

KEY FEATURES

- A deadly hunter that masquerades as a piece of drifting seaweed among coral reefs.

- Uses large pectoral fins to trap prey in rock crevices before sucking it into its mouth whole.

- Protective spines inject a powerful venom into any creature that brushes against them.

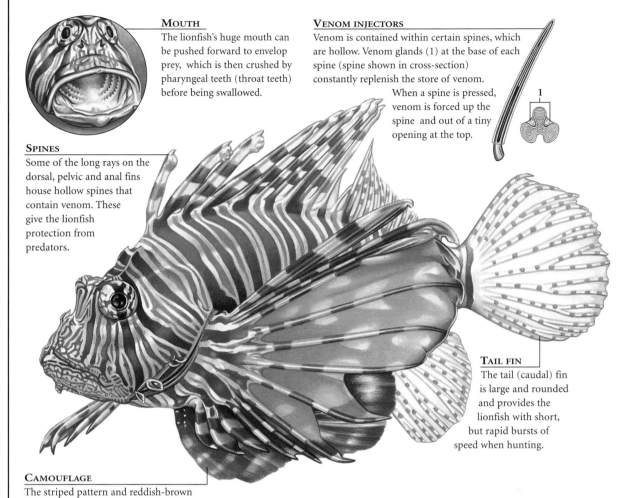

MOUTH
The lionfish's huge mouth can be pushed forward to envelop prey, which is then crushed by pharyngeal teeth (throat teeth) before being swallowed.

VENOM INJECTORS
Venom is contained within certain spines, which are hollow. Venom glands (1) at the base of each spine (spine shown in cross-section) constantly replenish the store of venom.

When a spine is pressed, venom is forced up the spine and out of a tiny opening at the top.

SPINES
Some of the long rays on the dorsal, pelvic and anal fins house hollow spines that contain venom. These give the lionfish protection from predators.

TAIL FIN
The tail (caudal) fin is large and rounded and provides the lionfish with short, but rapid bursts of speed when hunting.

CAMOUFLAGE
The striped pattern and reddish-brown colour, along with the long flowing fins, disguise the lionfish by breaking up its outline as it lies motionless against the multicoloured backdrop of coral and seaweed.

VITAL STATISTICS

WEIGHT	1–2kg (2.2–4.4lb)
LENGTH	35–38cm (13.8–15in)
SEXUAL MATURITY	Unknown
BREEDING SEASON	Varies with location; spring in temperate waters
NUMBER OF EGGS	Up to 20,000
BREEDING INTERVAL	1 year
TYPICAL DIET	Smaller fish, small crabs, prawns and shrimps
LIFESPAN	I5–10 years in captivity

CREATURE COMPARISONS

The family Scorpaenidae contains several species that closely resemble the lionfish in appearance and habits. The zebrafish, Dendrochirus zebra, for example,which is found on the coral reefs of temperate and tropical oceans, is very similar to the lionfish in several ways. Smaller than the lionfish, it has wing-like pectoral fins but its fin rays extend well past the fins' webbing. The zebrafish has the same hunting method as the lionfish, using its fins as a net to drive prey into rock crevices. Another shared feature is the venomous spines that protect these fish from predators while they drift among the coral looking for their next meal. Patterning and colouring are also similar, although the zebrafish is more of a rusty brown with dark blotches.

Zebrafish

Lionfish

WHERE IN THE WORLD?

Found on reefs and in coastal shallows from the Red Sea east through the Indian Ocean and from Japan south through the southwestern Pacific to Australia.

RELATED SPECIES

There are approximately 300 species in the family Scorpaenidae. Although a few species live in freshwater, most are found in the Indian and Pacific Oceans, although the scorpionfish, Scorpaena scrofa, lives in the Mediterranean and eastern Atlantic. The redfish, Sebastes marina, is found in the northern Atlantic. Most have venomous spines for protection and live on the the seabed waiting to ambush prey.

• ORDER • *Scorpiones* • FAMILY • *Buthidae* • GENUS & SPECIES • *Androctonus australis*

FAT-TAILED SCORPION

The scorpion's body is primitive but effective: it is armed with powerful weapons at head and tail, and armour-plated against predators.

KEY FEATURES

- Uses the sting in its tail to paralyze struggling prey as well as for defence against predators.
- Venom has a strength similar to that of a cobra, and is the most potent of any species in the genus.
- One of 50 scorpions that are dangerous to humans.
- Venom can kill humans by paralyzing heart muscles.

VITAL STATISTICS

WEIGHT	25g (0.9oz)
LENGTH	10cm (3.9in)
SEXUAL MATURITY	6 months to 3 years
MATING SEASON	Unknown
GESTATION PERIOD	About 6 months
NUMBER OF YOUNG	40 to 50
BREEDING INTERVAL	1 year
TYPICAL DIET	Invertebrates, such as beetles, cockroaches and spiders
LIFESPAN	3–5 years

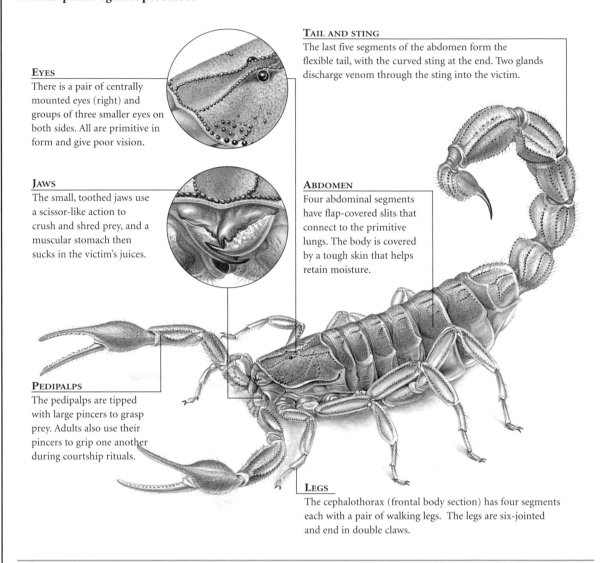

EYES
There is a pair of centrally mounted eyes (right) and groups of three smaller eyes on both sides. All are primitive in form and give poor vision.

JAWS
The small, toothed jaws use a scissor-like action to crush and shred prey, and a muscular stomach then sucks in the victim's juices.

PEDIPALPS
The pedipalps are tipped with large pincers to grasp prey. Adults also use their pincers to grip one another during courtship rituals.

TAIL AND STING
The last five segments of the abdomen form the flexible tail, with the curved sting at the end. Two glands discharge venom through the sting into the victim.

ABDOMEN
Four abdominal segments have flap-covered slits that connect to the primitive lungs. The body is covered by a tough skin that helps retain moisture.

LEGS
The cephalothorax (frontal body section) has four segments each with a pair of walking legs. The legs are six-jointed and end in double claws.

CREATURE COMPARISONS

Scorpions are most commonly found in desert or semi-arid land. Most are of a yellow or brown colour to match their surroundings, with a few notable exceptions, including the emperor scorpion of Africa. At up to 20cm (7.9in) long, this black scorpion is also one of the largest species, second only to the lobster scorpion of Sumatra. The smallest species, Microbuthus pusillus, is little more than 1cm (0.4in) in length.

Emperor scorpion

Microbuthus pusillus

Fat-tailed scorpion

WHERE IN THE WORLD?

Found in northern Africa and the Middle East, in Algeria, Arabia, Egypt, Israel, Libya, Palestine, Sudan and Tunisia. May occur more widely, since subspecies have been recorded in Pakistan and eastern India.

RELATED SPECIES

There are some 800 species of scorpion. Most are found in tropical regions, with a few in warm or warm-temperate parts. Most of the truly dangerous species occur in the family Buthidae. In southern Europe, the sting of Buthus occitanus causes mild pain in humans, but in North Africa and the Middle East the same species can kill. Of the 40 or so species of scorpion found in North America, only two Mexican species can kill humans.

• ORDER • *Scyliorhiniformes* • FAMILY • *Scyliorhinidae* • GENUS & SPECIES • *Scyliorhinus spp.*

DOGFISH

KEY FEATURES

- Small, seabed-dwelling sharks that prey on fish, as well as molluscs and other invertebrates.

- During the mating act, the male wraps himself around the female entirely before fertilizing her eggs internally.

- Large, single eggs are individually protected by a leathery purse, which attaches itself to the seabed by means of fine, coiled tendrils.

VITAL STATISTICS

WEIGHT	Up to 9.5kg (20.9lb) depending on species
LENGTH	80–160cm (31–63in)
SEXUAL MATURITY	1–2 years
SPAWNING SEASON	Autumn for North Atlantic species. Other species not known
NUMBER OF EGGS	18 to 20
HATCHING PERIOD	5–11 months
BREEDING INTERVAL	1 year
TYPICAL DIET	Molluscs, crustaceans, fish
LIFESPAN	Unknown

Swimming sinuously as it searches for food, the dogfish relies on its spots and sandy colouring to camouflage it against the seabed.

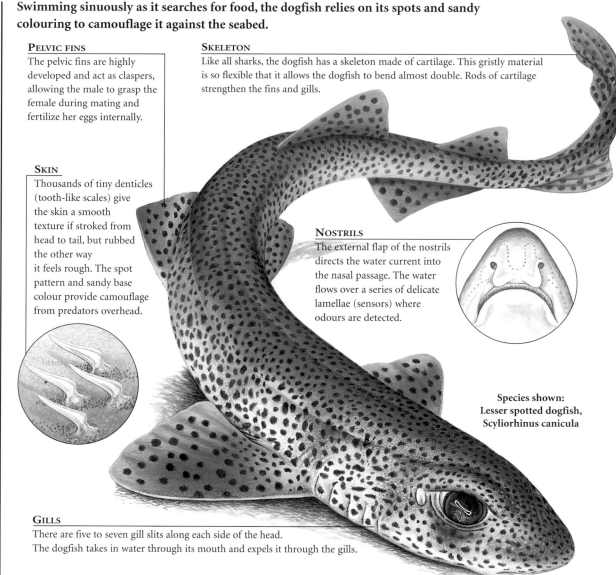

PELVIC FINS
The pelvic fins are highly developed and act as claspers, allowing the male to grasp the female during mating and fertilize her eggs internally.

SKIN
Thousands of tiny denticles (tooth-like scales) give the skin a smooth texture if stroked from head to tail, but rubbed the other way it feels rough. The spot pattern and sandy base colour provide camouflage from predators overhead.

SKELETON
Like all sharks, the dogfish has a skeleton made of cartilage. This gristly material is so flexible that it allows the dogfish to bend almost double. Rods of cartilage strengthen the fins and gills.

NOSTRILS
The external flap of the nostrils directs the water current into the nasal passage. The water flows over a series of delicate lamellae (sensors) where odours are detected.

Species shown:
Lesser spotted dogfish,
Scyliorhinus canicula

GILLS
There are five to seven gill slits along each side of the head. The dogfish takes in water through its mouth and expels it through the gills.

CREATURE COMPARISONS

Sharing much of the lesser spotted dogfish's range, the starry smooth hound (Mustelus asterias) is also a seabed predator. Lurking in packs from the intertidal zone to depths of 100m (328ft), the smooth hound hunts crustaceans, such as crabs and lobsters, as well as fish. Its diet may even include the dogfish, which only reaches half the size of the smooth hound. The smooth hound has the prominent dorsal and pectoral fins typical of big sharks, giving it a more 'menacing' profile. It takes its name from the overlapping alignment of the denticles on its skin, making it smoother than that of other sharks. The smooth hound's eggs hatch internally and the young are born live — unlike the dogfish, which lays eggs on the seabed.

Starry smooth hound

Dogfish

WHERE IN THE WORLD?

Most species found in coastal waters throughout the world including Mediterranean and Black Seas. Absent from Arctic and Antarctic seas. Several species found in deeper water.

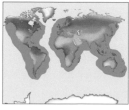

RELATED SPECIES

There are 13 species in the genus Scyliorhinus, including the lesser spotted dogfish, greater spotted dogfish and chain dogfish. There are a total of 15 genera within the family Scyliorhinidae, containing 89 species of dogfish, which, rather confusingly, are also known as catsharks. Another family in the order Scyliorhiniformes is Pseudotriakidae, which contains just 1 species, the false catshark. There are a total of 12 orders of sharks.

• **ORDER** • *Semaeostomeae* • **FAMILY** • *Ulmaridae* • **GENUS & SPECIES** • *Chrysaora hysoscella*

COMPASS JELLYFISH

KEY FEATURES

- A stunning sea invertebrate that reaches sexual maturity after completing a complex lifecycle.
- Equipped with powerful stinging cells on its bell and tentacles that shoot out microscopic 'harpoons' to stun or kill prey.
- Has an exceedingly delicate but efficient body composed mainly of water.

VITAL STATISTICS

WEIGHT	Unknown
LENGTH OF TENTACLES	Up to 60cm (23.6in)
DIAMETER OF BELL	25–30cm (9.8–11.8in)
BREEDING SEASON	Variable
TIME FROM LARVA TO ADULT	2–4 years, depending on water conditions
TYPICAL DIET	Small fish, crustaceans and animal plankton
LIFESPAN	Unknown

Beneath the umbrella-like bell, the compass jellyfish reveals its full complexity with an array of delicate bodyparts and a central cavity.

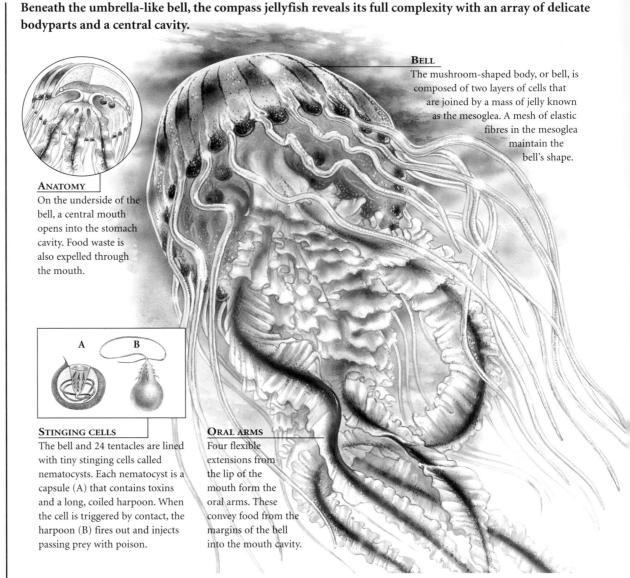

ANATOMY
On the underside of the bell, a central mouth opens into the stomach cavity. Food waste is also expelled through the mouth.

STINGING CELLS
The bell and 24 tentacles are lined with tiny stinging cells called nematocysts. Each nematocyst is a capsule (A) that contains toxins and a long, coiled harpoon. When the cell is triggered by contact, the harpoon (B) fires out and injects passing prey with poison.

ORAL ARMS
Four flexible extensions from the lip of the mouth form the oral arms. These convey food from the margins of the bell into the mouth cavity.

BELL
The mushroom-shaped body, or bell, is composed of two layers of cells that are joined by a mass of jelly known as the mesoglea. A mesh of elastic fibres in the mesoglea maintain the bell's shape.

CREATURE COMPARISONS

Like the compass jellyfish, the lion's mane jellyfish (Cyanea capillata, not shown to scale) has a widespread distribution. However, it is not nearly as common in coastal waters. This is fortunate for the human population, as the lion's mane is not only the largest jellyfish known, but it also delivers particularly powerful stings. It even feeds on other jellyfish.

The red-brown bell of the lion's mane jellyfish measures up to 2m (6ft 6in) in diameter, the four oral arms are up to 2m (6ft 6in) long, and the array of fine tentacles hanging from its rim reach a length of 10m (32.8ft). The young of at least one species of shrimp and a species of anglerfish often take refuge among its tentacles, where they are immune to its stings.

Lion's mane jellyfish

Compass jellyfish

WHERE IN THE WORLD?

Inhabits the North Atlantic Ocean from the Hudson Strait on the east coast of Canada south to the Venezuelan coast,

and from the Norwegian Sea south to the coast of Senegal. Also found in the Mediterranean Sea.

RELATED SPECIES

The compass jellyfish is a member of the family Ulmaridae, part of the order Semaeostomeae. This order contains most of the large 'typical' jellyfish, such as the common jellyfish, Aurelia aurita. There are 5 orders of jellyfish in the class Scyphozoa with a total of around 200 species.

• ORDER • *Siluriformes* • FAMILY • *Siluridae* • GENUS & SPECIES • *Silurus glanis*

EUROPEAN CATFISH

The European catfish is scaleless and has a wide, flat head and a huge mouth. Long, sensitive barbels help this fearsome predator locate its prey.

KEY FEATURES

- Voracious predatory fish that lives in sluggish and stagnant freshwater habitats.
- Three pairs of whisker-like barbels surround the huge mouth and give the catfish its name.
- Much prized by anglers because of its power and enormous size.

FRY
For their first ten days or so the fry look more like tadpoles than young catfish.

DORSAL FIN
The dorsal fin contains three to five rays and is very small. By contrast, the anal fin extends nearly to the tail — almost 60 per cent of the body length.

COLOURING
Colour varies greatly among individual fish. The dark back may have a green, blue or brownish tinge. The sides have light marbled markings and the belly is a dirty white. Albinos with red eyes occur regularly.

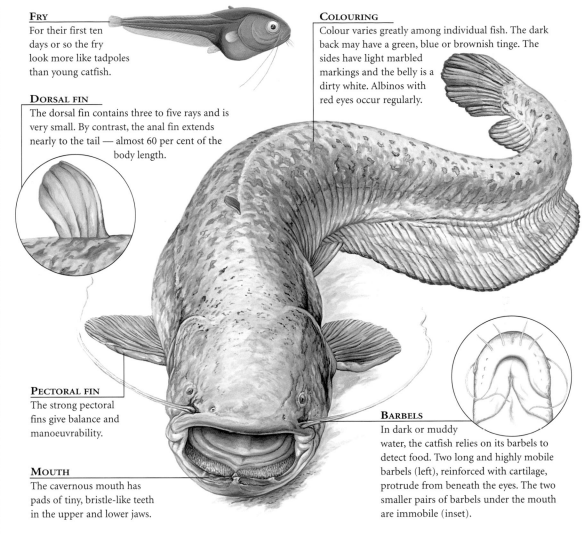

PECTORAL FIN
The strong pectoral fins give balance and manoeuvrability.

MOUTH
The cavernous mouth has pads of tiny, bristle-like teeth in the upper and lower jaws.

BARBELS
In dark or muddy water, the catfish relies on its barbels to detect food. Two long and highly mobile barbels (left), reinforced with cartilage, protrude from beneath the eyes. The two smaller pairs of barbels under the mouth are immobile (inset).

VITAL STATISTICS

WEIGHT	50–300kg (110.2–661.4lb)
LENGTH	Up to 3m (9ft 8in)
SEXUAL MATURITY	3–4 years
BREEDING SEASON	May–June
HATCHING PERIOD	2–3 days
NUMBER OF EGGS	130,000 to 500,000
BREEDING INTERVAL	1 year
TYPICAL DIET	Mainly fish, invertebrates and crustaceans; also frogs, newts, small mammals and waterfowl
LIFESPAN	Up to 40 years

CREATURE COMPARISONS

The eel-tail catfish (Plotosus lineatus) is smaller than the European catfish, growing to around 30cm (11.8in) in length. It is found off the coasts of southern and eastern Asia, but is also able to survive in brackish and even freshwater. Where the European catfish has an extended anal fin, the torpedo-shaped eel-tail takes this a step further with a fringed fin that combines the anal, caudal and second dorsal fins to encircle the entire hind part of the body. Some of the fins contain highly venomous spines. The adult eel-tail has the same dark back and pale underbelly as its European cousin. However, younger eel-tails have longitudinal stripes which vary from bluish-white to yellowish-white.

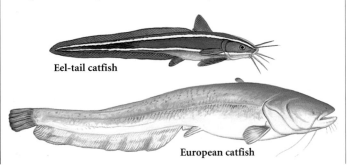

Eel-tail catfish

European catfish

WHERE IN THE WORLD?

Distributed across central and eastern Europe, from the Alps and the River Rhine to the Caspian Sea. Introduced to many other countries for sport.

RELATED SPECIES

The European catfish belongs to the family Siluridae, 1 of 34 families of catfish in the order Siluriformes. The order contains 2250 species including the glass catfish, Physailia pellcuia. Two catfish families, Plotosidae and Ariidae, contain marine catfish.

• **ORDER** • *Sirenia* • **FAMILY** • *Dugongidae* • **GENUS & SPECIES** • *Dugong dugon*

DUGONG

The dugong is an entirely aquatic mammal that never leaves the water. Its streamlined body is adapted to a life spent cruising lazily in the shallows.

KEY FEATURES

- Exclusively aquatic mammal that cruises through tropical and subtropical coastal waters.
- A large but gentle vegetarian, it specializes in eating sea grasses growing in shallow waters just offshore.
- A victim of hunting, pollution and the activities of fishermen, its population is now greatly reduced.

MOUTH
Incisor teeth project forward from the upper jaw of adult males to form a pair of short tusks. Their exact function is unclear, but some experts believe that they are used to guide the females during courtship. Very few females develop tusks.

EARS
Though it possesses only minuscule ear openings and no external ear flaps, the dugong's hearing is acute, and it can sense danger from a distance of 100m (328ft) or more.

TAIL
The notched tail is dolphin-like. It is the dugong's main means of propulsion and it beats it up and down to power itself along.

SKIN
The skin is tough and thick and overlies an insulating layer of blubber. Apart from a few stiff, blunt bristles on the snout, the body has only a sparse covering of hair.

FLIPPERS
The forelimbs are paddle-shaped and are used to help the dugong steer. Young dugongs also use their flippers for propulsion.

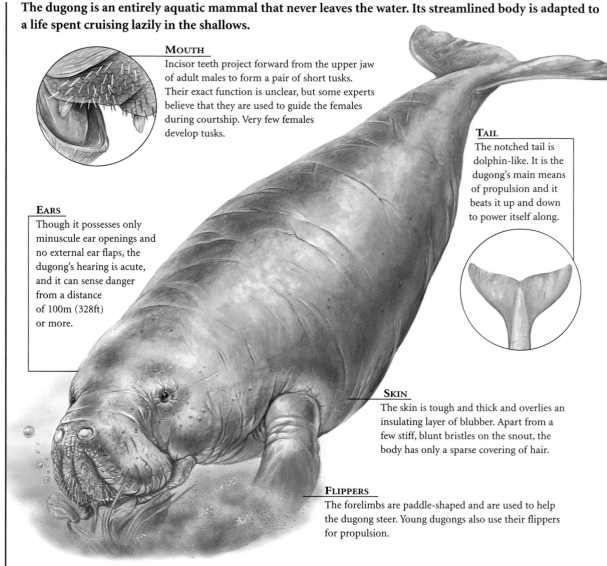

VITAL STATISTICS

WEIGHT	Up to 900kg (1984lb), but usually 230–360kg (507.1–793.7lb)
LENGTH	2.5–4m (8ft 2in–13ft 1in)
SEXUAL MATURITY	9–10 years, but may be delayed until 15 years
MATING SEASON	All year
GESTATION PERIOD	13–14 months
NUMBER OF YOUNG	1; rarely, twins
BIRTH INTERVAL	3–7 years
TYPICAL DIET	Sea grasses; some seaweed
LIFESPAN	Up to 50 years

CREATURE COMPARISONS

The West African manatee, Trichechus senegalensis, leads a similar life to the dugong, feeding on marine plants in the coastal waters and lowland rivers of West Africa from Senegal to Angola.

The clearest differences between the two are that the West African manatee has a broad, rounded tail and a longer, downward pointing snout with a less deeply cleft upper lip. Less obvious are the manatee's nostrils, which are positioned lower than the dugong's. Also, unlike the dugong, the adult male manatee does not possess any tusks.

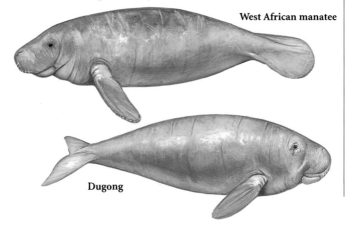

West African manatee

Dugong

WHERE IN THE WORLD?

Found in the Red Sea, African and Indian coastal waters in the Indian Ocean, Southeast Asia, south China and Australia, and around western Pacific islands.

RELATED SPECIES

The dugong and the manatees are the only surviving members of the Sirenians — an order of aquatic mammals that were much more abundant about 10 million years ago. The other member of the order Sirenia, Steller's sea cow, became extinct in 1768. The dugong is the only member of its family but there are 3 species of manatee — the West African, the West Indian, and the Amazonian — in the family Trichechidae.

• ORDER • *Sirenia* • FAMILY • *Trichechidae* • GENUS & SPECIES • *Trichechus manatus*

WEST INDIAN MANATEE

The hefty West Indian manatee is a slow-motion swimmer that lazily wafts its broad, flattened tail and paddle-like foreflippers to cruise in search of food.

KEY FEATURES

- Large and bulky aquatic mammal, fully adapted to a life spent swimming in warm coastal waters.
- Slow-moving and placid by nature, it rarely shows aggression towards other animals.
- Feeds almost exclusively on plants, unlike most other marine mammals, which are predators.

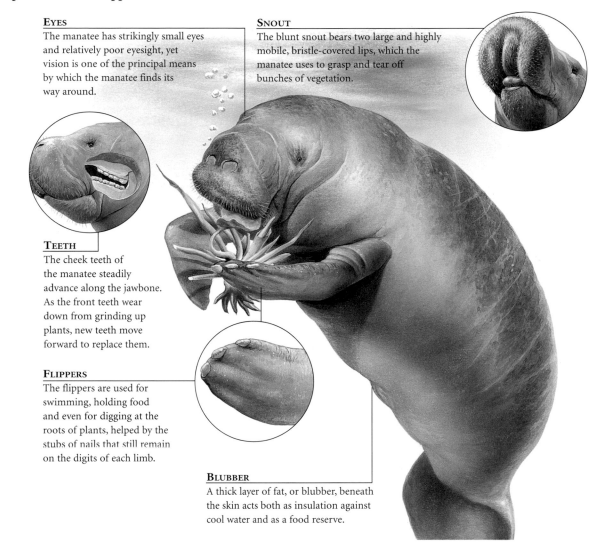

EYES
The manatee has strikingly small eyes and relatively poor eyesight, yet vision is one of the principal means by which the manatee finds its way around.

SNOUT
The blunt snout bears two large and highly mobile, bristle-covered lips, which the manatee uses to grasp and tear off bunches of vegetation.

TEETH
The cheek teeth of the manatee steadily advance along the jawbone. As the front teeth wear down from grinding up plants, new teeth move forward to replace them.

FLIPPERS
The flippers are used for swimming, holding food and even for digging at the roots of plants, helped by the stubs of nails that still remain on the digits of each limb.

BLUBBER
A thick layer of fat, or blubber, beneath the skin acts both as insulation against cool water and as a food reserve.

VITAL STATISTICS

WEIGHT	Up to 1600kg (3527lb), but usually 200–500kg (440.9–1102lb)
LENGTH	2.5–4.5m (8ft 2in–14ft 8in)
SEXUAL MATURITY	6–10 years
MATING SEASON	No set mating season
GESTATION PERIOD	Approximately 12 months
NUMBER OF YOUNG	1
BIRTH INTERVAL	2–2.5 years
TYPICAL DIET	Vegetation, especially sea grasses
LIFESPAN	Up to 30 years in captivity, probably longer in the wild

CREATURE COMPARISONS

The dugong, a marine mammal of the Red Sea and Indian and Pacific oceans, belongs to the same order as the manatees. Like the West Indian manatee, it is a non-ruminant herbivore dwelling in warm coastal shallows. Both species gain most of their propulsion through the water from up and down strokes of their flat tails. But whereas the manatee's tail is rounded in shape, the dugong's is wider and flared, with a concave trailing edge that is notched in the middle, rather like the tail flukes of a dolphin.

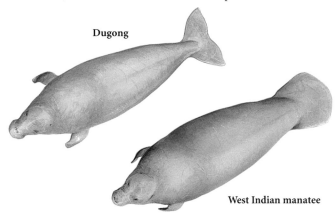

Dugong

West Indian manatee

WHERE IN THE WORLD?

Ranges along the Atlantic and Caribbean coastlines of the Americas, from eastern United States to northeastern Brazil, and around the larger islands of the Caribbean.

RELATED SPECIES

The West Indian manatee is one of three species in the genus Trichechus, all of which are similar in appearance. The Amazonian manatee, T. inunguis, inhabits the vast, inland waterways of the Amazon river system in Brazil, Colombia, Ecuador and Peru. The West African manatee, T. senegalensis, lives on the other side of the Atlantic Ocean occupying coastal waters and lowland rivers of West Africa from Senegal to Angola.

• **ORDER** • *Spihenisciformes* • **FAMILY** • *Spheniscidae* • **GENUS & SPECIES** • *Eudyptes chrysocome*

ROCKHOPPER PENGUIN

Specially adapted circulation in its exposed feet and individually muscled feathers enable the rockhopper penguin to thrive close to the South Pole.

HEAD PLUMES
The rich yellow and black plumes characterize birds of the Eudyptes genus. In the rockhopper, the extent to which they project or droop varies according to the subspecies. They reach their full glory on adults of more than two years old.

BILL
Composed of several horny plates, the rockhopper's short, stout bill is designed for seizing krill and squid.

FEATHERS
The rockhopper has a covering of short and stiff, lance-shaped feathers. Each quill has an additional row of downy filaments that creates a dense, warming layer beneath the sleek, waterproof exterior.

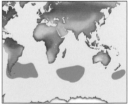

FLIPPER
The long pectoral flippers are supported by heavy, blade-like bones in the forearm, wrist and hand. The penguin uses its flippers to propel itself through the water.

JUVENILE
Downy at first, the juvenile reaches full size just prior to starting its moult into adult plumage. At this stage, it may weigh more than its parents; every gram is an advantage in its first winter.

FEET
The naked feet are a potential source of heat loss. To compensate, the rockhopper has a special circulatory system that allows the temperature in its feet to drop to 6–9°C (42.8–48.2°F), while its core body temperature remains at 39°C (102.2°F).

KEY FEATURES

- Perfectly streamlined for swimming, it dives to 100m (328ft) or more beneath the surface to catch krill (shrimps) and squid.
- Its dense coat of body feathers can be flattened to form a watertight barrier against freezing Antarctic waters.
- Colonies containing thousands of jostling pairs assemble to raise their young on remote oceanic islands.

VITAL STATISTICS

WEIGHT	2–5kg (4.4–11lb); maximum weight attained prior to moulting
LENGTH	55–62cm (21.6–24.4in)
SEXUAL MATURITY	4 years
BREEDING SEASON	Variable; mainly November to March
NUMBER OF EGGS	2, although only 1 chick usually survives
INCUBATION PERIOD	28–38 days
FLEDGING PERIOD	About 70 days
BREEDING INTERVAL	1 year
TYPICAL DIET	Crustaceans and fish
LIFESPAN	10–15 years

CREATURE COMPARISONS

The rockhopper shares part of its ocean habitat with the chinstrap penguin (Pygoscelis antarctica), so called because of the black marking under its chin. Slightly larger than the rockhopper, the chinstrap has an almost identical body shape and physiology. It lacks the yellow-crested plumes of the rockhopper, but has white markings on its chin, throat and cheeks.

The chinstrap has a more southerly distribution than the rockhopper, nesting on mainland Antarctica as well as more northerly islands and the tip of South America. Like the rockhopper, it gathers in huge, densely packed breeding colonies. It dives among areas of light pack ice for crustaceans and fish.

Chinstrap

Rockhopper

WHERE IN THE WORLD?

Lives in the southern oceans near Antarctica. Comes ashore on islands in the South Pacific and South Atlantic, including the Falklands, the Bounty and Antipodes islands and Tristan da Cunha.

RELATED SPECIES

The rockhopper penguin belongs to the genus Eudyptes, a group of 6 species characterized by golden head plumes. The penguin family, Spheniscidae, contains 17 species in 6 genera. The gentoo penguin, Pygoscelis papua, shares its range with the rockhopper.

• **ORDER** • *Spinulosida* • **FAMILY** • *Acanthasteridae* • **GENUS & SPECIES** • *Acanthaster planci* CROWN OF THORNS SEA STAR

KEY FEATURES

- A many-armed sea star (starfish) covered with poisonous spines.
- Has a radially symmetrical body plan, with a central mouth on its underside.
- Turns its stomach inside-out to dissolve and devour the soft, living parts of branching, and other, corals.
- Able to regrow any of its limbs that are bitten off by predators.

VITAL STATISTICS

WEIGHT	Up to 500g (17.6oz)
DIAMETER	Up to 70cm (27.6in) across the legs
SEXUAL MATURITY	2 years
BREEDING SEASON	December to January, perhaps longer
NUMBER OF EGGS	12 to 24 million
TYPICAL DIET	Polyps (living parts) of corals, especially the soft, branching, and plate corals, rather than the hard encrusting types.
LIFESPAN	6–7 years

The crown of thorns sea star is equipped with up to 23 muscular, sucker-footed arms, on which it creeps slowly but steadily across the reefs.

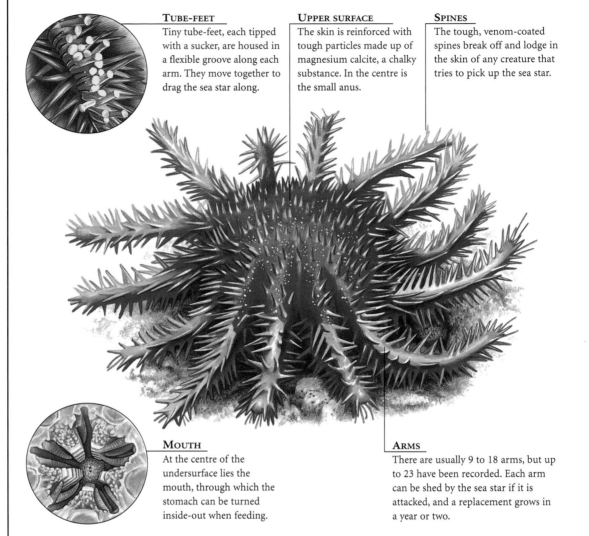

TUBE-FEET
Tiny tube-feet, each tipped with a sucker, are housed in a flexible groove along each arm. They move together to drag the sea star along.

UPPER SURFACE
The skin is reinforced with tough particles made up of magnesium calcite, a chalky substance. In the centre is the small anus.

SPINES
The tough, venom-coated spines break off and lodge in the skin of any creature that tries to pick up the sea star.

MOUTH
At the centre of the undersurface lies the mouth, through which the stomach can be turned inside-out when feeding.

ARMS
There are usually 9 to 18 arms, but up to 23 have been recorded. Each arm can be shed by the sea star if it is attacked, and a replacement grows in a year or two.

CREATURE COMPARISONS

Most sea stars are five-legged, but their shape and size vary greatly according to their habits. A typical five-legged sea star has short arms to burrow in sand in search of seashells and other molluscs. With its spectacular array of limbs and tube-feet, the crown of thorns can climb and curl around the stems of branching corals to feed.

Fromia ghardagna   Crown of thorns

WHERE IN THE WORLD?

Found on coral reefs in the tropical regions of the Indian and Pacific oceans, notably around the Great Barrier Reef off the eastern coast of Australia, and the atolls and lagoons of the Indonesian islands.

RELATED SPECIES

There are about 1600 species of sea star, or starfish, in about 300 genera. Acanthaster is the only genus in its family, and the crown of thorns is the only coral-eating species. A. brevispinus, for example, has shorter spines and feeds on molluscs.

• **ORDER** • *Squamata* • **FAMILY** • *Agamidae* • **GENUS & SPECIES** • *Chlamydosaurus kingii*

FRILLED LIZARD

The frilled lizard resembles a creature from the primordial past, especially when it bounds along on its hindlegs just like a diminutive dinosaur.

KEY FEATURES

- Can rapidly erect a neck frill to increase its apparent size and scare off would-be predators.
- Able to stand upright on its hindlegs and run 50m (164ft) or more at relatively high speed.
- Possesses keen eyesight and can identify predators or prey at distances of up to 25m (82ft).

TEETH
The sharp, conical front teeth and flat, chisel-shaped rear teeth are fused to the side of the jaw: the front teeth are replaceable. The mouth may be pink or yellow inside.

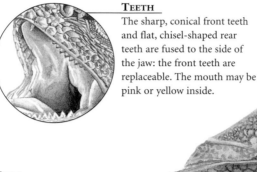

FRILL
The frill is a U-shaped collar of skin, open at the back of the neck. It is supported by two bony rods that extend backwards on each side. By contracting the muscles at the base of these rods, the lizard can rapidly erect the skin into a ruff-like frill.

TAIL
The long, whip-like tail can be lashed aggressively at an attacker, or used to counterbalance the lizard's bodyweight when it stands erect on its hindlegs.

CLAWS
Sharp, curved claws on all five digits enable the frilled lizard to climb trees with speed and dexterity.

VITAL STATISTICS

WEIGHT	Up to 740g (26.1oz)
LENGTH	Head & Body 25cm (9.8in) Tail 51cm (20.1in)
SEXUAL MATURITY	2–3 years
BREEDING SEASON	Spring
NUMBER OF EGGS	4 to 13, average 8
INCUBATION PERIOD	75–95 days at 30°C (86°F)
BIRTH INTERVAL	More than one clutch may be laid in each breeding season
TYPICAL DIET	Chiefly moth and butterfly larvae, termites and ants; also small mammals
LIFESPAN	Up to about 5 years in the wild

CREATURE COMPARISONS

Although the frilled lizard is the longest of the Australian dragon lizards, which are second only to monitor lizards in size, it is dwarfed by the giant Komodo dragon. The largest lizard in the world, this mighty monitor is, in fact, a near neighbour of the frilled lizard. The komodo dragon inhabits the tiny Lesser Sunda Islands, located about 145km (90.1 miles) off the northwestern coast of Australia. The Komodo dragon grows to 4m (13ft 1in) and weighs 135kg (297.6lb)— only about five times the length of the frilled lizard but almost 200 times heavier. An aggressive predator, it hunts prey as large as deer and young water buffalo.

Komodo dragon

Frilled lizard

WHERE IN THE WORLD?

Found in Australia, from Western Australia across Northern Territory to Cape York Peninsula and the eastern coast of Queensland; also southern New Guinea.

RELATED SPECIES

The Australian frilled lizard is a member of the dragon lizard family, the Agamidae, of which there are estimated to be about 320 species worldwide. Other family members include the bearded dragon, *Pogona minor*, and the bizarre-looking thorny devil, *Moloch horridus*.

• ORDER • *Squamata* • FAMILY • *Agamidae* • GENUS & SPECIES • *Moloch horridus*

KEY FEATURES

- Covered from head to tail in spiky, modified scales, presenting predators with a thorny problem.
- Bluffs predators by showing a false head and changing the tone of its colours if attacked.
- Able to survive in the hottest regions of the Australian Outback, living mainly on a diet of ants.

VITAL STATISTICS

WEIGHT	35–90g (1.2–3.2oz)
LENGTH	13–16cm (5.1–6.3in). Female larger than male
SEXUAL MATURITY	1–2 years
MATING SEASON	Late winter to early summer
NUMBER OF EGGS	6 to 8
INCUBATION PERIOD	90–130 days
BIRTH INTERVAL	1 year
TYPICAL DIET	Black ants, occasionally termites
LIFESPAN	Up to 20 years

The distinctive body armour that gives the thorny devil its name is essential protection against predators, but it also helps this lizard to trap water.

HEAD SPINES
Two especially prominent spines on the head warn predators that the thorny devil might be a painful mouthful to swallow.

COLOURATION
In the sun, the thorny devil's colouration is a broken pattern of burnt red, yellow and brown. However, the vibrant colours become drab when the thorny devil is cold or alarmed.

FALSE HEAD
The thorny devil has a curious spiked bulge on the back of its neck. When threatened, it tries to trick predators by tucking its real head between its forelegs and leaving the head-like bulge exposed instead.

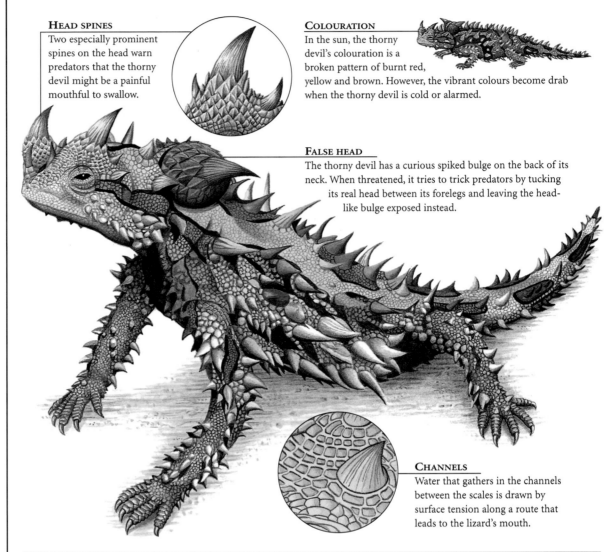

CHANNELS
Water that gathers in the channels between the scales is drawn by surface tension along a route that leads to the lizard's mouth.

CREATURE COMPARISONS

When the thorny devil was first studied about 100 years ago, naturalists noted its similarities to the horned lizards of North America. Further study indicated that these lizards belong to entirely different families, yet the external similarities are striking. The most obvious similarity is in the armoured skin. Like the thorny devil, the short-horned lizard, Phrynosoma douglassii, has a pair of horns on its head. But while the thorny devil is almost fully protected by hard spines, the short-horned lizard has spiky scales that extend only to the edge of its flattened body. Like many lizards, both species have triangular-shaped heads.

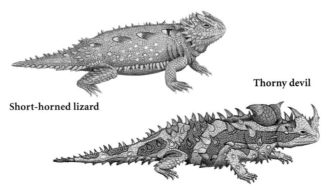

Short-horned lizard

Thorny devil

WHERE IN THE WORLD?

Found throughout most of the arid interior of Australia, particularly on sandy, rather than stony, soils. Also occurs on parts of the western and southern coasts.

RELATED SPECIES

The thorny devil is one of over 300 lizard species in the family Agamidae. Most of the lizards in this family have chisel-like teeth to feed on insects. Some members, such as the frilled lizard, Chlamydosaurus kingii, have flaps on their necks which are used to startle predators.

• **ORDER** • *Squamata* • **FAMILY** • *Boidae* • **GENUS & SPECIES** • *Morelia viridis*

GREEN TREE PYTHON

The green tree python is adapted to hunt among the branches of the forests, killing prey in the suffocating grip of its powerful coils.

KEY FEATURES

- Bright colour provides perfect camouflage in the trees where this predator spends much of its time.
- Well adapted for climbing, it ambushes passing prey from overhanging branches.
- Equipped with a heat-seeking system for targeting warm-blooded victims in total darkness.
- Uses its powerful coils to suffocate large prey.

VITAL STATISTICS

WEIGHT	Up to 9kg (19.8lb), but usually 3–6kg (6.6–17.6lb)
LENGTH	Up to 2m (6ft 6in), but usually about half this length
SEXUAL MATURITY	2 years
BREEDING SEASON	End of wet season
NUMBER OF EGGS	10 to 20
HATCHING PERIOD	About 60 days
BREEDING INTERVAL	1 year
TYPICAL DIET	Mainly birds; also bats and other small mammals
LIFESPAN	Up to 35 years in captivity

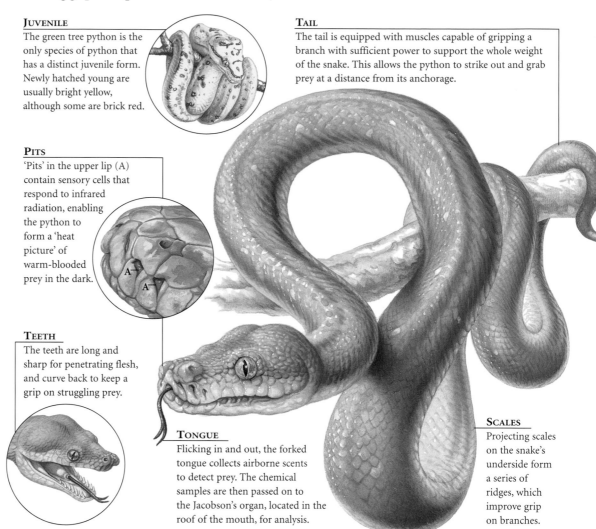

JUVENILE
The green tree python is the only species of python that has a distinct juvenile form. Newly hatched young are usually bright yellow, although some are brick red.

PITS
'Pits' in the upper lip (A) contain sensory cells that respond to infrared radiation, enabling the python to form a 'heat picture' of warm-blooded prey in the dark.

TEETH
The teeth are long and sharp for penetrating flesh, and curve back to keep a grip on struggling prey.

TONGUE
Flicking in and out, the forked tongue collects airborne scents to detect prey. The chemical samples are then passed on to the Jacobson's organ, located in the roof of the mouth, for analysis.

TAIL
The tail is equipped with muscles capable of gripping a branch with sufficient power to support the whole weight of the snake. This allows the python to strike out and grab prey at a distance from its anchorage.

SCALES
Projecting scales on the snake's underside form a series of ridges, which improve grip on branches.

CREATURE COMPARISONS

The emerald tree boa, Corallus caninus, is a distant cousin of the green tree python that lives in the rainforests of South America. Although, at 2.5m (8ft 2in), the emerald tree boa is generally longer than its relation, the two snakes are very similar in several respects. Both share an arboreal (tree-living) lifestyle, similar hunting methods and, most strikingly, colour. This is an example of parallel evolution: the process by which species in different places develop in the same way because they are faced with similar conditions.

Emerald tree boa

Green tree python

WHERE IN THE WORLD?

Occurs on the island of New Guinea, the nearby Bismark Archipelago and the islands scattered across the Torres Strait between New Guinea and mainland Australia. Also found in northern Queensland, Australia.

RELATED SPECIES

The family Boidae contains around 80 species of boas and pythons. It is usually divided into 7 subfamilies: Boinae (large boas); Erycinae (sand, rosy and rubber boas); Pythoninae (pythons); Calabariinae (burrowing pythons); Loxoceminae (Mexican python); Bolyeriinae (Round Island boas); and Tropidophiinae (wood snakes and dwarf boas). The Boidae are part of the order Squamata, which also contains lizards.

• ORDER • *Squamata* • FAMILY • *Boidae* • GENUS & SPECIES • *Eunectes murinus*

GREEN ANACONDA

Most powerful of all the giant snakes, the green anaconda uses its massive coils to squeeze the life out of prey that seems too large to eat.

KEY FEATURES

- Largest snake in the world, measuring up to 7.6m (24ft 9in) long and weighing almost 135kg (297.6lb).
- Kills using its powerful coils to suffocate or drown its hapless prey.
- Hunts by night, preying on large animals like deer, capybara and young caimans.

BODY
The green anaconda is the largest snake in the western hemisphere and the heaviest snake in the world. Its muscular coils have the power to kill even large prey with a deadly, suffocating embrace.

EYES
The lidless eye is protected by a layer of skin called the brille. The oval iris helps the snake to see by night; day-active snakes have round irises.

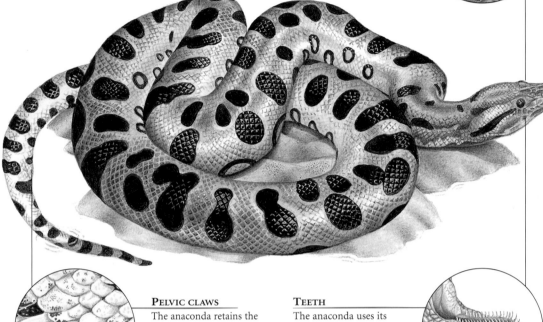

PELVIC CLAWS
The anaconda retains the remnants of what were once hindlimbs. These are larger in the male: he uses them during mating to stimulate the female.

TEETH
The anaconda uses its sharp teeth to hold prey in an inescapable grip. They point backward, to draw prey ever deeper into the snake's mouth.

VITAL STATISTICS

WEIGHT	Up to about 135kg (297.6lb)
LENGTH	5.4–7.6m (17.7–24.9ft)
SEXUAL MATURITY	4 years
MATING SEASON	Chiefly December and January
GESTATION PERIOD	6–7 months
NUMBER OF YOUNG	Varies with the size of the adult
BIRTH INTERVAL	1–2 years
TYPICAL DIET	Aquatic and semi-aquatic animals, including fish, caimans, capybaras and waterbirds
LIFESPAN	Up to 20 years in captivity

CREATURE COMPARISONS

The regal, or reticulated, python of Southeast Asia is another large and powerful snake, growing to 9m (29ft 5in) or more. Its slim body bears a pattern of interwoven lines, and a narrow line runs from its snout to the back of its head. Like the anaconda, it is highly aquatic.

Green anaconda

Reticulated python

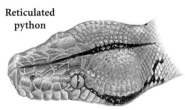

WHERE IN THE WORLD?

Found in rainforests and swamp areas on Trinidad and throughout most of tropical South America east of the Andes mountain range, from Venezuela south to Bolivia and northern Paraguay.

RELATED SPECIES
There are three other anaconda species in the genus Eunectes: E. barbouri, E. deschauenseei and E. notaeus. The yellow anaconda, E. notaeus, lives in southern Brazil, Bolivia, Paraguay and Argentina. This snake is highly aquatic, and grows to about 3m (9ft 8in) in length.

• ORDER • *Squamata* **• FAMILY •** *Boidae* **• GENUS & SPECIES •** *Python reticulatus*

RETICULATED PYTHON

KEY FEATURES

- Competes with the South American anaconda for the title of the world's largest snake.
- Locates its prey in the gloom of tropical rainforests, despite being unable to see or hear its victims clearly.
- Wraps its powerful coils around prey in a deadly embrace and slowly squeezes the life from it.

VITAL STATISTICS

LENGTH	Average adult 5–6m (16ft 4in–19ft 7in). Occasionally reaches 9m (29ft 5in)
WEIGHT	Up to 115kg (253.5lb)
SEXUAL MATURITY	5 years
BREEDING SEASON	Variable
NUMBER OF EGGS	Up to 100, but usually 20 to 50
GESTATION PERIOD	10–12 weeks
HATCHING PERIOD	11–13 weeks
BREEDING INTERVAL	1 year
TYPICAL DIET	Small mammals, birds, reptiles
LIFESPAN	Unknown in wild; up to 27 years in captivity

The reticulated python is a gigantic tube of muscle, capable of coiling around branches to climb trees with ease and killing prey with a suffocating grip.

JAWS
Elastic ligaments connecting the lower jaw to the rest of the skull allow the jaw to stretch wide. The python is able to swallow prey considerably wider than its head.

SKIN
The python periodically sloughs, or sheds, its entire skin as it grows. An adult reticulated python sloughs its skin up to seven times a year.

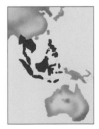

PITS
Prominent diagonal 'pits' in the upper lip contain heat sensory cells that can detect the most minute sources of heat radiating from animals.

EYES
Like other snakes, the python has no eyelids but, instead, has a layer of transparent skin over its eyes. During the day, its pupils narrow to vertical slits. At night the pupils open fully, but the eyes can see prey only at very close range.

TONGUE
The snake's forked tongue picks up traces of scent from the air and transfers the 'taste' to a scent organ — Jacobsen's Organ — in the roof of the mouth, where it is analyzed.

CREATURE COMPARISONS

'Reticulated' refers to the net of dark, intersecting lines overlying the paler patches along the python's body. Another Asian python — Python molurus — has two subspecies decorated with a similar pattern: the Indian python (P. m. molurus) of India and Sri Lanka has cream bands on dark patches. The Burmese python (P. m. bivittatus) has bands of orange-brown.

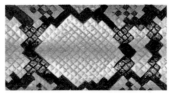

Reticulated python

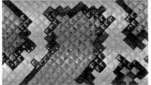

Indian python

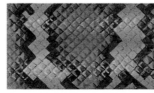

Burmese python

WHERE IN THE WORLD?

Found in the tropical rainforests of Southeast Asia, including Myanmar (Burma), Thailand, Laos, Cambodia, North and South Vietnam, Malaysia, the Philippine Islands and most of the islands of Indonesia.

RELATED SPECIES

The genus Python has 10 species, distributed across Africa, southern Asia and Australasia. Large specimens of several species can exceed 4m (13ft 1in) in length, including the African rock python (Python sebae), the Indian pythons of Asia, and the amethystine python (Liasis amethystinus), which ranges into Australia. No pythons are venomous, but all share the common feature of using their powerful constricting coils for subduing prey.

• ORDER • *Squamata* • FAMILY • *Chamaeleontidae* • GENUS & SPECIES • *Chamaeleo jacksonii*

JACKSON'S CHAMELEON

Jackson's chameleon has the remarkable ability to change its body colour to blend in with the shades of yellow, green and brown of its habitat.

KEY FEATURES

- Usually camouflaged green, but can change colour to blend in with the natural colours of its habitat.
- Male has three large horns at the tip of the snout; female has a single, shorter horn in front of the eyes.
- Can move each eye independently and so watch out for danger in two directions at once.

HORNS
The male possesses three horns, which he uses to intimidate rivals during territorial and breeding disputes. The female has only one horn.

EYES
Each eye lies at the tip of a swivelling turret. The eyes move independently of each other, allowing the chameleon to see in two directions at once.

SKIN
Skin cells contain pigments that can be changed at will, allowing the chameleon to turn pale or dark when irritated, green when relaxing, or darken to absorb heat.

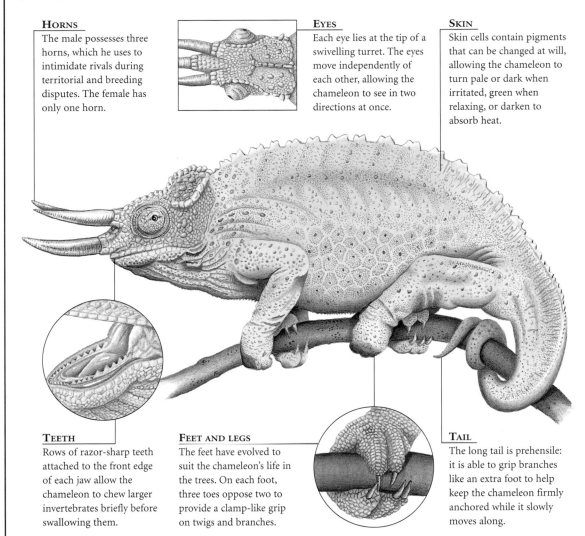

TEETH
Rows of razor-sharp teeth attached to the front edge of each jaw allow the chameleon to chew larger invertebrates briefly before swallowing them.

FEET AND LEGS
The feet have evolved to suit the chameleon's life in the trees. On each foot, three toes oppose two to provide a clamp-like grip on twigs and branches.

TAIL
The long tail is prehensile: it is able to grip branches like an extra foot to help keep the chameleon firmly anchored while it slowly moves along.

VITAL STATISTICS

WEIGHT	Not recorded
LENGTH	15–30cm (5.9–11.8in)
SEXUAL MATURITY	Not recorded
MATING SEASON	Throughout most of the year
GESTATION PERIOD	Not recorded
NUMBER OF YOUNG	20 to 40
BIRTH INTERVAL	Not recorded
TYPICAL DIET	Insects, spiders and scorpions
LIFESPAN	10 years in captivity

CREATURE COMPARISONS

Most chameleons have a similar body shape, with turret-shaped eyes and a prehensile tail, but their heads vary greatly in detail. Some have horns, while others have crests, like that of the crested chameleon, Chamaeleo cristatus. Still others possess helmet-like casques: the most dramatic is that of the Yemeni veiled chameleon, C. calyptratus.

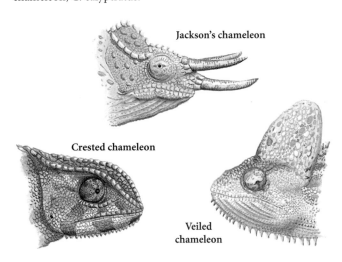

Jackson's chameleon

Crested chameleon

Veiled chameleon

WHERE IN THE WORLD?

Found in trees and bushes in the East African highlands, from Nairobi to the western slopes of Mount Kenya, the Aberdare Mountains of Kenya, and the Usambara Mountains of Tanzania.

RELATED SPECIES
Jackson's chameleon is one of 85 known species of chameleon that are found mainly in Mediterranean lands, Africa and many parts of Asia. These include the flap-necked chameleon, Chamaeleo dilepis. The longest horns, up to 15cm(5.9in) long, belong to the male Owen's chameleon.

• ORDER • *Squamata* • FAMILY • *Colubridae* • GENUS & SPECIES • *Natrix natrix*

GRASS SNAKE

Several colour variations have been recorded across this snake's range, but the yellow-and-black collar is usually present to aid identification.

KEY FEATURES

- A sleek, sinuous hunter that preys mainly on small mammals and various aquatic animals.
- As a non-venomous snake, it relies on surprise and strength to catch and overpower its prey.
- Wary and hard to approach, it is quick to escape its many enemies by slipping into cover.

VITAL STATISTICS

LENGTH	Up to 2m (6ft 6in) (female is usually longer)
SEXUAL MATURITY	Male 3 years; female 4 years
BREEDING SEASON	April to May
NUMBER OF EGGS	8 to 40, depending on the size of the mother; laid about 2 months after mating
INCUBATION PERIOD	40–55 days, depending on temperature
BREEDING INTERVAL	1 year
TYPICAL DIET	Small mammals, birds, reptiles and amphibians
LIFESPAN	Up to 25 years

SKIN
The protective scales are tough and flexible, but cannot stretch to accommodate the growing body. The snake overcomes this problem by shedding its skin several times a year.

SKULL AND JAW
The jaw bones are loosely connected to the skull by elastic ligaments, enabling the snake to stretch its jaws around large prey.

DARK FORM
Some grass snakes are almost black, or melanistic. They can be confused with adders, but have a less wedge-shaped head.

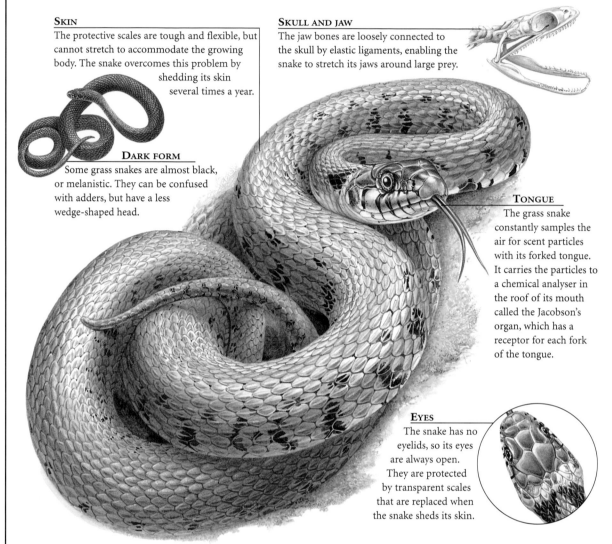

TONGUE
The grass snake constantly samples the air for scent particles with its forked tongue. It carries the particles to a chemical analyser in the roof of its mouth called the Jacobson's organ, which has a receptor for each fork of the tongue.

EYES
The snake has no eyelids, so its eyes are always open. They are protected by transparent scales that are replaced when the snake sheds its skin.

CREATURE COMPARISONS

In southeastern Europe, the grass snake lives alongside the horned viper (Vipera ammodytes), a southern relative of the adder. Like all vipers, it is shorter and stockier than the grass snake, with a broad, triangular head and a diamond-patterned back. It gets its name from the strange rhino-like horn that grows on its snout: a soft, pliable projection that has no obvious use. The horned viper favours drier, stonier country than the grass snake, and feeds mainly on small mammals such as mice and moles. It sinks its fangs into victims and injects them with venom, which can also be fatal to humans.

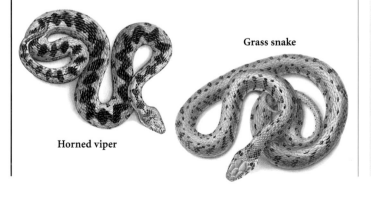

Grass snake

Horned viper

WHERE IN THE WORLD?

Occurs in much of Europe. Found in Asia, eastwards as far as Siberia, and also in northwestern Africa. Absent from Ireland and some Mediterranean islands.

RELATED SPECIES

The grass snake is 1 of 4 semi-aquatic, non-venomous species in the genus Natrix, which are found in Europe and western Asia and include the viperine snake and the highly aquatic dice snake. They are part of the family Colubridae, the 'typical snakes', which contains 2200 species. In all, there are 2700 species of snake, placed in 11 families in the suborder Serpentes. The order Squamata, which includes lizards, is placed in the class Reptilia.

GARTER SNAKE

• **ORDER** • *Squamata* • **FAMILY** • *Colubridae* • **GENUS & SPECIES** • *Thamnophis sirtalis*

KEY FEATURES

- North America's most common species of snake.
- A highly adaptable animal, at home both on land and in water.
- Escapes freezing winters by hiding underground, sometimes sharing communal dens with up to a hundred or more snakes.

VITAL STATISTICS

WEIGHT	Varies; average 300–400g (10.6–14.1oz)
LENGTH	30–130cm (11.8–51.2in); female larger than male
SEXUAL MATURITY	2–3 years
BREEDING SEASON	Variable, but normally spring
NUMBER OF EGGS	3 to 85; usually 11 to 26
INCUBATION PERIOD	87–116 days
BREEDING INTERVAL	1 year
TYPICAL DIET	Frogs, toads, salamanders, fish, small mammals, birds, invertebrates
LIFESPAN	Up to 12 years

Using stealth and a battery of senses, the muscle-packed garter snake attacks with little warning. Its lack of venom is no hindrance to hunting success.

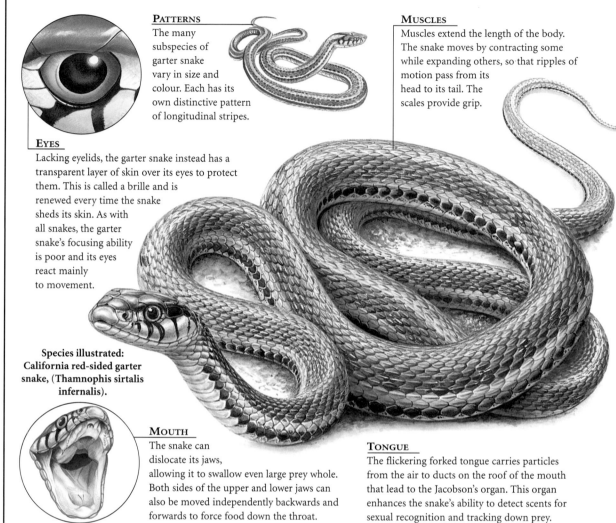

PATTERNS
The many subspecies of garter snake vary in size and colour. Each has its own distinctive pattern of longitudinal stripes.

MUSCLES
Muscles extend the length of the body. The snake moves by contracting some while expanding others, so that ripples of motion pass from its head to its tail. The scales provide grip.

EYES
Lacking eyelids, the garter snake instead has a transparent layer of skin over its eyes to protect them. This is called a brille and is renewed every time the snake sheds its skin. As with all snakes, the garter snake's focusing ability is poor and its eyes react mainly to movement.

Species illustrated:
California red-sided garter snake, (Thamnophis sirtalis infernalis).

MOUTH
The snake can dislocate its jaws, allowing it to swallow even large prey whole. Both sides of the upper and lower jaws can also be moved independently backwards and forwards to force food down the throat.

TONGUE
The flickering forked tongue carries particles from the air to ducts on the roof of the mouth that lead to the Jacobson's organ. This organ enhances the snake's ability to detect scents for sexual recognition and tracking down prey.

CREATURE COMPARISONS

Like the California red-sided garter snake, the western aquatic garter snake (Thamnophis couchii) varies widely in size and colouration between subspecies. But while the California garter snake is just striped, its cousin normally has a clear pattern of dark spots as well.

The western aquatic garter snake is confined to a thin band along the west coast of the USA, from southwestern Oregon south to central California. Even more of a water creature than its relative, it lives exclusively around rivers, streams, marshes and other aquatic environments. It has a similar diet to the California garter snake, feeding on fish, amphibians and invertebrates.

California garter snake

Aquatic garter snake

WHERE IN THE WORLD?

Has a broad range that extends from coast to coast across southern Canada and the USA. Also occurs in parts of northern Mexico.

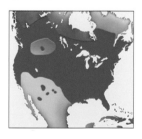

RELATED SPECIES

There are 11 subspecies of garter snake: the red-sided, California red-sided, blue-striped, valley, eastern, New Mexico, Texas, Chicago, Puget Sound, red-spotted and San Francisco garter snakes. The garter snake belongs to the family Colubridae, which includes all snakes other than front-fanged venomous species, burrowing snakes and constrictors such as boas and pythons. Snakes belong to the order Squamata and class Reptilia.

• **ORDER** • *Squamata* • **FAMILY** • *Crotalidae* • **GENUS & SPECIES** • *Crotalus atrox*

DIAMONDBACK RATTLESNAKE

KEY FEATURES

- Lives in the 'badlands' and semi-desert areas of North America, where its tough skin prevents it from losing too much moisture.

- Conserves water by excreting urine as a thick paste.

- Adjusts its daily behaviour to regulate its body heat, alternately basking in the sun and seeking shade.

VITAL STATISTICS

WEIGHT	Up to 6.8kg (15lb)
LENGTH	Up to 2.1m (6ft 9in)
SEXUAL MATURITY	About 3 years
MATING SEASON	Spring
INCUBATION PERIOD	About 165 days
NUMBER OF YOUNG	Up to 46, but usually 10 to 20
BIRTH INTERVAL	2 years
TYPICAL DIET	Small mammals, such as mice and voles; also ground squirrels, rabbits and prairie dogs, small birds, frogs and lizards
LIFESPAN	Up to 24 years in captivity, usually much less in the wild

The rattlesnake's heat-sensing pit organs guide the snake towards its prey, allowing it to strike with deadly accuracy even in total darkness.

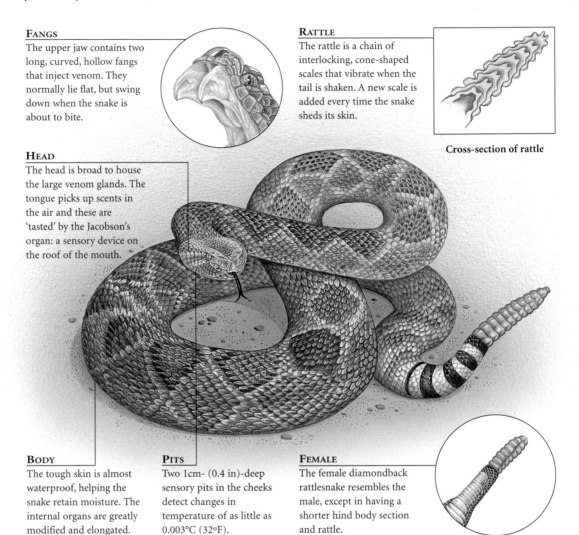

FANGS
The upper jaw contains two long, curved, hollow fangs that inject venom. They normally lie flat, but swing down when the snake is about to bite.

RATTLE
The rattle is a chain of interlocking, cone-shaped scales that vibrate when the tail is shaken. A new scale is added every time the snake sheds its skin.

Cross-section of rattle

HEAD
The head is broad to house the large venom glands. The tongue picks up scents in the air and these are 'tasted' by the Jacobson's organ: a sensory device on the roof of the mouth.

BODY
The tough skin is almost waterproof, helping the snake retain moisture. The internal organs are greatly modified and elongated.

PITS
Two 1cm- (0.4 in)-deep sensory pits in the cheeks detect changes in temperature of as little as 0.003°C (32°F).

FEMALE
The female diamondback rattlesnake resembles the male, except in having a shorter hind body section and rattle.

CREATURE COMPARISONS

Faced with danger, many snakes adopt a threat display or a defensive posture. The prairie rattler (1) coils into a rising spiral, its rattle held clear and buzzing out a warning. The rubber boa (2) rolls into a ball, protecting its head in its coils, but leaving its tail waving like a threatening head. The Tartar sand boa (3) also makes its head look like its tail, to tempt an enemy into attacking the least sensitive body part. The spectacled cobra (4) rears up and flattens its neck into a 'hood' that looks like a fearsome head.

WHERE IN THE WORLD?

Found in the drier states of North America, from California, east through Nevada, Arizona, New Mexico, Texas and Kansas, and south to Mexico.

RELATED SPECIES

The western diamondback rattlesnake is a member of the Crotalidae family. Snakes in this group are known as pit vipers because of the heat-sensing 'pits' on their heads. There are about 130 species of pit viper, and among them the western diamondback's closest relative is the largest of all rattlesnakes — the 2.4m (7ft 9in) eastern diamondback. The pit vipers are considered to be the most evolutionarily advanced of all snake species.

SEA SNAKE

• **ORDER** • *Squamata* • **FAMILY** • *Elapidae* • **GENUS & SPECIES** • *Hydrophiinae, Laticaudinae*

KEY FEATURES

- Most species spend their entire lives at sea; others come ashore to shelter and to breed.
- Equipped with venom more powerful than that of all other snakes, including their cobra relatives.
- Females of wholly aquatic species keep their eggs inside their body, giving birth to independent young.

VITAL STATISTICS

WEIGHT	1.5–2kg (3.3–4.4lb)
LENGTH	Up to 2m (6ft 6in)
SEXUAL MATURITY	2–3 years
BREEDING SEASON	All year
GESTATION PERIOD	150–180 days (Hydrophiinae only)
NUMBER OF YOUNG	2 to 12 (Hydrophiinae only)
NUMBER OF EGGS	5 to 10 (Laticaudinae only)
INCUBATION PERIOD	Not known
BIRTH INTERVAL	Not known
TYPICAL DIET	Mainly fish; some species eat fish eggs
LIFESPAN	Up to 20 years

Able to survive underwater for long periods, the sea snake fills its enlarged lung with air before diving down to the reefs and seaweed forests to hunt.

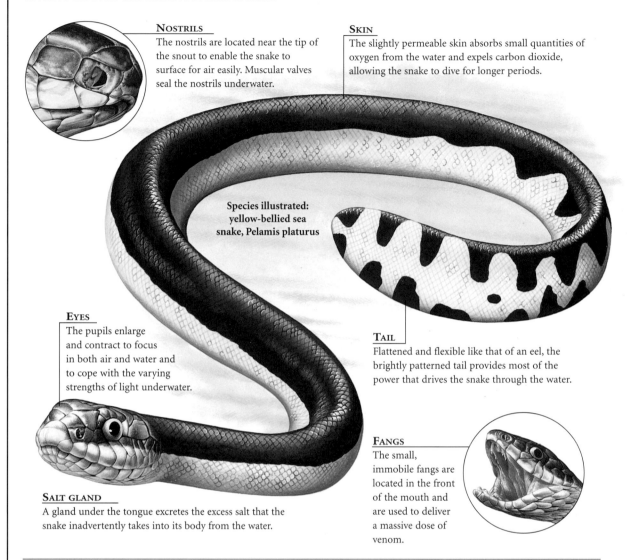

NOSTRILS
The nostrils are located near the tip of the snout to enable the snake to surface for air easily. Muscular valves seal the nostrils underwater.

SKIN
The slightly permeable skin absorbs small quantities of oxygen from the water and expels carbon dioxide, allowing the snake to dive for longer periods.

Species illustrated: yellow-bellied sea snake, Pelamis platurus

EYES
The pupils enlarge and contract to focus in both air and water and to cope with the varying strengths of light underwater.

TAIL
Flattened and flexible like that of an eel, the brightly patterned tail provides most of the power that drives the snake through the water.

SALT GLAND
A gland under the tongue excretes the excess salt that the snake inadvertently takes into its body from the water.

FANGS
The small, immobile fangs are located in the front of the mouth and are used to deliver a massive dose of venom.

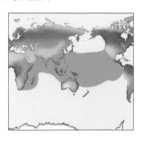

CREATURE COMPARISONS

While the sea snakes of the subfamily Hydrophiinae, such as the yellow-bellied sea snake, are totally marine and bear their young at sea, those of the subfamily Laticaudinae, such as the yellow-lipped sea snake (Laticauda colobrina), spend more time on land where they also lay their eggs. The Laticaudinae retain many of the features of terrestrial snakes including the scale and muscle arrangement that permits land movement. All sea snakes possess flattened tails for swimming, and most hunt fish, killing their prey with powerful venom.

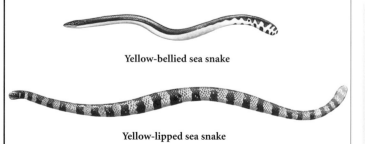

Yellow-bellied sea snake

Yellow-lipped sea snake

WHERE IN THE WORLD?

Found in the shallow coastal seas of the Indo-Pacific from Africa to southeast Asia and Australia. Also ranges to the west coasts of Central and South America.

RELATED SPECIES

The subfamily Laticaudinae contains only 5 species of sea snake whereas there are at least 48 species in the subfamily Hydrophiinae, and probably several more that have not yet been scientifically described. Both subfamilies belong to the family Elapidae. This contains 169 species including some of the most venomous land snakes, such as the tiger snake and the cobras. There are 11 snake families in the order Squamata.

• ORDER • *Squamata* • FAMILY • *Elapidae* • GENUS & SPECIES • *Ophiophagus hannah*

KING COBRA

The heavy and muscular king cobra can kill other snakes with its powerful venom, and uses its menacing hood to warn off other animals.

KEY FEATURES

• The largest venomous snake in the world, growing to a length of almost 5m (16ft 4in).

• Preys on other snakes — even other venomous species — subduing them with its highly potent venom and swallowing them whole.

• Rears its head off the ground and spreads out its neck into a 'hood' to present a menacing threat display towards intruders and predators.

FANGS
The hollow fangs grow to a length of 1.25cm (0.5in). The snake punches them into its prey, using them like hypodermic needles to inject its powerful venom.

HEAD
The cobra can dislocate its jaw to engulf large prey. The venom glands lie behind the eyes.

HOOD
The cobra spreads its neck ribs to form the hood, which has a double chevron marking on the back.

TONGUE
The cobra detects prey by flicking its tongue out to collect scents from the air. Inside the mouth, the tongue passes over the Jacobson's organ — a receptor with which the snake analyzes scents.

SKIN
The skin is olive-green, tan, or black, with faint, pale yellow crossbands down the entire length of the body. The underbelly is cream or pale yellow.

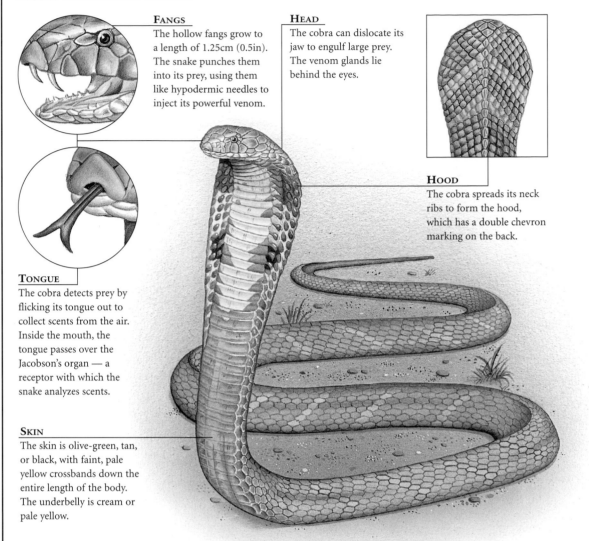

VITAL STATISTICS

WEIGHT	5.5–8kg (12.1–17.6lb)
LENGTH	Up to 4.9m (16ft 1in); average 4m (13.1lb)
SEXUAL MATURITY	About 4 years
MATING SEASON	January
NUMBER OF EGGS	18 to 51, usually 40 to 50; laid about 2 months after mating
INCUBATION PERIOD	70–77 days
BIRTH INTERVAL	1 year
TYPICAL DIET	Mainly snakes, plus some lizards
LIFESPAN	20 years on average

CREATURE COMPARISONS

The family Elapidae, to which the king cobra belongs, is sometimes called the cobra family. There are over 200 species of elapid, distributed over most of the world, with the exception of Antarctica and Europe. All are venomous and have short, fixed fangs, but they differ greatly in appearance and in habit.

The coral snake flaunts its bold colours, which warn animals not to attack it and risk a lethal bite; the death adder hides under sand by day and hunts by night, and the green mamba rests hidden among tree foliage.

Coral snake

Death adder

Green mamba

King cobra

WHERE IN THE WORLD?

Widespread, but nowhere common, across southern and Southeast Asia: through Bangladesh, India, Burma (Myanmar),

Thailand, Cambodia, Laos, Vietnam, Malaysia, Indonesia, parts of China and the Philippines.

RELATED SPECIES

The king cobra's relatives include the six species of the genus Naja. These include the Egyptian cobra, N. haje, found across Africa; the forest cobra, N. melanoleuca, which lives in rainforests in Africa south of the Sahara, and the Asian cobra, N. naja. The Asian cobra has a distinctive marking on its hood that looks like a pair of spectacles. There are ten subspecies, or races, of the Asian cobra, including the Indian cobra, N. naja naja.

• ORDER • *Squamata* **• FAMILY •** *Gekkonidae* **• GENUS & SPECIES •** *Palmatogecko rangei*

WEB-FOOTED GECKO

KEY FEATURES

- A small lizard that thrives in Africa's Namib Desert, despite energy-sapping temperature extremes.
- Webbed feet act like snowshoes to support its weight on the fine, dry sand, but also help it to burrow.
- Hunts by night, in the few hours when the desert temperature is neither too hot nor too cold.

VITAL STATISTICS

LENGTH	12.5cm (4.9in)
SEXUAL MATURITY	Not known
MATING SEASON	Any time of year
NUMBER OF EGGS	2 per clutch
INCUBATION PERIOD	Varies with temperature
BREEDING INTERVAL	Several times each year
TYPICAL DIET	Insects, including flies, beetles and crickets; spiders
LIFESPAN	5 years

This slender reptile picks its moments in order to survive: it is active only during the cooler hours, spending the rest of the day lying low.

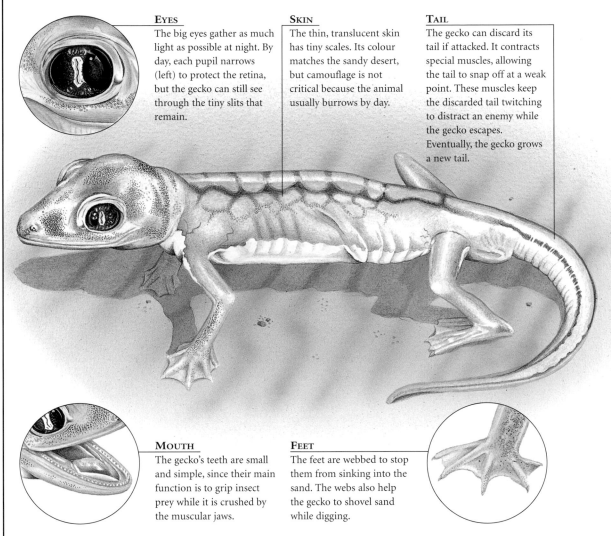

EYES
The big eyes gather as much light as possible at night. By day, each pupil narrows (left) to protect the retina, but the gecko can still see through the tiny slits that remain.

SKIN
The thin, translucent skin has tiny scales. Its colour matches the sandy desert, but camouflage is not critical because the animal usually burrows by day.

TAIL
The gecko can discard its tail if attacked. It contracts special muscles, allowing the tail to snap off at a weak point. These muscles keep the discarded tail twitching to distract an enemy while the gecko escapes. Eventually, the gecko grows a new tail.

MOUTH
The gecko's teeth are small and simple, since their main function is to grip insect prey while it is crushed by the muscular jaws.

FEET
The feet are webbed to stop them from sinking into the sand. The webs also help the gecko to shovel sand while digging.

CREATURE COMPARISONS

The gecko family includes the smallest lizards in the world: Sphaerodactylus parthenopion measures little more than 1cm in length from head to tail. At 12.5cm (4.9in) long, the web-footed gecko is much larger, but it is still a tiddler when compared to a typical lizard like the six-lined racerunner of the southern USA, which grows to about 25cm (9.8in).

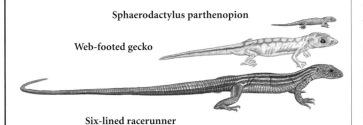

Sphaerodactylus parthenopion

Web-footed gecko

Six-lined racerunner

WHERE IN THE WORLD?

Found in the arid Namib Desert on the Atlantic coast of southwestern Africa. Other gecko species are widespread throughout the world's warmer regions.

RELATED SPECIES

There are at least 830 species of gecko, including the Madagascar leaftail gecko. More than 600 species share the subfamily Gekkoninae with the web-footed gecko. Many of these species can climb, using sucker-like toe-pads to cling to walls and other smooth surfaces.

• **ORDER** • *Squamata* • **FAMILY** • *Helodermatidae* • **GENUS & SPECIES** • *Heloderma suspectum*

GILA MONSTER

KEY FEATURES

• One of only two venomous lizard species in the world.

• Has been known to kill humans with its bite, although such instances are very rare.

• Preys on infant mammals, birds' eggs and nestlings, but tends not to use its venom for hunting, reserving it usually for defence against coyotes, eagles and other predators.

The Gila monster's thick tail contains fat stores to nourish it in the desert, and its tough, beaded skin helps retain water.

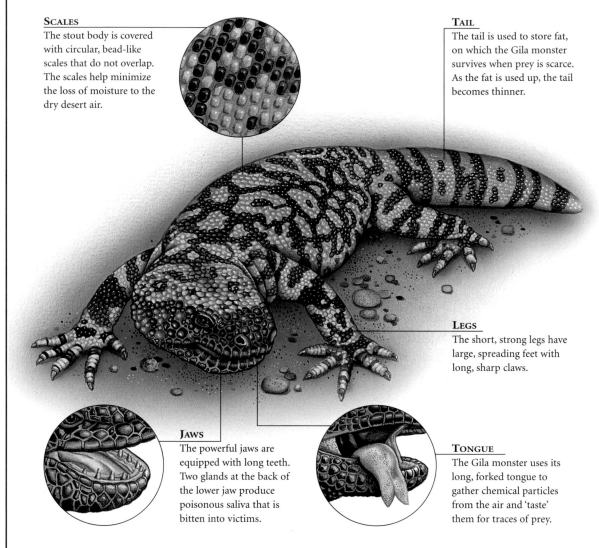

SCALES
The stout body is covered with circular, bead-like scales that do not overlap. The scales help minimize the loss of moisture to the dry desert air.

TAIL
The tail is used to store fat, on which the Gila monster survives when prey is scarce. As the fat is used up, the tail becomes thinner.

LEGS
The short, strong legs have large, spreading feet with long, sharp claws.

JAWS
The powerful jaws are equipped with long teeth. Two glands at the back of the lower jaw produce poisonous saliva that is bitten into victims.

TONGUE
The Gila monster uses its long, forked tongue to gather chemical particles from the air and 'taste' them for traces of prey.

VITAL STATISTICS

WEIGHT	4.5–5kg (9.9–11lb)
LENGTH	40–55cm (15.7–21.6in)
SEXUAL MATURITY	3–4 years
MATING SEASON	Spring
NUMBER OF EGGS	3 to 13
INCUBATION PERIOD	117–130 days
BREEDING INTERVAL	1 year
TYPICAL DIET	Young mammals and birds, as well as the eggs of birds and reptiles
LIFESPAN	About 20 years

CREATURE COMPARISONS

The Gila monster and beaded lizard are among the very few lizards that are dangerous to humans. Their poison can kill, but only if the victim is young or very unfit. The only other lizard species that pose a threat to humans are big monitor lizards, such as the common Asiatic monitor, which can deliver a deep and wounding bite. The biggest of all the monitors, the Komodo dragon of Indonesia, is powerful enough to kill a human without the help of poison. It is an active predator but also feeds on carrion.

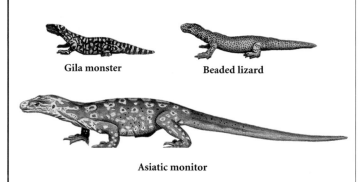

Gila monster   **Beaded lizard**

Asiatic monitor

WHERE IN THE WORLD?

Found in grassland, desert, woodland and chaparral (scrubland) in western parts of Mexico, and in Nevada, Utah, Arizona, California and New Mexico, in the southwestern USA.

RELATED SPECIES

The Gila monster has only one close relative: the very similar Mexican beaded lizard, Heloderma horridum. It, too, is venomous and lives in the hot, arid deserts of the southwestern United States and Mexico. The large and widespread order Squamata, to which the Gila monster belongs, contains about 95 per cent of all reptile species. Members of the Squamata are further divided into two suborders: the lizards, Sauria, and the snakes, Serpentes.

• ORDER • *Squamata* • FAMILY • *Iguanidae* • GENUS & SPECIES • *Amblyrhynchus cristatus*

MARINE IGUANA

KEY FEATURES

- The only lizard fully adapted for marine life, being able to remain underwater for long periods.
- Prevents itself from overheating by crowding into shady crevices and plunging into the cold sea.
- One of the few lizards that is known to survive on an exclusively vegetarian diet.

VITAL STATISTICS

WEIGHT	Male 7kg (15.4lb); female 4.3kg (9.5lb)
LENGTH	1.2–1.5m (3ft 9in–4ft 9in)
SEXUAL MATURITY	4–7 years
MATING SEASON	Usually at the end of the tropical rainy season, which occurs during the first few months of the year.
NUMBER OF EGGS	2 to 4
INCUBATION PERIOD	120 days
BREEDING INTERVAL	1 year
TYPICAL DIET	Seaweed
LIFESPAN	20–40 years

The primitive, almost prehistoric-looking marine iguana has the remarkable ability to live among crashing waves and the rocky shore.

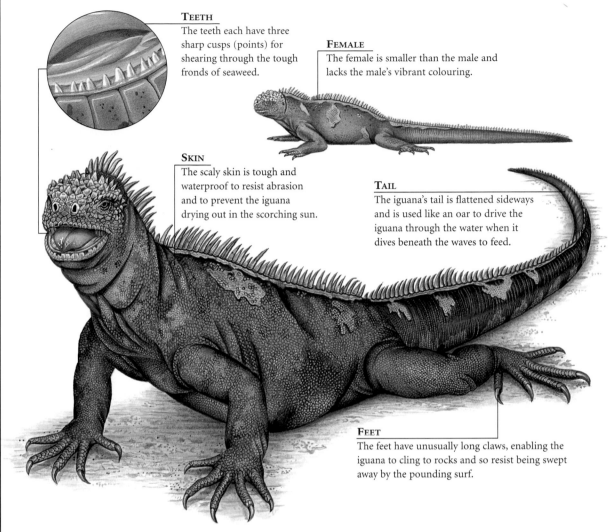

TEETH
The teeth each have three sharp cusps (points) for shearing through the tough fronds of seaweed.

FEMALE
The female is smaller than the male and lacks the male's vibrant colouring.

SKIN
The scaly skin is tough and waterproof to resist abrasion and to prevent the iguana drying out in the scorching sun.

TAIL
The iguana's tail is flattened sideways and is used like an oar to drive the iguana through the water when it dives beneath the waves to feed.

FEET
The feet have unusually long claws, enabling the iguana to cling to rocks and so resist being swept away by the pounding surf.

CREATURE COMPARISONS

Although the marine iguana is the only lizard that feeds at sea, it has a lot in common with other iguanas found on the mainland of South America. The common iguana, Iguana iguana, for example, has a similar crest of comb-like spines extending down its back. It can also swim well, but it normally forages in the trees of its rainforest habitat, where its banded green colouration helps conceal it from predators, such as eagles. Marine iguanas vary in colour according to their native island. Some are dark grey to black; others are bright red or turquoise.

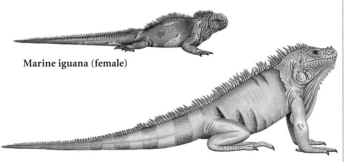

Marine iguana (female)

Common iguana (male)

WHERE IN THE WORLD?

Found on the rocky coasts of the Galapagos Islands in the eastern Pacific, 1000km (621.4 miles) west of Ecuador. Reduced by predators introduced by humans, it is now most numerous on the uninhabited islands of the group.

RELATED SPECIES
The marine iguana is one of over 650 species distributed in 55 genera in the large and diverse family Iguanidae. It is closely related to the cactus-eating land iguana, Conolophus subcristatus, which is also found on the Galapagos Islands.

• ORDER • *Squamata* • FAMILY • *Iguanidae* • GENUS & SPECIES • *Iguana iguana*

GREEN IGUANA

KEY FEATURES

- The largest lizard in South America.
- Adept at climbing trees and leaping from branch to branch, despite its ungraceful physique.
- Equipped with a long, whip-like tail that is used as a weapon in fights, and as a propeller when the reptile is swimming.
- Male is territorial, deterring rivals with threat displays.

Camouflaged by the disruptive pattern of its green and brown scales, the iguana moves stealthily through the branches of its rainforest habitat.

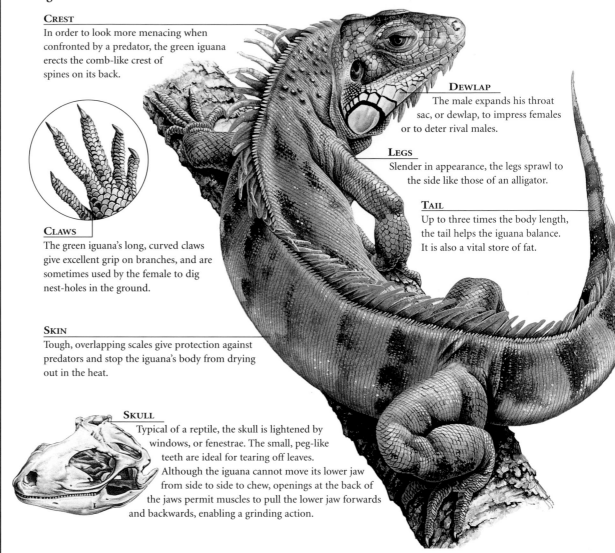

CREST
In order to look more menacing when confronted by a predator, the green iguana erects the comb-like crest of spines on its back.

CLAWS
The green iguana's long, curved claws give excellent grip on branches, and are sometimes used by the female to dig nest-holes in the ground.

SKIN
Tough, overlapping scales give protection against predators and stop the iguana's body from drying out in the heat.

SKULL
Typical of a reptile, the skull is lightened by windows, or fenestrae. The small, peg-like teeth are ideal for tearing off leaves. Although the iguana cannot move its lower jaw from side to side to chew, openings at the back of the jaws permit muscles to pull the lower jaw forwards and backwards, enabling a grinding action.

DEWLAP
The male expands his throat sac, or dewlap, to impress females or to deter rival males.

LEGS
Slender in appearance, the legs sprawl to the side like those of an alligator.

TAIL
Up to three times the body length, the tail helps the iguana balance. It is also a vital store of fat.

VITAL STATISTICS

WEIGHT	Up to 4kg (8.8lb)
LENGTH	1.6–2m (5ft 2in–6ft 6in) (including tail)
SEXUAL MATURITY	2–3 years
BREEDING SEASON	Onset of the dry season, which varies according to location
GESTATION PERIOD	21–49 days
NUMBER OF EGGS	20 to 70
HATCHING PERIOD	90 days
BREEDING INTERVAL	1 year
TYPICAL DIET	Plant matter for adults; uveniles feed mainly on insects
LIFESPAN	About 10 years

CREATURE COMPARISONS

The rhinoceros iguana (Cyclura cornuta) is smaller than its rainforest-dwelling cousin, the green iguana, but it still grows to lengths of over a metre. Large, pointed tubercles (hard projections of skin) on the male's snout give the rhinoceros iguana its common name. Like the green iguana, it has a crest of horny scales extending from the back of the neck to the tip of its tail.

Unlike the tree-climbing green iguana, the rhinoceros iguana is a ground lizard, restricted to the dry, rocky areas of the Caribbean islands of Haiti and the Dominican Republic. Found among thorn bush and thickets of cacti, the rhinoceros iguana feeds during the day on plants and berries. Like the green iguana, it is surprisingly agile. When disturbed, it flees into its burrow in the ground.

Green iguana

Rhinoceros iguana

WHERE IN THE WORLD?

Native to Central and South America, from northern Mexico south to southern Brazil and west to Paraguay. Introduced into the US state of Florida and several islands in the West Indies.

RELATED SPECIES

The green iguana shares the genus Iguana with the Antillean green iguana, I. delicatissima, of the Lesser Antilles, a group of islands off the coast of Venezuela. The 2 species belong to the family Iguanidae, which contains the spiny-tailed iguana, Ctenosaura similis.

• ORDER • *Squamata* • FAMILY • *Teiidae* • GENUS & SPECIES • *Tupinambis teguixin*

COMMON TEGU

KEY FEATURES

- A large lizard and a powerful predator that is equally at home in the trees, on the ground or in the water.
- Tracks down live prey and eggs by flicking out its forked tongue to pick up airborne scent particles.
- Female often lays her egg clutch within a termite mound to exploit its stable, protective conditions.

Despite its great size, the tegu can cling like a limpet to branches, aided by its long, sharp claws.

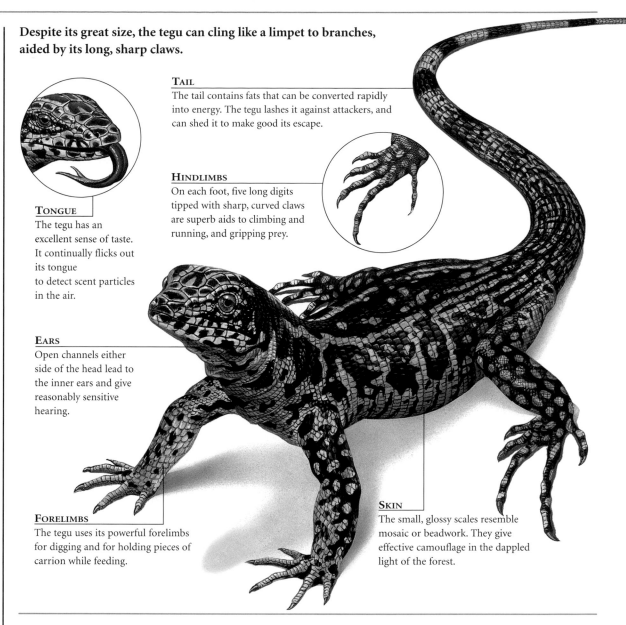

TAIL
The tail contains fats that can be converted rapidly into energy. The tegu lashes it against attackers, and can shed it to make good its escape.

TONGUE
The tegu has an excellent sense of taste. It continually flicks out its tongue to detect scent particles in the air.

HINDLIMBS
On each foot, five long digits tipped with sharp, curved claws are superb aids to climbing and running, and gripping prey.

EARS
Open channels either side of the head lead to the inner ears and give reasonably sensitive hearing.

FORELIMBS
The tegu uses its powerful forelimbs for digging and for holding pieces of carrion while feeding.

SKIN
The small, glossy scales resemble mosaic or beadwork. They give effective camouflage in the dappled light of the forest.

VITAL STATISTICS

LENGTH	Up to 1.4m (4ft 6in)
WEIGHT	Unknown
SEXUAL MATURITY	At least 3 years
BREEDING SEASON	Varies with locality and depends on climatic conditions
NUMBER OF EGGS	4 to 32
GESTATION PERIOD	90 days
HATCHING PERIOD	140–160 days
TYPICAL DIET	Insects, spiders, birds and their eggs, and other lizards. Also feeds on carrion
LIFESPAN	Unknown

CREATURE COMPARISONS

The leopard lizard (Gambelia wislizenii) belongs to the family Iguanidae. Found in northwestern Mexico and southwestern United States, it lives mainly in dry deserts with rocky outcrops and sparse vegetation. Already suitably coloured to blend in with its arid surroundings, the leopard lizard can also change the colour of its spots, depending on temperature and activity.

Reaching only 40cm (15.7in) in length, the leopard lizard feeds on smaller prey than the tegu, but has a similar diet. Hunting a variety of insects, spiders, and other lizards, it overcomes prey using its powerful jaws and then smashes the victim against the ground until it stops struggling.

Common tegu

Leopard lizard

WHERE IN THE WORLD?

Found in South America, from Colombia, Venezuela and Guyana, through the Amazon Basin, and along the larger rivers to Paraguay and northern Argentina.

RELATED SPECIES

The common tegu belongs to the family Teiidae, which contains 118 species of lizard in 9 genera. Restricted to the New World, members of the Teiidae are especially abundant in South America. All members of the family are highly alert and can move fast. There are 20 lizard families in the suborder Lacertilia, which shares the order Squamata with the snakes, suborder Serpentes. All belong to the class Reptilia.

• ORDER • *Squamata* • FAMILY • *Varanidae* • GENUS & SPECIES • *Varanus komodoensis*

KOMODO DRAGON

An armoury of shark-like teeth, powerful claws and muscle-packed limbs enables the Komodo dragon to overpower animals far larger than itself.

KEY FEATURES

- Heaviest and strongest of all lizards and top predator in its range; hunts prey as large as water buffaloes, despatching them with slashing claws and bites from its massive jaws.
- Population is under threat on its island home; listed as rare by the IUCN (World Conservation Union).

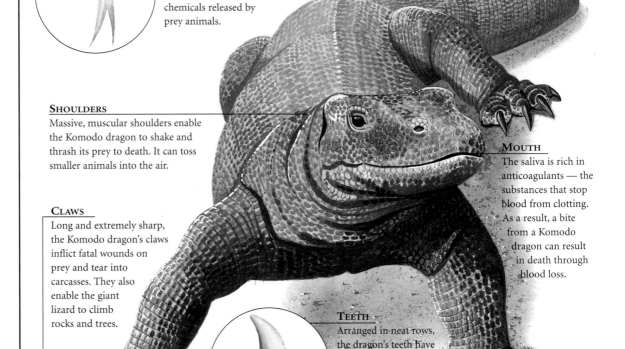

TONGUE
The long, deeply forked tongue flicks out constantly to 'taste' the air for traces of the chemicals released by prey animals.

SHOULDERS
Massive, muscular shoulders enable the Komodo dragon to shake and thrash its prey to death. It can toss smaller animals into the air.

CLAWS
Long and extremely sharp, the Komodo dragon's claws inflict fatal wounds on prey and tear into carcasses. They also enable the giant lizard to climb rocks and trees.

MOUTH
The saliva is rich in anticoagulants — the substances that stop blood from clotting. As a result, a bite from a Komodo dragon can result in death through blood loss.

TEETH
Arranged in neat rows, the dragon's teeth have more in common with sharks' teeth than with those of other lizards. Serrated edges slice through tough hide and muscle.

VITAL STATISTICS

WEIGHT	Up to 165kg (363.8lb)
LENGTH	Up to 3m (9ft 8in)
SEXUAL MATURITY	5–6 years
BREEDING SEASON	All year; usually June to July
NUMBER OF EGGS	4 to 30
INCUBATION PERIOD	32–36 weeks
BREEDING INTERVAL	Annual
TYPICAL DIET	Carrion, scraps; a wide variety of prey, from insects, lizards, snakes and birds to rats, wild pigs, deer and water buffalo
LIFESPAN	About 50 years

CREATURE COMPARISONS

Up to 2m (6ft 6in) in length, the Nile monitor (Varanus niloticus) is the largest lizard found in Africa, but it is still dwarfed by a fully grown Komodo dragon. Both species have a bulky, flattened body with broad shoulders, stout legs and a long tail. But the Nile monitor is considerably slimmer and has a striking pattern of yellow stripes.

It is a stronger swimmer than its heavyweight relative, and is rarely found far from water, where it hunts crabs, fish, frogs and waterbirds. During the early hours of the day, the monitor hauls out of the water to warm itself up in the morning sun.

Nile monitor

Komodo dragon

WHERE IN THE WORLD?

Found only on four islands in Indonesia — Komodo, Rinca, Gili Motang and Flores, part of the Lesser Sunda group of islands.

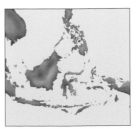

RELATED SPECIES

The Komodo dragon is 1 of 30 or so species of monitor in Varanus, the sole genus in the family Varanidae. The monitors include some of the world's largest lizards, such as the 4.5m (14ft 8in) Salvadori monitor, and the Yemen monitor, V. yemenensis, first known to science in 1985.

• ORDER • *Squamata* **• FAMILY •** *Viperidae* **• GENUS & SPECIES •** *Bitis arietans*

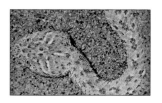

KEY FEATURES

- Takes its name from the way it puffs up its thick-set body to intimidate both predators and prey.
- Young are able to hunt and kill small prey almost immediately after their 'live birth'.
- Colouration and skin patterning help it to merge into its surroundings.

VITAL STATISTICS

WEIGHT	1.5–2kg (3.3–4.4lb)
LENGTH	70–150cm (27.6–59.1in)
SEXUAL MATURITY	About 2 years
BREEDING SEASON	Dependent on rainfall; usually during the early rains
NUMBER OF YOUNG	Usually 20 to 30; occasionally over 50
INCUBATION PERIOD	About 5 months; eggs hatch inside female
BIRTH INTERVAL	1 year
TYPICAL DIET	Rodents and other small mammals, birds, lizards and amphibians
LIFESPAN	Up to 15 years

Using stealth, camouflage and concealment, the puff adder strikes at any unsuspecting animal that crosses its path with its quick and venomous bite.

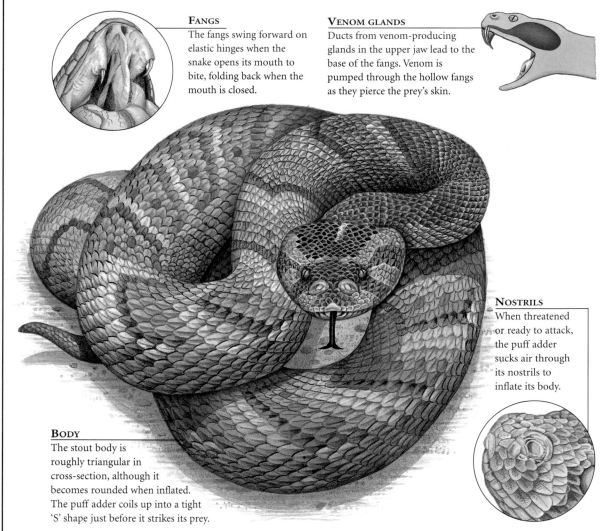

FANGS
The fangs swing forward on elastic hinges when the snake opens its mouth to bite, folding back when the mouth is closed.

VENOM GLANDS
Ducts from venom-producing glands in the upper jaw lead to the base of the fangs. Venom is pumped through the hollow fangs as they pierce the prey's skin.

NOSTRILS
When threatened or ready to attack, the puff adder sucks air through its nostrils to inflate its body.

BODY
The stout body is roughly triangular in cross-section, although it becomes rounded when inflated. The puff adder coils up into a tight 'S' shape just before it strikes its prey.

CREATURE COMPARISONS

Like the puff adder, the highly venomous gaboon viper (Bitis gabonica), a native of African rainforests, is noted for its geometric skin pattern. The gaboon viper has a brown, beige, yellow, black and purplish skin pattern, resembling an oriental carpet, that is ideal camouflage among the leaf litter of the forest floor. The puff adder's skin pattern is more variable. It can be yellow, yellowish-brown, reddish-brown or grey, patterned with brown or black V-shaped markings. Puff adders living in forests tend to be darker than those living in more open, drier regions.

Puff adder

Gaboon viper

WHERE IN THE WORLD?

Found throughout Africa and parts of the Arabian Peninsula. It is absent only from rainforest interiors, the most arid desert regions and altitudes above 2000m.

RELATED SPECIES

The puff adder is one of 187 species in the family Viperidae, which is made up of mainly short, sturdy snakes that ambush their prey on the ground. The puff adder, like the related Rhinoceros viper (Bitis nasicornis) of Africa, is a 'true' viper, lacking the heat-sensitive pits on the head that characterizes pit vipers. Pit vipers, such as rattlesnakes, number about 125 species, and are sometimes classed in a separate family (Crotalidae).

• **ORDER** • *Squamata* • **FAMILY** • *Viperidae* • **GENUS & SPECIES** • *Vipera berus*

COMMON ADDER

With its flicking tongue tasting the air for chemical scents and its fangs primed with venom, the adder patiently slips after its prey.

KEY FEATURES

- An advanced and adaptable species occupying the most northerly range of any snake.
- Britain's only native venomous snake — but a shy and non-aggressive animal.
- Males engage in ritualized contests for females.
- Hibernates in large communal dens.

SCALES
Each individual scale has a central ridge, or 'keel', running along its length.

FANGS
Like all members of the viper family, the adder has a pair of hollow, hinged fangs that fold away into the roof of its mouth. Throughout its life it grows sets of replacement fangs, which dislodge the existing pair.

COLOURATION
The zigzag pattern is more pronounced on the male than on the female, who is more brownish overall. A few individuals are black or melanistic (left).

BODY
A relatively stocky body shape minimizes the adder's surface area, cutting down its rate of heat loss — a factor that is critical to the snake's survival in cool climates.

VITAL STATISTICS

WEIGHT	1.5–1.8kg (3.3–4lb)
LENGTH	65–90cm (25.6–35.4in)
SEXUAL MATURITY	3 years
BREEDING SEASON	Spring
NUMBER OF YOUNG	3 to 20
INCUBATION PERIOD	3–4 months; eggs hatch inside female
BIRTH INTERVAL	1–3 years
TYPICAL DIET	Small mammals, lizards, birds, frogs
LIFESPAN	25 years or more

CREATURE COMPARISONS

The horn-nosed or sand viper (Vipera ammodytes) is a close relative of the adder, although it is larger and has a conspicuous 'horn' on the tip of its snout. It also tends to be more brightly coloured, although there is a great deal of local variation between populations.

In Europe, the horn-nosed viper's range overlaps with the southern part of the adder's range, but they remain separated by their habitat preferences. The horn-nosed viper prefers dry, rocky hillsides to the adder's more thickly overgrown home. Both species are active during the day and give birth to live young.

Adder

Horn-nosed viper

WHERE IN THE WORLD?

Inhabits a broad zone from Britain and Spain, across Europe, southern Siberia and northern China, to the shores of the North Pacific.

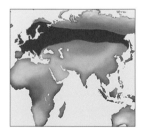

RELATED SPECIES

The adder, also known as the crossed viper, is 1 of 23 species in the genus Vipera, the true vipers, which are only found in Europe, Asia and Africa. Another true viper is the asp, Vipera aspis. All are part of the viper family, Viperidae, which has 187 species worldwide.

EAGLE OWL

• ORDER • *Strigiformes* • FAMILY • *Strigidae* • GENUS & SPECIES • *Bubo bubo*

Equipped with exceptional hearing and special feathers for silent flight, the eagle owl swoops in surprise attacks, killing prey in its lethal talons.

KEY FEATURES

- The world's largest owl, but very shy and elusive despite its great size and fearsome appearance.
- Highly sensitive ears are able to detect the faintest sounds of prey at a distance of 10m, and then pinpoint its position even in total darkness.
- A powerful predator, it can tackle prey as large as hares and ducks, killing its quarry with its deadly curved talons.

VITAL STATISTICS

WEIGHT	2–4kg (4.4–8.8lb)
LENGTH	65–70cm (25.6–27.6)
WINGSPAN	1.4–2.1m (4ft 6in–6ft 9in)
SEXUAL MATURITY	2 to 3 years
BREEDING SEASON	February to August
NUMBER OF EGGS	1 to 6, but usually 2 or 3
INCUBATION PERIOD	34–36 days
FLEDGING PERIOD	50–60 days
BREEDING INTERVAL	1 year
TYPICAL DIET	Mammals from small rodents to adult hares, and birds up to the size of ducks
LIFESPAN	20 years

FLIGHT FEATHERS
The flight feathers have soft, bristly fringes along their edges, and those forming the top layer are also downy. This softens the sound of rushing air when in flight, so that prey can be taken by surprise.

EARS
The ears are buried deep under the head feathers behind the eyes — the 'ear' tufts on the head are unrelated to hearing. The owl can pick up sounds coming from behind it by raising a flap of skin over each ear-opening to direct the sound waves into its ears.

CHICKS
Chicks are born covered with soft, dense down of a uniform white or creamy-white colour. The down insulates young chicks against the cold of early spring.

FEET
The powerful feet are equipped with long, curved talons, which are used to pierce the body of prey. To grip struggling prey more tightly, it swivels the outer front toe of each foot around to assist the rear toe.

CREATURE COMPARISONS

Vying with the eagle owl for the title of the world's largest owl, and often found alongside it in northern Europe and Russia, is the great grey owl (*Strix nebulosa*). Their similarity in size is deceptive, however, since the great grey is lighter and not as powerful. Its dense plumage, needed to survive the harsh winters of northern coniferous forests, accounts for much of its bulk.

The great grey's massive head appears even larger when viewed head-on, and its yellow eyes are set close together in a distinctly round facial disc. The eagle owl's orange eyes are set in a much flatter-shaped facial disc.

Great grey owl

Eagle owl

WHERE IN THE WORLD?

Ranges from the Iberian peninsula and North Africa in the west, east through parts of Europe, the Middle East, central Asia, including India, as far as Siberia and China. Uncommon or rare across most of its range.

RELATED SPECIES

The family Strigidae contains nearly all the owls. Of these, the 14 or so species of eagle owl are the largest and the pygmy owls are the smallest. The medium-sized spectacled owl lives in South American forests.

• **ORDER** • *Strigiformes* • **FAMILY** • *Strigidae* • **GENUS & SPECIES** • *Nyctea scandiaca*

SNOWY OWL

The snowy owl's dense plumage insulates it against the cold. In the female, barred feathers help camouflage her as she sits on her eggs.

KEY FEATURES

- Most northerly breeding owl, and one of the very few birds that lives permanently in the High Arctic.
- Biggest, most powerful bird of the far north.
- Has adapted its diet to include carrion, and is able to go without food for up to 40 days, but is nevertheless forced to move south when prey is in short supply.

VITAL STATISTICS

WEIGHT	1–2.7kg (2.2–5.9lb)
LENGTH	53–66cm (20.9–26in)
WINGSPAN	1.42–1.65m (4ft 6in–5ft 4in)
SEXUAL MATURITY	Probably 3–5 years
BREEDING SEASON	May to early September
NUMBER OF EGGS	Commonly 5 to 7 but ranges from 2 to 16, depending upon prey availability
INCUBATION PERIOD	30–33 days
FLEDGING PERIOD	60 days
BREEDING INTERVAL	1 year
TYPICAL DIET	Lemmings, voles, rabbits, hares; various seabirds
LIFESPAN	8–10 years

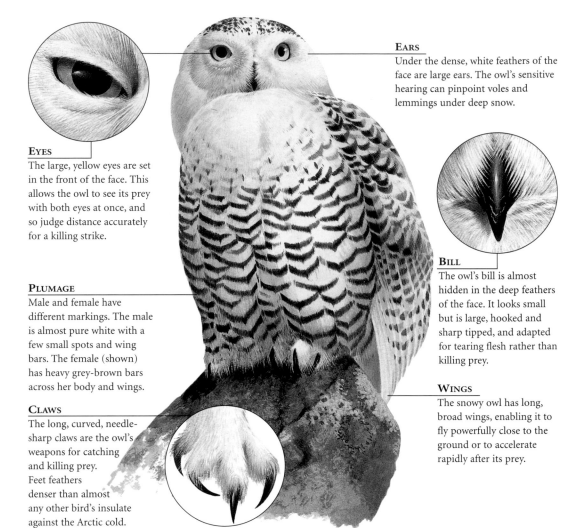

EYES
The large, yellow eyes are set in the front of the face. This allows the owl to see its prey with both eyes at once, and so judge distance accurately for a killing strike.

PLUMAGE
Male and female have different markings. The male is almost pure white with a few small spots and wing bars. The female (shown) has heavy grey-brown bars across her body and wings.

CLAWS
The long, curved, needle-sharp claws are the owl's weapons for catching and killing prey. Feet feathers denser than almost any other bird's insulate against the Arctic cold.

EARS
Under the dense, white feathers of the face are large ears. The owl's sensitive hearing can pinpoint voles and lemmings under deep snow.

BILL
The owl's bill is almost hidden in the deep feathers of the face. It looks small but is large, hooked and sharp tipped, and adapted for tearing flesh rather than killing prey.

WINGS
The snowy owl has long, broad wings, enabling it to fly powerfully close to the ground or to accelerate rapidly after its prey.

CREATURE COMPARISONS

Most owls hunt at night or in twilight, but the snowy owl hunts by day — in the Arctic summer, when the sun never fully sets, it has little choice. Like the snowy owl, the Eurasian eagle owl of northern Europe is powerfully built, and preys on small rodents. But it lives in more temperate conditions, hunting by night on the margins of woodlands and forests. Because its prey species are not subject to large fluctuations in numbers, the eagle owl is much less migratory than the snowy owl and tends to stay in one region.

Snowy owl

Eurasian eagle owl

WHERE IN THE WORLD?

Found in a ring around the North Pole in the High Arctic. Breeds in the tundra in the far north of Alaska, Canada, Greenland, Europe and Asia but may migrate farther south.

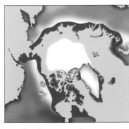

RELATED SPECIES

There are about 175 species of true owl, family Strigidae, distributed all over the world, and a further 10 barn owls in the family Tytonidae. The snowy owl has no close relatives among the Strigidae, but it is thought to have evolved from species similar to the big eagle owls, which occupy a similar ecological niche. The northern treeline marks the northern limit of the Eurasian eagle owl's range, and the southern border of the snowy owl's range.

BARN OWL

• ORDER • *Strigiformes* • FAMILY • *Tytonidae* • GENUS & SPECIES • *Tyto alba*

Totally silent in flight and with incredibly sharp hearing, the barn owl is an efficient and successful nighttime hunter, particularly over grassland.

KEY FEATURES

- Spectacularly acute hearing enables it to locate mice and voles in total darkness by the faint noises they make while moving or eating.
- Superbly sensitive and telescopic vision allows it to spot small mammals on the ground by day or in dim light.
- Flies silently, because the comblike tips of its wings and its feathered legs muffle noise.

VITAL STATISTICS

WEIGHT	226.8–453.6g (8–16oz)
LENGTH	33–43.2cm (13–17in)
WING SPAN	83.2–92.7cm (33–36.5in)
SEXUAL MATURITY	1 year, sometimes 2
BREEDING SEASON	Late February or March through November in northern hemisphere
NUMBER OF EGGS	Up to 20, but usually 4 to 7
INCUBATION PERIOD	30–31 days
FLEDGING PERIOD	50–55 days
BREEDING INTERVAL	1 year
TYPICAL DIET	Rodents, shrews, small birds, frogs, and toads
LIFE SPAN	Nearly 18 years

WINGS
Broad, rounded wings are typical of most owls, providing powerful lift and great maneuverability.

FACE
The two concave facial disks of short, stiff feathers help funnel sound toward the ears.

FEET
The three toes are bare or slightly bristly, with needle-sharp talons. The outer toe can be directed backward to hold a branch, and scales on the pads of the foot give a firm grip.

FEATHERS
A fringe along the rear edge of the wing feathers deadens the noise of air through the feathers in flight — a sound that often betrays the presence of other hunting birds.

EAR
The large ear openings are hidden beneath feathers (shown naked right). The left ear is higher on the head than the right ear, so sounds reach them at different times, helping the owl to locate prey.

Ear opening

CREATURE COMPARISONS

The barn owl differs strongly from all other owls. It has smaller eyes and relies more on its acute hearing, which is enhanced by the dish-shaped facial region. The barn owl also lacks the ear tufts of species such as the great horned owl. Although owls have hooked beaks and sharp talons like eagles and kestrels, they are not related: the two groups have simply evolved the means of hunting by the same basic method.

American kestrel

Barn owl

Great horned owl

Golden eagle

WHERE IN THE WORLD?

Found in open grasslands, wetlands, and semidesert in North and South America, the Caribbean, central

and southern Europe, much of Africa, and Australasia. Absent from many far northern regions, much of Asia, and Antarctica.

RELATED SPECIES

There are 35 subspecies of the common barn owl, known from localized areas or island groups. Ten other species of barn owl live on islands or in small areas of rain forest. One barn owl species from Indonesia may be extinct, and others are rare. The family Tytonidae also includes two species of bay owl, genus Phodilus. The other 150 or so species of owl are all classified in the diverse family Strigidae: the hawk owls or true owls.

• **ORDER** • *Struthioniformes* • **FAMILY** • *Apterygidae* • **GENUS & SPECIES** • *Apteryx*

KIWI

An oddity of the bird world, the flightless kiwi has no visible wings and plumage that looks more like a coat of long hair than feathers.

KEY FEATURES

- Nocturnal, flightless bird that spends the day sheltering in dense cover or hollow logs.
- Uses a long, probing bill and its highly developed sense of smell to search out underground prey.
- Produces enormous eggs that are incubated for longer than any other species of bird.

BILL
The female's bill is up to a third longer than the male's, which means that she can reach food at a deeper level and avoid competition for the same resources.

NOSTRILS
Unlike other birds, the kiwi has nostrils set at the tip of its bill. This helps it to sniff out prey hidden in the ground.

PLUMAGE
The kiwi's plumage is dense and hair-like, protecting the kiwi when it moves through prickly vegetation. Two short wings, no more than 5cm (2in), are hidden beneath the feathers.

BRISTLES
Long bristles around the bill act as feelers, helping the kiwi to find its way around at night.

LEGS AND FEET
The kiwi has powerful, muscular legs with large, clawed, stout-toed feet for running swiftly, scraping soil and kicking out in defence.

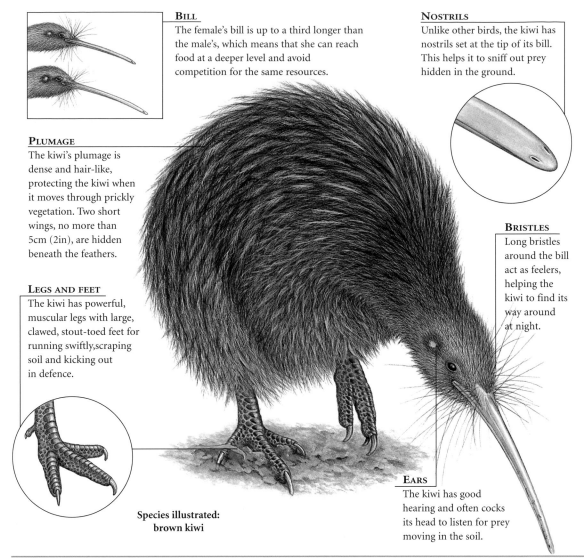

EARS
The kiwi has good hearing and often cocks its head to listen for prey moving in the soil.

Species illustrated:
brown kiwi

VITAL STATISTICS

WEIGHT	1–3.5kg (2.2–7.7lb); female is heavier than the male
LENGTH	35–65cm (13.8–25.6in)
WINGSPAN	4–5cm (1.6–2in); wings are useless for flight
SEXUAL MATURITY	5–6 years
BREEDING SEASON	August to January
NUMBER OF EGGS	1 or 2
INCUBATION PERIOD	71–84 days
FLEDGING PERIOD	14–20 days
BREEDING INTERVAL	1 year
TYPICAL DIET	Insects, worms and berries
LIFESPAN	Unknown in the wild; up to 30 years in captivity

CREATURE COMPARISONS

Size is the principal difference between the three species of kiwi. The largest is the brown kiwi, with some females weighing 3.5kg (7.7lb). At the other end of the scale is the little spotted kiwi, which weighs only 1kg (2.2lb). The great spotted kiwi is slightly larger. The species can also be told apart by their colouring. The plumage of the brown kiwi is uniform brown, while the little spotted kiwi is brown with lighter barring. The great spotted kiwi has an overall brown-streaked appearance.

Little spotted kiwi

Great spotted kiwi

Brown kiwi

WHERE IN THE WORLD?

The brown kiwi is found only on North, South and Stewart Islands, New Zealand. The little spotted kiwi is confined to four offshore islands, and the great spotted kiwi is found on South Island.

RELATED SPECIES

There are 3 species of kiwi in the genus Apteryx: the brown, A. australis, the great spotted, A. haasti, and the little spotted, A. owenii. They belong to the order of flightless birds known as Struthioniformes, which includes the emu, Dromaius novaehollandiae.

• **ORDER** • *Struthioniformes* • **FAMILY** • *Struthionidae* • **GENUS & SPECIES** • *Struthio camelus*

The ostrich's powerful legs equip it to roam the open plains with ease, while other special features help it cope with the relentless heat and dust.

KEY FEATURES

- Lives on open plains, where its 'watchtower' vision helps it spot predators before they spot it. Its group-based lifestyle also gives the protection essential for exposed plains-dwellers.
- Gapes its bill and spreads its wings to dissipate body heat.
- Manages to glean all of its water needs from plant food — except during the driest months.

VITAL STATISTICS

WEIGHT	Female about 113kg (249.1lb); male up to 154kg (339.5lb)
HEIGHT	1.8–2.7m (5ft 9in–8ft 8in)
SEXUAL MATURITY	Female 2 years; male 3–4 years
MATING SEASON	Variable, often dependent on local climatic conditions
NUMBER OF EGGS	Each female lays 5 to 11 eggs
INCUBATION PERIOD	42–46 days
BREEDING INTERVAL	Unknown
TYPICAL DIET	Mostly plant material; some invertebrates
LIFESPAN	Up to 40 years

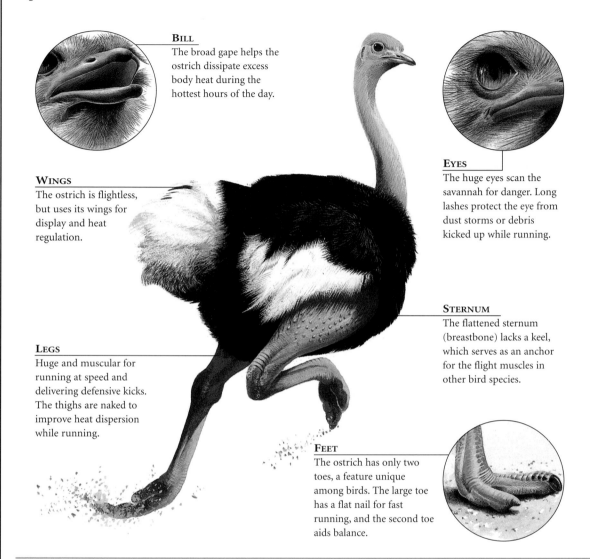

BILL
The broad gape helps the ostrich dissipate excess body heat during the hottest hours of the day.

WINGS
The ostrich is flightless, but uses its wings for display and heat regulation.

LEGS
Huge and muscular for running at speed and delivering defensive kicks. The thighs are naked to improve heat dispersion while running.

EYES
The huge eyes scan the savannah for danger. Long lashes protect the eye from dust storms or debris kicked up while running.

STERNUM
The flattened sternum (breastbone) lacks a keel, which serves as an anchor for the flight muscles in other bird species.

FEET
The ostrich has only two toes, a feature unique among birds. The large toe has a flat nail for fast running, and the second toe aids balance.

CREATURE COMPARISONS

At up to 2.7m (8ft 8in) tall, the male ostrich is the largest living bird. Its flightless relative, the Australian emu, stands almost 2m (6ft 6in) tall. Forest-dwelling birds called moas, which were even taller and heavier than ostriches, roamed New Zealand as recently as 300 years ago. Of the 12 moa species, the largest was the giant moa, which stood 3m (9ft 8in) tall or more.

Emu　　　　　Ostrich　　　　Giant moa

WHERE IN THE WORLD?

Found in a strip across Africa between 10° and 20° north of the equator. Its range in East Africa extends south down the Rift Valley to Tanzania. Also inhabits South Africa, Namibia, southern Angola and Botswana.

RELATED SPECIES

The ostrich is the only member of the family Struthionidae. Other flightless birds around the world are the rheas of South America, the kiwis of New Zealand and the cassowaries and emus of Australia.

• **ORDER** • *Tetraodontiformes* • **FAMILY** • *Tetraodontidae* • **GENUS & SPECIES** • *Various*

PUFFER FISH

With a flick of its fins, the puffer fish can change direction in an instant, enabling it to slip into the cover of a rock crevice at the first sign of danger.

KEY FEATURES

- A group of small to medium-sized fish that often sport intricate, colourful patterns.
- When threatened, they inflate their body in order to appear more formidable.
- Immune to the stinging cells of corals, they exploit a food source unappetizing to most other reef fish.

VITAL STATISTICS

WEIGHT	Up to 6.5kg (14.3lb)
LENGTH	8–60cm (3.1–23.6in); exceptionally 90cm (35.4in)
SEXUAL MATURITY	Varies according to species
SPAWNING SEASON	Varies according to region and species
NUMBER OF EGGS	200–300
BREEDING INTERVAL	Several spawnings a year
TYPICAL DIET	Corals, crustaceans and molluscs; occasionally fish
LIFESPAN	Not known

TEETH
The two teeth in both the upper and lower jaws are fused together to form a beak-like structure. This is used for biting into tough prey, such as hard corals and crab shells.

INFLATED BODY
The fish inflates its body by pumping its stomach full of air or water. It has neither ribs nor a pelvic bone to restrict the size to which it can swell.

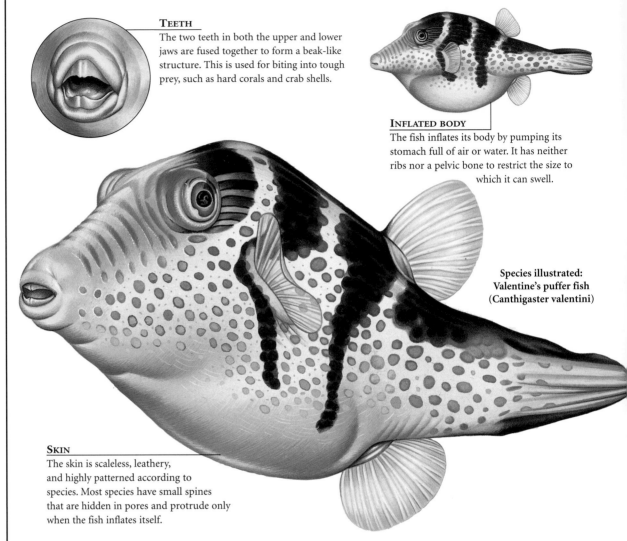

Species illustrated: Valentine's puffer fish (Canthigaster valentini)

SKIN
The skin is scaleless, leathery, and highly patterned according to species. Most species have small spines that are hidden in pores and protrude only when the fish inflates itself.

CREATURE COMPARISONS

Porcupine fish range in length from 30–90cm (11.8–35.4in). Like puffer fish, they can inflate their body when threatened. As their name suggests, they too possess defensive spines: these are permanently erect in smaller species but can be relaxed and held flat in larger fish. Feeding on molluscs, porcupine fish have only two beak-like teeth in contrast to the four teeth of the puffer fish. Porcupine fish range less widely than puffer fish, living exclusively in tropical seas on coral reefs and surrounding waters.

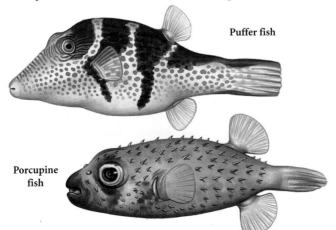

Puffer fish

Porcupine fish

WHERE IN THE WORLD?

Widespread in temperate and tropical seas around the world. Some species live in brackish or freshwater.

RELATED SPECIES

There are more than 100 species of puffer fish in the family Tetraodontidae, grouped into six genera: Chonerhinus, Tetraodon, Carinotetraodon, Sphaeroides, Colomesus and Canthigaster. Marine species include the white-spotted puffer, Arothron hispidus, of the Indo-Pacific region. The spotted puffer, Tetraodon fluviatilis, is a freshwater species found throughout most of India, Malaysia and Burma (Myanmar).

TINAMOU

• ORDER • *Tinamiformes* • FAMILY • *Tinamidae* • GENUS & SPECIES • *Various*

With its compact build and dappled brown plumage, the elegant crested tinamou is equipped for living on the ground in open grasslands.

KEY FEATURES

- Ground-dwelling birds with a distinctive call; live in grasslands and forests in Central and South America.
- Well camouflaged to hide from predators.
- Male mates with several females before incubating all their eggs in one nest.
- Glossy eggs are among the most brightly coloured of all birds' eggs.

VITAL STATISTICS

WEIGHT	Smallest species 160g; (5.6oz) largest species 2kg (4.4lb)
LENGTH	13–49cm (5.1–19.3in)depending on species
SEXUAL MATURITY	1 year
BREEDING SEASON	Year-round in tropics; seasonal in temperate regions
NUMBER OF EGGS	Up to 16
INCUBATION PERIOD	17–24 days
FLEDGING PERIOD	25–42 days
BREEDING INTERVAL	1 or 2 clutches a year
TYPICAL DIET	Plant matter, invertebrates
LIFESPAN	Unknown

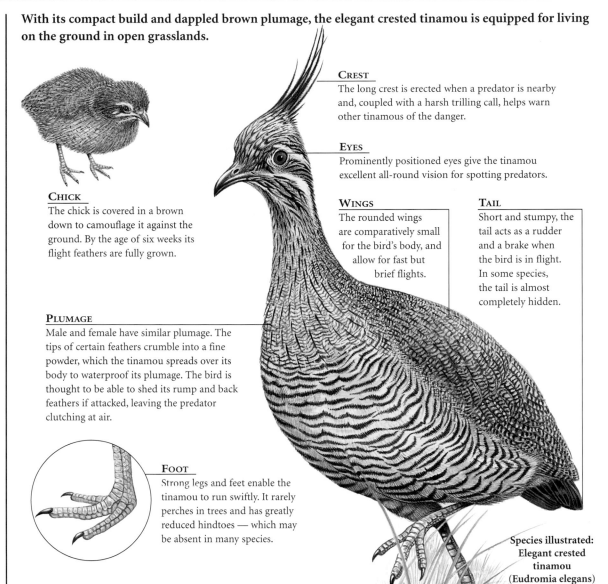

CHICK
The chick is covered in a brown down to camouflage it against the ground. By the age of six weeks its flight feathers are fully grown.

PLUMAGE
Male and female have similar plumage. The tips of certain feathers crumble into a fine powder, which the tinamou spreads over its body to waterproof its plumage. The bird is thought to be able to shed its rump and back feathers if attacked, leaving the predator clutching at air.

FOOT
Strong legs and feet enable the tinamou to run swiftly. It rarely perches in trees and has greatly reduced hindtoes — which may be absent in many species.

CREST
The long crest is erected when a predator is nearby and, coupled with a harsh trilling call, helps warn other tinamous of the danger.

EYES
Prominently positioned eyes give the tinamou excellent all-round vision for spotting predators.

WINGS
The rounded wings are comparatively small for the bird's body, and allow for fast but brief flights.

TAIL
Short and stumpy, the tail acts as a rudder and a brake when the bird is in flight. In some species, the tail is almost completely hidden.

**Species illustrated:
Elegant crested tinamou
(Eudromia elegans)**

CREATURE COMPARISONS

Like the elegant crested tinamou, the Himalayan monal pheasant (Lophophorus impejanus) has a broad diet of plant and animal matter. But the pheasant forages in steep, wooded valleys at high altitudes, whereas the tinamou keeps to lowland grasslands. The male pheasant (left) has a spur on the back of each leg, which he is thought to use in battle against breeding rivals. His bright plumage includes a showy crest, which he flaunts to attract a mate. The female pheasant has much more subdued plumage, like that of the tinamou. The dull brown colouring is vital, however, as it hides the female pheasant — and the male tinamou — from predators, as each incubates its egg clutches in deep undergrowth.

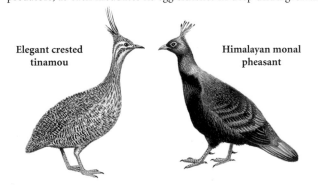

Elegant crested tinamou

Himalayan monal pheasant

WHERE IN THE WORLD?

Found throughout South and Central America north as far as Mexico. Absent from Tierra del Fuego and the Falkland Islands.

RELATED SPECIES

There are 45 species of tinamou divided into 2 subfamilies within the family Tinamidae. All tinamous are exclusively ground-dwelling and are found only within Central and South America. However, the subfamily Tinaminae contains forest-dwelling tinamous whereas the subfamily Rhynchotinae holds grassland species. Tinamous belong to the order Tinamiformes — thought to be one of the world's oldest bird orders.

• **ORDER** • *Tubulidentata* • **FAMILY** • *Orycteropodidae* • **GENUS & SPECIES** • *Orycteropus afer*

AARDVARK

The thickset, muscular aardvark uses its sensitive snout to locate termites, and rips into their mounds with a set of powerful, shovel-shaped claws.

KEY FEATURES

- Nocturnal animal that specializes in feeding on termites and ants, which it collects on its long, sticky tongue.
- Possesses an elongated snout and a finely tuned sense of smell to sniff out its tiny insect prey.
- Can burrow incredibly fast into hard soil to escape from predators.
- Lives alone in a complex burrow system.

VITAL STATISTICS

WEIGHT	40–100kg (88.2–220.5lb)
LENGTH	Head & Body: 1–1.58m (3ft 3in–5ft 2in) Tail: 44–71cm (14.3–27.9in)
SHOULDER HEIGHT	60–65cm (23.6–25.6in)
SEXUAL MATURITY	About 2 years
MATING SEASON	Varies according to region
GESTATION PERIOD	About 30 weeks
NUMBER OF YOUNG	1, occasionally twins
BIRTH INTERVAL	About 18 months
TYPICAL DIET	Mainly termites and ants
LIFESPAN	Up to 10 years in captivity, probably longer in the wild

TEETH
The aardvark has no canines or incisors, but is equipped with continuously growing cheek teeth that are used to grind up crunchy insects.

EARS
The ears can detect the tiny scrabblings of termites. They are held erect when the aardvark forages, but folded back to shut out soil when it digs (above).

SNOUT
The trunk-like snout is tipped with a disc-like, mobile nose that is used to sniff out prey. The dense hairs around the circular nostrils keep out soil and sand.

TOES
The digits end in long claws with sharp edges for tearing into and shovelling aside hard soil. Flaps of skin joining the bases of the toes form a partial webbing.

CREATURE COMPARISONS

The giant pangolin (Manis gigantea) of West and central Africa is quite distinct from the aardvark in taxonomic terms, belonging to the order Pholidota, but the two mammals share some similar adaptations fitting their common habit of raiding termite nests.

Like the aardvark, the giant pangolin has a thickset body, sturdy limbs equipped with stout claws, and a long snout housing a sticky tongue. It is slightly smaller, however, with a total length of up to 1.5m (4ft 9in) and weighing some 30kg (66.1lb). The pangolin's most striking feature is the armour-plating of overlapping scales that coats its body. The scales have sharp tips and can inflict serious wounds.

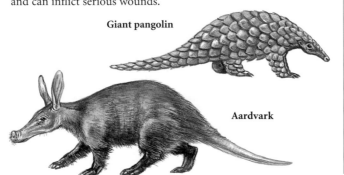

Giant pangolin

Aardvark

WHERE IN THE WORLD?

Ranges over most of sub-Saharan Africa, from west to east across the Sahel and south to the Cape of Good Hope. It is absent only from the most arid and the most densely forested regions.

RELATED SPECIES

The aardvark has no close relatives living today. It is the only species within its genus, and there are no other genera within its family. Indeed, it is the sole representative of the order Tubulidentata. It was once classified with anteaters, sloths, armadillos and pangolins in the order Edentata, but it is now thought that the similarities between these anteating animals are the result of a similar way of life and not of common ancestry.

• **ORDER** • *Urodela* • **FAMILY** • *Plethodontidae* • **SPECIES** • *Various* NORTH AMERICAN LUNGLESS SALAMANDER

Lungless salamanders spend the daylight hours hidden in burrows, sheltering from the potentially fatal drying effects of the sun's heat.

KEY FEATURES

- Breathe with fish-like gills during their aquatic larval stage but, as adults, absorb oxygen directly through the surface of their thin skin.
- Secretive amphibians that emerge from their damp hiding places only at night and during wet weather.
- Many adults are equally at home on land or in water.

VITAL STATISTICS

WEIGHT	Varies from a few grams up to 30g (1.1oz)
LENGTH	5–22cm (2–8.7in)
SEXUAL MATURITY	Up to 5 years
BREEDING SEASON	Summer to late winter; varies between species
NUMBER OF EGGS	10 to 100
HATCHING PERIOD	1.5–12 months
LARVAL STAGE	1–36 months
BREEDING INTERVAL	1 year
TYPICAL DIET	Larva feeds on small aquatic animals; adult feeds on snails, earthworms, insects and smaller species of salamander
LIFESPAN	Up to 25 years

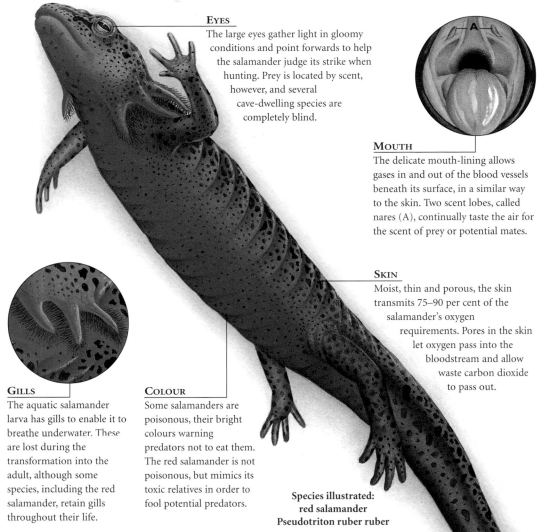

EYES
The large eyes gather light in gloomy conditions and point forwards to help the salamander judge its strike when hunting. Prey is located by scent, however, and several cave-dwelling species are completely blind.

MOUTH
The delicate mouth-lining allows gases in and out of the blood vessels beneath its surface, in a similar way to the skin. Two scent lobes, called nares (A), continually taste the air for the scent of prey or potential mates.

SKIN
Moist, thin and porous, the skin transmits 75–90 per cent of the salamander's oxygen requirements. Pores in the skin let oxygen pass into the bloodstream and allow waste carbon dioxide to pass out.

GILLS
The aquatic salamander larva has gills to enable it to breathe underwater. These are lost during the transformation into the adult, although some species, including the red salamander, retain gills throughout their life.

COLOUR
Some salamanders are poisonous, their bright colours warning predators not to eat them. The red salamander is not poisonous, but mimics its toxic relatives in order to fool potential predators.

Species illustrated:
red salamander
Pseudotriton ruber ruber

CREATURE COMPARISONS

The lungless salamanders of North America have a truly enormous, rather bizarre-looking relative: the Japanese giant salamander (*Andrias japonicus*). This creature can grow to over 1.5m long (4ft 9in), and has a broad, flattened head with huge jaws. Its size and strength enable it to hunt much larger prey than most other salamanders, including fish, frogs and other amphibians.

The Japanese giant salamander lives entirely underwater and breathes through the skin, like other lungless salamanders. However, its skin is loose-fitting and folded to maximize its absorbent surface area.

Japanese giant salamander

Red salamander

WHERE IN THE WORLD?

Found in and near pools, streams, humid forests and underground caves in much of eastern North America, and from central USA south to northeastern Mexico.

RELATED SPECIES

There are about 90 species of North American lungless salamander. All are distributed in 22 genera within 2 subfamilies (Plethodontinae and Desmognathinae) in the family Plethodontidae. Lungless salamanders are related to the many species of salamanders with functioning lungs in the families Salamandridae and Ambystomatidae, such as the boldly coloured tiger and fire salamanders, and to the similarly shaped newts.

• **ORDER** • *Urodeles* • **FAMILY** • *Salamandridae* • **GENUS & SPECIES** • *Triturus cristatus*

GREAT CRESTED NEWT

KEY FEATURES

* One of the largest newts; in the breeding season the male courts the female with an elaborate display.

* Breeds in water but spends much of its active time on land, foraging on the woodland floor for invertebrates.

* Has rough, warty skin equipped with glands that produce toxic secretions to ward off predators such as snakes.

VITAL STATISTICS

WEIGHT	Up to 14g (0.5oz)
LENGTH	13–17cm (5.1–6.7in)
SEXUAL MATURITY	2–4 years, usually 3
BREEDING SEASON	March–June
NUMBER OF EGGS	200 to 300
HATCHING PERIOD	14–21 days
LARVAL PERIOD	About 4 months
BREEDING INTERVAL	1 year
TYPICAL DIET	Aquatic invertebrates, tadpoles, worms, slugs, insects, other newts
LIFESPAN	27 years

Sporting a jagged crest and a fiery belly in the breeding season, the great crested newt is a voracious predator of ponds and sluggish waterways.

TAIL
Both sexes have a long and thick, slightly flattened tail that provides propulsion through the water.

FEMALE
Similar in colouration to the male, the female newt does not acquire the breeding crest. She can, however, grow slightly longer than the male.

CREST
During the breeding season, the male develops a high, jagged crest running the length of his back and tail. His skin also pales to reveal a sprinkling of white dots.

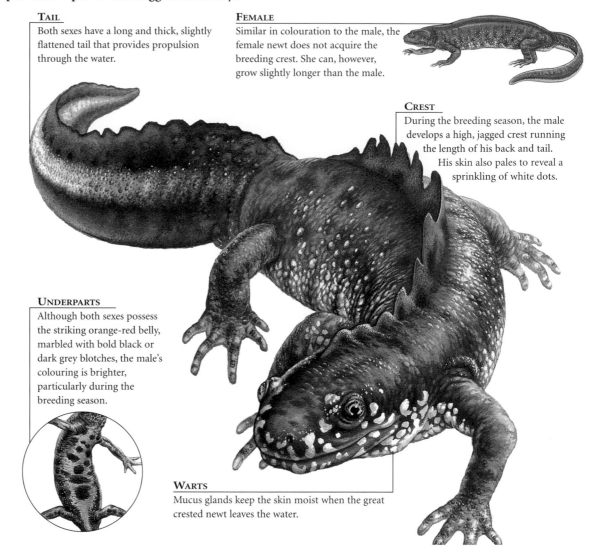

UNDERPARTS
Although both sexes possess the striking orange-red belly, marbled with bold black or dark grey blotches, the male's colouring is brighter, particularly during the breeding season.

WARTS
Mucus glands keep the skin moist when the great crested newt leaves the water.

CREATURE COMPARISONS

The alpine newt (Triturus alpestris) has a similar Europe-wide distribution to the great crested newt. Preferring cool, damp climates, the alpine newt spends the bulk of its life in or close to water. Its overall colouration resembles that of its larger cousin, although its spots and pale patches are larger and more prominent, and its belly varies from pale yellow to bright red. A medium-sized newt, the alpine newt is much smaller than its cousin, and in the breeding season the male alpine newt's crest is smooth, not jagged.

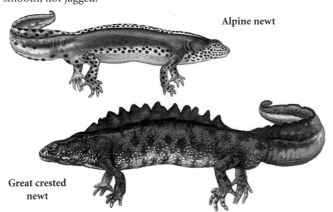

Alpine newt

Great crested newt

WHERE IN THE WORLD?

Distributed throughout northern and central Europe, from Britain, France and Scandinavia east as far as Russia, Ukraine and Belarus.

RELATED SPECIES

The great crested newt belongs to the largest genus of newts, Triturus, which includes the smooth newt, the alpine newt and the marbled newt, Triturus marmoratus. Triturus is 1 of 15 genera in the family Salamandridae, which is part of the order Urodeles in the class Amphibia.

• ORDER • *Xenarthra* • FAMILY • *Myrmecophagidae* • GENUS & SPECIES • *Tamandua tetradactyla*

SOUTHERN TAMANDUA

KEY FEATURES

- An agile, tree-climbing anteater that spends up to 15 hours a day asleep.
- This solitary creature thrives in a variety of habitats in its tropical home — from rainforest to dry grassland.
- Equipped with a long, tubular nose and extendable, sticky tongue to locate and capture prey.
- Readily defends itself with sharp, curved claws.

VITAL STATISTICS

WEIGHT	2–7kg (4.4–15.4lb)
LENGTH	Head & Body: 47–77cm (18.5–30.3in) Tail: 40–67cm (15.7–26.4in)
SEXUAL MATURITY	2–3 years
MATING SEASON	March to May: the southern autumn
GESTATION PERIOD	130–190 days
NUMBER OF YOUNG	Normally 1; occasionally twins
BIRTH INTERVAL	1 year
TYPICAL DIET	Ants and termites, occasionally bees and their honey
LIFESPAN	Up to 10 years in captivity

The southern tamandua's odd-looking body may look clumsy but is in fact perfectly adapted for a tree-dwelling, insect-eating lifestyle.

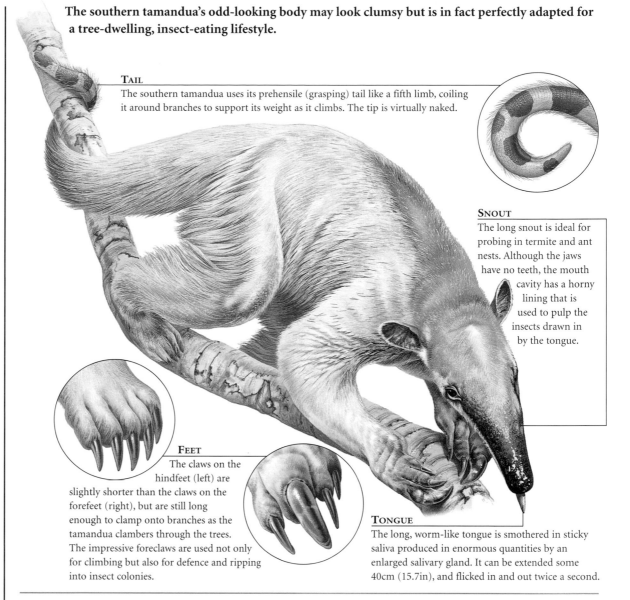

TAIL
The southern tamandua uses its prehensile (grasping) tail like a fifth limb, coiling it around branches to support its weight as it climbs. The tip is virtually naked.

SNOUT
The long snout is ideal for probing in termite and ant nests. Although the jaws have no teeth, the mouth cavity has a horny lining that is used to pulp the insects drawn in by the tongue.

FEET
The claws on the hindfeet (left) are slightly shorter than the claws on the forefeet (right), but are still long enough to clamp onto branches as the tamandua clambers through the trees. The impressive foreclaws are used not only for climbing but also for defence and ripping into insect colonies.

TONGUE
The long, worm-like tongue is smothered in sticky saliva produced in enormous quantities by an enlarged salivary gland. It can be extended some 40cm (15.7in), and flicked in and out twice a second.

CREATURE COMPARISONS

Ants and termites may be small, but they live in huge colonies. This makes them a good source of food for any animal that can catch and eat them in sufficient numbers. Several animals have taken up the challenge, including the pig-like aardvark (*Orycteropus afer*) of the African grasslands. This species feeds much like the southern tamandua, by breaking into ant and termite nests, inserting its long, tube-like snout and scooping up the occupants with its elongated, sticky tongue. But unlike the tamandua it cannot climb, and its hoof-like claws are adapted for digging rather than clinging to branches and bark.

Aardvark

Southern tamandua

WHERE IN THE WORLD?

The southern tamandua is a New World mammal found east of the Andes mountain range from Venezuela south to northern Argentina and southern Brazil. It also occurs on the island of Trinidad.

RELATED SPECIES

The closest relative of the southern tamandua is the northern tamandua (Tamandua mexicana), which is virtually identical in appearance and habits. It occurs in Mexico and Central and South America. The tamanduas belong to the family Myrmecophagidae, which also includes the silky anteater (Cyclopes didactylus) and the giant anteater (Myrmecophaga tridactyla), both of which are found in Mexico and Central and South America.

• **ORDER** • *Xenarthra* • **FAMILY** • *Dasypodidae* • **GENUS & SPECIES** • *Tolypeutes tricinctus* # THREE-BANDED ARMADILLO

KEY FEATURES

- Armour-plated mammal that rolls into a ball when threatened, to protect its soft underparts from attack.
- Shelters under a bush during the day, confident in the protection afforded by its tough upperparts.
- Extends its extra-long, sticky tongue to lick up masses of ants and termites.

VITAL STATISTICS

WEIGHT	1.5kg (3.3lb)
LENGTH	Head & Body: 35–45cm (13.8–17.7in) Tail: 6–9cm (2.4–3.5in)
SEXUAL MATURITY	9–12 months
MATING SEASON	October to January
GESTATION PERIOD	120 days
NUMBER OF YOUNG	1
BIRTH INTERVAL	1 year
TYPICAL DIET	Ants, termites and other invertebrates, carrion, fruit
LIFESPAN	12–15 years

The powerful forelimbs and sharp claws of the three-banded armadillo enable it to dig for insects in the sunbaked soil.

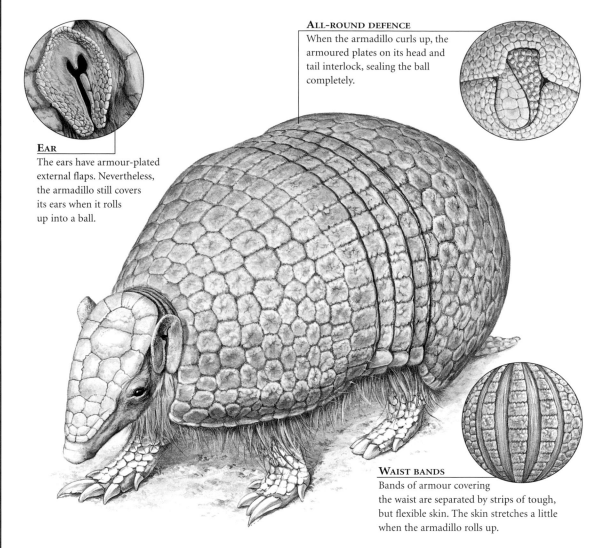

EAR
The ears have armour-plated external flaps. Nevertheless, the armadillo still covers its ears when it rolls up into a ball.

ALL-ROUND DEFENCE
When the armadillo curls up, the armoured plates on its head and tail interlock, sealing the ball completely.

WAIST BANDS
Bands of armour covering the waist are separated by strips of tough, but flexible skin. The skin stretches a little when the armadillo rolls up.

CREATURE COMPARISONS

Two species of pichiciego, or fairy armadillo (Chlamyphorus truncatus and C. retusus) occur on the sandy and grassy plains of Argentina, Bolivia and Paraguay. C. truncatus is the smallest of all armadillos, reaching only 5cm (2in) in length and weighing no more than 85g (3oz). Like the three-banded armadillo, pichiciegos have strong claws for digging. They burrow to escape predators, tending not to roll into a ball. Once inside a burrow, both species of pichiciego use a bony shield on their flat rump to plug the entrance. In common with the three-banded armadillo, the pichiciego is declining through habitat loss and predation by domestic dogs.

Pichiciego (life size) Species shown: Chlamyphorus retusus

Three-banded armadillo (not to scale)

WHERE IN THE WORLD?

Occurs in the open savannah and dry woodland of eastern Brazil in South America, just south of the Equator. Seldom found west of longitude 50°W.

RELATED SPECIES

The three-banded armadillo is 1 of 2 species in the genus Tolypeutes. The other species is the southern three-banded armadillo, Tolypeutes matacus, which lives in central Brazil, southern Argentina, and Bolivia. In all, there are 20 species of armadillo. All are found in South America, with the exception of the common long-nosed armadillo, Dasypus novemcinctus, which lives in southern parts of the USA.

• ORDER • *Xiphosura* **• FAMILY •** *Limulidae* **• SPECIES •** *Limulus polyphemus* NORTH AMERICAN HORSESHOE CRAB

The horseshoe crab is an intriguing survivor from a group of animals that dominated the world's seas long before the age of the dinosaurs.

KEY FEATURES

- A 'living fossil', whose enormous ancestors prowled the seas about 300 million years ago.
- Not a true crab, but more closely related to scorpions and spiders.
- Burrows into sandy seabeds to crack clam shells with its hindlegs.
- Threatened with extinction, according to the IUCN (World Conservation Union).

VITAL STATISTICS

LENGTH	51–61cm (20.1–24in)
SEXUAL MATURITY	9–12 years
BREEDING SEASON	March to August, during full and new moon high tides
NUMBER OF EGGS	2000 to 30,000
HATCHING PERIOD	About six weeks
TYPICAL DIET	Worms; molluscs and other shellfish; algae and carrion
LIFESPAN	Up to 19 years

BOOK GILLS
Five pairs of leaf-like gill structures (1) behind the legs enable the crab to extract oxygen from water.

SHELL
The shell comprises two jointed sections capable of bending. The forward section covers the head and prosoma (thorax). The hindpart protects the opisthosoma (abdomen).

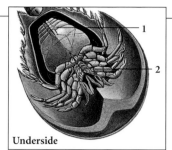
Underside

LEGS
The ten legs (2) are used for walking and shredding prey. The hindmost pair cleans the book gills, burrows and crushes prey.

TAIL
The long, mobile tail, or telson, aids movement and helps the animal right itself if overturned. Although the tail is stiff, sharp and dangerous-looking, it is not used as a weapon.

EYES
Two compound eyes (above) on the sides of the shell each contain 8 to 14 lenses. There are also two more simple eyes towards the front of the shell.

CREATURE COMPARISONS

Today's horseshoe crabs once had many more relatives and were far more widespread. The aquatic euryupterids, or water scorpions, lived 600–230 million years ago.

Eurypterids looked like horseshoe crabs, with a dome-fronted, armoured body and a spike-like tail. They also had similar, though simpler, compound eyes. They ranged more widely in size, however: some eurypterids were no more than 10cm (3.9in) long, while others grew to 2m (6ft 6in) or more. They would have preyed on early fish, which were equipped with armoured bodies to fend off such mighty hunters.

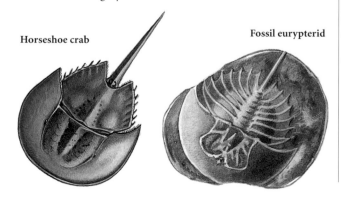
Horseshoe crab

Fossil eurypterid

WHERE IN THE WORLD?

Found in shallow, coastal waters along the eastern seaboard of North America, from Nova Scotia in Canada south to the Yucatan coast of Mexico. Related species occur along the coasts of Japan, Korea and other countries in Asia.

RELATED SPECIES

The North American **Limulus polyphemus** is the largest of the 5 species of horseshoe crab. The other 2 genera, **Carcinoscorpius** and **Tachypleus**, are found along the coasts of Asia from Japan and Korea south through the Philippines and the Malay Archipelago. The smallest species is **Carcinoscorpius rotunda**, at 30cm (11.8in) from head to tail. Horseshoe crabs are related to sea spiders, spiders and scorpions.

ANIMAL NAME INDEX Page numbers in **bold** refer to main entries.

A
aardvark **496,** 499
aardwolf 141, 142, 143, **144**
acouchi 431, 432
addax **39**
African buffalo 43
African bullfrog 29
African bushpig **96**
African civet **176,** 177
African clawed toad 28
African elephant 418, **419**
African fish eagle 10
African golden cat 121
African grey mongoose 179
African jacana 197
African lion 125, 133, **139**
African malachite sunbird 233
African moon moth 300
African palm civet 176
African pygmy goose 21
African pygmy kingfisher 230
African striped weasel 148
African white-backed vulture 259
African wild ass **357,** 358
African wild cat 128
African wild dog **114**
aga toad 25, 26
agile wallaby 315
agouti **431**
Aldabran giant tortoise 208
alpaca 75, **76**
alpine marmot **453**
alpine newt 498
Amazon river dolphin 188
American alligator **234,** 236
American avocet 200
American badger 147, 153, **162**
American bison **43**
American black bear **169,** 170, 173
American bullfrog **29**
American cockroach **100**
American crocodile 234
American eel 13
American harpy eagle **257**
American kestrel 266, 491
American marten 147
American mink **159**
American moon moth 300
American mountain goat 64
American paddlefish 11
American purple gallinule 197
American swallow-tailed kite 258
American white pelican 345
Amur leopard 135
Andean avocet 200
Andean condor 262, **263**
angelfish **351**
anglerfish **303**
angwantibo 412
Antarctic fur seal 373
antlion **327**
archaeopteryx 240
Arctic fox 17, 172

arctic fox **105**
Arctic ground squirrel **455**
arctic hare **295**
Arctic skua **203**
Arctic tern **204**
Arctic wolf 109
argali 63
army ant 282
Asian birdwing 299
Asian black bear **173**
Asian elephant **418,** 419
Asian false-vampire bat 211
Asian open-bill stork 223
Asiatic black bear 169
Asiatic golden cat 132
Asiatic lion **133,** 139
Asiatic water shrew 288
Asiatic wild ass 357
Atlantic cod 303
Atlantic puffin **194**
Atlantic salmon 459
Australian cockroach 100
Australian hopping mouse 442
Australian king parrot 422
avahi 407
avicularia 34
axis deer **79,** 83
aye-aye **404**

B
babirusa **94,** 95
Bactrian camel 74
Baikal seal 377
bald eagle 261
bald uakari **388**
banded blackwing 327
banded mongoose **180**
banded stingaree 99
bandicoot 317
bank swallow 338
bank vole **439**
banteng 45
bar-headed goose 16
Barbary ape **397**
barking deer 86
barn owl **491**
barnacle goose 19
barracuda 457
Barrier Reef clownfish 355
bat-eared fox **115,** 118
beaded lizard 482
bearded saki 388
bearded seal **371,** 375
bee hummingbird 32
beira 60
beluga 11, **190**
Bengal tiger **137**
Bennett's cassowary 181
big brown bat 212, **216**
bighorn sheep 61, **62,** 63
bilby **323**
binturong **175**
bittern 221

black-backed jackal 106, **110**
black brant goose 19
black-breasted buzzard 260
black-crowned night heron **221**
black-faced impala 40
black-faced sheathbill 195
black-footed cat 125
black-footed ferret 156, 158
black guillemot 193
black-headed blenny 349
black-headed gull **199**
black kite 258
black lemur 409
black millipede 302
black-necked grebe 380
black-necked stork 224
black rat 446, **447**
black-red modern game bantam 270
black rhinoceros **360**
black stork 223
black-tailed jackrabbit **294**
black-tailed prairie dog **451**
black-thighed falconet 265
black-throated diver 274
black toad 26
black tufted-eared marmoset 382
black widow spider **35**
black wildebeest 48
black-winged stilt 200
black wolf 109
blacktip shark 102, 104
Blanford's fox 113
blenny **349**
blesbok 49
blue and yellow macaw **421**
blue bird of paradise 342
blue chaffinch 337
blue-cheeked bee-eater 233
blue duck 21
blue-faced booby 347
blue land crab 245
blue-ringed octopus **328**
blue shark 104
blue-spotted stingray 99
blue whale 183
blue-winged kookaburra **231**
boat-billed heron 221, 225
bobcat **127**
bongo **71,** 73
bonnethead shark 103
bonobo **414**
bontebok 41, **49**
boodie 312
Botta's pocket gopher 435
bottlenose dolphin **188**
bowhead whale 189
brahminy kite 258
brain coral 460
Brazilian tapir **363**
broad-nosed caiman 235
brow-antlered deer 81
brown bear 170, 172
brown capuchin monkey **389,** 390

brown hyena **142,** 143
brown kiwi 492
brown lacewing 327
brown long-eared bat **215**
brown pelican 345
brown rat **446,** 447
brown spine-tailed swift 31
brown trout 458
brush-turkey 269
buff-faced pygmy parrot 422
bull shark 219
bulldog ant **282**
bulldog bat 209, **211,** 212
bumble-bee 280
Burmese python 474
bush baby **411,** 417
bush dog 114, **116**
bush duiker **66**
bush hyrax 284
bush-tailed mongoose 140
bushbuck 37, **72**
bushpig 96
bushy-tailed cloud rat 425
butterfly bat 218
butterfly blenny 349

C
cacomistle 163
Californian garter snake 477
Canada goose **19**
cane toad 26
Cape buffalo 43, **67**
Cape dune mole rat 424
Cape fox 113
Cape fur seal 369
Cape pangolin **365**
Cape porcupine **438**
capercaillie 271
capuchin monkey **389,** 390
capybara **437**
caracal **121,** 124
Carolina wood duck 14
carp **241**
carrion crow 336
Caspian pond turtle 207
Caspian tiger 137
cattle egret 333
cedar waxwing 332
Celebes wild boar 95
centipede **302**
Chacoan peccary 98
chaffinch **337**
chamois 47, 52, **64**
cheetah **120,** 135
Chilean beaver 428
chimpanzee 413, 414, **415**
chinchilla **430**
Chinese alligator 234
Chinese desert cat 131
Chinese ferret badger 162
Chinese water deer 85
chinstrap penguin 468
circus pygargus 255
cleaner wrasse **353**
clouded leopard **132,** 135, 138

coati **164,** 166
coatimundi 165
collared flycatcher 341
collared peccary **98**
colpeo fox 111
colugo **247,** 452
common adder **488**
common blue damselfly 330
common brushtail possum 308, 321, **322**
common carp 241
common clownfish **355**
common dolphin **184**
common dormouse 436, **449**
common eider duck **24**
common European lobster 246
common frog **30**
common genet **177**
common hawker damselfly 330
common iguana 483
common kestrel 264, **266**
common marmoset **382**
common octopus **329**
common palm civet 176
common potoo 101
common reedbuck 54
common seahorse 273
common seal **378**
common tegu **485**
common tenrec **291**
common tern 204
common vole 439
common wallaroo 314
common wildebeest **48**
common wombat **324**
compass jellyfish 279, **464**
conger eel 13
coral snake 480
corncrake **278**
cotton-top tamarin 385, **386**
cougar see puma
coyote 105, **108**
coypu **426,** 428, 437
Cozumel coati 164
crab-eating racoon 166
crabeater seal 374, **375**
crested caracara **267**
crested chameleon 475
crested gibbon 405
cross fox 119
crossed viper **488**
crown of thorns sea star **469**
crowned crane 276
crowned eagle 253
crowned lemur 410
Cuban hutia **425**
cuscus **321**
cuttlefish 328

D
Daubenton's bat 214, 218
death adder 480
death's head hawk-moth **301**
deep-sea anglerfish 303
deep-sea squid 244
demoiselle crane 276

Derby eland 68, 70
desert hedgehog **286**
desert jerboa **433,** 450
desert locust **331**
dhole 107, **112,** 114, 115
diamondback rattlesnake **478**
Diana monkey **392**
dibatag 55
dik-dik **56,** 60
dipper **335**
discus fish 351
dogfish **463**
domestic ass 358
domestic ferret 156, 158
domestic pig 96, 97
domestic rabbit 294, 295, **296**
domestic sheep 63
domestic tabby cat 129
dorcas gazelle **50**
Doria's tree kangaroo 248
double-wattled cassowary **181,** 182
douc langur **401**
drill 398
dromedary camel **74**
duckbill platypus **325**
dugong **466,** 467
dung beetle **228**
dwarf cassowary 181
dwarf mongoose 140, **178**
dwarf sperm whale 191

E
eagle owl **489,** 490
eastern quoll 307
eclectus parrot **422**
edible dormouse **436**
eel-tail catfish 465
Egyptian plover **196**
Egyptian spiny mouse 444
Egyptian vulture 256, **260**
eland **68,** 70
Eleonora's falcon 266
elephant seal **376**
elephant shrew **304**
elk 78
emerald tree boa 472
emperor scorpion 462
emperor tamarin **385**
emu 181, **182,** 493
Ethiopian wolf 110
Eurasian avocet **200**
Eurasian badger **153**
Eurasian buzzard **254**
Eurasian cuckoo 239
Eurasian curlew **201**
Eurasian eagle owl 490
Eurasian kingfisher **230**
Eurasian otter 146, **150**
Eurasian pine marten **151**
Eurasian shrew **289**
Eurasian swallow 338
Eurasian swift **31**
Eurasian toad **25**
Eurasian treecreeper **334**
Eurasian water shrew 287, **288**

European beaver 427, **428**
European bison 43
European catfish **465**
European eel **13**
European hedgehog **285**
European mole **290**
European mountain goat 64
European nightjar 101
European polecat 156, **158**
European rabbit 294, 295, **296**
European shag 346
European sturgeon **11**
European swallowtail 298, **299**
European widow spider 35
European wildcat **129**

F
fairy armadillo 500
fallow deer **83**, 88
false gharial 238
false killer whale 185
fat-tailed gerbil 440
fat-tailed scorpion **462**
fathead minnow 242
Fea's muntjac 86
fennec fox **113**
fiddler crab **245**
field vole **443**
fiery-breasted bush-shrike 339
firecrest 343
fisher 145, **152**
fisherman's bat 209, **211**, 212
five-legged sea star 469
flat-headed cat 131
flounder **379**
flower mantis 305
flycatcher 332
flying lemur 452
fogstand beetle **229**
forest buffalo 67
forest wallaby 309
four-horned antelope **69**
freshwater crocodile 237
freshwater eel 13
frilled lizard **470**
fungus ant 281
funnel-web spider 35

G
gaboon viper 487
Galapagos hawk 254
Gambian mongoose 180
garden dormouse 449
garter snake **477**
gaur **44**, 45
gelada baboon 398, **403**
gemsbok **59**
Geoffroy's cat **123**
Geoffroy's tamarin 385
gerenuk 50, **55**
German cockroach 100
German wasp 283
gharial 235, **238**
ghost bat **209**
ghost crab 245

giant anteater **252**
giant armadillo 251
giant eland 68
giant forest hog **95**
giant hammerhead shark 103
giant land crab 243
giant moa 493
giant oriental honeybee 280
giant otter 146, 150, **160**
giant otter shrew 287
giant panda **167**, 168
giant pangolin 496
giant toad 25, 26
gibel carp 241
Gila monster **482**
giraffe **90**, 91
Goeldi's monkey **381**
goldcrest **343**
golden eagle **253**, 261, 491
golden-handed tamarin 386
golden jackel **107**, 108
golden lion tamarin **384**
golden seahorse 273
golden snub-nosed monkey **399**, 401
goldfish 241
goliath heron 220
goliath spider 34
gopher tortoise **208**
gorilla 413, 415
Grant's gazelle 51
grass snake **476**
great black-backed gull 198
great black-headed gull 199
great bustard **277**
great cormorant **346**
great crested newt **498**
great diving beetle **227**
great grey owl 489
great grey shrike **339**
great horned owl 491
great northern diver **274**
great plains toad 25
great silver water beetle 227
great skua 203
great spotted kiwi 492
great white pelican **345**
great white shark **297**
greater crested grebe **380**
greater dwarf lemur 404
greater flamingo **364**
greater horseshoe bat **214**
greater kudu 68, 70, **73**
greater rhea 182
greater roadrunner **239**
greater spotted dogfish 219
greater spotted woodpecker **366**
green acouchi **432**
green anaconda **473**
green darner 330
green iguana **484**
green mamba 480
green tree python **472**
green turtle **205**, 206
grey cuscus 321
grey fox 108, **117**

grey heron **220**
grey seal **372**
grey squirrel **454**
grey whale **189**
grey-winged teal 23
grey wolf 105, **109**
greyhound 114
greylag goose **16**
grizzled leaf monkey 402
grizzled sureli 402
grizzled tree kangaroo 248
grizzly bear 167, **170**
grysbucks 60
guanaco **75**, 77
guereza **393**
guinea-pig 429
gyr falcon 264, **265**

H
hairy-eared dwarf lemur 408
hairy-legged vampire bat 212
hamadryas baboon **400**, 403
hamerkop 222, **225**
hammerhead shark **103**
Hanuman langur **402**
harbour porpoise 184
hard coral **460**
Harris' hawk 254
hartebeest 40, **41**, 49
harvest mouse **442**
Hawaiian sabre-tooth blenny 192
hedgehog 326
hen harrier **255**
hermit crab 12, 243
herring gull **198**
high mountain vole 448
Himalyan monal pheasant 495
hippopotamus 92, **93**, 359
hispid hare 293
hoatzin **240**
hog badger 153
hog-nosed skunk 155
honey bear **165**
honeybee **280**
hooded seal **370**, 376
hooded skunk 155
hooded vulture **259**, 260
Hooker's sea lion 368
horn-nosed viper 488
horned grebe 380
horned viper 476
hornet **283**
horseshoe bat 213, 215
horseshoe crab 501
houbara bustard 277
house marten 338
house mouse **444**
hummingbird 32
hummingbird hawk-moth 301
humpback whale **183**, 189
Huon tree kangaroo 248

I
Iberian wolf 109
ibex **47**, 61

impala 40
imperial eagle 253
Indian flying fox **213,** 247
Indian giant squirrel 456
Indian grey mongoose 180
Indian moon moth **300**
Indian muntjac **86**
Indian python 474
Indian rhinoceros **361**
Indochinese tiger 137
indri **407**
Irish elk 78
isard 64

J
jackal buzzard 254
Jackson's chameleon **475**
jaguar 120, **134,** 135
jaguarundi **131**
Japanese crane **276**
Japanese giant salamander **497**
Japanese macaque **394**
Japanese waxwing 332
jumping mouse 433

K
kakapo **423**
kea 423
king cobra **480**
king eider duck 24
king vulture **262**
kinkajou 163, **165,** 166
kit fox 117, **118**
kiwi **492**
klipspringer **58,** 60
Kloss's gibbon 406
koala **249**
kob **54**
kodkod 131
koi carp 241
Komodo dragon 470, 482, **486**
kookaburra 230
kouprey 44
kowari 306

L
lammergeier **256,** 260
lappet-faced vulture 259
lar gibbon **405,** 416
large-spotted genet 177
laughing kookaburra **231**
leadbetter's possum 318
leafcutter ant **281**
leafcutter bee 280
leafy sea-dragon 273
least weasel 147, 154
leather carp 241
leatherback turtle 205, **206**
lechwe 53
lemon shark **219**
leopard 120, **135,** 139
leopard lizard 485
leopard seal **373,** 374
lesser octopus 329
lesser panda *see* red panda

lesser roadrunner 239
lesser spotted eagle 253
lilac-breasted roller 233
lion **139**
lion-tailed macaque **396,** 397
lionfish **461**
lion's mane jellyfish 464
little auk **193**
little goblin bat 210
little shearwater 420
little spotted cat 130
little spotted kiwi 492
llama 75, 76
long-eared bat 213, 215
long-eared desert hedgehog **285**
long-fingered triok 318
long-nosed armadillo 365
long-nosed bandicoot **317**
long-nosed echidna 325, 326
long-tailed weasel 159
lowland gorilla **413**

M
magnificent frigatebird **344**
Malayan gymnure 286
Malayan porcupine 434
Malayan sun bear **171,** 174
Malayan tapir **362,** 363
mallard **15**
mallethead shark 103
Manchurian crane **276**
mandarin duck **14**
mandrill **398**
maned seahorse 273
maned wolf **111**
mantis **305**
Manx shearwater **420**
marabou stork 263, 268, **429**
marbled polecat 158
margay 123, **130,** 134
marine iguana **483**
marine otter 149
marine toad 25, **26**
markhor 47
marsh deer 84
marsh frog 30
marsh harrier 255
martial eagle 253, **261**
Masai giraffe 90
masked booby 347
masked palm civet 175
mastiff bat 210
Mediterranean monk seal 373
Mediterranean water shrew 288
meerkat **140**
merlin 264
Mexican free-tailed bat **210**
Mexican red-kneed spider 33, **34**
migratory locust 331
minke whale 186
minnow **242**
mirror carp 241
Mongolian gazelle 65
mongoose **179**
mongoose lemur **408**

monk seal **377**
Montagu's harrier 255
moonrat 286
Moor macaque 395
moose **78,** 88, 89
moray eel 13
moss forest rat 446
mothercare spider **36**
mouflon **63**
mountain beaver **427**
mountain coati 165
mountain goat **57**
mountain lion *see* puma
mountain nyala 71
mountain tapir 362
mountain viscacha 430
mountain zebra **358**
mouse-eared bat **217**
mudskipper **352**
mule deer **87**
musk deer **85**
musk ox 47, **61**
musk shrew 304
muskrat 443, **445**
musky rat kangaroo 314
mute swan **20**

N
nail-tailed wallaby 313
naked mole rat **424**
narwhal 190
nautilus 328
neotropical toad 25, 26
New Guinea harpy eagle 257
night monkey 390
Nile crocodile **236**
Nile monitor 486
nilgai **46,** 69
nine-banded armadillo **251**
nine-spined stickleback 272
North American beaver **427**
North American grey fox 117
North American horseshoe crab **501**
North American lungless salamander **497**
North American otter **149,** 160
North American porcupine **434**
North American swift fox 105
North Atlantic bottlenose whale 190
northern flying squirrel 452
northern fur seal **369**
northern gannet **347**
northern lynx **124**
northern pudu 89
northern pygmy gerbil **440**
northern shelduck 15
northern short-tailed shrew **287**
northern tamandua 499
Norway lemming **441**
Nubian woodpecker 366
numbat **316,** 317
nyala **70,** 72

O
ocellated turkey 269
ocelot **126,** 130

okapi 90, **91**
Old World bittern 275
olingo 163, 164
olive baboon 398, 400
olive ridley turtle 205
opalescent squid **244**, 328
orang-utan 413, **416**
orb-web spider 33
orca **186**
orchid mantis 305
oribi **60**
oriental cockroach 100
oriental small-clawed otter 146
osprey **10**
ostrich **493**
owl butterfly **298**
oxpecker **333**

P
paca 432
pacarana 426
Pacific ridley turtle 205
Pacific salmon 459
pacu toba 192
pademelon 312, **315**
painted snipe 197
pampas cat 122
pampas deer 79
parma wallaby 311
parrotfish **356**
Patagonian weasel 157
Pel's scaly-tailed flying squirrel 319
perch **354**
Père David's deer 80, **84**
peregrine falcon **264**, 265
pheasant-tailed jacana **197**
pichiciego 500
piebald shrew 289
pied flycatcher **341**
pied tamarin 383
pig-tailed macaque 396
pike **457**
pike-perch 354
pilot whale **185**
pipa toad **28**
pipistrelle bat 214, **218**
piranha **192**
plaice 379
plains pocket gopher 435
plate coral 460
pocket gopher **435**
poison-arrow frog **27**
polar bear 170, **172**
porcupine fish 494
Port Jackson shark 102
Portuguese man-of-war **279**
pot-bellied pig 96
potter wasp 283
potto 411
prairie rattlesnake 478
praying mantis 305
proboscis monkey **399**
pronghorn **37**
ptarmigan **271**
pudu **89**

puff adder **487**
puffer fish **494**
puma **122**, 130, 136
pygmy antelope 60
pygmy hippopotamus **92**, 93
pygmy marmoset **383**, 384
pygmy palm swift 31
pygmy sperm whale 191

Q
quokka **314**
quoll **306**, 307, 316

R
raccoon **166**
racoon dog 107
Raggiana bird of paradise **342**
rainbow trout **458**
ratel **154**
raven **336**
recluse spider 35
red acouchi 431, 432
red ant 282
red-backed saki 388
red-breasted goose 17
red brocket deer 89
red colobus monkey 393
red-crested bustard 277
red deer **81**, 82
red-eared terrapin **207**
red-footed booby 344
red fox 105, 113, **119**
red grouse 271
red howler monkey **387**
red junglefowl **270**
red kangaroo **312**, 314
red kite **258**
red-necked avocet 200
red-necked wallaby **311**
red panda **163**, 165
red squirrel 454, **456**
red-tailed guenon 392
red-tailed hawk 254
red throated diver 274
red uakari 388
red wolf 111
redback spider 35
Reeve's muntjac 80
reticulated giraffe 90
reticulated python 473, **474**
rhebok 52
rhesus macaque 394, **395**
rhinoceros iguana 484
ribbon seal 378
ring-tailed lemur **409**
ring-tailed possum **320**
ringed seal 372
ringtail 163
Rio Grande perch 350
river otter 149, 160
roan antelope 38, **52**
robber crab **243**
rock cavy 429
rock hyrax **284**
rock wallaby **313**

rockhopper penguin **468**
rocky mountain goat 64
roe deer 37, **80**
rook 336
roseate spoonbill 364
Ross seal 370
Rothschild's giraffe 90
round-tailed muskrat 445
royal antelope 55
royal tern 204
rubber boa 478
ruby-throated hummingbird 32
ruddy duck **23**
ruff **202**
ruffed lemur **410**
rusa deer 82
rusty-spotted cat 123

S
sable 145
sable antelope **38**
sacred ibis **226**
saddle-bill stork **224**
saiga **65**
saki monkey 389
salt desert cavy 429
saltwater crocodile **237**
sambar deer **82**
Samoan flying fox 213
sand cat **125**
sand fox 112
sand marten **338**
sand viper 488
sandhill crane 276
sargassum fish 303
scaly-tailed possum 322
scarlet ibis 226
scarlet macaw 421
scaup 18
Schomburgk's deer 82
scimitar-horned oryx 39
scrub wallaby 315
sea anemone **12**
sea otter **146**, 147
sea snake **479**
seahorse **273**
secretary bird **268**
serow 57
serval 121, 127, **128**
sewellel 427
sexton beetle 228
ship rat 446, **447**
shoebill **222**
short-horned lizard 471
short-nosed bandicoot 323
short-nosed echidna 325, **326**
siamang gibbon **406**
Siamese fighting fish **348**
Siberian tiger **136**, 137
side-striped jackal **106**
sika deer 82
silkworm 300
silver fox 119
silvery gibbon 405
six-lined racerunner 481

slender loris 381
sloth bear **174**
slow loris 411, **412**
small-eared dog 116
smew **22**
snail kite 258
snow goose **17**
snow leopard 135, 136, **138**
snowshoe hare **293,** 295
snowy owl **480**
snowy sheathbill **195**
sockeye salmon **459**
Sonoran Desert toad 25
South African ground squirrel 451
South American cichlids **350**
South American tree porcupine 438
south polar skua 195
southern bulldog bat 211
southern flying squirrel 319, **452**
southern fur seal **368**
southern ground hornbill 232
southern hairy-nosed wombat 324
southern hawker dragonfly **330**
southern pudu 78, 88, 89
southern tamandua 252, **499**
Spanish lynx 124
spectacled bear **168,** 171, 173
spectacled caiman **235**
spectacled cobra 478
Speke's gazelle 42
sperm whale **191**
spine-cheeked clownfish 355
spiny anteater 325
spiny lobster **246**
spoon-billed sandpiper **202**
spot-necked otter 160
spotted cuscus 321
spotted dolphin 186, **187**
spotted hyena **141,** 142, 143
spotted seal 371
spotted skunk **161**
springbok 40, **42**
springhare **450**
squirrel monkey **391**
staghorn coral 460
star coral 460
star-nosed mole 290
starry smooth hound 463
steenbuck 60
Steller sea lion 367
sterlet 11
stingray **99**
stink badger 154
stoat **156,** 157
stone-curlew 201
streaked tenrec 291
striated caracara 267
striped ground squirrel 453
striped hyena 142, **143,** 144
striped possum **318,** 320
striped skunk 150, **155,** 161
sugar glider **319**
Sulawesi macaque 395
Sumatran rhinoceros 361
Sumatran short-eared rabbit 296

Sumatran tiger 137
sun bittern **275**
Sunda sambar deer 82
suni 58
superb lyrebird **340**
Surinam toad 28
swallow-tailed gull 198
swallowtail butterfly 298, **299**
swamp deer 87
swamp minnow 242
swift fox 117
sword-billed hummingbird 32
Sydney funnel-web spider 35

T
takin 61
tambaqui 192
tammar wallaby 310
tarsier 411, **417**
Tartar sand boa 478
Tasmanian devil **307**
tawny frogmouth **101**
tayra **145,** 147
tent-building bat 217
termite **292**
Texas tortoise 208
thirteen-lined ground squirrel 455
Thomson's gazelle 40, **51**
thorny devil **471**
three-banded armadillo 251, **500**
three-banded courser 196
three-spined stickleback **272**
three-toed sloth **250**
tiger quoll 306
tiger shark **102,** 219
tinamou **495**
toco toucan 232
topi 46
torrent duck **21**
Transcaucasian water shrew 288
tree hyrax 284
tree kangaroo **309**
tree ocelot *see* margay
tufted deer 86
tufted duck **18**
tufted puffin 194
turbot 379
two-toed sloth 250

V
vampire bat 209, **212**
veiled chameleon 475
veiltail fighting fish 348
Verreaux's eagle 253
vicuna **77**
Virginia opossum **308**
viscacha 430

W
Walia ibex 47
Wallace's standardwing 342
wallcreeper 334
walrus **367**
wapiti 78
warthog 97

water buffalo 67
water rail 278
water vole **448**
waterbuck **53**
waxwing **332**
weasel **157**
web-footed gecko **481**
Weddell seal **374**
West African manatee 466
West Indian manatee **467**
Western capercaillie 340
whale shark 297
whimbrel 201
whiptail wallaby **310**
whirligig beetle 227
white-billed diver 274
white-faced saki monkey 387
white-fronted bee-eater **233**
white-lipped peccary 94, 98
white rhinoceros **359,** 360
white-sided dolphin 187
white stork **223**
white-tailed deer 87, **88**
white-tipped sicklebill 32
white-winged vampire bat 212
whitetip reef shark **104**
whooper swan 20, 21
whooping crane 276
wild boar 96, **97**
wild goat 47
wild turkey **269**
willow ptarmigan 271
Wilson's storm-petrel **420**
winghead shark 103
wingless hissing cockroach 100
wolf spider **33**
wolverine **147**
wombat 249
wood lemming 441
woolly lemur 407
woolly monkey **390**
wrinkled-face bat 216

Y
yak **45**
yellow anaconda 473
yellow-bellied sea snake 479
yellow-billed cuckoo 239
yellow-billed hornbill **232**
yellow-lipped sea snake 479
yellow mongoose 140, 178
yellow-throated marten 152
Yemen monitor 486

Z
zander 354
zebra cichlid 350
zebra duiker 66
zebrafish 461
zeren 65
zorilla **148**

General Index

A
Africa
   antelopes 38
   birds 222, 345
   carnivores 121, 144
   hyrax 284
   snakes 487
   see also Central Africa; East Africa;
      North Africa; South Africa; sub-Saharan
      Africa; West Africa
alkaline lakes 364
alligators 234
Amazon basin 27, 160, 275, 351, 381, 383, 385,
   388
America
   armadillo 251
   bats 210–11, 216
   birds and fowl 23, 32, 98, 267, 344
   carnivores 108, 117, 122, 131, 164
   deer 88
   fish 350
   see also Central America; North America;
      South America
amphibious fish 352, 497
Andes mountains 21, 76–7, 89, 168, 263, 430
Antarctic circle 195, 373–6, 468
antelopes 38–42, 46, 49–56, 58–60, 66, 68–73
ants 281–2
aquatic
   mammals 146, 149–150, 159–160, 287–8, 325,
      362–3, 466–7
   newts 498
   reptiles 479, 483
   rodents 426–8, 445, 448
Arctic circle
   birds 17–18, 193–4, 202–4, 265, 271, 332
   carnivores 124, 147, 172
   fox 105
   hares 295
   musk ox 61
   owls 490
   rodents 455
   seals 370–1
   walruses 367
   whales 190
Asia
   bovines 44
   carnivores 112, 132, 138
   deer 85
   fowl 14
   primates 395
   see also Central Asia; China; Eurasia;
      Himalayas; Japan; South Asia
Atacama desert 75
Atlantic ocean 194, 279, 347, 349, 370, 372, 464
auks 193–4
Australia
   bats 209
   birds 101, 181–2, 231, 340, 422
   duckbill platypus 325

echidna 326
   insects 282
   koala 249
   marsupials 306, 309–24
   reptiles 237, 470–2
avocets 200

B
baboons 400, 403
badgers 153, 162
bandicoots 317
bats 209–18
bears 168–73
   see also pandas
beavers 427–8
bee-eaters 233
bees 280
beetles 227–9
birds 9, 31–2, 230–3, 239–40, 332–43, 366
   see also birds of prey; ducks; geese; gulls;
      pelicans; seabirds; waders
birds of prey 10, 253–68, 489–91
bison 43
Brazil 382, 384, 500
   see also Amazon basin
breeding battles 43, 62–3, 78, 81–3
bubonic plague 447
buffalo 67
burrows 245, 251, 296, 324, 496
   carnivores 148, 153, 156, 162
   insectivores 288, 290
   rodents 424, 426, 433, 435, 438–40, 443, 445,
      451, 453, 455
bushland 55, 72, 96
butterflies 298–9
buzzards 254

C
camels 74–7
camouflage
   antelopes 66, 70
   birds 101, 201, 271, 275, 343, 421, 495
   carnivores 117, 133–4, 138, 140
   chameleon 475
   colugo 247
   deer 83, 88
   fish 303, 354, 379, 457, 461, 463
   hares 295
   moths 301
   octopus 329
   owls 490
   reptiles 472, 484, 487
   sloth 250
   squid 244
   toads 28–9
Canada *see* North America
Caribbean islands 210–12, 216, 267, 281, 467,
   473
cats 120–38
caviar 11

Central Africa 54, 71, 91, 95, 222, 393, 413–15
Central America 126, 130, 145, 161, 165, 212
   anteater 252
   birds 257, 262, 275, 495
   iguana 484
   insects 281, 298
   reptiles 235
   rodents 431, 435, 437, 452
   sloth 250
   toads 27–8
   see also Mexico
Central Asia 45, 65
China 14, 84, 136, 167, 276
civets 176
cockroaches 100
coral reefs 102, 104, 243, 246, 328, 353, 355–6,
   460–1, 469, 494
cormorants 346
crabs 243, 245
cranes 277
crocodiles 235–8
crustaceans 243–6
Cuba 425
curlews 201

D
deer 78–89
deserts 39, 59, 62, 74–5, 113
   beetles 229
   birds 239
   carnivores 125, 139
   horses 357
   insectivores 286
   locust 331
   marsupials 323
   rodents 433, 440
   snakes 481
dinosaurs 8, 234, 326, 470
   see also primitive animals
divers 274
dogs 112, 114, 116
   see also foxes; jackals; wolves
dolphins 186–8
domesticated animals 45, 74, 76, 280, 348
dormice 436, 449
dragonflies 330
dragons 486
ducks 14–15, 18, 21–4

E
eagles 253, 257, 261
East Africa 51, 55–6, 110, 114–15, 400, 424, 475
echolocation 184, 217–18
eels 13
elephants 418–19
endangered species 9
   antelopes 39, 41, 68
   birds of prey 257
   bovines 44
   carnivores 114, 126, 133, 138, 167

horseshoe crab 501
marsupials 309
pangolin 365
primates 386, 388, 396, 401–2, 404, 407–8
reptiles 238
rodents 425, 430
seals 377
turtles 205
see also threatened species; vulnerable species
Ethiopia 403
eucalyptus 249, 310, 320
Eurasia
    bats 214–15
    birds 199–201, 230, 254, 334, 343, 366
    carnivores 150, 153
    deer 80
    fish 242, 354
    fowl 18, 20, 22
    frogs 30
    insectivores 288–90
    insects 36, 227
    rodents 442, 448, 456
    snakes 476, 488
    toads 25
    see also Asia; Europe
Europe
    bats 217–18
    birds 258, 341
    carnivores 151, 158
    dragonflies 330
    fish 457, 465
    goats 63–4
    insectivores 285
    newts 498
    rodents 428, 436, 439, 443, 449
    see also Eurasia
evolution 9

F
falcons 264–5, 267
fish 11, 13, 241–2, 272–3, 303, 348–56, 379,
    457–67, 494, 497
    see also sharks; whales
forests 9, 69, 126, 145, 152
    carnivores 173–4
    elephants 418
    marsupials 316–17, 320
    see also rainforests; tree climbers; woodlands
foxes 8, 105, 113, 115, 117–18, 119
frogs 27, 29–30
fur farming 76–7, 159, 426, 428

G
Galapagos Islands 344, 483
gannets 347
gazelles 50–1
geese 16–17, 19
genets 177
gerbils 440
gibbons 405–6
Gibraltar 397
Gir Protected area 133, 139

goat-antelopes 65
goats 47, 57, 64–5
gorillas 413
grasslands 41–2, 79, 263, 429, 495
Great Britain
    aquatic animals 150, 153
    birds 255, 258, 341, 343
    deer 84
    fish 99
    fowl 14, 23
    insectivores 285, 289–90
    rodents 454
    snakes 488
grebes 380
guinea pigs 429
gulls 198–9

H
habitat loss 9, 69, 94
    birds 222, 277–8, 423
    carnivores 133, 149, 171, 173–4
    pangolin 365
    primates 396, 402, 407–8, 412
    turtles 205
hares 293–5
harriers 255
hedgehogs 285–6
herons 220–1
hibernation 169, 207
    bats 214–15, 217–18
    hedgehogs 283
    reptiles 234, 488
    rodents 449, 453, 455
Himalayas 45, 47, 163, 402
hornbills 232
'horse-antelopes' 52
horses 357
human habitats 108, 162, 166, 177, 119, 198–9
    bats 214, 216, 218
    hornets 283
    marsupials 306
    rodents 444, 446–7, 454
    waders 223, 226
humans
    threat from 112, 143, 158, 255, 371, 404, 413
        (*see also* hunting)
    threat to 35, 100, 237, 279, 282, 331, 462, 482
hunting 65, 466
    carnivores 123, 126–7, 133, 138, 168, 170–71
    pangolin 365
    reptiles 234, 237
    rhinoceros 359
    rodents 430
    sea life 191, 205, 377
hyenas 141–4

I
India 213, 238, 300, 361, 396, 402
    carnivores 137, 174
    herbivores 46, 69, 79, 82, 87
Indian ocean 104, 328, 353, 355–6, 461, 466
Indonesia 94, 247, 399, 406, 486

insects 280–3, 330–1
invertebrates 8

J
jackals 106–7, 110
Japan 14, 276, 394

K
kangaroos 248, 309, 312
    see also wallabies
kestrels 266
kingfishers 230–1
kites 258

L
leks 54, 202
lemmings 441
lemurs 404, 407–10
leopards 9, 132, 135, 138
lions 133, 139
living fossils 11, 326, 417, 501
lizards 470–1, 481
lobsters 246
lure 303
lynx 124

M
macaques 394–7
Madagascar 225–6, 236, 291
    primates 404, 407–10
mangrove swamps 352, 399
marmosets 382–3
marsupials 248–9, 306–24
martens 151–2
Mediterranean 63, 83, 121
metamorphosis 227
Mexico 34–5, 87, 207, 239, 269, 477–8, 482
mice 442, 444
Middle East 50, 74, 113, 197, 433, 440, 462, 487
migration
    birds 31–2, 200–4, 274, 278, 337–8, 341
    birds of prey 264–5
    fish 13, 459
    gazelles 51
    lemmings 441
    moths 301
    sharks 103
    storks 223
    turtles 205–6
    whales 183, 185, 189, 191
    wild fowl 16–17, 19, 22
    wildebeest 48
mink 159
mobs 310
moles 290
mongooses 140, 178–9
monkeys 381–403
moths 300–1
mountains
    birds 335
    carnivores 138
    ducks 21

herbivores 47, 57–8, 62–4, 75, 85
  rodents 453
  snakes 475
  zebras 358
  see also Andes mountains; Himalayas
Mozambique 70
musk 85, 155, 445

N
Namib desert 42, 229, 481
national parks *see* nature reserves
nature reserves 43–4, 49, 84, 92, 133, 167, 359, 361
New Guinea 101, 181, 237, 248, 326, 342, 422
  marsupials 306, 309, 315, 318–19, 321
  snakes 472
North Africa 50, 74, 113, 331, 397, 440, 462
  horses 357
  rodents 433
North America
  birds 239
  carnivores 118, 127, 149, 152, 155, 159, 161–2, 166, 169–170
  fish 497
  fowl 18, 20, 22, 269
  frogs 29
  hares 293–4
  herbivores 37, 43, 57, 62, 87
  horseshoe crab 501
  insectivores 287
  marsupials 308
  reptiles 234, 477–8, 482
  rodents 427, 434–5, 445, 451–2, 454
  spiders 35
  tortoises 207–8
North Atlantic 194, 347, 349, 370, 372, 464
North Pacific 146, 244, 369, 376, 458–9

O
oceans 102–4, 184–91, 206, 368, 420, 460
  see also Atlantic ocean; Indian ocean; Pacific ocean; tropical oceans
octopuses 8, 328–9
opossums 308
opportunistic
  birds 198, 231, 258, 267, 336
  fish 192
  hunters 106–8, 159, 119
  marsupials 317
  primates 412
  reptiles 234
  rodents 454
otters 146, 149–150, 160
owls 489–91
oxen 44–5, 61, 67

P
Pacific ocean 104, 189, 328, 353, 355–6, 461
  see also North Pacific
pandas 163, 167
parrots 421–3
patagium 319, 452

pelicans 344–7
penguins 468
pheasants 270
pigs 94–8
plains 43, 67–8, 140–41, 144, 451, 493
polecats 158
pollution 149, 205, 466
polyps 460
porcupines 434, 438
possums 318, 320, 322
prairies *see* plains
prehensile tail 165, 175, 273, 321, 389–90, 442
primitive animals 69, 208, 238, 282
puffins 194

R
rabbits 296
raccoons 163–5
rainforests 71, 91–2, 95
  birds 240, 262, 275, 421–2
  carnivores 116, 130, 132, 164, 175
  insects 281, 298
  primates 381, 384–5, 387–9, 391–2, 396, 398–9, 416
  rodents 432
  snakes 474
  toads 27–8
  tree kangaroo 248
  see also tree climbers
rats 424–5, 446–7
rhinoceros 359–61
roadrunners 239

S
Sahara desert 39, 113, 125, 286
salmon 459
Sargasso Sea 13
savannahs
  birds 268
  carnivores 106, 115, 119, 128, 139, 154
  insectivores 38, 48, 51–4, 58, 67, 90
  rodents 424, 450
  see also bushland; grasslands
Scandinavia 441
scavengers 8, 142–3, 195, 199, 246
  birds 339
  falcons 256, 258–60, 262, 267
  marsupials 307
  primates 395
scent glands 60, 148, 158, 161
scrubland 70, 121, 131
sea anemone 355
seabirds 193–204, 420
seals 368–78
'sentry duty' 140
sharks 8, 102–4, 219, 297
sheep 62–3
shrews 287–9, 304
skuas 203
skunks 155, 161
'skydancing' 254–5, 260
snakes 472–4, 476–80, 487–8

South Africa 49, 358
  antelopes 68
  carnivores 110, 114–15, 140, 142
South America
  anteater 252
  bats 212
  birds 21, 240, 257, 262, 421, 495
  carnivores 111, 116, 123, 126, 130, 134, 145, 165
  fish 192
  guanaco 75
  insects 281, 298
  mammals 363
  primates 386–7, 389–91
  reptiles 235, 484–5
  rodents 426, 429, 431–2, 437
  sloth 250
  snakes 473
  tamandua 499
  toads 27–8
  see also Amazon basin; Andes mountains
South Asia 82, 86, 237, 247, 348, 362
  birds 197, 270, 422
  carnivores 171, 173, 175
  elephants 418
  primates 401, 405–6, 412
  snakes 474, 480
  see also India; Indonesia
speed 37, 50–1, 54, 81, 118–20, 294, 450
spiders 33–6
squid 8, 244
squirrels 451–2, 454–6
stench 53, 148, 158, 161
sticklebacks 272
storks 223–4
sub-Saharan Africa
  aardvark 496
  antelopes 40–2, 53–4, 58–60, 66, 71–3
  birds 196, 232–3, 259, 261, 268, 333
  buffaloes 67
  carnivores 106, 119, 128, 139, 141, 148, 154, 176, 178, 180
  elephants 418
  giraffes 90
  hippopotamus 93
  ostrich 493
  pangolin 365
  pigs 95–6
  primates 398, 411
  reptiles 236
  rhinoceros 359–60
  rodents 438, 450
  shrews 304
  waders 224–6
  wildebeest 48
swamps 84, 92, 137, 222, 240, 348, 352, 399
swans 20
swifts 31

T
tamarins 384–6
tapirs 362–3

tenrecs 291
terns 204
threatened species
  carnivores 160
  dragons 486
  herbivores 71, 89, 94
  tamarins 384
  see also endangered species; vulnerable species
tigers 136–7
toads 25–6, 28
tortoises 208
toxins *see* venom
tree climbers 117, 145, 152, 163, 165, 171, 247–50, 309
  birds 334
  lizards 484–5
  marsupials 318–22
  primates 381–3, 385–7, 389–93, 399, 401, 405–8, 410–12, 414–17
  rodents 434, 436, 449, 452, 454, 456
  snakes 472, 474
  tamandua 499
  see also forests; rainforests
treecreepers 334
tropical oceans 102–4, 187, 205, 219, 243, 245–6, 273, 469, 479

see also Indian ocean
tundra 61, 455, 490
tunnels *see* burrows
turkeys 269
turtles 205–7

U
United States *see* North America

V
venom
  ants 282
  duckbill platypus 325
  insectivores 287–8
  jellyfish 464
  octopus 328
  scorpion 462
  sea anenome 12
  snakes 479–80, 482, 487–8
  spiders 33–5
  toads 25–7
vertebrates 8
voles 443, 448
vulnerable species
  birds 277
  carnivores 116, 171, 173

  marsupials 323
  primates 392
  reptiles 237
  tapir 362
  wolves 111–12
  see also endangered species; threatened species
vultures 256, 259–60, 262–3, 267

W
waders 195–6, 200–2, 220, 222, 224–6, 275, 364
wallabies 310–11, 313
  see also kangaroos
wasps 283
West Africa 92, 392, 415
wetlands 200, 222, 224, 235
whales 8, 183–5, 189–91
wildebeest 48
Woburn Abbey, England 84
wolves 109, 111
wombats 324
woodlands 69, 78–80, 215

Z
zebras 358

PICTURE CREDITS

Henderson/Stock.Xchng; 172: Photos.com; 173: shmuel152/Webshots; 174: robingame/Webshots; 175: chilentos/Webshots; 176: Animal Pictures Archive; 177: kpoko4/Webshots; 178: U.S. Fish and Wildlife Services; 179: Photos.com; 180: etwilliamsf/Webshots; 119: Photos.com; 181: jacob79/Webshots; 182–184: Photos.com; 185: mikegreers/Webshots; 186: Photos.com; 187: Commander Grady Tuell/NOAA Photo Library; 188: Photos.com; 189: NOAA Photo Library; 190: Photos.com; 191: NOAA Photo Library; 192: Photos.com; 193: bdbruijn/Webshots; 194: Photos.com; 195: mikenett55/Webshots; 196: jacob79/Webshots; 197: segye.com/Animal Pictures Archive; 198: U.S. Fish and Wildlife Services; 199: Casey Ramos-Violante/Dreamstime; 200: Pascal Dubois; 201: Choi Soon-kyoo/Animal Pictures Archive; 202: gunnar1953/Webshots; 203: U.S. Fish and Wildlife Services; 204–205: Photos.com; 206: Fah mun Kwan/Dreamstime; 207: Pascal Nardi; 208: zeedeep/Webshots; 209: htsorioles2000/Webshots; 210: Animal Pictures Archive; 211: Armando Rodriguez; 212: magikeith/Webshots; 213: Philip Date/Fotolia; 214–215: Kim Jinsuk/Animal Pictures Archive; 216: Charlie Conn/Webshots; 217: Marek Polchowski/Istockphoto; 218: Webshots; 219: skattle16/Webshots; 220–221: Photos.com; 222: Mary Lane/Fotolia; 223: Michal Koralewski/Stock.Xchng; 224: Steffen Foerster/Fotolia; 225: Layette Gifford; 226: Photos.com; 227: peatlandsni.gov.uk; 228: Photos.com; 229: Oleg Korsun/nature.chita.ru; 230: avalon2/Webshots; 231: Photos.com; 232: Jurie Maree/Dreamstime; 233–237: Photos.com; 238: Steve Geer/Istockphoto; 239: Dave Kahn/Stock.Xchng; 240: Photos.com; 241: Marlon Bruin/Stock.Xchng; 242: Kim Jinsuk/Animal Pictures Archive; 243: tampacutie/Webshots; 244: Stevene Billings/Webshots; 245: grey_mare/Webshots; 246: Stefan Otto/Stock.Xchng; 247: sarah_wino/Webshots; 248: wantok_man/Webshots; 249: Photos.com; 250: lisainmexico/Webshots; 251: U.S. Fish and Wildlife Services; 252–254: Photos.com; 255: gunnar1953/Webshots; 256: Pardosa/Animal Pictures Archive; 257: U.S. Fish and Wildlife Services; 258: Marilyn Barbone/Dreamstime; 259: 7storm77/Webshots; 260: Stock.Xchng; 261: Norman Reid/Fotolia; 262: Photos.com; 263: Josue adib Cervantes Garcia/Dreamstime; 264: Geoffrey Kuchera/Dreamstime; 265: Photos.com; 266: Jeremy Henderson/Stock.Xchng; 267: larson57/Webshots; 268: Photos.com; 269: Bruce MacQueen/Dreamstime; 270–271: U.S. Fish and Wildlife Services; 272: Curlyq/Animal Pictures Archive; 273: Photos.com; 274: kusnij/Animal Pictures Archive; 275: jacob79/Webshots; 276: Radu Razvan/Dreamstime; 277: Animal Pictures Archive; 278: gunnar1953/Webshots; 279: Bill Storage/Istockphoto; 280: Photos.com; 281: Animal Pictures Archive; 282: roolike/Webshots; 283: Photos.com; 284: U.S. Fish and Wildlife Services; 285: jamallucas/Webshots; 286: usinfantryboy/Webshots; 287–288: Kim Jinsuk/Animal Pictures Archive; 289: rasmab/Webshots; 290: santerre/Animal Pictures Archive; 291: fantasmicchic/Webshots; 292–296: Photos.com; 297: pnrphotography/Dreamstime; 298: Ron Sherwood/Dreamstime; 299: Photos.com; 300–301: The Magic of Life Butterfly House/magicoflife.org; 302: John Valenti/Dreamstime; 303: Steffen Foerster/Dreamstime; 304: vikki627/Webshots; 305: Photos.com; 306: huskygirl2009/Webshots; 307: Pete Langshaw/Stock.Xchng; 308: Corbis RF; 309: imawkward/Webshots; 310: Glenn Threlfo/Animal Pictures Archive; 311: monster_ray/Webshots; 312: Photos.com; 313: tomgame/Webshots; 314: aquaterp3/Webshots; 315: bowerbird48/Webshots; 316: htsorioles2000/Webshots; 317: rdavis/Animal Pictures Archive; 318: Dan Irby; 319: williamjfisher/Webshots; 320: Stuart Creegan/Stock.Xchng; 321: Animal Pictures Archive; 322: Gary Unwin/Istockphoto; 323: fluffy249/Webshots; 324: Cecilia Alegro/Stock.Xchng; 325: Dennis Haugen/Forestry Images; 326: David Hewitt /Stock.Xchng; 327: Ismael Montero/Fotolia; 328: Dan Schmitt/Istockphoto; 329: John Abramo/Dreamstime; 330: Barry Flammia/Istockphoto; 331: Photos.com; 332: petebest101/Webshots; 333: Photos.com; 334: petebest101/Webshots; 335: giuss95/Webshots; 336: U.S. Fish and Wildlife Services; 337: Dave Green/Stock.Xchng; 338: riflegunn/Webshots; 339: addan104/Webshots;

340: slugu/Animal Pictures Archive; 341: Animal Pictures Archive; 342: riflegunn/Webshots; 343: allcreation/Webshots; 344–345: Photos.com; 346: lonican99/Webshots; 347: Photos.com; 348: Sasha Dubovski/Stock.Xchng; 349: Photos.com; 350: bernierenee/Webshots; 351: Photos.com; 352: jl_walk/Webshots; 353: Maya Paulin/Dreamstime; 354: scubapete100/Webshots; 355–357: Photos.com; 358: Trisha Shears/Stock.Xchng; 359–361: Photos.com; 362: md72/Webshots; 363–364: Photos.com; 365: tomneuhaus/Webshots; 366: Gertjan Hooijer/Istockphoto; 367: Captain Budd Christman/NOAA Photo Library; 368: thomp4071/Webshots; 369: Captain Budd Christman/NOAA Photo Library; 370: Donald Mathis/Animal Pictures Archive; 371: Captain Budd Christman/NOAA Photo Library; 372: Photos.com; 373: kramg100/Webshots; 374: canoechic13/Webshots; 375: Uriel Avron; 376: Photos.com; 377: Dr. James P. McVey/NOAA Photo Library; 378: Photos.com; 379: pbase.com/kiml/Dreamstime; 380: Uwe Ohse/Dreamstime; 381: Joël Kuiper/Stock.Xchng; 382: Alan O'Donovan; 383: jacob79/Webshots; 384: urbanmdcowboy/Webshots; 385: jacob79/Webshots; 386: baldr369/Webshots; 387: rocktheseas/Webshots; 388: Animal Pictures Archive; 389: Shay Altshuler; 390: brazilx/Webshots; 391: Peter Caulfield/Stock.Xchng; 392: Layette Gifford; 393: Martina Berg/Dreamstime; 394: Jeanie Peterson; 395: samsegar/Webshots; 396: tkostov/Webshots; 397: James Maskrey/Stock.Xchng; 398: Photos.com; 399: Ray Ng Soo Meng; 400: Photos.com; 401: Michael Lynch/Istockphoto; 402: Martina Berg/Dreamstime; 403: paulandlone/Webshots; 404: goradok/Animal Pictures Archive; 405: Photos.com; 406: Gary Unwin/Istockphoto; 407: florence67/Webshots; 408: Garth Irvine/Webshots; 409: Joanne Cannon/Stock.Xchng; 410: Andy Biggs/Stock.Xchng; 411–412: Animal Pictures Archive; 413: Photos.com; 414: marksfinepix/Webshots; 415–416: Photos.com; 417: Matej Mraz/Webshots; 418–419: Photos.com; 420: jessiezyy/Webshots; 421: Photos.com; 422: Ausphotofriend/Istockphoto; 423: benandthebus1/Webshots; 424: Animal Pictures Archive; 425: jacob79/Webshots; 426: Dria Peterson/Stock.Xchng; 427: Photos.com; 428: Jill Batchelor; 429: Anthony Hathaway/Dreamstime; 430: Jameson Weston/Istockphoto; 431: dimitrisokolenko/Webshots; 432: John White; 433: Abdulrahman Al-Sirhan/www.alsirhan.com; 434: Photos.com; 435: Zygmund Zee/Istockphoto; 436: michael_lucas9/Webshots; 437: Quinn Kuiken/Stock.Xchng; 438: Rob S/Stock.Xchng; 439: Animal Pictures Archive; 440: Abdulrahman Al-Sirhan/www.alsirhan.com; 441: Solvin Zonkl; 442: vespa125125/Webshots; 443: Animal Pictures Archive; 444: john286/Animal Pictures Archive; 445: Photos.com; 446: Tamara Bauer/Istockphoto; 447: Ian McCann/Parks Victoria; 448: Les Borg; 449: Joachim Ruhstein; 450: Curly Q/Animal Pictures Archive; 451: U.S. Fish and Wildlife Services; 452: Donald Mathis/Animal Pictures Archive; 453: Jason Cheever/Stock.Xchng; 454: Photos.com; 455–456: U.S. Fish and Wildlife Services; 457: Tim Haynes/Dreamstime; 458–459: U.S. Fish and Wildlife Services; 460: Bartlomiej Kwieciszewski/Dreamstime; 461: Photos.com; 462: Kirubeshwaran Ganeshan/Dreamstime; 463: 59albion/Webshots; 464: Eli Mordechai/Dreamstime; 465: Pam Roth/Stock.Xchng; 466: helodriver2004/Webshots; 467: U.S. Fish and Wildlife Services; 468: Photos.com; 469: Christopher Waters/Dreamstime; 470: Photos.com; 471: alanm00/Webshots; 472: Who10/Dreamstime; 473: Animal Pictures Archive; 474–475: Photos.com; 476: Juha Blomberg/Stock.Xchng; 477: U.S. Fish and Wildlife Services; 478: Pam Roth/Stock.Xchng; 479–480: Photos.com; 481: flyliz/Animal Pictures Archive; 482: Animal Pictures Archive; 483–484: Photos.com; 485: rjward79/Webshots; 486: Nicholas Hinks/Stock.Xchng; 487: Animal Pictures Archive; 488: john286/Animal Pictures Archive; 489–491: Photos.com; 492: Ian Thacker; 493–494: Photos.com; 495: D. Murray Sullivan; 496: kusnij/Animal Pictures Archive; 497: chuckguy2/Webshots; 498: www.highclerevillage.com; 499: Anthony Hathaway/Dreamstime; 500: Bug-a-Boo/Animal Pictures Archive; 501: Steffen Foerster/Dreamstime